The Hvac/r Professional's Field Guide to ALTERNATIVE REFRIGERANTS

Richard Jazwin

BNP
Business News Publishing Company
Troy, Michigan USA

Library of Congress Cataloging in Publication Data

Jazwin, Richard
Alternative refrigerants / Richard Jazwin.
p. cm.
ISBN 1-885863-12-8
1. Refrigerants I. Title.
TP492.7.J387 1995 95-22895
621.5'64--dc20 CIP

Editor: Joanna Turpin
Art Director: Mark Leibold
Copy Editor: Carolyn Thompson

Printed in the United States of America
7 6 5 4 3 2 1

Dedication

To all of the contractors and technicians, present and future, who will be using the new alternative refrigerants. The future is full of uncertainty, however, you provide the expertise to make the world a better place.

Table of Contents

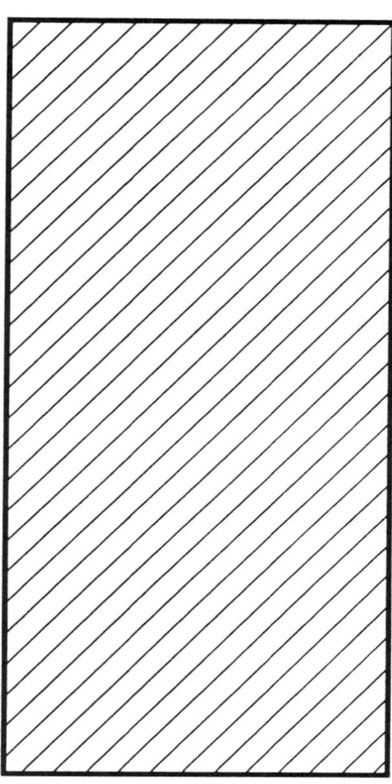

Introduction

Production of R-12 (a CFC) ceases in December, 1995. This is because environmental concerns at international and national levels demanded that R-12 use come to a halt. Before the mandated phaseout of CFCs came about, many manufacturers voluntarily cut their CFC production capabilities. Production bans will not be limited to CFCs; other refrigerants such as R-22 (an HCFC) will also be banned. It is just a question of time.

Many systems that require service will still have the "old regulated" refrigerants running through them. In time, the supply of these "old" refrigerants will disappear, and retrofitting to the new alternatives will not be a matter of choice. Supplies of recovered and recycled refrigerant will also eventually disappear. At some point in time, we will all have to use alternative refrigerants.

It is the job of the contractor and technician to ensure that a change over to the *proper* alternative occurs. Are you ready? Do you know what to do?

Hopefully, this book will provide many of the answers. Retrofitting a unit requires information. Never has so much information been necessary in order to perform service in the hvac/r industry. At the same time, never has so much confusing information been available. This confusion is due to the fact that as fast we learn how to use and handle the new alternative refrigerants, we find that another method will offer some additional benefits or at least alleviate some concerns that developed during the retrofit process.

Since the passage of the Clean Air Act in 1990, it has become very apparent that the CFC and HCFC refrigerants we use *will* be replaced with alternatives. Which alternatives and in what mixture or charge size is dependent on the particular application.

The Clean Air Act made the hvac/r industry look at service practices from an environmental standpoint. This is helpful, because it helps preserve the environment for the future. It is also a hindrance, because we are attempting to legislate the laws of physics. In reality, we do not have all the answers on how to phase out ozone-destroying refrigerant. Arguments will rage for years about whether or not a chlorine-based refrigerant is in fact the culprit in the destruction of the ozone layer. From a service standpoint, the arguments are unnecessary, because alternative refrigerants are here to stay.

The book is divided into two parts. Part One discusses the new alternatives from creation to retrofit in a system. Part Two provides information furnished directly from the refrigerant manufacturers on their products. No one understands the alternatives better than the people who make them. Together, Parts One and Two will provide information in the following areas:

- How should a blended refrigerant be charged into a system?
- What is a blend?
- What can happen when a leak occurs with a blended refrigerant?
- What is glide?
- What is the difference between R-134a (an HFC) and R-12, and do you understand how the difference affects system operation?

Alternative Refrigerants will help you understand the choices you must make in order to do your job properly.

Everyone in the hvac/r industry is familiar with the tremendous advances that have been made in system efficiency ratings. Unfortunately, some of the new refrigerants may not perform to the same efficiency levels that the unit previously achieved. In a time when industry has been pushed to improve efficiency, it is odd that certain alternative refrigerants when used in specific applications are going in the opposite direction. The fact is that the "old" refrigerants were in many cases more suited to certain applications than the new ones.

In most cases, there is no "drop-in replacement" available for a particular application. Therefore, technicians will have to make changes to ensure that the system will function properly. Changing over from R-12 to R-134a will require technicians who understand what they are doing.

This book is not the last work on the subject of alternative refrigerants. As the years go by, many new facts will be learned about the long-term operation of systems using the new refrigerants. We will have to alter our approaches to service as more information becomes available. In the future, your success in service will be based on how much time you devote to learning about the new environmentally-based world of service. This book is your first step towards that success. Good luck with your venture into the world of alternative refrigerants.

Richard Jazwin

Phoenix, Arizona

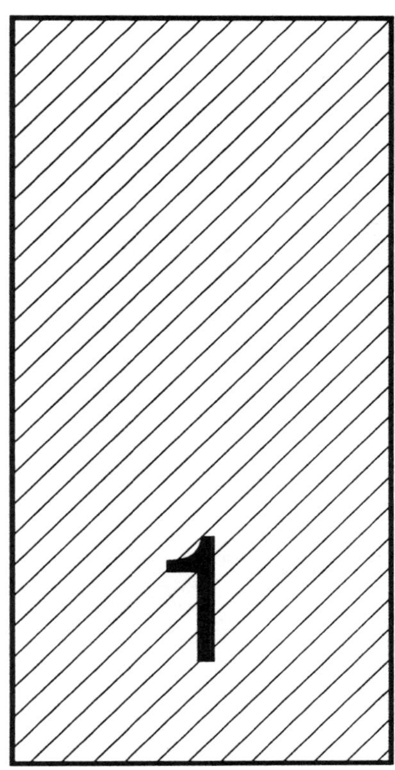

The World, Ozone, and Refrigerants

It all started with a hole. Normally a hole is not much of a problem, but in this case, the hole turned out to be a big problem. If you haven't guessed by now, I am talking about the hole in the ozone layer. The hole got bigger, and that's where the problem started.

In 1978, scientists discovered a hole in the ozone layer. Scientists began to study the ozone layer and debate whether or not the hole was a natural phenomenon or a man-made problem. After years of research, the majority of scientists believed that man's use of chemicals was creating the problem. Major contributors to that problem were the CFCs and halons that were being released into the atmosphere.

The bigger the hole in the ozone layer, the more problems we will encounter on earth. The ozone layer screens us from some of the ultraviolet (UV) radiation that reaches the earth. A decrease in the size of the ozone layer will result in more ultraviolet radiation reaching the earth. UV radiation reaching the earth is normal; however the ozone layer, which exists in the stratosphere, acts as a filter that allows a correct percentage of UV to reach us. The percentage of UV reaching the earth will increase as the ozone layer (filter) decreases.

The ozone layer can be viewed as a giant pair of sunglasses that filters out some of the sun's ultraviolet radiation. Decrease the strength of the sunglasses, and the entire protection factor of the glasses changes. Decrease the size of the ozone layer, and the protection that the layer affords us will also decrease. Increased UV radiation will cause:

- increased number of skin cancer cases;
- increased number of cataract cases;
- decreased crop yields;
- increased smog;
- a change in weather patterns;
- damage to plant and marine life;
- an upset in the very delicate balance of nature.

Individually none of these changes will destroy life on earth; however, collectively, they will wreak havoc for everyone on earth.

Scientists tell us that most of what occurs in nature is a result of cause and effect. The cause in this case is certain refrigerants used by the majority of the systems in operation today are entering the stratosphere where they are destroying the ozone layer. The effect is the reduction in size of the ozone layer. The refrigerants are entering the stratosphere primarily due to venting to the atmosphere and leaking systems.

Not all refrigerants are guilty of causing the hole in the ozone layer. The prime culprits are CFCs and HCFCs and a chemical family called halons used in applications such as fire extinguishers.

Global Warming

Many scientists believe there is a change occurring in our weather patterns, which is causing the average temperatures on earth to rise. This rise in temperature, also known as the *greenhouse effect*, could cause major problems on earth.

For years we have been sending pollutants such as carbon dioxide, which results from burning fossil fuels, into the atmosphere. The presence of these pollutants can trap heat that is normally radiated to space, thereby interfering with upper atmospheric wind patterns and raising average earth temperatures. We are trapping heat and light that has been "released" by the earth to the atmosphere and are resending a portion of it back to the earth.

CFCs, HCFCs, and some alternative refrigerants are considered to be contributors to this problem. CFCs in the atmosphere absorb and reflect infrared light and may be responsible for retaining a percentage of the heat energy trapped by the greenhouse effect. The pollutant make-up of the greenhouse gases includes carbon dioxide, carbon monoxide, sulfur oxide, CFCs, and other gases created in our usage of energy and manufacturing. Essentially we are polluting the atmosphere with the discharge of CFCs, while creating additional pollution by burning fossil fuels to create electricity to run the systems using the CFCs.

Because of this concern, refrigerants are rated as to their *global warming potential* (GWP). Table 1-1 presents some typical ratings for various refrigerants in use today. Remember that all of the numbers shown are ratios and are intended to show one refrigerant's potential GWP against another.

Refrigerant	Global Warming Potential (GWP)
R-11 (CFC)	1.0
R-12 (CFC)	3.1
R-500 (CFC)	2.4
R-113 (CFC)	1.3
R-22 (HCFC)	0.34
R-134a (HFC)	0.285
R-123 (HCFC)	0.02

Table 1-1. Global warming potentials

Much has yet to be learned about global warming, and many also disagree with the concept. Regardless of your viewpoint, GWPs must be considered when dealing with alternative refrigerants.

Atoms, Elements, and Molecules

Before continuing into our discussion of alternative refrigerants, it is first necessary to remember the definitions of atoms, elements, and molecules.

An *atom* is the smallest part of an element. An *element* is the smallest part of a substance that cannot be separated into different substances by ordinary chemical methods. For example, hydrogen is an element that cannot be separated into something else. Matter is made up of elements. When elements combine in certain combinations they form molecules.

A *molecule* is the smallest part of a substance having all the components of that substance. A molecule is a compound made up of different atoms. For example, a molecule of water consists of two hydrogen atoms and one oxygen atom, Figure 1-1. Therefore, a single molecule of water would have two hydrogen atoms and one oxygen atom. The chemical formula for water is written as H_2O.

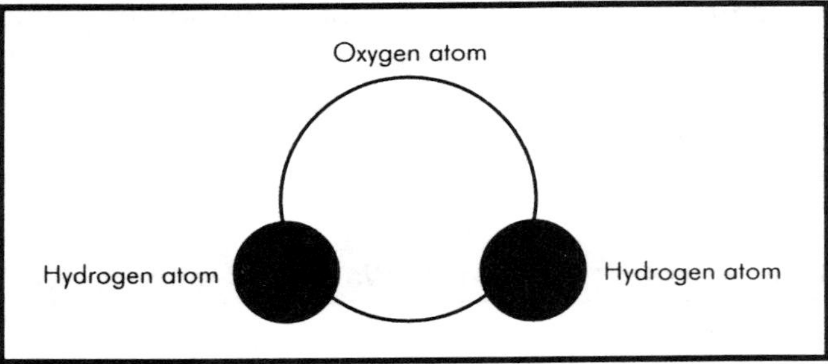

Figure 1-1. Water molecule

Another molecule that we are familiar with is an oxygen molecule. An ordinary oxygen molecule contains two atoms of oxygen and is written as O_2. If you add one atom of oxygen to ordinary oxygen, ozone (O_3) is created, Figure 1-2.

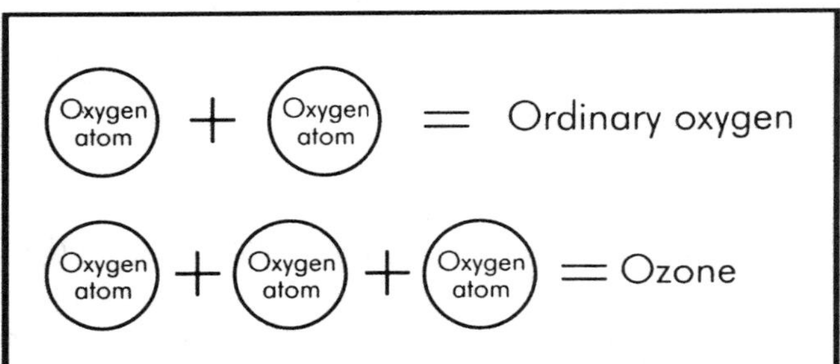

Figure 1-2. Ozone molecule

The refrigerants we handle are also composed of molecules. For example, a molecule of R-12 (chlorofluorocarbon) is composed of chlorine, fluorine, and carbon atoms combined into a molecule. The chemical formula for R-12 is written as CCl_2F_2. R-12 contains one atom of carbon, two atoms of chlorine, and two atoms of fluorine. While this book discusses different refrigerants, what is really being discussed is the arrangement and structure of atoms and molecules into a refrigerant.

CFC and Ozone Destruction

The ozone layer, which is located in the stratosphere, is composed of many ozone molecules. It is currently believed that the following steps occur, resulting in the destruction of ozone:

1. When a CFC refrigerant is vented to the atmosphere, a molecule of the CFC refrigerant finds its way to the ozone layer.
2. At the same time, UV radiation reaching the ozone layer breaks off a chlorine atom from a CFC molecule. The resultant chlorine atom is now free and finds an ozone molecule with three atoms of oxygen.
3. The chlorine atom attacks the ozone molecule and breaks off an oxygen atom. When one atom of oxygen is removed from the ozone (O_3) molecule, oxygen (O_2) and a free atom of oxygen are left over.
4. The ozone molecule is destroyed.
5. The left-over oxygen atom and the chlorine atom unite and form chlorine monoxide. (The presence of chlorine monoxide is considered proof that the layer is being destroyed by chlorine.)
6. Along comes another free oxygen atom, which breaks up the chlorine monoxide molecule, resulting in a chlorine atom and an oxygen molecule to start the whole ozone destruction process again.

The scientists studying this cycle believe chlorine may remain in the ozone layer for over 120 years. During that time, one chlorine molecule can destroy 100,000 ozone molecules. There is also a concern that HCFCs in the ozone layer will support a destructive cycle; however, HCFCs have a lower ozone depletion potential.

Ozone Depletion Potential

The ozone depletion potential is a scale that measures how destructive a refrigerant is to the ozone layer. The measurement involves setting a baseline number for a refrigerant that can be compared to other refrigerants. This baseline uses R-12, which has a value of one, Table 1-2.

Refrigerant	Ozone Depletion Potential (ODP)
R-11 (CFC)	1.0
R-12 (CFC)	1.0
R-500 (CFC)	0.7
R-113 (CFC)	0.8
R-22 (HCFC)	0.05
R-134a (HFC)	.0
R-123 (HCFC)	0.02

Table 1-2. Ozone depletion potentials

As you can see from the chart, it is the CFC refrigerants that are the major contributors to the destruction cycle.

Regulation

The world reacted to the ozone problem by creating a document called the *Montreal Protocol.* The original and subsequent Protocols attempted to establish production limits and phase out schedules of chemical production. A timetable was established that would result in the ultimate phase out of ozone-depleting substances. Signers of the Protocol established production limits and phase out schedules of chemicals for their particular countries.

In the United States, an amendment was passed that impacted just about every facet of the hvac/r industry. The Clean Air Act Amendment signed by then President George Bush established a set of standards that greatly affected service in this country. The standards include a prohibition on venting refrigerants to the atmosphere, mandatory technician certification, and mandated phase out of certain refrigerants.

Unfortunately, the mandated phase out resulted in targeting refrigerants that are heavily used by the service community, including R-12, R-502, and R-22. From automobiles to chillers, these refrigerants will soon be unavailable. The refrigerant manufacturers have worked hard to create new refrigerants that will not deplete the ozone level and at the same time meet the needs of the service industries. These refrigerants are known as *alternative refrigerants.*

The Future

For years if a unit required R-12, we just charged it with R-12. Now technicians or contractors will be faced with the decision of retrofitting a system with alternative refrigerants or replacing the entire system with an equal or higher efficiency system. Many factors must be considered when making this choice, and the following questions should be answered before making a decision:

- How old is the existing system?
- How much longer is the existing system expected to operate?
- What is the daily run time of the system?
- When will the existing refrigerant no longer be available?
- Is there an alternative available that will work well enough and be safe enough to maintain the customer's needs?
- What is the ODP and GWP of the alternative refrigerant?
- What are the energy considerations in your area? Will a higher efficiency unit offer the customer a payback on the energy side?
- What are the customer's circumstances? Will they occupy the space long enough to warrant a replacement unit?

All of these factors must be carefully considered before a decision to retrofit or replace is made. One of the primary considerations is whether or not there is an acceptable alternative available that can be installed at a reasonable cost and still meet the system's needs. Much research is going on to determine the *best* alternatives to the phased out refrigerants. However, no one has any idea of how the alternative refrigerants will behave under field operating conditions for a long period of time. In our industry it is not uncommon to have systems operating relatively maintenance free under every type of condition for 15 to 20 years. There is no history in the area of alternative refrigerants. Reality tells us that you cannot substitute years and years of operational experience with "new" refrigerants without some concerns.

Systems operate in low, medium, and high temperature ranges, cooling every conceivable product or population that exists. It will be years before we know for sure that refrigerant "X" has successfully replaced refrigerant "Y". There may be many more new alternatives to replace the existing alternatives. One company that committed to replacing R-12 with another refrigerant developed substantial concerns at the last moment. These concerns involved the newly specified alternative refrigerant, which could not perform as well as R-12 in a small percentage of test cases.

There are no drop-in replacements for current refrigerants. Many technicians have played with substitute refrigerants and found that they work; however, these same technicians have not followed manufacturer recommendations for the retrofit. These technicians seem to think the new refrigerants are working just fine, but they do not know for how long and at what price to the system. A premature compressor failure does not indicate the system is working just fine with the new alternative, but it may take time for that failure to appear. And, the compressor failure may not be the fault of the refrigerant but rather of the procedures used during the retrofit process.

We all have much to learn about the new alternatives, and the time to start learning is now.

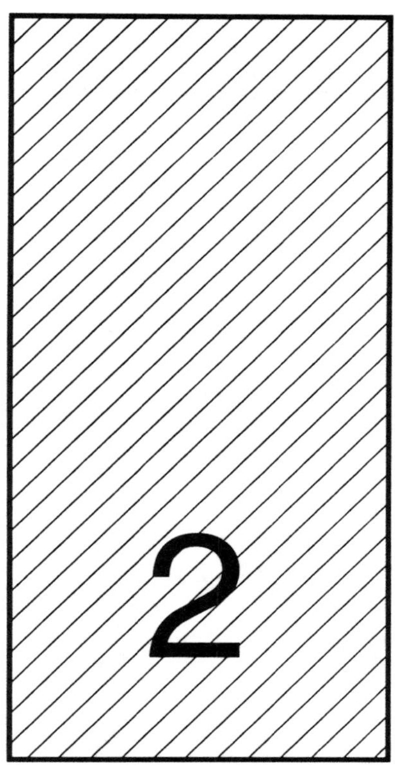

Refrigerant Fundamentals

The refrigeration process moves heat from one place to another. Refrigerants are the vehicles that allow the entire cooling or heating process to occur. If we are trying to move a load from one place to another, tools such as dollies greatly aid the moving process. However, the device used to move an object must fit the intended application; for example, a dolly would not be used to move a house. The same is true of refrigerants. Refrigerants are tools that allow us to move heat. Refrigerants are also sized to do the job, which is why there are so many different refrigerants designed to work under so many different conditions.

Terminology

There are certain terms that must be understood when learning about refrigerants. These terms describe the refrigeration process and give us the ability to understand refrigerant behavior.

Atmospheric pressure: The pressure that gases exert on the earth. A pressure of 14.7 psia (pounds per square inch absolute) at sea level is considered atmospheric pressure.

Boiling point: The temperature and pressure at which a liquid changes state to a gas. A refrigerant boiling point (saturation point) is the precise temperature and pressure point at which the liquid refrigerant changes state from a liquid to a gas. Temperature-pressure charts indicate the boiling point of a refrigerant. At sea level, the boiling point of water is 212°F.

At its boiling point, a refrigerant can exist as a liquid or vapor or a combination of liquid and vapor. The laws of thermodynamics state that flow is from a hotter to a colder place; therefore, the boiling point of a refrigerant must be lower than the temperature we want to maintain in order for heat transfer to occur.

British thermal unit (Btu): One Btu is the amount of heat necessary to raise one pound of water one degree Fahrenheit.

Change of state: When a liquid changes to a gas or a gas changes to a liquid.

Condensation: The change of state from a gas to a liquid. Condensation is the opposite of evaporation.

Condenser: The component in the refrigeration system where the refrigerant releases heat and changes from a vapor to a liquid.

Critical temperature: The highest temperature a gas can reach and still be able to be condensed by applying pressure.

Enthalpy: The amount of heat contained in a pound of liquid or gas, expressed in Btu per pound.

Evaporation: The process whereby a liquid absorbs sufficient heat to change state to a gas. Water changing to steam is a common example of evaporation or boiling.

Evaporator: The component in the refrigeration system that absorbs heat, thereby allowing liquid refrigerant to change to vapor.

Gas: The term that describes the state of a substance. For our purposes, the terms vapor and gas can be used interchangeably.

Latent (hidden) heat: Heat energy that causes a change of state without a corresponding change in sensible temperature. *Latent heat cannot be measured with a thermometer.* Applying the definition of a Btu, the addition of one Btu at a sea level temperature of 211°F will increase the temperature to 212°F. However, more than one Btu is required to increase the temperature of the same pound of water from 212° to 213°F. At sea level, a pound of water cannot exist in the liquid state at 213°F; the water will boil at 212°F and change state to a gas. It takes 970 Btu of latent heat to make water change state to a gas.

Latent heat of condensation: Amount of heat loss necessary to change a substance from a vapor to a liquid.

Latent heat of evaporation: Amount of heat gain necessary to change a substance from a liquid to a vapor.

Saturation: When a substance contains all of another substance that it can hold at a given temperature and pressure. For example, air holding as much moisture as it possibly can for a given temperature and pressure is saturated. The saturation point is the point at which a change of state can occur, at a given temperature and pressure.

Sensible heat: Heat energy which, when added or removed from a substance, causes a rise or fall in temperature. A thermometer measures sensible heat.

Specific density: Mass per unit volume expressed in pounds per cubic foot.

Specific volume: The space occupied by a substance per unit of mass. It is expressed in cubic feet per pound.

Standard conditions: An agreed upon criterion that is set to compare different refrigerants. Standard conditions are 5°F evaporating temperature and 86°F condensing temperature.

Subcooling: The removal of heat from a liquid that is below its condensation point. Only liquids may be subcooled.

Superheat: The addition of heat to a gas after change of state has occurred. Only gases may be superheated.

Toxicity: A measure of how poisonous a substance can be.

What is a Refrigerant?

Before we discuss alternative refrigerants, we must first thoroughly understand refrigerants in general. A refrigerant is a fluid that easily changes state from a liquid to gas or a gas to liquid. During this process, the refrigerant absorbs or rejects heat.

The basic cycle consists of a refrigerant absorbing heat at the evaporator and releasing heat at the condenser. While in a mostly liquid state, the refrigerant absorbs heat at a low pressure and then changes state to a vapor. The vapor is compressed, raised to a higher pressure and temperature, and sent to the condenser. In the condenser, the vapor changes back to a reusable liquid (condenses), giving up the heat it acquired as a low-pressure liquid. The refrigerant can then be used over and over to transfer heat.

For years we have enjoyed a simple approach to refrigerant usage. If a unit needed refrigerant, we simply replaced or added to the refrigerant already in the system. The equipment manufacturer designated the refrigerant for the system based on the design of the system. Boiling point, latent heat capacity, enthalpy, and all properties of the refrigerant were usually not the concern of the technician. This is no longer the case! In order to properly service refrigeration systems today, a complete change to an alternative refrigerant and oil may be necessary. Alternative refrigerants are different than the refrigerants we have been working with for years. The old "one refrigerant, one designation" to charge the system is gone.

Refrigerant Properties

In order to be effective, a refrigerant should possess certain properties. Some of these properties include the following:

- Chemical stability so that it does not come apart easily
- Non-toxic and non-flammable
- Solubility so that a lubricant can easily mix with and be carried by the refrigerant
- High latent heat. The higher the latent heat potential of the refrigerant, the more Btu per pound it can absorb. High latent heat capacity means that less refrigerant will be required to move heat.
- Ease of handling
- Resistant to breakdown under high temperatures or pressures
- Compatible with materials used in the system
- Low affinity for moisture. Moisture is the enemy of a refrigeration system. Moisture can cause pressure to change in the system and also cause components to deteriorate.
- Ease of locating leaks
- Always available. Refrigeration equipment has an extremely long useful life.
- Not harmful to the environment

If you look at the last two points, you understand why you are reading this book. Many of the refrigerants we use today will no longer be available. In addition, they can harm the environment. These are two of the main reasons that alternative refrigerants were created.

When using alternative refrigerants, you will soon discover that many of them will not perform as well as the refrigerant being replaced. Alternatives may also be flammable or toxic, have different latent heat characteristics, or not be easy to handle. There is no single refrigerant that will work in all systems and deliver the necessary range of cooling. From an operational standpoint, there is, in most cases, nothing wrong with the refrigerant being replaced.

High, Medium, or Low

Refrigeration systems operate in three different temperature ranges: high, medium, or low. High, medium, and low ranges are not boundaries that always must be adhered to; they are merely a practical guide to meeting the refrigerant needs of a system. With the number of available refrigerants and the number of system needs that must be met, there are times when overlap between the ranges will occur.

The most prevalent application of *high-temperature* systems is air conditioning. These systems are designed to keep the space around 70°F. R-22 is a prime example of a high-temperature refrigerant. R-22 is not normally used in a system designed to maintain a temperature of 5°F.

Medium-temperature systems generally maintain a space in the 30° to 40°F temperature range. R-12 is an example of a refrigerant that can be used as a medium-temperature refrigerant. A walk-in box or household refrigerator at 70°F is not very desirable, so a medium-temperature refrigerant is used in this application.

Freezers and freezing processes operating in a range of 5° to 50°F are considered *low-temperature* applications.

There are other temperature ranges such as ultra low and cryogenic that are designed for very specific applications. For our purposes, the focus will be on the most commonly accepted applications.

When faced with a situation of using an alternative refrigerant, one of the most difficult problems is finding the *best* refrigerant to meet the system's needs. At times the high-medium-low range boundary will be crossed, because the goal is to achieve the highest possible operating efficiency using the alternative.

Building a Refrigerant

Early refrigerants were generally made of methane or ethane molecules and did not use chlorine. Methane and ethane are pure hydrocarbons that contain hydrogen and carbon. Halogen refrigerants were created later. A halogen is one of five non-metallic elements (fluorine, bromine, chlorine, iodine, and astatine). The term *halogenate* means to combine another element with one of the five halogens. Fluorine and chlorine (halogens) atoms replaced *some* (partially halogenated) or *all* (fully halogenated) of the hydrogen atoms in the methane- and ethane-based refrigerants, thereby creating a halogenated refrigerant.

When the halogens were combined with hydrocarbons, halide refrigerants were born. Common halide refrigerants include CFCs, HCFCs, and HFCs. Unfortunately, both CFC and HCFC refrigerants contain the chlorine atom. Remember that chlorine (particularly in CFCs) is the primary culprit in the destruction of the ozone layer.

Single Compound Refrigerant

Refrigerants are compounds that are made by combining different elements into a molecule. An element is any substance that cannot be separated into different substances by ordinary chemical means. All matter is composed of such substances.

When hydrogen combines with oxygen in the proper mix, a single compound called water (H_2O) is created. When chlorine, carbon, and fluorine atoms are combined into a molecule, a single compound refrigerant is created. An important point to understand is that *a single refrigerant compound has a single boiling point for a given pressure and temperature.* Knowledge of a refrigerant's boiling point at a given temperature and pressure is essential for performing proper service.

Most of us work with single compound refrigerants such as R-12 or R-22 every day. There are other types of refrigerants that are not single compounds. CFCs are a good example, because while R-12 is a single compound, R-502 is not. A refrigerant designated as a CFC does not have to be a single compound; for example, R-502 is an azeotropic mixture (see Chapter Three). Single compound refrigerants are discussed in more detail in Chapter Four.

CFCs, HCFCs, HFCs

CFC is short for chlorofluorocarbon. Some of the more familiar CFCs include R-12, R-11, R-113, and R-502. CFCs are characterized by the following points:

- Contain chlorine
- Have one carbon atom, two chlorine (chloro) atoms, and two fluorine (fluoro) atoms
- Are fully halogenated, which means no hydrogen atoms
- Have a high ozone depletion potential (ODP)
- Are a cause for global warming concerns
- Will cease production December 31, 1995

Most of us have been working with single compound refrigerants such as R-12 for years. R-12 maintains a given temperature for a given pressure at all times. It is composed of one molecule that is chemically written as CCl_2F_2.

HCFC is short for hydrochlorofluorocarbon. The most commonly used HCFCs include R-21, R-22, R-123, and R-124. HCFCs contain some hydrogen (hydro), chlorine (chloro), fluorine (fluoro), and carbon atoms and are characterized by the following points:

- Not considered the prime offender in the ozone crisis
- Partially halogenated, which means some hydrogen atoms
- Much lower ODP and global warming concerns
- Usually will not reach the upper atmosphere
- Will decompose sooner due to the presence of hydrogen
- Will eventually cease production
- Contains chlorine but also contains hydrogen, which lessens ODP concerns

HFC stands for hydrofluorocarbon. Common examples of HFCs include R-32, R-125, R-134a, R-134, and R-143a. HFCs are characterized by the following points:

- Contain fluorine but not chlorine, which means it is safer for the environment
- Do not deplete the ozone layer and are rated very low in global warming potential

R-134a is the refrigerant of choice in the automotive industry and also replaces R-12 in medium- and high-temperature refrigeration and automotive air conditioning applications. However, R-134a has a lower heat carrying capacity than R-12 in certain temperature applications. R-134a is also incompatible with mineral oils that are used in many of today's systems.

HFCs are the major new and widely used alternatives. This family of refrigerants is one that must be thoroughly understood.

ASHRAE Classification

There is much confusion regarding the numbering of refrigerants. When reading about different refrigerants you may not be aware that the same refrigerant can be referred to by different names or numbers. This is because refrigerant manufacturers assign their own numbers to their refrigerants. To eliminate this confusion, the American Society of Heating, Refrigerating and Air-Conditioning Engineers (ASHRAE) has developed a uniform refrigerant numbering system. This numbering system is defined in ASHRAE Standard 34-1992, which is shown in Table 2-1.

Designation	Definition
000 Series	Uses methane compounds
100 Series	Uses ethane compounds
200 Series	Uses propane compounds
300 Series	Uses cylic organic compounds
400 Series	Zeotropes
500 Series	Azeotropes

Table 2-1. ASHRAE Standard 34-1992, *Refrigerant Number Classification*

Until now, we have been discussing the single compound group of refrigerants. Many of the new alternatives are not single compound but rather a mixture of refrigerants designed to duplicate as closely as possible the properties of the refrigerant they will replace. These refrigerants will be discussed in the next chapter.

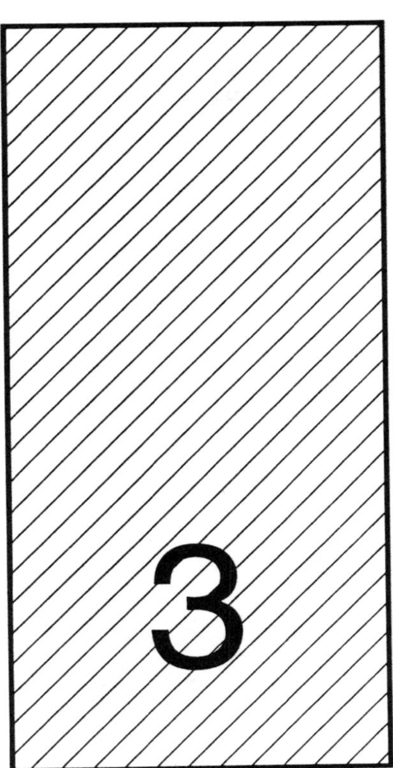

Blends/Mixtures

One of the big changes in the refrigerant world is the emergence of blends or mixtures. For our purposes, the terms blends and mixtures are interchangeable.

Blends are refrigerants that are mixed (blended) together and behave as a replacement refrigerant. When a refrigerant is made up of one type of molecule, it is a single compound refrigerant. Blends are not single compound refrigerants, because they contain more than one component (more than one type of molecule). A binary blend contains two components, and a ternary blend contains three components.

When building a blend, refrigerants are combined to create a refrigerant that will be as close as possible to a working replacement for a CFC or HCFC refrigerant. The phrase *as close as possible to* is the key to understanding alternative refrigerant blends. A blend is designed to replace an existing refrigerant, while at the same time meeting an environmental need. From a performance standpoint, there is no need to replace the original refrigerant, because R-12, for example, is sufficient to handle many system refrigeration needs. However, from a supply, cost, and environmental standpoint, R-12 must someday be replaced.

In building a blend, manufacturers try to accommodate the needs of particular applications by mixing refrigerants together. Different blends are created by using the same refrigerants in different proportions. For example, MP39 and MP66 are composed of R-22, R-152a, and R-124.

Blends are classified as *azeotropes*, *zeotropes,* or *near azeotropic mixtures (NARMs).* Most of these terms are new and describe the molecular composition of the refrigerant. Some manufacturers define azeotropes, zeotropes, and NARMs more narrowly than others. For our purposes, we will look at the terms as practically as possible. If, for example, you feel the term *NARM* should be used rather than the term *zeotrope* that's fine; what is important is that you understand the difference between the terms.

For years we have all used azeotropes such as R-502. When using zeotropes or NARMs, the handling of refrigerant will differ significantly from that of an azeotrope. In addition, some modifications may have to be made to a system when using the new blends. These modifications may include changing components and/or oil and utilizing different service procedures.

Most of the blends are HCFC or HFC based and have a lower ODP rating. All of the refrigerant manufacturers are researching and developing alternative blends to meet industry needs. Eventually, HCFC refrigerants will be phased out, and some of the current accepted blends will have to be replaced.

When dealing with blends, change is a constant. For some applications there are alternatives that cannot be considered blends. Ammonia-based refrigerants have been around for years and may replace refrigerants in certain applications. However, whenever a blend is installed, a trade-off occurs. The blend may require major changes to the system or may not have the performance factor of the original refrigerant. The new world of refrigerants is not a simple one. Questions such as which blend to use, how much to charge, and what changes may occur in system operation will have to be dealt with by every technician. (See Part Two of this book for detailed information on specific refrigerants.)

Equipment manufacturers are involved with blends from both a usage and warranty standpoint. Consider the compressor manufacturer who finds a blend in use that satisfies all the thermodynamic needs of the system but does not return oil to compressor satisfactorily. If you were the manufacturer, would you want that blend used in your system? Approval of blends for use as acceptable alternatives to ozone-depleting substances rests with the EPA group called SNAP (Significant New Alternative Program), which will be covered later.

One of the primary concerns with the new blends is that many will not perform with the mineral oils used in existing systems. The use of different oils has become necessary (oils are covered in Chapter Four), and there is continuing research into which blend will work with which oil to meet a system's needs. In the world of alternative refrigerants, we have just started to meet industry needs.

Fractionation and Glide

Blends may have two or three molecules present in the refrigerant mixture. Because of this construction, certain blends are subject to *fractionation.* Fractionation occurs when one of the refrigerants behaves as a single refrigerant rather than a part of the blend.

An example of fractionation is when a leak develops and one of the refrigerant molecules in the blend leaks faster than another refrigerant molecule present in the blend. When this leakage occurs, the composition of the blend can change. If the blend is in a pure liquid or entirely vapor state, then the composition of the mixture is complete. Fractionation occurs when both liquid and vapor are present at the same time — *not* when the refrigerant is in a pure liquid or vapor state. If a leaking system is improperly topped off with a blend, the proportion of the blend may change. One of the best ways to reduce the possibility of fractionation is to charge with liquid. Charging with liquid helps ensure that the original composition of the blend is maintained as much as possible.

Temperature glide is a new phenomenon in the world of refrigerants. Some blends may evaporate or condense over a range of temperatures at a constant pressure, rather than at just one temperature for a constant pressure. This range can vary from 2° to 12°F for a given pressure. The amount of glide depends on the composition of the refrigerant blend.

In the past when we handled a refrigerant, the temperature-pressure relationship was the absolute guide. When setting superheat, the temperature-pressure chart stated that at a certain pressure the refrigerant was at a precise temperature. When setting superheat with a blended refrigerant, glide must be considered. As change of state occurs, there can be a different temperature-pressure relationship for each component in the blend. At a stated pressure, one refrigerant component may be evaporating or condensing at one temperature, while another component is at another temperature. The different temperatures occur at the same pressure. The difference between the two temperatures is *glide.*

Table 3-1 illustrates the difference between a single compound refrigerant and a NARM composed of R-22, R-152a, and R-124.

Refrigerant	Pressure (psia)	Phase	Temperature (° F)
R-12	100	Liquid phase	80.83
	100	Vapor phase	80.83
Blended mixture	100	Vapor phase	75.08
	100	Liquid phase	67.79

Table 3-1. Single compound refrigerant compared to a NARM

Azeotropic, Zeotropic, and Near Azeotropic Mixtures

As stated earlier, blends are classified as azeotropic, zeotropic, or near azeotropic mixtures (NARMs). These classifications are based on the structure and behavior of the refrigerant. Retrofitting a system with blends will be discussed in a later chapter, but for now, it is important to remember that when charging a system with a blend, the charge should be liquid and weighed in to the high side of the system.

AZEOTROPES

A pure azeotropic refrigerant is a blend which, for all practical purposes, will behave as a single refrigerant at a specified temperature and pressure. When mixed in precise proportions, an azeotropic mixture can be viewed as two refrigerants behaving as if they were a single compound refrigerant. The mixture has a single boiling point at a given temperature and pressure. This single boiling point does not necessarily exist throughout the full range of pressures; however, the variation is generally not of concern in system operation. *Note: When the azeotropic mixture is in the system it may not always behave as a single compound because under certain conditions separation may occur. If separation occurs, the effect of this separation is negligible and normally is not a cause for concern.*

Azeotropic mixtures have been around a long time. Two of the more familiar azeotropic mixtures are R-500 and R-502. When system service is performed, azeotropic mixtures can be treated the same as a single compound refrigerant. Beyond the azeotropic application defined maximum and minimum boiling point, minimal fractionation and glide can occur. These occurrences should not be a concern for the technician. Use the azeotrope for the recommended application, and handle the azeotrope as the manufacturer recommends.

Chlorine is present in certain azeotropic refrigerants. Refrigerant manufacturers are attempting to solve this problem by developing azeotropes that do not contain chlorine. Earlier we discussed a single compound refrigerant (HFC), which does not contain chlorine. Table 3-2 shows the composition and usage of several azeotropic refrigerants. Note that R-152a, R-125, and R-143a are HFCs.

ASHRAE Number	Composition	Usage
R-500	R-12 (73.8%) R-152a (26.2%)	Chillers
R-502	R-22 (48.8%) R-115 (51.2%)	Low-temperature, transport, and industrial refrigeration
R-507	R-125 (50%) R-143a (50%)	Low- and medium-temperature R-22 replacement, AZ50 blend to replace R-502

Table 3-2. Azeotropic refrigerants

Because azeotropic mixtures are easy to handle, refrigerant manufacturers are continuing to explore the creation of replacement refrigerants that behave as azeotropes.

ZEOTROPES

A zeotropic refrigerant blend uses two or more refrigerants that have different vapor pressures and boiling points. A zeotropic refrigerant contains two or more molecules and can be a different composition when it evaporates or condenses. When the zeotrope is under a constant pressure, the evaporating and condensing temperatures can change with composition. During change of state, the boiling point of the refrigerant changes under constant pressure, because the composition of the refrigerant changes over a defined temperature range called glide.

An easy way to understand the behavior of a zeotrope is to imagine two dissimilar fluids in a state where both liquid and vapor are present. Assume the first fluid has a different boiling point than the second fluid. When heat is applied to this fluid mixture, the first fluid boils and turns to vapor sooner than the second fluid. When this occurs, the composition of the liquid changes, because the first fluid has boiled first, leaving more of the second fluid.

Table 3-3 illustrates some of the alternative zeotropic refrigerants that are currently in use. Detailed information on the particular refrigerants is available in Part Two of this book. The inclusion or exclusion of a particular refrigerant does not represent either an endorsement or lack of endorsement.

ASHRAE Number	Composition	Alternative Designation	Alternative Usage
R-400	R-12 (60%) R-114 (40%)	Genetron 12/114 Freon 12/114	Industrial air conditioning, high condensing temperatures
R-401A	R-22 (53%) R-152a (13%) R-124 (34%)	Genetron MP39 Suva MP39	R-12 alternative
R-401B	R-22 (61%) R-152a (11%) R-124 (28%)	Suva MP66	R-12 alternative
R-402A	R-125 (60%) R-290 (2%) R-22 (38%)	Suva HP80	R-502 alternative
R-402B	R-125 (38%) R-290 (2%) R-22 (60%)	Suva HP81	R-502 alternative
R-403A	R-290 R-22 R-218	Isceon 69S	R-502 alternative
R-403B	R-290 (5%) R-22 (56%) R-218 (39%)	Isceon 69L	R-502 alternative
R-404A	R-125 (44%) R-143a (52%) R-134a (4%)	Suva HP62 Forane FX70	R-502 alternative
R-406A	R-22 (55%) R-142B (41%) R-600a (4%)	Indianapolis Refrigerant Products R-406a	R-12 substitute as a drop-in for certain applications

R-407A	R-32 (20%) R-125 (40%) R-134a (40%)	KLEA 60	R-22 high-temperature replacement used in a/c and HP applications
R-407B	R-32 (10%) R-125 (70%) R-134a (20%)	KLEA 61	R-502 alternative for low- and medium-temperature applications
R-407C	R-32 (23%) R-125 (25%) R-134a (52%)	Suva AC9000 KLEA 66	Alternative for R-22 and R-502 applications
R-408A	R-22 (47%) R-125 (7%) R-143a (46%)	Forane FX10	R-502 alternative for medium- and low-temperature applications
R-409A	R-22 (60%) R-124 (25%) R-142b (15%)	Forane FX56	R-12 alternative for low- to medium-temperature, small hermetic applications where R134a cannot be used
R-410A	R-32 (50%) R-125 (50%)	AZ20	Azeotropic replacement for R-22

Table 3-3. Zeotropic mixtures

NARMs

As you read various manufacturer's information, you will find that certain manufacturers discuss azeotropes and zeotropes while other manufacturers discuss azeotropes and NARMs and do not mention zeotropes. We are discussing all three so that you are familiar with the terms. Current conventions state that a NARM is a zeotropic mixture that will exhibit a lesser degree of glide. In behavior, a NARM is closer to an azeotrope. A zeotrope, on the other hand, exhibits a much larger glide range. The actual range of glide is subject to interpretation. What is important to remember is that *all zeotropes are NARMs*. Temperature glide is the key to their difference.

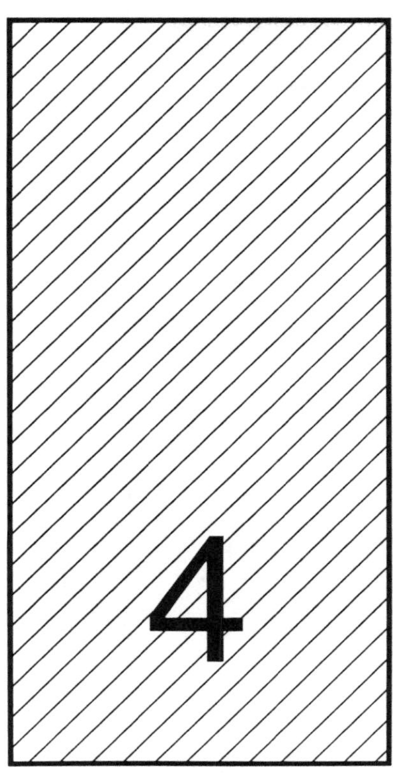

Single Compound Refrigerants

For years our industry used single compound refrigerants and azeotropes, such as R-12, R-22, R-11, R-502, and R-500. In response to the ozone layer crisis, alternative refrigerants such as R-134a and R-123 were created, and a whole new world of refrigerants was born.

A major advantage of single compound refrigerants is that they are not subject to fractionation or glide. In the event of a system leak, a single compound refrigerant may be added to the system without changing the overall composition of the refrigerant. As discussed in the previous chapter, this is not necessarily the case when using blends.

Refrigerants used to be constructed of hydrocarbons, which meant their molecular composition consisted of hydrogen and carbon atoms (pure hydrocarbon). The hydrogen and carbon atoms built molecules of methane and ethane. In later refrigerants, the pure hydrocarbon molecule was changed by removing all of the hydrogen and adding chlorine and fluorine (halocarbons), creating a chlorofluorocarbon (CFC). When all of the hydrogen is removed and replaced by halocarbons, a fully halogenated refrigerant (no hydrogen atoms) is created. When some of the hydrogen atoms were removed and chlorine and fluorine were added, a partially halogenated refrigerant (HCFC) was created. It is important to understand that the presence of hydrogen in the molecule causes the molecule to be less stable.

In chemistry, the term *stable* can be defined as less likely to decompose or fall apart. In the case of refrigerants as they relate to the atmosphere, less stable is better. A CFC is very stable, an HCFC is less stable, and both contain chlorine. Chlorine is the villain in the destruction of the ozone layer. The less stable the molecule, the better the chance it will "fall apart" in the atmosphere. The quicker the molecule falls apart, the less danger chlorine poses to the ozone layer. The fact that the HCFC family is less of a threat to the ozone layer does mean that HCFCs are excluded from regulation. Legally at this point, R-22 production will cease in the year 2030; however, there are forces driving to remove HCFCs from production as early as the year 2005.

By now you must know that a CFC or an HCFC refrigerant cannot be vented to the atmosphere. *Note: Effective November 14, 1995 you cannot vent any refrigerant to the atmosphere, including the HFC family.* Many equipment manufacturers are studying the use of an HCFC alternative because of the impending phaseout. The presence of chlorine in refrigerants such as R-12, R-11, and R-22 is the concern, and chlorine-based refrigerants will eventually disappear.

Single Compound Alternatives

Wherever possible, the focus is on single compound refrigerants such as R-134a (an HFC) and R-123 (an HCFC), because they are easier to handle. R-134a and R-123 are two alternatives that are widely used in specific applications. Currently, there is considerable research being conducted with these two refrigerants for both original and retrofit applications. Intended applications cover everything from automobiles to chillers.

R-134a is used as the original refrigerant in automobiles rolling off the assembly lines today. As a replacement for R-12, R-134a is also being used in residential, commercial, and industrial air conditioning and refrigeration applications. The use of R-134a in foam blowing and aerosol applications is also being pursued. R-134a is a single compound refrigerant. Remember that fractionation and glide are not concerns with single compound refrigerants. However, R-134a is not a drop-in replacement for R-12.

R-134a

R-134a is characterized by the following points:

- Contains hydrogen, fluorine, and carbon (CF_3CH_2F)
- Has an ODP of zero and a GWP of 0.285
- Has a boiling point of -14.9°F (R-12 has a boiling point of -21.6°F)
- Has a low toxicity (allowable exposure limit (AEL) is 1,000 ppm)
- Is not flammable; however, as with most refrigerants, it will displace oxygen, which may cause asphyxiation. In addition, at pressures as low as 5.5 psig, R-134a can be combustible when mixed with air concentrations greater than 60%.

When R-134a is used on a retrofit, there are concerns about lubrication. The mineral-based oils that are used with R-12 are fully miscible, and in an R-12 application, the mineral-based oil returns to the compressor without a problem. This is not the case with R-134a. The lack of chlorine in R-134a may cause concerns in relation to miscibility, which is why the mineral oil lubricants may not work with R-134a.

Polyalkylene glycol (PAG) and *polyol ester* (POE) are the two lubricants currently favored for R-134a retrofit. The PAG family of lubricants was first favored in automotive applications. In hvac applications, most compressor manufacturers are recommending POEs. When retrofitting a system to R-134a, it will be necessary to change the mineral-based oil and follow a flushing procedure. These flushing procedures are time consuming, but they are extremely important for system survival. You must consult the manufacturer's data for the proper flushing method, and then check for any residual mineral-based oils that may have been missed. Later chapters will offer an overview of the oil changing procedure, and Part Two of this book gives manufacturers' specific recommendations.

Current equipment is now being delivered with R-134a as the original refrigerant. From a service perspective, it is important to know which refrigerant is in the system before attempting service. Consult the manufacturer's data to ensure you are working with the correct refrigerant. The addition of R-134a into a system containing R-12 will cause disaster. Always use the temperature-pressure relationship and accepted field techniques to identify the refrigerant if it is unknown.

There are concerns about material compatibility when retrofitting a system. Depending on the application, components may have to be changed to function correctly. When R-134a replaces R-12 in a chiller application, the compressor may require modifications. There are also compatibility concerns in automotive applications when R-134a is used with existing system components. As with everything else, check the manufacturer's data before undertaking a major change.

R-123

R-123 is a replacement for R-11; however, it will eventually be phased out, because it is an HCFC. R-123 is not a drop-in replacement. R-123 is a single compound refrigerant that has the following characteristics:

- Contains chlorine, fluorine, hydrogen, and carbon ($CHCl_2CF_3$)
- Has an ODP of 0.02 and a GWP of 0.02
- Has a boiling point of 82°F
- Has an AEL between 10 ppm and 30 ppm. *Note: Technicians should be trained on the hazards of R-123 and be aware of the exposure limits. Consult the manufacturer's data when handling this or other refrigerants. R-123 is not a cleaning agent and should not be used where it cannot be contained inside the equipment.*
- Is not flammable; however, as with most refrigerants, it will displace oxygen, which may cause asphyxiation.
- Fractionation and glide are not a concern
- Classified as B1 under ASHRAE 34-1992

R-123 is not compatible with certain materials in existing chiller applications. For a retrofit, changes may have to be made to the existing system. Material compatibility concerns exist in areas such as gaskets, o-rings, seals, and insulation in hermetic compressors. In addition, gear sets and impellers may have to be replaced because of possible capacity and efficiency loss in unmodified equipment.

Because of the potential difference in capacity and efficiency, any possible retrofit must be analyzed from an efficiency standpoint. If the existing system is undersized, a retrofit will only create more problems. When considering a retrofit, seek competent advice from professionals — *do not just change refrigerants and hope for the best.*

OTHER ALTERNATIVES

Other alternative refrigerants are being used in applications that are more specialized in nature. These refrigerants include the following:

- R-23 (an HFC) - A low-temperature replacement for R-13 and R-503, which is used in the low stage of cascade systems.
- R-32 (an HFC) - Replacement for R-22 applications; however, there are flammability concerns. When used in blends, there will be fewer concerns about flammability; however, leakage in blends can also raise concerns.
- R-124 (an HCFC) - Alternative for R-12 in sterilizing gas; alternative for R-11 and R-12 in foam applications. It is an R-114 replacement in air conditioning and refrigeration marine chillers.
- R-125 (an HFC) - Replacement for R-502 in low-temperature applications. R-125 has a low critical temperature, therefore, its use as a stand alone is limited.

AMMONIA

There are other refrigerants, such as ammonia, that are non-ozone depleting and have been used in the past. Ammonia contains nitrogen and hydrogen and is not considered a threat to the ozone layer. Many in the industry are looking at using ammonia and other refrigerants as a replacement for the ozone-depleting groups. As with every alternative, there are trade-offs. The application of ammonia to a system that is piped through a public area could eventually cause considerable damage and also violate codes. When it comes to replacement refrigerants, the technician will have to consider each unit individually.

What Refrigerant to Use

You can no longer walk up to a unit, change out the evaporator, and let the charge go flying into the breeze. From a technician's standpoint, you are now faced with decisions on refrigerant applications that did not even exist ten years ago.

When repairing a unit, consider the future use of the unit and the customer's pocketbook. Refrigerant management is a new term that must become a part of every technician's vocabulary. The majority of our customers do not understand how a system functions and more importantly what should be done to meet future needs. From a practical standpoint, a technician must consider whether or not it is time to replace the existing refrigerant with an alternative.

A system containing a CFC is not illegal or even dangerous to the environment if the system is operating and leak free. Anyone who proposes changing the refrigerant to an environmentally acceptable refrigerant in an existing system should consider that the change may not be necessary. As a technician you cannot ignore the existing refrigerant; however, the decision to replace the refrigerant must be based on both technical and economic factors.

Some of the technical questions that should be asked include the following:

- Is the refrigerant environmentally acceptable? Does it have a low ODP, meet GWP ratings, and at least meet an acceptable TEWI rating (discussed later in this chapter)?

- Is the refrigerant safe from a toxicity, exposure, and flammability standpoint? Think of the potential for concern in using propane in an automotive R-12 application.

- Will the operational pressures and temperatures exceed the system's capabilities? A replacement that creates a high discharge temperature will not work for long from the compressor's standpoint.

- How will the refrigerant react with the existing materials in the system? In some cases using an alternative may require that certain components be changed.

- Is there a usable and available oil to replace the existing mineral oil base?

- How difficult will the oil changeover be?

Some of the economic questions that should be asked include the following:

- What is the estimated remaining useful life of the system? If the system's expected remaining life is short, does it make sense to retrofit?

- Is the system currently operating as required and leak free? If the system is operating to expectations, why is the change being made?

- Who owns the equipment? Many of the questions that will occur can only be answered by the owner of the equipment. Most tenants do not know the landlord's long-term plans.
- Is the currently used refrigerant available at an appropriate cost? It may be better to stay with the existing refrigerant, because age and application become critical factors.
- Is there a single drop-in replacement available? If not, what will it cost to retrofit the system as opposed to continuing use of the existing refrigerant?

Total Equivalent Warming Impact (TEWI)

An earlier chapter referred to the term global warming potential (GWP). GWP is a *direct* calculated measure of a refrigerant's effect on the environment when it enters the atmosphere. While global warming is a consideration in using a refrigerant, there are other factors that must be considered.

Total equivalent warming impact (TEWI) is the measured calculation that considers these other factors, which are really *indirect* contributors to global warming. Consider, for example, a unit that has a low efficiency rating. Replacement of the unit with a higher SEER would use less power to accomplish the same amount of cooling. The same is also true of the refrigerant; however, if the system is less efficient because the alternative refrigerant has a lower ODP and GWP efficiency, we can be trading concerns. If the system does not vent to the atmosphere, there is no direct effect on ODP or GWP; however, if the system is less efficient because the alternative refrigerant is less efficient, there may be increased concern from an environmental standpoint. This example is considered to be an indirect contributor to GWP. The energy to run the system can come from a fossil fuel source. If the system is using more energy to accomplish the same amount of cooling, more CO_2 is being exhausted to the atmosphere by the coal-fueled power plant. CO_2 is considered a prime culprit in global warming. An alternative refrigerant should have zero ODP and a lower GWP than the refrigerant it is replacing. TEWI measures both the *direct* and *indirect* effects of the alternative refrigerant and will be a baseline measurement in the future.

Much has yet to be learned about alternative refrigerants. Oils, applications, service procedures, and long-term performance are still under study. A system that is sound, well maintained, and leak free is not hurting the environment. Change for the sake of change just will not work. The answers to the earlier questions should be the basis for any retrofit situation.

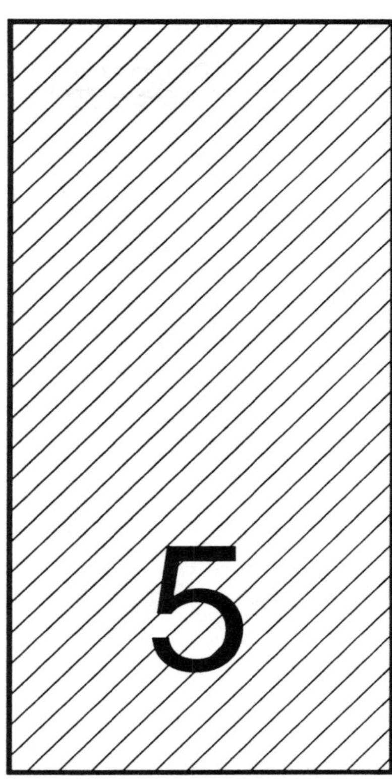

Oils

Until the introduction of alternative refrigerants, the oils used in hvac/r applications were standard. Currently, there is no acceptable oil that meets all the needs of different systems using alternative refrigerants. New systems coming from the factory using alternative refrigerants will use a new generation of oils. On a retrofit application, this will not be the case. The technician will be responsible for specifying the refrigerant and the appropriate oil, which will not always be easy. The safest oil to use is the one the manufacturer specifies; however, the origin of the equipment being serviced will be questionable. Whether to use a mineral-based oil or one of the new generation of lubricants is a decision you must be prepared to make.

Oil in a refrigeration system serves many purposes. Oils used in refrigeration are different from those used in automobiles. This difference exists because the composition and properties of refrigerant oils have been designed to meet the specific needs of refrigeration systems. For an oil to work effectively within a refrigeration system, the oil must behave in a manner that meets the needs of the system under every conceivable operating temperature range. With alternative refrigerants, questions arise as to material compatibility, moisture capacity, and what effect the new oil will have on the lubrication needs of the compressor.

R-134a is an approved, environmentally acceptable, chlorine-free replacement for R-12 in specific applications. One of the biggest concerns in retrofitting an R-12 system is that the mineral-based oil used with R-12 *cannot be used in a system using R-134a.* The oil that is used with R-12 is incompatible with HFC-based refrigerants. Incompatibility between oils and the new alternatives is not limited to R-12 and R-134a. Many of the alternatives have identical concerns. Therefore, when changing to alternative blends, the oil that will be used becomes a serious consideration.

Oil Function

Everyone knows that oils are used to lubricate a system. Try running your automobile without oil and you will very shortly find out the effects of not providing lubrication. An oil's basic function is to reduce the wear between two moving parts. When two pieces of metal rub against each other, wear and friction result. The presence of oil between the two metal surfaces forms a film that reduces the wear/friction. The oil film allows the parts to last longer and to move against each other more smoothly. When parts move with less friction they not only last longer but less energy is required to move them. Oil may also serve to seal the two surfaces being lubricated.

Oil's first function in a refrigeration system is lubricating the surfaces between moving parts. A thin film of oil is present between the connecting rod and the crankshaft. The presence of this film keeps the surfaces from touching each other. The lesser degree of physical contact between the two surfaces ensures they will last longer.

The second function is that oil acts as a seal. The space between the piston and the cylinder walls of a reciprocating compressor are covered with a film of oil. Not only is lubrication occurring, but the film of oil is acting as a seal to help prevent gases from blowing by. Oil also acts to absorb noise and assist in heat transfer between the components.

An important difference in many refrigeration systems is that the oil is carried by the refrigerant through the system in order to return to the compressor. If the properties of the oil are such that oil return is impeded, then partial or total system failure will result. If oil is coating the walls of the evaporator, what do you think happens to heat transfer in the system?

Properties of Oil

The following terminology is important to know when working with oils. The definitions that follow are not precise scientific definitions but rather definitions designed to give you a basic understanding of certain oil properties.

Cloud point: Wax settling out of the oil at a given temperature will cause the oil to become cloudy. A low cloud point for an oil in a low-temperature system is important. Wax can reduce heat transfer and plug orifices.

Compatibility: One of the concerns with alternative refrigerants is whether or not an oil or refrigerant mixture is compatible with the materials used in the system. The oil and refrigerant must not react with the materials or problems will occur.

Dielectric strength: A measurement of an oil's electrical resistance capability. Low dielectric strength can result in grounded windings in a hermetic compressor.

Flash point: When the vapor from a heated oil flashes at a given temperature.

Floc point: The temperature at which wax settles out of oil. The measurement is based on a mixture that is 10% oil and 90% refrigerant.

Foaming: The pressure drop that occurs at start-up that can cause the refrigerant to boil out of the oil in the crankcase.

Hygroscopicity: The ability of an oil to absorb water. Certain new oils are more hygroscopic than oils previously used. Improper storage of the oil will allow an unacceptable level of moisture in the oil.

Miscibility: The ability of substances to mix together. Refrigerant and oil must mix together. The refrigerant acts as a carrier to return the oil to the compressor. *Note: Mineral oils are not miscible with pure HFC refrigerants.*

Pour point: The lowest temperature at which oil will flow. An oil's pour point should always be below the lowest evaporating temperature.

Solubility: A quality of a substance that allows it to be dissolved in another substance (usually liquid) under a given set of conditions. Refrigerant oils and refrigerant should be soluble with each other, or else at certain temperatures they may separate into phases and the refrigerant oil may not return to the compressor.

Stability: The measure of an oil's ability to do its job. An oil should not break down or react with other components in the system.

Viscosity: The oil's resistance to flow. The viscosity of an oil is measured in *Saybolt Seconds Universal* (SSU). The SSU number is a measurement of how fast oil will flow through a capillary tube of measured length and diameter at a given temperature. If it takes 100 seconds for oil to flow through the tube, the oil has an SSU number of 100. A higher number indicates a higher viscosity, hence a thicker oil. Operating temperatures and the percentage of refrigerant within a system will also affect the viscosity of an oil. An increase in temperature and refrigerant presence will generally decrease the viscosity of oil.

Oil Types

Oils have usually been classed as animal, vegetable, or mineral. However, many alternative refrigerants use synthetic oils, which are showing the most promise for a wide variety of applications.

ANIMAL AND VEGETABLE

Animal and vegetable oils are not widely used in the refrigeration industry, because they are subject to composition change and have a narrow viscosity range. After animal and vegetable oils are processed, they can easily change composition, and they have a natural tendency to form acid or gum. The refrigeration industry requires a wide range of viscosities to satisfy the wide temperature ranges of various systems.

MINERAL

The mineral oil family is made up of three different types: paraffinic, naphthenic, and aromatics.

Paraffinic oil may be used to oil an electric motor. It comes directly from crude oil. It is not used much in the refrigeration industry, because paraffinics have a high wax content and solubility problems.

Naphthenic oils used in refrigeration may come from naphthenic crude. These oils are refined directly from crude oil. Naphthenic-based oils have low wax content, low pour point, and low viscosity. The difference between paraffinic and naphthenic oil is where the crude oil originates; paraffinic crude comes from the eastern United States and naphthenic crude comes from the western United States.

Many synthetic oils in use today are derived from aromatic oils. These synthetic oils are of most interest to the industry at this point in time.

An important point to remember is that mineral oil cannot be used with pure HFC refrigerants, due to concerns regarding mineral oil's ability to lubricate when chlorine is not present. Miscibility is also a problem with pure HFCs. Some research shows that there may also be a solubility problem with the HCFC family of refrigerant blends and mineral oils. Alkylbenzene synthetics (discussed later) appear to work much better with the HCFC blends compared to paraffinic and naphthenic mineral oils.

Using the wrong oil in a system will result in performance/efficiency and possibly component failure. The correct oil for a particular application is the one that the manufacturer specifies. In many cases, total removal of the previous oil will be required. Compressor, refrigerant, and equipment manufacturers are now researching the long-term effects of new oils in systems.

SYNTHETIC

Alkylbenzenes, esters, and glycol are three types of synthetics currently being researched for specific applications. Research shows there is no single synthetic that will work best for all different refrigerant applications. Some oils will not work with the HFC family, others are not soluble with HCFCs, and many are very hygroscopic.

Alkylbenzene (AB)

Alkylbenzene is made from propylene and benzene. Because it is a synthetic oil, AB's composition can be uniform. It does not rely on the quality of crude oil as mineral oils do. Uniform consistency over the wide range of temperatures is a crucial requirement for an oil.

HCFC blends can work with alkylbenzene oils with up to a 20% maximum concentration of mineral oil. Using an AB helps resolve the solubility problem that exists when paraffinic- or naphthenic-based oils are used with blends. When retrofit to certain blends occurs, the flushing that is necessary compared with some of the other oils (e.g., POEs) can be minimized.

Polyalkylene Glycol (PAG)

Polyalkylene glycol was first used with R-134a in automotive applications. PAG oils are being tested for use with R-134a; however, they are not completely soluble, and separation has been known to occur in the condenser. PAG oils can attract and hold moisture (hygroscopic), which is not a good characteristic for a refrigeration oil. PAG oils are also incompatible with chlorine and have poor lubrication ability with certain metal combinations. Retrofit use on a R-12 system requires total removal of all CFCs and mineral oils. Overall, PAGs do not appear to be a very good candidate for refrigeration applications.

Polyol Ester (POE)

A major focus in refrigeration is the use of polyol esters (POEs) as lubricants. More and more of the alternatives are chlorine-free refrigerants, and POEs show definite potential. The increased use of HFC refrigerants has driven the need for an oil that works with HFCs and still provides the necessary lubrication characteristics of mineral oil-based lubricants.

Some of the positive characteristics of POEs are as follows:

- Potentially, they are the closest to an "all around" lubricant for some of the new alternatives.
- They have better thermal stability.
- Manufacturer specified and tested POEs can provide the same lubrication qualities as a mineral-based oil.
- Manufacturer specified POEs in a compressor can be used in a system containing mineral oil.
- Copeland states that POEs are "backward compatible with mineral oil," which means that a compressor containing POE can be installed in a refrigeration system that contains mineral oil. Furthermore, they state that "POEs we recommend are compatible with all refrigerants, so that a compressor containing POE can be installed in a system that contains CFCs, HCFCs, or the new HFCs."
- They are similar to a mineral-based oil from a lubrication and miscibility standpoint.
- They are completely wax free.
- Replacing a portion of the original mineral oil with a POE can begin the flushing process for later HFC conversion.

- They are more polar than mineral oils, therefore they can be "designed" to meet the solubility and miscibility needs of an HFC refrigerant.
- Their viscosity varies less with temperature than mineral oils.
- They are biodegradable.

Some of the negative characteristics of POEs are as follows:

- When exposed to air, POEs will attract moisture more readily than mineral oils. Introducing the moisture laden oil to the system will cause system problems.
- Their greater ability to hold moisture makes vacuuming a system much more difficult.
- When using a POE-based oil, the container must be kept sealed and the oil stored in its original container. A plastic storage container may be permeable. Copeland only approves POEs that are stored in metal cans because of the moisture permeability problem. *Note: Make sure the system is kept sealed except when actually working on it. Leaving a system open during a break or overnight will cause unacceptable moisture levels. Do not add POE oil to a system if the maximum moisture content exceeds 50 ppm.*
- Filter driers may remove some of the additives from a POE-based oil. New drier designs that work with POE and HFC systems should be used in POE systems.
- They are currently more expensive.
- There is no long-term operating experience to find out what POEs will do to a system.

As with everything else, use the manufacturer's recommendations for the system you are servicing.

Flushing

Retrofitting is always a complicated procedure. In today's service environment, a major portion of a retrofit is the flushing of oil that exists in the system being retrofitted. Procedures are being developed that will make flushing easier, but for now, certain basic steps must be followed.

Choosing the type of oil and following a proper flushing process are the keys to success. Depending on the refrigerant and the oil, you may be required to flush many times, add another type of oil to an existing mineral oil-based system to complete service, and/or establish a platform for removing an oil that is not compatible with the new alternative.

Always make sure that the old oil in the system is identified before being removed and/or replaced with an oil that will function with the new refrigerant.

The oil used with the new refrigerant is specified by the compressor, refrigerant, and component manufacturers. Compressor manufacturers provide data sheets that are specific to the compressor, which contain the data on the oil that must be used with the new refrigerant.

The following is a generic flushing procedure for a system that contains R-12 and mineral oil, which is being retrofitted to R-134a with POE:

1. Identify the oil that will be used with the replacement refrigerant. Depending on the refrigerant to be used, total removal of the existing mineral oil will probably be necessary.
2. Isolate the compressor from the system.
3. Drain the existing mineral oil. Mineral oil is compatible with CFC and HCFC refrigerants but not HFC refrigerants.
4. Fill the reservoir with the new manufacturer specified ester oil having the recommended viscosity. The presence of the CFC refrigerant with the ester oil will help remove any remaining mineral oil.
5. Run the system for 24 hours.
6. Check a sample of the system's oil for cloudiness and discoloration. If the sample is not close to the clarity of the new oil, repeat steps 3, 4, and 5. Repeating these steps more than once may be necessary depending on the size and the piping of the system.
7. When the sample appears to be acceptable, check it with a refractometer or test kit to determine what concentration of mineral oil remains in the system. The current acceptable level of residual mineral oil concentration is 5% or less.
8. Recover the CFC refrigerant.
9. Charge the system with R-134a.

Table 5-1 shows some of the possibilities that exist when retrofitting to an alternative. The percentages at the bottom of the chart represent the degree of cross contamination possible when changing oils.

Refrigerant	First Choice	Second Choice
R-11	MO	———
R-12	MO or AB	POE
R-13	MO or AB	POE
R-22	MO or AB	POE
R-23	POE[A]	———
Suva 123	MO or AB	———
Suva 134a	POE[A]	———
R-500	MO or AB	POE
R-502	MO or AB	POE
R-503	MO or AB	POE
Suva AC9000	POE[A]	———
Suva HP62	POE[A]	———
Suva HP80	AB[B]	POE[B]
Suva HP81	AB[B]	POE[B]
Suva MP39	AB[B]	POE[B]
Suva MP66	AB[B]	POE[B]

MO = Mineral Oil AB = Alkylbenzene POE = Polyol Ester
[A] = Maximum 5% MO or AB in POE
[B] = Maximum 20% MO in AB or POE

Note: Where possible use OEM recommended oil type, charge size, and viscosity.

Table 5-1. Suggested oil guide *(Courtesy, Dupont)*

Oil Disposal

Much has been written on the procedures that are involved in handling oil. In most cases, the oil used in refrigeration systems is not considered a hazardous waste. EPA took this position in order to encourage refrigerant recovery, recycling, and reclaiming. A primary rule to follow when dealing with refrigerant oil is that the oil must be stored in a proper container and properly labeled. From a practical standpoint, the safest way to deal with oil is to establish a working relationship with a local oil reclaimer and follow the procedures that the firm requires. Certain states have regulations that require oil to be handled as a hazardous waste. These rules are superior to the federal government's position, and you are required to conform to these regulations. As a technician or contractor, you must learn the requirements for handling oil in your area.

There are already regulations in place that govern the handling of oil, particularly waste oil. The regulations establish requirements such as the quantity of oil handled, condition of the oil, and handling procedures. Under these regulations, specific procedures exist for waste oil storage and handling. As a service technician, you must follow those regulations; you cannot just throw oil removed from a compressor into the trash bin. You have a legal obligation to dispose of oil properly. EPA maintains information lines that will help you understand the requirements for handling oil properly.

Retrofit

Oil retrofit was discussed in the previous chapter. This chapter will look at what is involved in changing the refrigerant and oil to allow the system to operate with the new alternatives. R-12 is disappearing and in its place are HCFC and HFC alternatives. R-134a will replace R-12 in certain applications, but the removal of mineral oil that is used with R-12 must be accomplished. Using alternative blends that are HCFC based lessens concerns about oil; however, HCFC refrigerants are also targeted for major regulations and eventual phaseout.

The usual retrofits will either involve R-134a and a POE oil or a blend such as MP39 with an AB-based oil.

Retrofitting a System

The following procedures were compiled from different sources and are intended to provide a guideline for a retrofit. The first step in a successful retrofit is to identify the system being serviced and research what the manufacturer recommends for that unit. The manufacturer may recommend that certain components be changed or identify certain materials that are incompatible with the new refrigerant. With R-134a, component change or material compatibility is not as much of a concern as it is with R-123. Between equipment manufacturers, refrigerant manufacturers, associations, and oil manufacturers, information is available to ensure the best possible chance for a successful retrofit.

SINGLE COMPOUND POE RETROFIT WITH R-134a

Before starting the retrofit, measure and record data from the current system. If the system being retrofitted is operating, then take measurements to establish an operational baseline with R-12. Measurements should include: temperatures and pressures at the evaporator, condenser, compressor suction, and discharge; superheat; subcooling; and amperage draw. If readings indicate a problem, correct the problem before proceeding with the retrofit. If the readings are on target, then record them for use when setting up the system after the retrofit is complete.

At this point, different manufacturers recommend different paths. The following instructions are compiled from recommendations made by different manufacturers. You must check the data for the system you are servicing. In certain pieces of equipment Path A may start the process, while in other pieces of equipment Path B may start the process. The possible paths are different because of compressor type and system size. The major difference is whether or not refrigerant recovery will occur before the oil changeover is undertaken.

Path A

1. Recover the refrigerant from the system, then weigh and store the recovered refrigerant. Recovery not only helps ensure supplies for the future, it is also illegal to vent refrigerant. Weighing the recovered charge will provide a basis for the amount of new refrigerant to be added to the system.

Path B

1. Drain the oil from the compressor and system. If there are no drain plugs, you may have to remove the compressor to drain the oil. If the system has drain plugs, drain at the crankcase. Depending on the size and piping of the system, you may also have to look for low spots in the system where oil may be accumulating. Do not forget that the accumulator and the oil separator can also hold oil. The ultimate goal is to have a mineral oil content of 5% or less.

2. Drain the oil from the compressor and system. If there are no drain plugs, you may have to remove the compressor to drain the oil. If the system has drain plugs, drain at the crankcase. Depending on the size and piping of the system, you may also have to look for low spots in the system where oil may be accumulating. Do not forget that the accumulator and the oil separator can also hold oil. The ultimate goal is to have a mineral oil content of 5% or less.	2. Measure the amount of oil that is removed from the compressor. Measuring the oil will tell you how much to replace. Knowing how much oil has been removed will allow you to check the unit's specifications against the original charge to see how much oil you have recovered.
3. Measure the amount of oil that is removed from the compressor. Measuring the oil will tell you how much to replace. Knowing how much oil has been removed will allow you to check the unit's specifications against the original charge to see how much oil you have recovered.	3. Replace the oil in the system with the POE oil of equal volume. Adding the POE at this point will help ensure miscibility of the two oils.
4. Replace the oil in the system with the POE oil of equal volume. Overcharging oil can lead to serious problems. Check specifications for the POE oil and add the proper amount.	4. Operate the system with the existing refrigerant charge. The system will now be operating with R-12 and mineral oil/POE. The goal is to reach a 5% or less concentration of mineral oil. Run the system and recheck oil until the 5% goal is achieved. During the run time the oil may have to be drained and replaced two or three times.

5. Install the new filter-drier and any component that may be required by the equipment manufacturer. Replace the filter-drier core with a new core or compacted bead desiccant. Make sure that the refrigerant is compatible with existing seals. If the system has a sight glass, check that it will register moisture at a level of 150 ppm.	5. Recover the refrigerant from the system, then weigh and store the recovered refrigerant. Recovery not only helps ensure supplies for the future, it is also illegal to vent refrigerant. Weighing the recovered charge will provide a basis for the amount of new refrigerant to be added to the system.
6. Evacuate and leak test the system. Today's service procedures require a deep vacuum to at least 1500/1000/500 microns. Many manufacturers recommend a different minimum; however, they all agree that electronic measurement of vacuum is essential. Use a micron gauge when measuring vacuum. Manifold gauges are not as accurate.	6. Install the new filter-drier and any component that may be required by the equipment manufacturer. Replace the filter-drier core with a new core or compacted bead desiccant. Make sure that the refrigerant is compatible with existing seals. If the system has a sight glass, check that it will register moisture at a level of 150 ppm.
7. Charge the system with R-134a. A rule of thumb is that the new charge in a medium- or high-temperature system will be 90% of the original charge. Charging by using the sight glass with the new refrigerant and oil is not recommended.	7. Evacuate and leak test the system. Today's service procedures require a deep vacuum to at least 1500/1000/500 microns. Many manufacturers recommend a different minimum; however, they all agree that electronic measurement of vacuum is essential. Use a micron gauge when measuring vacuum. Manifold gauges are not as accurate.

8. Turn the system on.	8. Charge the system with R-134a. A rule of thumb is that the new charge in a medium- or high-temperature system will be 90% of the original charge. Charging by using the sight glass with the new refrigerant and oil is not recommended.
9. Check, adjust, repair, or replace expansion valve and pressure controls. The new refrigerant will have different operating pressures than the CFC. An expansion valve may have to be adjusted as will both high- and low-pressure controls. Operating pressures with R-134a on the low side are generally 2% to 5% lower and 2% to 5% higher on the high side.	9. Turn the system on.
10. Test the oil in the system for cross contamination. Use a mineral oil check kit or refractometer to verify any remaining concentration of oil in the system. In an HFC conversion with a POE oil, the maximum amount of mineral oil or AB oil that can remain is 5%. In the event that oil is not within an acceptable tolerance, then additional oil changes will be necessary. Two or three additional oil changes may be necessary before the system reaches the desired level of mineral oil.	10. Check, adjust, repair, or replace expansion valve and pressure controls. The new refrigerant will have different operating pressures than the CFC. An expansion valve may have to be adjusted as will both high- and low-pressure controls. Operating pressures with R-134a on the low side are generally 2% to 5% lower and 2% to 5% higher on the high side.

11. Test the oil in the system for cross contamination. Use a mineral oil check kit or refractometer to verify any remaining concentration of oil in the system. In an HFC conversion with a POE oil, the maximum amount of mineral oil or AB oil that can remain is 5%. In the event that oil is not within an acceptable tolerance, then additional oil changes will be necessary. Two or three additional oil changes may be necessary before the system reaches the desired level of mineral oil.

Whichever path is used, always apply appropriate labels to the system. The labels on the system should indicate that it contains R-134a, as well as the size of the charge. Also indicate the presence of the new POE oil and the appropriate quantity.

BLENDS

The other major type of retrofit is changing out a CFC refrigerant to a blend. For a retrofit from a CFC to a blend such as MP39 it is important to remember that a blend is not a single compound; therefore, it can separate. Using a blend that has an HCFC refrigerant as one of its components can also cause concerns in the future. This is because HCFC refrigerants are targeted to be phased out, and at some point, a retrofit may again be necessary.

Blends are not drop-in replacements; therefore, some changes will have to be made. Under ideal conditions a retrofit to R-134a is preferable; however, the oil change is a concern and R-134a will not work in all systems and operating conditions. The following procedure is a general guide for an HCFC-based blend with an AB-based oil. *Note: Always check with the manufacturer of the equipment before undertaking any retrofit.*

1. Measure and record data from the current system. If the system being retrofitted is operating, take measurements to establish an operational baseline with R-12. Measurements should include: temperatures and pressures at the evaporator, condenser, compressor suction, and discharge; superheat; subcooling; and amperage draw. If readings indicate a problem, correct the problem before proceeding with the retrofit. If the readings are on target, then record them for use when tuning the system after the retrofit is complete.

2. Recover the refrigerant from the system, then weigh and store the recovered refrigerant. Recovery not only helps ensure supplies for the future, it is also illegal to vent refrigerant. Weighing the recovered charge will provide a basis for the amount of new refrigerant to be added to the system.

3. Drain the oil from the compressor and system. If there are no drain plugs, you may have to remove the compressor to drain the oil. If the system has drain plugs, drain at the crankcase. Depending on the size and piping of the system, you may also have to look for low spots in the system where oil may be accumulating. Do not forget that the accumulator and the oil separator can also hold oil. The use of the alkylbenzene lubricant may allow a greater amount of residual mineral oil to remain in the system. Currently the allowable limit of mineral oil in the system is 20%.

4. Measure the amount of oil that is removed from the compressor. Measuring the oil will tell you how much to replace. Knowing how much oil has been removed will allow you to check the unit's specifications against the original charge to see how much oil you have recovered.

5. Replace the oil in the system with the AB oil of equal volume. If 14 oz of mineral oil are removed, then 14 oz of alkylbenzene oil should be charged into the system. In smaller systems, the remaining mineral oil and AB oil may be miscible enough to achieve compressor oil return. The proper viscosity for the AB oil is the one the compressor manufacturer recommends.

6. Check the expansion device. If the unit has an expansion valve it probably will operate with a blend such MP39 or MP66. If the unit uses a capillary tube then it will probably have to be changed. Check with the manufacturer for the new sizing. If it is not possible to come up with that information, the rule of thumb is to increase the length of the tube by 50% but leave the orifice the same size. For example, replace a 30-in. tube with a 45-in. tube having the same orifice diameter. Another

practice that can be considered is to replace the capillary tube with an expansion device. Some technicians purposely undercharge a capillary tube system; however, there are legitimate operating concerns about high and low end operation. Just because a unit operates on target when you are there does not mean it will operate properly with an ambient change.

7. Install a new filter-drier and any other component that may be required by the equipment manufacturer. Check the refrigerant manufacturer information to find out what type of drier is compatible with the blend. The loose fill or solid core drier may not be compatible with the blend.

8. Evacuate and leak test the system. Today's service procedures require a deep vacuum to at least 1500/1000/500 microns. Many manufacturers recommend a different minimum; however, they all agree that electronic measurement of vacuum is essential. Use a micron gauge when measuring vacuum. Manifold gauges are not as accurate.

9. Charge the system with the refrigerant blend. Charge the system with liquid only. If vapor charging is used, the refrigerant will have the wrong composition when you are finished. Use a throttling valve on the suction side so that vapor conversion occurs. A standing rule is that liquid cannot be charged directly to the suction side of the system. Not using a throttling valve can damage the compressor. For blends such as MP39 or MP66, the final charge will be less than the original R-12 charge. By weight, the final charge will be about 90% of the original charge if the expansion device or capillary tube has been adjusted or changed. Refrigerant manufacturers such as AlliedSignal recommend, in some cases, an initial charge of 75% by weight of the original charge. If the original capillary tube is used, refer back to section #6 for procedures and dangers of undercharging.

10. Turn the system on and check system operation. The following is from an AlliedSignal procedures list and discusses what must be checked:

    Start the systems and let conditions stabilize. If the system is undercharged, add additional Genetron® MP Blend in increments of 5 percent by weight of the original R-12 charge. For example, if the original charge was 100 lbs, charge in increments of 5 lbs. Continue until desired operating conditions are achieved.

Compressor-suction pressures for Genetron MP39 after stabilization should be within about 1 psi of normal system operation with R-12. For Genetron MP66, the suction pressure will be close to that of R-12 at low evaporator temperature (-20°F), but may be as much 8 or 9 psi higher at medium temperature (+25°F). The discharge pressure may be as much as 70 psi higher when exposed to extreme ambient conditions.

It may be necessary to reset the high pressure cut-out to compensate for the higher discharge pressures of MP blend system. This procedure should be done carefully to avoid exceeding the recommended operation limits of the compressor and other system components. The use of an expansion device not optimized for the system, such as the original capillary tube, will make the system more sensitive to charge and/or operating conditions. As a result, system performance will change more quickly if the system is overcharged (or undercharged) with MP39 or MP66.

To avoid overcharging, it is best to charge the system by first measuring the operation conditions (including discharge and suction pressures, suction line temperature, compressor amps, superheat) instead of using the liquid line sight glass as a guide.

11. Test the oil in the system for cross contamination. Use an oil check kit or refractometer to verify any remaining mineral oil concentration in the system. In a CFC to HCFC blend conversion using an AB oil, the maximum amount of mineral oil that can remain is 20%. In the event that oil is not within an acceptable tolerance, then additional oil changes will be necessary.

12. Always apply appropriate labels to the system. The labels on the system should indicate that it contains a blend, as well as the size of the charge. Also indicate the presence of the new AB oil and the appropriate quantity.

Superheat and Subcooling

One of the measurements that allows us to establish satisfactory operating conditions for a system is superheat. When working with a refrigerant such as R-12, superheat is relatively easy. All that is necessary is to measure the evaporator outlet temperature at the suction line and convert the low side gauge pressure to saturation temperature. Subtract the saturation temperature from the outlet temperature, and the result is superheat. *Note: For this discussion we are ignoring pressure drop in the system.*

Blends are different, because the pressure gauge shows one pressure but there is more than one temperature involved. A blend has a saturated vapor phase and a saturated liquid phase temperature (remember glide). In calculating superheat for the unit, you must use the blend's saturated vapor phase pressure converted to temperature, not the blend's saturated liquid phase. Superheat always measures vapor not liquid.

Subcooling is calculated in the liquid phase temperature of the refrigerant. The amount of subcooling that has occurred is measured by converting the condensing pressure to saturated liquid temperature and then subtracting the condenser outlet (liquid line temperature). Once again, the superheat and subcooling values for the system should be obtained from the manufacturer.

Throughout this book there is a constant reference to obtaining manufacturer information. Understand that we have much to learn about working with alternative refrigerants. It is the equipment manufacturers who are doing the research on their equipment, and they know best what works *now*.

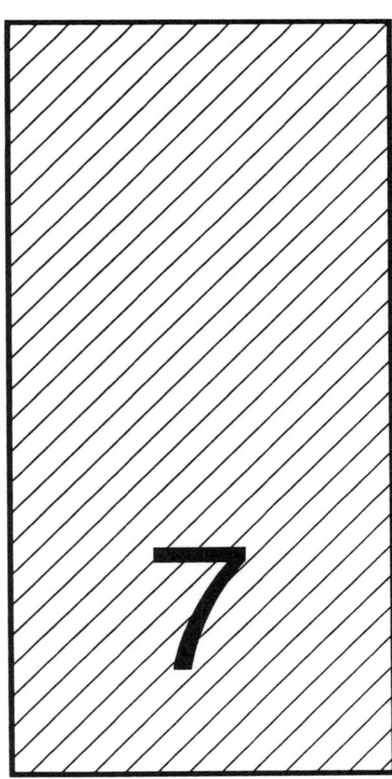

Safety

While this chapter is tough to write, it is even tougher to read. No one likes to be told what to do or what not to do; however, ***this is the most important chapter in the book***. Not every safe practice or warning is covered, but many safe practices should already be part of your daily routine. If they are not, remember that accidents will happen but most can be avoided.

Most of us view safety as wearing safety glasses and gloves when handling refrigerant. Safe working practices ensure our safety, but there are other factors to consider, such as the safety considerations for the public and the equipment.

A few years ago in Alaska, 34 people were injured and one person died when an accidental release of R-22 occurred. When an accident occurs with refrigerant, the greatest single danger is asphyxiation. All halogenated refrigerants are heavier than air, so you can literally drown in a sea of refrigerant. The second danger is oil. A burnout can produce acid, heavy metals, decomposed refrigerants, and other interesting chemical combinations.

Two terms that you should be familiar with are *allowable exposure limit* (AEL) and *emergency exposure limit* (EEL). These terms appear throughout safety literature and are a measurement of how much exposure to refrigerant can be tolerated.

AEL is a long-term exposure limit, which is defined as an 8 hour day in a 5 day work week. During a working lifetime, a technician exposed to an average concentration of a chemical in the air should have no adverse affects when working within the rated AEL.

EEL is a short-term exposure limit, which is defined as up to one hour without any consequences. To check the limits for a particular refrigerant, look up the refrigerant in the information provided in Part Two of this book.

Much of the data that covers health and safety guidelines for refrigerants is available from the refrigerant manufacturers in documents titled *Material Safety Data Sheets*. Part Two of this book contains these MSDSs. MSDSs are required in the work place, and they should be on your required reading list. The fact that a refrigerant is non-toxic or non-flammable does not preclude health hazards from occurring. How you handle the refrigerant and what you know about the refrigerant is what makes it "safe" to work with.

Safety must also be considered from the standpoint of the equipment. Is the refrigerant safe for the equipment? When retrofitting to an alternative will the new refrigerant destroy existing components? be compatible with the existing oil? operate within an acceptable temperature-pressure range or ruin the compressor? All are factors that must be considered when choosing a refrigerant. Choosing the wrong refrigerant or oil will damage the equipment.

Technician Safety

This chapter was not designed to cover every aspect of safety. It will, however, offer some common sense guidelines and discuss some of the regulations you must follow. It is your responsibility to know and follow safety codes, standards, and regulations.

The following are just some of the suggestions and questions technicians should consider regarding safety:

- Wear safety glasses with side shields regardless of the temperature. Refrigerant that is accidentally sprayed into the eye can cause permanent damage. Many technicians are now wearing full face shields to afford added protection against skin damage, frostbite, or being blinded.

- Wear butyl-lined gloves when handling and using refrigerants. If you have ever burned your fingers taking off a hose, you understand why the gloves are so important.

- Wear proper shoes. Safety shoes should be worn before you drop the compressor on your foot.

- Wear long sleeve shirts and pants to help protect you from frostbite and sun exposure, particularly if you spend a lot of time on rooftops.
- Hard hats are required on some sites by regulations. In other cases, common sense tells you that the person working above you may have a tremendous impact on your life.
- Ensure access to a device called a *self-contained breathing apparatus* (SCBA). Its purpose is to allow you to continue to breath safely in the event of a refrigerant spill contaminating the work area. SCBAs work well, and you will continue to work if you have access to one in the event of a spill.
- Remember that when handling oil you may be handling acid-laden material.
- Always be on solid footing. Hoses can rupture and spray refrigerant all over the place. A ruptured hose can cause discomfort, but falling because of the surprise is even more deadly.
- Do you know how to set a ladder? If not, please learn.
- Electricity is dangerous. Do you carry lockout devices and use them when performing service?
- Check to make sure power is disabled before performing service. The boxes should be locked out to protect against accidental energizing.
- Most of us focus on the power at the unit. However, you should not leave fully energized tools and equipment lying around while you are working. Why are they energized if you are not using them? If they are not in use, unplug them.
- Do you place signs indicating that power lines or extension cords are on the ground and are hot?
- Set up access barriers to keep people out of the area. In many cases, this is the law.
- If exposed to refrigerant, use lukewarm water to flush the area and get to a doctor.
- Applying a torch to a sealed system causes the creation of gas, which is not safe to breathe or come into contact with.

Flammability

Some of the new refrigerants contain components that by themselves can be flammable. Other refrigerants are flammable due to their composition. ASHRAE Standard 34 sets standards for refrigerant safety. This standard classifies refrigerants into groups, which establish their toxicity and flammability levels. Table 7-1 is typical of the information that Standard 34 furnishes.

	Level	Group	Group
Higher flammability	↑	A3	B3
Lower flammability	↑	A2	B2
No flame	↑	A1	B1
Increasing toxicity		®	®
		Lower	Higher

Table 7-1. Flammability/toxicity rating (ASHRAE Standard 34)

A classification of A1 means the refrigerant has the lowest toxicity and is non-flammable in its manufactured form. A classification of A2 means the refrigerant has a lower flammability rating and could be weakly flammable when the composition changes due to something such as a leak. (When a refrigerant is weakly flammable, it will burn but not sustain a flame.) A3 indicates a highly flammable refrigerant, such as R-290 (propane).

In the world of blends, there are refrigerants that are rated as non-flammable (e.g., A1/A2). The rating shows that the refrigerant is non-flammable in its original mix (A1); however, if a leak occurs, it can move to the A2 category. Blends can contain flammable components such as isobutane (R-600a), propane, R-142b, and R-152a, but the blend may not be considered flammable. In these blends, the flammable component of the blend has been diluted to the point where it is not flammable as long as the blend remains intact. If a leak develops in the system, fractionation of the blend will allow the refrigerant with the highest pressure to leave the system first. The remaining refrigerant could be partially flammable since it is no longer diluted. If the blend was originally composed of three different refrigerants and one of the components left the scene, the remaining components are present but in a different concentration. Remember, the blend was rated nonflammable because the different refrigerants mixed in the blend diluted the flammable refrigerant component.

Certain refrigerants may form a combustible mixture when they are mixed with air. Some of these include butane (R-600), ethane (R-170), and propane (R-290).

Flammable refrigerants were becoming a thing of the past; however, the ozone situation has created some interesting situations. There are appliances being sold that are touted as being environmentally friendly. Some of the appliances coming from overseas contain refrigerants that are flammable. The environmentally friendly label refers to the fact that these appliances do not contain a CFC-based refrigerant, so they will not deplete ozone. The effect of these refrigerants on the environment from a global warming standpoint is being studied. From a practical standpoint, do not assume every unit you work on is non-flammable. Hopefully the equipment you are servicing will have the content labeled, but be careful and know what you are working on. If you don't know, then find out.

Refrigerants can be classified as non-flammable at ambient temperatures and atmospheric pressures. Dupont literature states, "Tests have shown R-134a to be combustible at pressures as low as 5.5 psig at 350°F when mixed with air at concentrations generally greater than 60 volume % air." At lower temperatures, higher pressures are required for combustibility. R-22 can also be flammable at pressures above atmospheric in the presence of high air concentration. From a safety standpoint, never leak test a system with air. The "no-air" standard has always been a requirement. With the new refrigerants the requirement is even more important.

When complying with the regulations on recovery, the system may be "pulled" into a vacuum, then air may enter the system. If some refrigerant is still present in the compressor oil, the refrigerant may leave the oil and mix with the air. A partially flammable mixture is now present in the system. If you use a torch to "un-sweat" the lines, you can create problems. And, of course, you should not smoke when working with partially, weakly, or totally flammable vapors.

If the system contains a leak, topping off a blend can be a questionable procedure. You may not have the correct percentage of refrigerants present in the system after a leak occurs. Topping off the system may result in a refrigerant that does not resemble the original charge. This could result in potentially dangerous properties for the system and the technician. ***Repeated topping off of a leaking system will create problems.*** The location and size of the leak are critical factors. Leaks in areas where change of state occurs will certainly impact the proportion of the refrigerant mixture. If the proportion is not correct, performance will suffer.

Some additional rules to live by:

- Repairing a leak should be a required practice.
- Recovered refrigerant may be reusable, depending on where the leak occurs.
- If a leak occurs in the evaporator or condenser and the system uses a blend, it is good practice to replace the charge with new refrigerant.
- Liquid charging is the best approach with a blend. When charging on the low side, use a metering type device to flash the refrigerant.
- Refrigerants cannot be vented to the atmosphere.
- A good source for refrigerant safety information is the MSDS.
- Read ASHRAE Standards 15 and 34.

Cylinders

You can work safely and still get hurt by improperly handling refrigerant cylinders. The following are important facts you should know:

- Hydrostatic pressure will result from overfilling the cylinder. Hydrostatic pressure can be avoided by never filling the cylinder more than 80% of its volume. If the cylinder will experience temperatures in excess of 130°F, then only fill to 60% of the cylinder's volume.
- Disposable cylinders are not reusable. They should not be refilled or used for other purposes such as storing compressed air. Recover any remaining refrigerant, puncture the cylinder, and dispose of the cylinder conforming to regulations.
- A cylinder containing residual refrigerant may explode with any type of heat application.
- Transporting a refilled disposable cylinder could lead to a $25,000 fine and 5 years in prison.
- Use a DOT refillable approved cylinder for storage and transfer of used refrigerants.

- If the cylinder is over five years old, do not reuse it. Retest it per DOT requirements. DOT regulations require that the cylinder be retested and recertified every five years.
- Store the cylinder in a vertical position with the valve at the top.
- Knocking the valve off the cylinder could result in a torpedo effect.
- Keep cylinders chained.
- If it doesn't look good, do not use it. Dents, rust, and gouges may indicate unsafe refrigerant cylinders.
- Know the weight of the cylinder and be sure the weight is correct. Use equipment that will accurately weigh the cylinder and shut down in the event of overfilling.
- Relief devices could fail on a cylinder. Do not overfill just because the cylinder has a relief device.
- You cannot vent refrigerant to the atmosphere; you must recover, store, and ship according to local, state, and federal regulations.
- Cylinders and drums that are to be shipped must carry the green diamond "Non-Flammable Gas" label and classification tag. If you are using a drum, do not forget to allow vapor space of at least 10% of the drum height between the liquid and the drum top.
- Mixing refrigerants is bad business. Evacuate the cylinder before you use it to store refrigerant. If the refrigerant is used, it should be the proper color code.
- The container that you are transferring refrigerant to should be initially evacuated to 28 mm.

Codes and Standards

Every time a service call is made, you are responsible for ensuring that the appropriate codes and standards are met. Meeting code requirements starts with the local building code and goes all the way to federal regulations such as Section 608 of the Clean Air Act. The regulations or rules we are required to obey were created to prevent people from getting hurt.

There are many different codes, standards, and guidelines that you should know, including the following:

Section 608 of the Clean Air Act — Establishes requirements for refrigerants, equipment, service procedures, and technicians. Section 608 started the age of regulation for the hvac/r industry.

Section 609 of the Clean Air Act — Establishes requirements for motor vehicle repair and guidelines for recovery/recycling equipment.

DOT Title 49 CFR — Deals primarily with the testing, certifying, labeling, and transportation of refrigerants. Today, shipping the refrigerant to a reclaimer is as much a part of the job as getting the refrigerant out of the system.

ASHRAE Standard 15 — Defines requirements for safety of persons and premises where refrigeration systems work. Standard 15 covers safe practices and sets standards for monitoring, alarms, ventilation, and handling refrigerants.

ASHRAE Standard 34 — Sets standards for safety groups on refrigerants.

SAE J Standards — Sets standards for handling, servicing, recovering, recycling, and establishing purity for refrigerants used in vehicles.

Underwriters Laboratories (UL) Guidelines — Proposes guidelines in 2154 series for handling conversions and retrofit of ozone-depleting chemicals.

ARI 700 — Sets standards for refrigerant purity.

ARI 740 — Sets performance standards for refrigerant recovery, recycling, and reclaiming equipment.

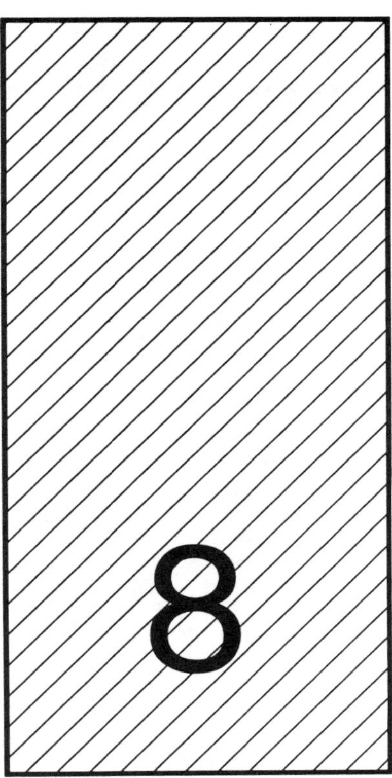

SNAP

By now you probably understand that it would be impossible for a technician to evaluate all of the different alternatives and their applications. As technicians, you have neither the time nor the facilities to research all of the different applications for alternative refrigerants. In addition, there is a practical aspect of what environmental concerns could arise from using an alternative. The EPA program that helps overcome these concerns is called *Significant New Alternatives Policy*, or SNAP for short.

Section 612 of the Clean Air Act requires EPA to publish lists of new alternative refrigerants that can be used as substitutes for ozone-depleting substances. Existing refrigerants that could be used as alternatives also appear on the lists. The lists cover more than the hvac/r industry. Industries such as foam blowing, fire extinguishing, and electronic component cleaning also use refrigerants that have ozone depletion potential. SNAP's list contains acceptable alternatives for different industries and applications.

Evaluation of new and existing alternatives occurs in areas such as the following:

- Ozone depletion potential
- Global warming potential
- Flammability

- Toxicity
- Exposure
- Risks involved from a technical and economic standpoint

An alternative refrigerant must be EPA SNAP approved for use. There are also other approvals that must be considered:

- Alternative refrigerants and lubricants must be approved by Underwriters Laboratories (UL) in order for equipment to retain its UL safety certification. Many building codes and jurisdictions require that equipment be UL safety certified.
- Alternative refrigerants and lubricants should be approved by the equipment and compressor manufacturer. Compressor manufacturers are doing extensive research into how alternatives and oils will relate to their unit.

As time progresses, local jurisdictions will become involved in refrigerant applications and how they meet codes. Building codes are designed to protect the public. The changeover to an alternative can be designed into a new piece of equipment by a manufacturer. Retrofitting older equipment is also a manufacturer concern. If the alternative does not work, it is the equipment manufacturer that takes the blame.

The pages that follow contain the latest listing from SNAP.

United States
Environmental
Protection Agency

Office of Air and Radiation
Stratospheric Protection
Division (6205-J)

April 1995
Rev. 2

Significant New Alternatives Policy (SNAP) Program Substitutes List for Class I Ozone Depleting Chemicals

INTEGRATED LISTS FROM FEDERAL REGISTER NOTIFICATIONS OF DETERMINATIONS OF ACCEPTABILITY OF ALTERNATIVES FOR CLASS I OZONE DEPLETING CHEMICALS UNDER THE SIGNIFICANT NEW ALTERNATIVES POLICY (SNAP) PROGRAM
(Comprehensive as of April 1995)

Section 612 of the Clean Air Act (CAA) requires EPA to review alternatives to ozone depleting substances and to publish lists of acceptable and unacceptable substitutes. It is illegal to replace an ozone depleting chemical with a substitute which has been listed as unacceptable. In addition, any person who produces a substitute must notify EPA at least 90 days before new or existing alternatives are introduced into interstate commerce for significant new use as substitutes.

For further detail on the attached decisions refer to the following Federal Register Notices: 59 FR 13044 (March 18, 1994); and 59 FR 44240 (August 26, 1994); 60 FR 3318 (January 13, 1995).

FOR MORE INFORMATION ON FEDERAL REGULATIONS UNDER THE STRATOSPHERIC OZONE PROTECTION PROGRAM, PLEASE CALL THE STRATOSPHERIC OZONE PROTECTION HOTLINE AT **1-800-296-1996** (OUTSIDE THE U.S. CALL (202) 783-1100).

ADHESIVES, COATINGS, AND INKS
ACCEPTABLE SUBSTITUTES
Updated January 1995

END-USE	SUBSTITUTE	DECISION	COMMENTS
Methyl Chloroform Adhesives, Coatings, and Inks	**Petroleum Hydrocarbons**	Acceptable	OSHA standards exist for many of these chemicals. Formulators should use chemicals with lowest toxicity, where possible.
	Oxygenated solvents (Alcohols, Ketones, Ethers, and Esters)	Acceptable	OSHA standards exist for many of these chemicals. Formulators should use chemicals with lowest toxicity, where possible.
	Chlorinated solvents (methylene chloride, trichloro-ethylene, perchloro-ethylene)	Acceptable	High inherent toxicity. Use only when necessary. OSHA and RCRA standards must be met.
	Terpenes	Acceptable	
	Water-based formulations	Acceptable	
	High-solid formulations	Acceptable	
	Alternative technologies (e.g., powder, hot melt, thermoplastic plasma spray, radiation-cured, moisture-cured, chemical-cured, and reactive liquid)	Acceptable	

ADHESIVES, COATING, AND INKS

PENDING DECISIONS

APPLICATION	SUBSTITUTE	COMMENTS
Methyl Chloroform Adhesives, Coatings and Inks	Monochloro-toluene/benzo-trifluorides	Agency has not completed review of data.

AEROSOLS

ACCEPTABLE SUBSTITUTES
Updated February 1995

End Use	Substitute	Decision	Comments
CFC-11, HCFC-22, HCFC-142b as aerosol propellants	Saturated light hydrocarbons, C3-C6 (e.g., propane, isobutane, n-butane)	Acceptable	Hydrocarbons are flammable materials. Use with the necessary precautions.
	Dimethyl ether	Acceptable	DME is flammable. Use with the necessary precautions. Blends of DME with HCFCs are subject to section 610 restrictions.
	HFC-152a, HFC-134a, HFC-125	Acceptable	HFC-134a, HFC-125 and HFC-152a are potential greenhouse gases.
	Alternative processes (pumps, mechanical pressure dispensers, non-spray dispensers)	Acceptable	
	Compressed Gases (Carbon dioxide, air, nitrogen, nitrous oxide)	Acceptable	

CFC-11 as aerosol propellant	HCFC-22, HCFC-142b	Acceptable (in applications not restricted under S. 610 of the CAA)	All aerosol propellant uses of HCFC-22 and HCFC-142b are already prohibited as of January 1, 1994 under Section 610 (d) of the Clean Air Act. Only one exemption exists. It is described in the section on aerosol substitutes in 59 FR 13044.

End Use	Substitute	Decision	Comments
CFC-11, CFC-113, MCF, HCFC-141b as aerosol solvents	C6-C20 Petroleum hydrocarbons	Acceptable	Petroleum hydrocarbons are flammable. Use with the necessary precautions. Pesticide aerosols must adhere to FIFRA standards.
	Chlorinated solvents (trichloroethylene, perchloro-ethylene, methylene chloride)	Acceptable	Extensive regulations under other statutes govern use of these chemicals, including VOC standards, workplace standards, waste management standards, and pesticide formulation and handling standards. Should be used only for products where nonflammability is a critical feature.
	Oxygenated organic solvents (esters, ethers, alcohols, ketones)	Acceptable	These substitutes are flammable. Use with the necessary precautions.
	Terpenes	Acceptable	These substitutes are flammable. Use with the necessary precautions.

	Water-based formulations	Acceptable	
	Trans-1,2-dichloroethylene	Acceptable	
CFC-11, CFC-113, MCF as aerosol solvents	HCFC-141b and its blends	Acceptable (in applications not restricted under S. 610 of the CAA)	All aerosol solvent uses of HCFC-141b, either by itself or blended with other compounds, are already prohibited as of January 1, 1994 under Section 610 (d) of the Clean Air Act. Limited exemptions exist. These are described in the section on aerosol substitutes in 59 FR 13044.

PENDING SUBSTITUTES

End Use	Substitute	Comments
CFC-12 as aerosol propellant	**HFC-227**	FDA approval still required in metered dose inhalers. Likely to have low environmental impacts.
CFC-11, CFC-113, MCF, HCFC-141b as aerosol solvents	**Monochlorotoluene/ benzotrifluorides**	Agency has not yet completed review of data.
	Volatile methyl siloxanes	EPA investigating feasibility of meeting exposure standards for this class of chemicals when used in occupational settings.
	HFC-4310mee	Agency has not completed review of data. Premanufacture Notice review under the Toxic Substances Control Act not yet completed.
	Volatile methyl siloxanes	EPA investigating feasibility of meeting exposure standards for this class of chemicals when used in occupational settings.
	Perfluorocarbons (C6F14) and Perfluoropolyethers	Agency has not completed review of data.

FIRE SUPPRESSION AND EXPLOSION PROTECTION
Updated April, 1995

ACCEPTABLE SUBSTITUTES
STREAMING AGENTS

APPLICATION	SUBSTITUTE	DECISION	COMMENTS
Halon 1211 Streaming Agents	HCFC-123	Acceptable	This agent is banned in residential applications per section 610(d) of the CAAA.
	HCFC-124	Acceptable	This agent is banned in residential applications per section 610(d) of the CAAA.
	[HCFC Blend] B	Acceptable	This agent is banned in residential applications per section 610(d) of the CAAA.
	[HCFC Blend] C	Acceptable	This agent is banned in residential applications per section 610(d) of the CAAA.
	[HCFC Blend] D	Acceptable	The intended market for this agent is large, outdoor applications. This agent is banned in residential applications per section 610(d) of the CAAA.
	Gelled Halocarbon/Dry Chemical Suspension	Acceptable	This agent was formerly identified as Powdered Aerosol B.
	[Surfactant Blend] A	Acceptable	This blend is not a clean agent, but can reduce the quantity of water required to extinguish a fire.
	Carbon Dioxide	Acceptable	
	Dry Chemical	Acceptable	
	Water	Acceptable	
	Foam	Acceptable	

STREAMING AGENTS
SUBSTITUTES ACCEPTABLE SUBJECT TO NARROWED USE LIMITS

END-USE	SUBSTITUTE	DECISION	CONDITIONS	COMMENTS
Halon 1211 Streaming Agents	HBFC-22B1	Acceptable in nonresidential uses only.		Proper procedures regarding the operation of the extinguisher and ventilation following dispensing the extinguishant is recommended. Worker exposure may be a concern in small office areas. HBFC-22B1 is considered an interim substitute for Halon 1211. Because the HBFC-22B1 has an ODP of .74, production will be phased out (except for essential uses) on January 1, 1996. This agent was submitted to the Agency as a Premanufacture Notice (PMN) and is presently subject to requirements contained in a Toxic Substance Control Act (TSCA) Consent Order. See additional comments 1, 2
	C_6F_{14}	Acceptable for nonresidential uses where other alternatives are not technically feasible due to performance or safety requirements: a. due to the physical or chemical properties of the agent, or b. where human exposure to the extinguishing agent may approach cardiac sensitization levels or result in other unacceptable health effects under normal operating conditions.		Users must observe the limitations on PFC acceptability by making reasonable effort to undertake the following measures: (i) conduct an evaluation of foreseeable conditions of end use; (ii) determine that the physical or chemical properties or other technical constraints of the other available agents preclude their use; and (iii) determine that human exposure to the other alternative extinguishing agents may approach or result in cardiosensitization or other unacceptable toxicity effects under normal operating conditions; Documentation of such measures must be available for review upon request. The principal environmental characteristic of concern for PFCs is that they have high GWPs and long atmospheric lifetimes. Actual contributions to global warming depend upon the quantities of PFCs emitted. Guidance regarding applications in which PFCs may be appropriate is available from the Stratospheric Ozone Hotline, 1-800-296-1996 or 1-202-775-6677. See additional comments 1, 2

Additional Comments:
1 - Discharge testing and training should be strictly limited only to that which is essential to meet safety or performance requirements.
2 - The agent should be recovered from the fire protection system in conjunction with testing or servicing, and recycled for later use or destroyed.

FIRE SUPPRESSION AND EXPLOSION PROTECTION

STREAMING AGENTS

UNACCEPTABLE SUBSTITUTES

END-USE	SUBSTITUTE	DECISION	COMMENTS
Halon 1211 Streaming Agents	[CFC-11]	Unacceptable	This agent has been suggested for use on large outdoor fires for which non-ozone depleting alternatives are currently used. In addition, CAAA section 610 bans the use of CFCs in portable extinguishers.

TOTAL FLOODING AGENTS
SUBSTITUTES ACCEPTABLE SUBJECT TO USE CONDITIONS

END-USE	SUBSTITUTE	DECISION	CONDITIONS	COMMENTS
Halon 1301 Total Flooding Agents	HBFC-22B1	Acceptable	Until OSHA establishes applicable workplace requirements: Where egress from an area cannot be accomplished within one minute, the employer shall not use this agent in concentrations exceeding its cardiotoxic NOAEL of 0.3% Where egress takes longer than 30 seconds but less than one minute, the employer shall not use the agent in a concentration greater than its cardiotoxic LOAEL of 1.0%. HBFC-22B1 concentrations greater than 1.0% are only permitted in areas not normally occupied by employees provided that any employee in the area can escape within 30 seconds. The employer shall assure that no unprotected employees enter the area during agent discharge.	The comparative design concentration based on cup burner values is approximately 5.3%, while its cardiotoxic LOAEL is 1%. Thus, it is unlikely that this agent will be used in normally occupied areas. HBFC-22B1 can be considered only an interim substitute for Halon 1301. HBFC-22B1 has an ODP of .74; thus, production will be phased out January 1, 1996. This agent was submitted to the Agency as a Premanufacture Notice (PMN) and is presently subject to requirements contained in a Toxic Substance Control Act (TSCA) Consent Order. See additional comments 1, 2, 3, 4
	HCFC-22	Acceptable	Until OSHA establishes applicable workplace requirements: Where egress from an area cannot be accomplished within one minute, the employer shall not use this agent in concentrations exceeding its cardiotoxic NOAEL of 2.5%. Where egress takes longer than 30 seconds but less than one minute, the employer shall not use the agent in a concentration greater than its cardiotoxic LOAEL of 5.0%. HCFC-22 concentrations greater than 5.0% are only permitted in areas not normally occupied by employees provided that any employee in the area can escape within 30 seconds. The employer shall assure that no unprotected employees enter the area during agent discharge.	The comparative design concentration based on cup burner values is approximately 13.9% while its cardiotoxic LOAEL is 5.0%. Thus, it is unlikely that this agent will be used in normally occupied areas. See additional comments 1, 2, 3, 4

HCFC-124	Acceptable	Until OSHA establishes applicable workplace requirements: Where egress from an area cannot be accomplished within one minute, the employer shall not use this agent in concentrations exceeding its cardiotoxic NOAEL of 1.0%. Where egress takes longer than 30 seconds but less than one minute, the employer shall not use the agent in a concentration greater than its cardiotoxic LOAEL of 2.5%. HCFC-123 concentrations greater than 2.5% are only permitted in areas not normally occupied by employees provided that any employee in the area can escape within 30 seconds. The employer shall assure that no unprotected employees enter the area during agent discharge.	The comparative design concentration based on cup burner values is approximately 8.4% while its cardiotoxic LOAEL is 2.5%. Thus, it is unlikely that this agent will be used in normally occupied areas. See additional comments 1, 2, 3, 4
[HCFC BLEND] A	Acceptable	Until OSHA establishes applicable workplace requirements: Where egress from an area cannot be accomplished within one minute, the employer shall not use [HCFC Blend] A in concentrations exceeding its cardiotoxic NOAEL of 10.0% Where egress takes greater than 30 seconds but less than one minute, the employer shall not use [HCFC Blend] A in a concentration greater than its cardiotoxic LOAEL of 10.0%. [HCFC Blend] A concentrations greater than 10 percent are only permitted in areas not normally occupied by employees provided that any employee in the area can escape within 30 seconds. The employer shall assure that no unprotected employees enter the area during agent discharge.	The comparative design concentration based on full scale testing is approximately 8.6%. The agent should be recovered from the fire protection system in conjunction with testing or servicing, and should be recycled for later use or destroyed. Feasible for use in a normally occupied area. See additional comments 1, 2, 3, 4

HFC-23	Acceptable	Until OSHA establishes applicable workplace requirements: Where egress from an area cannot be accomplished within one minute, the employer shall not use HFC-23 in concentrations exceeding 30%. Where egress takes greater than 30 seconds but less than one minute, the employer shall not use HFC-23 in a concentration greater than 50.0%. HFC-23 concentrations greater than 50 percent are only permitted in areas not normally occupied by employees provided that any employee in the area can escape within 30 seconds. The employer shall assure that no unprotected employees enter the area during agent discharge. The design concentration must result in an oxygen level of at least 16%.	The comparative design concentration based on cup burner values is approximately 14.4% while data indicates that its cardiotoxicity NOAEL is 30% without added oxygen and 50% with added oxygen. Its LOAEL is likely to exceed 50%. Feasible for use in a normally occupied area. See additional comments 1, 2, 3, 4
HFC-125	Acceptable	Until OSHA establishes applicable workplace requirements: Where egress from an area cannot be accomplished within one minute, the employer shall not use this agent in concentrations exceeding its cardiotoxic NOAEL of 7.5%. Where egress takes longer than 30 seconds but less than one minute, the employer shall not use the agent in a concentration greater than its cardiotoxic LOAEL of 10.0%. HFC-125 concentrations greater than 10.0% are only permitted in areas not normally occupied by employees provided that any employee in the area can escape within 30 seconds. The employer shall assure that no unprotected employees enter the area during agent discharge.	The comparative design concentration based on cup burner values is approximately 11.3% while its cardiotoxic LOAEL is 10.0%. Thus, it is unlikely that this agent will be used in normally occupied areas. See additional comments 1, 2, 3, 4

HFC-134a	Acceptable	Until OSHA establishes applicable workplace requirements: Where egress from an area cannot be accomplished within one minute, the employer shall not use this agent in concentrations exceeding its cardiotoxic NOAEL of 4.0%. Where egress takes longer than 30 seconds but less than one minute, the employer shall not use the agent in a concentration greater than its cardiotoxic LOAEL of 8.0%. HFC-134a concentrations greater than 8.0% are only permitted in areas not normally occupied by employees provided that any employee in the area can escape within 30 seconds. The employer shall assure that no unprotected employees enter the area during agent discharge.	The comparative design concentration based on cup burner values is approximately 12.6% while its cardiotoxic LOAEL is 8.0%. Thus, it is unlikely that this agent will be used in normally occupied areas. See additional comments 1, 2, 3, 4
HFC-227ea	Acceptable	Until OSHA establishes applicable workplace requirements: Where egress from an area cannot be accomplished within one minute, the employer shall not use HFC-227ea in concentrations exceeding its cardiotoxic NOAEL of 9.0%. Where egress takes longer than 30 seconds but less than one minute, the employer shall not use the agent in a concentration greater than its cardiotoxic LOAEL of 10.5%. HFC-227ea concentrations greater than 10.5% are only permitted in areas not normally occupied by employees provided that any employee in the area can escape within 30 seconds. The employer shall assure that no unprotected employees enter the area during agent discharge.	The comparative design concentration based on cup burner values is approximately 7.0% while data indicate that its cardiotoxicity LOAEL is probably greater than 10.5%. EPA is accepting 10.5% as its LOAEL. This agent was submitted to the Agency as a Premanufacture Notice (PMN) agent and is presently subject to requirements contained in a Toxic Substances Control Act (TSCA) Significant New Use Rule (SNUR). Feasible for use in a normally occupied area. See additional comments 1, 2, 3, 4

	C_4F_{10}	Acceptable where other alternatives are not technically feasible due to performance or safety requirements: a. due to their physical or chemical properties, or b. where human exposure to the extinguishing agents may approach cardiosensitization levels or result in other unacceptable health effects under normal operating conditions.	Until OSHA establishes applicable workplace requirements: For occupied areas from which personnel cannot be evacuated in one minute, use is permitted only up to concentrations not exceeding the cardiotoxicity NOAEL of 40%. Although no LOAEL has been established for this product, standard OSHA requirements apply, i.e. for occupied areas from which personnel can be evacuated or egress can occur between 30 and 60 seconds, use is permitted up to a concentration not exceeding the LOAEL. All personnel must be evacuated before concentration of C_4F_{10} exceeds 40%. Design concentration must result in oxygen levels of at least 16%.	The comparative design concentration based on cup burner values is approximately 6.6%. Users must observe the limitations on PFC acceptability by making reasonable efforts to undertake the following measures: (i) conduct an evaluation of foreseeable conditions of end use; (ii) determine that human exposure to the other alternative extinguishing agents may approach or result in cardiosensitization or other unacceptable toxicity effects under normal operating conditions; and (iii) determine that the physical or chemical properties or other technical constraints of the other available agents preclude their use; Documentation of such measures must be available for review upon request. The principal environmental characteristic of concern for PFCs is that they have high GWPs and long atmospheric lifetimes. Actual contributions to global warming depend upon the quantities of PFCs emitted. Guidance regarding applications in which PFCs may be appropriate is available from the Stratospheric Ozone Hotline, 1-800-296-1996 or 1-202-775-6677. Feasible for use in a normally occupied area. See additional comments 1, 2, 3, 4
	[IG-541]	Acceptable	Until OSHA establishes applicable workplace requirements: The design concentration must result in at least 10% oxygen and no more than 5% CO_2. If the oxygen concentration of the atmosphere falls below 10%, personnel must be evacuated and egress must occur within 30 seconds.	Studies have shown that healthy, young individuals can remain in a 10% to 12% oxygen atmosphere for 30 to 40 minutes without impairment. However, in a fire emergency, the oxygen level may be reduced below safe levels, and the combustion products formed by the fire are likely to cause harm. Thus, the Agency does not contemplate personnel remaining in the space after system discharge during a fire without Self Contained Breathing Apparatus (SCBA) as required by OSHA. Feasible for use in a normally occupied area. See additional comments 1, 2
	Carbon Dioxide	Acceptable		System design must adhere to OSHA 1910.162(b)5 and NFPA Standard 12.
	Water Sprinklers	Acceptable		

Additional Comments

1 - Must conform with OSHA 29 CFR 1910 Subpart L Section 1910.160 of the U.S. Code.
2 - Per OSHA requirements, protective gear (SCBA) must be available in the event personnel must reenter the area.
3 - Discharge testing should be strictly limited only to that which is essential to meet safety or performance requirements.
4 - The agent should be recovered from the fire protection system in conjunction with testing or servicing, and recycled for later use or destroyed.

FIRE SUPPRESSION AND EXPLOSION PROTECTION

TOTAL FLOODING AGENTS
SUBSTITUTES ACCEPTABLE SUBJECT TO NARROWED USE LIMITS

END-USE	SUBSTITUTE	DECISION	CONDITIONS	COMMENTS
Halon 1301 Total Flooding Agents	C_4F_{10}	Acceptable where other alternatives are not technically feasible due to performance or safety requirements: a. due to their physical or chemical properties, or b. where human exposure to the extinguishing agents may approach cardiosensitization levels or result in other unacceptable health effects under normal operating conditions.	Until OSHA establishes applicable workplace requirements: For occupied areas from which personnel cannot be evacuated in one minute, use is permitted only up to concentrations not exceeding the cardiotoxicity NOAEL of 40%. Although no LOAEL has been established for this product, standard OSHA requirements apply, i.e. for occupied areas from which personnel can be evacuated or egress can occur between 30 and 60 seconds, use is permitted up to a concentration not exceeding the LOAEL. All personnel must be evacuated before concentration of C_4F_{10} exceeds 40%. Design concentration must result in oxygen levels of at least 16%.	The comparative design concentration based on cup burner values is approximately 6.6%. Users must observe the limitations on PFC approval by undertaking the following measures: (i) conduct an evaluation of foreseeable conditions of end use; (ii) determine that human exposure to the other alternative extinguishing agents may approach or result in cardiosensitization or other unacceptable toxicity effects under normal operating conditions; and (iii) determine that the physical or chemical properties or other technical constraints of the other available agents preclude their use; Documentation of such measures must be available for review upon request. The principal environmental characteristic of concern for PFCs is that they have high GWPs and long atmospheric lifetimes. Actual contributions to global warming depend upon the quantities of PFCs emitted. Guidance regarding applications in which PFCs may be appropriate is available from the Stratospheric Ozone Hotline, 1-800-296-1996 or 1-202-775-6677. Feasible for use in a normally occupied area. See additional comments 1, 2, 3, 4

Additional Comments

1 - Must conform with OSHA 29 CFR 1910 Subpart L Section 1910.160 of the U.S. Code.
2 - Per OSHA requirements, protective gear (SCBA) must be available in the event personnel must reenter the area.
3 - Discharge testing should be strictly limited only to that which is essential to meet safety or performance requirements.
4 - The agent should be recovered from the fire protection system in conjunction with testing or servicing, and recycled for later use or destroyed.

FIRE SUPPRESSION AND EXPLOSION PROTECTION

TOTAL FLOODING AGENTS
UNACCEPTABLE SUBSTITUTES

END-USE	SUBSTITUTE	DECISION	COMMENTS
Halon 1301 Total Flooding Agents	HFC-32	Proposed unacceptable, Sept. 26, 1994.	This agent is flammable.

PENDING SUBSTITUTES

END-USE	SUBSTITUTE	COMMENTS
Halon 1211 Streaming Agents	CF_3I	Proposed Acceptable in nonresidential applications (forthcoming).
	HFC-227ea	Complete SNAP submission and personal monitoring data required.
	Water Mist, without additives	Proposed Acceptable (forthcoming).

END-USE	SUBSTITUTE	COMMENTS
Halon 1301 Total Flooding Agents	C_3F_8	Proposed acceptable where other alternatives are not technically feasible, Sept. 26, 1994.
	CF_3I	Proposed acceptable in normally unoccupied areas, Sept. 26, 1994.
	[HFC Blend] A	Pending receipt of further data requested by the Agency.
	IG-55 (formerly [Inert Gas Blend] B)	Proposed Acceptable (forthcoming).
	IG-01 (formerly [Inert Gas Blend] C)	Proposed Acceptable (forthcoming).
	Gelled Halocarbon/Dry Chemical Suspension	Proposed acceptable in normally unoccupied areas, Sept. 26, 1994.
	Inert Gas/Powdered Aerosol Blend	Proposed acceptable in normally unoccupied areas, Sept. 26, 1994.
	SF_6	Proposed acceptable for use as a discharge test agent in military uses and civilian aircraft uses only, Sept. 26, 1994.
	Water Mist Systems with No Additives	Proposed Acceptable (forthcoming).
	Water Mist Systems with Additives	Must be individually submitted to EPA and reviewed on a case-by-case basis. Determination forthcoming.

FOAM SECTOR
ACCEPTABLE SUBSTITUTES
(Updated January 1995)

END-USE	SUBSTITUTE	DECISION	COMMENTS
CFC-11 Rigid Polyurethane and Polyisocyanurate Laminated Boardstock	HCFC-123	Acceptable	Worker monitoring studies indicate AEL for 123 (30 ppm) can be achieved with increased ventilation, where needed. Availability is limited.
	HCFC-141b	Acceptable	Has highest ODP of HCFCs.
	HCFC-142b	Acceptable	
	HCFC-22	Acceptable	
	HCFC-22/HCFC-141b blends	Acceptable	HCFC-141b
	HCFC-141b/ HCFC-123 blends	Acceptable	Recent worker monitoring studies indicate OEL for 123 (10 ppm) can be achieved with increased ventilation, where needed. Fairly good energy efficiency properties.
	HCFC-22/ HCFC-142b blends	Acceptable	
	HFC-134a	Acceptable	
	HFC-152a	Acceptable	Flammability may be an issue for workers and consumers.
	Saturated Light Hydrocarbons C3-C6	Acceptable	Flammability may be an issue for workers and consumers. Major sources of VOC emissions are subject to the New Source Review (NSR) program.
	2-Chloropropane	Acceptable	
	Electroset Technology	Acceptable	Proprietary technology
	Carbon Dioxide	Acceptable	Has highest thermal conductivity relative to other acceptable substitutes in this end-use.

CFC-11 Polyurethane, Rigid Appliance	HCFC-22 (or blends thereof)	Acceptable	
	HCFC-123 (or blends thereof)	Acceptable	Recent worker monitoring studies indicate OEL for 123 (30 ppm) can be achieved with increased ventilation, where needed. Easy to use as a retrofit; energy efficiency close to CFC-11. Current availability is limited.
	HCFC-141b (or blends thereof)	Acceptable	HCFC-141b has an ODP of 0.11, almost equivalent to that of methyl chloroform, a Class I substance. Fairly good energy efficiency properties.
	HCFC-142b (or blends thereof)	Acceptable	
	HFC-134a (or blends thereof)	Acceptable	
	HFC-152a (or blends thereof)	Acceptable	Flammability may be an issue for workers and consumers.
	Saturated Light Hydrocarbons C3-C6 (or blends thereof)	Acceptable	Flammability may be an issue for workers and consumers. Major sources of VOC emissions are subject to the New Source Review (NSR) program.
	Vacuum Panels	Acceptable	
	Electroset Technology	Acceptable	Proprietary technology.
	Carbon Dioxide (or blends thereof)	Acceptable	
CFC-11 Polyurethane, Rigid Commercial	HCFC-22 (or blends thereof)	Acceptable	
Refrigeration Foams, Spray Foams and Sandwich Panel Foams	HCFC-123 (or blends thereof)	Acceptable	Recent worker monitoring studies indicate AEL for 123 (30 ppm) can be achieved with use of increased ventilation, where needed. Easy to use as a retrofit; energy efficiency close to CFC-11. Availability is limited.

	HCFC-141b (or blends thereof)	Acceptable	HCFC-141b has an ODP of 0.11, almost equivalent to that of methyl chloroform, a Class I substance. Fairly good energy efficiency properties.
	HCFC-142b (or blends thereof)	Acceptable	
	HFC-134a (or blends thereof)	Acceptable	
	HFC-152a (or blends thereof)	Acceptable	Flammability may be an issue for workers and consumers.
	Saturated Light Hydrocarbons C3-C6 (or blends thereof)	Acceptable	Flammability may be an issue for workers and consumers. Major sources of VOC emissions are subject to the New Source Review (NSR) program.
	Electroset Technology	Acceptable	Proprietary technology.
	Carbon Dioxide (or blends thereof)	Acceptable	
CFC-11 Polyurethane, Rigid Slabstock and Other	HCFC-22 (or blends thereof)	Acceptable	
	HCFC-141b (or blends thereof)	Acceptable	HCFC-141b has an ODP of 0.11, almost equivalent to that of methyl chloroform, a Class I substance.
	HCFC-123 (or blends thereof)	Acceptable	Recent worker monitoring studies indicate AEL for 123 (30 ppm) can be achieved increased ventilation, where needed. Availability is limited.
	HFC-134a (or blends thereof)	Acceptable	
	HFC-152a (or blends thereof)	Acceptable	
	Saturated Light Hydrocarbons C3-C6 (or blends thereof)	Acceptable	Flammability may be an issue for workers and consumers. Major sources of VOC emissions are subject to the New Source Review (NSR) program.
	Electroset Technology	Acceptable	Proprietary technology.

	Carbon Dioxide (or blends thereof)	Acceptable	
CFC-12 Polystyrene, Extruded Boardstock and Billet	HCFC-22	Acceptable	
	HCFC-142b	Acceptable	
	HCFC-22/142b blends	Acceptable	
	HFC-134a	Acceptable	
	HFC-143a	Acceptable	Has relatively high global warming potential compared to other acceptable substitutes in this end-use.
	HFC-152a	Acceptable	Flammability may be an issue for workers and consumers.
	Saturated Light Hydrocarbons C3-C6	Acceptable	Flammability may be an issue for workers and consumers. Major sources of VOC emissions are subject to the New Source Review (NSR) program.
	HCFC-22/Saturated Light Hydrocarbons blends	Acceptable	Flammability may be an issue for workers and consumers. Major sources of VOC emissions are subject to the New Source Review (NSR) program.
	Electroset Technology	Acceptable	Proprietary technology.
	Carbon Dioxide	Acceptable	Relatively high thermal conductivity compared to other acceptable substitutes in this end-use.
CFC-11, CFC-113 Phenolic, Insulation Board and Bunstock	HCFC-141b	Acceptable	HCFC-141b has an ODP of 0.11, almost equivalent to that of methyl chloroform, a Class I substance. Fairly good energy efficiency properties.
	HCFC-142b	Acceptable	
	HCFC-22	Acceptable	
	HCFC-22/142b blends	Acceptable	

	HCFC-22/ Saturated Light Hydrocarbons C3-C6 blends	Acceptable	Flammability may be an issue for workers and consumers.
	Saturated Light Hydrocarbons C3-C6	Acceptable	Major sources of VOC emissions are subject to the New Source Review (NSR) program. Flammability may be an issue for workers and consumers.
	HFC-143a	Acceptable	Has relatively high global warming potential compared to other acceptable substitutes in this end-use.
	Electroset Technology	Acceptable	Proprietary technology.
	2-Chloropropane	Acceptable	Proprietary technology. Flammability may be an issue for workers and consumers.
	Carbon Dioxide	Acceptable	High thermal conductivity relative to other acceptable substitutes in this end-use.
CFC-11 Polyurethane, Flexible	HFC-134a (or blends thereof)	Acceptable	
	HFC-152a (or blends thereof)	Acceptable	Flammability may be an issue for workers and consumers.
	Saturated Light Hydrocarbons C3-C6 (or blends thereof)	Acceptable	
	Methylene Chloride (or blends thereof)	Acceptable	Revised OSHA PELs have been proposed at 25 ppm (TWA) for methylene chloride (Nov. 7, 1991). Subject to meeting all future ambient air controls for hazardous air pollutants under Title III section 112 of the 1990 CAAA. RCRA standards must be met.
	Acetone (or blends thereof)	Acceptable	Regulated as a VOC under Title I of the Clean Air Act. Major sources of VOC emissions are subject to the New Source Review (NSR) program. Flammability may be an issue for workers and consumers.
	AB Technology	Acceptable	AB generates more carbon monoxide (CO) than other blowing agents. OSHA has set a PEL for CO at 35 ppm TWA with a ceiling of 200 ppm.
	Electroset Technology	Acceptable	Proprietary technology.

	Carbon Dioxide (or blends thereof)	Acceptable	
CFC-11 Polyurethane, Integral Skin	HCFC-22 (or blends thereof)	Acceptable	Use restricted by section 610 Non-Essential Use Ban to motor vehicle safety foams. See HCFC discussion in Preamble for detail.
	HCFC-123 (or blends thereof)	Acceptable	Use restricted by section 610 Non-Essential Use Ban to motor vehicle safety foams. See HCFC discussion in Preamble for detail. Worker monitoring studies indicate AEL for HCFC-123 (30 ppm) can be achieved with increased ventilation, where needed. Very easy to use as a retrofit; energy efficiency close to CFC-11. Supply is currently limited.
	HCFC-141b (or blends thereof)	Acceptable	Use restricted by section 610 Non-Essential Use Ban to motor vehicle safety foams. See HCFC discussion in Preamble for detail. HCFC-141b has an ODP of 0.11, almost equivalent to that of methyl chloroform, a class I substance.
	HFC-134a (or blends thereof)	Acceptable	
	HFC-152a (or blends thereof)	Acceptable	Flammability may be an issue for workers and consumers.
	Saturated Light Hydrocarbons C3-C6 (or blends thereof)	Acceptable	Major sources of VOC emissions are subject to the New Source Review (NSR) program. Flammability may be an issue for workers and consumers.
	Methylene Chloride (or blends thereof)	Acceptable	Revised OSHA PELs have been proposed at 25 ppm (TWA) for methylene chloride (Nov. 7, 1991). Subject to meeting all future ambient air controls for hazardous air pollutant under Title III section 112 of the 1990 CAA Amendments. RCRA standards must be met.
	Electroset Technology	Acceptable	Proprietary technology.
	Carbon Dioxide (or blends thereof)	Acceptable	
CFC-12 Polystyrene, Extruded Sheet	HFC-134a (or blends thereof)	Acceptable	

	HFC-152a (or blends thereof)	Acceptable	Flammability may be an issue for workers and consumers.
	Saturated Light Hydrocarbons C3-C6 (or blends thereof)	Acceptable	Major sources of VOC emissions are subject to the New Source Review (NSR) program. Flammability may be an issue for workers and consumers.
	Electroset Technology	Acceptable	Proprietary technology.
	Carbon Dioxide (or blends thereof)	Acceptable	
CFC-12, CFC-114, CFC-11 Polyolefin	HCFC-22	Acceptable	Use restricted under section 610 Non-Essential Use Ban to polyethylene thermal insulating applications. See HCFC discussion in Preamble for detail.
	HCFC-142b	Acceptable	Use restricted under section 610 Non-Essential Use Ban to polyethylene thermal insulating applications. See HCFC discussion in Preamble for detail.
	HCFC-22/HCFC-142b blends	Acceptable	Use restricted under section 610 Non-Essential Use Ban to polyethylene thermal insulating applications. See HCFC discussion in Preamble for detail.
	HCFC-22/ Saturated Light Hydrocarbons C3-C6 blends	Acceptable	HCFC use restricted to thermal insulating applications under section 610 Non-Essential Use Ban. Major sources of VOC emissions are subject to the New Source Review (NSR) program. Flammability may be an issue for workers and consumers.
	HFC-152a/Saturated Light Hydrocarbons C3-C6 Blends	Acceptable	Flammability may be an issue for the manufacture and transport of products. Hydrocarbons are VOCs and are subject to control under Title I of the Clean Air Act.
	HFC-134a	Acceptable	
	HFC-143a	Acceptable	Has relatively high global warming potential compared to other acceptable substitutes in this end-use.
	HFC-152a	Acceptable	Flammability may be an issue for workers and consumers.
	Methylene Chloride	Acceptable	Revised OSHA PELs have been proposed at 25 ppm (TWA) for methylene chloride (11/7/91). Subject to meeting all future ambient air controls for hazardous air pollutants under Title III section 112, of the 1990 CAA Amendments. RCRA standards must be met.

	Saturated Light Hydrocarbons C3-C6	Acceptable	Major sources of VOC emissions are subject to the New Source Review (NSR) program. Flammability may be an issue for workers and consumers.
	Polyolefin Chemical Blend A	Acceptable	Proprietary blend.
	Electroset Technology	Acceptable	Proprietary technology.
	Carbon Dioxide	Acceptable	

FOAM SECTOR
UNACCEPTABLE SUBSTITUTES

END-USE	SUBSTITUTE	DECISION	COMMENTS
CFC-11 Polyolefin	HCFC-141b (or blends thereof)	Unacceptable	HCFC-141b has an ODP of 0.11, almost equivalent to that of methyl chloroform, a Class I substance. The Agency believes that non-ODP alternatives are sufficiently available to render the use of HCFC-141b unnecessary in polyolefin foams.

FOAM SECTOR
PENDING SUBSTITUTES

END-USE	SUBSTITUTE	COMMENTS
HCFC-141b, HCFC-22 Rigid polyurethane and polyisocyanurate laminated boardstock	Saturated light hydrocarbons C3-C6	Agency has not completed review of data.
HCFC-141b, HCFC-22 Polyurethane, rigid appliance	Saturated light hydrocarbons C3-C6	Agency has not completed review of data.
HCFC-141b, HCFC-22 Polyurethane, rigid commercial, refrigeration, spray and sandwich panels	Saturated light hydrocarbons C3-C6	Agency has not completed review of data.
	HFC-134a	Agency has not completed review of data.
HCFC-141b, HCFC-22, HCFC-142b Polyurethane, rigid slabstock and other	Saturated light hydrocarbons C3-C6	Agency has not completed review of data.
HCFC-22, HCFC-142b Polystyrene, extruded boardstock and billet	Saturated light hydrocarbons C3-C6	Agency has not completed review of data.
HCFC-141b, HCFC-22, HCFC-142b Phenolic, insulation boardstock and bunstock	Saturated light hydrocarbons C3-C6	Agency has not completed review of data.
HCFC-22 Polyurethane, integral skin	Saturated light hydrocarbons C3-C6	Agency has not completed review of data.
	HFC-134a	Agency has not completed review of data.
HCFC-22, HCFC-142b Polyolefin	Saturated light hydrocarbons C3-C6	Agency has not completed review of data.

End-Use	Substitute	Decision	Comments
CFC-11 Centrifugal Chillers (Retrofit)	HCFC-123	Acceptable	EPA worker-monitoring studies of 123 show that 8-hour TWA can be kept within 1 ppm (well under the AEL of 30 ppm) when recycling and ASHRAE standards are followed. This substitute is subject to containment and recovery regulations concerning HCFCs.
CFC-12 Centrifugal Chillers (Retrofit)	HFC-134a	Acceptable	EPA strongly recommends the containment and reclamation of this substitute.
CFC-113 Centrifugal Chillers (Retrofit)	None	Acceptable	
CFC-114 Centrifugal Chillers (Retrofit)	HCFC-124	Acceptable	This substitute is subject to containment and recovery regulations covering HCFCs.
R-500 Centrifugal Chillers (Retrofit)	HFC-134a	Acceptable	EPA strongly recommends the containment and reclamation of this substitute.
	R-406A	Acceptable	This substitute is subject to containment and recovery regulations covering HCFCs.
CFC-11, CFC-12, CFC-113, CFC-114, R-500 Centrifugal Chillers (New Equipment/NIKs)	HCFC-123	Acceptable	EPA worker-monitoring studies of 123 show that 8-hour TWA can be kept within 1 ppm (well under the AEL of 30 ppm) when recycling and ASHRAE standards are followed. This substitute is subject to containment and recovery regulations concerning HCFCs.
	HCFC-124	Acceptable	This substitute is subject to containment and recovery regulations covering HCFCs.
	HCFC-22	Acceptable	This substitute is subject to containment and recovery regulations covering HCFCs.
	HFC-134a	Acceptable	EPA strongly recommends the containment and reclamation of this substitute.
	HFC-227ea	Acceptable	EPA strongly recommends the containment and reclamation of this substitute.
	R-406A	Acceptable	This substitute is subject to containment and recovery regulations covering HCFCs.
	Ammonia Vapor Compression	Acceptable	Users should check local building codes related to the use of ammonia.
	Evaporative Cooling	Acceptable	Alternative technology that is currently commercially available; new developments have greatly expanded applicability.
	Desiccant Cooling	Acceptable	Alternative technology that is currently commercially available; new developments have greatly expanded applicability.
	Ammonia/water Absorption	Acceptable	Alternative technology that is currently commercially available; new developments have greatly expanded applicability.
	Water/lithium bromide absorption	Acceptable	Alternative technology that is currently commercially available; new developments have greatly expanded applicability.
	Stirling Cycle	Acceptable	Alternative technology.
CFC-12 Reciprocating Chillers (Retrofit)	HFC-134a	Acceptable	EPA strongly recommends the containment and reclamation of this substitute.
CFC-12 Reciprocating Chillers (New Equipment/NIKs)	HCFC-22	Acceptable	This substitute is subject to containment and recovery regulations covering HCFCs.
	HFC-134a	Acceptable	EPA strongly recommends the containment and reclamation of this substitute.
	HFC-227ea	Acceptable	EPA strongly recommends the containment and reclamation of this substitute.

	Evaporative Cooling	Acceptable	Alternative technology that is currently commercially available; new developments have greatly expanded applicability.
	Desiccant Cooling	Acceptable	Alternative technology that is currently commercially available; new developments have greatly expanded applicability.
	Stirling Cycle	Acceptable	Alternative technology.
CFC-11, CFC-12, R-502 Industrial Process Refrigeration (Retrofit)	HCFC-123	Acceptable	This substitute is subject to containment and recovery regulations covering HCFCs.
	HCFC-22	Acceptable	This substitute is subject to containment and recovery regulations covering HCFCs.
	HFC-134a	Acceptable	EPA strongly recommends the containment and reclamation of this substitute.
	R-401A	Acceptable	This substitute is subject to containment and recovery regulations covering HCFCs.
	R-401B	Acceptable	This substitute is subject to containment and recovery regulations covering HCFCs.
	R-402A	Acceptable	This substitute is subject to containment and recovery regulations covering HCFCs.
	R-402B	Acceptable	This substitute is subject to containment and recovery regulations covering HCFCs.
	R-404A	Acceptable	EPA strongly recommends the containment and reclamation of this substitute.
	R-406A (R-500 substitute only)	Acceptable	This substitute is subject to containment and recovery regulations covering HCFCs.
	R-407A	Acceptable	EPA strongly recommends the containment and reclamation of this substitute.
	R-407B	Acceptable	EPA strongly recommends the containment and reclamation of this substitute.
	R-507	Acceptable	EPA strongly recommends the containment and reclamation of this substitute.
	HCFC Blend Epsilon	Acceptable	This substitute is subject to containment and recovery regulations covering HCFCs.
	Ammonia Vapor Compression	Acceptable	Users should check local building codes related to the use of ammonia.
	Propane	Acceptable	EPA recommends that this substitute be used only at industrial facilities that manufacture or use hydrocarbons in the process stream.
	Propylene	Acceptable	EPA recommends that this substitute be used only at industrial facilities that manufacture or use hydrocarbons in the process stream.
	Butane	Acceptable	EPA recommends that this substitute be used only at industrial facilities that manufacture or use hydrocarbons in the process stream.
	Hydrocarbon Blend A	Acceptable	EPA recommends that this substitute be used only at industrial facilities that manufacture or use hydrocarbons in the process stream.
	Chlorine	Acceptable	EPA recommends that this substitute be used only at industrial facilities that manufacture or use chlorine in the process stream.
CFC-11, CFC-12, R-502 Industrial Process Refrigeration (New Equipment/NIKs)	HCFC-123	Acceptable	This substitute is subject to containment and recovery regulations covering HCFCs.
	HCFC-22	Acceptable	This substitute is subject to containment and recovery regulations covering HCFCs.
	HFC-134a	Acceptable	EPA strongly recommends the containment and reclamation of this substitute.
	HFC-227ea	Acceptable	EPA strongly recommends the containment and reclamation of this substitute.
	R-402A	Acceptable	This substitute is subject to containment and recovery regulations covering HCFCs.
	R-402B	Acceptable	This substitute is subject to containment and recovery regulations covering HCFCs.
	R-404A	Acceptable	EPA strongly recommends the containment and reclamation of this substitute.

	R-407A	Acceptable	EPA strongly recommends the containment and reclamation of this substitute.
	R-407B	Acceptable	EPA strongly recommends the containment and reclamation of this substitute.
	R-507	Acceptable	EPA strongly recommends the containment and reclamation of this substitute.
	Ammonia Vapor Compression	Acceptable	Users should check local building codes related to the use of ammonia.
	Propane	Acceptable	EPA recommends that this substitute be used only at industrial facilities that manufacture or use hydrocarbons in the process stream.
	Propylene	Acceptable	EPA recommends that this substitute be used only at industrial facilities that manufacture or use hydrocarbons in the process stream.
	Butane	Acceptable	EPA recommends that this substitute be used only at industrial facilities that manufacture or use hydrocarbons in the process stream.
	Hydrocarbon Blend A	Acceptable	EPA recommends that this substitute be used only at industrial facilities that manufacture or use hydrocarbons in the process stream.
	Chlorine	Acceptable	EPA recommends that this substitute be used only at industrial facilities that manufacture or use chlorine in the process stream.
	Evaporative Cooling	Acceptable	Alternative technology that is currently commercially available; new developments have greatly expanded applicability.
	Desiccant Cooling	Acceptable	Alternative technology that is currently commercially available; new developments have greatly expanded applicability.
	Stirling Cycle	Acceptable	Alternative technology.
CFC-13, R-13B1, R-503 Industrial Process Refrigeration (Retrofit and New Equipment/NIKs)	HFC-23	Acceptable	EPA strongly recommends the containment and reclamation of this substitute.
	R-403B	Acceptable	EPA strongly recommends the containment and reclamation of this substitute.
	PFC Blend Alpha	Acceptable	EPA strongly recommends the containment and reclamation of this substitute.
CFC-13, R-13B1, and R-503 Very Low Temperature Refrigeration (Retrofit and New Equipment/NIKs)	HFC-23	Acceptable	EPA strongly recommends the containment and reclamation of this substitute.
	R-403B	Acceptable	EPA strongly recommends the containment and reclamation of this substitute.
	PFC Blend Alpha	Acceptable	EPA strongly recommends the containment and reclamation of this substitute.
CFC-114 Industrial Process Air Conditioning (Retrofit)	HCFC-124	Acceptable	This substitute is subject to containment and recovery regulations covering HCFCs.
CFC-114 Industrial Process Air Conditioning (New Equipment/NIKs)	HCFC-124	Acceptable	This substitute is subject to containment and recovery regulations covering HCFCs.
CFC-12, R-502 Ice Skating Rinks (Retrofit)	HCFC-22	Acceptable	This substitute is subject to containment and recovery regulations covering HCFCs.
	HFC-134a	Acceptable	EPA strongly recommends the containment and reclamation of this substitute.
	R-401A	Acceptable	This substitute is subject to containment and recovery regulations covering HCFCs.
	R-401B	Acceptable	This substitute is subject to containment and recovery regulations covering HCFCs.
	R-407A	Acceptable	EPA strongly recommends the containment and reclamation of this substitute.
	R-407B	Acceptable	EPA strongly recommends the containment and reclamation of this substitute.
	Ammonia Vapor Compression	Acceptable	Users should check local building codes related to the use of ammonia.
CFC-12, R-502 Ice Skating Rinks (New Equipment/NIKs)	HCFC-22	Acceptable	This substitute is subject to containment and recovery regulations covering HCFCs.

	HFC-134a	Acceptable	EPA strongly recommends the containment and reclamation of this substitute.
	R-407A	Acceptable	EPA strongly recommends the containment and reclamation of this substitute.
	R-407B	Acceptable	EPA strongly recommends the containment and reclamation of this substitute.
	Ammonia Vapor Compression	Acceptable	Users should check local building codes related to the use of ammonia.
CFC-114 Uranium Isotope Separation Processing (Retrofit)	C_4F_8	Acceptable	EPA strongly recommends the containment and reclamation of this substitute.
	C_4F_{10}	Acceptable	EPA strongly recommends the containment and reclamation of this substitute.
	C_5F_{12}	Acceptable	EPA strongly recommends the containment and reclamation of this substitute.
	C_6F_{14}	Acceptable	EPA strongly recommends the containment and reclamation of this substitute.
	$C_5F_{11}NO$	Acceptable	EPA strongly recommends the containment and reclamation of this substitute.
CFC-12, R-502 Cold Storage Warehouses (Retrofit)	HCFC-22	Acceptable	This substitute is subject to containment and recovery regulations covering HCFCs.
	HFC-134a	Acceptable	EPA strongly recommends the containment and reclamation of this substitute.
	R-401A	Acceptable	This substitute is subject to containment and recovery regulations covering HCFCs.
	R-401B	Acceptable	This substitute is subject to containment and recovery regulations covering HCFCs.
	R-402A	Acceptable	This substitute is subject to containment and recovery regulations covering HCFCs.
	R-402B	Acceptable	This substitute is subject to containment and recovery regulations covering HCFCs.
	R-404A	Acceptable	EPA strongly recommends the containment and reclamation of this substitute.
	R-406A	Acceptable	This substitute is subject to containment and recovery regulations covering HCFCs.
	R-407A	Acceptable	EPA strongly recommends the containment and reclamation of this substitute.
	R-407B	Acceptable	EPA strongly recommends the containment and reclamation of this substitute.
	R-507	Acceptable	EPA strongly recommends the containment and reclamation of this substitute.
	HCFC Blend Epsilon	Acceptable	This substitute is subject to containment and recovery regulations covering HCFCs.
CFC-12, R-502 Cold Storage Warehouses (New Equipment/NIKs)	HCFC-22	Acceptable	This substitute is subject to containment and recovery regulations covering HCFCs.
	HFC-134a	Acceptable	EPA strongly recommends the containment and reclamation of this substitute.
	HFC-227ea	Acceptable	EPA strongly recommends the containment and reclamation of this substitute.
	R-402A	Acceptable	This substitute is subject to containment and recovery regulations covering HCFCs.
	R-402B	Acceptable	This substitute is subject to containment and recovery regulations covering HCFCs.
	R-404A	Acceptable	EPA strongly recommends the containment and reclamation of this substitute.
	R-407A	Acceptable	EPA strongly recommends the containment and reclamation of this substitute.
	R-407B	Acceptable	EPA strongly recommends the containment and reclamation of this substitute.
	R-507	Acceptable	EPA strongly recommends the containment and reclamation of this substitute.
	Ammonia Vapor Compression	Acceptable	Users should check local building codes related to the use of ammonia.
	Evaporative Cooling	Acceptable	Alternative technology that is currently commercially available; new developments have greatly expanded applicability.

	Desiccant Cooling	Acceptable	Alternative technology that is currently commercially available; new developments have greatly expanded applicability.
	High to Low Pressure Stepdown	Acceptable	Alternative technology.
	Stirling Cycle	Acceptable	Alternative technology.
CFC-12, R-500, R-502 Refrigerated Transport (Retrofit)	HCFC-22	Acceptable	This substitute is subject to containment and recovery regulations covering HCFCs.
	HFC-134a	Acceptable	EPA strongly recommends the containment and reclamation of this substitute.
	R-401A	Acceptable	This substitute is subject to containment and recovery regulations covering HCFCs.
	R-401B	Acceptable	This substitute is subject to containment and recovery regulations covering HCFCs.
	R-402A	Acceptable	This substitute is subject to containment and recovery regulations covering HCFCs.
	R-402B	Acceptable	This substitute is subject to containment and recovery regulations covering HCFCs.
	R-404A	Acceptable	EPA strongly recommends the containment and reclamation of this substitute.
	R-406A	Acceptable	This substitute is subject to containment and recovery regulations covering HCFCs.
	R-407A	Acceptable	EPA strongly recommends the containment and reclamation of this substitute.
	R-407B	Acceptable	EPA strongly recommends the containment and reclamation of this substitute.
	R-507	Acceptable	EPA strongly recommends the containment and reclamation of this substitute.
	HCFC Blend Gamma	Acceptable	This substitute is subject to containment and recovery regulations covering HCFCs.
	HCFC Blend Epsilon	Acceptable	This substitute is subject to containment and recovery regulations covering HCFCs.
CFC-12, R-500, R-502 Refrigerated Transport (New Equipment/NIKs)	HCFC-22	Acceptable	This substitute is subject to containment and recovery regulations covering HCFCs.
	HFC-134a	Acceptable	EPA strongly recommends the containment and reclamation of this substitute.
	R-402A	Acceptable	This substitute is subject to containment and recovery regulations covering HCFCs.
	R-402B	Acceptable	This substitute is subject to containment and recovery regulations covering HCFCs.
	R-404A	Acceptable	EPA strongly recommends the containment and reclamation of this substitute.
	R-407A	Acceptable	EPA strongly recommends the containment and reclamation of this substitute.
	R-407B	Acceptable	EPA strongly recommends the containment and reclamation of this substitute.
	R-507	Acceptable	EPA strongly recommends the containment and reclamation of this substitute.
	Stirling Cycle	Acceptable	Alternative technology that is currently commercially available.
	Nitrogen Direct Gas Expansion	Acceptable	Alternative technology.
CFC-12, R-502 Retail Food Refrigeration (Retrofit)	HCFC-22	Acceptable	This substitute is subject to containment and recovery regulations covering HCFCs.
	HFC-134a	Acceptable	EPA strongly recommends the containment and reclamation of this substitute.
	R-401A	Acceptable	This substitute is subject to containment and recovery regulations covering HCFCs.
	R-401B	Acceptable	This substitute is subject to containment and recovery regulations covering HCFCs.
	R-402A	Acceptable	This substitute is subject to containment and recovery regulations covering HCFCs.

	R-402B	Acceptable	This substitute is subject to containment and recovery regulations covering HCFCs.
	R-404A	Acceptable	EPA strongly recommends the containment and reclamation of this substitute.
	R-406A	Acceptable	This substitute is subject to containment and recovery regulations covering HCFCs.
	R-407A	Acceptable	EPA strongly recommends the containment and reclamation of this substitute.
	R-407B	Acceptable	EPA strongly recommends the containment and reclamation of this substitute.
	R-507	Acceptable	EPA strongly recommends the containment and reclamation of this substitute.
	HCFC Blend Gamma	Acceptable	This substitute is subject to containment and recovery regulations covering HCFCs.
	HCFC Blend Epsilon	Acceptable	This substitute is subject to containment and recovery regulations covering HCFCs.
CFC-12, R-502 Retail Food Refrigeration (New Equipment/NIKs)	HCFC-22	Acceptable	This substitute is subject to containment and recovery regulations covering HCFCs.
	HFC-134a	Acceptable	EPA strongly recommends the containment and reclamation of this substitute.
	HFC-227ea	Acceptable	EPA strongly recommends the containment and reclamation of this substitute.
	R-402A	Acceptable	This substitute is subject to containment and recovery regulations covering HCFCs.
	R-402B	Acceptable	This substitute is subject to containment and recovery regulations covering HCFCs.
	R-404A	Acceptable	EPA strongly recommends the containment and reclamation of this substitute.
	R-407A	Acceptable	EPA strongly recommends the containment and reclamation of this substitute.
	R-407B	Acceptable	EPA strongly recommends the containment and reclamation of this substitute.
	R-507	Acceptable	EPA strongly recommends the containment and reclamation of this substitute.
	Ammonia Vapor Compression	Acceptable	Users should check local building codes related to the use of ammonia.
	Stirling Cycle	Acceptable	Alternative technology.
CFC-12, R-502 Commercial Ice Machines (Retrofit)	R-401A	Acceptable	This substitute is subject to containment and recovery regulations covering HCFCs.
	R-401B	Acceptable	This substitute is subject to containment and recovery regulations covering HCFCs.
	R-402A	Acceptable	This substitute is subject to containment and recovery regulations covering HCFCs.
	R-402B	Acceptable	This substitute is subject to containment and recovery regulations covering HCFCs.
	R-404A	Acceptable	EPA strongly recommends the containment and reclamation of this substitute.
	R-406A	Acceptable	This substitute is subject to containment and recovery regulations covering HCFCs.
	R-407A	Acceptable	EPA strongly recommends the containment and reclamation of this substitute.
	R-407B	Acceptable	EPA strongly recommends the containment and reclamation of this substitute.
	R-507	Acceptable	EPA strongly recommends the containment and reclamation of this substitute.
	HCFC Blend Gamma	Acceptable	This substitute is subject to containment and recovery regulations covering HCFCs.
	HCFC Blend Epsilon	Acceptable	This substitute is subject to containment and recovery regulations covering HCFCs.
CFC-12, R-502 Commercial Ice Machines (New Equipment/NIKs)	HCFC-22	Acceptable	This substitute is subject to containment and recovery regulations covering HCFCs.
	HFC-134a	Acceptable	EPA strongly recommends the containment and reclamation of this substitute.
	R-402A	Acceptable	This substitute is subject to containment and recovery regulations covering HCFCs.

	R-402B	Acceptable	This substitute is subject to containment and recovery regulations covering HCFCs.
	R-404A	Acceptable	EPA strongly recommends the containment and reclamation of this substitute.
	R-407A	Acceptable	EPA strongly recommends the containment and reclamation of this substitute.
	R-407B	Acceptable	EPA strongly recommends the containment and reclamation of this substitute.
	R-507	Acceptable	EPA strongly recommends the containment and reclamation of this substitute.
	Ammonia Vapor Compression	Acceptable	Users should check local building codes related to the use of ammonia.
	Stirling Cycle	Acceptable	Alternative technology.
CFC-12 Vending Machines (Retrofit)	HCFC-22	Acceptable	This substitute is subject to containment and recovery regulations covering HCFCs.
	HFC-134a	Acceptable	EPA strongly recommends the containment and reclamation of this substitute.
	R-401A	Acceptable	This substitute is subject to containment and recovery regulations covering HCFCs.
	R-401B	Acceptable	This substitute is subject to containment and recovery regulations covering HCFCs.
	R-404A	Acceptable	EPA strongly recommends the containment and reclamation of this substitute.
	R-406A	Acceptable	This substitute is subject to containment and recovery regulations covering HCFCs.
	R-507	Acceptable	EPA strongly recommends the containment and reclamation of this substitute.
	HCFC Blend Gamma	Acceptable	This substitute is subject to containment and recovery regulations covering HCFCs.
CFC-12 Vending Machines (New Equipment/NIKs)	HCFC-22	Acceptable	This substitute is subject to containment and recovery regulations covering HCFCs.
	HFC-134a	Acceptable	EPA strongly recommends the containment and reclamation of this substitute.
	R-404A	Acceptable	EPA strongly recommends the containment and reclamation of this substitute.
	R-507	Acceptable	EPA strongly recommends the containment and reclamation of this substitute.
	Stirling Cycle	Acceptable	Alternative technology.
CFC-12 Water Coolers (Retrofit)	HFC-134a	Acceptable	EPA strongly recommends the containment and reclamation of this substitute.
	R-401A	Acceptable	This substitute is subject to containment and recovery regulations covering HCFCs.
	R-401B	Acceptable	This substitute is subject to containment and recovery regulations covering HCFCs.
	R-406A	Acceptable	This substitute is subject to containment and recovery regulations covering HCFCs.
	HCFC Blend Gamma	Acceptable	This substitute is subject to containment and recovery regulations covering HCFCs.
CFC-12 Water Coolers (New Equipment/NIKs)	HCFC-22	Acceptable	This substitute is subject to containment and recovery regulations covering HCFCs.
	HFC-134a	Acceptable	EPA strongly recommends the containment and reclamation of this substitute.
	Stirling Cycle	Acceptable	Alternative technology.
CFC-12 Household Refrigerators (Retrofit)	HCFC-22	Acceptable	This substitute is subject to containment and recovery regulations covering HCFCs.
	HFC-134a	Acceptable	EPA strongly recommends the containment and reclamation of this substitute.
	R-401A	Acceptable	This substitute is subject to containment and recovery regulations covering HCFCs.
	R-401B	Acceptable	This substitute is subject to containment and recovery regulations covering HCFCs.
	R-406A	Acceptable	This substitute is subject to containment and recovery regulations covering HCFCs.

End-use	Substitute	Decision	Comments
	HCFC Blend Alpha	Acceptable	EPA strongly recommends the containment and reclamation of this substitute.
	HCFC Blend Gamma	Acceptable	This substitute is subject to containment and recovery regulations covering HCFCs.
CFC-12 Household Refrigerators (New Equipment/NIKs)	HCFC-22	Acceptable	This substitute is subject to containment and recovery regulations covering HCFCs.
	HFC-134a	Acceptable	EPA strongly recommends the containment and reclamation of this substitute.
	HFC-152a	Acceptable	EPA strongly recommends the containment and reclamation of this substitute.
	HCFC Blend Alpha	Acceptable	This substitute is subject to containment and recovery regulations covering HCFCs.
	R200b	Acceptable	This substitute's composition is confidential. Its use may be governed by regulations concerning the use of ozone-depleting substances.
	Stirling Cycle	Acceptable	Alternative technology currently under development for this end-use.
CFC-12, R-502 Household Freezers (Retrofit)	HCFC-22	Acceptable	This substitute is subject to containment and recovery regulations covering HCFCs.
	HFC-134a	Acceptable	EPA strongly recommends the containment and reclamation of this substitute.
	R-401A	Acceptable	This substitute is subject to containment and recovery regulations covering HCFCs.
	R-401B	Acceptable	This substitute is subject to containment and recovery regulations covering HCFCs.
	R-402A	Acceptable	This substitute is subject to containment and recovery regulations covering HCFCs.
	R-402B	Acceptable	This substitute is subject to containment and recovery regulations covering HCFCs.
	R-404A	Acceptable	EPA strongly recommends the containment and reclamation of this substitute.
	R-406A	Acceptable	This substitute is subject to containment and recovery regulations covering HCFCs.
	R-507	Acceptable	EPA strongly recommends the containment and reclamation of this substitute.
	HCFC Blend Gamma	Acceptable	This substitute is subject to containment and recovery regulations covering HCFCs.
CFC-12, R-502 Household Freezers (New Equipment/NIKs)	HCFC-22	Acceptable	This substitute is subject to containment and recovery regulations covering HCFCs.
	HFC-134a	Acceptable	EPA strongly recommends the containment and reclamation of this substitute.
	HFC-152a	Acceptable	EPA strongly recommends the containment and reclamation of this substitute.
	R-402A	Acceptable	This substitute is subject to containment and recovery regulations covering HCFCs.
	R-402B	Acceptable	This substitute is subject to containment and recovery regulations covering HCFCs.
	R-404A	Acceptable	EPA strongly recommends the containment and reclamation of this substitute.
	R-507	Acceptable	EPA strongly recommends the containment and reclamation of this substitute.
	Stirling Cycle	Acceptable	Alternative technology.
CFC-12, R-500 Residential Dehumidifiers (Retrofit)	HCFC-22	Acceptable	This substitute is subject to containment and recovery regulations covering HCFCs.
	HFC-134a	Acceptable	EPA strongly recommends the containment and reclamation of this substitute.
	R-401A	Acceptable	This substitute is subject to containment and recovery regulations covering HCFCs.
	R-401B	Acceptable	This substitute is subject to containment and recovery regulations covering HCFCs.
	R-406A	Acceptable	This substitute is subject to containment and recovery regulations covering HCFCs.
	HCFC Blend Gamma	Acceptable	This substitute is subject to containment and recovery regulations covering HCFCs.

CFC-12, R-500 Residential Dehumidifiers (New Equipment/NIKs)	HCFC-22	Acceptable	This substitute is subject to containment and recovery regulations covering HCFCs.
	HFC-134a	Acceptable	EPA strongly recommends the containment and reclamation of this substitute.
CFC-12 Motor Vehicle Air Conditioners (Retrofit)	HFC-134a	Acceptable	EPA strongly recommends the containment and reclamation of this substitute.
	R-401C	Acceptable	This substitute is subject to containment and recovery regulations covering HCFCs.
CFC-12 Motor Vehicle Air Conditioners (New Equipment/NIKs)	HFC-134a	Acceptable	EPA strongly recommends the containment and reclamation of this substitute.
	R-401C	Acceptable	This substitute is subject to containment and recovery regulations covering HCFCs.
	CO_2	Acceptable	Alternative technology.
	Stirling Cycle	Acceptable	Alternative technology currently under development for this end-use.
CFC-12 Non-Automobile Motor Vehicle Air Conditioners (Retrofit and New)	Evaporative Cooling	Acceptable	
	HCFC-22	Acceptable	HCFC-22 may damage automobile AC systems, which is why it is acceptable only for non-automobile use such as buses. This substitute is subject to containment and recovery regulations covering HCFCs.

REFRIGERANTS
UNACCEPTABLE SUBSTITUTES

END-USE	SUBSTITUTE	DECISION	COMMENTS
CFC-11 Centrifugal Chillers (Retrofit)	HCFC-141b	Unacceptable	Has a high ODP relative to other alternatives.
CFC-12 Centrifugal Chillers (Retrofit)	HCFC-22/HFC-142b/CFC-12	Unacceptable	As a blend of both Class I and Class II substances, it has a higher ODP than use of Class II substances.
	Hydrocarbon Blend A	Unacceptable	Flammability is a serious concern. Data have not been submitted to demonstrate it can be used safely in this end-use.
CFC-11, CFC-12, CFC-113, CFC-114, R-500 Centrifugal Chillers (New Equipment/NIKs)	HCFC-22/HFC-142b/CFC-12	Unacceptable	As a blend of both Class I and Class II substances, it has a higher ODP than use of Class II substances.
	Hydrocarbon Blend A	Unacceptable	Flammability is a serious concern. Data have not been submitted to demonstrate it can be used safely in this end-use.
	HCFC-141b	Unacceptable	Has a high ODP relative to other alternatives.
CFC-12 Reciprocating Chillers (Retrofit)	HCFC-22/HFC-142b/CFC-12	Unacceptable	As a blend of both Class I and Class II substances, it has a higher ODP than use of Class II substances.
	Hydrocarbon Blend A	Unacceptable	Flammability is a serious concern. Data have not been submitted to demonstrate it can be used safely in this end-use.
CFC-12 Reciprocating Chillers (New Equipment/NIKs)	HCFC-22/HFC-142b/CFC-12	Unacceptable	As a blend of both Class I and Class II substances, it has a higher ODP than use of Class II substances.
	Hydrocarbon Blend A	Unacceptable	Flammability is a serious concern. Data have not been submitted to demonstrate it can be used safely in this end-use.
CFC-11, CFC-12, R-502 Industrial Process Refrigeration (Retrofit)	HCFC-22/HFC-142b/CFC-12	Unacceptable	As a blend of both Class I and Class II substances, it has a higher ODP than use of Class II substances.
CFC-11, CFC-12, R-502 Industrial Process Refrigeration (New Equipment/NIKs)	HCFC-22/HFC-142b/CFC-12	Unacceptable	As a blend of both Class I and Class II substances, it has a higher ODP than use of Class II substances.
CFC-12, R-502 Ice Skating Rinks (Retrofit)	HCFC-22/HFC-142b/CFC-12	Unacceptable	As a blend of both Class I and Class II substances, it has a higher ODP than use of Class II substances.
	Hydrocarbon Blend A	Unacceptable	Flammability is a serious concern. Data have not been submitted to demonstrate it can be used safely in this end-use.
CFC-12, R-502 Ice Skating Rinks (New Equipment/NIKs)	HCFC-22/HFC-142b/CFC-12	Unacceptable	As a blend of both Class I and Class II substances, it has a higher ODP than use of Class II substances.
	Hydrocarbon Blend A	Unacceptable	Flammability is a serious concern. Data have not been submitted to demonstrate it can be used safely in this end-use.
CFC-12, R-502 Cold Storage Warehouses (Retrofit)	HCFC-22/HFC-142b/CFC-12	Unacceptable	As a blend of both Class I and Class II substances, it has a higher ODP than use of Class II substances.
	Hydrocarbon Blend A	Unacceptable	Flammability is a serious concern. Data have not been submitted to demonstrate it can be used safely in this end-use.
CFC-12, R-502 Cold Storage Warehouses (New Equipment/NIKs)	HCFC-22/HFC-142b/CFC-12	Unacceptable	As a blend of both Class I and Class II substances, it has a higher ODP than use of Class II substances.
	Hydrocarbon Blend A	Unacceptable	Flammability is a serious concern. Data have not been submitted to demonstrate it can be used safely in this end-use.

CFC-12, R-500, R-502 Refrigerated Transport (Retrofit)	HCFC-22/HFC-142b/CFC-12	Unacceptable	As a blend of both Class I and Class II substances, it has a higher ODP than use of Class II substances.
	Hydrocarbon Blend A	Unacceptable	Flammability is a serious concern. Data have not been submitted to demonstrate it can be used safely in this end-use.
CFC-12, R-500, R-502 Refrigerated Transport (New Equipment/NIKs)	HCFC-22/HFC-142b/CFC-12	Unacceptable	As a blend of both Class I and Class II substances, it has a higher ODP than use of Class II substances.
	Hydrocarbon Blend A	Unacceptable	Flammability is a serious concern. Data have not been submitted to demonstrate it can be used safely in this end-use.
CFC-12, R-502 Retail Food Refrigeration (Retrofit)	HCFC-22/HFC-142b/CFC-12	Unacceptable	As a blend of both Class I and Class II substances, it has a higher ODP than use of Class II substances.
	Hydrocarbon Blend A	Unacceptable	Flammability is a serious concern. Data have not been submitted to demonstrate it can be used safely in this end-use.
CFC-12, R-502 Retail Food Refrigeration (New Equipment/NIKs)	HCFC-22/HFC-142b/CFC-12	Unacceptable	As a blend of both Class I and Class II substances, it has a higher ODP than use of Class II substances.
	Hydrocarbon Blend A	Unacceptable	Flammability is a serious concern. Data have not been submitted to demonstrate it can be used safely in this end-use.
CFC-12, R-502 Commercial Ice Machines (Retrofit)	HCFC-22/HFC-142b/CFC-12	Unacceptable	As a blend of both Class I and Class II substances, it has a higher ODP than use of Class II substances.
	Hydrocarbon Blend A	Unacceptable	Flammability is a serious concern. Data have not been submitted to demonstrate it can be used safely in this end-use.
CFC-12, R-502 Commercial Ice Machines (New Equipment/NIKs)	HCFC-22/HFC-142b/CFC-12	Unacceptable	As a blend of both Class I and Class II substances, it has a higher ODP than use of Class II substances.
	Hydrocarbon Blend A	Unacceptable	Flammability is a serious concern. Data have not been submitted to demonstrate it can be used safely in this end-use.
CFC-12 Vending Machines (Retrofit)	HCFC-22/HFC-142b/CFC-12	Unacceptable	As a blend of both Class I and Class II substances, it has a higher ODP than use of Class II substances.
	Hydrocarbon Blend A	Unacceptable	Flammability is a serious concern. Data have not been submitted to demonstrate it can be used safely in this end-use.
CFC-12 Vending Machines (New Equipment/NIKs)	HCFC-22/HFC-142b/CFC-12	Unacceptable	As a blend of both Class I and Class II substances, it has a higher ODP than use of Class II substances.
	Hydrocarbon Blend A	Unacceptable	Flammability is a serious concern. Data have not been submitted to demonstrate it can be used safely in this end-use.
CFC-12 Water Coolers (Retrofit)	HCFC-22/HFC-142b/CFC-12	Unacceptable	As a blend of both Class I and Class II substances, it has a higher ODP than use of Class II substances.
	Hydrocarbon Blend A	Unacceptable	Flammability is a serious concern. Data have not been submitted to demonstrate it can be used safely in this end-use.
CFC-12 Water Coolers (New Equipment/NIKs)	HCFC-22/HFC-142b/CFC-12	Unacceptable	As a blend of both Class I and Class II substances, it has a higher ODP than use of Class II substances.
	Hydrocarbon Blend A	Unacceptable	Flammability is a serious concern. Data have not been submitted to demonstrate it can be used safely in this end-use.
CFC-12 Household Refrigerators (Retrofit)	HCFC-22/HFC-142b/CFC-12	Unacceptable	As a blend of both Class I and Class II substances, it has a higher ODP than use of Class II substances.

	Hydrocarbon Blend A	Unacceptable	Flammability is a serious concern. Data have not been submitted to demonstrate it can be used safely in this end-use.
CFC-12 Household Refrigerators (New Equipment/NIKs)	HCFC-22/HFC-142b/CFC-12	Unacceptable	As a blend of both Class I and Class II substances, it has a higher ODP than use of Class II substances.
	Hydrocarbon Blend A	Unacceptable	Flammability is a serious concern. Data have not been submitted to demonstrate it can be used safely in this end-use.
CFC-12, R-502 Household Freezers (Retrofit)	HCFC-22/HFC-142b/CFC-12	Unacceptable	As a blend of both Class I and Class II substances, it has a higher ODP than use of Class II substances.
	Hydrocarbon Blend A	Unacceptable	Flammability is a serious concern. Data have not been submitted to demonstrate it can be used safely in this end-use.
CFC-12, R-502 Household Freezers (New Equipment/NIKs)	HCFC-22/HFC-142b/CFC-12	Unacceptable	As a blend of both Class I and Class II substances, it has a higher ODP than use of Class II substances.
	Hydrocarbon Blend A	Unacceptable	Flammability is a serious concern. Data have not been submitted to demonstrate it can be used safely in this end-use.
CFC-12, R-500 Residential Dehumidifiers (Retrofit)	HCFC-22/HFC-142b/CFC-12	Unacceptable	As a blend of both Class I and Class II substances, it has a higher ODP than use of Class II substances.
	Hydrocarbon Blend A	Unacceptable	Flammability is a serious concern. Data have not been submitted to demonstrate it can be used safely in this end-use.
CFC-12, R-500 Residential Dehumidifiers (New Equipment/NIKs)	HCFC-22/HFC-142b/CFC-12	Unacceptable	As a blend of both Class I and Class II substances, it has a higher ODP than use of Class II substances.
	Hydrocarbon Blend A	Unacceptable	Flammability is a serious concern. Data have not been submitted to demonstrate it can be used safely in this end-use.
CFC-12 Motor Vehicle Air Conditioners (Retrofit)	HCFC-22/HFC-142b/CFC-12	Unacceptable	As a blend of both Class I and Class II substances, it has a higher ODP than use of Class II substances.
	Hydrocarbon Blend A	Unacceptable	Flammability is a serious concern. Data have not been submitted to demonstrate it can be used safely in this end-use.
CFC-12 Motor Vehicle Air Conditioners (New Equipment/NIKs)	HCFC-22/HFC-142b/CFC-12	Unacceptable	As a blend of both Class I and Class II substances, it has a higher ODP than use of Class II substances.
	Hydrocarbon Blend A	Unacceptable	Flammability is a serious concern. Data have not been submitted to demonstrate it can be used safely in this end-use.

REFRIGERANTS
PENDING DECISIONS

APPLICATION	SUBSTITUTE	COMMENTS
CFC-12 Motor Vehicle Air Conditioning	HCFC Blend Delta	EPA has requested additional data.
HCFC-22 Heat Pumps	HFC-134a	EPA has not yet evaluated Class II substitutes.
	HFC-152a	EPA has not yet evaluated Class II substitutes.
	HFC-32	EPA has not yet evaluated Class II substitutes.
HCFC-22 Conventional (Household) Air Conditioning	R-407C	EPA has not yet evaluated Class II substitutes.

SOLVENT CLEANING
ACCEPTABLE SUBSTITUTES
Updated February 1, 1994

END USE	SUBSTITUTE	DECISION	COMMENTS
Metals cleaning w/ CFC-113, MCF	**Aqueous cleaners**	Acceptable	EPA expects to issue effluent guidelines for this industry under the Clean Water Act by as early as 1994.
	Semi-aqueous cleaners	Acceptable	EPA expects to issue effluent guidelines for this industry under the Clean Water Act by as early as 1994.
	Straight organic solvent cleaning (with terpenes, C6-C20 petroleum hydrocarbons, oxygenated organic solvents such as ketones, esters, ethers, alcohols, etc.)	Acceptable	OSHA standards must be met, if applicable.
	Trichloroethylene, perchloroethylene, methylene chloride	Acceptable	OSHA and RCRA standards must be met. EPA expects to issue Maximum Achievable Control Technology requirements under the Clean Air Act for this application by 1994.
	Vanishing oils	Acceptable	Depending on geographic region, may be subject to VOC controls.
	Supercritical fluids	Acceptable	
	Volatile methyl siloxanes	Acceptable	Approval is granted for the whole class of compounds.
	Trans-1,2-dichloroethylene	Acceptable	

END USE	SUBSTITUTE	DECISION	COMMENTS
Electronics cleaning w/ CFC-113, MCF	**Aqueous cleaners**	Acceptable	EPA expects to issue effluent guidelines for this industry under the Clean Water Act by as early as 1994.
	Semi-aqueous cleaners	Acceptable	EPA expects to issue effluent guidelines for this industry under the Clean Water Act by 1994.
	Straight organic solvent cleaning (with terpenes, C6-C20 petroleum hydrocarbons, oxygenated organic solvents such as ketones, esters, ethers, alcohols, etc.)	Acceptable	OSHA standards must be met, if applicable.
	Trichloroethylene, perchloroethylene, methylene chloride	Acceptable	OSHA and RCRA standards must be met. EPA expects to issue Maximum Achievable Control Technology requirements under the Clean Air Act for this application by 1994.
	No-clean alternatives	Acceptable	Substitutes found acceptable include low solids fluxes and inert gas soldering.
	Supercritical fluids, plasma cleaning, UV/Ozone cleaning	Acceptable	OSHA standards for ozone must be met.
	Volatile methyl siloxanes	Acceptable	Approval is granted for the whole class of compounds.
	Trans-1,2-dichloroethylene	Acceptable	

END USE	SUBSTITUTE	DECISION	COMMENTS
Precision cleaning w/ CFC-113, MCF	Aqueous cleaners	Acceptable	EPA expects to issue effluent guidelines for this industry under the Clean Water Act by as early as 1994.
	Semi-aqueous cleaners	Acceptable	EPA expects to issue effluent guidelines for this industry under the Clean Water Act by as early as 1994.
	Straight organic solvent cleaning (with terpenes, C6-C20 petroleum hydrocarbons, oxygenated organic solvents such as ketones, esters, ethers, alcohols, etc.)	Acceptable	OSHA standards must be met, if applicable.
	Trichloroethylene, perchloroethylene, methylene chloride	Acceptable	OSHA and RCRA standards must be met. EPA expects to issue Maximum Achievable Control Technology requirements for this application by 1994.
	Supercritical fluids, plasma cleaning, UV/Ozone cleaning	Acceptable	OSHA standards for ozone must be met.
	HCFC-123	Acceptable	Has an AEL of 30ppm.
	Trans-1,2-dichloroethylene	Acceptable	
	Volatile methyl siloxanes	Acceptable	Approval is granted for the whole class of compounds.

SUBSTITUTES ACCEPTABLE SUBJECT TO NARROWED USE LIMITS

END USE	SUBSTITUTE	DECISION	COMMENTS
Electronics cleaning w/ CFC-113, MCF	Perfluorocarbons (C5F12, C6F12, C6F14, C7F16, C8F18, C5F11NO, C6F13NO, C7F15NO, and C8F16)	Acceptable for high-performance, precision-engineered applications only where reasonable efforts have been made to ascertain that other alternatives are not technically feasible due to performance or safety requirements	The principal environmental characteristic of concern for PFCs is that they have long atmospheric lifetimes and high global warming potentials. Although actual contributions to global warming depend upon the quantities of PFCs emitted, the effects are for practical purposes irreversible. Users must observe this limitation on PFC acceptability by conducting a reasonable evaluation of other substitutes to determine that PFC use is necessary to meet performance or safety requirements. Documentation of this evaluation must be kept on file. For additional guidance regarding applications in which PFCs may be appropriate, users should consult the Preamble for this rulemaking.
Precision cleaning w/ CFC-113, MCF	Perfluorocarbons (C5F12, C6F12, C6F14, C7F16, C8F18, C5F11NO, C6F13NO, C7F15NO, and C8F16)	Acceptable for high-performance, precision-engineered applications only where reasonable efforts have been made to ascertain that other alternatives are not technically feasible due to performance or safety requirements	The principal environmental characteristic of concern for PFCs is that they have long atmospheric lifetimes and high global warming potentials. Although actual contributions to global warming depend upon the quantities of PFCs emitted, the effects are for practical purposes irreversible. Users must observe this limitation on PFC acceptability by conducting a reasonable evaluation of other substitutes to determine that PFC use is necessary to meet performance or safety requirements. Documentation of this evaluation must be kept on file. For additional guidance regarding applications in which PFCs may be appropriate, users should consult the Preamble for this rulemaking.

UNACCEPTABLE SUBSTITUTES

END USE	SUBSTITUTE	DECISION	COMMENTS
Metals cleaning w/ CFC-113	**HCFC 141b and its blends**	Unacceptable	High ODP; other alternatives exist. **Effective date: As of** 30 days after final rule for uses in new equipment (including retrofits made after the effective date); as of January 1, 1996 for uses in existing equipment. **EPA will** grant, if necessary, narrowed use acceptability listings for CFC-113 past the effective date of the prohibition.
Metals cleaning w/ MCF	**HCFC 141b and its blends**	Unacceptable	High ODP; other alternatives exist. **Effective date: As of** 30 days after final rule for uses in new equipment (including retrofits made after the effective date); as of January 1, 1996 for uses in existing equipment.
Electronics cleaning w/ CFC-113	**HCFC 141b and its blends**	Unacceptable	High ODP; other alternatives exist. **Effective date: As of** 30 days after final rule for uses in new equipment (including retrofits made after the effective date); as of January 1, 1996 for uses in existing equipment. **EPA will** grant, if necessary, narrowed use acceptability listings for CFC-113 past the effective date of the prohibition.
Electronics cleaning w/ MCF	**HCFC 141b and its blends**	Unacceptable	High ODP; other alternatives exist. **Effective date: As of** 30 days after final rule for uses in new equipment (including retrofits made after the effective date); as of January 1, 1996 for uses in existing equipment.
Precision cleaning w/ CFC-113	**HCFC 141b and its blends**	Unacceptable	High ODP; other alternatives exist. **Effective date: As of** 30 days after final rule for uses in new equipment (including retrofits made after the effective date); as of January 1, 1996 for uses in existing equipment. **EPA will** grant, if necessary, narrowed use acceptability listings for CFC-113 past the effective date of the prohibition.
Precision cleaning w/ MCF	**HCFC 141b and its blends**	Unacceptable	High ODP; other alternatives exist. **Effective date: As of** 30 days after final rule for uses in new equipment (including retrofits made after the effective date); as of January 1, 1996 for uses in existing equipment.

PENDING SUBSTITUTES

END USE	SUBSTITUTE	COMMENTS
Metals cleaning w/ CFC-113, MCF	**Monochlorotoluene/ benzotrifluorides**	Agency has not completed review of data. Evaluation of exposure and toxicity data still ongoing.
	HCFC-122	Agency is still reviewing ODP. This HCFC is a new chemical and must also complete Premanufacture Notice requirements under the Toxic Substances Control Act.
	Dibromomethane	On 9/26/94 (59 FR 49108), EPA proposed dibromomethane as unacceptable for metals, electronics and precision cleaning.
Electronics cleaning w/ CFC-113, MCF	**Monochlorotoluene/ benzotrifluorides**	Agency has not completed review of data. Evaluation of exposure and toxicity data still ongoing.
	HCFC-225ca/cb	On 9/26/94 (59 FR 49108), EPA proposed HCFC-225 as acceptable for electronics and precision cleaning with the regulatory condition that users meet the the AEL of 25ppm for the ca-isomer.
	HCFC-122	Agency is still reviewing ODP. This HCFC is a new chemical and must also complete Premanufacture Notice requirements under the Toxic Substances Control Act.
	HFC-4310mee	Agency has not completed review of data. Premanufacture Notice review under the Toxic Substances Control Act not yet completed.
	Perfluorocarbons (C_5F_{12}, C_6F_{12}, C_6F_{14}, C_7F_{16}, C_8F_{18}, $C_5F_{11}NO$, $C_6F_{13}NO$, $C_7F_{15}NO$, and C_8F_{16})	Agency in process of evaluating global warming concerns.
	Dibromomethane	On 9/26/94 (59 FR 49108), EPA proposed dibromomethane as unacceptable for metals, electronics and precision cleaning.

Precision cleaning w/ CFC-113, MCF	**Monochlorotoluene/ benzotrifluorides**	Agency has not completed review of data. Evaluation of exposure and toxicity data still ongoing.
	HCFC-225ca/cb	On 9/26/94 (59 FR 49108), EPA proposed HCFC-225 as acceptable for electronics and precision cleaning with the regulatory condition that users meet the the AEL of 25ppm for the ca-isomer.
	HCFC-122	Agency is still reviewing ODP. This HCFC is a new chemical and must also complete Premanufacture Notice requirements under the Toxic Substances Control Act.
	HFC-4310mee	Agency has not completed review of data. Premanufacture Notice review under the Toxic Substances Control Act not yet completed.
	Perfluorocarbons (C5F12, C6F12, C6F14, C7F16, C8F18, C5F11NO, C6F13NO, C7F15NO, and C8F16)	Agency in process of evaluating global warming concerns.
	Dibromomethane	On 9/26/94 (59 FR 49108), EPA proposed dibromomethane as unacceptable for metals, electronics and precision cleaning.
	Chlorobromomethane	Agency has not yet completed review of data.

STERILANTS
ACCEPTABLE SUBSTITUTES
Updated April 1995

Application	Substitute	Decision	Conditions	Comments
12/88 Blend of EtO/CFC-12 **Sterilant**	CO_2/ETO	Acceptable		CO_2/EtO blends can serve as drop-in replacements to 12/88 in some but not in all existing equipment because they require a higher operating pressure. As a HAP, use of EtO must comply with Title III of the CAA. This agent is FIFRA registered.
	HCFC-124/ETO	Acceptable		HCFC-124 is an ozone depleting substance; it should be use to sterilize only that equipment that cannot be sterilized using other alternatives such as steam or CO_2/EtO blends. As a HAP, use of EtO must comply with Title III of the CAA. This agent is FIFRA registered.
	[HCFC Blend] A	Acceptable		This blend contains HCFC-124, an ozone depleting substance; it should be use to sterilize only that equipment that cannot be sterilized using other alternatives such as steam or CO_2/EtO blends. As a HAP, use of EtO must comply with Title III of the CAA. This agent is FIFRA Registered.

	Pure ETO	Acceptable		EtO is a toxic, carcinogenic substance and is considered a hazardous air pollutant. Potential exposures of the general population to EtO releases can be limited either through the use of catalytic converters which convert waste EtO into CO_2 and water, or through the use of acid water scrubbers which convert waste EtO into ethylene glycol. Must be used in accordance with manufacturer recommendations to address flammability concerns. Must be used in accordance with OSHA standards to limit occupational exposures. As a HAP, use of EtO must comply with Title III of the CAA.
	Steam	Acceptable		Applicable only to devices resistant to heat and moisture.

STERILANTS
PENDING

END-USE	**SUBSTITUTE**	**COMMENTS**
12/88 Blend of EtO/CFC-12 Sterilant	HFC-125/EtO	Pending FIFRA registration and completion of Agency review.
	HFC-227ea/EtO	Pending FIFRA registration and receipt of complete SNAP submission.

TOBACCO EXPANSION
ACCEPTABLE SUBSTITUTES
Updated April 1995

APPLICATION	SUBSTITUTE	DECISION	CONDITIONS	COMMENTS
CFC-11 Tobacco Expansion	Carbon Dioxide	Acceptable		Carbon Dioxide cannot be used as a drop-in or a retrofit, but requires new equipment.
	Propane	Acceptable		Propane tobacco expansion is a patented process. Flammability may be of concern for workers. Major sources of VOC emissions are subject to the New Source Review (NSR) program under the CAA.

TOBACCO EXPANSION
PENDING SUBSTITUTES

END-USE	SUBSTITUTE	COMMENTS
CFC-11 Tobacco Expansion	HFC-227ea	Agency has not completed review of data.

EPA

United States
Environmental Protection Agency

Air and Radiation
(6205J)

January 1995

Acceptable Substitute Refrigerants under SNAP

EPA has created the Significant New Alternatives Policy (SNAP) program under section 612 of the Clean Air Act Amendments. SNAP evaluates alternatives to ozone-depleting substances. Substitutes are reviewed on the basis of ozone depletion potential, global warming potential, toxicity, flammability, and exposure potential as described in the final SNAP rule (59 FR 13044). Lists of acceptable and unacceptable substitutes will be updated quarterly in the Federal Register. The latest Notice was published on January 13, 1995 (60 FR 3318). For information about future SNAP notices, please call the Stratospheric Ozone Protection Hotline at (800) 296-1996.

Acceptable Substitutes for Air Conditioning under the Significant New Alternatives Policy (SNAP) Program as of January 13, 1995

Substitutes (Name Used in the Federal Register)	Trade Name	CFC-11 Centrifugal Chillers	CFC-12, R-500 Centrifugal Chillers	CFC-12 Reciprocating Chillers	CFC-12 Motor Vehicle AC	Non Automotive Motor Vehicle AC	CFC-114 Industrial Process AC	CFC-12, R-500 Residential Dehumidifiers
HCFC-123		R, N	N					
HCFC-22		N	N	N		R, N	N (only <115F)	R, N
HFC-134a		N	R, N	R, N	R, N		N (only <125F)	R, N
HFC-227ea		N	N	N				
HCFC-124							R, N	
R-401A	MP-39			R, N			R	R, N
R-401B	MP-66			R, N			R	R, N
R-401C	MP-52				R, N			
R-406A	GHG		R, N (R-500 only)					R
R-409A (HCFC Blend Gamma)	FX-56							R
Ammonia Vapor Compression		N	N					
Evaporative Cooling		N	N	N		N		
Desiccant Cooling		N	N	N				
Ammonia/water Absorption		N	N					
Water/Lithium Bromide Absorption		N	N					

Key: R = Retrofit Uses, N = New Uses

Acceptable Substitutes for Commercial Refrigeration under the Significant New Alternatives Policy (SNAP) Program as of January 13, 1995

Substitutes (Name used in Fed. Reg.)	Trade Name	ODS being replaced	Cold Storage Warehouses	Refrigerated Transport	Retail Food Refrigeration	Ice Machines	Vending Machines	Water Coolers
HCFC-22		12, 502	R, N	R, N	R, N	N	R, N	N
HFC-134a		12	R, N	R, N	R, N	N	R, N	R, N
HFC-227ea		12	N		N			
R-401A, R-401B	MP-39, MP-66	12	R, N	R, N	R, N	R, N	R, N	R, N
R-402A, R-402B	HP-80, HP-81	502	R, N	R, N	R, N	R, N		
R-404A	HP-62, FX-70	502	R, N	R, N	R, N	R, N	R, N	
R-406A	GHG	12, 500	R	R	R	R	R	R
R-407A, R-407B	Klea 407A, 407B	502	R, N	R, N	R, N	R, N		
R-408A (HCFC Blend Epsilon)	FX-10	502	R	R	R	R		
R-409A (HCFC Blend Gamma)	FX-56	12		R	R	R	R	R
R-507	AZ-50	502	R, N	R, N	R, N	R, N	R, N	
Ammonia Vapor Compression		all	N		N	N		
Evaporative/Desiccant Cooling		all	N					
Stirling Cycle		all		N				
Direct Nitrogen Expansion		all		N				
Pressure Stepdown		all	N					

Key: R = Retrofit Uses, N = New Uses

Acceptable Substitutes for Non-Commercial Refrigeration under the Significant New Alternatives Policy (SNAP) Program as of January 13, 1995

Substitutes (Name used in Fed. Reg.)	Trade Name	ODS being replaced	Industrial Process Refrigeration	Ice Skating Rinks	Household Refrigerators	Household Freezers
HCFC-123		11	R, N			
HCFC-22		12, 502	R, N	R, N	R, N	R, N
HFC-23		13, 13B1, 503	R, N			
HFC-134a		12	R, N		R, N	R, N
HFC-152a		12			N	N
HFC-227ea		12	N			
R-401A, R-401B	MP-39, MP-66	12	R, N	R	R, N	R, N
R-402A, R-402B	HP-80, HP-81	502	R, N			R, N
R-403B	Isceon 69-L	13, 13B1, 503	R, N*			
R-404A	HP-62, FX-70	502	R, N			R, N
R-406A	GHG	12, 500	R		R	R
R-407A, R-407B	Klea 407A, 407B	502	R, N	R, N		
R-408A (HCFC Blend Epsilon)	FX-10	502	R			
R-409A (HCFC Blend Gamma)	FX-56	12			R	R
R-507	AZ-50	502	R, N			R, N
CO2		13, 13B1, 503	R, N			
Ammonia Vapor Compression		12, 502	R, N	R, N		
Propane, Propylene, Butane, Hydrocarbon Blend A, B		all	R, N*			
Chlorine		all	R, N			
Evaporative/Desiccant Cooling		all	N			
(PFC Blend Alpha)		13, 13B1, 503	R, N			
(HCFC Blend Alpha)		12			R, N	

* Prohibited or proposed unacceptable for other end-uses.

Key: R = Retrofit Uses, N = New Uses

SNAP Refrigerants and Blend Contents

Trade Name	HP-80	HP-81	Isceon 69-L	HP-62, FX-70	KLEA 407A	KLEA 407B	FX-10	AZ-50	AZ-20
Name Used in Federal Register	ASHRAE designation	ASHRAE designation	ASHRAE designation	ASHRAE designation	ASHRAE designation	ASHRAE designation	HCFC Blend Epsilon	ASHRAE designation	HFC Blend Alpha
ASHRAE R-	402A	402B	403B	404A	407A	407B	408A	507	
File Number	IV-D-161	IV-D-161	IV-D-154	IV-D-161	VI-D-8	VI-D-9	VI-D-7	IV-D-156	IV-D-173
Replacing	502	502	503 (Proposed Unacceptable to replace R-502)	502	502	502	502	502	22
HCFC-22	38	60	56				46		
HCFC-124									
HFC-125	60	38		44	40	70	7	50	50
HCFC-142b									
HFC-134a				4	40	20			
HFC-143a				52			47	50	
HFC-152a									
HFC-32					20	10			50
Propane	2	2	5						
Perfluoropropane			39						
Butane									
Isobutane									

SNAP Refrigerants and Blend Contents

Trade Name	MP-39	MP-66	MP-52	GHG	FX-56	HCFC Blend Alpha	FRIGC	Freezone
Name Used in Federal Register	ASHRAE designation	ASHRAE designation	ASHRAE designation	ASHRAE designation	HCFC Blend Gamma	HCFC Blend Alpha	HCFC Blend Beta	HCFC Blend Delta
ASHRAE R-	401A	401B	401C	406A	409A			
File Number	IV-D-161	IV-D-161	IV-D-161	IV-D-167	IV-D-174		IV-D-184	VI-D-6
Replacing	12	12	12	12	12	12	12	12
HCFC-22	53	61	33	55	60			
HCFC-124	34	28	52		25			
HFC-125								
HCFC-142b				41	15			
HFC-134a								
HFC-143a								
HFC-152a	13	11	15					
HFC-32								
Propane								
Perfluoropropane								
Butane								
Isobutane				4				

United States Environmental Protection Agency

Office of Air and Radiation Stratospheric Protection Division

April 1995

SIGNIFICANT NEW ALTERNATIVES POLICY (SNAP) PROGRAM

SUMMARY OF RULES & NOTICES

STATUTORY REQUIREMENTS

Section 612 of the Clean Air Act (CAA) requires EPA to establish a program to identify alternatives to Class I (CFC, Halon, Carbon Tetrachloride, Methyl Chloroform, Methyl Bromide, HBFC) and Class II (HCFC) ozone-depleting substances and to publish lists of acceptable and unacceptable substitutes. Upon promulgation of the final rule, it is illegal to replace a Class I or Class II substance with any substitute which the Administrator determines may present adverse effects to human health or the environment where other substitutes have been identified that reduce overall risk and are currently or potentially available. Any person may petition EPA to add a substitute to either of the lists. Such petitions will be granted or denied within 90 days of receipt of a complete petition. In addition, any person who produces a substitute for a Class I substance must notify EPA at least 90 days before new or existing alternatives are introduced into interstate commerce for significant new use as substitutes for a Class I substance.

THE FINAL RULE

On March 18, 1994 EPA published the Final Rulemaking (FRM) (59 FR 13044) which described the process for administering the SNAP program and issued EPA's first acceptability lists for substitutes in the major industrial use sectors. These sectors include refrigeration and air conditioning, solvents, foam blowing, fire suppression and explosion protection, sterilants, aerosols, adhesives, coatings, and inks, and tobacco expansion. To assess the acceptability of a substitute, the Agency completes a screening analysis in which overall risks to human health and the environment in use-specific applications were examined.

QUARTERLY UPDATES

EPA intends to publish Quarterly Updates to the SNAP rule. These updates may be in two parts, a 'Notice' or a 'Rulemaking.' A 'Notice' contains no regulatory controls and thus does not need to go through the public comment process. It contains technical corrections to the original rule as well as listings of new agents which are 'Acceptable' without restrictions. It enters into force upon publication in the Federal Register.

A Rulemaking requires a public notice-and-comment process, beginning with a 'Notice of Proposed Rulemaking (NPRM)'. An NPRM contains proposed lists of agents deemed 'Acceptable Subject to Use Conditions,' 'Acceptable Subject to Narrowed Use Limits,' and 'Unacceptable'. There is a 45-day public comment period beginning with the date of publication in the Federal Register, after which a 'Final Rulemaking' is published.

Quarterly Updates comprise of Notices for acceptable substitutes and a Rulemakings for unacceptable or restricted substitutes. Notices were published on August 26, 1994 (59 FR 44240) and January 13, 1995 (60 FR 3318). A Notice of Proposed Rulemaking was published on September 26, 1994 (59 FR 49180).

WHO MUST APPLY FOR LISTING

Under SNAP, the Agency defines a "substitute" as any chemical, product, substitute, or alternative manufacturing process, whether existing or new, that could replace a Class I or Class II substance. Anyone who produces a substitute must provide the Agency with health and safety studies, as well as notify the Agency at least 90 days before introducing it into interstate commerce for use as an alternative. This requirement applies to chemical manufacturers, but may include importers, formulators or end-users when they are responsible for introducing a substitute into commerce.

INFORMATION FOR SNAP SUBMISSION

To develop the lists of acceptable and unacceptable substitutes, the Agency must assess and compare "overall risks to human health and the environment" posed by use of substitutes in the context of particular applications. EPA requires submission of information covering a wide range of health and environmental factors. These include intrinsic properties such as physical and chemical information, ozone depleting potential, global warming potential, toxicity, and flammability, and use-specific data such as substitute applications, process description, environmental release data, environmental fate and transport, and cost information.

Once a completed submission has been received, a 90 day review period under the SNAP program will commence. Any substitute which is a new chemical must also be submitted to the Agency under the Premanufacture Notice (PMN) program under the Toxic Substances Control Act (TSCA). Alternatives that will be used in pesticide formulations must be filed jointly with EPA's Office of Pesticide Programs and with SNAP.

Any information submitted as Confidential Business Information (CBI) will be treated in a manner consistent with 40 CFR Part 2, Subpart B. All claims of confidentiality must be substantiated at the time of submission.

SNAP Notification Forms and the SNAP notification guidance manual may be requested from the Stratospheric Hotline at 1-800-296-1996 or contact the SNAP Coordinator at (202) 233-9152.

THE SNAP LISTS

EPA has identified three mechanisms for revising or expanding the list of SNAP determinations published in the final regulation:

- First, as new substitutes are developed for commercial sale, producers must notify EPA at least 90 days before introduction of a chemical into interstate commerce for significant new use as an alternative to Class I or Class II substances;
- Second, any person may petition EPA to add or delete substances from the SNAP lists of acceptable and unacceptable alternatives; and
- Third, EPA may revise the SNAP lists outside the context of petitions or notifications, based on new data or on characteristics of substitutes previously reviewed.

EFFECTIVE DATE

The effective date of the March 18, 1994 Final Rule is April 18, 1994.

PUBLIC COMMENT PERIOD

The public comment period for the September 26 NPRM expires on November 10, 1994.

FOR MORE INFORMATION

Lists of acceptable and unacceptable substitutes for the industrial use sectors covered under the SNAP program can be obtained from the Stratospheric Protection Hotline at 1-800-296-1996, M-F 10:00 a.m. to 4:00 p.m. (EST). International callers dial direct (202) 783-1100.

The SNAP Federal Register notices can be ordered from the Government Printing Office Order Desk (202) 783-3238; the citations for each are: March 18, 1994 (Final Rule); August 26, 1994 (Notice); January 13, 1995 (Notice) and Sept. 26, 1994 (Proposed Rule).

Each Rule and Notice can be retrieved electronically from EPA's Technology Transfer Network (TTN) Bulletin Board. For a 1200 or 2400 bps modem, dial (919) 541-5742. For a 9600 bps modem dial (919) 541-1447. For assistance, call (919) 541-5384 during normal business hours, EST.

United States
Environmental Protection
Agency

Air and Radiation
Stratospheric Protection Division
6205J

March 1994

Qs & As ON OZONE-DEPLETING REFRIGERANTS AND THEIR SUBSTITUTES

Ozone Protection Hotline toll-free (800) 296-1996 • Ozone Protection Hotline direct dial (202) 775-6677

• How do I know what I'm allowed to use?

Lists of acceptable and unacceptable substitutes are published quarterly in the Federal Register. In addition, you may call the Ozone Protection Hotline at (800) 296-1996. If the Hotline cannot answer your question, it will refer you to the appropriate SNAP analyst for more information.

• What are use conditions? Do I have to meet them?

In some cases, EPA believes that substitutes must be deemed unacceptable, unless the user meets specific conditions on <u>*how*</u> *the substitute is used. Such substitutes will be listed as acceptable subject to use conditions. For example, EPA may require the use of a detector to warn users of leakage. Users must meet such conditions, or they will be in violation of the SNAP rule.*

• Will EPA recommend the best substitute for my equipment?

No, EPA only determines what substitutes are acceptable from an environmental and health perspective. In the refrigeration and air conditioning sector, EPA firmly believes that the market should determine which of the acceptable alternatives will work the best and gain the largest market share.

• When can I start buying new alternatives?

EPA has divided the alternatives into two categories. Existing substitutes, defined as being on the market as of the effective date of the final SNAP rule, may be sold continuously until the effective date of any unacceptability determination. New substitutes must be submitted for SNAP review at least 90 days prior to sale. Once those 90 days have passed, regardless of whether EPA has made a decision about the substitute, sales may begin.

• I don't see any substitutes listed for my equipment. How do I find out what's available?

The SNAP program has identified eight major industrial use sectors, and several end-uses within each sector. The SNAP rule only applies to those end-uses included in the lists. However, EPA is interested in receiving information about significant end-uses not included in the lists. For definitions of the end-uses within a sector or to report information on a potential new end-use, read the SNAP rule or call the Ozone Protection Hotline. If the Hotline cannot answer your question, it will refer you to the appropriate SNAP analyst.

• Are there any safety considerations for new refrigerants in chillers?

EPA strongly believes that adherence to standard 15 of the American Society of Heating, Refrigerating and Air Conditioning Engineers (ASHRAE) will ensure the safety of technicians and building occupants. This standard applies to the use of all alternative refrigerants. In addition, systems designed and operated in accordance with ASHRAE Guideline 3 will leak minimal amounts of refrigerant, thereby reducing ozone depletion and global warming impacts.

• I keep hearing that HCFC-123 isn't safe to use in centrifugal chillers and that it causes cancer in rats. Why is EPA listing it as acceptable?

Toxicity in general is a complex issue. The two types of toxicity, chronic and acute, pose completely different sets of hazards. Chronic toxicity relates to long-term exposures over a lifetime of experience with refrigeration equipment. Acute toxicity, in contrast, relates to the dangers posed by short-term exposure to very high concentrations of refrigerant, especially catastrophic releases.

Short-term exposure levels measure several types of risk. Cardiotoxicity indicates the concentration at which a worker's heart becomes sensitized to adrenalin; thus, in an emergency, exposure to this level may result in a heart attack. The asphyxiation level indicates when the amount of oxygen in the area is reduced to the point that a worker may become unconscious and therefore unable to escape.

All refrigerants pose each type of toxicity. HCFC-123 actually poses less acute risk than CFC-11. In other words, in the event of a major leak, you're safer with HCFC-123 than with CFC-11.

As for chronic toxicity, it is true that HCFC-123 caused tumors in several organs in rats, including the testes. However, the critical facts are that, in all cases: a) the tumors were <u>*benign*</u>*, b) they only appeared after long exposures to very high concentrations, c) the tumors were never life-threatening, and d) the exposed rats actually lived longer at these higher concentrations.*

The Acceptable Exposure Limit (AEL) set by the HCFC-123 manufacturers is 30 ppm. This represents the concentration to which a worker could be exposed 8 hours/day for a working lifetime without effects. In other words, the AEL is a chronic exposure limit. EPA conducted a study to determine the typical exposure level found in actual equipment rooms. The study concluded that if appropriate measures are taken (for instance, complying with ASHRAE 15), the concentration of HCFC-123 can be kept below 1 ppm.

EPA believes that HCFC-123 is a necessary transition refrigerant as the world phases out the CFCs, and SNAP lists it as acceptable for use in chillers. It is safe to use in the long-term, and is actually safer in emergencies than CFC-11.

- Are flammable refrigerants automatically unacceptable?

  EPA considers flammability as one factor in the SNAP risk screen. Rather than serving to disqualify a substitute, flammability may necessitate additional testing and assessment of risk. The risks from using a flammable refrigerant are extremely dependent on the conditions and type of equipment. EPA believes that it may well be possible to safely use flammable refrigerants, and encourages manufacturers to contact SNAP to discuss the information needed to support such a submission.

- I manage an industrial plant which switched years ago from a CFC-12 based industrial process cooling to an alternative. This switch was made long before EPA's rules governing substitutes were issued; it may have been as long as twenty years ago, and the plant still uses this non-ozone depleting substitute. Must I apply under SNAP to continue using this substitute?

  No, because you are not yourself introducing the substitute into interstate commerce for use as an alternative to an ozone depleting substance. You are responsible, though, to make sure you're not using a substitute which has been deemed unacceptable by EPA.

- I bought a can of a substitute for CFC-12 which I used to charge my auto's air conditioning system myself. When I went to buy more, the store clerk told me it was illegal to use it as a substitute under EPA regulations. Am I breaking the law if I continue to use my car's air conditioner with this material as the cooling fluid?

  No. It is perfectly legal to continue to use your existing supply after the effective date of the final SNAP rule, as long as you bought it before the rule's publication date. However, once your air conditioner needs a recharge and you've exhausted your supply of the alternative, you must switch to a substitute deemed acceptable under SNAP. To assure your safety or the safety of anyone servicing your vehicle, please inform yourself and technicians about the flammability of any substitute you may have used.

- What are my choices for mobile air conditioning? How much will it cost me to replace my car's system?

  EPA has deemed HFC-134a and R-401C acceptable for use in cars. Both of these new refrigerants require some retrofitting. In addition, evaporative cooling is acceptable in this end-use, although it's currently only available in transit buses. Although there are currently no drop-in substitutes, EPA has received submissions for such alternatives and is currently reviewing them. EPA estimates that it will cost $200-$800 to retrofit most cars, with a cost of over $1000 only occurring for the oldest models. EPA does not require retrofitting, however, nor does it require leak repair in cars. Rather, retrofitting is mainly recommended when an air conditioning system needs major repairs anyway.

- What is evaporative cooling?

  Evaporative cooling is an alternative technology to classic vapor compression and absorption cycle equipment. It uses the evaporation of water to effect cooling. It is currently available in systems designed to cool homes, office buildings, and transit buses. Recent advancements in technology have expanded its applicability nationwide.

- How does EPA define the drop-in, retrofit, and new use categories?

  Drop-in substitutes require no changes to existing equipment other than draining the old refrigerant. For purposes of SNAP determinations, EPA does not distinguish between drop-in and retrofit substitutes. The intention of the retrofit designation is to identify substitutes which may be used in systems that retain at least some of the original equipment. Retrofits will generally be less expensive than total replacements. This category will also include not-in-kind replacements, such as evaporative cooling. Note, however, that acceptability in both categories is certainly possible and even likely for chemical substitutes. Alternative technologies will usually be deemed acceptable only in new equipment, since they cannot utilize parts of existing systems.

- When should I let EPA know I'm selling a new substitute?

  You must notify EPA at least 90 days prior to sale of a new substitute. This time period allows SNAP staff to review the health and environmental implications of use of your alternative.

- I've been selling a refrigerant since before the SNAP rule was published. Do I need to notify EPA?

  Possibly. First, you should check the lists that were published with the rule. If your substitute fits into one of the end-uses and does not appear anywhere, then you meet EPA's definition of selling an existing substitute, and you must submit the substitute for SNAP review within 90 days of the publication of the final rule. If, however, your substitute is listed as acceptable, you need do nothing. Finally, if your substitute is listed as unacceptable, you must stop selling it as of the effective date of the rule.

- What information should I send EPA about a new substitute?

  The information is listed in the SNAP final rule. Jeffrey Levy is the SNAP analyst for the refrigeration and air conditioning sector. Prior to submitting a substitute for review, call him at (202) 233-9727.

- How are SNAP-reviewed refrigerants described in the SNAP updates?

  Wherever possible, EPA will use ASHRAE designations for refrigerants. In cases when refrigerant compositions are confidential, EPA will use generic greek names that describe the major components. In particular, EPA believes it is necessary to alert users if a blend contains HCFCs, necessitating adherence to other regulations such as those issued under section 608 and 609. It is not possible to list trade names in the Federal Register, but lists will be available that connect generic names to trade names.

- Is there a list of companies who sell SNAP-acceptable substitutes?

  EPA will maintain a vendors list for substitutes. The list will include all companies who request that EPA include them. You will still have to assure that you are using a refrigerant that EPA has not deemed unacceptable. Contact Jeffrey Levy at (202) 233-9727 to be added to the vendors list.

United States Environmental Protection Agency | Air and Radiation (6205J) | EPA-430-F-94-010 Revised April 1994

EPA Stratospheric Ozone Protection

Action Guide

COOLING & REFRIGERATING WITHOUT CFCs

Beginning January 1, 1996, chlorofluorocarbons (CFCs), with some exceptions, will no longer be produced in the United States. This significant step to protect the ozone layer has major implications for owners and managers of commercial refrigeration and air-conditioning equipment. Rising costs and shortages of domestic and imported CFC refrigerants can be expected. Manufacturers and service technicians warn of difficulties in delivery of new equipment and retrofits if owners postpone decision making. EPA urges equipment owners to act now and prepare for the phaseout of CFCs.

This fact sheet provides important background information, suggestions for an action plan, and a list of additional resources on this issue.

BACKGROUND

CFC Refrigerants and the Ozone Layer

EPA estimates show that in 1992 there were over 80,000 centrifugal chillers, 1.6 million retail food refrigeration units, 540,000 transport refrigeration units, and 537 million cubic feet of cold storage warehousing in service in the United States. CFC refrigerants emitted during the use, maintenance, and disposal of this equipment contribute to the destruction of the ozone layer--Earth's shield against harmful ultraviolet radiation. Stratospheric ozone is being eroded at an accelerated rate over North America and other regions, posing serious threats to human, animal, and plant life.

Phasing Out CFCs: A Global Effort

The United States and 22 other countries first agreed to limit the production and use of CFCs in 1987, with the signing of the Montreal Protocol on Substances that Deplete the Ozone Layer. The Protocol initially required a 50 percent reduction in CFC production worldwide by the year 2000. Now signed by over 125 nations, the Protocol has since been amended to require a virtual phaseout of CFC production by January 1, 1996.

Ozone Protection at Home

Under the authority of the Clean Air Act Amendments of 1990, EPA has issued regulations that accelerate the domestic phaseout schedules for ozone-depleting substances to meet U.S. obligations for the new international deadlines. The CFC refrigerants that will be phased out of production at the end of 1995 include but are not limited to: CFC-11, CFC-12, CFC-13, CFC-113, CFC-114, CFC-115, R-500, R-502, and R-503. Two replacements for CFCs will also be phased out over a longer timetable: HCFC-22 for new equipment in 2010 with total phaseout in 2020; and HCFC-123 for new equipment in 2020, with total phaseout in 2030.

Besides mandating the phaseout of ozone-depleting refrigerants, the Clean Air Act contains other requirements that will affect equipment owners and managers. Effective July 1, 1992, it became illegal to intentionally release CFC or HCFC refrigerants into the atmosphere during the servicing, maintenance, or disposal of refrigeration and air-conditioning equipment. EPA has issued regulations under Title VI to reduce emissions of CFCs and to maximize recycling with the goal of creating a supply of refrigerant for use after 1995. The regulations specify performance standards for refrigerant-recovery equipment and will impose various certification requirements for equipment and owners, reclaimers, contractors, and disposers. For more information on this regulation, please refer to the *Final Rule Summary: Complying with the Refrigerant Recycling Rule.*

Phasing In CFC Alternatives

Alternative refrigerants, retrofit parts, and new equipment are now available for all CFC refrigeration and air-conditioning equipment. On March 18, 1994, EPA published the final rule establishing procedures for administering the Significant New Alternatives Policy program (SNAP). Lists of acceptable and unacceptable substitutes for each use sector will be regularly published by EPA in the *Federal Register* and are available through the Stratospheric Ozone Information Hotline. Equipment owners will need to consult these lists when making decisions.

GETTING STARTED: THREE STEPS FORWARD

Although there is no single best approach to the transition from CFC refrigerants to substitutes, it is clear that the worst action in refrigerant management is no action. There are three steps that owners and managers can take immediately:

Recycled/Recyclable
Printed with Soy/Canola Ink on paper that contains at least 50% recycled fiber

1. Designate a Facility Refrigerant Manager

Every equipment owner should put someone in charge of writing and carrying out a plan to manage refrigerant. The refrigerant manager will need clear authority and the necessary budget to effect change. The candidate should be knowledgeable about the facility's HVAC/R operations, industry standards, and relevant federal, state, and local regulations. The manager must also be able to successfully coordinate and communicate with other facility departments.

2. Conduct an Inventory of Equipment and Refrigerants

Detailed records of equipment stocks and refrigerant are essential for making informed decisions about the transition to new refrigerants. Priority should be given to equipment with the largest charge. Inventory sheets should individually list chillers and pieces of commercial refrigeration equipment. Information is needed on the manufacturer, model, serial number, year installed, capacity in tons, charge size, leak rates (based on records of recharging or "topping off"), refrigerant type (CFCs, HCFCs, and HFCs), and location. Small appliances–such as household refrigerators and window air conditioners, package units, vending machines, water coolers, and ice machines–should also be inventoried and can be recorded as groups.

Refrigerant stock will become an increasingly valuable asset as the price rises and supplies decrease each year. The quantity purchased, consumed, disposed of, or reclaimed should be monitored and analyzed. Refrigerant inventories should be kept by type and should include the volume contained in each piece of existing equipment, as well as amounts that are currently stored. These inventories should be updated regularly. Local codes for storage limits should be consulted.

3. Develop a Refrigerant Management Plan

A sound refrigerant management plan is the road map for making the transition to refrigerants that do not destroy the ozone layer. A good plan is based on accurate equipment and refrigerant inventories and takes account of the unique business environment. The plan will help to minimize capital outlays and operating costs while achieving these goals: compliance with applicable laws and regulations, continued supplies and service, reduced emissions, and increased recycling. The plan should combine these actions:

▶ **Maintaining Existing Equipment.** Conserving CFCs through leak detection, equipment repairs, refrigerant recovery, and installation of high-efficiency purges (in CFC-11 machines) is critically important. Reliance on recycled or reclaimed refrigerants to maintain existing equipment, however, is most viable with large equipment inventories where units can be gradually retired to keep others going. Equipment owners should consider the fact that avoiding capital costs for new equipment now may be offset by increased operating costs later. Purchasing or renting on-site recovery and recycling equipment may keep costs down. Equipment owners and managers should become familiar with EPA regulations governing recovery, recycling, and reclaiming refrigerants.

▶ **Retrofitting Equipment to Alternative Refrigerants.** The best solution for equipment with a long anticipated lifetime is likely to be its conversion for use with substitute refrigerants. Scheduling retrofits at the time of servicing or major equipment overhauls will keep costs down. Most original equipment manufacturers can be consulted for information on special design requirements (such as compatibility of materials and lubrication) and may be able to analyze the energy and capacity trade-offs of retrofitting.

▶ **Replacing Old or Inefficient Equipment.** Replacing aging equipment is an opportunity to improve energy efficiency and performance while lessening the impact on the ozone layer. This option requires the greatest initial outlay of capital, but in the long run may yield savings in energy, maintenance, and refrigerant costs. Only equipment that does not use CFCs should be purchased.

Consideration of these eight factors will be useful in assessing whether to maintain, retrofit or replace each piece of equipment: (1) age and remaining life of existing equipment; (2) hours of usage; (3) maintenance and repair history; (4) refrigerant and equipment supply and possible alternatives; (5) energy and capacity trade-offs; (6) equipment upgrades; (7) building modernization schedule; (8) energy efficiency rebates or other incentives from utility companies.

FOR ADDITIONAL INFORMATION

EPA's Stratospheric Ozone Information Hotline maintains an extensive library of scientific, technical, and regulatory documents pertaining to the depletion of the ozone layer. The hotline is open Monday through Friday, 10:00 a.m. to 4:00 p.m. (Eastern time), except on federal holidays. The number is 800 296-1996.

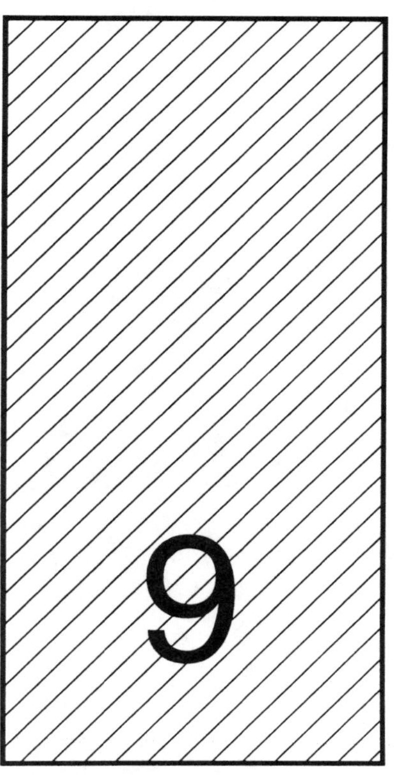

Moving to Alternative Refrigerants

Courtesy, EPA

United States
Environmental Protection
Agency

Air and Radiation
(6205J)

EPA 430-K-93-002
November 1993

Stratospheric Ozone Protection

Moving to Alternative Refrigerants

Ten Case Histories -- Comfort Coolers, Industrial Process, and Commercial Refrigeration

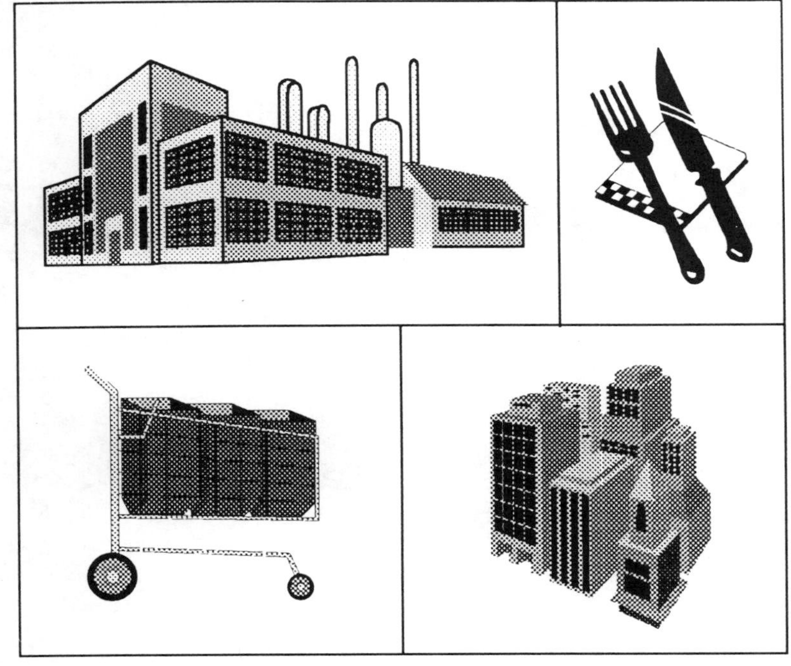

Foreword

The United States and over 125 other countries have signed the Montreal Protocol, the international agreement to protect the stratospheric ozone layer. Under the authority of the Clean Air Act, EPA has issued regulations to phase out the production of ozone-depleting substances. With very limited exceptions, CFC production and importation will cease in the U.S. at the end of 1995. Production of HCFCs will be phased out in stages, with a complete phaseout by 2030. Other EPA regulations require recycling of CFC and HCFC refrigerants and designate acceptable alternative refrigerants.

To assist equipment owners in the transition to non-ozone-depleting refrigerants, EPA has undertaken a "Cooling and Refrigerating Without CFCs" initiative. As part of this initiative, EPA is publishing these case histories which describe equipment retrofits and replacements actually implemented by companies around the United States. EPA has endeavored to present a diverse sample of types of facilities, equipment, and alternative refrigerants. The Agency knows, however, that there are many other situations not covered by these case histories; we therefore intend to publish additional case histories. If your company, institution, or agency has completed a retrofit or replacement of its CFC equipment and would like to become a candidate for one of these case histories, please let us know.

Every effort has been made to see that these case histories accurately reflect the actions taken by the companies profiled. However, recommendations about retrofit/replacement procedures can vary. Companies are urged to check with manufacturers and local authorities in implementing programs to make the transition away from CFC refrigerants.

For fact sheets on refrigerant conversions and replacements, or to suggest possible case histories, call the Stratospheric Ozone Information Hotline number at 1-800-296-1996.

Table of Contents

United States Environmental Protection Agency | Air and Radiation (6205J) | November 1993

EPA

Stratospheric Ozone Protection

Case History

Houston High-Rise Successfully Converted to HCFC-123

Case Study	Texaco Heritage Plaza
Owner	Coventry Fund III, Ltd.
Manager	Coventry Management Systems
Type of Facility	Office Building
Location	Houston, Texas

Coventry Management Systems, a property management firm located in Houston, has successfully eliminated CFC-11 from three chillers at the Texaco Heritage Plaza. Coventry Fund III, Ltd., the owner of Texaco Heritage Plaza, commissioned the conversions and Coventry Management Systems, its subsidiary and the day-to-day manager of the building, worked closely with Trane (the manufacturer of the chillers) throughout the entire three-year process. The high-rise is one of the largest buildings in Houston, with 53 floors and over 1.2 million square feet of commercial office space.

Trane was chosen to perform the actual conversions because it had originally installed the chillers and had the capability to engineer the conversions. The first chiller was converted in 1991, the second in 1992, and the last in 1993. Because all of the conversions were custom-engineered, cooling capacity losses were limited to three percent and energy efficiency improved by three percent. Trane reports similar results from conversions it has performed for other chiller owners.

Mr. Roma Kirkland, head of building operations at Texaco Heritage Plaza, has been following the ozone depletion issue since the 1980s, when he first saw television reports about ozone depletion and read about the possibility of a CFC phaseout in trade journals. Upon passage of the Clean Air Act Amendments of 1990, he decided that Coventry needed to take action regarding the use of CFC refrigerants at Texaco Heritage Plaza. Soon thereafter, he met with representatives of Trane to discuss what could be done. Together, they developed three options:

- Continue operating the existing chillers with CFC-11
- Purchase new non-CFC chillers
- Convert the chillers to a non-CFC refrigerant

Coventry decided to convert the chillers to a non-CFC refrigerant for two reasons:

1. To continue to use CFCs, Coventry would have had to stockpile CFC-11 for future use. The tax on stockpiled CFCs made this option very expensive. More importantly, stockpiling is severely restricted by the Uniform Mechanical Code, which is legally binding in Houston. (For safety, the Code restricts the quantity of refrigerant that can be stored at the same site as the refrigeration equipment.) Coventry knew the allowed amount would not be satisfactory for the life of its chillers.

2. The machines were only five years old when Coventry began its planning process. The expense of new chillers could not be justified given that the existing chillers were mechanically sound and could conceivably be used for another two decades.

Texaco Heritage Plaza's Converted Chillers

Type	3-stage centrifugal
Size	1,050 tons each
Old Refrigerant	CFC-11
New Refrigerant	HCFC-123

HCFC-123 was the obvious replacement refrigerant because it is the only alternative to CFC-11 for low-pressure centrifugal chillers. Coventry chose to proceed with only one conversion initially; it would convert the remaining two only if the first conversion yielded positive results.

A Conservative Approach

At the time of the first conversion, there was still considerable uncertainty about how a conversion would affect the performance of the chillers. Of particular concern were reports that this procedure might reduce the cooling capacity of the equipment by 20 percent or more. Coventry viewed this scenario as unacceptable because it could not meet its cooling requirements with 20 percent capacity loss and because the equipment room at Texaco Heritage Plaza had no extra space for the installation of supplemental chillers. Accordingly, an effort was made to engineer the conversion to minimize capacity loss. Computer modeling predicted that both capacity and energy efficiency would be reduced by six percent if the conversions were custom-engineered. This amount of capacity loss was still significant, but acceptable to Coventry. The original modeling predictions turned out to be quite conservative, and only small reductions in cooling capacity and actual increases in energy efficiency resulted from the conversions.

Winter Conversions

The first conversion took approximately nine weeks to complete. Conversions of the two remaining chillers took between four and six weeks. All of the conversions were done in the winter months when cooling demands were at a minimum. If Coventry had needed a faster turnaround, Trane estimated that each job could have been completed in three weeks with mechanics working eight hours a day, or in one week with mechanics working overtime.

Conversion Priorities

The tasks performed during the conversions can be divided into four general areas:

- Procedures to ensure that the new refrigerant is compatible with equipment parts that come into contact with it
- Procedures that enhance the performance of the chillers after conversion
- Procedures that reduce future refrigerant loss during service or operation
- Procedures that enhance the safety of building occupants and operations and maintenance staff

Ensuring Compatibility

Trane replaced several of the components in the chillers because they were made of materials that would slowly deteriorate if in contact with the new refrigerant, eventually causing a system failure. Most of the items that were replaced (e.g., O-rings, gaskets, and seals) would have been replaced in a few years anyway when the equipment's scheduled overhaul was performed. Because the overhaul was performed during the conversion, Coventry believes that the chillers at Texaco Heritage Plaza will not need major service for another 10 years. The motor winding insulation, also made with a material incompatible with HCFC-123, could not be replaced on site. Instead, the entire motor was sent back to Trane headquarters in Wisconsin where all of the windings were replaced with a new set that had insulation compatible with HCFC-123.

Performance Enhancement

To minimize capacity loss to levels acceptable to Coventry, Trane changed two of the components in the chillers. First, it replaced the orifice plates that meter refrigerant to the evaporator with plates that would provide the correct outlet pressures for the new refrigerant. Second, it modified the impellers in each chiller to provide the proper pressure increase for the new refrigerant. Like the compressor motor, the impellers were sent back to Trane headquarters for modification. Both of the tasks were completed in less than a week, since Trane headquarters already had remanufacturing and testing equipment in place.

Minimizing Leaks

To reduce future refrigerant loss, a high-efficiency purge unit was installed on each of the chillers. In addition, new valves were installed around the oil sumps so that mechanics could isolate the sumps when changing the lubricant. The new valves prevent refrigerant releases during oil change procedures, which are performed two or three times annually. The efforts to prevent refrigerant loss have proved to be remarkably successful. The machines have not required any additional refrigerant since the conversions, the first of which occurred two years ago. Prior to the conversions, each of the machines was typically charged with an additional 100 pounds of replacement refrigerant annually.

New Chiller Components

Replaced

- **O-rings**
- **Gaskets**
- **Seals**
- **Motor Windings**
- **Orifice Plates**
- **Impellers**

Added

- **High-Efficiency Purge Unit**
- **Valves around Oil Sumps**

Increasing Safety

Coventry also commissioned a number of modifications to the equipment room to increase worker safety and comply with the American Society of Heating, Refrigeration and Air-conditioning Engineers (ASHRAE) Standard 15-1992. Building owners in Houston are required to follow the provisions of the Standard. Since HCFC-123 is classified as a B1 refrigerant in ASHRAE Standard 34-1992, it must be installed in a mechanical room with refrigerant vapor sensors, an adjoining alarm system, ventilation piping leading from the purge units to the outside air, and ventilation exhaust fans.

Costs

The three conversions cost a total of approximately $250,000. In addition, $50,000 was spent to purchase the new HCFC-123 refrigerant for the three machines. The equipment room modifications and new peripherals (e.g., the refrigerant monitor, alarm system, and high-efficiency purge units) cost an extra $100,000. These costs, however, were offset by returning recovered CFCs to a reclaimer for credit. These costs also continue to be offset by savings from higher chiller energy efficiency and lower refrigerant emissions. In addition, the tenants of Texaco Heritage Plaza will not experience disruptions in comfort cooling as a result of the impending lack of available refrigerant. Finally, the tenants are now protected by state-of-the-art safety systems. The conversions at Texaco Heritage Plaza were so successful that Coventry is now planning to eliminate CFC use in comfort cooling applications at its five other commercial office buildings in the Houston area.

COSTS	
Convert three chillers	$250,000
Purchase new HCFC-123 refrigerant	$50,000
Make equipment room modifications & purchase new peripherals	$100,000

With very limited exceptions, CFC production and importation will cease in the U.S. at the end of 1995. It is EPA's goal to assist equipment owners in the transition to non-CFC refrigerants. This case history is part of a series on equipment retrofits and replacements by specific companies or agencies. Every effort has been made to see that these case histories accurately reflect the actions taken by the companies profiled. However, recommendations about retrofit/replacement procedures can vary. Companies are urged to check with manufacturers and local authorities in implementing programs to make the transition away from CFC refrigerants. Mention of any trade names or commercial products does not constitute endorsement or recommendation for use. For more information on the CFC phaseout, EPA information on refrigerant management, and acceptable alternative refrigerants, write: CFC Outreach, Stratospheric Protection Division, USEPA (6205J), Washington, DC, 20460.

United States Environmental Protection Agency | Air and Radiation (6205J) | November 1993

EPA

Stratospheric Ozone Protection
Case History

Life Insurance Company Cools Headquarters with CFC-Free Refrigerants

Case Study	New York Life Insurance Co.
Type of Facility	Office Building
Location	New York City

New York Life Insurance Company, one of the largest life insurance companies in the U.S., has a refrigerant problem. Its headquarters, spanning two city blocks in midtown Manhattan, had eight large chillers containing two different refrigerants soon to be phased out -- CFC-11 and R-500. Centrifugal Associates, the contractor responsible for maintaining the chillers, is helping solve this problem. The contractor converted two of the chillers in the headquarters building to HCFC-123, making New York Life Insurance Company headquarters the first large building in the city to be converted to a non-CFC refrigerant. A third chiller was converted to HFC-134a.

Centrifugal Associates, the largest mechanical contractor in the New York City area, is known throughout the chiller service industry for its technical expertise. DuPont recognized that expertise and asked the company to join a group known as the DuPont Mechanical Services Network. This group was formed by DuPont to share information about CFC alternatives, gain experience converting chillers to the new refrigerants, and accelerate the usage of CFC-free refrigerants. Recognizing that DuPont was offering access to the latest information on the new refrigerants as well as a good business opportunity, Centrifugal Associates gladly accepted the invitation. "What DuPont liked about our company best," said El Tangel, President of Centrifugal Associates, "was that we were capable of working on very large machines." Stephen Yager, CEO of Centrifugal Associates, elaborated: "Centrifugal Associates was founded on large centrifugal chillers. We know this type of machine inside and out. DuPont realized that in order to convince chiller owners to get out of CFCs, it needed to reach out to contractors for help."

In the spring of 1992, Centrifugal Associates contacted Tom Carney, Corporate Vice President of the Building Operations Group at New York Life, and proposed converting the chillers in the headquarters building to more environmentally acceptable refrigerants, specifically HFC-134a and HCFC-123. "I knew Tom Carney understood the necessity of converting his equipment away from CFCs. He had been following the issue for a number of years, and had been anticipating the phaseout," Mr. Yager remarked. "However, he had major concerns about the performance of the new refrigerants as well as the cost of converting his chillers. He needed additional technical information from another source."

To encourage Mr. Carney, Mr. Yager contacted Ed Kramer, the DuPont sales representative who had recruited Centrifugal Associates for the DuPont Mechanical Services Network, and asked him to present some of DuPont's findings on chiller conversions and answer any technical questions Mr. Carney might have. After listening to the representative from DuPont and examining the data, Mr. Carney decided to proceed with the conversions. Tom Carney explained: "We wanted to get started with our first conversion to learn the details about the new refrigerants. Our company has direct responsibility over a number of properties, and we needed to get insight into the matter to intelligently act on the problem in the rest of our properties."

New York Life's Chiller Conversions

Number	3
Size	3,000 tons each
Age	25-40 years
Refrigerant Conversion	CFC-11 → HCFC-123 R-500 → HFC-134a

"I've conducted my own research on the CFC issue by attending seminars and reading journals," Mr. Carney explained, "and after looking at the facts presented by Centrifugal Associates and DuPont, I became confident that getting out of CFCs made good business and environmental sense. The law is not going to be changed. Now is the right time to convert to the alternatives. Waiting any longer just means that more and more money will be chasing after less and less available refrigerant. I don't want my business impaired because I can't cool my buildings."

A Smooth Conversion

The first conversion at New York Life took place in July 1992. A 40-year-old, 750-ton open-drive chiller was converted from CFC-11 to HCFC-123. Mr. Carney took advantage of the fact that the chiller would be out of service and instructed Centrifugal Associates to perform an overhaul of the chiller. Centrifugal Associates inspected all of the moving parts in the chiller and replaced its old gaskets, O-rings and seals with new parts that were compatible with the new refrigerant. This overhaul saved New York Life money because HCFC-123 is a potent solvent that eventually would have ruined some of the old parts if they had not been replaced during the overhaul, causing the chiller to leak the new refrigerant.

Mr. Carney was surprised by how easy it was to convert the chiller. He was also pleased with the performance of the new refrigerant. "I thought that a chiller conversion would be complex, but it actually turned out to be no more difficult than the many chiller overhauls I have observed," recalled Mr. Carney. "I expected significant losses in capacity, but we haven't seen any losses at all."

Second Conversion

In November 1992, Centrifugal Associates began a second chiller conversion at New York Life. This time an appreciably larger chiller was converted from R-500 to HFC-134a. All of the components in the chiller were compatible with HFC-134a except for the mineral oil, which was flushed thoroughly from the chiller and replaced with polyol ester lubricant. The chiller, a 25-year-old, 1,250-ton open-drive centrifugal unit, has been in full operation this year, including during one of the hottest summers on record, and has maintained essentially the same capacity as before the conversion. Once again, New York Life was pleased with the ease with which the conversion was made. "This total conversion procedure took only a matter of weeks. What's more, the cost of the conversion and new refrigerant was less than 15 percent of the cost of a new machine installation."

Additional Conversions

Based on the ease of the previous conversions and the resulting high levels of performance, New York Life decided to convert two more large chillers in its headquarters. The third conversion has already been completed. Centrifugal Associates converted a 30-year-old, 1,000-ton open-drive centrifugal chiller from CFC-11 to HCFC-123, following the same procedure as for the first chiller. Again, no appreciable change in capacity or energy use was noted. The fourth chiller to be converted is the same size and model as the second chiller converted at the site, and will be CFC-free before the end of Spring 1994.

"We were surprised at how well our first conversions went," Mr. Tangel recalled. "The conversion process was not as difficult a job as we were led to believe. For one thing, it didn't take as long as we had heard. We put two mechanics on the job, and it only took them two to four weeks for each of the conversions. It did help that all of the machines were open-drive chillers, so we didn't have to change any of the motor windings when we converted to HCFC-123."

Inexpensive Conversions

Centrifugal Associates is now becoming increasingly proficient at converting large chillers to the alternative refrigerants. In fact, its labor time has decreased to the point where a conversion for an open-drive R-500 centrifugal chiller costs only about 10 percent of the cost of a new chiller. "Hermetic chillers take a little more time, and the job ends up costing about twenty percent of the cost of a new chiller. If the customer wants the motor, gears, and impeller replaced, the costs run about 30 percent of a new chiller," Mr. Tangel said. "But all things considered, it seems that conversions are the way to go in most cases. Some of the costs can always be recouped by returning the recovered CFCs to a reclaimer for credit."

Centrifugal Associates' Checklist for Converting Open-Drive Chillers from CFC-11 to HCFC-123

- ☑ **Recover CFC in system and send back for reclamation.**
- ☑ **Overhaul chiller, inspecting all moving parts for wear.**
- ☑ **Replace seals, gaskets and O-rings.**
- ☑ **Thoroughly flush old mineral oil from system and replace with new mineral oil.**
- ☑ **Thoroughly check for leaks.**
- ☑ **Charge with HCFC-123.**
- ☑ **Clearly indicate on unit the type of refrigerant it now contains.**
- ☑ **Take all steps necessary to ensure compliance with ASHRAE Standard 15-1992.**

With very limited exceptions, CFC production and importation will cease in the U.S. at the end of 1995. It is EPA's goal to assist equipment owners in the transition to non-CFC refrigerants. This case history is part of a series on equipment retrofits and replacements by specific companies or agencies. Every effort has been made to see that these case histories accurately reflect the actions taken by the companies profiled. However, recommendations about retrofit/replacement procedures can vary. Companies are urged to check with manufacturers and local authorities in implementing programs to make the transition away from CFC refrigerants. Mention of any trade names or commercial products does not constitute endorsement or recommendation for use. For more information on the CFC phaseout, EPA information on refrigerant management, and acceptable alternative refrigerants, write: CFC Outreach, Stratospheric Protection Division, USEPA (6205J), Washington, DC, 20460.

United States Environmental Protection Agency | Air and Radiation (6205J) | November 1993

EPA

Stratospheric Ozone Protection
Case History

Electronics Manufacturer Successfully Converts Chiller to HFC-134a

Case Study	Westinghouse ESG
Type of Facility	Manufacturing Plant
Location	Baltimore, Maryland

One of the first-ever field conversions of a chiller from CFC-12 to HFC-134a was performed at a Westinghouse Electric Corporation facility in Baltimore, Maryland. The chiller, a 493-ton centrifugal unit located at the headquarters of the Westinghouse Electronic Systems Group (ESG), has been running smoothly now for three years. Westinghouse ESG has gained useful first-hand knowledge from this experience and has begun planning a facility-wide CFC elimination campaign.

The process leading up to the first chiller conversion actually began one year prior to the actual procedure when corporate executives at Westinghouse ESG, acting on information regarding the CFC situation, decided to appoint a CFC elimination team. The team members appointed were George Duncan (Senior Facilities Design Engineer), Robert Stryjewski (Manager of Facilities Engineering), and Steve McKew (Manager of Hazardous Materials). The team was headed by Kay Rand, Manager of Regulatory Compliance, who also bore responsibility for the success of the phaseout program.

The team knew that unlimited resources were not available to eliminate CFC use from the many pieces of equipment located in the three main buildings at Westinghouse ESG Headquarters. Rather than develop a strategy to phase out CFCs on a set timetable, the team decided to evaluate each piece of equipment individually and decide what action to take based on the overall economics of each available option. The primary concerns of the company were its chillers, since these large pieces of equipment contain the most refrigerant.

Westinghouse ESG's decision to replace or retrofit each chiller will involve a number of logistical, engineering and financial factors.

- **Location** -- Conversions are the favored option for chillers located in inaccessible areas since they present difficult replacement logistics. In addition, a replacement strategy would likely severely disrupt normal operations.
- **Cooling Capacity** -- In some instances, the company may not be able to tolerate the loss of cooling capacity from the chiller being considered for conversion.
- **Cash Flow** -- Both first costs and operating costs (e.g., energy costs of new and converted equipment, and future prices of service refrigerant) must be considered.
- **Refrigerant Availability** -- The refrigerant that the chiller uses must be quickly available if needed.

Westinghouse ESG's Converted Chiller	
Type	Centrifugal
Original Capacity	493 tons
New Capacity	498 tons
Old Refrigerant	CFC-12
New Refrigerant	HFC-134a
Age	16 years

The team decided that the most cost-effective action to take would be to implement a refrigerant conservation program immediately. Westinghouse ESG purchased portable recovery machines for each of the buildings and developed a proactive program for detecting refrigerant leaks and fixing them immediately. Leak checks became part of the regular preventive maintenance program for the company.

Refrigerant Management Tools

Westinghouse ESG also began to install and utilize computerized monitoring panels on many of its chillers so that their performance could be monitored from a remote location. On a weekly basis, the maintenance personnel for the company take a readout of the temperatures and pressures to determine trends in the performance and efficiency of the chillers. The monitoring panels also act indirectly as refrigerant leak monitors, since refrigerant loss in chillers is eventually reflected by negative trends in performance and energy efficiency.

Even though Westinghouse ESG Headquarters has many large pieces of CFC equipment, the company believes it can substantially reduce CFC purchases before the end of 1995. "We've saved a lot of time in the economic analysis of the various pieces of equipment because we have extensive documentation of all of our refrigeration and air-conditioning equipment. We are confident that we already have most of the data we need, so all we need to do is finish crunching the numbers," said Mr. Duncan.

Westinghouse ESG has an advanced equipment inventory system based on a nine-digit number that identifies each piece of CFC equipment by type and location. This number reflects the location of each piece of equipment, including the exact building, section, and floor. This type of information has been invaluable in keeping track of the refrigerant used by each piece of equipment. This excellent inventory tracking system has put the team in a good position to develop extensive CFC-phaseout plans with confidence that cost estimates will be accurate. The system also tracks the many pieces of small equipment in the buildings, including water coolers, refrigerators in the cafeteria, and cooling units for very-low-temperature environmental testing chambers. "These types of equipment will be subjected to the same economic scrutiny as the chillers in determining their eventual disposition," said Ms. Rand.

Factors Involved in Making CFC Elimination Decisions

- **Equipment Location**
- **Cooling Capacity Changes**
- **First Costs**
- **Operating Costs**
- **Refrigerant Price**
- **Refrigerant Availability**

Besides the CFC-12 chillers previously mentioned, the company also owns chillers that use CFC-11 and R-500. "We will be retiring the CFC-11 chillers in a few years rather than converting them, since they are 35 years old and can be replaced with much higher efficiency equipment," said Mr. Stryjewski. "The R-500 equipment will be either converted or retired."

Chiller Retrofit

In 1990, McQuayService, the service arm of SnyderGeneral Corporation, approached Westinghouse ESG and offered financial and engineering assistance to convert one of the CFC-12 McQuay brand chillers at Westinghouse ESG to HFC-134a. Westinghouse ESG Headquarters was selected by McQuay -Service because Westinghouse is a leader in testing new technologies, and also because Westinghouse ESG had a backup chiller in place, so even though reliability of the pilot project was desirable, it was not crucial.

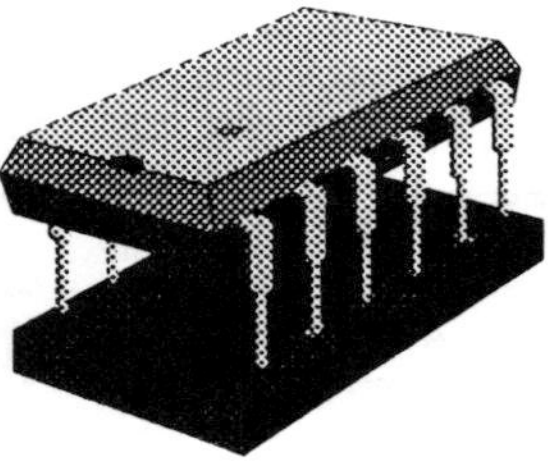

Mr. Duncan proposed to McQuay-Service that a chiller originally manufactured by Westinghouse be converted. The chiller was an ideal piece of equipment to convert since it had many more years of useful life left in it, and was still fairly energy efficient. (Westinghouse sold its Commercial-Industrial Air Conditioning Services division to McQuay, Inc. in 1982, which then was acquired by SnyderGeneral in 1984.) "McQuayService agreed with our choice, and even offered a full-year warranty on the entire machine after the conversion," exclaimed Mr. Duncan.

The company only had two requirements of McQuayService. First, the original cooling conversion capacity of the chiller was to be maintained. Second, business could not be interrupted. Consequently, McQuay-Service engineered the conversion so that the cooling capacity would either remain the same or increase slightly. McQuayService also advised scheduling the conversion for the fall or winter because during these seasons the air conditioning systems operated primarily on "free cooling." In this method of air conditioning, outdoor air is used to cool the conditioned air inside the building or to chill the water circulated to the air handler. Thus, some of the comfort

New Chiller Components

Replaced

- **Gaskets**
- **Impeller**
- **Bearings**
- **Lubricant**

Added

- **Expansion Valve (Replaced High-Side Float)**

cooling chillers were idle and could be called upon to provide extra cooling capacity, if necessary.

The two companies began converting the chiller in September 1990. During the conversion, 1,500 pounds of CFC-12 were recovered. The gearset and impeller were replaced so that the chiller would operate with no loss in cooling capacity after the conversion. The chiller was then subjected to a complete compressor inspection, where it was revealed that some bearings were worn and required replacement. The conversion also included a complete condenser and evaporator vessel cleaning and eddy-current testing of the condenser and evaporator tubes. The tests revealed that the walls of two of the tubes were thin, so they were subsequently plugged to prevent leaks in the future. In addition, a panel connected to a dedicated telephone line was installed to allow Westinghouse ESG to monitor operation of the converted chiller from a remote location.

After these overhaul procedures were completed, the lubricant was flushed out and replaced with new ester-based lubricant because the original lubricant was incompatible with HFC-134a. The chiller was checked for leaks and then charged with the new refrigerant. Finally, the chiller was started up and its operation was closely monitored. The chiller has been running since October 2, 1990 without any significant problems.

The conversion took two mechanics approximately 30 days to complete. This time included all of the overhaul procedures as well as the conversion itself. Mr. Duncan estimates that without the overhaul, a conversion of this type can be completed in about one week. He remarked, "For a first effort, we got excellent results. The conversion of the chiller proceeded surprisingly well. Its cooling capacity increased by about one percent and its energy efficiency increased by five percent. I believe that this conversion demonstrates that with engineered hardware changes, HFC-134a can perform as well as or better than CFC-12 in the same chiller."

Money-Saving Opportunities

Mr. Duncan also remarked that the CFC phaseout has had a big impact on the economics of the HVAC operations of the company.

- Because of increasing refrigerant costs, the first piece of equipment to be repaired is now the one with the biggest leaks and not the equipment in the poorest mechanical condition, unless the equipment no longer functions. However, these two criteria frequently fit the same piece of equipment.
- Because large machines consume more refrigerant than smaller ones do, large machines are often considered as candidates for conversion/replacement before small ones.
- Because large machines contain large charges, converting or retiring large machines will significantly increase the stock of service CFC refrigerant without any additional expense.

Energy savings are of prime concern to Westinghouse ESG. The company plans to achieve energy savings in two ways. First, during any future chiller conversions, the high-side float will be replaced with an expansion valve to better control the superheat of the chiller to match its cooling load. Second, the company plans to replace existing reciprocating chillers with energy-saving dual-compressor centrifugal chillers. "These types of chillers may cost more up front, but they will be able to match our cooling loads much more effectively than the old chillers and with a lower power consumption. We'll make up the cost difference pretty quickly," said Mr. Duncan.

New Equipment

At the time of the conversion, several Westinghouse ESG facilities were scheduled for a change in utilization. For example, one of the manufacturing areas was to be converted into a clean room. The company took advantage of the opportunity to install a new HFC-134a chiller at the same time the space was reconfigured. Mr. Duncan remarked, "This was another joint project with SnyderGeneral. This was one of the first HFC-134a chillers to roll off the assembly line at SnyderGeneral. We would have had to replace the existing chiller serving this area anyway because of the different cooling requirements of clean rooms. SnyderGeneral gave us a choice to use a non-CFC refrigerant."

Westinghouse ESG is now planning to replace eight 100-ton CFC-12 reciprocating chillers because of their condition and age. (These chillers are forty years old.) The chillers are scheduled to be replaced in the spring of 1994 with two new double-effect gas-fired absorption chillers. One factor in this decision is the sizeable rebate being offered by the local gas company for new installations of gas-fired air conditioning equipment. Another factor is that Westinghouse ESG plans to use the gas-fired chillers in the summer months when natural gas is less expensive and during peak electrical demand periods, thereby allowing the company to take some of its electric chillers off-line. By reducing its peak electrical demand, the company will save on energy costs.

Westinghouse ESG considers both the chiller conversion and new installation successes, and is now planning to eliminate CFCs in all of its chillers in the near future.

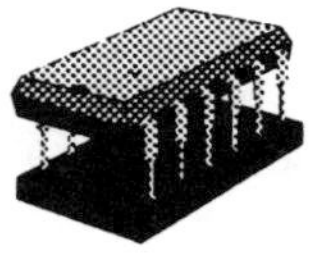

With very limited exceptions, CFC production and importation will cease in the U.S. at the end of 1995. It is EPA's goal to assist equipment owners in the transition to non-CFC refrigerants. This case history is part of a series on equipment retrofits and replacements by specific companies or agencies. Every effort has been made to see that these case histories accurately reflect the actions taken by the companies profiled. However, recommendations about retrofit/replacement procedures can vary. Companies are urged to check with manufacturers and local authorities in implementing programs to make the transition away from CFC refrigerants. Mention of any trade names or commercial products does not constitute endorsement or recommendation for use. For more information on the CFC phaseout, EPA information on refrigerant management, and acceptable alternative refrigerants, write: CFC Outreach, Stratospheric Protection Division, USEPA (6205J), Washington, DC, 20460.

United States Environmental Protection Agency | Air and Radiation (6205J) | November 1993

EPA

Stratospheric Ozone Protection

Case History

Tennessee Chemical Manufacturer to End CFC Purchases By 1995

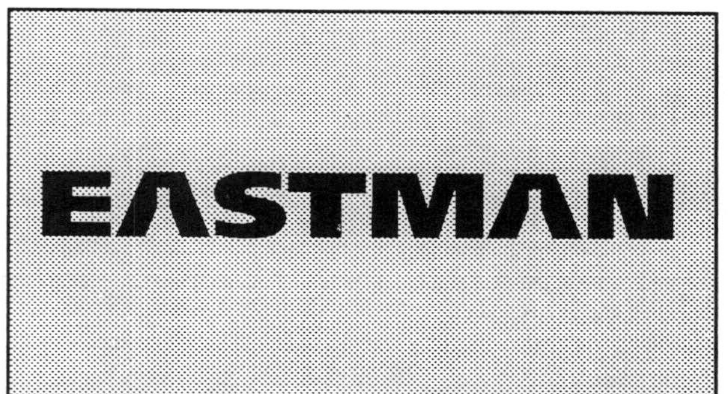

Case Study	Eastman Chemical Co.
Type of Facility	Manufacturing Plant
Location	Kingsport, Tennessee

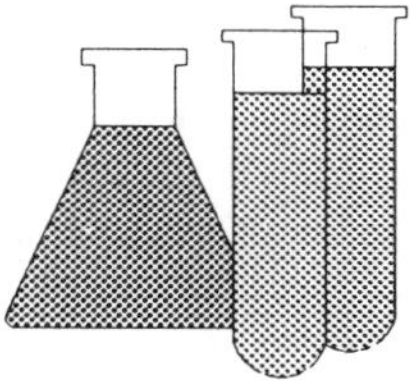

The Tennessee Eastman Division of Eastman Chemical Company has illustrated the importance of a well-planned strategy for equipment repair, conversions, and replacements as part of a CFC phaseout program. York International has recognized the plan as a model for the industry by presenting the division with its Refrigerant Leadership Award. This recognition comes as a result of successfully handling the complexities involved in coordinating 400 buildings, more than 50 chillers, and a wide variety of different CFCs in use.

To manufacture the materials necessary to produce its chemical, fiber, and plastics products, the company uses CFC-12, CFC-114, HCFC-22, and R-500 in its process chillers. For its comfort cooling chillers, the company uses CFC-11 and CFC-12. In addition, Eastman owns a number of other types of smaller equipment, mostly containing CFC-12. The age of the equipment varies from brand new for some of the appliances to over 50 years for some of the chillers. Eastman's problems are compounded by the fact that its chillers were made by almost every manufacturer in America.

Eastman took its first step toward a CFC-free workplace in 1990 when Michael Logan, operations manager in the refrigeration department, attended a CFC phaseout seminar at Purdue University. Upon his return, he formed a problem-solving team composed of his operations and maintenance staff. The team produced a two-phase plan: first, conserve CFCs by improving service and maintenance practices; and second, eliminate use of CFCs by buying non-CFC equipment and converting existing equipment to alternative refrigerants.

Eastman's plan focuses on its 42 CFC chillers because these units account for the majority of its refrigerant loss and are integral to the production processes of the company. The company did not prepare a detailed plan for its smaller equipment because it concluded early on that converting the smaller equipment would be uneconomical. This equipment, therefore, would be maintained with CFCs recovered from the larger units until retirement.

Tennessee Eastman Division's Chiller Stock	
Quantity	42
Size Range	500-1500 tons
Age Range	1-50+ years
Refrigerants Used	CFC-11, CFC-12, CFC-114, HCFC-22, R-500

At the very first meeting of the problem-solving team, several major types of refrigerant loss were identified: tube leaks, seal leaks, purge losses, losses during refrigerant recovery or transfer procedures, and losses during refrigerant handling and storage. For each of these categories, the team then developed procedures and practices that would reduce refrigerant losses. No additional labor time or personnel were required to implement the conservation plan since most of Eastman's mechanics had already been trained in these procedures. Mr. Logan's major challenge was to persuade employees who had always viewed CFCs as cheap and expendable to improve their refrigerant conservation practices.

Eastman's Two-Phase Plan

1. Conserve CFCs
2. Eliminate CFCs

Setting the Stage

To set the tone of the new program and define his expectations, Mr. Logan gave a lecture to the employees that maintain and operate the chillers on the topics of (1) the CFC issue and (2) his plan to eliminate CFC use in the company. The company implemented the improved conservation procedures soon thereafter and intends to continue the procedures even after CFC refrigerants have been eliminated at the facility.

Improved Procedures

From the start, Eastman was ahead of many other companies in conservation measures because it had always recovered its refrigerant during servicing operations. (Companies can typically reduce refrigerant loss by 40 percent by instituting a basic refrigerant recovery program.) Eastman has reduced refrigerant loss even further by identifying and correcting improper recovery techniques. For example, in the past, mechanics had occasionally handled transfer hoses that connect the refrigeration equipment to recovery devices in a careless manner, thereby increasing the probability of contamination. Refrigerant transfer procedures have since been improved. Eastman has also upgraded its recovery and recycling equipment and now has a dedicated unit for each refrigerant, avoiding problems associated with mixing refrigerants of different types.

Eliminating Leaky Tubes

The second major area of refrigerant loss was leakage from evaporator and condenser tubes. Maintenance staff performed eddy current testing to determine the thickness of the tubes in order to assess the likelihood of future leaks. When testing revealed that tube walls were too thin and, therefore, likely to leak in the future, the mechanics plugged or replaced them.

Refrigerant Conservation Priorities

- Refrigerant Recovery Program
- Improved Transfer Procedures
- Dedicated Recovery Units
- Tube Eddy Current Testing
- Tube Repair and Replacement
- Immediate Leak Repair
- Chiller Pressurization During Offseason
- High-Efficiency Purge Devices (For New and Converted Chillers)
- Refrigerant Tracking System

Better Connections

The company also placed a greater emphasis on checking seals, flanges and connections for leaks. Before the conservation plan began, mechanics would search for leaks on a monthly basis using halide torches and solid state testers. Whenever they located a leak, they would tag it and write a work order for its repair, returning sometime in the future to fix it. Now they search for leaks weekly and fix them before the chillers have a chance to leak further. Work orders are issued only if it is determined that a job is too complex to handle in a short time.

Reducing Purge Losses

Eastman has also taken steps to reduce emissions from the purges on its low-pressure chillers. Eastman leaves its comfort cooling chillers idle in the winter because cold water taken from a nearby river provides for most of the comfort cooling needs of the facility. However, considerable amounts of air and moisture can leak into low-pressure chillers when left idle. To prevent this, Eastman uses dry nitrogen to increase the pressure inside the equipment above ambient levels. This prevents moisture-laden air from leaking in, avoiding excessive purging when the system starts up. Eastman has also reduced purge losses by ensuring that the purge devices themselves are operating properly. Finally, the company has installed high-efficiency purge units on several of its low-pressure chillers and plans to make them standard with every conversion.

Keeping Track

To monitor its success and to help plan for the future, Eastman maintains a refrigerant tracking system. It periodically records the existing quantity of refrigerant on site (in both equipment and in storage) and the quantity of new refrigerant purchased, thereby allowing it to determine the extent of the company's refrigerant emissions. Calculations show that Eastman has reduced its refrigerant loss by 55 percent relative to 1989 levels -- an excellent performance, especially given that the company was already recovering refrigerant prior to improving its conservation program. Nevertheless, Mr. Logan believes that Eastman can reduce refrigerant loss by an additional 10 percent in the next couple of years as the program matures.

Progress Can Be Inexpensive

Importantly, Eastman is well on its way to accomplishing all its refrigerant conservation objectives without additional staff, much additional training, or help from outside firms. This program is evidence that companies can implement successful refrigerant conservation without significant expense.

Eastman has just begun both to purchase new CFC-free equipment and to convert existing equipment to alternative refrigerants in order to totally eliminate CFCs from its stock of chillers. This approach required approval from the corporate executives because of the size of the investment. Accordingly, Mr. Logan and his team provided a briefing on the CFC phaseout to the president of the company and other corporate executives. They also presented a plan based on two key objectives: (1) maintaining existing cooling capacity and (2) limiting future disruptions.

Applications where CFCs are to be Eliminated

- **Comfort Cooling**
- **Laboratory Refrigeration**
- **Industrial Processes**

A Silver Lining

About 75 percent of Eastman's chillers are scheduled for conversion. The company is making the most of the situation by turning each conversion into an opportunity to standardize its refrigeration equipment. It is choosing conversion options that will place identical parts in many of the systems even though these systems may currently have very different characteristics. The company believes standardization will significantly reduce its service and maintenance costs in the years ahead. Standardization will also simplify service tasks for the mechanics, thereby giving them more time to concentrate on refrigerant conservation methods.

Converting to HCFC-123

For its soon-to-be-converted CFC-11 chillers, Eastman plans to replace each compressor driveline (compressor and motor) with new compressor drivelines intended for use with HCFC-123. This conversion option essentially involves replacing everything but the heat exchangers. Each conversion is expected to cost approximately 50 percent of the cost of new equipment. Some of this cost can be recouped by returning recovered CFCs to a reclaimer for credit. After being converted, the equipment is expected to last for another 20 to 30 years. Replacing the entire compressor driveline rather than just some its parts is consistent with Eastman's goal of standardization.

Converting to HFC-134a

Eastman plans to convert its high pressure equipment (both the CFC-12 and R-500 units) to HFC-134a. Because it has more complete information on the components of these chillers, it intends to have all of these conversions fully engineered (including modeling the operation of the equipment and modifying the equipment in such a way as to minimize capacity and energy efficiency losses).

Leakiest First

Rather than convert all of its equipment at once, the company plans to perform its conversions in stages. Chillers that are losing the most refrigerant (and that are consequently due for complete overhauls) will be converted first. This will reduce emissions, save money, and create a supply of CFC refrigerant for the remaining equipment.

Maintaining Capacity

Mr. Logan projects that converting equipment to the alternative refrigerants will unfortunately reduce cooling capacity. To solve this problem, Eastman will first increase its cooling capacity by purchasing new HCFC-22 screw chillers. The company's operating standard is to be able to handle peak cooling loads with its largest chiller out of operation. The company has a thorough knowledge of its current situation because it tests the maximum capacity of its chillers every year and electronically monitors required cooling capacity. The company will measure the new maximum post-conversion capacity of each chiller to determine if even more units need to be installed.

New CFC-Free Chillers

Eastman also plans to purchase HCFC-22 screw chillers to replace older equipment. In general, equipment will only be replaced if either it cannot be converted to non-CFC alternatives or if its energy efficiency has deteriorated to the point where the expense of converting the equipment is not economically worthwhile. For example, Eastman has eight CFC-114 chillers for which it could not find conversion kits. The company plans to retire these units over the next two years.

Eastman's CFC Elimination Checklist

- ☑ **Assess Plant Capacity**
- ☑ **Estimate Minimum Required Capacity**
- ☑ **Project Future Requirements for Capacity Expansion**
- ☑ **Estimate Costs of Conversions and Replacements**
- ☑ **Estimate Capacity after Conversions**
- ☑ **Conduct Engineering Analysis to Determine Most Appropriate Action**
- ☑ **Add Capacity as Required Before Beginning Conversions**
- ☑ **Replace Equipment for Which There Are No Conversion Options**
- ☑ **Combine Projects to Minimize Costs (i.e., Equipment Overhaul, Standardization, or Upgrade)**
- ☑ **Fully Engineer All Conversions to Minimize Energy Costs and Maintain Cooling Capacity**
- ☑ **Convert Leakiest Chillers First**
- ☑ **Use Recovered Refrigerant for Future Servicing**

A primary reason why Eastman chose HCFC-22 screw chillers over other options is because these types of chillers can be converted to a variety of refrigerants. The company insists on having an option that would allow it to discontinue use of HCFCs or HFCs for ozone depletion and global warming reasons. Given that the company would like to operate its new equipment for up to 50 years, it wants to ensure that its new equipment could potentially use a refrigerant that is likely to be available for several decades.

When Eastman made its decision to purchase these chillers, it believed that it would most likely convert them to ammonia when HCFC-22 was no longer available. Due to recent advances in refrigerant blends, the company now believes other attractive conversion options will also be available in the near future.

The Big Picture

Eastman installed four screw chillers in 1993 to ensure that it can maintain its refrigeration capacity throughout and after its CFC phaseout. In 1994, it plans to buy another two screw chillers and convert two existing machines. In 1995 and each year thereafter, it plans to convert approximately five to eight chillers per year. Under this schedule, the company will convert approximately one-third of its chillers by the December 31, 1995 CFC phaseout date and it will no longer use CFCs in any of its chillers after 1999. Moreover, because the company can use the refrigerant recovered from chillers to service other refrigeration equipment, it will no longer need to purchase CFC refrigerant for any of its refrigeration or air conditioning systems after 1994.

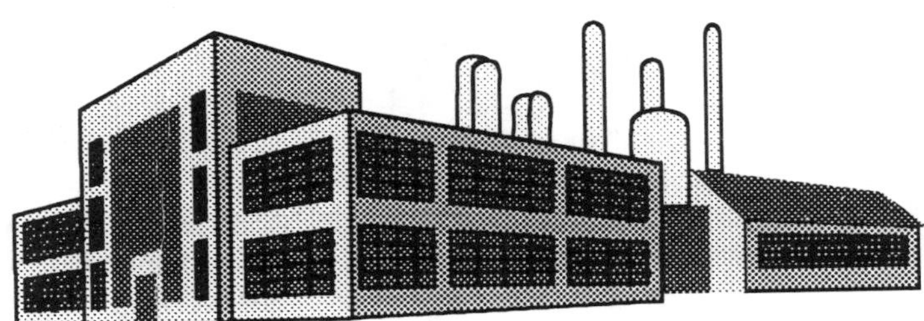

With very limited exceptions, CFC production and importation will cease in the U.S. at the end of 1995. It is EPA's goal to assist equipment owners in the transition to non-CFC refrigerants. This case history is part of a series on equipment retrofits and replacements by specific companies or agencies. Every effort has been made to see that these case histories accurately reflect the actions taken by the companies profiled. However, recommendations about retrofit/replacement procedures can vary. Companies are urged to check with manufacturers and local authorities in implementing programs to make the transition away from CFC refrigerants. Mention of any trade names or commercial products does not constitute endorsement or recommendation for use. For more information on the CFC phaseout, EPA information on refrigerant management, and acceptable alternative refrigerants, write: CFC Outreach, Stratospheric Protection Division, USEPA (6205J), Washington, DC, 20460.

United States
Environmental Protection
Agency

Air and Radiation
(6205J)

November 1993

EPA

Stratospheric Ozone Protection
Case History

Manufacturer of Alternative Refrigerants Converts Own Facilities

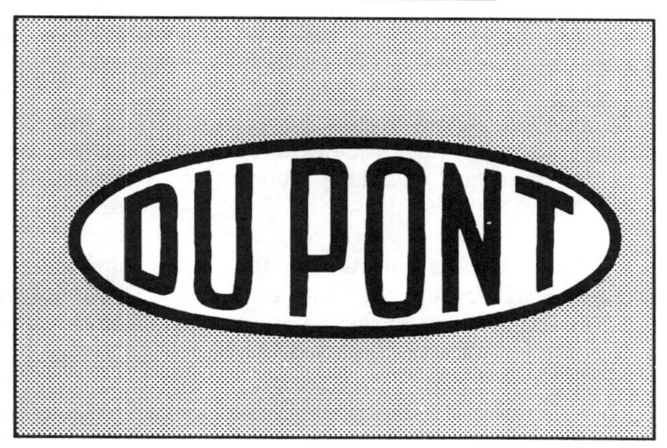

Case Study	**DuPont**
Type of Facility	**Manufacturing Plant**
Location	**Camden, South Carolina**

DuPont is one of the world's largest manufacturers of alternative refrigerants that can be used to replace CFCs. When it launched its alternative refrigerant business, DuPont knew that it would have to convince its customers that the alternatives could meet both performance and operating specifications. Doing so required hands-on experience with the process of converting equipment from CFCs. DuPont decided that the best place to start was in its own facilities.

DuPont has over 550 chillers in its plants around the world operating in a wide variety of industrial process and HVAC applications. This provided a large variety of machine types and models in which to evaluate the new refrigerants. To focus its efforts, DuPont management formed a Corporate Retrofit Leadership Team (CRLT) charged with demonstrating conversion feasibility and developing a strategy for converting the CFC chillers in the corporation.

The DuPont team includes a cross-functional mix of DuPont employees from Engineering, Fluorochemicals, Purchasing, Safety and Health, and Marketing. Ben Smith, a Facilities Maintenance Consultant for DuPont, coordinates and leads the activities of the team. Bob Bates, an Energy and Refrigeration Consultant for DuPont, provides technical guidance for the refrigerant conversion effort and is also a member of the team.

The first item on the team's agenda was to establish a list of candidate chillers within DuPont to serve as conversion demonstrations. A variety of manufacturer's equipment types and models were targeted to gain as broad an understanding of the conversion process as possible in the least amount of time.

The next step was to reach agreement with the operating groups dependent on the chillers to allow the team to proceed with the conversions. This was no small task, as the risks associated with converting production equipment concerned the operating groups, which could not afford significant downtime.

Finally, to successfully apply the lessons learned from the conversions to the remainder of the equipment in the company required a partnership arrangement with the original equipment manufacturers (OEMs). Since over half of the chillers in the company were manufactured by Carrier Corporation, the company proposed to Carrier that they form a partnership to develop a methodology for chiller conversions.

The success of the partnership required both a commitment of resources and a streamlining of communications between the engineering groups of the companies. Under this arrangement, the companies could more easily identify and resolve any technology issues arising from the conversion and more widely transfer the lessons learned from the conversions to the remainder of the chillers in the company.

Converted Chillers at the Camden Plant	
Number	**3**
Size	**3,000 tons**
Original Refrigerant	**CFC-12**
New Refrigerant	**HFC-134a**

The Test

In 1990, DuPont and Carrier made plans to convert a chiller from CFC-12 to HFC-134a at a DuPont Fibers Plant in Camden, South Carolina. This plant produces synthetic fibers for the carpet and textile industries and requires approximately 10,000 tons of cooling for temperature and humidity control of its spinning processes. Three 3,000-ton Carrier centrifugal chillers provide the majority of this cooling capacity. All capacity is needed throughout the peak cooling season from May through September, but opportunities to shut down equipment for maintenance and conversions are available during the cooler months.

The machine selected for the first conversion was the first Carrier Model 17DA open-drive chiller ever manufactured and also the first large-tonnage chiller ever to be converted to HFC-134a. In addition, this chiller would be among the first of DuPont's chiller conversions to use the new polyol ester lubricant. The search for a lubricant compatible with HFC-based refrigerants had so far yielded polyol esters and polyalkaline glycols as candidates in chiller applications. However, only polyalkaline glycols had been evaluated in field applications. Jeff Coleman, one of Carrier's Senior Product Managers remarked, "This project was very exciting since this was the first time Carrier had used a polyol ester lubricant in a chiller conversion."

The partners developed a conversion strategy and a list of objectives they wanted to achieve in the conversion. "We had a few major goals going into this project," said Mr. Bates. "But most important of all, we wanted to be able to transfer any lessons learned from this conversion to other CFC-12 chiller conversions scheduled across the corporation." Issues that the companies wanted to investigate included:

- Post-conversion cooling capacity changes
- Post-conversion energy efficiency changes
- Performance of polyol ester lubricant in existing equipment
- Timing and logistical requirements

Conversion Details

A key consideration in the conversion process was an assessment of the compatibility of the components in the chiller with the new refrigerant. "We knew that HFC-134a compatibility with traditional metallurgical materials found in chillers (e.g., copper, copper-nickel, steel, aluminum) was not an issue," Mr. Bates said. "But we also knew that components such as seals, gaskets or O-rings made of certain materials could exhibit unacceptable property changes when exposed to HFC-134a. Because incompatible materials had been used in refrigeration equipment applications in the past, Carrier researched its records to identify the elastomers originally used in the manufacturing of the chiller. Fortunately, all the components were compatible with HFC-134a."

Mr. Bates continued: "Since HFC-134a is a lighter refrigerant than CFC-12, we were concerned with the capability of the compressor to produce the thermodynamic lift required for HFC-134a." (The molecular weight of HFC-134a is 102.0 versus 120.9 for CFC-12.) Carrier's assistance became critical to understanding the compressor's operational limitations in the system as originally built. Carrier's computer model predicted that a 12 percent compressor speed increase was necessary to achieve the thermodynamic lift required to produce the design cooling capacity at rated design operating conditions.

The model also predicted that system power requirements would increase by 10 percent as a result of the compressor speed increase. The existing motor was originally designed to handle 15 percent more power than the maximum required in the original application, so we felt that it would be adequate for use with the new refrigerant. The heat dissipation capability of the electrical transformer was enhanced to allow its use with the slightly higher electrical load.

During this conversion, 10,900 pounds of CFC-12 refrigerant were recovered from the chiller and reclaimed. After draining the mineral oil from the oil sump, the compressor lubrication system was flushed three times with the polyol ester lubricant to minimize the presence of mineral oil. The objective was to reduce the residual mineral oil concentration to below three percent by weight. Approximately 60 gallons of polyol ester lubricant were used in the flushing process.

Conversion Results

After reassembling the chiller, the conversion team members performed a leak check of the machine followed by a thorough dehydration and a standing vacuum test. They then charged the chiller with HFC-134a and ran it for several weeks under partial load until the operators of the chiller became comfortable with the operating characteristics of the new refrigerant (e.g., slightly higher condenser pressures, slightly lower evaporator temperatures).

Under partial load conditions, the chiller produced a cooling capacity of about 2,750 tons. When the chiller was subjected to full load conditions, it met its original design cooling capacity of 3,000 tons. Power consumption under rated design conditions approached the 10 percent increase predicted by Carrier. Overall, the conversion went smoothly. The cost to convert this large chiller amounted to approximately $50/ton, including all labor and materials.

Results of First Chiller Site Conversion	
Change in Cooling Capacity	**None**
Change in Energy Consumption	**10% increase**
Quantity of CFC-12 Recovered	**10,900 lb.**
Quantity of Polyol Ester Oil Required	**90 gallons**

"The most important lesson from this conversion was the importance of having a detailed plan," Mr. Bates stated. "Only by running a conversion operation like a construction project, with critical path items clearly identified, could we complete the conversion on schedule. For example, this particular conversion required a gearset replacement. As a result, we included in our plans the several month lead time required to obtain the new gearset. Also, because the compressor speed was being increased, we felt it was imperative to inspect all rotating components and overspeed test the impeller. The time required for these procedures had to be factored into the schedule as well. Having a detailed task list with defined roles, responsibilities and timing provided the road map for the conversion."

Refrigerant Management Strategy

In addition to conversion issues, DuPont and Carrier believe that a comprehensive refrigerant management plan is essential to minimize total costs and protect the environment. Mr. Bates stated that to assess objectively the future refrigerant needs at each site or to develop a conversion strategy, equipment owners must first determine the service refrigerant needs for the existing equipment.

One of the first objectives of DuPont's CRLT in 1990 was to focus on reducing refrigerant loss from its chillers. While conversion feasibility was being demonstrated on selected equipment around DuPont in 1989 and 1990, the CRLT also had a strong focus on refrigerant conservation for all of DuPont's chillers. High efficiency purge units, refrigerant recovery units, and additional leak detectors were purchased for use at the sites. In addition, site teams aggressively repaired all refrigerant leaks to reduce refrigerant consumption.

Another important component of the refrigerant management plan is a refrigerant tracking system. At DuPont, refrigerant use trends were recorded, and these records became the benchmark for improvement. "If you're not keeping score, you're only practicing," remarked Mr. Bates. "Monitoring and reducing refrigerant consumption is not only sound environmental practice, it makes economic sense."

Conversion Planning/Methodology

- ☑ **Develop a refrigerant management strategy**
- ☑ **Assess refrigeration needs**
- ☑ **Obtain equipment data survey sheet from OEM**
- ☑ **Complete survey and transmit survey sheet to the OEM**
- ☑ **Review OEM engineering report for conversion cost and post-conversion cooling capacity and energy use**
- ☑ **Conduct life cycle cost appraisal of converted vs. new equipment**
- ☑ **Review mechanical limitations of equipment**
- ☑ **Develop the conversion plan**
- ☑ **Issue purchase order to proceed with conversion**

With very limited exceptions, CFC production and importation will cease in the U.S. at the end of 1995. It is EPA's goal to assist equipment owners in the transition to non-CFC refrigerants. This case history is part of a series on equipment retrofits and replacements by specific companies or agencies. Every effort has been made to see that these case histories accurately reflect the actions taken by the companies profiled. However, recommendations about retrofit/replacement procedures can vary. Companies are urged to check with manufacturers and local authorities in implementing programs to make the transition away from CFC refrigerants. Mention of any trade names or commercial products does not constitute endorsement or recommendation for use. For more information on the CFC phaseout, EPA information on refrigerant management, and acceptable alternative refrigerants, write: CFC Outreach, Stratospheric Protection Division, USEPA (6205J), Washington, DC, 20460.

United States Environmental Protection Agency | Air and Radiation (6205J) | November 1993

EPA Stratospheric Ozone Protection
Case History

Supermarket Chain Converts Two Entire Stores from CFC-12 to HFC-134a

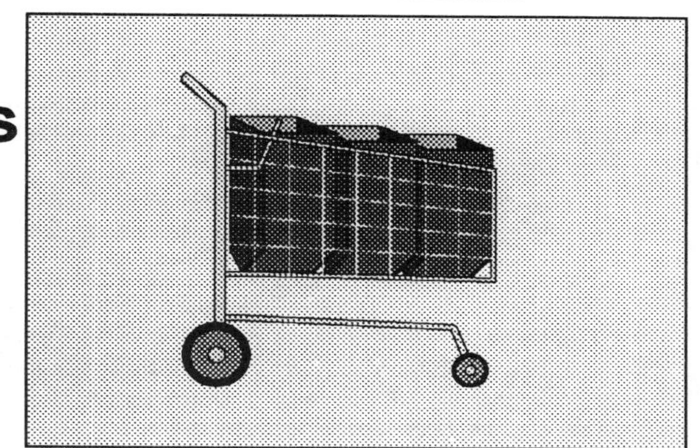

Case Study	**Market Basket**
Type of Facility	**Supermarket**
Location	**New England**

Market Basket, a supermarket chain operating in the Massachusetts/New Hampshire area, has successfully embarked on a chain-wide CFC conservation program. In addition, the company has also completed pilot HFC-134a conversion projects in two of its 52 stores. The company plans to initiate a campaign to totally eliminate new purchases of CFCs before 1995 and all use of CFCs before the year 2000. It will likely meet this goal if it can identify suitable substitutes for R-502 in the near future.

John Patinskas, the manager of refrigeration, knew that the chain would soon have a problem getting CFC refrigerants to service its equipment. He decided the best action to take was to first reduce the amount of service refrigerant his equipment required. Mr. Patinskas and his staff of mechanics formed a CFC elimination team and began thinking of ways to conserve their existing refrigerant. They also began thinking about ways to get experience working with the new refrigerants so that the team could effectively design a chain-wide CFC elimination plan.

The first step the team took was to implement a leak detection and repair program, assigning two mechanics full-time responsibility for these tasks. "With the price of CFC refrigerant what it is, the work that the leak detection crew does pays for itself," remarked Mr. Patinskas. Mr. Patinskas also justified purchasing a recovery unit for every truck in the department: "Since some of our stores are pretty far from headquarters, driving to and from our maintenance shop would have wasted valuable time and money. Buying a recovery unit for every truck just made good sense."

Cases Converted to HFC-134a at Woburn, MA Store

- 76' Meat Cases
- 48' Poultry Cases
- 56' Front Dairy Cases
- 44' Middle Dairy Cases
- 24' Rear Dairy Cases
- 32' Service Deli Cases
- Island Produce Cases
- Wall Produce Cases
- Meat Prep Room
- 2 Deli Coolers
- Meat Cooler
- Poultry Cooler
- Fish Cooler
- 3-Door Reach-In Cooler
- Dairy Cooler
- Produce Cooler

Converting an Average Market Basket Store from CFC-12 to HFC-134a

Quantity of HFC-134a Required	2,300 lb.
Total Number of Refrigerated Systems	17
Number of Refrigeration Racks	3
Size of Racks	2 @ 20 HP 1 @ 10 HP

Working Smart

The team has also installed in-store refrigeration controllers with refrigerant leak-detection capabilities. By monitoring the controller via a modem, the team can now tell when a system is leaking significantly, even when the leak detection crew is at other stores.

Every morning before beginning their rounds, the members of the team share their views on the activities of the previous day, highlighting ways to improve their operating procedures as well as recapping news from the converted stores. By combining their knowledge, they get the job done in an effective manner and keep everyone up to speed on the new refrigerants.

"Our only problem occurs when we are building a new store or remodeling an older one," Mr. Patinskas remarked. "This usually means 'all hands on deck' at the construction site, and preventive maintenance takes lower priority. It is during these times that all the steps we've taken to reduce leaks during the slower times really pay off, since we have a chance to fix leaks only between construction jobs. But since our systems really don't leak that much because of our improved maintenance program, we don't lose any sleep at night worrying about whether our systems will have enough expensive refrigerant to make it through the month. The CFC issue is really making supermarkets manage in a whole new way, and that's not necessarily bad."

First Conversion

Mr. Patinskas had wanted to try out the new refrigerants for some time, and as HFC-134a became more available, he decided to move forward. He chose two of the older stores in the chain to convert to HFC-134a. "We planned to reduce CFC-12 purchases in those stores to zero and get experience with HFC-134a in one stroke," stated Mr. Patinskas.

Market Basket initially tested the new refrigerant at its store in Wilmington, Massachusetts, replacing the CFC-12 in all of the medium-temperature equipment. First, the mineral oil was flushed from the systems four times with new polyol ester lubricant to reduce mineral oil concentrations to levels that would not interfere with the performance of the converted systems. The systems were then charged with HFC-134a. All the work was performed at night, so business was not interrupted.

Lessons Learned

The team learned two lessons from this first conversion:

1. HFC-134a leaks readily through some gaskets that CFC-12 cannot penetrate. The team obtained much better results after performing minor overhauls on valves with those types of gaskets and then thoroughly checking for leaks before recharging with the new refrigerant.

2. Polyol ester lubricant is a potent solvent, capable of cleaning up pipe scale, sludge, and other system contaminants. Mr. Patinskas said that for future conversions, filters will definitely be replaced prior to charging systems with the new refrigerant.

Mr. Patinskas commented on these difficulties: "It would have been nice for the test conversions to have proceeded without a hitch, but our whole purpose in conducting these tests was to find out what kinds of problems would occur. It's much better for these types of unforeseeable events to occur in a test installation only once, rather than chain-wide."

Second Conversion

With these lessons in mind, the team converted the store in Woburn, Massachusetts using the new procedure of thoroughly checking for leaks, overhauling gasketed valves, replacing filters, and then checking for leaks again after completing these tasks. So far, the results of the conversions have been good enough for Mr. Patinskas to decide that all of the CFC-12 systems in the chain should be converted to the new refrigerant.

Outside Assistance

Mr. Patinskas sought and received technical advice from all of his equipment manufacturers and chemical suppliers, including Hill, Hussman, Phoenix, DuPont, Allied-Signal, and Elf Atochem. By contacting more than one source of information, he felt that he got a more balanced assessment of his options than if he had contacted only one equipment or chemical supplier.

Market Basket's Conversion Checklist CFC-12 → HFC-134a

- ☑ Record temperatures and pressures of system operating with CFC-12 to determine baseline performance. Perform preliminary leak check to identify leaks to be repaired during conversion procedure.
- ☑ Remove CFCs and store in recovery container. *DO NOT VENT TO ATMOSPHERE.* Remove lubricant from compressor(s). Measure amount removed and recharge with equal amount of pure polyol ester lubricant and run for at least 48 hours. Use test kit to determine concentration of remaining mineral oil. Properly dispose of removed lubricant.
- ☑ Repeat above procedure for a total of four times or until concentration of mineral oil has been reduced to acceptable levels as indicated by test kit.
- ☑ Replace all HFC-134a-permeable gaskets in system.
- ☑ Replace liquid filter/drier and suction filters with HFC-134a-compatible type.
- ☑ Leak check and evacuate. Charge with new HFC-134a refrigerant. Use 80% by weight of original CFC charge.
- ☑ Start up system and adjust charge and expansion device until desired temperatures and pressures are reached. Label components and system with type of refrigerant and lubricant.
- ☑ Return recovered CFC refrigerant to reclaimer for banking purposes.
- ☑ Monitor system performance closely during initial weeks of operation.
- ☑ Revert to routine maintenance.

Energy Studies

Mr. Patinskas has heard that the energy use of HFC-134a compares favorably with that of CFC-12, but has not yet conducted any energy studies comparing the two refrigerants on his own. He explained: "The problem is that in order to 'work smart,' I'm obligated to convert and overhaul my older stores first. None of these older stores have state-of-the-art computerized monitoring equipment with energy analysis capabilities like our newer stores. So reducing our use of CFCs practically and at the same time comparing energy use between refrigerants isn't possible. Besides, most of our newer stores lack CFC-12 systems anyway because we quit installing them in 1989."

No More CFC-12 Purchases

Mr. Patinskas projects that by converting his main refrigeration racks, he will have sufficient recovered refrigerant in storage to service all of the small remaining equipment for the rest of their useful mechanical lives. "By doing things this way, I can feel comfortable that my company is protected from future shortages of CFC-12. Our improved refrigerant conservation program also makes me feel more secure. We have reduced our consumption of CFC-12 by one-third already, and I anticipate that we will be able to cut our consumption to half of what it was."

Future Plans

Mr. Patinskas plans to convert all of the R-502 systems in the chain to the new replacement refrigerants as soon as they become commercially available. "I don't know what the price will be for the new refrigerants and equipment, but I believe that there will be enough competition out there among manufacturers that prices won't be too out of line. What I do know is that it is already beginning to get awfully expensive to keep operating with the refrigerants that I have now."

Even though Mr. Patinskas feels comfortable using HFC-134a now, he leans towards using HCFC-22 in new medium-temperature equipment. But again, he insists on working smart. "From now on, we will only install new HCFC-22 equipment in combination with the new polyol ester lubricant, thereby saving ourselves the trouble of flushing mineral oil out of the systems when they are eventually converted to the new HFC-based replacements."

Costs

Converting each of the stores in the chain to HFC-134a has cost approximately $31,000 on average, including labor and materials. Materials costs included the new refrigerant, which cost $24,000 for 2,300 pounds, the new lubricant, which cost $2,100 for 60 gallons, and gaskets and filters, which cost approximately $600. Labor costs included 32 hours spent flushing the old mineral oil out of the systems, 30 hours recovering and recharging refrigerant, 20 hours replacing gaskets and filters, and 20 additional hours thoroughly checking for and repairing leaks. However, these costs can be partially offset by returning recovered CFCs to a reclaimer for credit.

COSTS

Materials ($)		Labor (hours)	
2,300 Pounds New Refrigerant:	24,000	Flushing Out Old Mineral Oil:	32
60 Gallons New Lubricant:	2,100	Recovering and Recharging Refrigerant:	30
Gaskets and Filters/Driers:	600	Replacing Gaskets and Filters:	20
		Checking and Repairing Leaks:	20

With very limited exceptions, CFC production and importation will cease in the U.S. at the end of 1995. It is EPA's goal to assist equipment owners in the transition to non-CFC refrigerants. This case history is part of a series on equipment retrofits and replacements by specific companies or agencies. Every effort has been made to see that these case histories accurately reflect the actions taken by the companies profiled. However, recommendations about retrofit/replacement procedures can vary. Companies are urged to check with manufacturers and local authorities in implementing programs to make the transition away from CFC refrigerants. Mention of any trade names or commercial products does not constitute endorsement or recommendation for use. For more information on the CFC phaseout, EPA information on refrigerant management, and acceptable alternative refrigerants, write: CFC Outreach, Stratospheric Protection Division, USEPA (6205J), Washington, DC, 20460.

United States Environmental Protection Agency

Air and Radiation (6205J)

November 1993

EPA

Stratospheric Ozone Protection

Case History

Supermarket Chain Builds First Store to Use Non-CFC Blends Exclusively

Case Study	Jitney Jungle Stores of America
Type of Facility	Supermarket
Location	AL, AR, FL, LA, MS, TN

Jitney Jungle's CFC-free supermarket in Forest, Mississippi is a good example of what a supermarket chain can accomplish through careful planning and implementation of an aggressive CFC phaseout program. Jitney Jungle, established in 1914, is headquartered in Jackson, Mississippi. The chain has 108 stores operating in six states throughout the South. Jitney Jungle was the first chain in the U.S. to design and build a new store that exclusively used the new non-CFC refrigerant HP-80 in all of its large refrigeration systems. The chain now plans to open a store using only HP-62 soon, as this non-ozone-depleting refrigerant has recently become available commercially.

The CFC phaseout program began in 1991 when James Riley, Vice President of Engineering, began to gather information to assess CFC phaseout options for new and existing stores. In his quest for an alternative refrigerant that could be used for all temperature ranges (like the old refrigerant R-502), he began by looking at HCFC-22 and the recently developed DuPont blend HP-80.

"HCFC-22 is a very versatile refrigerant, but we chose HP-80 for energy-efficiency reasons," Mr. Riley said. "In medium-temperature applications, such as produce cases, both HCFC-22 and HP-80 perform quite well. But as the temperatures of the applications fall, the cooling capacity and energy efficiency of HCFC-22 systems decrease markedly compared to HP-80 systems. HP-80 mimics the performance of R-502 much more closely than HCFC-22 across the board. Although the energy efficiency of two-stage HCFC-22 systems is acceptable, we are not convinced that two-stage HCFC-22 compound systems are practical in the field, because they have high maintenance costs due to their complexity. We prefer to use common single-stage systems."

Once Mr. Riley had identified a good candidate for a replacement refrigerant, he made a presentation on the situation to the senior executives in the company. Although they were cautious at first, the executives warmed to Mr. Riley's suggestions after reading articles that he had distributed on the subject. In fact, the executives even began to push for an accelerated CFC phaseout program. Mr. Riley formed a CFC elimination team consisting of himself, the senior executives of the company, some of his best mechanics, and Norman Twisdale, a refrigeration applications consultant.

Equipment Conversion at a Typical Jitney Jungle Store	
Number of Conversions: CFC-12 to HFC-134a	15
Number of Conversions: R-502 to HP-80	9
Quantity of HFC-134a Required	1,400 pounds
Quantity of HP-80 Required	1,100 pounds
Quantity of Polyol Ester Lubricant Required	75 gallons
Labor Hours Required	32

First Non-CFC Installation

The first step the team took was to construct an entirely CFC-free refrigeration installation. Construction of a new store in Forest, Mississippi was underway and the team decided that this store would be a good test case. At this time, DuPont was testing HP-80 as a replacement for R-502. Although the new refrigerant was available only on an experimental basis, DuPont agreed to supply sufficient refrigerant for an entire store if Jitney Jungle could persuade its equipment manufacturers to approve the use of HP-80 in new equipment.

Shortly thereafter, Jitney Jungle scheduled a meeting of its equipment and refrigerant manufacturers. The meeting was attended by representatives from Copeland, Sporlan Valve, DuPont, and Novar Controls. In addition, Mobil Oil submitted test data and asked to be included in the project. The response from the manufacturers' representatives was very positive and details were quickly worked out so that the refrigeration systems could be constructed on schedule. The refrigeration systems were designed, built, and ready for operation by December 1992.

Since the new store was installed with a computerized refrigeration controller/monitor that could be read remotely via a modem, Jitney Jungle was able to watch the new systems closely. In addition, extra monitoring sensors were installed so that Jitney Jungle could obtain detailed performance data on the systems, such as temperatures and pressures at various key points. From the data obtained during the first few months of operation at the Forest installation, Jitney Jungle found that the performance of the systems exceeded expectations, with no maintenance problems to report and energy efficiency better than similar R-502 installations.

Persuading the Mechanics

The successful installation gave confidence to the in-house maintenance and construction department and became an operating classroom as well. "At first we encountered a little resistance to the new refrigerants from some of the mechanics. Once we got all of the mechanics out to the Forest store, however, they saw that there was nothing magical about the new refrigerants. This demonstration convinced them to get on board," Mr. Riley said.

Although not all of the maintenance staff has had the opportunity to convert a refrigeration system to the new refrigerants, fully one-third of the staff has become proficient at the procedure. Mr. Riley plans to assign some of the more experienced staff to a conversion task force to perform conversions full-time. He remarked that the biggest problem he faces in continuing his CFC phaseout program is not training his staff on the technical aspects of the conversions, but getting them focused on adopting procedures that conserve refrigerant. In this regard, he has purchased electronic leak detectors for all of his mechanics and refrigerant recovery units for all of the maintenance trucks.

Next Steps

Using the experience gained from the Forest store, the company began to implement an extensive program to eliminate CFCs from all equipment by the end of 1995. CFC-12 equipment was to be converted to HFC-134a and R-502 equipment to HP-80. In May 1993, Jitney Jungle committed $4.9 million to phase out all CFC-12 and R-502 to meet its goal. However, in July 1993, the company found out that the testing of HP-62 was nearly complete. Consequently, use of HP-80 was suspended because it conflicted with the goal of using only non-ozone-depleting refrigerants if these were commercially available.

Problems Solved

The retrofit program has progressed smoothly, with only a few problems encountered. Mr. Twisdale elaborated: "Some valves were prone to leak HP-80. However, we found this problem involved only a single model of solenoid valve made by one manufacturer. We simply replaced these valves with new ones and the problem was solved. Typically we don't need to replace any of our rack components for refrigerant compatibility reasons during conversions."

Mr. Twisdale spoke about an additional problem the chain had encountered. "We were experiencing moisture problems with the new HFC-134a systems because the new polyol ester lubricant quickly absorbs moisture when exposed to the air. To solve this problem we first installed access valves on the compressors to ease lubricant changes during the conversions. Then we transferred the polyol ester lubricant from its original shipping container to a clean evacuated refrigerant recovery container, and pressurized the container with nitrogen. While charging the lubricant into the compressor, we made sure to minimize contact with the air. Finally, we evacuated the system immediately after charging the lubricant."

Jitney Jungle's Conversion Checklist to Prevent Moisture Contamination

- ☑ **Install access valves on compressors to ease lubricant changes during conversions.**
- ☑ **Transfer polyol ester lubricant from its original shipping container to a clean evacuated refrigerant recovery container.**
- ☑ **Pressurize container with dry nitrogen.**
- ☑ **Take care when charging lubricant into compressor to minimize contact with air.**
- ☑ **Immediately evacuate system after charging with new lubricant.**

Conversion at McComb

The company believes that converting its stores now is a prudent business decision. In fact, fourteen of its stores have been either partially or completely converted to the new refrigerants. "It really doesn't cost that much to convert our stores to the new refrigerants, in relative terms, if the conversions are planned properly," said Mr. Twisdale. "For example, we converted an entire 39,000 square foot store in McComb, Mississippi from CFC-12 and R-502 to HFC-134a and HP-80 using only 32 labor hours. This time included operations conducted to flush out the old mineral oil from the systems with pure polyol ester lubricant. The only parts we replaced were the filters and the lubricant. Those systems are now much cleaner inside and will probably run much better because of it. And the HP-80 systems have already been prepared for HP-62 by adding a compatible lubricant, so we can just drop that refrigerant right in without changing a thing."

Phasing in HP-62

Jitney Jungle is now well underway with its phase-in of HP-62. In mid-1993, a store expansion required the addition of a new medium-temperature parallel compressor system. DuPont provided HP-62 for this system and the same group that was so successful in the Forest store installation contributed to this effort as well. Shortly thereafter, the company undertook an extensive expansion at a different store, which required installing a new refrigeration system. This time, the CFC elimination team decided to go with new HP-62 systems in all temperature ranges. Construction is under way for a new store which will open in early 1994. Jitney Jungle plans to make this the first exclusively HP-62 store in the chain.

No more CFC Purchases

The chain plans to stop purchasing new CFC refrigerant in 1994 and begin using the refrigerant recovered from converted systems to service its remaining stock of CFC equipment. Jitney Jungle anticipates that approximately half of its stores will be CFC-free in nine months. "That sounds like a fast-paced program, but when you consider that there are only 26 more months to finish all of the work, we really are just getting in under the deadline."

Proceeding Carefully

Mr. Riley feels that his program is solidly underway and that the training for his mechanics is progressing well. He remarked on the lessons he has learned: "In the last two years we have felt as if we are climbing a wet ladder. Each step had to be very carefully taken, and each successive step well studied before we took it. The lessons we learned in the first test conversions speak to the wisdom of that approach. Now that we have developed good methods to keep our systems dry and leak-free, we believe our conversions will proceed smoothly. But we also believe that there is still more to learn before we reach the top. In fact, you never stop learning. But that's no justification not to act. We did, and we are confident we will be comfortably out of CFCs and into the new refrigerants while others are still scrambling."

With very limited exceptions, CFC production and importation will cease in the U.S. at the end of 1995. It is EPA's goal to assist equipment owners in the transition to non-CFC refrigerants. This case history is part of a series on equipment retrofits and replacements by specific companies or agencies. Every effort has been made to see that these case histories accurately reflect the actions taken by the companies profiled. However, recommendations about retrofit/replacement procedures can vary. Companies are urged to check with manufacturers and local authorities in implementing programs to make the transition away from CFC refrigerants. Mention of any trade names or commercial products does not constitute endorsement or recommendation for use. For more information on the CFC phaseout, EPA information on refrigerant management, and acceptable alternative refrigerants, write: CFC Outreach, Stratospheric Protection Division, USEPA (6205J), Washington, DC, 20460.

United States Environmental Protection Agency | Air and Radiation (6205J) | November 1993

EPA

Stratospheric Ozone Protection
Case History

Supermarket Chain Accelerates Its CFC Elimination Program

Case Study	Furr's Supermarkets
Type of Facility	Supermarket
Location	New Mexico & Texas

Furr's, a chain of 69 supermarkets based in Albuquerque, New Mexico has decided to accelerate its CFC elimination program. After carefully observing the results of test installations of non-CFC refrigerants that other supermarkets have conducted, the company feels confident it can successfully eliminate the CFC refrigerants in its systems by the end of 1995.

"We've been gathering all the information we can find on the issue for some time now," remarked Lee Stokes, the Manager of Refrigeration and the person in charge of the CFC elimination program at Furr's. "The articles we obtained at the annual energy conferences of the Food Marketing Institute have really boosted our confidence. We felt sure that our company could obtain the same kinds of results with the new refrigerants as other supermarkets have, but first we wanted to confirm what we had learned by actually conducting our own field tests. We also wanted to get practice converting our systems to the new refrigerants before proceeding chain-wide with our CFC elimination program."

Mr. Stokes has worked closely with his maintenance contractor in El Paso, Texas on several test installations. Although the territory of the chain covers all of New Mexico and parts of West Texas, the company had been concentrating its tests in the El Paso stores. El Paso was chosen because Mr. Stokes wanted the same maintenance contractor to perform all of the test conversions.

Furr's first tested the new refrigerants in March 1993 by converting a beer cooler to MP-39 and monitoring its operation for three sweltering summer months. The results of the test conversion were reassuring, so the company decided to proceed with a program to eliminate CFC-12 chain-wide.

Mr. Stokes discussed the original test: "In our initial test conversion, we first brought the system up to design specifications. We performed an extensive leak check and repaired all the leaks. We then cleaned up the system thoroughly, changing the oil and replacing the filter/driers. Only after the system was fully prepared for the conversion did we convert it to the new refrigerant."

Cases Converted to MP-39 at Store #935 in El Paso, Texas

- 84' Dairy Cases
- 72' Packaged Meat Cases
- 72' Wall Produce Cases
- 60' Meat Cases
- 44' Beer Cases
- 16' Service Deli Cases
- 12' Service Fish Case
- Meat Prep Room
- Meat Cooler
- Meat Holding Cooler
- Deli Cooler
- Fish Cooler
- 3-Door Floral Cooler
- Dairy Cooler
- Produce Cooler

CFC-12 Out First

"We chose MP-39 for the first test for two reasons. First, MP-39 was the most cost-effective alternative with which to gain experience, since it was cheaper than CFC-12 at the time. Second, it is a replacement for CFC-12, which we use exclusively in single-compressor systems. These types of systems are easier to convert than parallel-compressor racks," said Mr. Stokes.

Based on the results, Furr's decided to convert an entire store to MP-39 in August 1993. The maintenance contractor first "tuned up" the store, taking three weeks to bring the systems up to specifications. The fifteen CFC-12 systems in the store were converted in a matter of four days. During the conversions, 1,200 pounds of CFC-12 were recovered and the systems were charged with 1,000 pounds of MP-39. Half of the mineral oil in the systems was replaced with alkylbenzene lubricant for better oil return. The whole process cost $20,000, including 200 hours of labor time. A large portion of these costs reflects the time taken for the "tune up." In addition, some of these costs were recouped from credits received from a reclaimer for recovered CFC refrigerant.

"One interesting by-product of having to bring all of our systems up to specifications before converting them is that we realized exactly how good a job our maintenance contractors have been doing," remarked Mr. Stokes. "The contractors who have been doing a good job are eager to do the conversions. All the rest are raising their standards."

R-502 Out Next

Despite the initial focus on CFC-12, Furr's does not plan to wait to phase out R-502. After a successful test of HP-80 in another El Paso store, the company felt confident enough to begin planning to eliminate R-502 on a fast track. The program starts January 1, 1994, and by mid-1995, all of the R-502 systems in the chain will have been converted to HP-80.

Good Financial Sense

Another reason Furr's accelerated its CFC phaseout program was that its refrigerant costs were dramatically increasing. "We have records of our refrigerant consumption that are updated every week on a per-store basis," explained Mr. Stokes. "The executives of the company noticed that our refrigerant costs had been increasing steadily over the last five years. When we presented the estimate of how much it would cost to complete our phaseout of CFC refrigerant, the financial officers approved the plan immediately. To the officers of the company, it just made good financial sense to get out of CFCs now. It also made good environmental sense. We were given enough money to eliminate CFC-12 in twelve stores this year, and we have worked out a long-term budget to finish converting the entire chain by mid-1994."

During any future remodeling projects, Furr's plans to replace old single-compressor equipment with new energy-efficient non-CFC parallel-compressor racks. The 40 oldest stores in the chain use both CFC-12 and R-502 in single-compressor refrigeration equipment. At this time, Furr's plans to eventually replace all of the equipment in these stores with HCFC-22 parallel racks. The other 29 stores in the chain now operate with parallel racks using R-502 for the freezers and frozen food cases and HCFC-22 for the medium-temperature coolers and display cases. Furr's plans to eliminate R-502 in these pieces of equipment by converting them to HCFC-22 rather than replacing them. The company expects to complete this conversion process within 18 months of obtaining some experience converting the single-compressor equipment. Furr's hopes to eventually convert all parallel racks to HFC-based blends, but desires conversion experience before beginning any conversions of parallel racks.

"We have a lot of planning to do for the phaseout projects for next year. We are gearing up to remodel 15 stores, and plan to build the new stores using HCFC-22 exclusively. We will do this only as long as it makes financial sense. When the HFC-based alternatives become cheaper than HCFC-22, we plan to switch over. In the meantime, we will no longer install systems that contain CFCs," Mr. Stokes stated.

Increased Maintenance Saves Money

Since the costs of CFC-based refrigerants have escalated greatly in the last three years, Furr's has directed its maintenance contractors to increase preventive maintenance and perform leak checking more frequently. Furr's believes that the increased maintenance costs have been more than offset by the decreased refrigerant purchases. In addition, the company has been working on reducing refrigerant loss by installing refrigerant sensors in newly constructed stores. "The alarm for the sensors is located in the store manager's office, so we can notify someone immediately if a leak occurs."

By decreasing its consumption of CFC refrigerants, Furr's has protected itself against refrigerant shortages in the short term. Its success in converting some systems to new refrigerants has given Furr's confidence that its phaseout program is on target.

Converting the El Paso Store from CFC-12 → MP-39

Quantity of CFC-12 Recovered	1,200 lbs.
Quantity of MP-39 Required	1,000 lbs.
Number of Systems	15
Compressor Size Range	3 to 10 HP

With very limited exceptions, CFC production and importation will cease in the U.S. at the end of 1995. It is EPA's goal to assist equipment owners in the transition to non-CFC refrigerants. This case history is part of a series on equipment retrofits and replacements by specific companies or agencies. Every effort has been made to see that these case histories accurately reflect the actions taken by the companies profiled. However, recommendations about retrofit/replacement procedures can vary. Companies are urged to check with manufacturers and local authorities in implementing programs to make the transition away from CFC refrigerants. Mention of any trade names or commercial products does not constitute endorsement or recommendation for use. For more information on the CFC phaseout, EPA information on refrigerant management, and acceptable alternative refrigerants, write: CFC Outreach, Stratospheric Protection Division, USEPA (6205J), Washington, DC, 20460.

United States Environmental Protection Agency | Air and Radiation (6205J) | November 1993

EPA

Stratospheric Ozone Protection

Case History

California Restaurant Chain Leads Conversion to Refrigerant Blends

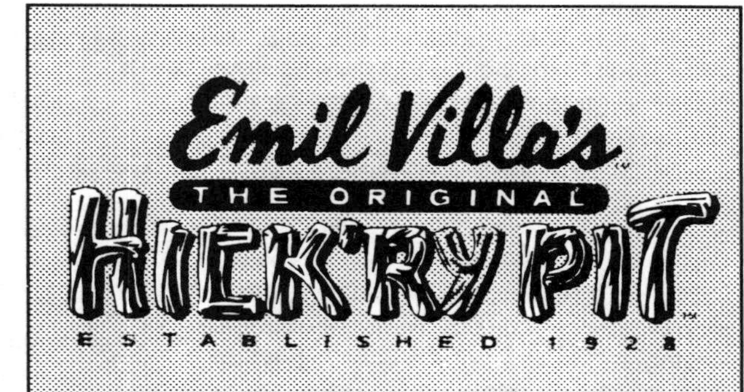

Case Study	Emil Villa's Hick'ry Pit
Type of Facility	Restaurant
Location	Northern California

Emil Villa's Hick'ry Pit, a popular restaurant chain located in the San Francisco Bay area, has been a leader in switching to the new generation of CFC substitute refrigerants. After successfully converting the CFC refrigeration equipment in one of its restaurants to the new DuPont blends, the chain launched a campaign to eliminate use of CFCs in all of its restaurants before the end of 1993.

Hick'ry Pit has expanded from a single restaurant in 1928 to a chain of twelve restaurants today. The company is committed to more than just providing large portions of good food made from scratch, however. "We want to be at the forefront of the environmental movement and be good neighbors as well," said Thomas Crane, Hick'ry Pit's head of maintenance.

DuPont had its blend refrigerants ready for field testing in January 1991 and approached Hick'ry Pit about conducting such a test. Thomas Crane jumped at the chance. A conversion team was formed that included the in-house maintenance staff, George Fisher of DuPont, local contractor Bob Evans, and Robert Wurzbach, the owner of William Wurzbach Company, the local refrigeration supply house.

The team tested the new refrigerants at the restaurant in Campbell, California, replacing all CFC-12 with MP-39 in the medium-temperature equipment and MP-66 in the low-temperature equipment. They tested HP-80 in another store in a low-temperature R-502 system. The positive results of the conversions convinced Mr. Crane that the entire chain should be converted as soon as possible. His enthusiasm was rewarded with a "full steam ahead" response from Nancy Ontko, Hick'ry Pit's Vice President of Operations.

Refrigerant Conversion

Low Temperature
CFC-12 → MP-66
R-502 → HP-80

Medium Temperature
CFC-12 → MP-39

Mr. Crane feels that his strategy is both economically and environmentally sound. When asked why his company is converting all locations to the new blends at such an early date, Mr. Crane responded, "To get ahead of the game, to save money in the long run, and to set a good example environmentally. That's what we want to be known for. CFC prices are rising, and what we have done was eventually going to have to happen anyway. At the rate we are going, we will be finished with CFCs by the end of October."

Converted Equipment

- walk-in coolers
- walk-in freezers
- ice cream freezer
- reach-in pie case
- milk dispenser
- reach-in beer case
- ice machine
- salad bar

Average Refrigerant Quantity Required per Restaurant	MP-39: 20 lbs. MP-66: 3 lbs. HP-80: 4 lbs.
Systems	9-12 units per Restaurant
Compressor Size Range	1/4 to 3 HP

Support from Management

Management supports Mr. Crane's CFC elimination program and has given him full responsibility and authority. As a result, the chain will be CFC-free well ahead of the phaseout. "Since I'm the person that maintains the converted equipment, I make absolutely sure that each conversion is done correctly. If I note that a particular system component is unable to perform adequately with the original CFC refrigerant, I am authorized to upgrade the equipment before I convert to the new refrigerant," remarked Mr. Crane.

Outside Assistance

Because the chain was the first to try the new blends, Hick'ry Pit's two-man maintenance staff received a lot of help from DuPont and the local refrigeration supply house. They do not need any help now, however. After converting nine restaurants to the new blends, the two men now require only one day to convert a restaurant. With only three more restaurants to go, Emil Villa's Hick'ry Pit will soon be totally CFC-free.

Attention to Detail

Mr. Crane remarked: "Attention to detail is very important. When converting the equipment, I always replace the filter/drier and the expansion valves. This practice helps keep the system clean and dry, a necessity for these new refrigerants. I believe it also helps prevent the system from malfunctioning later, and will probably reduce my maintenance costs in the long run. I want the job done right. That's why I check the performance of the equipment on each converted site three times before I feel confident that I can let the equipment go to the usual monthly maintenance routine." So far the new refrigerants have performed better than the original refrigerants; the cooling units operate less frequently and maintain proper refrigerated space temperatures more consistently.

Minor Adjustments

The maintenance staff did have to make a few minor adjustments because the new refrigerants were not thermodynamically identical to the CFCs . The new blends operated with different pressures than the pure refrigerants. Also, the boiling point of the new blends rose a set amount as the boiling proceeded in the evaporator. The average evaporator temperature, however, was about the same as the old single component refrigerant. This characteristic required a different method of adjusting the system's expansion valve. The converted units had to be very clearly marked to avoid confusion if outside repair people were required to add refrigerant in an emergency.

Emil Villa's Hick'ry Pit Conversion Checklist

- ☑ Record temperatures and pressures of system operating with CFCs to determine baseline performance.
- ☑ Remove CFCs and store in recovery container for off-site reclamation. Weigh CFCs. *DO NOT VENT TO ATMOSPHERE.*
- ☑ Remove mineral oil from compressor. Measure amount removed and recharge with equal amount of alkylbenzene or polyol ester lubricant.
- ☑ Replace filter/drier with DuPont-approved type.
- ☑ Totally evacuate system, check for leaks, and re-evacuate. Charge with new refrigerant (liquid only). For MP-blends use 70% by weight of original CFC charge; for HP-blends, 90%.
- ☑ Start up system and adjust charge and expansion valve until desired temperatures and pressures are reached. Label components and system with type of refrigerant and lubricant.
- ☑ Check system performance 3 times during initial weeks of operation.
- ☑ Revert to routine monthly maintenance.

"Conversion Aces"

The maintenance staff has become so proficient that it can convert an entire restaurant to the alternative refrigerants in an eight-hour work day. The total bill for converting a restaurant is about $600, including labor and materials, according to Mr. Crane.

Next Steps

All the chain's new ice makers will use the blend HP-81. The chain is also looking at other types of CFC-free equipment. "Although we are happy with the performance of these new blends, we realize that these particular blends are only a temporary solution because they contain HCFCs," stated Mr. Crane. "But how can you argue against putting in a refrigerant that contains no CFCs, is cheaper than R-12, and performs better, too? We are curious about HFCs and HFC blends and plan to try them so that we can also be prepared for the HCFC phaseout."

Composition of Blends

Name	Pure Refrigerant Constituents
MP-39	HCFC-22 (53%), HFC-152a (13%), HCFC-124 (34%)
MP-66	HCFC-22 (61%), HFC-152a (11%), HCFC-124 (28%)
HP-80	HCFC-22 (38%), HFC-125 (60%), Propane (2%)
HP-81	HCFC-22 (60%), HFC-125 (38%), Propane (2%)

With very limited exceptions, CFC production and importation will cease in the U.S. at the end of 1995. It is EPA's goal to assist equipment owners in the transition to non-CFC refrigerants. This case history is part of a series on equipment retrofits and replacements by specific companies or agencies. Every effort has been made to see that these case histories accurately reflect the actions taken by the companies profiled. However, recommendations about retrofit/replacement procedures can vary. Companies are urged to check with manufacturers and local authorities in implementing programs to make the transition away from CFC refrigerants. Mention of any trade names or commercial products does not constitute endorsement or recommendation for use. For more information on the CFC phaseout, EPA information on refrigerant management, and acceptable alternative refrigerants, write: CFC Outreach, Stratospheric Protection Division, USEPA (6205J), Washington, DC, 20460.

United States Environmental Protection Agency | Air and Radiation (6205J) | November 1993

EPA

Stratospheric Ozone Protection
Case History

Convenience Store Chain Launches Aggressive CFC Phaseout Campaign

Case Study	Wawa
Type of Facility	Convenience Store
Location	CT, DE, MD, NJ, PA

Wawa, a large chain of convenience stores, continues to demonstrate a proactive stance towards the CFC phaseout. The chain is now in the fifth year of its phaseout program and has progressed past the stage of testing non-CFC refrigerants. Wawa has begun to accelerate the elimination of CFCs in its stores and has targeted 1995 as the year that it will have all 512 of its stores totally CFC-free.

Fred Wood, Corporate Facilities and Energy Manager at Wawa, explained his philosophy this way: "Most convenience stores are still waiting for the government to regulate use of CFCs before they begin taking steps to get out. What they don't realize is that regulations already exist that control the *production* of CFCs. Regulations that affect the *use* of these refrigerants are unnecessary. At any rate, soon there just won't be any CFCs around to regulate. I saw this coming about five years ago and immediately instructed my regional managers to begin getting experience with the new refrigerants." He feels that his two biggest hurdles, (1) convincing corporate executives that there is a concern with continuing CFC use and (2) testing the new refrigerants, are already out of the way.

Henry Anderson, one of the five Regional Facilities Managers for the chain, elaborated: "Back in 1988, we quit purchasing CFC-12 medium-temperature equipment and began buying HCFC-22 equipment instead. We also began to convert some of our R-502 systems to HCFC-22." The company installed its first new HFC-134a system in November 1992. Soon thereafter, the company began testing the HCFC-based blends. So far, 70 conversions have been done, mostly in Mr. Anderson's region since it is the closest to corporate headquarters in Philadelphia, where Mr. Wood can monitor the progress more closely.

"All the conversions turned out quite well, with the systems running normally or even a little better than before. Our maintenance contractors have really learned a lot about the new refrigerants. At present, they now have standing orders to convert any system that requires a compressor change: CFC-12 systems are to be converted to HFC-134a and R-502 systems are to be converted to HCFC-22," said Mr. Wood. The chain has tested many of the alternative refrigerants, and even has one store with equipment containing MP-39, MP-66, HP-80, HCFC-22 and HFC-134a.

Systems Converted to Alternative Refrigerants in a Typical Wawa Store

- 8' Open Dairy Case
- 8' Produce Case
- Walk-In Cooler
- Sandwich Station
- Deli Case

Converting a Typical Wawa Store from CFC-12 to HFC-134a

Quantity of HFC-134a Required	60 pounds
Number of Existing CFC-12 Systems	5
Range of Equipment Size	1/3 - 5 HP

One of the maintenance contractors for Wawa remarked, "The new polyol ester lubricants are expensive, but you really get what you pay for. Equipment charged with these lubricants runs substantially more quietly and has no oil return problems to speak of. In fact, when we changed the oil in one of the CFC-12 systems during an HFC-134a conversion to polyol ester, we were able to remove 10 ounces more lubricant in the second oil change than in the first oil change. This indicated to me that the new lubricant returned to the compressor better than the original mineral oil, and actually flushed out old oil that was trapped somewhere in the system."

The contractor went on to say that during a pilot conversion of one of the freezer systems from R-502 to HP-62, the decrease in the electrical current that the compressor drew was substantial, on the order of 20 percent. This reduction in operating current also applied in the CFC-12 to HFC-134a conversions: "Essentially, across the board we noticed a decrease in electrical current of one-half to a full ampere for the equipment after the conversions were completed."

Reduced Conversion Costs

The maintenance contractors for Wawa have gained enough experience converting CFC-12 systems to HFC-134a that the conversion costs have dropped substantially. To convert an average store containing five CFC-12 systems, Wawa spends about $2,000, of which approximately 60 percent is for chemicals, lubricant, and parts, while the rest is for labor. However, some of these costs can be recovered from credits given by a reclaimer for recovered CFC refrigerant.

Egging them On

Wawa's stores contain a number of different refrigerators and freezers, including a flower case, a frozen carbonated beverage machine, and an ice freezer, which are all owned and operated by equipment manufacturers. Although the chain is not directly responsible for eliminating CFCs from these pieces of equipment, the executives in the chain have begun to put pressure on the manufacturers to develop a plan to phase out CFCs. Wawa knows that store operations will suffer should this equipment become unusable due to a lack of refrigerant.

Use of Maintenance Contractors

Wawa has changed the way it maintains its stores. Mr. Wood elaborated: "Four years ago we used to have 11 districts, each operating its own in-house maintenance department. This configuration proved to be very wasteful and inefficient. Now we operate under only five districts, and leave the maintenance to local maintenance contractors. We want to focus on selling food, and that's why we are getting out of CFCs just as soon as we can. With today's competition, we can't afford to have one of our stores down, even for a little while."

Wawa's Typical Conversion Costs CFC-12 → HFC-134a

Labor	$800
Refrigerant	$700
Lubricant	$400
Parts	$100
Total	$2,000

Gathering Information

For five years, Mr. Wood and the five regional managers have collected information about alternative refrigerants and equipment and have shared this information with their maintenance contractors. They have encouraged the various maintenance contractors that service the five regions to do the same, and this information-sharing program has worked well. After attending the Food Marketing Institute's 1992 Energy Conference in Boston for a "reality check," they agreed that enough testing had been conducted in the food industry to give them confidence in their phaseout program.

Accelerating the Phaseout

Mr. Wood and the regional managers decided to accelerate their CFC phaseout program and have instructed their maintenance contractors to begin conducting equipment and refrigerant inventories and estimating conversion costs. The five managers want to be prepared with a realistic budget when they meet with corporate executives at the end of 1993. The managers have decided to request funding for a two-year CFC phaseout program, with half of the money to be disbursed in 1994 and half in 1995. "Since we also plan to remodel 70 of our stores in the next two years, we thought that it would be a good idea to combine the remodeling and CFC elimination projects to save money," said Mr. Wood.

Attitude Adjustments

Mr. Wood said that he is constantly surprised at what he perceives to be lackadaisical attitudes on the part of other convenience store corporate managers at the national convenience store association conferences. His advice to convenience store owners: "Educate yourself about the issue before it's too late, and begin to act soon."

With very limited exceptions, CFC production and importation will cease in the U.S. at the end of 1995. It is EPA's goal to assist equipment owners in the transition to non-CFC refrigerants. This case history is part of a series on equipment retrofits and replacements by specific companies or agencies. Every effort has been made to see that these case histories accurately reflect the actions taken by the companies profiled. However, recommendations about retrofit/replacement procedures can vary. Companies are urged to check with manufacturers and local authorities in implementing programs to make the transition away from CFC refrigerants. Mention of any trade names or commercial products does not constitute endorsement or recommendation for use. For more information on the CFC phaseout, EPA information on refrigerant management, and acceptable alternative refrigerants, write: CFC Outreach, Stratospheric Protection Division, USEPA (6205J), Washington, DC, 20460.

United States
Environmental Protection Agency
(6205-J)
Washington, DC 20460

EPA 430-K-93-002
November 1993

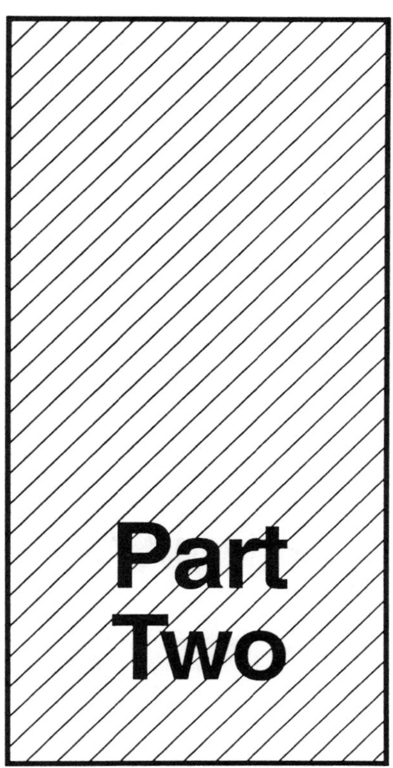

Manufacturer's Data

The information contained herein has been furnished by refrigerant manufacturers and is reproduced as originally published by those manufacturers. The omission or inclusion of any particular manufacturer's information does not represent an endorsement or lack of endorsement of a particular manufacturer's product(s). The information is arranged in no particular order, and no order of preference is implied or intended by the author or publisher.

The author and publisher wish to thank the manufacturers for their participation and cooperation.

Copeland Corporation

The following information is reprinted with the permission of Copeland Corporation:

- *The CFC Report: The New Age of HFC Technology*
- *Introduction to Refrigerant Mixtures*
- *The Demand Cooling Report: HCFC-22 Low Temperature Comparison*
- *Refrigerant Changeover Guidelines:*
  - *— CFC-12 to HFC-134a*
  - *— CFC-12 to R-401A*
  - *— CFC-12 to R-401B*
  - *— R-502 to R-402A*
  - *— CFC R-502 to HFC R-404A*

The CFC Report

The New Age of HFC Technology

1994

Introduction

Copeland is pleased to provide the industry with another edition of our CFC Report. In this publication, we continue to provide our interpretation of the complex challenges involved in providing chlorine-free products and solutions to our customers. We have learned a great deal since publishing the last CFC Report and continue to gain valuable experience through our research, field testing, qualification and release of new compressor products. Over the last year, we have introduced many product lines for use with commercially available HFCs and will continue to do so in 1994. We continue to evaluate all available options to provide you the broadest range of alternatives, and as always, Copeland encourages a critical review from our valued customers, suppliers, and end users of our products.

Use only Copeland approved refrigerants and lubricants in the manner prescribed by Copeland Corporation. In some circumstances, non-approved refrigerants and lubricants may be dangerous and could cause fires, explosions or electrical shorting. For more information, contact Copeland Corporation and your original equipment manufacturer.

Regulatory Update

The1992 Copenhagen revision to the Montreal Protocol CFC phase-out schedule will ban CFCs after December 31, 1995 (see Table 1).

As a result of U.S. regulations and producer decisions, U.S. production of CFCs will end by December 31, 1995. Therefore, both OEM and aftermarket usage of R-12 and R-502 must be shifted to alternatives (HCFCs and HFCs) or rely on reclaimed or recycled refrigerants. In fact, some refrigerant manufacturers are accelerating the phase-out.

The International Protocol does not discourage the use of HCFC-22 in transitioning from CFCs. HCFC consumption will be limited relative to historic usage of CFC and HCFC usage on an ozone depletion weighted basis beginning in 1996. This agreement will enable the EPA to establish regulations in the U.S. that control future HCFC use according to a schedule that both the agency and industry believe is appropriate. This reasonable transition schedule permits substantial conversion to HCFC-22 from CFCs during the 1990s. Even though the EPA estimates that HCFC usage will more than double between 1993 and 2000, it will stay well within Montreal Protocol limits set in Copenhagen in November, 1992.

In Germany and northern European countries, there are restrictions being placed on HCFC-22 by the end of 1994 or 1995.

The amendments to the Clean Air Act were signed into law on November 15, 1990. This legislation contains comprehensive regulations for the production and use of Class I compounds (CFCs, halons, carbon tetrachloride, methyl chloroform and Class II compounds (HCFC and HCFC containing substitutes). The major provisions of the Clean Air Act include:

- *Phase Out Schedules for the U.S.*
- *Mandates for recovery of refrigerants in auto air conditioning and stationary refrigeration equipment.*
- *Bans on "nonessential" products.*
- *Dictates concerning safe alternatives.*
- *Labeling for containers and/or products containing or made with Class I or Class II compounds.*

The 1990 Clean Air Act Amendments called for a phase-out of Class I substances by January 1, 2000. The EPA has finalized regulations which are expected to occur as demonstrated by the schedule in Table 1.

EPA regulations are expected to permit the use of HCFC (Class II substances) in new refrigeration equipment until January 1, 2010. HCFC production will only be allowed for service of in-place refrigeration equipment after this date with a total HCFC production ban effective January 1, 2020. The intentional venting of CFC and HCFC refrigerants was illegal as of July 1, 1992.

The EPA is developing lists of safe alternatives for Class I and II substances which reduce risk to health and the environment and will be the only acceptable refrigerants.

EPA regulations require warning labels to be used on all products containing or manufactured with Class I (CFC) substances by May 15, 1993. EPA enforcement began in October, 1993. All products containing or made with HCFCs for which suitable alternatives have been defined by the EPA must similarly be labeled one year after EPA definition. Copeland products do not require such labels when purchased from Copeland.

Table 2 (following page) shows current tax rates for R-12 and R-502. HFCs and HCFCs are not covered by any ozone depletion tax at this time.

While global warming continues to be of concern, International Protocols have not set specific limits for refrigerants based on global warming potential. President Clinton announced his "Climate Change Action Plan" in October, 1993 which set limits for global warming for the year 2000. Essentially all alternatives to R-12 and R-502 have substantially less direct global warming potential (GWP) and are therefore considered a move in the

TABLE 1
CFC Phaseout Schedule
(Percent of 1986 Production)

Year	1992 Copenhagen	1990 Clean Air Act	Proposed EPA Regulations
1993	—	75	75
1994	25	65	25
1995	25	50	25
1996	0	40	0

right direction. As a result, refrigerants with a GWP less than about 1.0 have generally been accepted. Some European countries are using 0.5 as a reference maximum GWP.

The best widely accepted measure of global warming takes into account both direct and indirect warming. Total Equivalent Warming Impact (TEWI) not only considers the direct GWP but also the sizable indirect global warming resulting from the CO_2 produced by fossil fuel energy. Higher energy efficiency of some refrigerants can offset a somewhat higher GWP.

In dealing with the changing refrigerant environment, Copeland has adhered to a strategy that permits us to serve our markets with products that provide proven performance, demonstrated reliability, and minimum risk —while moving as rapidly as possible to chlorine-free alternatives. The HCFC and HFC alternatives are now widely available in production quantities.

TABLE 2
Current Tax Rate for R-12 and R-502

Base Tax, $ Per ODP Pound		$ Per Refrigerant Pound	
		R-12	**R-502**
Year	**Amount**	**(1.00 ODP)**	**(0.37 ODP)**
1991	$1.37	$1.37	$0.42
1992	$1.67	$1.67	$0.51
1993	$3.35	$3.35	$1.03
1994	$4.35	$4.35	$1.34
1995	$5.35	$5.35	$1.64

As in previously published "CFC Reports," Copeland continues to follow its long-term direction to lead the way in providing environmentally responsible solutions and products for our industry.

To reiterate our position, Copeland fully supports the elimination of environmentally harmful refrigerants as quickly as possible. However, an orderly approach is essential for a successful transition to HFCs. We believe that such an approach will permit Copeland to develop superior products which meet the industry's needs, are rapidly accepted, and will motivate users to abandon environmentally harmful refrigerants quickly and effectively.

HFC Overview

The situation surrounding chlorine-free alternative refrigerants has cleared up significantly in the last year, especially for refrigeration applications where CFCs have been commonly used for decades. Several chemical manufacturers have commercialized or announced commercialization schedules for HFCs which have properties similar to the refrigerants they are intended to replace. In addition, refrigeration component manufacturers have products available for use with these refrigerants. As a result, refrigeration systems using HFC refrigerants are beginning to appear in the market.

The situation in the air conditioning market is not quite as clear as it is for the refrigeration market. Historically, air conditioning has used HCFC-22, which has a much longer product life under EPA regulations than CFCs, and in fact, is viewed by most people as part of the solution to the CFC issue. As a result, there has not been as much urgency on finding a replacement for HCFC-22 as was the case for CFCs. The Air Conditioning and Refrigeration Institute (ARI) has a program underway where many of its members are performing substantial testing of possible HCFC-22 replacements, and until that work is done, it will be difficult to determine what the most viable replacements for HCFC-22 will be. We anticipate this program will provide the industry with recommended options later in 1994.

Although the HFCs being commercialized for refrigeration appear to be satisfactory, there are several areas where they differ from CFCs. One major difference is that HFCs must use polyol ester oil instead of mineral oil. In many cases, the HFCs are mixtures, as opposed to pure or azeotropic fluids (see Copeland Corporation's *Introduction to Refrigerant Mixtures*, publication No. 92-81). As a result, some service practices may have to be revised. Many HFCs also have a somewhat higher saturation pressure for any given temperature, which may result in the need to set controls at different values as well as review the pressure handling capability of all components.

A positive aspect of HFCs is they tend to have better heat transfer characteristics in the evaporator and condenser than CFCs or HCFCs which should lead to higher efficiency. In addition, several HFCs have lower discharge temperatures which should further improve compressor reliability and durability.

In summing up the status of the new HFC refrigerants, all of the laboratory and field testing indicates that the refrigerants work well in systems and should provide long and satisfactory service. Of course, the refrigerants' viability will only be proven when the industry accumulates data from long periods of successful service.

Service Refrigerants

Copeland does not encourage widespread conversion of systems away from the refrigerants they were designed to use unless there is a strong economic or technical reason to do so. We believe that a system containing CFCs which is leak-free and operating properly should be left alone.

December 31, 1995 is the last day that CFCs (including R-12 and R-502) will be produced by DuPont, AlliedSignal or any other refrigerant manufacturer for use in the United States. The availability of CFC refrigerants for servicing existing equipment will become limited and very expensive. Copeland believes one of the following three "alternatives" will become more attractive for equipment owners.

1. Remove the CFC containing equipment and replace it with equipment that uses HCFC-22 or new HFC refrigerants.
2. Convert the equipment to a low-ozone depleting HCFC-containing refrigerant. This will involve removing most of the mineral oil and replacing it with either approved polyol ester or alkyl benzene. Lower labor and material (oil) costs will be incurred. The system will be much more environmentally acceptable and the HCFC-containing refrigerant will be available as long as HCFC-22 is available.
3. Convert the equipment to a non-ozone depleting HFC. This will involve repeated flushing with polyol ester oil to remove the mineral oil and recharging the system with the HFC refrigerant. Considerable labor will need to be expended, but the system will be environmentally acceptable and serviceable for the remainder of its useful life.

For many equipment owners, the second approach (HCFC) will be the preferred decision for existing equipment. Several major refrigerant manufacturers are offering products which are equal to the CFCs in capacity and efficiency. As a result, Copeland expects a considerable amount of existing equipment will be converted to these service HCFC containing mixtures.

We believe it is important to realize that service HCFC mixtures are not identical to the refrigerants they are designed to replace. Some areas where they differ from the original refrigerant include:

1. The intermediate HCFC mixtures are near azeotropes with varying amounts of glide. Although this is not expected to affect system operation, prolonged and extensive leakage may result in capacity changes for some applications. The cost of replacement refrigerant will likely make continuous leakage economically unacceptable.
2. Equipment converted from its original refrigerant will lose its U.L. listing. An industry group is working with U.L. to resolve this issue; guidelines have been published.
3. All of the low-ozone depleting HCFC-containing refrigerant blends have higher system pressures than the CFC refrigerant they are replacing. This could create a safety issue and a low side pressure relief valve may be required. Refer to the Copeland retrofit guidelines to determine if the relief valve is required.
4. Limited testing has been performed by component and system manufacturers with these refrigerants. Copeland's research indicates there should not be any major durability or performance issues on the refrigerants we recommend. We will provide normal warranty coverage for compressors converted in accordance with our specific published guidelines to the recommended refrigerants. Equipment owners should check with their extended warranty providers to verify warranty policies with regard to retrofitting to new refrigerants.
5. Copeland does not have performance data for these refrigerants nor do we have U.L. approvals for the refrigerants with our compressors.
6. Not all of the available service HCFC mixtures are alike in terms of their operating characteristics. Some of them have not provided acceptable performance in our tests. Before a conversion is performed, it is imperative to review the list of Copeland-approved refrigerants and lubricants for acceptability. See Copeland publication No. 93-11.

Copeland believes that circumstances will arise which will result in decisions to convert some equipment to appropriate interim HCFC blends in order to achieve more of the equipment's useful life. If the decision is made to convert to a new refrigerant, there are refrigerants and guidelines available as follows:

TABLE 3

Copeland Retrofit Guidelines	Form No.
• R-12 to R-401A	93-02
• R-12 to R-401B	93-03
• R-12 to R-134a	93-04
• R-502 to R-402A	93-05
• R-502 to R-404A/R-507	94-15

Definitions

• Blends (Mixtures): Refrigerants consisting of mixtures of two or more different chemical compounds, often used individually as refrigerants for other applications.

• Azeotrope: Blends, when used in refrigeration cycles, that do not change volumetric composition or saturation temperature appreciably as they evaporate (boil) or condense at constant pressure.

• Zeotrope: Blends, when used in refrigeration cycles, that change volumetric composition and saturation temperatures to varying extents as they evaporate (boil) or condense at constant pressure.

• Glide: The difference between the starting and ending temperatures of a phase-change process by a refrigerant within a component of a refrigerating system, exclusive of any subcooling or superheating. This term usually describes condensation or evaporation of a zeotrope.

• Near-Azeotrope: A zeotropic blend with a small temperature and composition glide over the application range and no significant effect on system performance, operation and safety.

• Fractionation: A change in composition of a blend by preferential evaporation of the more volatile component(s) or condensation of the less volatile component(s).

Long Term Refrigerants

For a refrigerant to be considered a long-term option, it must have zero ozone depletion and low global warming potential. These refrigerants can be grouped into three primary classes according to their vapor pressure/temperature characteristics.

1. Medium Pressure (pressures similar to R-12)
2. High Pressure (pressures similar to R-502 or HCFC-22)
3. Very High Pressure (pressures significantly higher than R-502 and HCFC-22)

Most of the currently proposed long-term refrigerants are HFCs. The polarity of HFC refrigerants make them immiscible with mineral oils. As a result, HFC refrigerants must be used with polyol ester oil, discussed elsewhere in this report.

Current U.S. regulations require the long term refrigerant to have zero ozone depletion. There are two ways to measure global warming:

1. Global Warming Potential (GWP) - This is the direct measure of global warming potential. The calculation only considers the direct effect of the refrigerant as a greenhouse gas when it escapes into the atmosphere.
2. Total Equivalent Warming Impact (TEWI) - This is a global warming calculation which includes the effects of system efficiency, the source of the electricity (coal, nuclear, hydrodynamic, etc.), as well as the direct effect of the refrigerant when it escapes into the atmosphere. The actual number varies according to the leakage rate and type of power used.

Note again that all alternative refrigerants have substantially lower direct global warming potential than CFC refrigerants. The new "Climate Change Action Plan" announced by President Clinton will limit the global warming potential of refrigerants by the year 2000.

Medium Pressure Refrigerants

HFC R-134a

R-134a is the first non-ozone depleting fluorocarbon refrigerant to be commercialized. Developed more than 20 years ago to have characteristics similar to R-12, it is a viable candidate for use in medium and high temperature applications where R-12 has been successfully used. R-134a has been generally accepted by the automotive air conditioning industry because of its low hose permeability and high critical temperature. Domestic refrigerator producers also find R-134a to be a viable refrigerant for their products. R-134a is available from several refrigerant manufacturers.

Copeland's laboratory and field tests show that refrigeration capacity and energy efficiency of R-134a are similar to R-12 for medium and high temperature applications. At evaporating temperatures below -10°F, R-134a loses its attractiveness for several reasons, including:

1. Significant loss of capacity and efficiency compared to R-12.
2. Pressure ratios become very high, compromising compressor reliability.
3. Low side pressures are sub-atmospheric (i.e. vacuum), resulting in system reliability concerns.

With the exception of ozone depletion potential, Copeland believes that R-134a possesses the same deficiencies as R-12 and represents a step backward for most commercial refrigeration and air conditioning applications. These deficiencies include larger displacement compressors and larger diameter tubing compared to what is required for use with high pressure refrigerants.

For customers who plan to use R-134a, Copeland has developed product lines for applications above -10°F evaporator temperatures. We do not expect it to be a widely used refrigerant except in refrigeration applications where the benefits of high pressure refrigerants cannot be practically achieved (primarily fractional horsepower).

High Pressure Refrigerants

Refrigerant manufacturers have been unsuccessful in developing single component high pressure alternatives that meet all requirements including zero ozone depletion, adequate performance, good reliability and safety. Consequently, the possibility of using mixtures (also called blends, azeotropes, near-azeotropes, zeotropes, etc.) has gained increased attention. The refrigeration industry has considerable experience with mixtures such as R-502 and R-500.

Mixtures have both advantages and disadvantages when compared to pure substances. Mixtures allow the advantage of tailoring the final refrigerant characteristics for superior efficiency, performance and reliability. Disadvantages of zeotropic mixtures include the following:

• Temperature Glide — Because the composition of a zeotrope changes during a phase change, there is a slight change in evaporating and condensing temperature at constant pressure. This phenomenon is known as "glide." Most zeotropic mixtures under consideration exhibit low glide. The magnitude of this phenomenon is little different than similar effects seen with single component refrigerants due to normal pressure drop within the heat exchanger. As a result, little or no effect on system performance is expected.

• Fractionation — Since the components of a zeotropic mixture possess different vapor pressures, under certain conditions they may leak from a system at different rates. As a result, the refrigerant composition may change over time with a corresponding change in performance. Zeotropic mixtures presently being offered in the marketplace are believed to be close enough to an azeotrope that fractionation will not be a serious problem. To ensure fractionation does not occur during charging, it is recommended that zeotropic mixtures be liquid charged rather than vapor charged. Liquid must be removed from the refrigeration cylinder. It then can be flashed through a metering device and charged into the system in its vapor state. The refrigerant manufacturers' recommendation should be closely followed.

R-502 Replacements — Low and Medium Temperature\Refrigeration Applications

HFC R-404A

This is commonly known as Suva® HP62 from DuPont and Forane® FX70 from Elf Atochem. The refrigerant is a near-azeotrope with characteristics very similar to R-502. It is commercially available. Copeland has announced a broad product line that uses R-404A.

HFC R-507

This is commonly known as Genetron® AZ50 from AlliedSignal. The refrigerant is a near-azeotrope with characteristics very similar to R-502. Copeland is developing a product line to be released later in 1994.

HCFC-22 Replacements — Air Conditioning Applications

Suva® AC9000

Suva AC9000 is a near-azeotrope from DuPont with characteristics similar to HCFC-22 for air conditioning applications. DuPont has announced plans to commercialize AC9000 in late 1995. The glide of this refrigerant is 10°F which may present some system concerns.

KLEA-66

KLEA-66 is a near-azeotrope proposed by ICI with characteristics similar to HCFC-22 for air conditioning applications. The glide of this refrigerant is 10°F which may present some system concerns.

Very High Pressure Refrigerants

Very High Pressure refrigerants operate at pressures significantly higher than those normally seen with refrigerants such as HCFC-22 and R-502. They cannot be used as retrofit refrigerants with existing equipment but only in new equipment (including compressors) specifically designed for them. Existing HCFC-22 compressors cannot meet U.L. and industry design standards with these higher pressures. (Advantages that may come from their use include smaller components.)

Very High Pressure mixtures have the same advantages and disadvantages as the High Pressure refrigerants previously described. Only one Very High Pressure refrigerant has been proposed so far. Genetron® AZ-20, by AlliedSignal, is being tested by some equipment manufacturers as a replacement for HCFC-22 for air conditioning. Genetron® AZ-20's vapor pressure at 130°F condensing is about 480 psig, where as HCFC-22 is about 300 psig. Only time will tell if the air conditioning industry will be willing to accept such a change from existing products and whether new compressors will be developed to use it.

Criteria for Refrigerant Selection

The selection and approval of acceptable long-term refrigerants is a complex and time consuming task. Many factors must be taken into consideration. The ever-shifting legislative environment, impending phase-out of CFCs, availability of alternate refrigerants, and numerous other issues are just a few of the things that must be taken into account. Based on these factors, Copeland recommends the following key criteria when evaluating and selecting refrigerants:

- Environmentally, candidates must have zero or low ozone depletion potential, low direct global warming potential, and energy efficiency must meet or exceed the refrigerant it is replacing. The Total Equivalent Warming Impact (TEWI) is a key measure.
- Safety must be maintained. New refrigerants must be non-toxic (TLV < 400 ppm) and non-flammable. Maximum system pressures must be no greater than current acceptable limits for retrofit applications.
- Reliability concerns require that compressor discharge temperatures not exceed the temperatures of the refrigerant they are replacing.
- It is desirable that lubricants work with current oil control technology, meet current or improved durability requirements, and be backward compatible with mineral oil systems. Material compatibility between the new refrigerants and traditional compressor materials must also be maintained.
- Service procedures for equipment must remain simple. The serviceability of the refrigerants with respect to fractionation of blends must not require unreasonable service procedures.
- It is highly desirable to have a single lubricant solution that works with all of the alternate refrigerants, including both HFC and HCFC retrofit chemicals. A single lubricant that works with all of the approved chemicals makes the service and long-term refrigerant strategies easier to navigate.
- The performance of new refrigerants should be very similar to the

refrigerants which they are replacing. R-502 for low and medium temperature refrigeration, R-12 for medium and high temperature applications, and HCFC-22 for high temperature air conditioning.

A variety of other factors should be taken into consideration when choosing a refrigerant. The following key questions should be asked:

1. Is the application for new equipment or as a replacement for a CFC in service?
2. What is the age and condition of the equipment?
3. How many more years of service is the equipment expected to have?
4. What are the available resources for the refrigerants and service requirements?

It is then possible to begin categorizing where the alternate refrigerants will begin to be used. Copeland is still learning many things about these new refrigerants, lubricants and their chemical interaction in refrigeration systems. We continue to test refrigerants from chemical manufacturers from around the world. Given our experience to date, we have outlined the following general groupings to select the proper refrigerant for particular application and service situations.

Service Replacement Refrigerants- HCFC blends intended only to be used in retrofit applications where the original refrigerant (R-12 and R-502) is no longer available or cost effective. These refrigerants require at least 50% alkyl benzene. Please refer to the Copeland Application Bulletin AE-12-1248 *Refrigeration Oils* for the list of approved lubricants to be used in Copeland compressors. Some of the approved service replacements follow:

- (HCFC) R-401A and (HCFC) R-401B can be used to replace R-12.
- (HCFC) R-402A can be used to replace R-502.

Long-Term Refrigerants - Although these refrigerants can also be used in a retrofit application, it is not easily accomplished. The refrigerants are HFCs which require at least 95% polyol ester lubricant. Please refer to the Copeland Application Bulletin AE-17-1248 *Refrigeration Oils* for the list of approved lubricants to be used in Copeland compressors.

To achieve less than 5% residual mineral oil in the system, a substantial flushing operation must be performed. Results of field tests have shown that at least three flushes with POE and at least one day to one week of operation are required to remove most of the residual mineral oil in the system. During this time, the system must be operated with the original CFC refrigerant. At the time that the residual mineral oil is less than 5%, the CFC refrigerant can be removed and replaced with the HFC refrigerant. Some of the long-term refrigerants follow:

- (HFC) R-404A or R-507 can be used to replace R-502.
- (HFC) R-134a can be used to replace R-12 in systems with operating temperatures above -10°F evaporating.

Please refer to Copeland's retrofit guidelines for detailed instructions on the retrofit procedures.

Lubricants

After considerable testing, Copeland has determined that polyol ester (POE) lubricants provide the best combination of characteristics for use with the new generation of chlorine-free, refrigerants. In addition to providing superior lubrication with the new refrigerants, POE has other advantages which increase its attractiveness for use in refrigeration. Several other refrigeration equipment manufacturers have drawn the same conclusion.

Copeland has qualified two specific POEs (which are compatible with each other) Mobil EAL™ Arctic 22 CC and ICI EMKARATE™ RL 32S. Specifications for Copeland-approved POEs are provided in Application Engineering Bulletin AE-17-1248.

What is Polyol Ester?

Polyol esters are a family of synthetic lubricants used primarily for jet engine lubrication. POE is manufactured by several companies. There are many types and grades of POEs and it is important to understand that all POEs are not the same. Areas of difference include lubricity, miscibility with refrigerant, viscosity, additive packages, pour point and moisture content. Unlike natural mineral oils, POE is completely wax free. In addition, POE has better thermal stability than refrigeration mineral oils.

POE is made from more expensive base stock materials than traditional refrigeration mineral oils and therefore costs more. However, some of the characteristics of POE help offset the higher cost. For instance, POE is backward compatible with mineral oil, which means that a compressor containing POE can be installed in a refrigeration system that contains mineral oil. Furthermore, POEs we recommend are compatible with all refrigerants, so that a compressor containing POE can be installed in a system which contains CFCs, HCFCs or the new HFCs. Thus, for the higher initial cost of POE, we obtain significant flexibility in the face of the changes brought on by the CFC issue.

A second positive aspect of POE is that it can be designed to meet lubricity requirements equivalent to those of mineral oils used with CFCs and HCFCs. Standard laboratory lubricant bench tests (Falex, pin on v-block and four ball wear tests) and accelerated compressor life tests are used to verify these results. Contributing to the superiority of POE is the fact that the viscosity of POE has less variation with temperature than mineral oil.

A third positive aspect of POE is that its miscibility with refrigerant can be matched easily to that of mineral oil in R-12, R-502 or HCFC-22. Thus, POE should have similar oil return characteristics to mineral oil with conventional chlorine-containing refrigerants.

Finally, from an environmental perspective, POE is highly biodegradable and should provide low ecotoxicity.

Mineral Oil Can't Be Used With Pure HFC Refrigerants

When a lubricant is evaluated for use in a compressor, the following characteristics must be considered in addition to basic considerations such as product safety and environmental impacts:

Lubricity is the ability of the lubricant to minimize friction and wear between the rotating or sliding surfaces under all operating conditions, including adverse conditions such as high load, flooded start and floodback. With regard to lubricity, the chlorine in CFCs and HCFCs significantly enhances boundary layer lubrication in bearings used with mineral oil. Since HFCs do not contain chlorine, POE must be formulated to provide the necessary anti-wear capabilities without the presence of chlorine in refrigerants.

Miscibility is the ability of oil to mix with refrigerant in all areas of the system so that it can return to the compressor without stagnating in the connecting lines, heat exchangers or receiver. Mineral oils are not miscible with pure HFCs. Thus, any mineral oil that leaves the compressor in a pure HFC system may get trapped in the connecting lines or evaporator. Since oil acts as an insulator in heat exchangers, oil trapped in the evaporator can significantly reduce system capacity and efficiency as well as jeopardize compressor reliability.

Stability and Compatibility with commonly used refrigeration components and the refrigerant itself are important. Copeland has performed extensive sealed tube material compatibility tests and has found that selected POEs have acceptable compatibility with materials commonly used in refrigeration systems.

POE Can Be Used With All Refrigerants

Because POE is used with all refrigerants and is compatible with mineral oils commonly used with CFCs and HCFCs, it offers the greatest level of flexibility in dealing with the uncertainties imposed by the CFC issue. For example:

1. Initially using POE in a new system will allow the easy transition to HFCs without the expensive, repetitive flushing procedure to remove the mineral oil from the system.

2. During system service, if POE is used to replace any mineral oil removed from a system, it begins the process to flush the system of mineral oil so that conversion to an HFC can be performed with fewer steps later on.

3. POE can also be used with the intermediate HCFC mixtures if they are used to replace CFCs. A mixture of at least 50% POE in mineral oil provides excellent lubrication, and will begin the flushing procedure if a switch to HFCs occurs in the future.

It is imperative that any system that contains POE be clearly marked to identify the composition of the oil and refrigerant in the system to avoid cross charging with the wrong lubricant or refrigerant.

Handling POE Lubricants

POE has one negative aspect in that it is substantially more hygroscopic (absorbs moisture) than mineral oil. Consequently, exposing POE to air will result in absorbing moisture quickly, reaching levels that are unacceptable in refrigeration systems.

POE also holds moisture tighter than mineral oil, so removing it with vacuum is more difficult. Copeland's specification for maximum moisture content of POE oil to be added to refrigeration systems is 50 parts per million (PPM). If the moisture content of the oil in a refrigeration system rises above 100 PPM, corrosion of various metallic materials and copper plating may occur. In addition, acids and alcohols can be formed (through a process called hydrolysis) which will have a negative impact on long term compressor and system durability and performance. It is imperative that system moisture levels be kept below 100 PPM. It is equally important that undesirable contaminants picked up as a result of POE's increased solvency be filtered out. Both can be achieved by proper installation and service techniques as well as use of the correct filters and driers. These components are available from leading suppliers and are clearly described in their literature as well as in Copeland's Refrigerant Retrofit Guidelines and Application Bulletins for the HFC refrigerants.

Figure A shows how the moisture level of POE can increase when it is exposed to air. Obviously, it is imperative that containers of POE be kept sealed except when the oil is actually being dispensed. Also, it is imperative that compressors and systems be kept closed except when work is actually being performed on the equipment. Leaving equipment open during work breaks, overnight or when performing

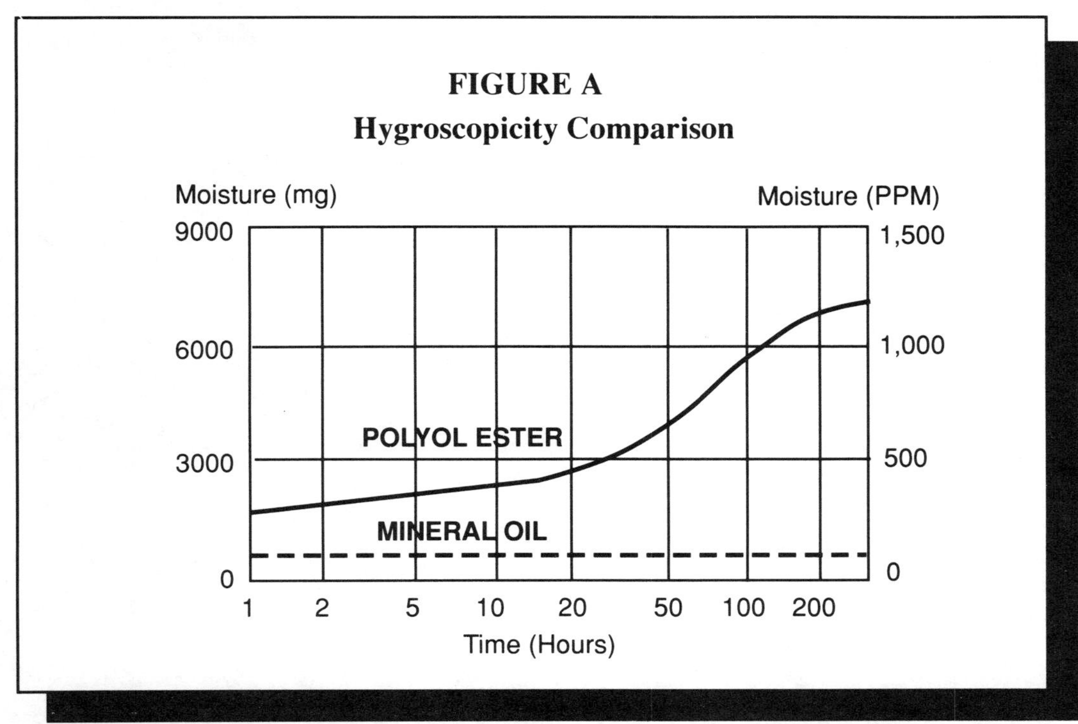

other work will quickly result in unacceptable levels of moisture in POE lubricants.

It is equally important that POE be properly stored in its original container, because many plastics used to package oils are permeable to moisture. Even though the cap is kept in place, moisture can permeate through the plastic and contaminate the POE. One of the requirements for Copeland to qualify a POE lubricant is proper packaging to prevent moisture contamination during normal shelf storage. For this reason, Copeland only approves POE oils that are presently packaged in metal cans.

The impending phase-out of chlorine based refrigerants mandates that the refrigeration industry move to lubricants which will work satisfactorily with the new HFC refrigerants. These lubricants must have as good or better levels of reliability and performance as previously experienced with traditional mineral oils used with chlorine containing refrigerants. It appears that selected POE lubricants meet this requirement. Because of its compatibility with all commonly used refrigerants, POE offers a large measure of flexibility in dealing with the many refrigerant options being introduced into the market. This flexibility should help reduce confusion over exactly which lubricants and refrigerants are compatible.

Alkyl Benzene Refrigeration Oils

Another lower cost option for use with the intermediate term service refrigerants, such as HCFCs R-401A, R-401B, R-402A and R-402B, is a mixture of alkyl benzene (AB) and mineral oil. In this case, at least half of the mineral oil should be removed from the compressor and replaced with a Copeland-approved AB, such as Zerol 200 TD. This option cannot be used with the chlorine-free refrigerants, which must use POEs. Specifications of Copeland-approved AB oils are provided in Application Engineering Bulletin No. 17-1248.

When making the decision of whether to use POE or AB with an intermediate term service refrigerant, remember that AB does not begin the flushing process to remove mineral oil from the system. If the system is converted to an HFC later on, the entire flushing process will have to be performed with a POE lubricant.

System Accessories

Copeland has worked with many refrigerant companies to ensure that new refrigerants are compatible with new and existing Copeland compressors currently used in the refrigeration industry.The materials used in Copelametic® and Copelametic Discus® compressors are generally compatible with the new refrigerants and oils. However there are exceptions to this general compatibility statement. The insulation material used in motors prior to 1973 may or may not be compatible with the HCFC blends or the new HFC refrigerants and/or lubricants. Copeland does not recommend retrofitting any system that uses a compressor with a serial number indicating the compressor was built in 1973 or earlier.

Copelametic 3D Discus compressors that have the original HCFC-22/R-502 "Moduload" unloader must have the unloader changed as part of the retrofitting process to HFCs. The original HCFC-22/R-502 Moduload unloader has a "Viton" seal as part of the unloader piston assembly. Viton is not compatible with HFC refrigerants. Unloader kits are available with seals that are compatible with HFC refrigerants as well as separate kits with seals that are compatible with HFC refrigerants. For more information, contact your Authorized Copeland Wholesaler.

Pressure Control Valves

The new refrigerants are not identical to the refrigerants they are replacing. In all cases, the new refrigerants have higher pressures thus all pressure controls and pressure operated valves may need to be reset for proper operation. Some of the controls or valves may need to be replaced. Pilot operated valves must be checked to be sure they are properly operating. The pilot operated valve, in many cases, requires a minimum pressure differential to open and the valve will not operate properly unless this pressure differential is correct. Valves or controls may need to be re-sized. Other system components will also be affected by the new refrigerants and lubricants. Consult your equipment manufacturer for guidelines and more information.

Sight Glass/Moisture Indicator

The sight glass/moisture indicators currently available can be used with the new refrigerants and lubricants; however, the moisture indicator will be incorrect. The actual moisture level of POE will be higher than the sight glass specifies. This is a result of the high hygroscopicity of the POE oil. The sight glass/moisture indicator should be used as a sight glass only and the system must be closely monitored to determine if there is moisture in the system. Oil samples will have to be taken from the system and analyzed at an independent laboratory to determine the true moisture level in the system. Sight glass/moisture indicator manufacturers are working to develop moisture indicators that can be used in systems with the new refrigerants and lubricants.

Liquid Control Device

The liquid control or metering device may be a capillary tube or a thermal expansion valve. The purpose of the liquid control device is to control the flow of refrigerant to the evaporator. The liquid control device will not have to be changed when an R-502 system is retrofit with R-402A, with R-404A, or with R-507. The capacity of the liquid control device is virtually the same. However, the flow capacity of the liquid control device in an existing R-12 system may increase up to 30% higher with the new refrigerants.

When an R-12 system is retrofit with either an HCFC blend or with R-134a, the liquid control device may have to be changed. However, a properly sized R-12 expansion valve may work with the new refrigerant by adjusting the evaporator superheat. The existing capillary tube can, in all probability, be made to work with the new refrigerant by adjusting the refrigerant charge. While most systems can retrofit without changing the liquid control device, it will be necessary to adjust the valve superheat or the system charge. Systems using expansion valves still require a solid column of liquid refrigerant ahead of the expansion valve. This means that the sight glass is clear (no bubbles).

Filter-Driers

Filter-driers currently available are compatible with the new refrigerants and lubricants as far as materials are concerned. The construction of the filter-drier must be solid core or compacted bead (spring-loaded). The desiccant must be XH-9 to assure compatibility with the new refrigerants and lubricants. Filter-driers with a high activated alumina content may remove additives from the lubricant which improve operating characteristics. We recommend that the filter-drier activated alumina content be limited to a maximum of 25-31% like the PureFlow™ filter-drier from Copeland.

Activated alumina is used in filter-driers to remove acids from the system and is not required unless there are acids in the system. Molecular sieve filter-driers are the best for moisture absorption. With the hygroscopic nature of POE lubricants, it is very important that the filter-drier have a high moisture absorbing capability. Oversized filter-driers may become the standard.

Summary

Let's review Copeland's chlorine-free strategy. We continue to support the use of HCFC-22 and HFC R-404A as the primary medium and low temperature refrigerants, and HCFC-22 for high temperature applications. HCFC-22, R-404A and R-507. Discus products are currently available. We understand these refrigerants and know how to apply them in order to maximize reliability and performance while minimizing risk. We believe HFCs developed to emulate both the performance and capacity of R-502 are the best long-term solution. To date, we have amassed the most experience with R-404A. We are now actively testing R-507 for a broad line of Copeland products with a goal to approve its use during 1994.

Copeland recognizes there are many refrigerant manufacturers and we are keenly aware of our responsibility to ensure the widest application of our products. To that end, we are continuing to work with the major refrigerant and lubricant manufacturers around the world to ensure that products acceptable for use in our compressors are available from multiple sources.

We have focused our attention on R-134a as the replacement for R-12 for many applications in both the service and OEM markets. R-134a has the widest application in small, fractional horsepower compressors and condensing units which are used in applications where a redesign to accommodate high pressure refrigerants would be impractical. At the same time however, some users and OEMs have expressed interest in using R-134a as either an interim or final solution in other applications. This interest is motivated by a desire to move as quickly as possible to chlorine-free chemicals. As a result, in 1992 we released a full line of R-134a Discus compressors for medium temperature supermarket applications.

We continue to view R-402A as the preferred alternative for R-502 in service and retrofit applications. Because it contains HCFC-22, it will be phased out of use at the same time as HCFC-22. Nevertheless, it is a useful alternative for users concerned about the availability of R-502 or who wish to move immediately away from CFCs in existing installations. As with R-134a, a few OEMs have expressed a desire to use R-402A in new installations. This desire stems from a concern over the availability of R-502 during the transition to full commercial availability of R-404A or R-507, and a desire to simplify their transition from systems using R-502 to those using R-404A or R-507. Copeland is prioritizing full qualification of R-404A and R-507, and our plans do not include the release of R-402A products for new equipment.

A major component of our developmental work has been our ongoing effort to minimize the proliferation of models that we manufacture. Much of Copeland's product line has always been cross-qualified; for example, qualified for both medium temperature R-12 and low temperature R-502 applications. To the maximum extent possible, we will continue this approach as we release products for use with the new refrigerants.

Our desire to adhere to a focused path is due to our ongoing commitment to bring to market only fully qualified products which continue to meet our standards for durability, reliability, safety, efficiency and performance. Doing so for even a small number of refrigerants represents a monumental challenge. Each model must undergo an extensive array of tests and qualifications to ensure the compatibility of the motor materials with the new refrigerants and lubricants to be used. Also, we demonstrate their long term durability and reliability and validate our capacity and efficiency projections to predict the performance data required by OEMs and contractors who will apply the products. Each model must also be submitted to a time and resource consuming battery of U.L. qualification tests over and above Copeland's own testing.

As contractors and end users attempt to retrofit new refrigerants in existing systems, Copeland has formalized its position on the use of a number of these refrigerants. Briefly, we have found R-401A, R-401B, R-402A and R-134a to be acceptable for field retrofit use providing you follow our guidelines.

Copeland's refrigerant strategy does not subscribe to "quick fix" or hasty near-term offerings for our customers. Rather, we are continuing to follow the long-term strategy we set forth and to deliver high-value, chlorine-free solutions, products and information for our customers and for our industry.

Copeland Product Offerings

Copeland was the first to bring to the industry R-134a products in October, 1992. This initial product offering was for Discus compressors in the three to 30 horsepower range. These compressors are charged from the factory with polyol ester oil and hold the same warranty as our current products.

Copeland followed these products with small hermetic compressors and condensing units in the 1/4 to one horsepower range for reach-in applications currently using R-12. These models were put in production in January, 1993 with excellent results to date. We have also taken the next step in releasing products for use with R-404A. The release schedule for HFC refrigerants follows in Table 4.

NOTE: The number of models includes all the various voltage combinations within each product family. Some compressors have up to five different voltage variations including both single and three-phase (where applicable).

Not all models in all families will be released on this timing. Copeland will not compromise when it comes to compressor reliability and durability.

Up to this point, our direction has been to offer HFC products necessary for the refrigeration industry. We believe only Copeland will have available the broad line of products to meet the needs of our industry. We will also continue work on our future HFC product offerings to take our customers into the next century. For more information on our chlorine-free product lines, please contact your Copeland District Sales Manager.

TABLE 4

Product Release Schedule for HFC Refrigerants

Refrigerant	Product Family	# of Models	Release Date
R-134a	Discus	31	Oct. 1992
R-134a	Copelaweld®	18	Jan. 1993
R-134a	Copelametic	4	Jan. 1994
R-404A	Discus	68	Oct. 1993
R-404A	Copelaweld	44	Jan. 1994
R-404A	Copelametic	56	June 1994
R-507	Discus	68	July 1994
R-507	Copelaweld	44	Sept. 1994
R-507	Copelametic	56	Sept./Oct. 1994

For more information, the following suggested reading materials are available from Copeland:

	Form No.
• Copeland Accepted Refrigerants/Lubricants	93-11
• Introduction to Refrigerant Mixtures	92-81
• New Refrigerant Smorgasbord	92-83
• Refrigeration Oils	AE-1248
• 134a Application Engineering Bulletin	AE-1295
• Refrigerant Changeover Guidelines	
- (CFC) R-12 to (HCFC) R-401A	93-02
- (CFC) R-12 to (HCFC) R-401B	93-03
- (CFC) R-12 to (HCFC) R-134a	93-04
- (CFC) R-502 to R-402A	93-05
- (CFC) R-502 to R-404A/R-507	94-15

Copeland Corporation
1675 W. Campbell Road
Sidney, Ohio 45365-0669

Form No. 94-13 R1 Revised 6-94
Supersedes 94-13

Printed in U.S.A.

Introduction to Refrigerant Mixtures

Table of Contents

Section 1
INTRODUCTION

The CFC/ozone depletion issue and resulting international regulations require the refrigeration and air conditioning industry world-wide to find new refrigerants to use in its equipment. Within a few years, CFCs will no longer be available to use in new systems and will be severely limited in availability for service use. Although exact timing is uncertain, HCFCs should be available for use in new systems for 10 to 12 years, and over 20 years for service.

Nature has not been kind enough to provide boundless numbers of chemicals which can be used for refrigerants. As a result, refrigerant manufacturers have been unsuccessful in developing single component replacement chemicals which meet all of the required or highly desirable characteristics for a widely used refrigerant. These requirements include no safety (such as flammability) or toxicity issues, environmental acceptability, chemical stability, materials compatibility, and good refrigeration cycle performance. Highly desirable characteristics include little or no major system component redesign or substantial increases in first cost over what is done today.

In order to achieve the requirements for acceptable refrigerants without incurring the enormous system and component changes which would occur with a change to an entirely different type of refrigerant (such as carbon dioxide, helium, or a very high pressure chemical), several refrigerant manufacturers have investigated zeotropic (also referred to as "non-azeotropic," a grammatically incorrect double negative) and near-azeotropic refrigerant mixtures ("Near-ARMs") of chemicals which can achieve all of the requirements while maintaining similar vapor pressure characteristics to those CFCs and HCFCs in common use today.

Zeotropes behave differently than single component and azeotropic refrigerant mixtures ("ARMs") during phase changes such as occur in a system's heat exchangers. In addition, changes in composition which might occur with zeotropes as a result of leaks and recharge can change system performance. It is important to verify that these differences in behavior do not seriously degrade either performance or reliability of the system.

The purpose of this manual is to provide a very brief introduction to the characteristics of mixtures and their appropriate lubricants and how they behave in refrigeration systems. It is by no means intended to be a comprehensive treatment of the subject. There is an enormous amount of excellent technical literature available on mixtures, some of which is listed in the Appendix, and you are encouraged to look to these sources for more detailed information.

Several of the figures used in this manual were adapted from Reference 2 listed in the Appendix.

Section 2
TERMINOLOGY AND EXAMPLES

The following definitions primarily deal with the way the described materials behave as a working fluid in a thermodynamic system. There may be more specific or technically complete definitions which deal with the chemistry, transport properties, or other aspects of these materials' composition or behavior which are unimportant in the present context.

2.1 PURE FLUID

A pure fluid is a single component fluid which does not change composition when boiling or condensing. A pure fluid is made up of one type of molecule.

EXAMPLES

CFC-11, CFC-12, HCFC-22, HFC-134a.

2.2 MIXTURE and BLEND

Technically, there is no difference in the terms mixture and blend. They include any fluids which are composed of more than one component (ie, more than one type of molecule). ARMs, Near-ARMs, and zeotropes (each is discussed below) are subsets of the larger group consisting of blends and mixtures.

The following definitions apply to dual component mixtures, but three ("ternary") or more component mixtures have similar but slightly more complicated characteristics. From a thermodynamic working fluid point of view, the number of components in the fluid has little or no effect.

2.2a AZEOTROPIC REFRIGERANT MIXTURE

An azeotropic refrigerant mixture (ARM) is a multi-component working fluid of specific composition which, at the azeotropic point, does not change composition when it evaporates or condenses since both components have exactly the same boiling temperature at that composition and pressure. It is made up of two or more types of molecules. In actuality, an ARM only exhibits such behavior at one temperature and pressure, but deviations from this behavior at other pressures are very slight and essentially undetectable.

ARMs are fairly complex mixtures whose properties depend upon molecular interactions which may result from polarity differences. They can be either minimum or maximum boiling point ARMs. Even more complicated behavior can occur with ARMs. However, factors such as these are relatively unimportant when considering their performance in a system. The most important factor is that they essentially behave as a pure substance when changing phase.

Examples of how minimum and maximum boiling point ARMs behave at their azeotropic and zeotropic composition ratios at constant pressure are shown in Figures 1 and 2. These figures show the "Dew Line" (the temperature at which droplets first appear as superheated vapor is cooled) and "Bubble Line" (the temperature at which bubbles first appear as subcooled liquid is heated) for mixtures at various fluid temperatures and concentrations for one pressure value. At concentration values away from the azeotropic value, the components ("A" and "B") have different boiling temperatures, and the liquid and vapor

FIGURE 1

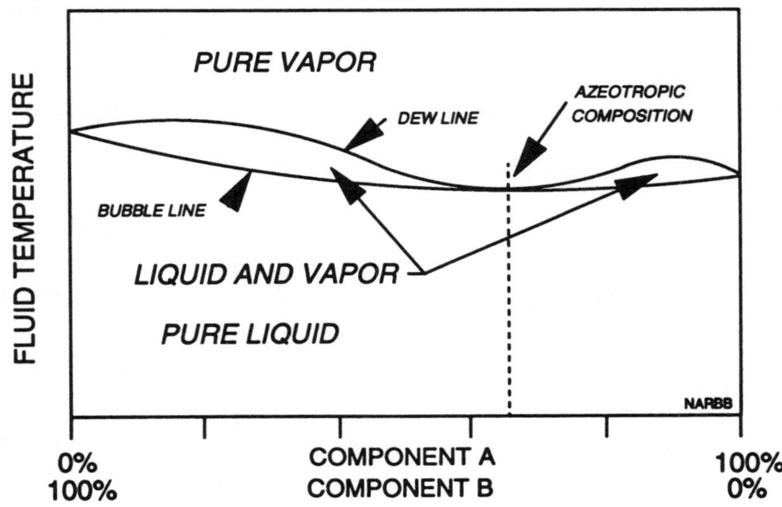

FIGURE 2

AZEOTROPIC MIXTURES

(MAXIMUM BOILING POINT AZEOTROPE)

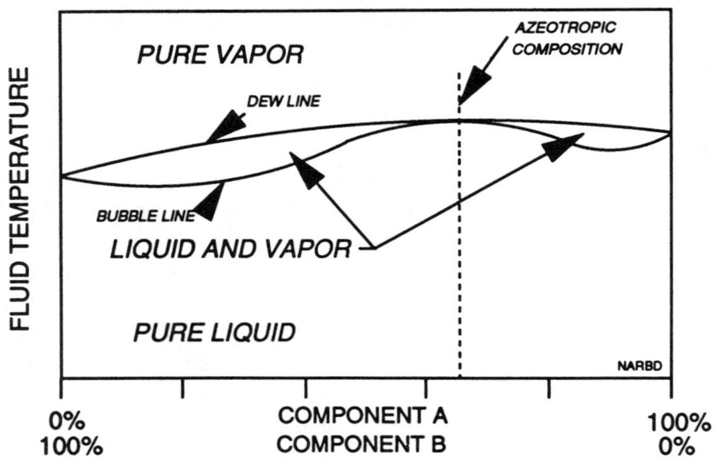

phases change percentage composition as the mixture evaporates or condenses.

EXAMPLES

R-502, an azeotrope of 48.8% HCFC-22 and 51.2% CFC-115 at -49 deg F., has lower discharge temperatures than does pure HCFC-22 for high compression ratio applications.

R-500, an azeotrope of 73.8% CFC-12 and 26.2% HFC-152a at -29 deg F, has approximately 15% more capacity than pure CFC-12 and is used to compensate for the capacity reduction arising from using a 60 hz. CFC-12 system on 50 hz.

R-507, a non-ozone depleting proprietary azeotrope from Allied-Signal, is 50% HFC-125 and 50% HFC-143a. It is a replacement for R-502.

2.2b ZEOTROPIC MIXTURE

A zeotrope is a working fluid with two or more components of different vapor pressure and boiling points whose liquid and vapor components have different compositions when the fluid evaporates or condenses. It is made up of two or more types of molecules. Under constant pressure, the evaporating and condensing temperatures change with composition. See Figure 3. This change in temperature during constant pressure phase change is called glide, and varies with the components used and their proportions. (See Section 3.5 on Glide.) The amount of glide exhibited by a particular zeotrope is a measure of its deviation from being an azeotrope. By definition, azeotropes have zero glide at their azeotropic point. At other conditions, however, they can exhibit glide.

EXAMPLES

CFC-12 is mixed with HCFC-22 to improve oil miscibility.

R-401A (MP39) is a mixture of HCFC-22, HFC-152a, and R-124 which closely approximates the vapor pressure and performance of CFC-12. (R-401A can also be considered a Near-azeotropic mixture.)

FIGURE 3

ZEOTROPIC MIXTURES

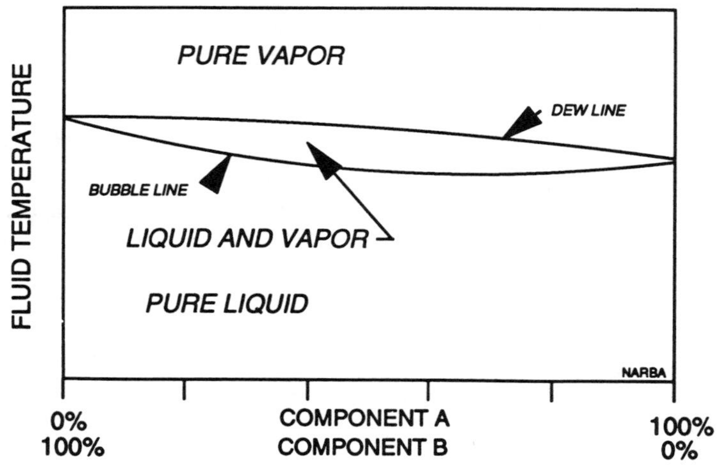

2.2c NEAR-AZEOTROPIC REFRIGERANT MIXTURE

A Near-ARM is a zeotropic fluid whose composition is such that it exhibits a "small" amount of glide. (See Section 3.5 on Glide.) Thus, "near-azeotropic" is a relative term. See Figure 4. Some researchers use a maximum glide temperature value of 10 deg F to distinguish Near-ARMs from zeotropes.

See Copeland's Refrigerant Smorgasbord chart for values of glide for several mixtures.

EXAMPLES

R-69l and R-69s are mixtures of HCFC-22, FC-218, and HC-290 (propane) from Rhone-Poulenc, which closely approximate the vapor pressure and performance characteristics of R-502.

R-404A is a proprietary ternary mixture from DuPont, which closely approximates the vapor pressure and performance characteristics of R-502.

R-402A (HP80) is a mixture of HCFC-22, HFC-125, and HC-290 (propane) which closely approximates the vapor pressure and performance characteristics of R-502.

FIGURE 4

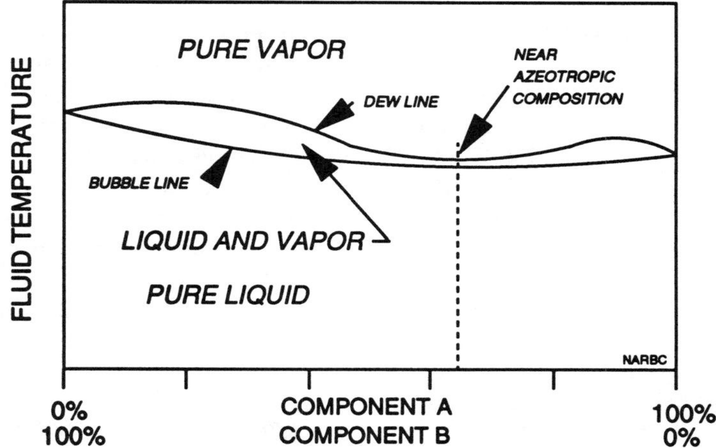

Section 3
CHARACTERISTICS OF MIXTURES

3.1 COMPONENTS

3.1a HOW ARE COMPONENTS CHOSEN?

Components are primarily chosen based on the final characteristics desired in the mixture. These characteristics could include vapor pressure, transport properties, lubricant and material compatibility, thermodynamic performance, cost, flammability, toxicity, stability, and environmental properties.

Availability of components to a particular chemical manufacturer may also be a factor in component selection.

3.1b HOW ARE PROPORTIONS OF COMPONENTS CHOSEN?

Proportions of components are chosen based on the exact characteristics desired in the final product. It is possible to modify the percentage composition of the components and alter such parameters as capacity, efficiency, discharge temperature, vapor pressure, etc. Of course, changing one parameter will likely change others as well. There may also be a need to balance proportions to guarantee that a given mixture cannot become flammable, toxic, or environmentally undesirable under any foreseeable circumstances, such as leakage.

In many cases, there are computer programs which can use the properties of the individual components and calculate the resulting mixture properties and performance with a fairly high degree of accuracy.

3.2 MIXTURE BEHAVIOR

3.2a HOW DO MIXTURES BEHAVE IN THE VAPOR STATE?

When a mixture (azeotropic or zeotropic) is entirely in the vapor state (ie, no liquid is present in the container) the composition is totally mixed and all properties are uniform throughout.

3.2b HOW DO MIXTURES BEHAVE IN THE LIQUID STATE?

When a mixture (azeotropic or zeotropic) is entirely in the liquid state (ie, no vapor is present in the container), the composition is totally mixed and all properties are uniform throughout.

3.2c HOW DO MIXTURES BEHAVE IN A LIQUID/VAPOR EQUILIBRIUM STATE (IE, WHERE BOTH LIQUID AND VAPOR ARE PRESENT) SUCH AS IN A PARTIALLY FULL SEALED DRUM OF THE MIXTURE?

In a partially full sealed container of a refrigerant mixture, the composition of the vapor and liquid phases can be different. The degree of difference depends upon whether the mixture is an azeotrope, zeotrope, or near-azeotrope.

3.2c1 AZEOTROPE

The percentage composition of an ARM will always be virtually the same in both the liquid and vapor phases, except its azeotropic mixture condition when its liquid and vapor components are identical in composition. At this condition each component has the same boiling point and each vaporizes in proportion to the amount present in the liquid phase. The resulting vapor is the same composition as the liquid. The same is true for the reverse (condensing) process. At other conditions, however, the percentage composition of liquid and vapor phases will be slightly different.

3.2c2 ZEOTROPE

The percentage composition of a zeotropic mixture may be substantially different in the liquid and vapor phases. This is because there is no unique boiling point for each component, and they will not vaporize at rates proportional to their composition in the liquid state. The higher vapor pressure component (with the lower boiling point) will vaporize faster than the lower vapor pressure component (with the higher boiling point), and result in percentage composition changes in both the liquid and vapor phases as vaporization progresses. The higher vapor pressure component will be in higher composition in the vapor phase above the liquid. This process is called "**fractionation**."

3.2c3 NEAR-AZEOTROPIC REFRIGERANT MIXTURES

The percentage composition of the liquid and vapor phases of a Near-ARM will be nearly identical, due to the very similar vapor pressure values of each component. Thus, a Near-ARM behaves essentially the same as an ARM from this standpoint.

3.3 WHAT HAPPENS TO MIXTURE COMPOSITION DURING SYSTEM CHARGING?

Depending on how system charging is performed (ie, with vapor or liquid being removed from the cylinder), the refrigerant may change phase in the cylinder.

Since pure fluids and ARMs (except as discussed in Section 3.2) do not change composition with changes in phase, there is no change in composition with these materials during system charging with vapor or liquid.

On the other hand vapor charging with a zeotropic mixture can result in significant composition changes due to fractionation of the components as discussed in Section 3.2c2.

If an entire cylinder of refrigerant is used to charge a system, then the composition change which occurs during the charging process has no effect since the entire contents of the cylinder will go into the system.

However, if only part of a cylinder of a zeotropic refrigerant is vapor charged into a system, the vapor composition can change substantially during the charging process. As a result, only liquid charging (ie, what leaves cylinder) should be used for zeotropes unless the entire cylinder is to be used for one system. Of course, proper protection against liquid ingestion by the compressor must be provided. This could be in the form of an accumulator-type device which meters liquid into the suction side of the system. Another choice is the "Dial-a-Charge" type of charging system, which takes a measured amount of liquid from the cylinder and puts all of it into the system.

Since Near-ARMs are actually zeotropes, they also result in composition changes during charging, but to a much smaller extent than occurs with zeotropes. When charging Near-ARM refrigerants, liquid (from the cylinder) should be used to avoid composition changes (unless the entire contents is going into one system), and the last few percent of the contents of a cylinder should not be used as this is when composition changes can be the greatest.

Guidelines for charging procedures and how much of cylinder's refrigerant to use during charging will be provided by the refrigerant manufacturers.

3.4 HOW DO MIXTURES BEHAVE DURING CHANGE OF PHASE (IE, BOILING OR CONDENSING)?

Azeotropes, as described above, essentially behave as a pure material during boiling and condensing, and do not appreciably change percentage composition.

Zeotropes, on the other hand, do not behave as a pure material during boiling and condensing, and the percentage composition of the liquid and vapor phases can be different. This characteristic can have a significant effect on the composition of the refrigerant left in the system after a leak in the vapor-containing region of a system, and to the subsequent composition after the leaked refrigerant has been replaced.

The magnitude of this effect depends strongly upon how much the mixture departs from being an ARM. (See Section 3.5 on "Glide.")

Leakage scenarios are discussed in Section 3.6.

3.5 WHAT IS TEMPERATURE GLIDE?

Figure 5 shows how a zeotropic two-component mixture behaves during change of phase at various concentrations for a constant pressure. As subcooled liquid is heated, the higher vapor pressure component eventually reaches its boiling point and begins to form vapor. This condition is called the "Bubble Point," and is the temperature at which bubbles begin to appear. The vapor is rich with the high vapor pressure component. As the temperature increases, more and more of the high vapor pressure component vaporizes, reducing its composition in the liquid phase. At the same time, the lower vapor pressure component eventually reaches its boiling point and begins to vaporize. Finally, the high vapor pressure component is fully evaporated and all that is left is the low vapor pressure component which, as the last drop evaporates, results in establishment of the "Dew Point." This is the temperature at which liquid begins to appear when the zeotropic vapor is cooled. The difference between the dew point and bubble point temperatures is known as "temperature glide." It varies with percentage composition of components as well as pressure.

The practical effect of glide in heat exchangers is that as the refrigerant mixture flows through the tubing at constant pressure, the evaporating (or boiling) temperature will change as the composition of the liquid and vapor phases change. Thus, a constant evaporating or condensing temperature process does not occur, even with constant pressure.

FIGURE 5

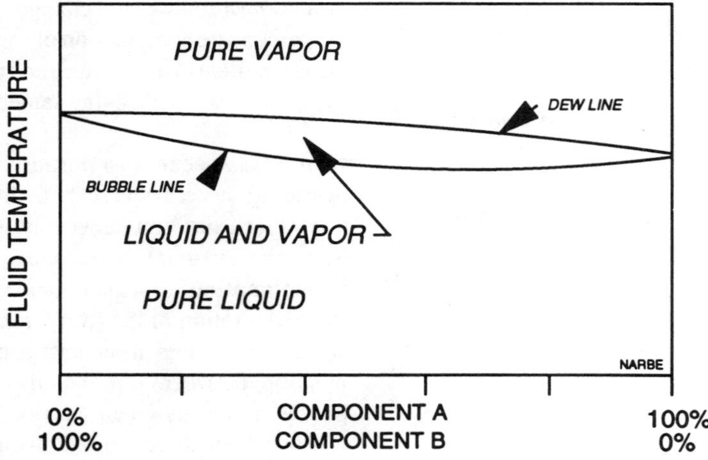

3.5a HOW LARGE A VALUE CAN GLIDE HAVE AND WHAT IS ITS EFFECT?

The amount of glide varies with the pressure and percentage composition of each component present in the mixture. Glide can vary from an imperceptible amount with a Near-ARM to ten or more degrees F with a zeotrope. Many researchers consider a Near-ARM to have glide less than ten degrees F. The glide of many mixtures is given in Copeland's Refrigerant Smorgasbord chart.

FIGURE 6
P-H DIAGRAM
ZEOTROPIC MIXTURES

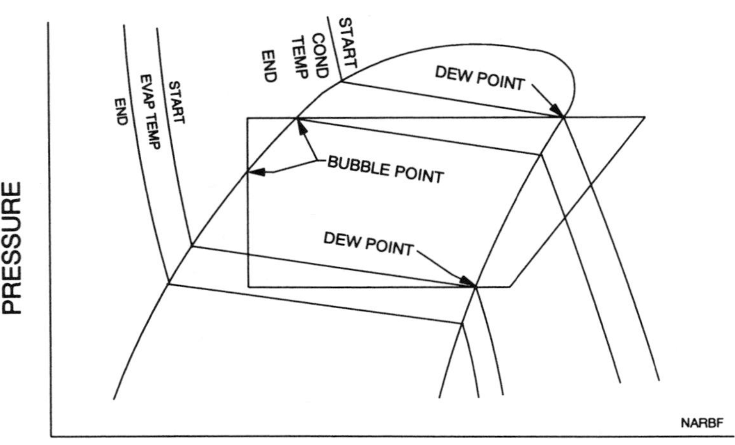

ENTHALPY

3.5b HOW IS GLIDE SIMILAR TO THE CHANGES IN EVAPORATING AND CONDENSING TEMPERATURE WHICH OCCUR IN HEAT EXCHANGERS WITH PURE OR AZEOTROPIC FLUIDS WITH PRESSURE DROPS?

In any heat exchanger, flow of refrigerant through the tubing results in a pressure drop from the entrance to the exit. Consequently, since the pressure at which the phase change is occurring is decreasing along the length of the heat exchanger, the evaporating or condensing temperature will decrease as the saturated refrigerant moves through the heat exchanger. Of course, the amount of change in evaporating or condensing temperature depends upon the magnitude of the pressure drop, but it can be several degrees. The change in evaporating and condensing temperature which occurs with today's pure fluids in many systems is similar to that which occurs with Near-ARMs due to glide as they pass through the heat exchangers.

A schematic example of how glide with a zeotrope affects temperatures in an evaporator and condenser in a system is shown in the Pressure-Enthalpy diagram in Figure 6. As a result of the composition change as the refrigerant flows through the heat exchangers the evaporating and condensing temperatures decrease. Of course, with Near-ARMs the temperature change is very slight and probably undetectable.

As a practical matter, the pressure drop in the evaporator tends to counteract the temperature glide, resulting in the actual glide being less than would be expected at constant pressure conditions. The effects are additive in the condenser.

3.6 WHAT HAPPENS TO REFRIGERANT COMPOSITION DURING A LEAK?

3.6a SINGLE COMPONENT REFRIGERANT

There is no change in percentage composition of the refrigerant.

3.6b AZEOTROPIC REFRIGERANT

There is virtually no change in percentage composition of the refrigerant.

3.6c ZEOTROPIC MIXTURE REFRIGERANT

If a leak occurs in a portion of an operating system where only vapor is present (such as the compressor discharge or suction line), the system's refrigerant composition will not change since the percentage composition of the vapor is identical to the mixture and each component will leak at the same rate.

If a leak occurs in a portion of an operating system where only liquid (such as in the liquid line) is present, the composition will not change since the percentage composition of the liquid is identical to the mixture and each component will leak at the same rate.

If a leak occurs in a portion of an operating system where both liquid and vapor exist simultaneously (such as in the evaporator or condenser), **"fractionation"** (unequal evaporation or condensation of the refrigerant resulting in a change in percentage composition between liquid and vapor phases as discussed in Section 3.2) will occur and there can be a change in percentage composition of the refrigerant left in the system. For example, if a leak occurs in the two-phase portion of the evaporator and only vapor leaks out, the vapor will be richer in the higher vapor pressure component, resulting in a change in the percentage composition of the remaining refrigerant in the system. If the system is recharged with the original composition, the mixture in the system can never get back to the original composition, and system performance (such as capacity or efficiency) may change to some degree. Repeated leak and recharge cycles will result in additional change. However, in most operating systems where two phases are present, turbulent mixing occurs and liquid will leak along with the vapor which minimizes the effect the vapor leakage effect.

It is important to keep in mind that to have a change in composition in an operating system, the leak must occur in a portion of the system where both liquid and vapor phases exist simultaneously, and only vapor leaks out.

While a system is off, there will be parts of the system where pure vapor exists and parts where pure liquid exists, and these locations can change with varying environmental conditions. Since the composition of the liquid and vapor phases will be different for a zeotrope in liquid-vapor equilibrium (as discussed in Section 3.2c), a leak in the area where vapor alone is present can result in a composition change in the system. Such a leak could be significant during the long wintertime off cycle of an air conditioning system, or during long periods of non-use for any system.

The effect of such leaks with **near-zeotropes** is much less due to the fact that the percentage composition difference between the liquid and vapor phases is very small. Theoretical leakage effect calculations (verified by initial laboratory testing) show that the leakage effects on performance (capacity and efficiency) with Near-ARMs are undetectable, even with several repeated leak and recharge cycles.

Section 4
APPENDIX

Below is a very brief listing of sources of information regarding refrigerant mixtures. Each of them contains many additional references.

1. **ADVANCES IN NONAZEOTROPIC MIXTURE REFRIGERANTS FOR HEAT PUMPS**, A Collection of Papers from the ASHRAE Annual Meeting at Honolulu, Hawaii, in June, 1985. ASHRAE Technical Bulletin; American Society of Heating, Refrigerating, and Air-Conditioning Engineers, Inc.

2. **THE ABCs OF NARBs (NONAZEOTROPIC REFRIGERANT BLENDS)**, by Theodore Atwood, Senior Research Engineer, Allied Chemical, Buffalo, New York. (Published in Number 1 (above)).

3. **THE CHARACTERISTICS OF FLUID MIXTURES AND THEIR UTILIZATION IN VAPOR COMRESSION REFRIGERATION SYSTEMS**, by U. W. Schulz, Engineer, Carrier Corporation, Syracuse, New York. (Published in Number 1 (above)).

4. **THE ADVANTAGES OF NON-AZEOTROPIC REFRIGERANT MIXTURES FOR HEAT PUMP APPLICATION**, by H. Kruse. **Int. J. of Refrigeration**, Vol. 4, No. 3, pp. 119-125, 1981.

Form No. 92-81 R2
Supersedes Form No. 92-81 R1

Printed in U.S.A.

April 1994

Copeland Corporation
1675 W. Campbell Road
Sidney, Ohio 45365-0669

The Demand Cooling Report

HCFC-22 Low Temperature Comparison

Summary

Copelametic® semi-hermetic Discus® compressors with Demand Cooling™ have superior energy efficiency as compared to internally compounded two-stage compressors, when measured under conditions similar to those encountered in commercial applications in North America.

Because energy efficiency relates directly to energy costs, Copelametic Discus compressors with Demand Cooling are less expensive to operate in commercial applications than internally compounded two-stage compressors.

NOTE: this report represents Copeland Corporation's analysis based on published competitive data and rigorous internal research and testing.

Background

The issue of CFC refrigerants depleting the ozone layer in the earth's atmosphere has resulted in the timed obsolescence of CFC-12 and CFC-502 refrigerants. These refrigerants are used in the refrigeration and air conditioning industry in low to medium temperature applications. Until non-ozone depleting HFC refrigerants are developed, tested, and approved, HCFC-22 is a suitable low temperature refrigerant in a properly designed and controlled refrigeration system. HCFC-22 has a lower ozone depletion potential than the CFC refrigerants.

However, under some operating conditions HCFC-22 has high discharge temperatures. These high discharge temperatures can degrade the long-term stability of refrigeration oil and result in poor lubrication and excessive wear of internal parts, thus causing early compressor failures.

Demand Cooling was developed by Copeland Corporation to allow the use of HCFC-22 without exposure to overheating problems. This report will show that Demand Cooling also *contributes to energy efficiency* when compared to other approaches to using HCFC-22 for low temperature applications.

The purpose of this report is to compare the energy efficiency of two methods of using HCFC-22 in low temperature systems, Copelametic Discus compressors with Demand Cooling and internally compounded two-stage compressors equipped with a subcooler (economizer). It is offered as an objective comparison for refrigeration professsionals.

Demand Cooling Compressor

Demand Cooling is an advanced method of controlling discharge temperatures used in R-22 low temperature Copeland Discus compressors. Demand Cooling is based on an electronic control system which monitors the compressor discharge temperature and injects saturated refrigerant directly into the compressor body as required. This provides the supplemental cooling needed to prevent the overheating of the compressor in low temperature refrigeration systems. Figure 1 shows a system block diagram of a Copelametic Discus compressor with Demand Cooling. For additional information, see Copeland Application Engineering Bulletin 1287.

Figure 1

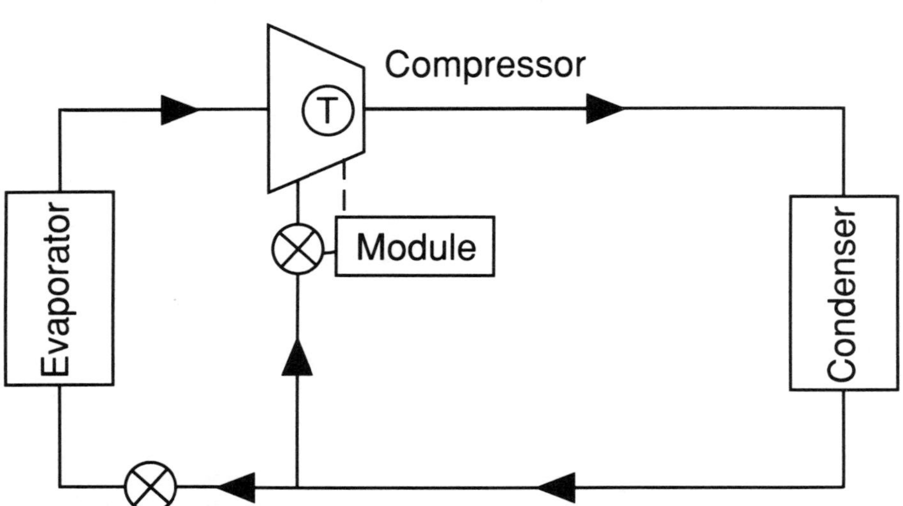

Figure 2

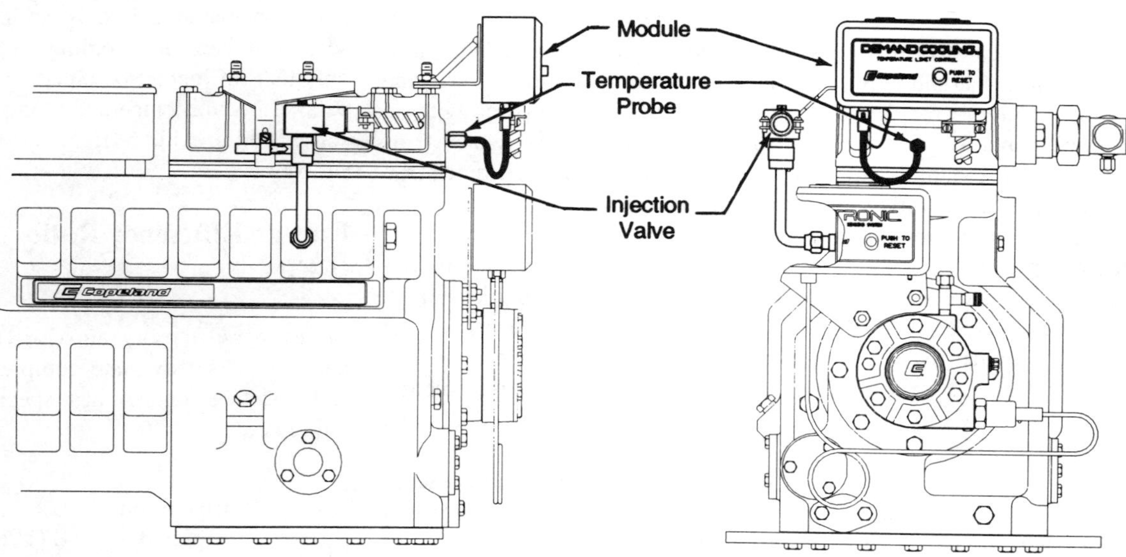

Figure 2 shows a Copelametic Discus compressor equipped with Demand Cooling.

Demand Cooling consists of three major components:

- **Temperature Probe** - Mounted in cylinder head; monitors compressor discharge temperature.
- **Solid State Control Module** - Monitors the signal from probe and sends a signal to actuate the injection valve at the appropriate discharge temperature.
- **Injection Valve** - Responds to signal from module and injects saturated refrigerant into the compressor.

Internally Compounded Two-Stage Compressors

Internally compounded two-stage compressors have both the low and high stages built into one compressor body. Refrigerant is injected between the stages to cool the low-stage discharge vapor to an acceptable temperature level entering the high stage. Figure 3 shows a simple system diagram of an internally compounded two-stage compressor. The subcooler (economizer) is normally located at the compressor.

Figure 3

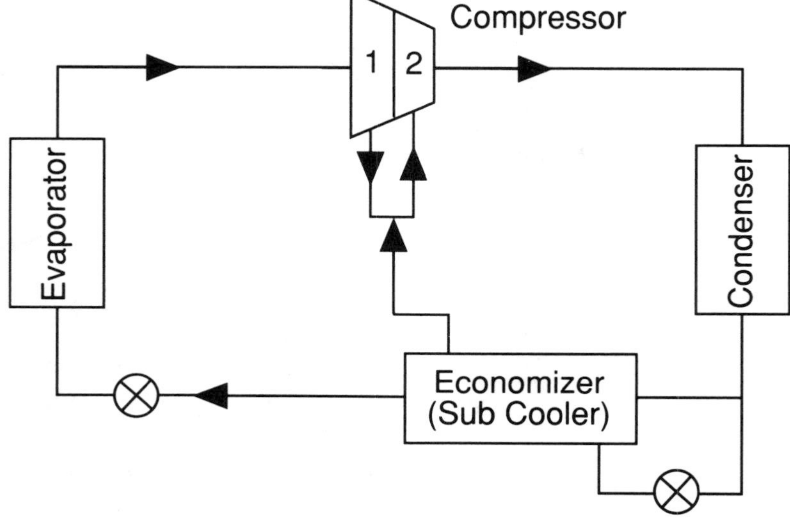

Subcooler Usage

A subcooler is a heat exchanger designed to reduce the liquid temperature below the saturation temperature. This causes an increase in system efficiency by providing part of the refrigeration at a higher evaporating temperature. The internally compounded two-stage compressors examined in this study rely on a subcooler to produce liquid refrigerant at 40°F. When subcooling is provided by a higher evaporating temperature than the application, it can enhance system performance and efficiency.

Copelametic Discus compressors with Demand Cooling must have a separate mechanical subcooler condensing unit or a source of refrigeration to provide equivalent liquid temperatures. The power required to provide this subcooling is a factor in the energy efficiency ratio (EER) rating of a compressor.

To obtain accurate efficiency comparisons, the two competing compressor systems were analyzed under similar subcooling conditions. First, the two systems were compared with no subcooling. Second, the two systems were compared with 40°F liquid at the expansion valve.

In single compressor applications, it is easier to provide 40°F liquid with an internally compounded two-stage compressor because the economizer is required to provide supplemental cooling between the two stages. Copelametic Discus compressors with Demand Cooling require either a separate mechanical subcooling unit or an economizer (subcooler) utilizing refrigerant piped from another system. Additional power is required and must be accounted for in any comparison. The additional power required has been included in this comparison.

In multiple-parallel compressor systems, Copelametic Discus compressors with Demand Cooling require only that refrigerant be piped from a parallel medium temperature compressor rack to provide refrigerant to the subcooler.

Energy Efficiency Ratio (EER)

The energy efficiency ratio (EER) is a measure of steady state compressor and system efficiency at a specified rating point.

$$\text{EER} = \frac{\text{Refrigeration Supplied}}{\text{Power Input}} = \frac{\text{BTU/Hr.}}{\text{Watts}}$$

Figure 4 shows the Energy Efficiency Ratio (EER) plotted against condensing temperature and/or ambient air temperature.

Figure 4

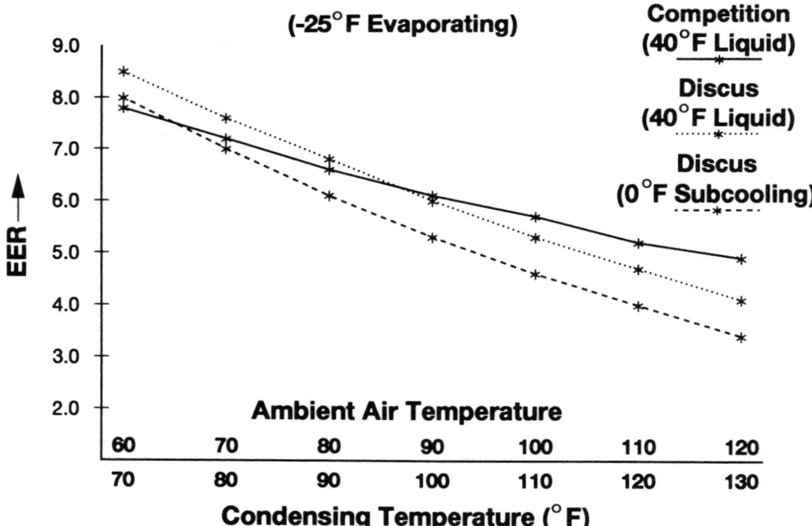

Figure 5

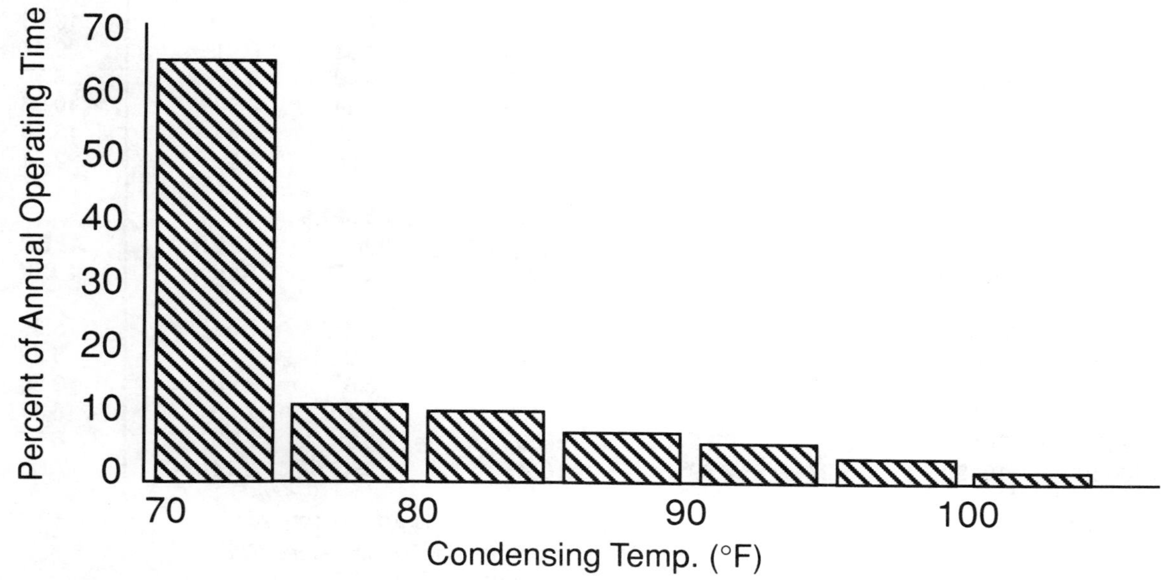

The solid line represents internally compounded two-stage compressors, economized to 40°F liquid temperature. The dashed line represents Copelametic "Discus" compressors with Demand Cooling with no subcooling. Looking at these two lines only, the crossover occurs at approximately 75°F condensing temperature—in other words, Demand Cooling compressors are more efficient than internally compounded two-stage compressors at 75°F condensing temperature and below.

The dotted line represents Copelametic Discus compressors with Demand Cooling economized to 40°F liquid temperature. In this case, the crossover occurs at approximately 95°F condensing temperature. *Thus, Demand Cooling is more efficient at 95°F condensing temperature and below.*

Annual Energy Efficiency Ratio (AEER)

In order to properly compare the relative energy efficiency of compressor systems, it is essential to duplicate the operating conditions under which the compressors are expected to perform—specifically their condensing ambient temperatures. It is important to understand not only the condensing temperatures which compressors are subject to, but also the relative time spent running at each temperature range.

The Energy Efficiency Ratio (EER) used to show energy efficiency in Figure 4 is simply a "snap shot" measurement at a single operating temperature. A better method to compare relative energy efficiencies is the Annual Energy Efficiency Ratio (AEER). AEER is a measure of the refrigeration supplied (BTU) on an annual basis divided by the annual energy consumed. The AEER takes into account the variations in the ambient air temperature throughout the year and the corresponding changes in condensing temperature. AEER is a calculation based on the number of hours per year that a compressor system operates at each condensing temperature.

Figure 5 is a typical U.S. condensing temperature profile—ambient temperatures plotted against the percentage of time spent at each temperature (weather data obtained from the U.S. Commerce Department). This chart illustrates that most of the time systems are operating at condensing temperatures of 70° or less.

Figure 6 AEER Calculation Based On St. Louis Weather Data

Copeland Model	No Liquid Subcooling Design RatingPoint Capacity	EER	AEER Rating	COMPETITIVE MODELS Design Rating Point Capacity	EER	AEER Rating	AEER % Diff
2DB3-0600	19300	4.82	7.44	19170	4.50	6.73	10.55
3DB3-0750	27300	4.83	7.56	22910	4.62	6.91	9.41
3DF3-0900	32500	4.74	7.44	31040	4.38	6.87	8.30
4DT3-2200	59900	4.61	7.29	55505	4.44	6.57	10.96
4DT3-2200	59900	4.61	7.29	62620	4.38	6.44	13.20
6DT3-3000	89500	4.57	7.34	80380	4.08	5.99	22.54

Copeland Model	Liquid Temperature 40°F Design Rating Point Capacity	EER	AEER Rating	COMPETITIVE MODELS Design Rating Point Capacity	EER	AEER Rating	AEER % Diff
2DB3-0600	24840	5.6	7.99	24672	5.8	7.57	5.55
3DB3-0750	35140	5.57	8.18	29483	5.9	7.77	5.28
3DF3-0900	41830	5.48	7.99	39945	5.6	7.72	3.50
4DT3-2200	77090	5.31	7.85	71436	5.7	7.38	6.37
4DT3-2200	77090	5.31	7.85	80593	5.6	7.23	8.58
6DT3-3000	115190	5.27	7.89	10345	35.3	6.74	17.06

DESIGN RATING POINT
Evaporator Temperature -25°F
Condensing Temperature 110°F
Return Gas'Temperature 65°F
Liquid Temperature:
Suitable Subcooler Available
0°F Subcooling
40°F Liquid Temperature
Ambient Air Temperature 95°F

AEER CALCULATION ASSUMPTIONS
Minimum Condensing Temperature 70°F
Constant Condenser TD 10°F
Evaporator Temperature -25°F
Suitable Subcooler Available

This issue is important since the energy efficiency of the alternate compressor designs vary with ambient temperature (as shown in Figure 4).

Performance Comparisons

The chart above (Figure 6) is a comparison of energy efficiencies of Demand Cooling versus internally compounded two-stage compressors based on St. Louis, Missouri weather data. Appendix A contains similar charts for 13 cities covering the United States.

This chart shows that, when compared with internally compounded two-stage compressors, Copelametic Discus compressors with Demand Cooling have *higher* EER ratings, as well as *higher* AEER ratings, when measured at 0°F subcooling (top half of Figure 6).

More importantly, at 40°F liquid temperature (bottom half of Figure 6), the internally compounded two-stage compressor has a slightly higher EER at design conditions; however, a relatively small percentage of time is spent running at these high temperatures. Copelametic Discus compressors with Demand Cooling have a significantly higher AEER rating than the internally compounded two-stage compressor because of their significantly higher efficiency at low condensing temperatures. Since the AEER rating is a better indicator of performance under actual conditions, the Copelametic Discus compressor with Demand Cooling will be less expensive to operate in commercial applications.

The chart on the next page (Figure 7) shows similar data for 13 cities in the U.S.

Column 1 shows the amount of time that a compressor system operates at 85°F or lower ambient temperatures. El Paso, Texas, has the lowest percentage; yet, even in El Paso, the ambient temperature is 85°F or lower a full 85.5% of the time. This is significant because Demand Cooling is more efficient than internally compounded two-stage compressors in these lower temperature ranges (see Figure 4).

Figure 7

Demand Cooling Versus Internally Compounded Two-Stage

City	% Time 85°F Amb. or Lower	Advantage Copeland Demand Cooling Liquid @ Sat. Cond. Temp. Min	Max	Liquid @ 40°F Min	Max
Atlanta, GA	93.1%	8.5%	22.1%	3.5%	16.5%
Boston, MA	97.9%	8.1%	23.5%	3.6%	18.8%
Chicago, IL	96.0%	8.2%	23.1%	3.5%	18.2%
Denver, CO	96.0%	8.1%	23.4%	3.5%	18.0%
El Paso, TX	85.5%	8.7%	21.5%	3.3%	15.5%
Galveston, TX	89.6%	9.1%	20.6%	3.1%	14.1%
Los Angeles, CA	99.5%	8.2%	23.2%	3.7%	18.4%
Miami, FL	88.4%	8.8%	18.9%	2.8%	11.5%
Minneapolis, MN	97.6%	8.1%	23.5%	3.6%	18.8%
Reno, NV	95.4%	8.1%	23.6%	3.5%	18.9%
San Francisco, CA	99.7%	7.9%	24.4%	3.6%	20.1%
Seattle, WA	99.6%	7.9%	24.4%	3.6%	20.3%
St. Louis, MO	92.4%	8.3%	22.5%	3.5%	17.0%

Figure 7 shows that various Copelametic Discus compressors with Demand Cooling have AEER ratings that range from 7.9% to 24.4% higher than internally compounded two-stage compressors with no subcooling applied. When subcooling to 40°F is applied, various Copelametic Discus compressors with Demand Cooling have AEER ratings that range from 2.8% to 20.3% higher than internally compounded two-stage compressors.

Equal Efficiency Point

Copelametic Discus compressors with Demand Cooling, with only 10°F liquid subcooling at the expansion valve, will have an AEER rating equal to an internally compounded two-stage compressor that is economized to 40°F liquid temperature. See Figure 8.

At 110°F condensing temperature, the 10°F ambient liquid subcooling results in a liquid temperature of 100°F for the Demand Cooling system. Typical supermarket indoor ambient design conditions of 75°FDB/55% RH and 110°F condensing temperature,

Figure 8

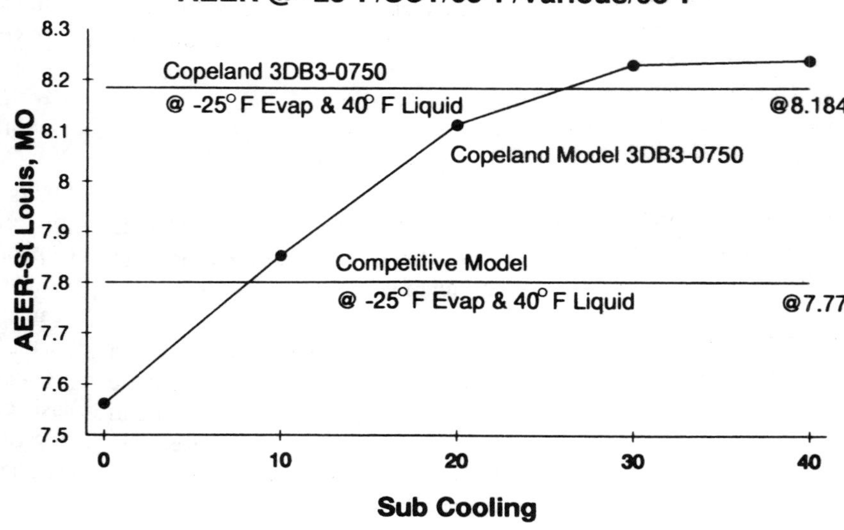

usually provide as much as 10°F of subcooling by oversizing the condenser. Each system is given this 10°F of *free* subcooling. Even with insulated liquid lines, some heat transfer always occurs. With an internally compounded two-stage system economized to 40°F, heat will be added to the liquid line causing the liquid temperature to rise. With a Demand Cooling system, with 100°F liquid, heat is removed and the actual liquid temperature drops. Therefore, the systems will have equal efficiencies with less subcooling provided by external means. And, as ambient temperatures increase, Demand Cooling will improve because of the large difference between 40° liquid and high ambients.

Conclusions

Copelametic Discus compressors with Demand Cooling, at equivalent operating conditions, will have a higher AEER rating than internally compounded two-stage compressors in all instances, translating into a lower annual operating cost.

Copelametic Discus compressors with Demand Cooling, at equivalent operating conditions, will have an EER rating higher than internally compounded two-stage compressors when the saturated condensing temperature is 95°F or lower (85°F ambient air temperature.)

Copelametic Discus compressors using Demand Cooling with 10°F ambient liquid subcooling will have an EER rating that is equivalent to a internally compounded two-stage compressor that is economized to 40°F liquid.

Figure 9

	0°F Subcooling	Economized 40° Liquid
Evaporating temp.	-25°F	-25°F
Condensing temp.	110°F	110°F
Return gas temp.	65°F	65°F
Subcooling Amount	0°F	70°F
Liquid temp.	110°F	40°F
Ambient air over	95°F	95°F

Test Conditions

The test results shown in the chart in Figure 6 were determined under the following conditions:

- AEER comparison is based on published data at the same rating conditions.
- Capacity/power adjustment factors for Copelametic Discus compressors with Demand Cooling from Appendix B.
- Capacity adjustment factors for internally compounded two-stage compressors from Appendix B.
- Minimum condensing temperature is 70°F.
- Return gas temperature is 65°F.
- Condenser TD = 10°F (constant).
- Suitable subcooling is available for Copelametic Discus compressors with Demand Cooling.
- Weather data from the U.S. Department of Commerce.

The EER ratings shown in the chart in Figure 6 were based on the conditions in Figure 9.

Figure 10, on the next page, shows a block diagram of the Copelametic Discus compressor with Demand Cooling with a subcooler. Refer to Figure 3 for a block diagram of the internally compounded two-stage compressor with subcooler. The return gas temperature is 65°F, and the liquid temperature has been economized to 40°F in both cases.

Competitive Claims

Competitive claims published in 1991 attempted to compare the relative energy efficiencies of Demand Cooling vs. internally compounded two-stage compressors. These claims were misleading because:

- It compared compressors based on displacement rather than on capacities.
- Internally compounded two-stage compressors were rated with 40°F liquid at the liquid control device (expansion valve) while the Copelametic Discus compressors with Demand Cooling were rated with 0°F subcooling.

Figure 11 shows the information as presented by the competition. Copelametic Discus Demand Cooling models are compared side by side against the competitive models based on the displacement in CFH. Compressors should be compared on the basis of their capacity, the true measure of the refrigeration that will be supplied.

Figure 10

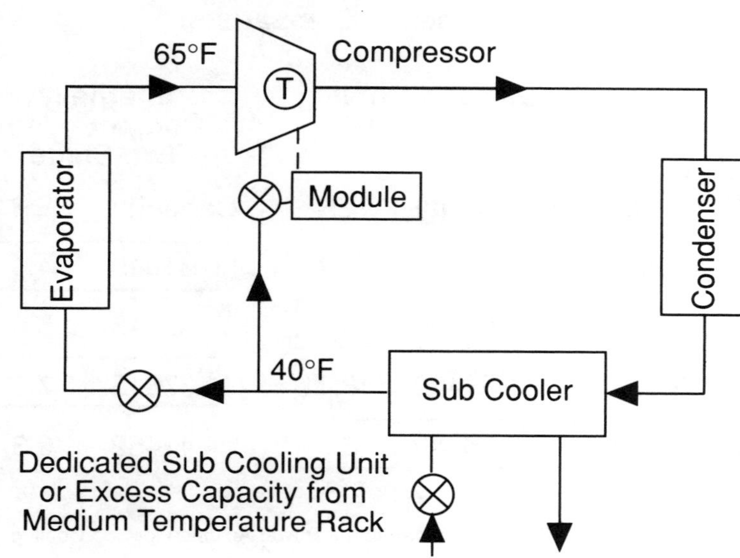

The data in Figure 11 is based on two different rating points. Copelametic Discus Demand Cooling models are rated and published using 0° subcooling where liquid temperature is equal to condensing temperature at the expansion valve. The competition publishes data with adequate subcooling to provide 40°F liquid temperature at the expansion valve. By comparing data based on two different operating conditions, the EER and capacity comparisons are misleading.

Figure 12 shows the performance comparison between a Model 3DS3-1000 Copelametic Discus compressor, and a competitive internally compounded two-stage compressor, comparably sized based on capacity. The unboxed

Figure 11

Demand Cooling Versus Competition

	Demand Cooling			Competition		
Model	CFH	HCFC 22 Capacity	EER	CFH	HCFC 22 Capacity	EER
2DF3-0300	904	12600	4.5			
2DL3-0400	1008	15200	4.6			
2DA3-0600	1135	17700	4.6			
2DB3-0600	1191	19300	4.8			
3DA3-0600	1375	22200	4.7	1434	24670	5.77
3DB3-0750	1620	27300	4.8	1680	29480	6.05
3DF3-0900	1915	32500	4.7			
3DS3-1000	2120	35700	4.7	2226	39945	5.60
4DA3-1000	2380	36600	4.5			
4DL3-1500	3020	49300	4.5			
4DT3-2200	3603	59900	4.6	4098	71440	5.72
6DL3-2700	4530	74700	4.6	4524	80590	5.64
6DT3-3000	5404	89500	4.6	5940	103450	5.40
Rating Point		-25/110/65/110/95			-25/110/65/40/95	

(T evap/T con/T ret gas/ T liquid/T ambient)

ratings are the published data where the rating points are not equal. Equivalent rating points were calculated using the adjustment factors for capacity and/or power input so that comparisons are accurate.

The calculated ratings (boxed) for the Copelametic Discus compressors have taken the additional subcooling power into account. The calculated ratings derive from adjustments based on refrigerant properties. We compare the two compressors at 70°F condensing temperature as well as the 110°F condensing temperature.

As the chart in Figure 12 shows, Copelametic Discus compressors with Demand Cooling have superior performance.

Appendices

Appendix A demonstrates a summary of AEER comparisons between Copelametic Discus compressors and internally compounded two-stage compressors for 13 cities across the nation. In addition, this appendix provides detailed comparison imformation for each of these major metropolitan areas.

Appendix B contains Demand Cooling performance factors that correct to 40°F liquid temperatures.

Figure 12

Demand Cooling Vs. Competitive Model

Performance Comparison

	Demand Cooling 3DS3-1000		Internally Compounded Two-Stage	
Rating Point	**Capacity**	**EER**	**Capacity**	**EER**
-25/110/65/110	35700	4.7	31040	4.4
-25/110/65/40	45950	5.4	39945	5.6
-25/70/65/70	51400	8.1	37615	7.5
-25/70/65/40	56640	8.6	41452	8.3

Rating = T evap/ T cond/ T ret gas/ T liquid
Copeland Rating at 40°F Liquid Temperature - Power Adjusted for Sub Cooling

APPENDIX A

Summary AEER
Percent Time Spent at Various Temperature Ranges

Ambient Air Temp.°F	60F	62F	67F	72F	77F	82F	87F	92F	97F	102F	
Condensing Temp.°F	70F	72F	77F	82F	87F	92F	97F	102F	107F	112F	
City/State											**TOTAL**
Atlanta,Ga.	42.4%	9.4%	10.6%	13.5%	10.1%	7.1%	4.6%	2.0%	0.3%		100.0%
Boston,Ma.	64.0%	9.2%	9.3%	7.7%	4.9%	2.8%	1.4%	0.4%	0.1%		99.8%
Chicago,Il.	60.5%	7.4%	8.8%	8.7%	6.4%	4.2%	2.5%	1.2%	0.3%		00.0%
Denver,Co.	64.2%	8.9%	7.8%	6.3%	5.0%	3.8%	2.7%	1.2%	0.1%		100.0%
El Paso,Tx.	37.7%	9.1%	9.6%	10.6%	10.0%	8.5%	6.8%	4.9%	2.3%	0.5%	100.0%
Galveston,Tx.	21.7%	11.4%	11.9%	11.5%	13.0%	20.1%	9.7%	0.7%			100.0%
Los Angeles,Ca.	40.0%	25.0%	18.9%	10.0%	4.3%	1.3%	0.%	0.1%			99.9%
Miami,Fl.	6.0%	5.1%	9.2%	19.5%	28.1%	20.5%	10.1%	1.4%			99.9%
Minneapolis,Mn.	66.0%	7.9%	7.9%	7.1%	5.3%	3.4%	1.3%	0.6%	0.1%		100.0%
Reno,Nv.	70.7%	6.5%	5.4%	4.8%	4.2%	3.8%	2.8%	1.4%	0.4%		100.0%
San Francisco,Ca.	72.9%	14.4%	7.6%	3.3%	1.1%	0.4%	0.2%				99.9%
Seattle,Wa.	80.9%	8.6%	5.1%	2.9%	1.4%	0.7%	0.4%				100.0%
St. Louis,Mo.	52.0%	7.4%	8.3%	9.4%	8.7%	6.6%	4.2%	2.3%	0.7%	0.2%	99.8%

AEER Calculation Based On Atlanta Weather Data

Copeland Model	No Liquid Subcooling Design Rating Point Capacity	EER	AEER Rating	COMPETITIVE MODELS Design Rating Point Capacity	EER	AEER Rating	AEER % Diff
2DB3-0600	19300	4.82	7.376	9170	4.5	6.673	10.53
3DB3-0750	27300	4.83	7.504	22910	4.62	6.852	9.52
3DF3-0900	32500	4.74	7.38	31040	4.38	6.797	8.58
4DT3-2200	59900	4.61	7.217	55505	4.44	6.511	10.84
4DT3-2200	59900	4.61	7.217	62620	4.38	6.387	13.00
6DT3-3000	89500	4.57	7.264	80380	4.08	5.949	22.1

Copeland Model	Liquid Temperature 40°F Design Rating Point Capacity	EER	AEER Rating	COMPETITIVE MODELS Design Rating Point Capacity	EER	AEER Rating	AEER % Diff
2DB3-0600	24840	5.6	7.936	24672	5.8	7.53	5.28
3DB3-0750	35140	5.57	8.128	29483	5.9	7.731	5.14
3DF3-0900	41830	5.48	7.935	39945	5.6	7.667	3.5
4DT3-2200	77090	5.31	7.834	71436	5.7	7.339	6.74
4DT3-2200	77090	5.31	7.834	80593	5.6	7.209	8.67
6DT3-3000	115190	5.27	7.818	103453	5.3	6.71	16.51

DESIGN RATING POINT
Evaporator Temperature -25°F
Condensing Temperature 110°F
Return Gas Temperature 65°F
Liquid Temperature:
0°F Subcooling
40°F Liquid Temperature
Ambient Air Temperature 95°F

AEER CALCULATION ASSUMPTIONS
Minimum Condensing Temperature 70°F
Constant Condenser TD 10°F
Evaporator Temperature -25°F
Suitable Subcooler Available

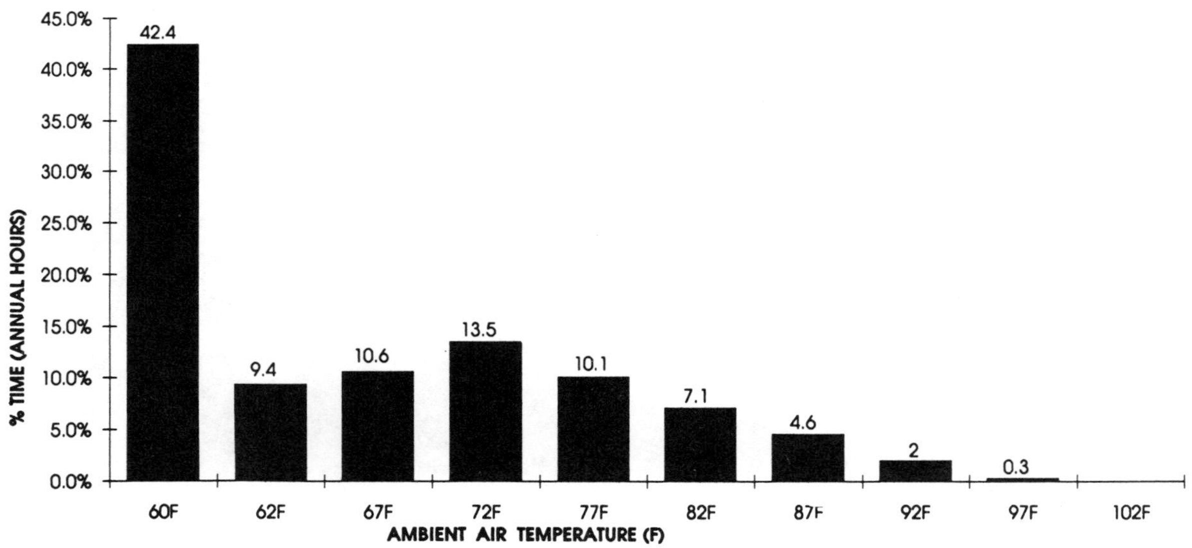

AEER Calculation Based on Boston Weather Data

Copeland Model	No Liquid Subcooling Design Rating Point Capacity	EER	AEER Rating	COMPETITIVE MODELS Design Rating Point Capacity	EER	AEER Rating	AEER % Diff
2DB3-0600	19300	4.82	7.731	19170	4.5	6.97	10.92
3DB3-0750	27300	4.83	7.848	22910	4.62	7.156	9.67
3DF3-0900	32500	4.74	7.732	31040	4.38	7.15	8.14
4DT3-2200	59900	4.61	7.599	55505	4.44	6.803	11.7
4DT3-2200	59900	4.61	7.599	62620	4.38	6.656	14.17
6DT3-3000	89500	4.57	7.672	80380	4.08	6.209	23.56

Copeland Model	Liquid Temperature 40°F Design Rating Point Capacity	EER	AEER Rating	COMPETITIVE MODELS Design Rating Point Capacity	EER	AEER Rating	AEER % Diff.
2DB3-0600	24840	5.6	8.259	24672	5.8	7.76	16.42
3DB3-0750	35140	5.57	8.457	29483	5.9	7.959	6.26
3DF3-0900	41830	5.48	8.259	39945	5.6	7.972	3.6
4DT3-2200	77090	5.31	8.166	71436	5.7	7.562	7.99
4DT3-2200	77090	5.31	8.166	80593	5.6	7.397	10.4
6DT3-3000	115190	5.27	8.198	103453	5.3	6.899	18.83

DESIGN RATING POINT
Evaporator Temperature -25°F
Condensing Temperature 110°F
Return Gas Temperature 65°F
Liquid Temperature:
0°F Subcooling
40°F Liquid Temperature
Ambient Air Temperature 95°F

AEER CALCULATION ASSUMPTIONS
Minimum Condensing Temperature 70°F
Constant Condenser TD 10°F
Evaporator Temperature -25°F
Suitable Subcooler Available

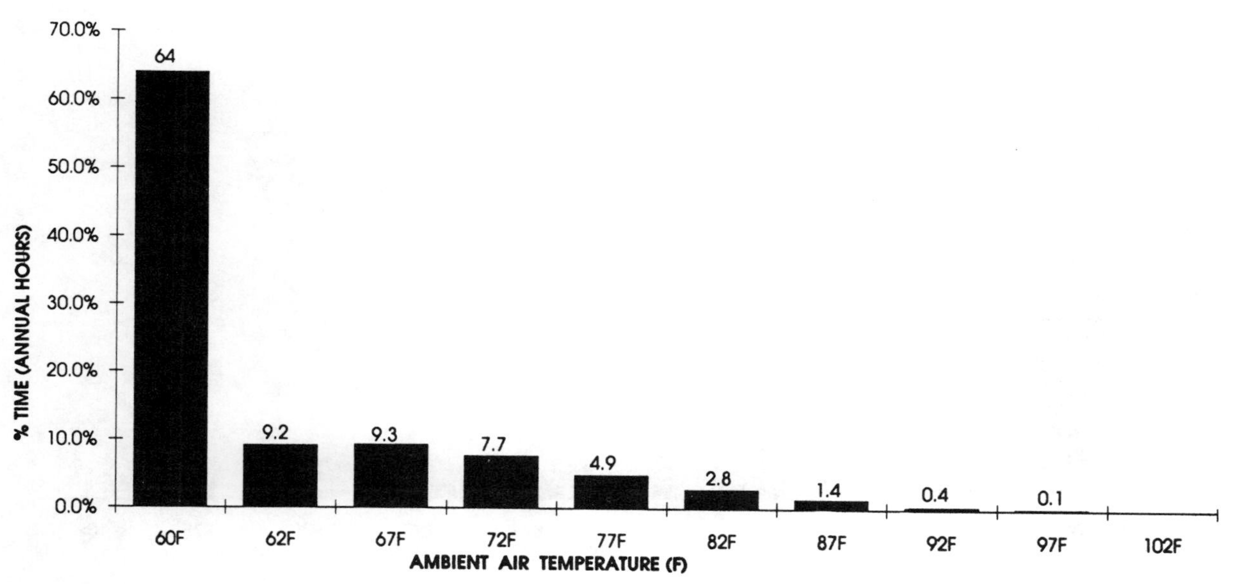

AEER Calculation Based On Chicago Weather Data

Copeland Model	No Liquid Subcooling Design Rating Point Capacity	EER	AEER Rating	COMPETITIVE MODELS Design Rating Point Capacity	EER	AEER Rating	AEER % Diff
2DB3-0600	19300	4.82	7.772	19170	4.5	6.892	12.77
3DB3-0750	27300	4.83	7.755	22910	4.62	7.075	9.61
3DF3-0900	32500	4.74	7.639	31040	4.38	7.056	8.26
4DT3-2200	59900	4.61	7.498	55505	4.44	6.726	11.48
4DT3-2200	59900	4.61	7.498	62620	4.38	6.586	13.85
6DT3-3000	89500	4.57	7.564	80380	4.08	6.14	23.19

Copeland Model	Liquid Temperature 40°F Design Rating Point Capacity	EER	AEER Rating	COMPETITIVE MODELS Design Rating Point Capacity	EER	AEER Rating	AEER % Diff
2DB3-0600	24840	5.6	8.175	24672	5.8	7.713	5.99
3DB3-0750	35140	5.57	8.37	29483	5.9	7.901	5.94
3DF3-0900	41830	5.48	8.174	39945	5.6	7.894	3.55
4DT3-2200	77090	5.31	8.077	71436	5.7	7.506	7.61
4DT3-2200	77090	5.31	8.077	80593	5.6	7.351	9.88
6DT3-3000	115190	5.27	8.099	03453	5.3	6.851	18.22

DESIGN RATING POINT
Evaporator Temperature -25°F
Condensing Temperature 110°F
Return Gas Temperature 65°F
Liquid Temperature:
0°F Subcooling
40°F Liquid Temperature
Ambient Air Temperature 95°F

AEER CALCULATION ASSUMPTIONS
Minimum Condensing Temperature 70°F
Constant Condenser TD 10°F
Evaporator Temperature -25°F
Suitable Subcooler Available

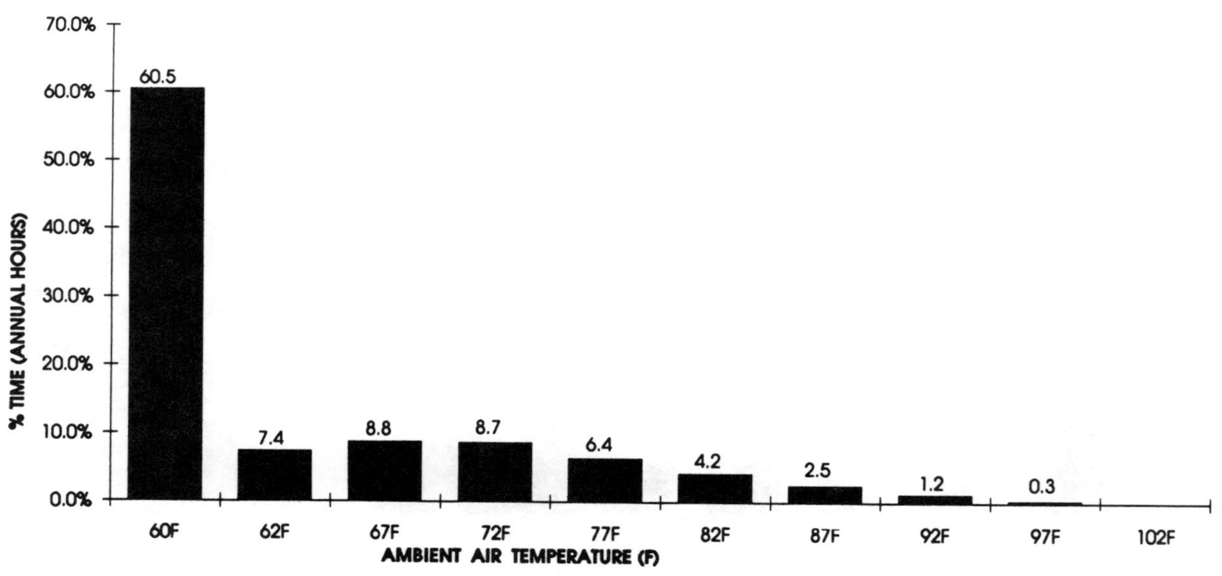

AEER Calculation Based On Denver Weather Data

Copeland Model	No Liquid Subcooling Design Rating Point Capacity	EER	AEER Rating	COMPETITIVE MODELS Design Rating Point Capacity	EER	AEER Rating	AEER % Diff
2DB3-0600	19300	4.82	7.7	19170	4.5	6.945	10.87
3DB3-0750	27300	4.83	7.816	22910	4.62	7.128	9.65
3DF3-0900	32500	4.74	7.702	31040	4.38	7.12	8.17
4DT3-2200	59900	4.61	7.567	55505	4.44	6.779	11.62
4DT3-2200	59900	4.61	7.567	62620	4.38	6.634	14.06
6DT3-3000	89500	4.57	7.637	80380	4.08	6.187	23.44

Copeland Model	Liquid Temperature 40°F Design Rating Point Capacity	EER	AEER Rating	COMPETITIVE MODELS Design Rating Point MCapacity	EER	AEER Rating	AEER % Diff
2DB3-0600	24840	5.6	8.233	24672	5.8	7.745	6.3
3DB3-0750	35140	5.57	8.429	29483	5.9	7.941	6.15
3DF3-0900	41830	5.48	8.233	39945	5.6	7.95	3.56
4DT3-2200	77090	5.31	8.134	71436	5.7	7.546	7.79
4DT3-2200	77090	5.31	8.134	80593	5.6	7.384	10.16
6DT3-3000	115190	5.27	8.168	03453	5.3	6.885	18.63

DESIGN RATING POINT
Evaporator Temperature -25°F
Condensing Temperature 110°F
Return Gas Temperature 65°F
Liquid Temperature:
0°F Subcooling
40°F Liquid Temperature
Ambient Air Temperature 95°F

AEER CALCULATION ASSUMPTIONS
Minimum Condensing Temperature 70°F
Constant Condenser TD10°F
Evaporator Temperature -25°F
Suitable Subcooler Available

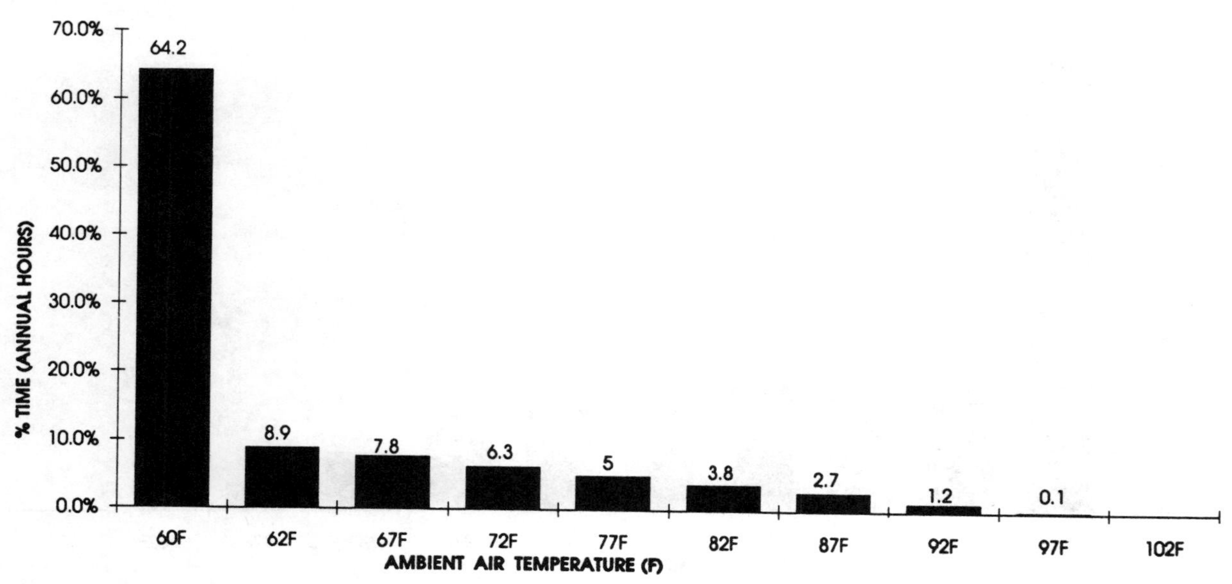

AEER Calculation Based On El Paso Weather Data

Copeland Model	No Liquid Subcooling Design Rating Point Capacity	EER	AEER Rating	COMPETITIVE MODELS Design Rating Point Capacity	EER	AEER Rating	AEER % Diff
2DB3-0600	19300	4.82	7.182	19170	4.5	6.507	10.37
3DB3-0750	27300	4.83	7.303	22910	4.62	6.681	9.31
3DF3-0900	32500	4.74	7.183	31040	4.38	6.609	8.69
4DT3-2200	59900	4.61	7.016	55505	4.44	6.352	10.45
4DT3-2200	59900	4.61	7.016	62620	4.38	6.236	12.51
6DT3-3000	89500	4.57	7.053	80380	4.08	5.803	21.54

Copeland Model	Liquid Temperature 40°F Design Rating Point Capacity	EER	AEER Rating	COMPETITIVE MODELS Design Rating Point Capacity	EER	AEER Rating	AEER % Diff
2DB3-0600	24840	5.6	7.755	24672	5.8	7.408	4.68
3DB3-0750	35140	5.57	7.938	29483	5.9	7.594	4.53
3DF3-0900	41830	5.48	7.752	39945	5.6	7.505	3.29
4DT3-2200	77090	5.31	7.64	71436	5.7	7.211	5.95
4DT3-2200	77090	5.31	7.64	80593	5.6	7.092	7.73
6DT3-3000	115190	5.27	7.619	103453	5.3	6.598	15.47

DESIGN RATING POINT
Evaporator Temperature -25°F
Condensing Temperature 110°F
Return Gas Temperature 65°F
Liquid Temperature:
0°F Subcooling
40°F Liquid Temperature
Ambient Air Temperature 95°F

SEER CALCULATION ASSUMPTIONS
Minimum Condensing Temperature 70°F
Constant Condenser TD10°F
Evaporator Temperature -25°F
Suitable Subcooler Available

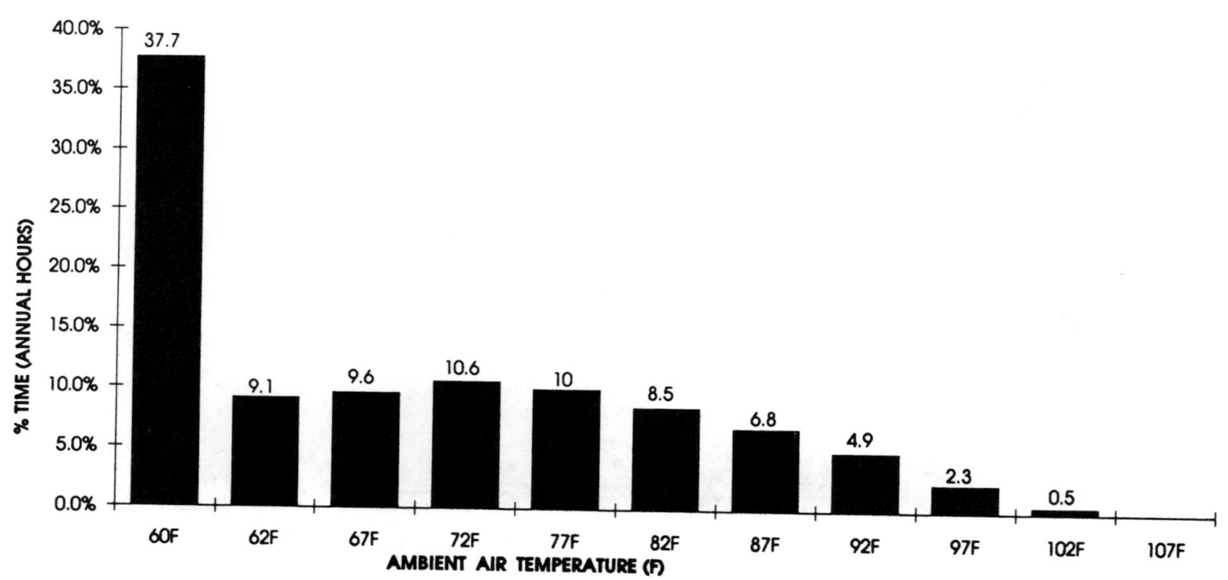

AEER Calculation Based On Galveston Weather Data

Copeland Model	No Liquid Subcooling Design Rating Point Capacity	EER	AEER Rating	COMPETITIVE MODELS Design Rating Point Capacity	EER	AEER Rating	AEER % Diff
2DB3-0600	19300	4.82	7.005	19170	4.5	6.361	10.12
3DB3-0750	27300	4.83	7.139	22910	4.62	6.532	9.29
3DF3-0900	32500	4.74	7.016	31040	4.38	6.428	9.15
4DT3-2200	59900	4.61	6.82	55505	4.44	6.205	9.91
4DT3-2200	59900	4.61	6.82	62620	4.38	6.106	11.69
6DT3-3000	89500	4.57	6.843	80380	4.08	5.673	20.62

Copeland Model	Liquid Temperature 40°F Design Rating Point Capacity	EER	AEER Rating	COMPETITIVE MODELS Design Rating Point Capacity	EER	AEER Rating	AEER % Diff
2DB3-0600	24840	5.6	7.593	24672	5.8	7.297	4.06
3DB3-0750	35140	5.57	7.781	29483	5.9	7.458	4.33
3DF3-0900	41830	5.48	7.593	39945	5.6	7.363	3.12
4DT3-2200	77090	5.31	7.475	71436	5.7	7.097	5.33
4DT3-2200	77090	5.31	7.475	80593	5.6	7.004	6.72
6DT3-3000	115190	5.27	7.42	103453	5.3	6.504	14.08

DESIGN RATING POINT
Evaporator Temperature -25°F
Condensing Temperature 110°F
Return Gas Temperature 65°F
Liquid Temperature:
0°F Subcooling
40°F Liquid Temperature
Ambient Air Temperature 95°F

AEER CALCULATION ASSUMPTIONS
Minimum Condensing Temperature 70°F
Constant Condenser TD 10°F
Evaporator Temperature -25°F
Suitable Subcooler Available

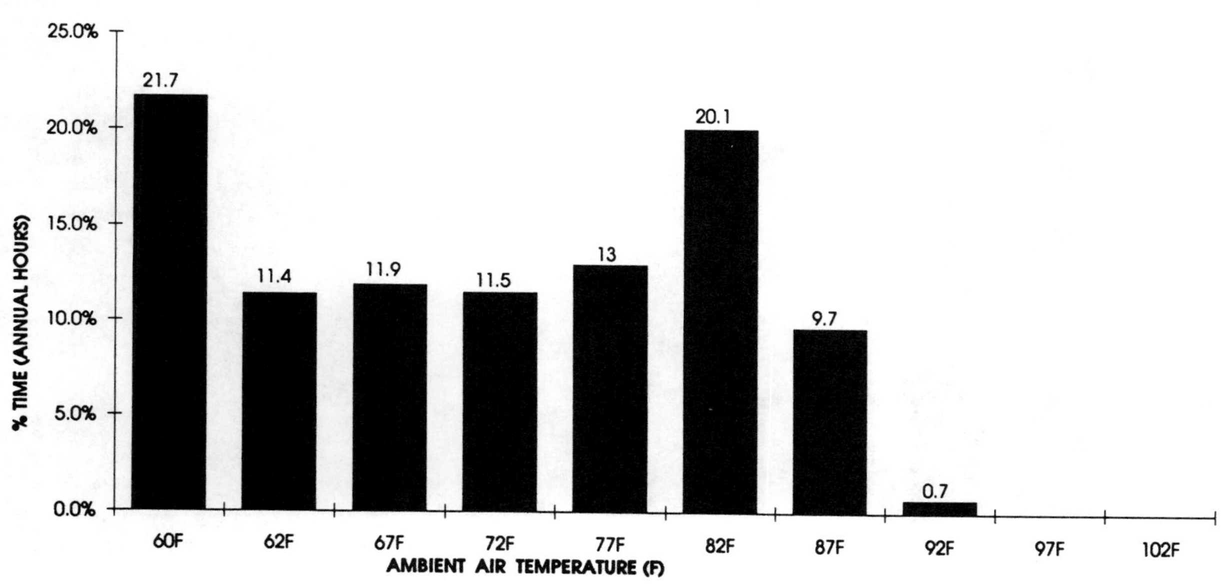

AEER Calculation Based On Los Angeles Weather Data

Copeland Model	No Liquid Subcooling Design Rating Point Capacity	EER	AEER Rating	COMPETITIVE MODELS Design Rating Point Capacity	EER	AEER Rating	AEER % Diff
2DB3-0600	19300	4.82	7.691	9170	4.5	6.939	10.84
3DB3-0750	27300	4.83	7.819	22910	4.62	7.124	9.76
3DF3-0900	32500	4.74	7.691	31040	4.38	7.107	8.22
4DT3-2200	59900	4.61	7.551	55505	4.44	6.769	11.55
4DT3-2200	59900	4.61	7.551	62620	4.38	6.625	13.98
6DT3-3000	89500	4.57	7.616	80380	4.08	6.183	23.18

Copeland Model	Liquid Temperature 40°F Design Rating Point Capacity	EER	AEER Rating	COMPETITIVE MODELS Design Rating Point Capacity	EER	AEER Rating	AEER % Diff
2DB3-0600	24840	5.6	8.226	24672	5.8	7.743	6.24
3DB3-0750	35140	5.57	8.425	29483	5.9	7.943	6.07
3DF3-0900	41830	5.48	8.226	39945	5.6	7.933	3.69
4DT3-2200	77090	5.31	8.146	71436	5.7	7.544	7.98
4DT3-2200	77090	5.31	8.146	80593	5.6	7.385	10.3
6DT3-3000	115190	5.27	8.15	103453	5.3	6.885	18.37

DESIGN RATING POINT
Evaporator Temperature -25°F
Condensing Temperature 110°F
Return Gas Temperature 65°F
Liquid Temperature:
0°F Subcooling
40°F Liquid Temperature
Ambient Air Temperature 95°F

AEER CALCULATION ASSUMPTIONS
Minimum Condensing Temperature 70°F
Constant Condenser TD10°F
Evaporator Temperature -25°F
Suitable Subcooler Available

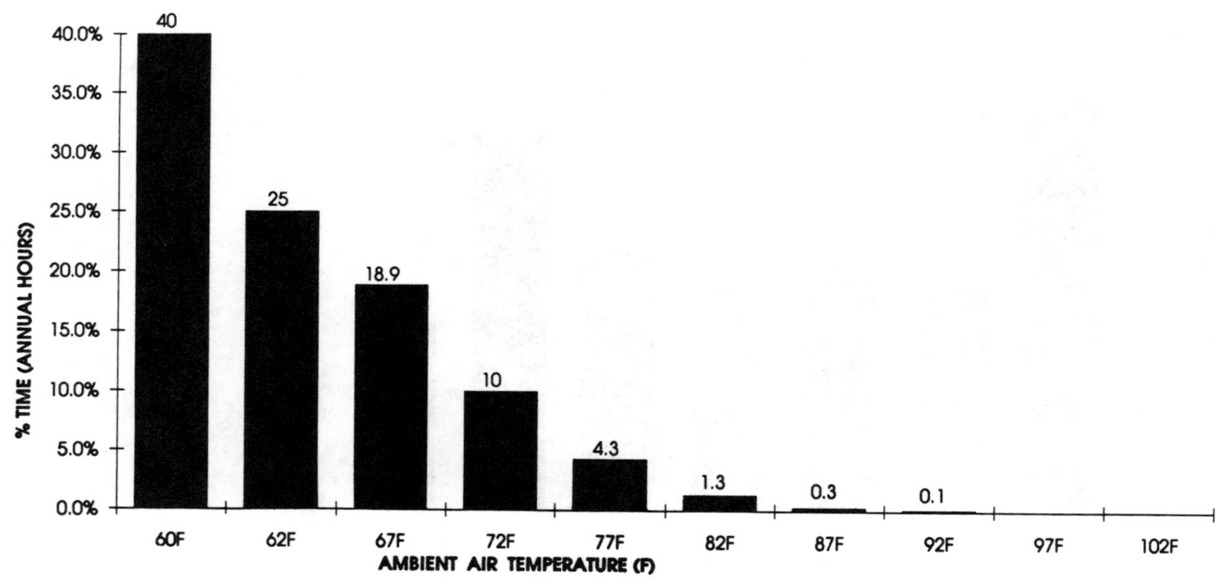

AEER Calculation Based On Miami Weather Data

Copeland Model	No Liquid Subcooling Design Rating Point Capacity	EER	AEER Rating	COMPETITIVE MODELS Design Rating Point Capacity	EER	AEER Rating	AEER % Diff
2DB3-0600	19300	4.82	6.658	19170	4.5	6.07	9.69
3DB3-0750	27300	4.83	6.805	22910	4.62	6.236	9.12
3DF3-0900	32500	4.74	6.674	31040	4.38	6.082	9.73
4DT3-2200	59900	4.61	6.444	55505	4.44	5.919	8.87
4DT3-2200	59900	4.61	6.444	62620	4.38	5.843	10.29
6DT3-3000	89500	4.57	6.445	80380	4.08	5.419	18.93

Copeland Model	Liquid Temperature 40°F Design Rating Point Capacity	EER	AEER Rating	COMPETITIVE MODELS Design Rating Point Capacity	EER	AEER Rating	AEER % Diff
2DB3-0600	24840	5.6	7.274	24672	5.8	7.072	2.86
DB3-0750	35140	5.57	7.461	29483	5.9	7.259	32.78
3DF3-0900	41830	5.48	7.273	39945	5.6	7.042	3.28
4DT3-2200	77090	5.31	7.149	71436	5.7	6.872	4.03
4DT3-2200	77090	5.31	7.149	80593	5.6	6.815	4.9
6DT3-3000	115190	5.27	7.044	103453	5.3	6.316	11.53

DESIGN RATING POINT
Evaporator Temperature -25°F
Condensing Temperature 110°F
Return Gas Temperature 65°F
Liquid Temperature:
0°F Subcooling
40°F Liquid Temperature
Ambient Air Temperature 95°F

SEER CALCULATION ASSUMPTIONS
Minimum Condensing Temperature 70°F
Constant Condenser TD 10°F
Evaporator Temperature -25°F
Suitable Subcooler Available

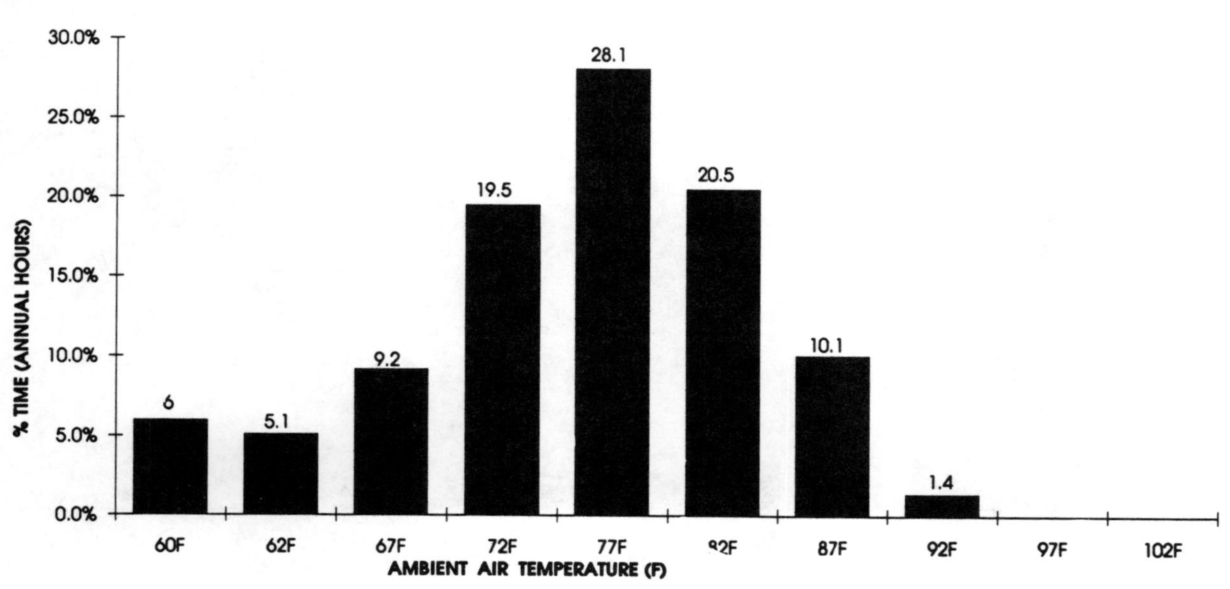

AEER Calculation Based On Minneapolis Weather Data

Copeland Model	No Liquid Subcooling Design Rating Point Capacity	EER	AEER Rating	COMPETITIVE MODELS Design Rating Point Capacity	EER	AEER Rating	AEER % Diff
2DB3-0600	19300	4.82	7.735	19170	4.5	6.975	10.9
3DB3-0750	27300	4.83	7.852	22910	4.62	7.159	9.68
3DF3-0900	32500	4.74	7.737	31040	4.38	7.155	8.13
4DT3-2200	59900	4.61	7.604	55505	4.44	6.808	11.69
4DT3-2200	59900	4.61	7.604	62620	4.38	6.661	14.16
6DT3-3000	89500	4.57	7.676	80380	4.08	6.213	23.55

Copeland Model	Liquid Temperature 40°F Design Rating Point Capacity	EER	AEER Rating	COMPETITIVE MODELS Design Rating Point Capacity	EER	AEER Rating	AEER % Diff
2DB3-0600	24840	5.6	8.266	24672	5.8	7.769	6.4
3DB3-0750	35140	5.57	8.463	29483	5.9	7.966	6.24
3DF3-0900	41830	5.48	8.265	39945	5.6	7.979	3.58
4DT3-2200	77090	5.31	8.169	71436	5.7	7.569	7.93
4DT3-2200	77090	5.31	8.169	80593	5.6	7.405	10.32
6DT3-3000	115190	5.27	8.204	103453	5.3	6.905	18.81

DESIGN RATING POINT
Evaporator Temperature -25°
Condensing Temperature 110°F
Return Gas Temperature 65°F
Liquid Temperature:
0°F Subcooling
40°F Liquid Temperature
Ambient Air Temperature 95°F

AEER CALCULATION ASSUMPTIONS
Minimum'Condensing Temperature 70°F
Constant Condenser TD 10°F
Evaporator Temperature -25°F
Suitable Subcooler Available

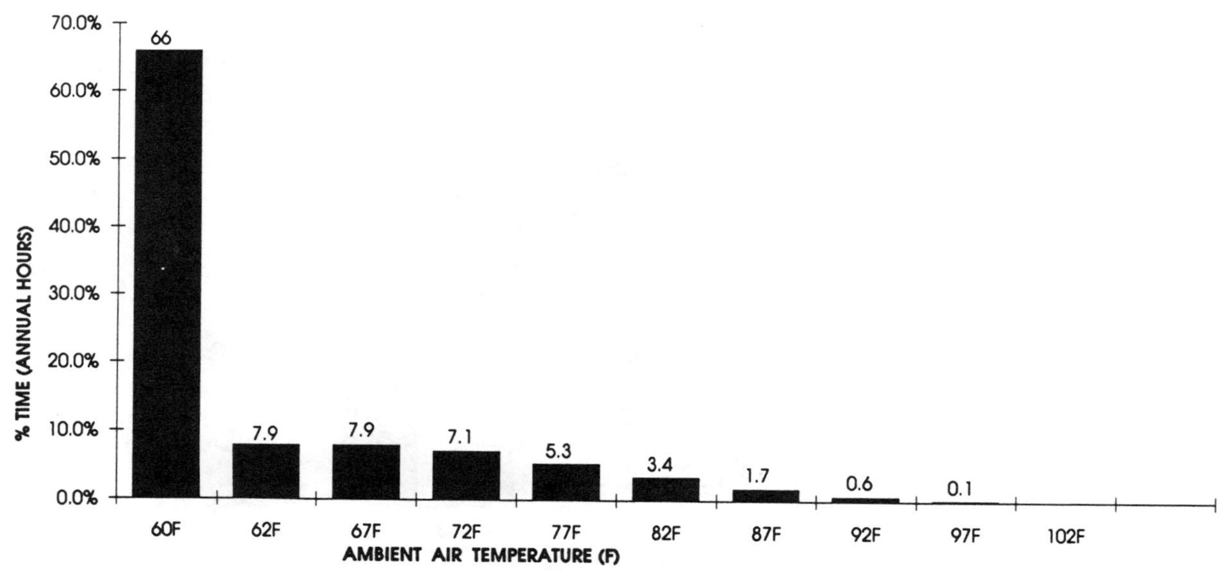

AEER Calculation Based On Reno Weather Data

Copeland Model	No Liquid Subcooling Design Rating Point Capacity	EER	AEER Rating	COMPETITIVE MODELS Design Rating Point Capacity	EER	AEER Rating	AEER % Diff
2DB3-0600	19300	4.82	7.735	19170	4.5	6.973	10.93
3DB3-0750	27300	4.83	7.846	22910	4.62	7.157	9.63
3DF3-0900	32500	4.74	7.736	31040	4.38	7.156	8.11
4DT3-2200	59900	4.61	7.606	55505	4.44	6.808	11.72
4DT3-2200	59900	4.61	7.606	62620	4.38	6.66	14.2
6DT3-3000	89500	4.57	7.68	80380	4.08	6.211	23.65

Copeland Model	Liquid Temperature 40°F Design Rating Point Capacity	EER	AEER Rating	COMPETITIVE MODELS Design Rating Point Capacity	EER	AEER Rating	AEER % Diff
2DB3-0600	24840	5.6	8.264	24672	5.8	7.766	6.41
3DB3-0750	35140	5.57	8.459	29483	5.9	7.961	6.26
3DF3-0900	41830	5.48	8.264	39945	5.6	7.982	3.53
4DT3-2200	77090	5.31	8.162	71436	5.7	7.566	7.88
4DT3-2200	77090	5.31	8.162	80593	5.6	7.401	10.28
6DT3-3000	115190	5.27	8.207	103453	5.3	6.902	18.91

DESIGN RATING POINT
Evaporator Temperature -25°
Condensing Temperature 110°F
Return Gas Temperature 65°F
Liquid Temperature:
    0°F Subcooling
    40°F Liquid Temperature
Ambient Air Temperature 95°F

AEER CALCULATION ASSUMPTIONS
Minimum'Condensing Temperature 70°F
Constant Condenser TD 10°F
Evaporator Temperature -25°F
Suitable Subcooler Available

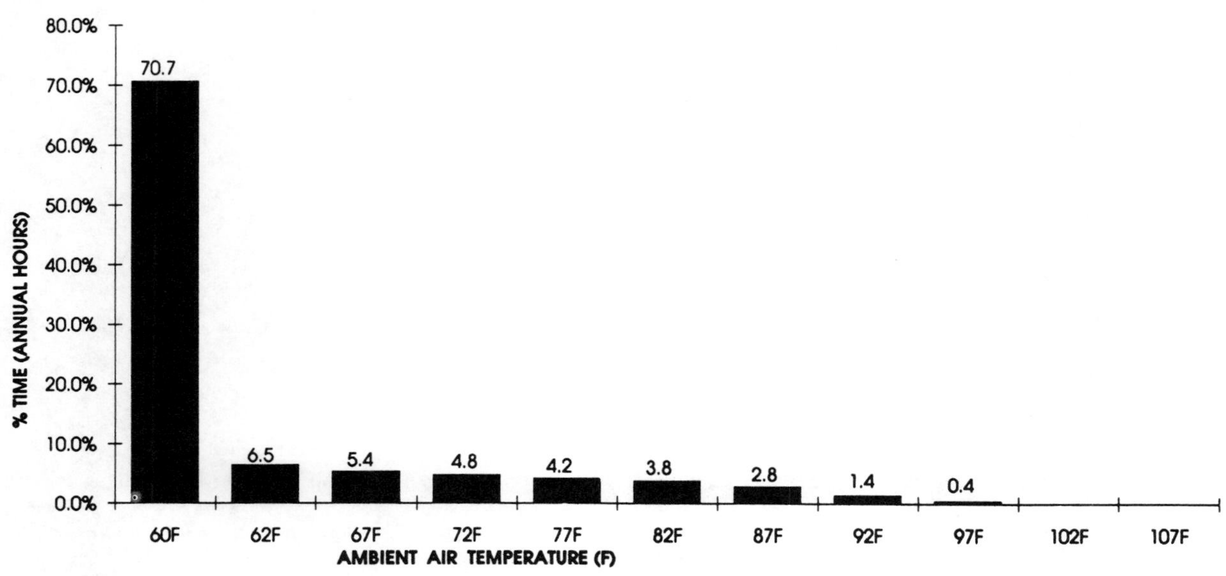

AEER Calculation Based On San Francisco Weather Data

Copeland Model	No Liquid Subcooling Design Rating Point Capacity	EER	AEER Rating	COMPETITIVE MODELS Design Rating Point Capacity	EER	AEER Rating	AEER % Diff
2DB3-0600	19300	4.82	7.942	19170	4.5	7.148	11.11
3DB3-0750	27300	4.83	8.053	22910	4.62	7.336	9.77
3DF3-0900	32500	4.74	7.942	31040	4.38	7.361	7.89
4DT3-2200	59900	4.61	7.827	55505	4.44	6.978	12.17
4DT3-2200	59900	4.61	7.827	62620	4.38	6.818	14.8
6DT3-3000	89500	4.57	7.913	80380	4.08	6.365	24.32

Copeland Model	Liquid Temperature 40°F Design Rating Point Capacity	EER	AEER Rating	COMPETITIVE MODELS Design Rating Point Capacity	EER	AEER Rating	AEER % Diff
2DB3-0600	24840	5.6	8.455	24672	5.8	7.9	7.03
3DB3-0750	35140	5.57	8.654	29483	5.9	8.099	6.85
3DF3-0900	41830	5.48	8.455	39945	5.6	8.157	3.65
4DT3-2200	77090	5.31	8.364	71436	5.7	7.7	8.62
4DT3-2200	77090	5.31	8.364	80593	5.6	7.515	11.3
6DT3-3000	115190	5.27	8.426	103453	5.3	7.016	20.1

DESIGN RATING POINT
Evaporator Temperature -25°
Condensing Temperature 110°F
Return Gas Temperature 65°F
Liquid Temperature:
0°F Subcooling
40°F Liquid Temperature
Ambient Air Temperature 95°F

AEER CALCULATION ASSUMPTIONS
Minimum'Condensing Temperature 70°F
Constant Condenser TD 10°F
Evaporator Temperature -25°F
Suitable Subcooler Available

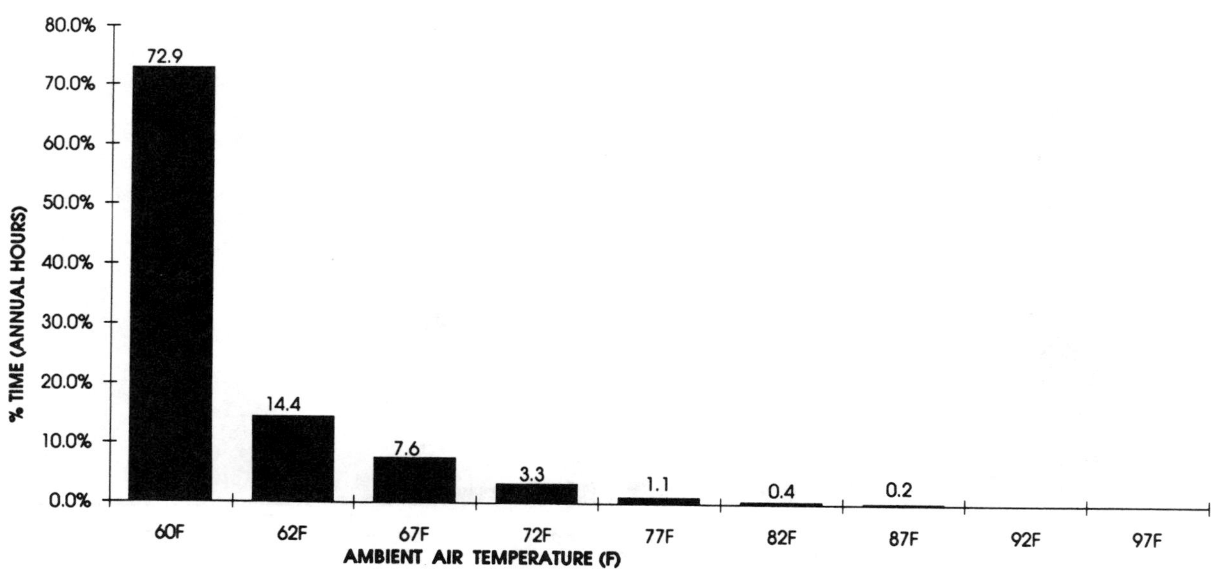

AEER Calculation Based On Seattle Weather Data

Copeland Model	No Liquid Subcooling Design Rating Point Capacity	EER	AEER Rating	COMPETITIVE MODELS Design Rating Point Capacity	EER	AEER Rating	AEER % Diff
2DB3-0600	19300	4.82	7.968	19170	4.5	7.17	11.13
3DB3-0750	27300	4.83	8.076	22910	4.62	7.358	9.76
3DF3-0900	32500	4.74	7.968	31040	4.38	7.387	7.87
4DT3-2200	59900	4.61	7.856	55505	4.44	7	12.23
4DT3-2200	59900	4.61	7.856	62620	4.38	6.839	14.87
6DT3-3000	89500	4.57	7.944	80380	4.08	6.384	24.44

Copeland Model	Liquid Temperature 40°F Design Rating Point Capacity	EER	AEER Rating	COMPETITIVE MODELS Design Rating Point Capacity	EER	AEER Rating	AEER % Diff
2DB3-0600	24840	5.6	8.48	24672	5.8	7.918	7.1
3DB3-0750	35140	5.57	8.679	29483	5.9	8.117	6.92
3DF3-0900	41830	5.48	8.48	39945	5.6	8.183	3.63
4DT3-2200	77090	5.31	8.385	71436	5.7	7.718	8.64
4DT3-2200	77090	5.31	8.385	80593	5.6	7.531	11.34
6DT3-3000	115190	5.27	8.456	103453	5.3	7.031	20.27

DESIGN RATING POINT
Evaporator Temperature -25°
Condensing Temperature 110°F
Return Gas Temperature 65°F
Liquid Temperature:
0°F Subcooling
40°F Liquid Temperature
Ambient Air Temperature 95°F

AEER CALCULATION ASSUMPTIONS
Minimum'Condensing Temperature 70°F
Constant Condenser TD 10°F
Evaporator Temperature -25°F
Suitable Subcooler Available

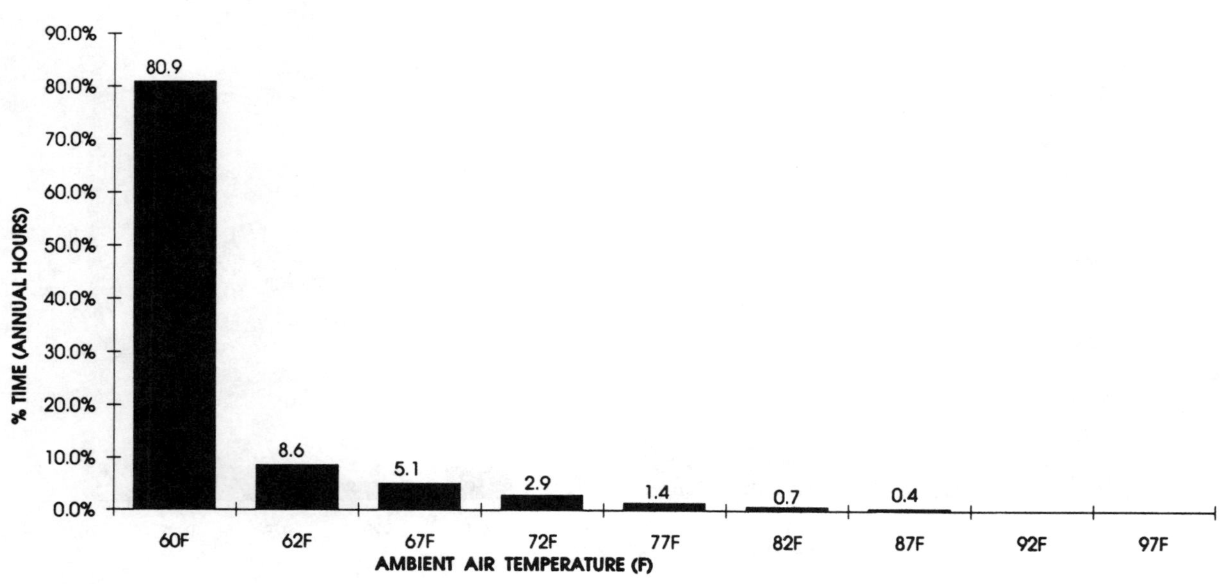

AEER Calculation Based On St. Louis Weather Data

Copeland Model	No Liquid Subcooling Design RatingPoint Capacity	EER	AEER Rating	COMPETITIVE MODELS Design Rating Point Capacity	EER	AEER Rating	AEER % Diff
2DB3-0600	19300	4.82	7.44	19170	4.50	6.73	10.55
3DB3-0750	27300	4.83	7.56	22910	4.62	6.91	9.41
3DF3-0900	32500	4.74	7.44	31040	4.38	6.87	8.30
4DT3-2200	59900	4.61	7.29	55505	4.44	6.57	10.96
4DT3-2200	59900	4.61	7.29	62620	4.38	6.44	13.20
6DT3-3000	89500	4.57	7.34	80380	4.08	5.99	22.54

Copeland Model	Liquid Temperature 40°F Design Rating Point Capacity	EER	AEER Rating	COMPETITIVE MODELS Design Rating Point Capacity	EER	AEER Rating	AEER % Diff
2DB3-0600	24840	5.6	7.99	24672	5.8	7.57	5.55
3DB3-0750	35140	5.57	8.18	29483	5.9	7.77	5.28
3DF3-0900	41830	5.48	7.99	39945	5.6	7.72	3.50
4DT3-2200	77090	5.31	7.85	71436	5.7	7.38	6.37
4DT3-2200	77090	5.31	7.85	80593	5.6	7.23	8.58
6DT3-3000	115190	5.27	7.89	10345	35.3	6.74	17.06

DESIGN RATING POINT
Evaporator Temperature -25°F
Condensing Temperature 110°F
Return Gas'Temperature 65°F
Liquid Temperature:
Suitable Subcooler Available
0°F Subcooling
40°F Liquid Temperature
Ambient Air Temperature 95°F

AEER CALCULATION ASSUMPTIONS
Minimum Condensing Temperature 70°F
Constant Condenser TD 10°F
Evaporator Temperature -25°F
Suitable Subcooler Available

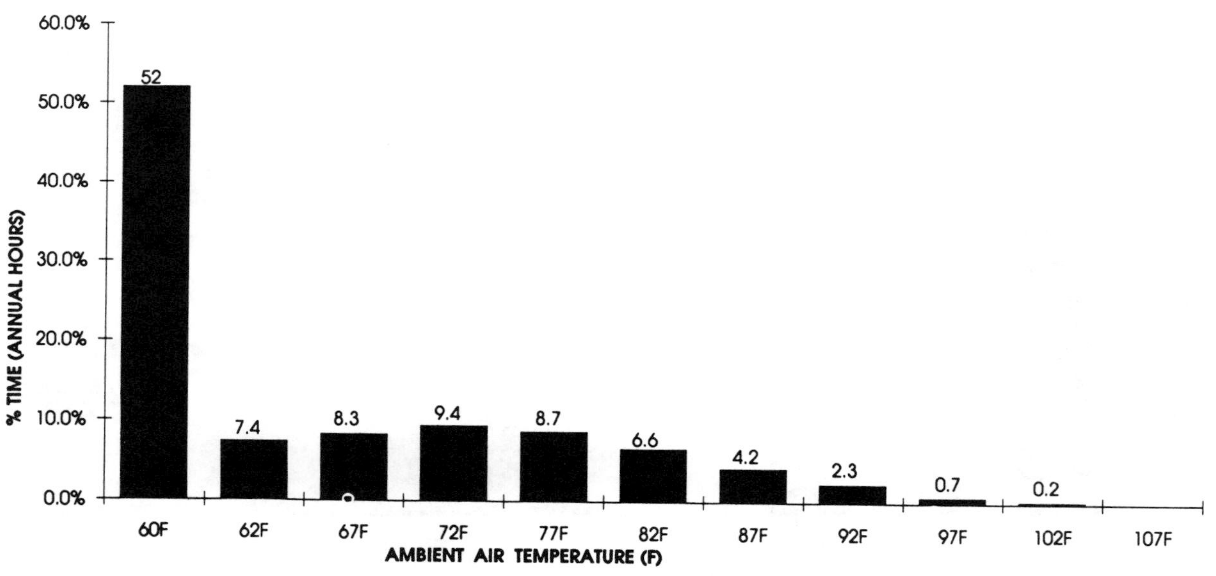

APPENDIX B

Demand Cooling Performance Factors

Standard Rating Conditions to 40°F Liquid Temperature

CAPACITY (Btu/Hr)

Cond. Temp. (°F)	Evaporating Temperature (°F)								
	-40	-35	-30	-25	-20	-15	-10	-5	0
70	1.101	1.101	1.102	1.102	1.102	1.102	1.102	1.102	1.103
80	1.141	1.141	1.141	1.142	1.142	1.142	1.142	1.143	1.143
90	1.185	1.185	1.185	1.185	1.186	1.186	1.186	1.187	1.187
100	1.233	1.233	1.233	1.234	1.234	1.235	1.235	1.236	1.236
110	1.286	1.286	1.287	1.287	1.288	1.288	1.289	1.290	1.291
120	1.346	1.346	1.347	1.347	1.348	1.349	1.349	1.350	1.351
130	1.413	1.414	1.414	1.415	1.416	1.417	1.418	1.419	1.420

*POWER (Watts)

Cond. Temp. (°F)	Evaporating Temperature (°F)								
	-40	-35	-30	-25	-20	-15	-10	-5	0
70	1.027	1.030	1.032	1.035	1.038	1.041	1.045	1.048	1.053
80	1.039	1.043	1.047	1.052	1.057	1.061	1.067	1.072	1.078
90	1.052	1.058	1.064	1.071	1.078	1.085	1.092	1.100	1.108
100	1.066	1.075	1.084	1.093	1.102	1.111	1.121	1.131	1.141
110	1.081	1.093	1.104	1.116	1.128	1.140	1.153	1.166	1.179
120	1.097	1.111	1.126	1.141	1.156	1.171	1.187	1.203	1.220
130	1.109	1.127	1.145	1.163	1.182	1.202	1.222	1.243	1.264

*EFFICIENCY (EER)

Cond. Temp. (°F)	Evaporating Temperature (°F)								
	-40	-35	-30	-25	-20	-15	-10	-5	0
70	1.072	1.070	1.067	1.064	1.061	1.058	1.055	1.051	1.048
80	1.099	1.094	1.090	1.085	1.081	1.076	1.071	1.066	1.060
90	1.126	1.120	1.113	1.107	1.100	1.094	1.087	1.079	1.072
100	1.156	1.147	1.138	1.129	1.120	1.111	1.102	1.093	1.083
110	1.189	1.177	1.165	1.153	1.142	1.130	1.118	1.107	1.095
120	1.227	1.211	1.196	1.181	1.166	1.152	1.137	1.122	1.107
130	1.274	1.255	1.236	1.217	1.198	1.179	1.160	1.142	1.124

•DEMAND COOLING compressor power consumption is not directly affected by liquid subcooling. The power correction factor represents the additional power required to operate a mechanical subcooler with DISCUS ® compressors operating at 30°F evaporating, 0°F subcooling, and at the specified condensing temperature.

Form No. 92-84

Printed in U.S.A.

October 1992

Copeland Corporation
1675 W. Campbell Road
Sidney, Ohio 45365-0669

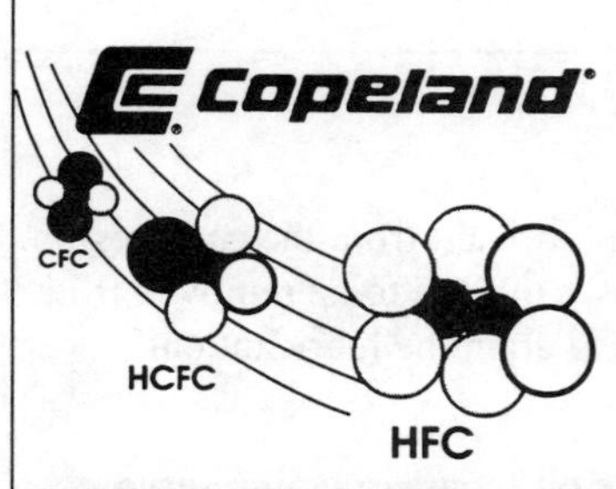

Refrigerant Changeover Guidelines

CFC-12 to HFC-134a

Leading the Industry with Environmentally Responsible Refrigerant Solutions

Copeland does not advocate the wholesale changeover of CFC refrigerants to HCFCs or HFCs. If a system is not leaking refrigerant to the atmosphere, and is operating properly, there is no technical reason to replace the CFC refrigerant. Changing the refrigerant may void the U.L. listing of the unit. However, once the decision has been made to make the change from CFC-12 (R-12) to HFC-134a (R-134a), the following guidelines are recommended.

CONSIDERATIONS

1. Retrofitting systems that employ compressors manufactured prior to 1973 is not recommended. This is due to the different materials used in motor insulation that have not been evaluated for compatibility with the new refrigerants and lubricants. Failure to heed this advice will violate the proposed U.L. Standard For Field Conversion/Retrofit Of Alternate Refrigerants In Refrigeration and Air Conditioning Equipment (U.L. 2170-2172).

2. Copeland's lubricant recommendation for use with HFC-134a is a Polyol Ester (POE), Mobil EAL™ Arctic 22 CC or ICI EMKARATE RL 32S. The use of any other POE lubricant may void the compressor warranty.

3. R-134a should be used only in systems where the saturated suction temperature is maintained at -10°F or higher. **It should not be mixed with any other refrigerant!**

4. The expansion valve may need to be changed. The existing R-12 valve when used with R-134a will have approximately 15% more capacity. Oversized expansion valves can result in hunting and refrigerant floodback. Consult with the thermostatic expansion valve manufacturer for the correct valve and size.

5. Filter-driers must be changed at the time of conversion. This is proper air conditioning/refrigeration practice.

   a. The recommended drier for use with all HFC refrigerants is the Copeland PureFlow or Alco UltraFlow.

   b. Solid core driers such as ALCO ADK are compatible with either R-12 or R-134a.

   c. Compacted bead type driers can use XH6 or XH9 molecular sieve material such as found in the ALCO EK or EKH series.

   d. If a loose fill type drier is to be used, XH9 molecular sieve is required.

6. R-134a exhibits marginally higher pressures than R-12 at normal condensing temperatures. We do not believe this will require readjustment of safety controls; however, you should verify this with the system manufacturer or component suppliers.

7. Systems that use a low pressure controller to maintain space temperature may need to have the cut-in and cut-out points changed due to the difference in Pressure/Temperature relationships.

8. Systems using R-134a may have a lower system pressure drop than with R-12. Because of the lower pressure drop, check with the manufacturer of any pressure regulators and pilot operated solenoid valves used in the system to be sure that they will operate with the lower pressure drop. It is possible that these controls may have to be downsized in order to operate properly.

9. Mineral oil lubricants, such as 3GS, **must not** be used as the compressor lubricant. Polyol Ester (POE) lubricant,

WARNING: Use only Copeland approved refrigerants and lubricants in the manner prescribed by Copeland. In some circumstances, other refrigerants and lubricants may be dangerous and could cause fires, explosions or electrical shorting. Contact Copeland Corp., Sidney, Ohio.

Mobil EAL Arctic 22 CC, or ICI EMKARATE RL 32S are the only lubricants that can be used in a Copeland compressor when using R-134a.

Before starting the changeover, it is suggested that at least the following items be ready:

1. Safety glasses
2. Gloves
3. Refrigerant service gauges
4. Electronic thermometer
5. Vacuum pump capable of pulling 250 microns
6. Thermocouple micron gauge
7. Leak detector
8. Refrigerant recovery unit including refrigerant cylinder
9. Proper container for removed lubricant
10. New liquid control device
11. Replacement liquid line filter-drier(s)
12. New lubricant, Mobil EAL Arctic 22 CC or ICI EMKARATE RL 32S (POE)
13. R-134a pressure temperature chart
14. R-134a refrigerant

CHANGEOVER PROCEDURE

NOTE: R-134a is not compatible with the seal material used in Moduload unloading. If your system has Moduload, it MUST be changed. Consult your Copeland wholesaler for the proper part number.

1. The system should be thoroughly leak tested with the R-12 still in the system. All leaks should be repaired before the R-134a refrigerant is added.

2. It is advisable that the system operating conditions be recorded with the R-12 still in the system. This will provide the base data for comparison when the system is put back into operation with the R-134a.

3. It is necessary to thoroughly remove the existing mineral oil lubricant from the system before the refrigerant is changed. No more than 5% residual mineral oil may be left in the system when it is recharged with R-134a for proper compressor operation. 1 to 2% residual mineral oil may be required to assure no loss of heat transfer if enhanced tube heat exchangers are used in the system.

I. Systems with service valves

a. Disconnect electrical power to system.

b. Front seat the service valves to isolate the compressor.

c. Properly remove the R-12 from the compressor.

d. Remove the mineral oil lubricant from the compressor. Hermetic compressors will have to be removed from the system and tipped up to drain the lubricant out through the suction stub.

e. Those systems that have oil separators, oil reservoirs, oil floats and suction line accumulators must have the mineral oil drained from them. Add POE lubricant to the oil separator and to the oil reservoir.

f. Replace the liquid line filter-drier with one that is compatible with R-134a.

g. Fill the compressor with the proper amount of POE lubricant. The oil charge is on the label of Copelaweld® compressors. Copelametic® compressor oil charges can be found in Application Engineering Bulletin 4-1281. If the lubricant charge is unknown, an authorized Copeland wholesaler can provide the technician with the information.

h. Reinstall the compressor in the system. Evacuate it to 250 microns. A vacuum decay test is suggested to assure the system is dry and leak free.

i. Recharge the system with R-12.

j. Operate the compressor in the system for a minimum of 24 hours, longer is better.

k. Repeat steps 3.I.a through j two more times. This will have provided three flushes of the system's lubricant.

l. To date, three complete flushes of the lubricant has shown to lower the mineral oil content down to 5% or less in the system. To be sure of the mineral oil content between flushes and to be sure that the system ultimately has 5% or less mineral oil, Copeland recommends the use of a refractometer.

m. Properly dispose of the lubricant removed from the system after each flush.

II. Systems without service valves

a. Disconnect electrical power to system.

b. Properly remove the R-12 from the system.

c. Remove the mineral oil lubricant from the compressor. Hermetic compressors will have to be removed from the system and tipped up to drain the lubricant out through the suction stub.

d. It may be advisable to add service valves at the compressor suction and discharge connections. The compressor will have to have its lubricant changed generally three times.

e. Those systems that have oil separators, oil reservoirs, oil floats and suction line accumulators must have the mineral oil drained from them. Add POE lubricant to the oil separator and to the oil reservoir.

f. Replace the liquid line filter-drier with one that is compatible with R-134a.

g. Fill the compressor with the proper amount of POE lubricant. The oil charge is on the label of Copelaweld compressors. Copelametic compressor oil charges can be found in Application Engineering Bulletin 4-1281. If the lubricant charge is unknown, an authorized Copeland wholesaler can provide the technician with the information.

h. Reinstall the compressor in the system. Evacuate it to 250 microns. A vacuum decay test is suggested to assure the system is dry and leak free.

i. Recharge the system with R-12.

j. Operate the compressor in the system for a minimum of 24 hours, longer is better.

k. Repeat steps 3.II.a through j two more times. This will have provided three flushes of the system's lubricant.

l. To date, three complete flushes of the lubricant has shown to get the mineral oil content down to 5% or less in the system. To be sure of the mineral oil level between flushes and to be sure that the system has 5% or less mineral oil, Copeland recommends the use of a refractometer to determine the residual mineral oil in the system. The refractometer (P/N 998-RMET-00) is available from your Copeland Wholesaler.

4. With the proper amount of polyol ester in the system, the R-12 can now be removed. Measure and note the amount removed.

5. Before the final flush, be sure all leaks are repaired, liquid control devices and any other system components are changed. Install the correct liquid line filter-drier. Driers must be compatible with the refrigerant and lubricant.

6. Be advised that POEs are very hygroscopic. They will very quickly absorb moisture from the air once the container is opened. Once the lubricant is added to the compressor, the compressor should be quickly installed. Like an open container, an open compressor with POE will absorb moisture. Add the correct amount of lubricant to the compressor. It is important that the system contain not more than 5% mineral oil. More than 5% may contribute to premature compressor failure and or system capacity problems. Mineral oils are not miscible with R-134a. The lubricant may log in the evaporator resulting in system capacity loss. It is for this reason that the flushing process must be done with the R-12 in the system.

7. Once the compressor is installed and the system is closed, the system must be evacuated to and hold 250 microns or lower.

8. Charge the system with the R-134a. Charge to 90% of the refrigerant removed in item 4.

9. Operate the system. Record the data and compare to the data taken in item 2. Check and adjust the TEV superheat setting if necessary. Make adjustments to other controls as needed. Additional R-134a may have to be added to obtain optimum system performance.

10. Properly label the components. Tag the compressor with the refrigerant used (R-134a) and the lubricant used (Mobil EAL Arctic 22 CC or ICI EMKARATE RL 32S). The proper color code for R-134a is Light Sky Blue PMS (Paint Matching System) 2975.

11. Clean up and properly dispose of the removed lubricant. Check local and state laws regarding the disposal of refrigerant lubricants. Recycle or reclaim the removed refrigerant.

CAUTION: These guidelines are intended for use with R-134a only, not for refrigerants which are similar to R-134a. *Other refrigerants may not be compatible with the materials used in our compressors or the lubricants recommended in this bulletin resulting in unacceptable reliability and durability of the compressor.*

Note: Retrofit videos are available from your Authorized Copeland Wholesaler. Ask for VT-026.

The information contained herein is based on technical data and tests which we believe to be reliable and is intended for use by persons having technical skill, at their own discretion and risk. Since conditions of use are beyond Copeland's control, we can assume no liability for results obtained or damages incurred through the application of the data presented.

R-134a Saturated Vapor/Liquid Temperature/Pressure Chart

Temperature °F	Pressure PSIG	Temperature °F	Pressure PSIG
-10	1.8	30	25.6
-9	2.2	31	26.4
-8	2.6	32	27.3
-7	3.0	33	28.1
-6	3.5	34	29.0
-5	3.9	35	29.9
-4	4.4	40	34.5
-3	4.8	45	39.5
-2	5.3	50	44.9
-1	5.8	55	50.7
0	6.2	60	56.9
1	6.7	65	63.5
2	7.2	70	70.7
3	7.8	75	78.3
4	8.3	80	86.4
5	8.8	85	95.0
6	9.3	90	104.2
7	9.9	95	113.9
8	10.5	100	124.3
9	11.0	105	135.2
10	11.6	110	146.8
11	12.2	115	159.0
12	12.8	120	171.9
13	13.4	125	185.5
14	14.0	130	199.8
15	14.7	135	214.8
16	15.3		
17	16.0		
18	16.7		
19	17.3		
20	18.0		
21	18.7		
22	19.4		
23	20.2		
24	20.9		
25	21.7		
26	22.4		
27	23.2		
28	24.0		
29	24.8		

Form No. 93-04-R3 Revised 3-94
Supersedes Form No. 93-04-R2

Printed in U.S.A.
Copeland Corporation
Sidney, OH 45365-0669

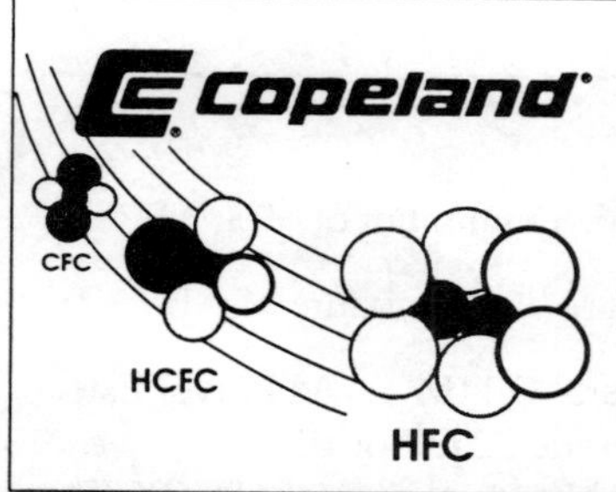

Refrigerant Changeover Guidelines

CFC-12 to R-401A (MP39)

Leading the Industry with Environmentally Responsible Refrigerant Solutions

Copeland does not advocate the wholesale changeover of CFC refrigerants to HCFCs or HFCs. If a system is not leaking refrigerant to the atmosphere, and is operating properly, there is no technical need to replace the CFC refrigerant. In fact, changing the refrigerant may void the U.L. listing of the unit. However, once the decision has been made to make the change from CFC-12 (R-12) to the interim R-401A, the following guidelines are recommended.

CONSIDERATIONS

1. Retrofitting systems that employ compressors manufactured prior to 1973 is not recommended. This is due to the different materials used in motor insulation that have not been evaluated for compatibility with the new refrigerants and lubricants. Failure to heed this advice will violate the proposed U.L. Standard For Field Conversion/Retrofit Of Alternate Refrigerants In Refrigeration and Air Conditioning Equipment (U.L. 2170-2172).

2. Copeland's lubricant recommendation for use with R-401A is a mixture of 50% mineral oil and 50% alkylbenzene (Zerol 200TD). Polyol ester lubricants, Mobil EAL™ Arctic 22 CC or ICI EMKARATE RL 32S, can also be used with R-401A if the system is expected to be changed in the near future to an HFC refrigerant such as HFC-134a. This will eliminate the need of having to flush the system again when making the R-134a retrofit.

Refer to item 11 in this section for a list of other approved lubricants for use with R-401A or Application Engineering Bulletin 17-1248 for a complete list of all Copeland approved lubricants.

3. R-401A should be used only in systems where the saturated suction temperature is maintained at -10°F or higher. **It should not be mixed with any other refrigerant!**

4. The expansion valve may need to be changed. The existing R-12 valve when used with R-401A will have approximately 25% more capacity. Oversized expansion valves can result in hunting and refrigerant floodback. Consult with the thermostatic expansion valve manufacturer for the correct valve and size.

5. Filter-driers must be changed at the time of conversion. This is proper air conditioning/refrigeration practice.

a. Solid core driers such as ALCO ADK, are compatible with either R-12 or R-401A.

b. Compacted bead driers can use XH6 or XH9 molecular sieve material such as found in the ALCO UltraFlow, EK or EKH series, or Copeland PureFlow.

c. If a loose fill type drier is to be used, XH9 molecular sieve is required.

6. R-401A exhibits marginally higher pressures than R-12 at normal condensing temperatures. We do not believe this will require readjustment of safety controls; however, you should verify this with the system manufacturer or component suppliers.

7. Systems that use a low pressure controller to maintain space temperature may have to have the cut-out and cut-in points changed. With R-401A, the pressure setting must reflect an average temperature of the refrigerant in the evaporator. Because of refrigerant glide (see Copeland booklet 92-81, "Guide To Refrigerant Mixtures"), the refrigerant entering the evaporator for a specific suction pressure will be approximately 8°F colder than the refrigerant vapor at the outlet of the evaporator (not

WARNING: Use only Copeland approved refrigerants and lubricants in the manner prescribed by Copeland. In some circumstances, other refrigerants and lubricants may be dangerous and could cause fires, explosions or electrical shorting. Contact Copeland Corp., Sidney, Ohio.

considering superheat). Therefore, the average refrigerant temperature will be at a midpoint pressure/temperature equivalent.

Example: A 35°F refrigerated space usually requires that the refrigerant temperature in the evaporator be approximately 25°F. Using R-401A, the liquid entering the evaporator may be as cold as 21°F, and the vapor temperature before superheat may be 29°F. Taking the saturated vapor pressure at 29°F gives us the exit pressure at the evaporator of 24.8 psig. Considering a 2 psig pressure drop in the suction line, the pressure control cut-out should be set at 22.8 psig.

The cut-in point will be based on the vapor pressure/ temperature value. Let's assume that the space temperature can rise to 37°F before the compressor is turned on. 37°F vapor pressure is 31.6 psig. Set the cut-in at 32 psig.

8. Because of glide, pressure regulators such as EPRs may have to be reset. Contact the EPR manufacturer for correct settings.

9. Due to refrigerant glide, it is important that when measuring and/or adjusting TEV superheat, the pressure and SATURATED VAPOR TABLES be used. Example: The pressure measured at the TEV bulb is 30 psig. The Pressure/Temperature (P/T) chart shows that the saturated vapor temperature for 30 psig is 35.2°F. If the actual refrigerant temperature measured is 45.0°F, the superheat is 9.8°F.

To measure sub-cooling at the condenser outlet or at the TEV inlet to verify that a solid column of liquid is present, measure the pressure and the refrigerant temperature at the location that the sub-cooling information is needed. Compare it to the saturated liquid temperature from the SATURATED LIQUID TABLES. Example: A pressure of 140 psig is measured at the condenser coil outlet. From the P/T chart, 140 psig is 100.2°F saturated liquid temperature. If the actual refrigerant temperature is 95°F, the liquid is sub-cooled 5.2°F.

10. Systems using R-401A may have a lower system pressure drop than with R-12. Because of the lower pressure drop, pilot operated solenoid valves and pressure regulators may not operate. Check with the manufacturer of any pressure regulators and pilot operated solenoid valves used in the system to be sure that they will operate properly. These controls may have to be downsized.

11. Mineral oil lubricant only, such as 3GS, cannot be used as the compressor lubricant. Copeland recommends the following lubricant choices:

1. A mixture of 3GS Mineral Oil (MO) and Zerol 200TD Alkyl Benzene (AB) with a minimum of 50% AB
2. Virginia KMP MS2212 (a 70/30 mixture of AB/MO)
3. A mixture of 3GS Mineral Oil (MO) and Polyol Ester (POE) ie; Mobil EAL Arctic 22 CC or ICI EMKARATE RL 32S with a minimum of 50% POE
4. 100% Mobil EAL Arctic 22 CC or ICI EMKARATE RL 32S.

Before starting the changeover, it is suggested that at least the following items be ready:

1. Safety glasses
2. Gloves
3. Refrigerant service gauges
4. Electronic thermometer
5. Vacuum pump capable of pulling 250 microns
6. Thermocouple micron gauge
7. Leak detector
8. Refrigerant recovery unit including refrigerant cylinder
9. Proper container for removed lubricant
10. New liquid control device
11. Replacement liquid line filter-drier(s)
12. New lubricant
    a. Zerol 200TD (AB) or Virginia KMP MS 2212 (AB)
    b. Mobil EAL Arctic 22 CC or ICI EMKARATE RL 32S (POE)
13. R-401A pressure temperature chart
14. R-401A refrigerant

CHANGEOVER PROCEDURE

1. The system should be thoroughly leak tested with the R-12 refrigerant still in the system. All leaks should be repaired before the R-401A refrigerant is added.

2. It is recommended that system operating conditions be recorded with the R-12 still in the system. This will provide the base data for comparison when the system is put back into operation with the R-401A.

3. The system should be electrically shut off and the refrigerant properly removed from the system. Measure the quantity of refrigerant removed. This will provide a guide for recharging the system with R-401A (see item 9 this section).

4. The mineral oil must be removed from the compressor crankcase. Hermetic compressors will have to be removed from the piping and the lubricant drained out through the suction stub. It is advisable to do an acid test on the oil.

5. Measure the amount of lubricant removed. It should be

within 4 to 6 ounces of the compressor's factory oil charge. The lubricant charge is indicated on the name plate of Copelaweld® compressors. Copelametic® compressor oil charges can be found in Application Engineering Bulletin 4-1281. If the lubricant charge is unknown, an authorized Copeland wholesaler can provide the technician with the information.

If the amount of lubricant removed is less than 50% of the factory charge, it will be necessary to flush the excess lubricant from the system.

Those systems that have oil separators, oil reservoirs, oil floats and suction line accumulators must have the oil drained from them. If the liquid control device is going to be replaced, it is advisable that the suction line, liquid line and evaporator coil be blown clean using properly regulated dry nitrogen.

NOTE: Properly dispose of the lubricant.

6. Before the new lubricant is installed into the compressor, be sure all leaks are repaired, liquid control devices and any other system components are changed. Install the correct liquid line filter-drier. Driers must be compatible with the refrigerant and lubricant.

7. Be advised that POEs are very hygroscopic. They will very quickly absorb moisture from the air once the container is opened. Once the lubricant is added to the compressor, the compressor should be quickly installed. Like an open container, an open compressor with POE will absorb moisture. Add the correct amount of lubricant to the compressor. It is important that the system contain at least 50% POE. On systems using enhanced surfaces in the heat exchanger, excessive mineral oil can adversely effect the heat transfer due to logging. Therefore, it is desirable to have no more than 20% mineral oil in systems employing these type surfaces.

8. Once the compressor is installed and the system is closed, the system must be evacuated to 500 microns or lower. A vacuum decay test is suggested at this time to assure the system is dry and free of leaks.

9. REFRIGERANT CHARGING WITH "NEAR AZEOTROPES." Refrigerant R-401A is a near azeotropic mixture (see Copeland booklet 92-81 "Guide to Refrigerant Mixtures"). It is important that during initial charging or "topping" off a system that the refrigerant be removed from the charging cylinder in the liquid phase. Many of the cylinders for the newer refrigerants use a dip tube so that in the upright position liquid is drawn from the cylinder. DO NOT vapor charge out of a cylinder unless the entire cylinder is to be charged into the system. Refer to charging instructions provided by the refrigerant manufacturer.

With the system in a 500 micron or lower vacuum, liquid can be charged into the system "high side." The initial charge should be about 80% of the amount of refrigerant removed from the system.

Put the system into operation and observe its performance. Additional refrigerant may have to be added to the operating system to obtain optimum performance.

When adding refrigerant to an operating system, it may be necessary to add the refrigerant through the compressor suction service valve. Because the refrigerant leaving the refrigerant cylinder must be in the liquid phase, care must be exercised to avoid damage to the compressor. It is suggested that a sight glass be connected between the charging hose and the compressor suction service valve. This will permit your adjusting the cylinder hand valve so that liquid can leave the cylinder while allowing vapor to enter the compressor.

10. Operate the system and record the operating conditions. Compare this data to the base data taken in item 2. Check and adjust the expansion valve superheat setting if necessary. Make adjustment to other controls as needed.

11. Properly label the components. Tag the compressor with the refrigerant used (R-401A) and the lubricant used. The proper color code for R-401A is Coral Red PMS (Paint Matching System) 177.

12. Clean up and properly dispose of removed lubricant. Check local and state laws regarding the disposal of refrigerant lubricants. Recycle or reclaim the removed refrigerant.

CAUTION: These guidelines are intended for use with R-401A only, not for refrigerants which are similar to R-401A. *Other refrigerants may not be compatible with the materials used in our compressors or the lubricants recommended in this bulletin resulting in unacceptable reliability and durability of the compressor.*

Note: Retrofit Videos are available from your Authorized Copeland Wholesaler. Ask for VT-025.

The information contained herein is based on technical data and tests which we believe to be reliable and is intended for use by persons having technical skill, at their own discretion and risk. Since conditions of use are beyond Copeland's control, we can assume no liability for results obtained or damages incurred through the application of the data presented.

R-401A Saturated Vapor/Liquid Pressure/Temperature Chart

Press. PSIG	Vapor Temp. °F	Liquid Temp. °F	Press. PSIG	Vapor Temp. °F	Liquid Temp. °F	Press. PSIG	Vapor Temp. °F	Liquid Temp. °F	Press. PSIG	Vapor Temp. °F	Liquid Temp. °F
1	-13.7	-24.3	51	55.8	45.7	101	90.3	80.3	151	113.9	105.1
2	-9.8	-22.0	52	56.7	46.5	102	91.3	80.9	152	114.3	105.5
3	-7.4	-18.5	53	57.5	48.2	103	91.8	81.5	153	114.8	106.0
4	-5.1	-16.2	54	58.3	49.1	104	91.4	82.0	154	115.2	106.4
5	-2.9	-14.0	55	59.1	49.6	105	92.0	82.6	155	115.6	106.8
6	-0.8	-11.9	56	60.0	50.2	106	92.5	83.1	156	116.0	107.2
7	1.2	-9.8	57	60.8	50.7	107	93.0	83.7	157	116.4	107.7
8	3.2	-7.8	58	61.5	51.5	108	93.5	84.2	158	116.8	108.1
9	5.1	-5.9	59	62.3	52.2	109	94.1	84.8	159	117.2	108.6
10	6.9	-4.1	60	63.1	53.1	110	94.7	85.3	160	117.6	108.9
11	8.7	-2.3	61	63.9	53.9	111	95.2	85.9	161	118.0	109.3
12	10.4	-0.5	62	64.6	54.6	112	95.7	86.4	162	118.4	109.7
13	12.1	1.2	63	65.4	55.4	113	96.2	86.9	163	118.8	110.1
14	13.7	2.8	64	66.1	56.2	114	96.7	87.4	164	119.2	110.6
15	15.3	4.4	65	66.9	57.0	115	97.2	88.0	165	119.6	111.0
16	16.8	6.0	66	67.6	57.7	116	97.7	88.5	166	120.0	111.4
17	18.3	7.5	67	68.3	58.4	117	98.2	89.0	167	120.4	111.8
18	19.8	9.0	68	69.1	59.2	118	98.7	89.5	168	120.8	112.2
19	10.5	21.2	69	59.9	69.8	119	90.0	99.2	169	112.6	121.2
20	22.6	11.9	70	70.5	60.6	120	99.7	90.5	170	121.6	113.0
21	24.0	13.3	71	71.2	61.3	121	100.2	91.0	171	122.0	113.4
22	25.4	14.7	72	71.9	62.0	122	100.7	91.5	172	122.4	113.8
23	26.7	16.0	73	72.6	62.8	123	101.2	92.0	173	122.8	114.2
24	28.0	17.3	74	73.2	63.5	124	101.7	92.5	174	123.2	114.6
25	29.2	18.6	75	73.9	64.1	125	102.2	93.0	175	123.6	115.0
26	30.5	19.9	76	74.6	64.8	126	102.6	93.5	176	124.0	115.4
27	31.7	21.1	77	75.3	65.5	127	103.0	94.0	177	124.3	115.8
28	32.9	22.3	78	76.0	66.2	128	103.5	94.5	178	124.7	116.2
29	34.0	23.5	79	76.6	66.9	129	104.1	95.0	179	125.1	116.5
30	35.2	24.7	80	77.2	67.5	130	104.6	95.5	180	125.4	116.9
31	36.3	25.9	81	78.4	68.2	131	105.0	97.2	181	125.8	117.2
32	37.4	27.0	82	78.8	68.8	132	105.5	96.4	182	126.2	117.5
33	38.5	28.1	83	79.1	69.5	133	105.9	96.9	183	126.6	118.1
34	39.6	29.2	84	79.8	70.1	134	106.4	97.4	184	126.9	118.5
35	40.7	30.3	85	80.4	70.8	135	106.9	97.9	185	127.3	118.5
36	41.7	31.3	86	81.0	71.4	136	107.3	98.3	186	127.6	119.2
37	42.7	32.4	87	81.6	72.5	137	107.8	98.8	187	128.0	119.6
38	43.8	33.4	88	82.2	72.6	138	108.2	99.2	188	128.4	120.0
39	44.8	34.4	89	82.8	73.2	139	108.7	99.7	189	128.7	120.4
40	45.8	35.5	90	83.4	73.9	140	109.1	100.2	190	129.1	120.8
41	46.7	36.4	91	84.0	74.5	141	109.5	100.6	191	129.5	121.1
42	47.7	37.4	92	84.6	75.1	142	110.0	101.0	192	129.8	121.5
43	48.6	38.4	93	85.2	75.7	143	110.4	101.5	193	130.2	121.8
44	49.6	39.3	94	85.8	76.3	144	110.9	101.9	194	130.6	122.2
45	50.5	40.3	95	86.4	76.9	145	111.3	102.4	195	130.9	122.6
46	51.4	41.2	96	87.0	77.5	146	111.8	102.9	196	131.3	122.9
47	52.3	42.1	97	87.5	78.0	147	112.2	103.3	197	131.6	123.3
48	53.2	43.0	98	88.1	78.6	148	112.6	102.9	198	132.0	123.7
49	54.1	43.9	99	88.7	79.2	149	113.0	104.2	199	132.3	124.0
50	54.7	44.8	100	89.2	79.8	150	113.4	104.7	200	132.7	124.6

R-401A Saturated Vapor/Liquid Temperature/Pressure Chart

Temp. °F	Vapor Pressure PSIG	Liquid Pressure PSIG	Temp. °F	Vapor Pressure PSIG	Liquid Pressure PSIG	Temp. °F	Vapor Pressure PSIG	Liquid Pressure PSIG
-10	1.9	6.9	40	34.4	44.7	90	101.4	119.0
-9	2.3	7.4	41	35.3	45.8	91	103.2	121.0
-8	2.7	7.9	42	36.3	46.9	92	105.1	123.0
-7	3.2	8.4	43	37.3	48.0	93	106.9	125.0
-6	3.6	9.0	44	38.2	49.0	94	108.8	127.0
-5	4.0	9.5	45	39.2	50.2	95	110.7	129.0
-4	4.5	10.0	46	40.3	51.4	96	112.6	131.1
-3	4.9	10.6	47	41.3	52.5	97	114.6	133.2
-2	5.4	11.1	48	42.3	53.7	98	116.6	135.4
-1	5.9	11.7	49	43.4	54.9	99	118.6	137.5
0	6.4	12.3	50	44.5	56.1	100	120.6	139.7
1	6.9	12.9	51	45.6	57.4	101	122.6	141.9
2	7.4	13.5	52	46.7	58.6	102	124.7	144.1
3	7.9	14.1	53	47.8	59.9	103	126.8	146.3
4	8.4	14.7	54	48.9	61.1	104	128.9	148.6
5	9.0	15.4	55	50.0	62.4	105	131.0	150.9
6	9.5	16.0	56	51.2	63.7	106	133.1	153.2
7	10.0	16.6	57	52.4	65.1	107	135.3	155.5
8	10.6	17.3	58	53.6	66.4	108	137.5	157.9
9	11.2	18.0	59	54.8	67.8	109	139.8	160.2
10	11.8	18.9	60	56.1	69.1	110	142.0	162.4
11	12.4	19.4	61	57.3	70.5	111	144.3	165.1
12	13.0	20.0	62	58.6	71.9	112	146.6	167.5
13	13.5	20.8	63	59.9	73.4	113	148.9	170.0
14	14.2	21.5	64	61.2	74.8	114	151.3	172.5
15	14.8	22.2	65	62.5	76.3	115	153.6	175.0
16	15.5	23.0	66	63.8	77.7	116	156.0	177.6
17	16.1	23.7	67	65.2	79.2	117	159.5	180.1
18	16.8	24.5	68	66.5	80.8	118	160.9	182.8
19	17.4	25.3	69	67.9	82.3	119	163.4	185.4
20	18.1	26.0	70	69.3	83.9	120	165.9	188.0
21	18.8	26.9	71	70.7	85.4	121	168.4	190.7
22	19.5	27.7	72	72.1	87.0	122	171.0	193.4
23	20.3	28.6	73	73.6	88.6	123	174.6	196.1
24	21.0	29.4	74	75.1	90.2	124	176.2	198.9
25	21.7	30.3	75	76.6	91.9	125	178.8	201.7
26	22.5	31.1	76	78.1	93.6	126	181.5	204.5
27	23.3	32.0	77	79.7	95.2	127	184.2	207.3
28	24.0	32.9	78	81.2	97.0	128	186.9	210.2
29	24.8	33.8	79	82.8	98.7	129	189.7	213.1
30	25.6	34.7	80	84.4	100.4	130	192.5	216.0
31	26.4	35.7	81	86.0	102.2			
32	27.3	36.6	82	87.6	104.0			
33	28.1	37.6	83	89.3	105.8			
34	29.0	38.6	84	91.0	107.6			
35	29.8	39.6	85	92.6	109.4			
36	30.7	40.6	86	94.4	111.3			
37	31.6	41.6	87	96.1	113.2			
38	32.5	42.6	88	97.8	115.1			
39	33.4	43.7	89	99.6	117.0			

Form No. 93-02-R3 Revised 3-94
Supersedes Form No. 93-02-R2

Printed in U.S.A.
Copeland Corporation
Sidney, OH 45365-0669

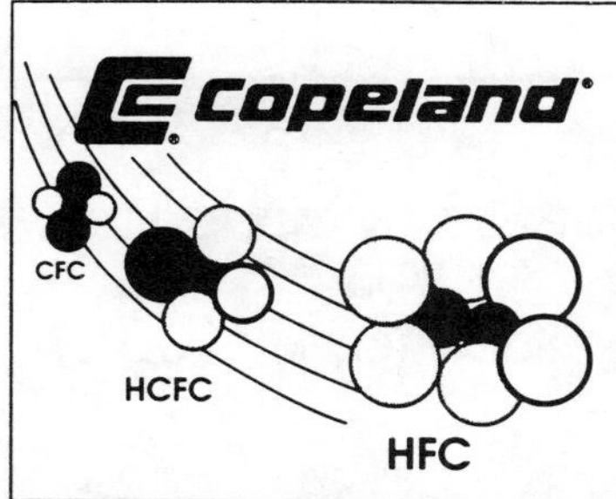

Refrigerant Changeover Guidelines

CFC-12 to R-401B (MP66)

Leading the Industry with Environmentally Responsible Refrigerant Solutions

Copeland does not advocate the wholesale changeover of CFC refrigerants to HCFCs or HFCs. If a system is not leaking refrigerant to the atmosphere, and is operating properly, there is no technical reason to replace the CFC refrigerant. In fact, changing the refrigerant may void the U.L. listing of the unit. However, once the decision has been made to make the change from CFC-12 (R-12) to the interim R-401B, the following guidelines are recommended.

CONSIDERATIONS

1. Retrofitting systems that employ compressors manufactured prior to 1973 is not recommended. This is due to the different materials used in motor insulation that have not been evaluated for compatibility with the new refrigerants and lubricants. Failure to heed this advice will violate the proposed U.L. Standard For Field Conversion/Retrofit Of Alternate Refrigerants In Refrigeration and Air Conditioning Equipment (U.L. 2170-2172).

2. Copeland's lubricant recommendation for use with R-401B is a mixture of 50% mineral oil and 50% alkylbenzene (Zerol 200TD). Polyol ester lubricants, Mobil EAL™ Arctic 22 CC or ICI EMKARATE RL 32S, can also be used with R-401B if the system is expected to be changed in the near future to an HFC refrigerant such as R-401B. This will eliminate the need of having to flush the system again when making the R-134a retrofit.

Refer to item11 in this section for a list of other approved lubricants for use with R-401B or Application Engineering Bulletin 17-1248 for a complete list of all Copeland approved lubricants.

3. R-401B should be used only in systems where the saturated suction temperature is maintained between -40°F and -10°F. **It should not be mixed with any other refrigerant!**

4. The expansion valve may need to be changed. The existing R-12 valve when used with R-401B will have approximately 25% more capacity. Oversized expansion valves can result in hunting and refrigerant floodback. Consult with the thermostatic expansion valve manufacturer for the correct valve and size.

5. Filter-driers must be changed at the time of conversion. This is proper air conditioning/refrigeration practice.

a. Solid core driers such as ALCO ADK, are compatible with either R-12 or R-401B.

b. Compacted bead driers can use XH6 or XH9 molecular sieve material such as found in the ALCO UltraFlow or EK or EKH series, or Copeland PureFlow.

c. If a loose fill type drier is to be used, XH9 molecular sieve is required.

6. R-401B exhibits marginally higher pressures than R-12 at normal condensing temperatures.We do not believe this will require readjustment of safety controls; however, you should verify this with the system manufacturer or component suppliers.

7. Systems that use a low pressure controller to maintain space temperature may have to have the cut-out and cut-in points changed. With R-401B, the pressure setting must reflect an average temperature of the refrigerant in the evaporator. Because of refrigerant glide (see Copeland booklet 92-81, "Guide To Refrigerant Mixtures"), the refrigerant entering the evaporator for a specific suction pressure will be approximately 8°F colder than the refrigerant vapor at the outlet of the evaporator (not considering superheat). Therefore, the average refrigerant

WARNING: Use only Copeland approved refrigerants and lubricants in the manner prescribed by Copeland. In some circumstances, other refrigerants and lubricants may be dangerous and could cause fires, explosions or electrical shorting. Contact Copeland Corp., Sidney, Ohio.

temperature will be at a midpoint pressure/temperature equivalent.

Example: A -5°F refrigerated space usually requires that the refrigerant temperature in the evaporator be approximately -15°F. Using R-402B, the entering liquid temperature may be as cold as -19°F and the vapor temperature before superheat may be -11°F. Taking the saturated vapor pressure at -11° F gives us the exit pressure at the evaporator of 3.3 psig. Considering a 2 psig pressure drop in the suction line, the pressure control cut-out should be set at 1.3 psig.

The cut-in point will be based on the vapor pressure/ temperature value. Let's assume that the space temperature can rise to -2°F before the compressor is turned on. -2°F vapor pressure is 7.6 psig. Set the cut-in at 8 psig.

8. Because of glide, pressure regulators such as EPRs may have to be reset. Contact the EPR manufacturer for correct settings.

9. Due to refrigerant glide, it is important that when measuring and/or adjusting TEV superheat, the pressure and SATURATED VAPOR TABLES be used. Example: The pressure measured at the TEV bulb is 7 psig. The Pressure/Temperature (P/T) chart shows that the saturated vapor temperature for 7 psig is -3.2°F. If the actual refrigerant temperature measured is 6°F, the superheat is 6.2°F.

To measure sub-cooling at the condenser outlet or at the TEV inlet to verify that a solid column of liquid is present, measure the pressure and the refrigerant temperature at the location that the sub-cooling information is needed. Compare it to the saturated liquid temperature from the SATURATED LIQUID TABLES. Example: A pressure of 175 psig is measured at the condenser coil outlet. From the P/T chart, 175 psig is 110.2°F saturated liquid temperature. If the actual refrigerant temperature is 105°F, the liquid is sub-cooled 5.2°F.

10. Systems using R-401B may have a lower system pressure drop than with R-12. Because of the lower pressure drop, pilot operated solenoid valves and pressure regulators may not operate. Check with the manufacturer of any pressure regulators and pilot operated solenoid valves used in the system to be sure that they will operate properly. These controls may have to be downsized.

11. Mineral oil lubricant only, such as 3GS, cannot be used as the compressor lubricant. Copeland recommends the following lubricant choices:

1. A mixture of 3GS Mineral Oil (MO) and Zerol 200TD Alkyl Benzene (AB) with a minimum of 50% AB
2. Virginia KMP MS2212 (a 70/30 mixture of AB/MO)
3. A mixture of 3GS Mineral Oil (MO) and Polyol Ester (POE) ie; Mobil EAL Arctic 22 CC or EMKARATE RL 32S with a minimum of 50% POE
4. 100% Mobil EAL Arctic 22 CC or ICI EMKARATE RL 32S

Before starting the changeover, it is suggested that at a minimum the following items be ready:

1. Safety glasses
2. Gloves
3. Refrigerant service gauges
4. Electronic thermometer
5. Vacuum pump capable of pulling 250 microns
6. Thermcouple micron gauge
7. Leak detector
8. Refrigerant recovery unit including refrigerant cylinder
9. Proper container for removed lubricant
10. New liquid control device
11. Replacement liquid line filter-drier(s)
12. New lubricant
    a. Zerol 200TD (AB) or Virginia KMP MS 2212 (AB)
    b. Mobil EAL Arctic 22 CC or ICI EMKARATE RL 32S (POE)
13. R-401B pressure temperature chart
14. R-401B refrigerant

CHANGEOVER PROCEDURE

1. The system should be thoroughly leak tested with the R-12 refrigerant still in the system. All leaks should be repaired before the R-401B refrigerant is added.

2. It is advisable that the system operating conditions be recorded with the R-12 still in the system. This will provide the base data for comparison when the system is put back into operation with the R-401B.

3. The system should be electrically shut off and the refrigerant properly removed from the system. Measure the quantity of refrigerant removed. This will provide a guide for recharging the system with R-401B (see item 9 this section).

4. The mineral oil lubricant must be removed from the compressor crankcase. Hermetic compressors will have to be removed from the piping and the lubricant drained out through the suction stub. It is advisable to do an acid test on the oil.

5. Measure the amount of lubricant removed. It should be within 4 to 6 ounces of the compressor's factory oil charge. The lubricant charge is indicated on the name plate of Copelaweld® compressors. Copelametic® compressor oil charges can be found in Application Engineering Bulletin 4-1281. If the lubricant charge is unknown, an authorized

Copeland wholesaler can provide the technician with the information.

If the amount of lubricant removed is less than 50% of the factory charge, it will be necessary to flush the excess lubricant from system.

Those systems that have oil separators, oil reservoirs, oil floats and suction line accumulators must have the oil drained from them. If the liquid control device is going to be replaced, it is advisable that the suction line, liquid line and evaporator coil be blown clean using properly regulated dry nitrogen.

NOTE: Properly dispose of the lubricant.

6. Before the new lubricant is installed into the compressor, be sure all leaks are repaired, liquid control devices and any other system components are changed. Install the correct liquid line filter-drier. Driers must be compatible with the refrigerant and lubricant.

7. Be advised that POEs are very hygroscopic. They will very quickly absorb moisture from the air once the container is opened. Once the lubricant is added to the compressor, the compressor should be quickly installed. Like an open container, an open compressor with POE will absorb moisture. Add the correct amount of lubricant to the compressor. It is important that the system contain at least 50% POE. On systems using enhanced surfaces in the heat exchanger, excessive mineral oil can adversely effect the heat transfer due to logging. Therefore, it is desirable to have no more than 20% mineral oil in systems employing these type surfaces.

8. Once the compressor is installed and the system is closed, the system must be evacuated to 250 microns or lower. A vacuum decay test is suggested to assure the system is dry and leak free.

9. REFRIGERANT CHARGING WITH "NEAR AZEOTROPES." Refrigerant R-401B is a near azeotropic mixture (see Copeland booklet 92-81 "Guide to Refrigerant Mixtures"). It is important that during initial charging or "topping" off a system that the refrigerant be removed from the charging cylinder in the liquid phase. Many of the cylinders for the newer refrigerants use a dip tube so that in the upright position liquid is drawn from the cylinder. DO NOT vapor charge out of a cylinder unless the entire cylinder is to be charged into the system. Refer to charging instructions provided by the refrigerant manufacturer.

With the system in a 250 micron or lower vacuum, liquid can be charged into the system high side. The initial charge should be about 80% of the amount of refrigerant removed from the system.

Put the system into operation and observe its performance. Additional refrigerant may have to be added to the operating system to obtain optimum performance.

When adding refrigerant to an operating system, it may be necessary to add the refrigerant through the compressor suction service valve. Because the refrigerant leaving the refrigerant cylinder must be in the liquid phase, care must be exercised to avoid damage to the compressor. It is suggested that a sight glass be connected between the charging hose and the compressor suction service valve. This will permit your adjusting the cylinder hand valve so that liquid can leave the cylinder while allowing vapor to enter the compressor.

10. Operate the system and record the operating conditions. Compare this data to the base data taken in item 2 this section. Make adjustments as needed.

11. Properly label the components. Tag the compressor with the refrigerant used (R-401B) and the lubricant used. The proper color code for R-401B is Light Gray Green PMS (Paint Matching System) 413.

12. Clean up and properly dispose of removed lubricant. Check local and state laws regarding the disposal of refrigerant lubricants. Recycle or reclaim the removed refrigerant.

CAUTION: These guidelines are intended for use with R-401B only, not for refrigerants which are similar to R-401B. *Other refrigerants may not be compatible with the materials used in our compressors or the lubricants recommended in this bulletin resulting in unacceptable reliability and durability of the compressor.*

Note: Retrofit videos are avialable from your Authorized Copeland Wholesaler. Ask for VT-025.

R-401B Saturated Vapor/Liquid Pressure/Temperature Chart

Pressure PSIG	Vapor Temp. °F	Liquid Temp. °F
(13)	-40.5	-51.1
(12)	-38.8	-49.1
(11)	-36.5	-47.1
(10)	-34.6	-45.2
(9)	-32.8	-43.4
(8)	-31.1	-41.6
(7)	-29.4	-40.0
(6)	-27.8	-38.4
(5)	-26.3	-36.8
(4)	-24.8	-35.3
(3)	-23.3	-33.8
(2)	-21.9	-32.4
(1)	-20.5	-31.0
0	-19.2	-29.6
1	-16.6	-26.9
2	-14.1	-24.4
3	-11.7	-22.0
4	-9.4	-19.7
5	-7.3	-17.5
6	-5.2	-15.4
7	-3.2	-13.4
8	-1.2	-11.4
9	0.6	-9.5
10	2.5	-7.6
11	4.2	-5.8
12	5.9	-4.1
13	7.6	-2.4
14	9.2	-0.8
15	10.8	0.8
16	11.7	2.3
17	13.8	3.9
18	15.3	5.3
19	16.7	6.8
20	18.1	8.2
21	19.4	9.6
22	20.8	10.9
23	22.1	12.3
24	23.3	13.6
25	24.6	14.9
26	25.8	16.1
27	27.0	17.3
28	28.2	18.5
29	29.4	19.7
30	30.5	20.9
31	31.6	22.0
32	32.7	23.2
33	33.8	24.3
34	34.9	25.4
35	35.9	26.4
36	37.0	27.5
37	38.0	28.5
38	39.0	29.6
39	40.0	30.6
40	41.0	31.6
45	45.7	35.4
50	50.1	40.8
55	53.4	45.0
60	58.1	49.0
65	61.9	52.9
70	65.1	56.5
75	68.8	60.0
80	72.1	63.3
85	75.2	66.5
90	78.2	69.6
95	81.1	72.5
100	83.9	75.4
105	86.6	76.2
110	89.3	80.9
115	91.8	83.5
120	94.3	86.0
125	96.7	88.5
130	99.1	91.4
135	101.3	93.3
140	103.6	95.5
145	105.7	98.8
150	107.9	100.4
155	109.9	102.1
160	112.0	104.2
165	114.0	106.2
170	115.9	108.2
175	117.8	110.2
180	119.7	112.1
185	121.4	114.0
190	123.3	115.9
195	125.1	117.7
200	126.8	119.8
205	128.5	121.2
210	130.0	123.0
215	131.8	124.7
220	133.5	126.3
225	135.0	128.0
230	138.6	129.5
235	138.2	131.1

( ) Inches Vacuum

Copeland Corporation • 1675 W. Campbell Road, Sidney, Ohio 45365-0669 • (513) 498-3011

R-401B Saturated Vapor/Liquid Temperature/Pressure Chart

Temp. °F	Vapor Press. PSIG	Liquid Press. PSIG	Temp. °F	Vapor Press. PSIG	Liquid Press PSIG	Temp. °F	Vapor Press. PSIG	Liquid Press. PSIG	Temp. °F	Vapor Press. PSIG	Liquid Press. PSIG
-40	(12.9)	(7.0)	10	14.5	21.3	60	62.5	75.0	110	155.1	174.5
-39	(12.3)	(6.4)	11	15.1	22.0	61	63.8	76.6	111	157.6	177.0
-38	(11.8)	(5.8)	12	15.8	22.8	62	65.2	78.1	112	160.1	179.7
-37	(11.3)	(5.1)	13	16.5	23.6	63	66.5	79.6	113	162.2	182.3
-36	(10.7)	(4.5)	14	17.1	24.3	64	68.0	81.1	114	165.2	185.0
-35	(10.2)	(3.8)	15	17.8	25.1	65	69.4	82.7	115	167.7	187.7
-34	(9.7)	(3.1)	16	18.5	25.9	66	70.8	84.2	116	170.2	190.4
-33	(9.1)	(2.4)	17	19.2	26.7	67	72.3	85.8	117	172.9	193.1
-32	(8.5)	(1.8)	18	19.9	27.5	68	73.8	87.4	118	175.5	195.9
-31	(7.9)	(1.0)	19	20.7	28.4	69	75.3	89.1	119	178.2	198.7
-30	(7.3)	(0.3)	20	21.4	29.3	70	76.8	90.7	120	180.9	210.5
-29	(6.7)	0.2	21	22.2	30.0	71	78.3	92.4	121	183.5	204.4
-28	(6.1)	0.6	22	22.9	31.0	72	79.9	94.1	122	186.4	207.2
-27	(5.5)	1.0	23	23.7	31.9	73	81.5	95.8	123	189.1	210.3
-26	(4.8)	1.4	24	24.5	32.8	74	83.1	97.5	124	191.9	213.1
-25	(4.2)	1.8	25	25.3	33.7	75	84.7	99.3	125	195.8	216.0
-24	(3.5)	2.2	26	26.1	34.6	76	86.3	101.1	126	197.7	219.0
-23	(2.8)	2.6	27	27.0	35.5	77	88.0	102.8	127	200.6	222.0
-22	(2.1)	3.0	28	27.8	36.5	78	89.6	104.7	128	203.5	225.1
-21	(1.3)	3.4	29	28.9	37.5	79	91.3	106.5	129	206.5	228.2
-20	(0.6)	3.9	30	29.5	38.4	80	93.1	108.3	130	209.5	231.3
-19	0.1	4.3	31	30.4	39.4	81	94.8	110.2			
-18	0.5	4.8	32	31.2	40.6	82	96.6	112.1			
-17	0.8	5.2	33	32.2	41.5	83	98.3	114.0			
-16	1.2	5.7	34	33.2	42.5	84	100.1	116.0			
-15	1.6	6.2	35	34.1	43.6	85	102.0	117.9			
-14	2.0	6.7	36	35.1	44.6	86	103.8	119.4			
-13	2.5	7.2	37	36.0	45.7	87	105.7	121.9			
-12	2.9	7.7	38	37.0	46.8	88	107.6	124.0			
-11	3.3	8.2	39	38.0	47.9	89	109.5	126.0			
-10	3.8	8.7	40	39.0	49.1	90	111.4	128.1			
-9	4.2	9.3	41	40.0	50.2	91	113.4	130.2			
-8	4.7	9.8	42	41.0	51.4	92	115.4	132.3			
-7	5.1	10.4	43	42.1	52.6	93	117.4	134.4			
-6	5.6	10.9	44	43.2	53.7	94	119.4	119.4			
-5	6.1	11.5	45	44.3	55.0	95	121.4	138.8			
-4	6.6	12.1	46	45.4	56.2	96	123.5	123.5			
-3	7.1	12.7	47	46.5	57.4	97	143.2	143.2			
-2	7.6	13.3	48	47.6	58.7	98	127.7	145.5			
-1	8.1	13.9	49	48.8	59.9	99	129.9	147.8			
0	8.7	14.5	50	49.9	61.2	100	132.0	150.1			
1	9.2	15.1	51	51.1	62.5	101	134.2	152.4			
2	9.7	15.8	52	52.3	63.9	102	136.5	154.8			
3	10.3	16.4	53	53.5	65.2	103	138.7	157.1			
4	10.9	17.1	54	54.7	66.5	104	141.0	159.6			
5	11.5	17.8	55	56.0	67.9	105	143.3	162.0			
6	12.0	18.5	56	57.3	69.3	106	145.6	164.4			
7	12.6	19.2	57	58.5	70.7	107	147.9	166.9			
8	13.2	19.9	58	59.8	72.2	108	150.3	169.4			
9	13.9	20.6	59	61.1	73.6	109	152.7	172.0			

( ) Inches Vacuum

Form No. 93-03-R3 Revised 3-94
Supersedes Form No. 93-03-R2

Printed in U.S.A.
Copeland Corporation
Sidney, OH 45365-0669

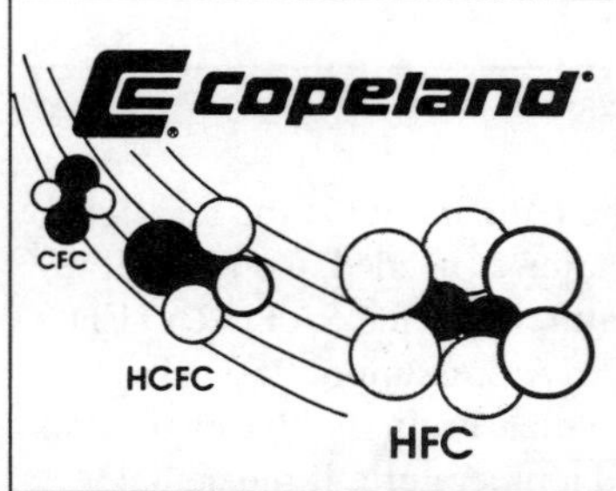

Refrigerant Changeover Guidelines

R-502 to R-402A (SUVA® HP80)

Leading the Industry with Environmentally Responsible Refrigerant Solutions

Copeland does not advocate the wholesale changeover of CFC refrigerants to HCFCs or HFCs. If a system is not leaking refrigerant to the atmosphere, and is operating properly, there is no technical need to replace the CFC refrigerant. In fact, changing the refrigerant may void the U.L. listing of the unit. However, once the decision has been made to make the change from R-502 to the interim R-402A (SUVA® HP80), the following guidelines are recommended.

CONSIDERATIONS

1. Retrofitting systems that employ compressors manufactured prior to 1973 is not recommended. This is due to the different materials used in motor insulation that have not been evaluated for compatibility with the new refrigerants and lubricants. Failure to heed this advice will violate the proposed U.L. Standard For Field Conversion/Retrofit Of Alternate Refrigerants In Refrigeration and Air Conditioning Equipment (U.L. 2170-2172).

2. Copeland's lubricant recommendation for use with R-402A is a mixture of 50% mineral oil and 50% alkylbenzene (Zerol 200TD). Polyol ester lubricants, Mobil EAL™ Arctic 22 CC or ICI EMKARATE RL 32S, can also be used with R-402A if the system is expected to be changed in the near future to an HFC refrigerant such as R-404A. This will eliminate the need of having to flush the system again when making the R-404A retrofit.

Refer to item 12 in this section for a list of other approved lubricants for use with R-402A or Application Engineering Bulletin 17-1248 for a complete list of all Copeland approved lubricants.

3. R-402A should be used only in systems that currently use R-502. It should not be mixed with R-502 or any other refrigerant nor should it be used to replace R-12 or R-22.

4. The capacity of the existing R-502 thermal expansion valve (TEV) will be approximately the same when using R-402A. However, the superheat setting must be checked and may have to be readjusted after the system is put back into operation.

Consult with the TEV manufacturer for correct sizing and superheat settings.

5. Filter-driers must be changed at the time of conversion. This is proper air conditioning/refrigeration practice.

a. Solid core driers, such as ALCO ADK, are compatible with either R-502 or R-402A.

b. Compacted bead driers can use XH6 or XH9 molecular sieve material such as found in the ALCO UltraFlow, EK or EKH series, or Copeland PureFlow.

c. If a loose fill type drier is to be used, XH9 molecular sieve is required.

6. Because of glide, pressure regulators such as EPR valves may have to be reset. Contact the EPR manufacturer for the correct settings.

7. R-402A exhibits higher pressures than R-502 at normal condensing temperatures. This may require the high pressure safety control be reset in order to operate as intended.

8. The higher pressure characteristics exhibited by R-402A will in some cases exceed the industry accepted safety factors on the compressor crankcase (low side). This will require the addition of a pressure relief valve on the

WARNING: Use only Copeland approved refrigerants and lubricants in the manner prescribed by Copeland. In some circumstances, other refrigerants and lubricants may be dangerous and could cause fires. explosions or electrical shorting. Contact Copeland Corp., Sidney, Ohio.

compressor crankcase, set at a maximum of 375 psig to adequately protect the compressor from the possibility of excessive pressure. Semi-hermetic compressors manufactured before 1993 that require this additional valve are:

- Discus® 3D, 4D, MD, and 9D
- All other semi-hermetic (non-Discus models)

> WARNING: IT IS POSSIBLE THAT EXCESS PRESSURE BUILD-UP ON MODELS INDICATED COULD RESULT IN THE COMPRESSOR EXPLODING UNLESS THE PRESSURE RELIEF VALVE SPECIFIED HAS BEEN PROPERLY INSTALLED ON THE ORIGINALLY BUILT COPELAND COMPRESSOR.

Pressure relief valves can be purchased from your Authorized Copeland wholesaler as part number 998-0051-02.

9. Systems that use a low pressure controller to maintain space temperature may need to have the cut in and cut out points changed. With R-402A, the pressure settings must reflect on average temperature of the refrigerant in the evaporator. Because of refrigerant glide (see Copeland booklet 92-81, "Guide To Refrigerant Mixtures"), the refrigerant entering the evaporator for a specific suction pressure will be approximately 2°F colder than the refrigerant vapor at the outlet of the evaporator (not considering superheat). Therefore, the average refrigerant temperature will be at a midpoint pressure/temperature equivalent.

Example: A -10°F refrigerated space usually requires that the refrigerant temperature in the evaporator be approximately -20°F. Using R-402A, the liquid entering the evaporator may be as cold as -21°F and the vapor temperature before superheat may be -19°F. Taking the saturated vapor pressure at -19°F gives us the exit pressure at the evaporator of 19.1 psig. Considering a 2 psig pressure drop in the suction line, the pressure control cut out should be set at 17.1 psig.

10. Due to refrigerant glide, it is important that when measuring and/or adjusting TEV superheat, the pressure and SATURATED VAPOR TABLES be used. Example: The pressure measured at the TEV bulb is 18 psig. The Pressure/Temperature (P/T) chart shows that the saturated vapor temperature for 18 psig is -20.7°F. If the actual refrigerant temperature measured is -15.7°F, the superheat is 5°F.

To measure sub-cooling at the condenser outlet or at the TEV inlet to verify that a solid column of liquid is present, measure the pressure and the temperature at the location that the sub-cooling information is needed. Compare it to the saturated liquid temperature from the SATURATED LIQUID TABLES. Example: A pressure of 250 psig is measured at the condenser outlet. From the P/T chart, 250 psig is 99°F saturated liquid temperature. If the actual refrigerant temperature is 89°F, the liquid is sub-cooled 10°F.

11. Systems using R-402A may have a lower system pressure drop than with R-502. Check with the manufacturer of any pressure regulators and pilot operated solenoid valves used in the system to be sure that they will operate properly. These controls may have to be downsized.

12. Mineral oil lubricant only, such as 3GS, cannot be used as the compressor lubricant. Copeland recommends the following lubricant choices:

1. A mixture of 3GS Mineral Oil (MO) and Zerol 200TD Alkyl Benzene (AB) with a minimum of 50% AB
2. Virginia KMP MS2212 (a 70/30 mixture of AB/MO)
3. A mixture of 3GS Mineral Oil (MO) and Polyol Ester (POE) ie; Mobil EAL Arctic 22 CC or ICI EMKARATE RL 32S with a minimum of 50% POE
4. 100% Mobil EAL Arctic 22 CC or ICI EMKARATE RL 32S

Before starting the changeover, it is suggested that at least the following items be ready:

1. Safety glasses
2. Gloves
3. Refrigerant service gauges
4. Electronic thermometer
5. Vacuum pump capable of pulling 250 microns
6. Thermocouple micron gauge
7. Leak detector
8. Refrigerant recovery unit including refrigerant cylinder
9. Proper container for removed lubricant
10. New liquid control device
11. Replacement liquid line filter-drier(s)
12. New lubricant
    a. Zerol 200TD (AB)
    b. or Virginia KMP MS 2212 (AB/MO mixture)
    b. or Mobil EAL Arctic 22 CC or ICI EMKARATE RL 32S (POE)
13. R-402A pressure temperature chart
14. R-402A refrigerant

CHANGEOVER PROCEDURE

1. The system should be thoroughly leak tested with the R-502 refrigerant still in the system. All leaks should be repaired before the R-402A refrigerant is added.

2. It is recommended that system operating conditions be recorded with the R-502 still in the system. This will provide the base data for comparison when the system is put back into operation with the R-402A.

3. The system should be electrically shut off and the refrigerant properly removed from the system. Measure the quantity of refrigerant removed. This will provide a guide for recharging the system with R-402A (see item 9 this section).

4. The mineral oil must be removed from the compressor crankcase. Hermetic compressors will have to be removed from the piping and the lubricant drained out through the suction stub. It is advisable to do an acid test on lubricant removed.

5. Measure the amount of lubricant removed. It should be within 4 to 6 ounces of the compressor's factory oil charge. The lubricant charge is indicated on the name plate of Copelaweld® compressors. Copelametic® compressor oil charges can be found in Application Engineering Bulletin 4-1281. If the lubricant charge is unknown, an authorized Copeland wholesaler can provide the technician with the information.

If the amount of lubricant removed is less than 50% of the factory charge, it will be necessary to flush the excess lubricant from the system.

Those systems that have oil separators, oil reservoirs, oil floats and suction line accumulators must have the oil drained from them. If the liquid control device is going to be replaced, it is advisable that the suction line, liquid line and evaporator coil be blown clean using properly regulated dry nitrogen.

NOTE: Properly dispose of the lubricant.

6. Before the new lubricant is installed into the compressor, be sure all leaks are repaired, liquid control device and any other system components are changed. Install the correct liquid line filter-drier. Driers must be compatible with the refrigerant and lubricant.

7. Be advised that POEs are very hygroscopic. They will very quickly absorb moisture from the air once the container is opened. Once the lubricant is added to the compressor, the compressor should be quickly installed. Like an open container, an open compressor with POE will absorb moisture. Add the correct amount of lubricant to the compressor. It is important that the system contain a minimum of 50% AB or POE. On systems using enhanced surfaces in the heat exchanger, excessive mineral oil can adversely effect the heat transfer due to logging. Therefore, it is desirable to have no more than 20% mineral oil in systems employing these type surfaces.

8. Once the compressor is installed and the system is closed, the system must be evacuated to 250 microns or lower.

9. REFRIGERANT CHARGING WITH "NEAR AZEOTROPES." R-402A is a near azeotropic mixture (see Copeland booklet 92-81 "Guide to Refrigerant Mixtures"). It is important that during initial charging or "topping" off a system that the refrigerant be removed from the charging cylinder in the liquid phase. Many of the cylinders for the newer refrigerants use a dip tube so that in the upright position liquid is drawn from the cylinder. DO NOT vapor charge out of a cylinder unless the entire cylinder is to be charged into the system. Refer to charging instructions provided by the refrigerant manufacturer.

With the system in a 250 micron or lower vacuum, liquid can be charged into the system "high side." The initial charge should be approximately 80% of the amount of refrigerant removed from the system.

10. Start the system and observe its operation. Additional refrigerant may have to be added to obtain optimum performance.

When adding refrigerant to an operating system, it may be necessary to add the refrigerant through the compressor suction service valve. Because the refrigerant leaving the refrigerant cylinder must be in the liquid phase, care must be exercised to avoid damage to the compressor. It is suggested that a sight glass be connected between the charging hose and the compressor suction service valve. This will permit your adjusting the cylinder hand valve so that liquid can leave the cylinder while allowing vapor to enter the compressor.

11. Operate the system and record the operating conditions. Compare this data to the data taken in item 2 of this section. Check and adjust the TEV superheat setting if necessary. Make adjustment to other controls as needed.

12. Properly label the components. Tag the compressor with the refrigerant used (R-402A) and the lubricant used. The proper color code for R-402A is Light Brown PMS (Paint Matching System) 461.

13. Clean up and properly dispose of removed lubricant.

Check local and state laws regarding the disposal of refrigerant lubricants. Recycle or reclaim the removed refrigerant.

CAUTION: These guidelines are intended for use with R-402A only, not for refrigerants which are similar to R-402A. *Other refrigerants may not be compatible with the materials used in our compressors or the lubricants recommended in this bulletin resulting in unacceptable reliability and durability of the compressor.*

Note: Retrofit Videos are available from your Authorized Copeland Wholesaler. Ask for VT-027.

The information contained herein is based on technical data and tests which we believe to be reliable and is intended for use by persons having technical skill, at their own discretion and risk. Since conditions of use are beyond Copeland's control, we can assume no liability for results obtained or damages incurred through the application of the data presented.

R-402A Saturated Vapor/Liquid Temperature/Pressure Chart

Temp. °F	Vapor Press. PSIG	Liquid Press. PSIG	Temp. °F	Vapor Press. PSIG	Liquid Press PSIG	Temp. °F	Vapor Press. PSIG	Liquid Press. PSIG	Temp. °F	Vapor Press. PSIG	Liquid Press. PSIG
-40	5.8	7.6	10	47.1	50.2	60	132.7	137.3	110	285.7	290.9
-39	6.4	8.1	11	48.3	51.5	61	135.0	139.6	111	289.6	294.9
-38	6.9	8.7	12	49.5	52.7	62	137.4	142.0	112	293.6	298.8
-37	7.4	9.2	13	50.8	54.0	63	139.7	144.4	113	297.6	302.8
-36	8.0	9.8	14	52.0	55.3	64	142.1	146.8	114	301.6	306.9
-35	8.5	10.4	15	53.3	56.6	65	144.6	149.2	115	305.7	311.0
-34	9.1	11.0	16	54.6	57.9	66	147.0	151.7	116	309.8	315.1
-33	9.7	11.6	17	55.9	59.3	67	149.5	154.2	117	314.0	319.2
-32	10.3	12.2	18	57.2	60.6	68	152.0	156.7	118	318.2	323.4
-31	10.9	12.9	19	58.6	62.0	69	154.6	159.3	119	322.4	327.6
-30	11.5	13.5	20	60.0	63.4	70	157.1	161.9	120	326.7	331.9
-29	12.1	14.2	21	61.4	64.8	71	159.7	164.5	121	331.0	336.2
-28	12.8	14.8	22	62.8	66.3	72	162.2	167.1	122	335.3	340.5
-27	13.4	15.5	23	64.2	67.8	73	165.0	169.8	123	339.8	344.9
-26	14.1	16.2	24	65.7	69.2	74	167.7	172.5	124	344.2	349.3
-25	14.8	16.9	25	67.2	70.7	75	170.4	175.3	125	348.7	353.8
-24	15.4	17.6	26	68.6	72.3	76	173.1	178.0	126	353.2	358.3
-23	16.2	18.3	27	70.2	73.8	77	175.9	181.0	127	357.8	365.9
-22	16.9	19.1	28	71.7	75.4	78	178.7	183.6	128	362.4	367.4
-21	17.6	19.8	29	73.2	77.0	79	181.5	186.6	129	367.1	372.1
-20	18.3	20.6	30	74.8	78.6	80	184.4	189.6	130	371.7	376.7
-19	19.1	21.4	31	76.4	80.2	81	187.3	192.4			
-18	19.8	22.1	32	78.0	81.8	82	190.2	195.2			
-17	20.6	23.0	33	79.7	83.5	83	193.2	198.2			
-16	21.4	23.8	34	81.3	85.2	84	196.2	201.2			
-15	22.2	24.6	35	83.0	86.9	85	199.2	204.2			
-14	23.0	25.4	36	84.7	88.6	86	202.2	207.3			
-13	23.8	26.3	37	86.5	90.4	87	205.3	210.4			
-12	24.7	27.2	38	88.2	92.2	88	208.4	213.5			
-11	25.6	28.1	39	90.0	94.0	89	211.6	216.7			
-10	24.4	29.0	40	91.8	95.8	90	214.7	219.9			
-9	27.3	29.9	41	93.6	97.6	91	218.0	223.1			
-8	28.2	30.8	42	95.4	99.5	92	221.2	226.4			
-7	29.1	31.8	43	97.3	101.4	93	224.5	229.7			
-6	30.0	32.7	44	99.2	103.3	94	227.8	233.0			
-5	31.0	33.7	45	101.1	105.2	95	231.2	236.4			
-4	32.0	34.7	46	103.0	107.2	96	234.6	239.8			
-3	33.0	35.7	47	105.0	109.2	97	238.0	243.2			
-2	33.9	36.7	48	107.0	111.2	98	241.4	246.6			
-1	34.9	37.8	49	109.0	113.2	99	244.9	250.2			
0	36.0	38.8	50	111.0	115.3	100	248.4	253.7			
1	37.0	39.9	51	113.1	117.4	101	252.0	257.3			
2	38.0	41.0	52	115.1	119.5	102	255.6	260.8			
3	39.1	42.0	53	117.3	121.6	103	259.2	264.5			
4	40.2	43.2	54	119.4	123.8	104	262.9	268.1			
5	41.3	44.3	55	121.5	126.0	105	266.6	271.9			
6	42.4	45.5	56	123.7	128.2	106	270.4	275.6			
7	43.6	46.6	57	125.9	130.4	107	274.2	279.4			
8	44.7	47.8	58	128.2	132.7	108	277.9	283.2			
9	45.9	49.0	59	130.4	135.0	109	281.8	287.1			

R-402A Saturated Vapor/Liquid Pressure/Temperature Chart

Press. PSIG	Vapor Temp. °F	Liquid Temp. °F	Press. PSIG	Vapor Temp. °F	Liquid Temp. °F	Press. PSIG	Vapor Temp. °F	Liquid Temp. °F	Press. PSIG	Vapor Temp. °F	Liquid Temp. °F
5	-41.6	-45.0	55	16.2	13.6	105	47.0	44.9	335	121.9	120.7
6	-39.8	-42.9	56	16.9	14.3	106	47.5	45.4	340	123.0	121.9
7	-37.9	-41.1	57	17.6	15.2	107	48.0	45.9	345	124.2	123.0
8	-36.0	-39.6	58	18.3	16.0	108	48.5	46.2	350	125.3	124.1
9	-34.6	-37.7	59	19.1	16.7	109	49.0	46.9	355	126.4	125.3
10	-33.2	-35.8	60	20.0	17.4	110	49.5	47.4	360	127.5	126.3
11	-31.4	-34.0	61	20.7	18.1	115	51.9	49.9	365	128.6	127.5
12	-29.8	-32.7	62	21.4	18.9	129	54.1	52.1	370	129.6	128.5
13	-27.8	-31.4	63	22.0	19.5	125	56.6	54.6	375	130.7	129.6
14	-26.6	-29.6	64	22.8	20.2	130	58.8	56.8	380	131.7	130.7
15	-25.3	-27.9	65	23.4	20.9	135	61.0	59.0	385	132.8	131.7
16	-23.6	-26.6	66	24.1	21.6	140	63.1	61.2	390	133.8	132.8
17	-21.9	-25.4	67	24.8	22.2	145	65.2	63.3	395	134.8	133.8
18	-20.7	-23.7	68	25.5	22.9	150	67.2	65.3	400	135.8	134.9
19	-19.6	-22.6	69	26.1	23.6	155	69.2	67.3			
20	-17.9	-21.4	70	26.8	24.3	160	71.1	69.3			
21	-16.8	-19.7	71	27.4	24.9	165	73.0	71.2			
22	-15.6	-18.6	72	28.1	25.6	170	74.9	73.1			
23	-14.5	-17.5	73	28.8	26.2	175	76.7	74.9			
24	-13.4	-15.9	74	29.4	26.9	180	78.5	76.7			
25	-11.8	-14.8	75	30.0	27.5	185	80.2	78.5			
26	-10.8	-13.7	76	30.7	28.2	190	81.9	80.1			
27	-9.7	-12.6	77	31.4	28.8	195	83.6	81.9			
28	-8.6	-11.5	78	32.0	29.5	200	85.3	83.6			
29	-7.6	-10.0	79	32.3	30.1	205	86.9	85.2			
30	-6.5	-8.9	80	33.2	30.8	210	88.5	86.9			
31	-5.5	-7.9	81	33.8	31.4	215	90.0	88.5			
32	-4.0	-6.9	82	34.2	32.1	220	91.6	90.0			
33	-3.0	-5.9	83	35.9	32.7	225	93.1	91.6			
34	-2.0	-4.6	84	35.6	33.3	230	94.6	93.1			
35	-1.0	-3.8	85	36.1	33.9	235	96.1	94.6			
36	0.0	-2.8	86	36.7	34.2	240	97.6	96.1			
37	0.8	-1.9	87	37.3	35.1	245	99.0	97.6			
38	1.5	-0.9	88	37.9	35.6	250	100.4	99.0			
39	2.2	0.1	89	38.2	36.1	255	101.8	100.4			
40	3.2	1.1	90	39.0	36.8	260	103.2	101.8			
41	4.2	2.0	91	39.6	37.3	265	104.6	103.1			
42	5.2	2.8	92	40.1	37.9	270	105.9	104.5			
43	6.2	3.5	93	40.7	38.5	275	107.2	105.8			
44	7.1	4.4	94	41.2	39.0	280	108.5	107.2			
45	8.1	5.3	95	41.8	39.6	285	109.8	108.5			
46	8.9	6.2	96	42.2	40.1	290	111.1	109.8			
47	9.6	7.2	97	42.8	40.7	295	112.4	111.0			
48	10.4	8.1	98	43.4	41.2	300	113.6	112.3			
49	10.4	8.1	98	43.4	41.2	300	113.6	112.3			
49	11.3	8.8	99	43.9	41.7	305	114.8	113.5			
50	12.2	9.6	100	44.2	42.1	310	116.0	114.8			
51	12.9	10.3	101	45.0	42.8	315	117.2	116.0			
52	13.6	11.2	102	45.7	43.3	320	118.4	117.2			
53	14.4	12.1	103	46.0	43.8	325	119.6	118.4			
54	15.3	12.8	104	46.3	44.2	330	120.8	119.6			

Form No. 93-05-R1 Revised 3-94
Supersedes Form No. 93-05

Printed in U.S.A.
Copeland Corporation
Sidney, OH 45365-0669

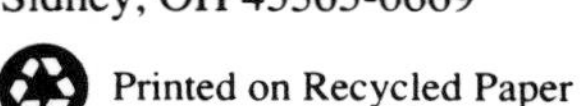

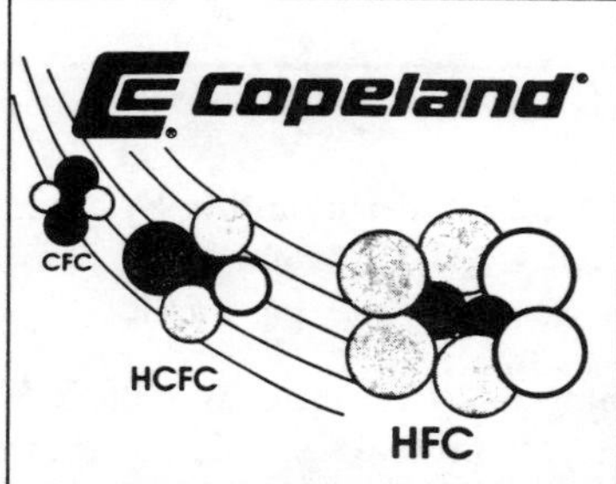

Refrigerant Changeover Guidelines CFC R-502 to HFC R-404A

Leading the Industry with Environmentally Responsible Refrigerant Solutions

Copeland does not advocate the wholesale changeover of CFC refrigerants to HCFCs or HFCs. If a system is not leaking refrigerant to the atmosphere, and is operating properly, there is no technical reason to replace the CFC refrigerant. In fact, changing the refrigerant may void the U.L. listing of the system. However, once the decision has been made to make the change from CFC R-502 to HFC R-404A (Suva® HP62 or FX70), the following guidelines are recommended.

CONSIDERATIONS

1. Retrofitting systems that employ compressors manufactured prior to 1973 is not recommended. This is due to the different materials used in motor insulation systems that have not been evaluated for compatibility with the new refrigerants and lubricants. Failure to heed this advice will violate the proposed U.L. Standard For Field Conversion/Retrofit Of Alternate Refrigerants In Refrigeration and Air Conditioning Equipment (U.L.2154).

2. Copeland's lubricant recommendation for use with R-404A is a Polyol Ester (POE), either Mobil EAL™ Arctic 22 CC or ICI EMKARATE™ RL 32S. These are the only POE lubricants approved for use in Copeland compressors and are available from all authorized Copeland wholesalers. The use of any other POE lubricant may void the compressor warranty.

It is important that the system contain not more than 5% residual mineral oil. More than 5% may contribute to premature compressor failure and or system capacity short-fall. Because mineral oils are not miscible with R-404A, they may log in the evaporator resulting in system capacity loss. It is for this reason that the flushing process must be done with the R-502 in the system.

3. R-404A can be used in either low or medium temperature systems. **R-404A should not be mixed with any other refrigerant!**

4. The expansion valve will not need to be changed. The existing R-502 valve when used with R-404A will have virtually the same capacity; however, it may be necessary to adjust the superheat.

5. Filter-driers must be changed at the time of conversion. This is proper air conditioning/refrigeration practice.

a. Solid core driers such as ALCO ADK are compatible with either R-502 or R-404A.

b. Compacted bead type driers can use XH6 or XH9 molecular sieve material such as found in the ALCO EK or EKH series.

c. If a loose fill type drier is to be used, XH9 molecular sieve material is required.

6. Pressure regulators such as EPR valves may have to be reset. Contact the EPR manufacturer for the correct settings.

7. R-404A exhibits higher pressures than R-502 at normal condensing temperatures. This may require that the high pressure safety controls be reset in order to operate as intended.

8. The higher pressure characteristics exhibited by R-404A will in some cases exceed the industry accepted safety factors on the compressor crankcase (low side). This will require the addition of a pressure relief valve on the compressor crankcase, set at a maximum of 375 psig to adequately protect the compressor from the possibility of excessive pressure. Pressure relief valves can be purchased from your Authorized

WARNING: Use only Copeland approved refrigerants and lubricants in the manner prescribed by Copeland. In some circumstances, other refrigerants and lubricants may be dangerous and could cause fires, explosions or electrical shorting. Contact Copeland Corp., Sidney, Ohio for more information.

Copeland wholesaler as part number 998-0051-02. Copeland semi-hermetic compressors that require this additional valve are:

* Discus® 3D and 4D

* All Other Semi-Hermetic (Non-Discus Models)

WARNING: IT IS POSSIBLE THAT EXCESS PRESSURE BUILD-UP ON MODELS INDICATED COULD RESULT IN THE COMPRESSOR EXPLODING UNLESS THE PRESSURE RELIEF VALVE SPECIFIED HAS BEEN PROPERLY INSTALLED ON THE ORIGINALLY BUILT COPELAND COMPRESSOR.

9. Systems that use a low pressure controller to maintain space temperature may need to have the cut in and cut out points changed. Although R-404A does exhibit "glide", the average evaporator or condenser temperature is within 0.5ºF of the saturated vapor temperature; therefore no correction is required.

10. Systems using R-404A should have approximately the same system pressure drop as with R-502. Check with the manufacturer of any pressure regulators and pilot operated solenoid valves used in the system to be sure that they will operate properly.

11. Mineral oil lubricants, such as 3GS, must not be used as the compressor lubricant with R-404A. Polyol Ester (POE) lubricant, Mobil EAL Arctic 22 CC or ICI Emkarate™ RL 32S, are the only lubricants that can be used in a Copeland compressor when using R-404A.

Before starting the changeover, it is suggested that at least the following items be ready:

1. Safety glasses
2. Gloves
3. Refrigerant service gauges
4. Electronic thermometer
5. Vacuum pump capable of pulling 250 microns
6. Thermocouple micron gauge
7. Leak detector
8. Refrigerant recovery unit including refrigerant cylinder
9. Proper container for removed lubricant
10. New liquid control device
11. Replacement liquid line filter-drier(s)
12. New POE lubricant, Mobil EAL Arctic 22 CC/ICI EMKARATE RL 32S
13. R-404A pressure temperature chart
14. R-404A refrigerant

CHANGEOVER PROCEDURE

NOTE: R-404A is not compatible with the seal material used in the R-502/R-22 Moduload Unloading System. If your system has Moduload, it MUST be changed. Consult your Copeland wholesaler for the proper part number.

1. The system should be thoroughly leak tested with the R-502 refrigerant still in the system. All leaks should be repaired before the R-404A refrigerant is added.

2. It is advisable that the system operating conditions be recorded with the R-502 still in the system. This will provide the base data for comparison when the system is put back into operation with the R-404A.

3. It is necessary to thoroughly remove the existing mineral oil lubricant from the system before the refrigerant is changed. No more than 5% residual mineral oil may be left in the system when it is recharged with R-404A for proper compressor operation. No more than 1 to 2% residual mineral oil may be required to assure no loss of heat transfer if enhanced tube heat exchangers are used in the system.

I. Systems with service valves

a. Disconnect electrical power to system.

b. Front seat the service valves to isolate the compressor.

c. Properly remove the R-502 from the compressor.

d. Remove the mineral oil lubricant from the compressor. Hermetic compressors will have to be removed from the system and tipped up to drain the lubricant out through the suction/process fitting.

e. Those systems that have oil separators, oil reservoirs, oil floats and suction line accumulators must have the mineral oil drained from them. Add POE lubricant to the oil separator and to the oil reservoir.

f. Replace the liquid line filter-drier with one that is compatible with R-404A.

g. Fill the compressor with the proper amount of POE lubricant. The oil charge is on the label of Copelaweld® compressors. Copelametic® compressor oil charges can be found in Application Engineering Bulletin 4-1281. If the lubricant charge is unknown, an authorized Copeland wholesaler can provide the technician with the information.

h. Reinstall the compressor in the system. Evacuate it to 250 microns. A vacuum decay test is suggested to assure the system is dry and leak free.

i. Recharge the system with R-502.

j. Operate the compressor in the system for a minimum of 24 hours. On large systems with long piping runs, experience indicates operating for several days to allow for thorough mixing of the remaining mineral oil and POE will minimize the number of flushes.

k. Repeat steps 3.I.a through j until the residual mineral oil is less than 5%. This may require three flushes of the system's lubricant.

l. In most cases, three complete flushes of the lubricant lowers the mineral oil content down to 5% or less in the system. To be sure of the mineral oil content between flushes and to be sure that the system ultimately has 5% or less mineral oil, test kits are available from Virginia KMP or Nu Calgon. A Refractometer may also be used to determine the residual mineral oil in the system. The Refractometer (p/n 998-RMET-00) is available from your Copeland Wholesaler.

m. Properly dispose of the lubricant removed from the system after each flush.

II. Systems without service valves

a. Disconnect electrical power to system.

b. Properly remove the R-502 from the system.

c. Remove the mineral oil lubricant from the compressor. Hermetic compressors will have to be removed from the system and tipped up to drain the lubricant out through the suction/process fitting.

d. It may be advisable to add service valves at the compressor suction and discharge connections. The compressor will have to have its lubricant changed generally three times.

e. Those systems that have oil separators, oil reservoirs, oil floats and suction line accumulators must have the mineral oil drained from them. Add POE lubricant to the oil separator and to the oil reservoir.

f. Replace the liquid line filter-drier with one that is compatible with R-404A.

g. Fill the compressor with the proper amount of POE lubricant. The oil charge is on the label of Copelaweld compressors. Copelametic compressor oil charges can be found in Application Engineering Bulletin 4-1281. If the lubricant charge is unknown, an authorized Copeland wholesaler can provide the technician with the information.

h. Reinstall the compressor in the system. Evacuate it to 250 microns. A vacuum decay test is suggested to assure the system is dry and leak free.

i. Recharge the system with R-502.

j. Operate the compressor in the system for a minimum of 24 hours. On large systems with long piping runs, experience indicates operating for several days to allow for thorough mixing of the remaining mineral oil and POE will minimize the number of flushes.

k. Repeat steps 3.II.a through j until the residual mineral oil is less than 5%. This may require three flushes of the system's lubricant.

l. To date, three complete flushes of the lubricant has shown to lower the mineral oil content down to 5% or less in the system. To be sure of the mineral oil content between flushes and to be sure that the system ultimately has 5% or less mineral oil, test kits are available from Virginia KMP or Nu Calgon. A Refractometer may also be used to determine the residual mineral oil in the system. The Refractometer (p/n 998-RMET-00) is available from the Copeland Wholesaler.

m. Properly dispose of the lubricant after each flush.

4. With the proper amount of polyol ester in the system, the R-502 can now be removed. Measure and note the amount removed.

5. Before the final flush, be sure all leaks are repaired, liquid control devices and any other system components are changed. Install the correct liquid line filter-drier. Driers must be compatible with the refrigerant and lubricant.

6. Be advised that POEs are very hygroscopic. They will very quickly absorb moisture from the air once the container is opened. Once the lubricant is added to the compressor, the compressor should be quickly installed. Like an open container, an open compressor with POE will absorb moisture. Add the correct amount of lubricant to the compressor. It is important that the system contain not more than 5% mineral oil. More than 5% may contribute to premature compressor failure and or system capacity problems. Mineral oils are not miscible with R-404A. The lubricant may log in the evaporator resulting in system capacity loss. It is for this reason that the flushing process must be done with the R-502 in the system.

7. Once the compressor is installed and the system is closed, the system must be evacuated to and hold 250 microns or lower.

8. Charge the system with the R-404A. Charge to 90% of the refrigerant removed in item 4. When charging R-404A it must leave the charging cylinder in the liquid phase. It is suggested that a sight glass be connected between the charging hose and compressor suction service valve to permit adjustment of the cylinder hand valve to assure the refrigerant entering the compressor is in the vapor state.

9. Operate the system. Record the data and compare to the data taken in item 2. Check and adjust the TEV superheat setting if necessary. Make adjustments to other controls as needed. Additional R-404A may have to be added to obtain optimum system performance.

10. Properly label the components. Tag the compressor with the refrigerant used (R-404A) and the lubricant used (Mobil

EAL Arctic 22 CC or ICI EMKARATE RL 32S). The proper color code for R-404A is Pantone Orange PMS (Paint Matching System) 021C.

11. Clean up and properly dispose of the removed lubricant. Check local and state laws regarding the disposal of refrigerant lubricants. Recycle or reclaim the removed refrigerant.

CAUTION: These guidelines are intended for use with R-404A only, not for refrigerants which are similar to R-404A. *Other refrigerants may not be compatible with the materials used in our compressors or the lubricants recommended in this bulletin resulting in unacceptable reliability and durability of the compressor.*

The information contained herein is based on technical data and tests which we believe to be reliable and is intended for use by persons having technical skill, at their own discretion and risk. Since conditions of use are beyond Copeland's control, we can assume no liability for results obtained or damages incurred through the application of the data presented.

R-404A Pressure/Temperature Chart

Press. PSIG	Vapor Temp. °F	Press. PSIG	Vapor Temp. °F	Press. Temp.	Vapor Temp. °F	Press. PSIG	Vapor Temp. °F	Press. PSIG	Vapor Temp. °F	Press. PSIG	Vapor Temp. °F
0	-50.0	29	-4.0	57	21.0	85	40.0	125	60.0	265	108.5
1	-48.0	30	-3.0	58	22.0	86	40.6	130	63.0	270	110.0
2	-46.0	31	-2.0	59	22.5	87	41.2	135	65.0	275	111.5
3	-43.5	32	-1.0	60	23.0	88	41.8	140	67.0	280	113.0
4	-41.0	33	0.0	61	24.0	89	42.4	145	69.0	285	114.0
5	-39.0	34	1.0	62	25.0	90	43.0	150	71.0	290	115.0
6	-37.0	35	2.0	63	25.5	91	43.4	155	73.0	295	116.5
7	-35.0	36	3.0	64	26.0	92	43.8	160	75.0	300	118.0
8	-33.0	37	4.0	65	27.0	93	44.2	165	77.0	305	119.0
9	-31.5	38	5.0	66	28.0	94	44.6	170	79.0	310	120.0
10	-30.0	39	6.0	67	28.5	95	45.0	175	81.0	315	121.0
11	-28.0	40	7.0	68	29.0	96	45.6	180	82.0	320	122.0
12	-26.0	41	8.0	69	29.5	97	46.2	185	84.0	325	123.5
13	-24.5	42	9.0	70	30.0	98	46.8	190	86.0	330	125.0
14	-23.0	43	10.0	71	31.0	99	47.4	195	88.0	335	126.0
15	-21.5	44	11.0	72	32.0	100	48.0	200	89.0	340	127.0
16	-20.0	45	11.5	73	32.5	101	48.6	205	90.5	345	128.0
17	-19.0	46	12.0	74	33.0	102	49.2	210	92.0	350	129.0
18	-18.0	47	13.0	75	33.5	103	49.8	215	94.0	355	130.5
19	-16.5	48	14.0	76	34.0	104	50.4	220	96.0	360	132.0
20	-15.0	49	15.0	77	34.5	105	51.0	225	97.5	365	133.0
21	-13.5	50	16.0	78	35.0	105	51.4	230	99.0	370	134.0
22	-12.0	51	16.5	79	36.0	107	51.8	235	100.5	375	135.0
23	-11.0	52	17.0	80	37.0	108	52.2	240	102.0	380	136.0
24	-10.0	53	18.0	81	37.6	109	52.6	245	103.0	385	137.0
25	-8.5	54	19.0	82	38.2	110	53.0	250	104.0	390	138.0
26	-7.0	55	19.5	83	38.8	115	56.0	255	105.5	395	139.0
27	-6.0	56	20.0	84	39.4	120	58.0	260	107.0	400	140.0
28	-5.0										

Note: Saturated Vapor Temperatures are shown. The average evaporator or condenser temperature is within .5° F of the saturated vapor temperature; therefore, no correction is required.

Form No. 94-15 R1 Revised 4-94
Supersedes Form No. 94-15

1675 W. Campbell Road
Sidney, OH 45365-0669
Printed in U.S.A.

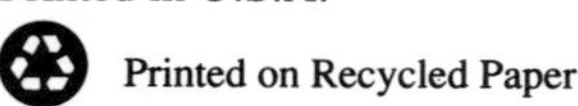

DuPont Fluoroproducts

The following information is used by permission of DuPont Fluoroproducts:

- *Material Safety Data Sheets for the following refrigerants: "SUVA" 9100, 9000, 95, 124, 123, HP81, MP39 and MP66, HP62, MP66, HP80, 134a.*
- *Safety of SUVA® Refrigerants*
- *DuPont HFC-134a: Properties, Uses, Storage and Handling*
- *Transport Properties of SUVA® Refrigerants HFC-134a and HCFC-123*
- *Retrofit Guidelines for SUVA® 134a in Stationary Equipment*
- *DuPont HCFC-123: Properties, Uses, Storage and Handling*
- *DuPont SUVA® HP Refrigerants: Properties, Uses, Storage and Handling*
- *Transport Properties of SUVA® Refrigerants HP62, HP80, HP81*
- *Retrofit Guidelines for SUVA® HP80*
- *Properties and Applications of SUVA® HP62 Refrigerant*
- *DuPont SUVA® MP Refrigerant Blends: Properties, Uses, Storage and Handling*
- *Transport Properties of SUVA® Refrigerants MP39, MP52, MP66*
- *Retrofit Guidelines for SUVA® MP39 and MP66*
- *SUVA® Refrigerants for Replacing R12 and R502-Quick Reference*
- *Properties and Performance of SUVA® AC9000 in Air Conditioners and Heat Pumps*
- *A Refrigerant for Every Strategy*
- *General Replacement Guide*

Du Pont Chemicals

6072FR | Revised 24-FEB-1995 | Printed 19-APR-1995

"SUVA" 9100 (R-410B)

CHEMICAL PRODUCT/COMPANY IDENTIFICATION

Company Identification

MANUFACTURER/DISTRIBUTOR

DuPont
1007 Market Street
Wilmington, DE 19898

PHONE NUMBERS

Product Information 1-800-441-9442
Transport Emergency CHEMTREC: 1-800-424-9300
Medical Emergency 1-800-441-3637

COMPOSITION/INFORMATION ON INGREDIENTS

Components

Material	CAS Number	%
PENTAFLUOROETHANE (HFC-125)	354-33-6	55
DIFLUOROMETHANE (HFC-32)	75-10-5	45

HAZARDS IDENTIFICATION

Potential Health Effects

Inhalation of high concentrations of vapor is harmful and may cause heart irregularities, unconsciousness, or death. Intentional misuse or deliberate inhalation may cause death without warning. Vapor reduces oxygen available for breathing and is heavier than air. Liquid contact can cause frostbite.

HUMAN HEALTH EFFECTS:

Overexposure to the vapors by inhalation may include temporary nervous system depression with anesthetic effects such as dizziness, headache, confusion, incoordination, and loss of consciousness. Higher exposures to the vapors may

(Continued)

HAZARDS IDENTIFICATION(Continued)

cause temporary alteration of the heart's electrical activity with irregular pulse, palpitations, or inadequate circulation. Gross overexposure may be fatal. Skin contact with the liquid may cause frostbite.

Individuals with preexisting diseases of the central nervous or cardiovascular system may have increased susceptibility to the toxicity of increased exposures.

Carcinogenicity Information

None of the components present in this material at concentrations equal to or greater than 0.1% are listed by IARC, NTP, OSHA or ACGIH as a carcinogen.

FIRST AID MEASURES

First Aid

INHALATION

If inhaled, immediately remove to fresh air. Keep person calm. If not breathing, give artificial respiration. If breathing is difficult, give oxygen. Call a physician.

SKIN CONTACT

Flush area with lukewarm water. Do not use hot water. If frostbite has occurred, call a physician.

EYE CONTACT

In case of contact, immediately flush eyes with plenty of water for at least 15 minutes. Call a physician.

INGESTION

Ingestion is not considered a potential route of exposure.

Notes to Physicians

THIS MATERIAL MAY MAKE THE HEART MORE SUSCEPTIBLE TO ARRHYTHMIAS. Catecholamines such as adrenaline, and other compounds having similar effects, should be reserved for emergencies and then used only with special caution.

FIRE FIGHTING MEASURES

Flammable Properties

Flash Point	Will not burn
Flammable limits in Air, % by Volume	
LEL	Not applicable
UEL	Not applicable
Autoignition	Not determined

(Continued)

FIRE FIGHTING MEASURES(Continued)

Fire and Explosion Hazards:

Cylinders may rupture under fire conditions. Decomposition may occur.

Potential Combustibility:

This material is not flammable at temperatures up to 100 deg C (212 deg F) and at atmospheric pressure. Data are not available at higher temperatures and pressures. However, one of the components, HFC-32 is flammable. At lower temperatures, higher pressures are required for combustibility. Therefore, this material should not be mixed with air for leak testing. In general, it should not be use or allowed to be present with high concentrations of air above atmospheric pressure.

Extinguishing Media
As appropriate for combustibles in area.

Fire Fighting Instructions
Cool cylinder with water spray or fog. Self-contained breathing apparatus (SCBA) is required if cylinders rupture and contents are released under fire conditions.

ACCIDENTAL RELEASE MEASURES

Safeguards (Personnel)
NOTE: Review FIRE FIGHTING MEASURES and HANDLING (PERSONNEL) sections before proceeding with clean-up. Use appropriate PERSONAL PROTECTIVE EQUIPMENT during clean-up.

Accidental Release Measures
Ventilate area, especially low or enclosed places where heavy vapors might collect. Extinguish open flames. Use self-contained breathing apparatus (SCBA) for large spills or releases. Eliminate electrical sources.

HANDLING AND STORAGE

Handling (Personnel)
Avoid breathing vapor. Avoid liquid contact with eyes and skin. Use with sufficient ventilation to keep employee exposure below recommended limits. See Fire and Explosion Data section.

Storage
Clean, dry area. Do not heat above 52 deg C (125 deg F).

(Continued)

EXPOSURE CONTROLS/PERSONAL PROTECTION

Engineering Controls

Avoid breathing vapors. Avoid contact with skin or eyes. Use with sufficient ventilation to keep employee exposure below the recommended exposure limit. Local exhaust should be used if large amounts are released. Mechanical ventilation should be used in low or enclosed places.

Personal Protective Equipment

Impervious gloves should be used to avoid prolonged or repeated exposure. Chemical splash goggles should be available for use as needed to prevent eye contact. Under normal manufacturing conditions, no respiratory protection is required when using this product provided exposure is maintained at or below occupational limits. Self-contained breathing apparatus (SCBA) is required if a large release occurs.

 # Exposure Guidelines

Applicable Exposure Limits

PENTAFLUOROETHANE (HFC-125)

PEL (OSHA)	None Established
TLV (ACGIH)	None Established
AEL * (Du Pont)	1000 ppm, 8 & 12 Hr. TWA

DIFLUOROMETHANE (HFC-32)

AEL * (Du Pont)	1000 ppm, 8 & 12 Hr. TWA
WEEL (AIHA)	1000 ppm, 8 Hr. TWA

* AEL is Du Pont's Acceptable Exposure Limit. Where governmentally imposed occupational exposure limits which are lower than the AEL are in effect, such limits shall take precedence.

PHYSICAL AND CHEMICAL PROPERTIES

Physical Data

Boiling Point	-61.8 F (-52.1 C) @ 1 atm
Vapor Pressure	239.7 psia 25 C (77 F)
% Volatiles	100 WT%
Evaporation Rate	(Cl4 = 1) Greater than 1
Solubility in Water	Not determined
Odor	Slight ethereal
Form	Liquefied gas
Color	Clear, colorless
Specific Gravity	1.066 @ 25 C (77 F)

STABILITY AND REACTIVITY

Chemical Stability

Material is stable. However, avoid open flames and high temperatures.

(Continued)

STABILITY AND REACTIVITY (Continued)

Incompatibility with Other Materials

Incompatible with active metals, alkali or alkaline earth metals--powdered Al, Zn, Be, etc.

Polymerization

Polymerization will not occur.

Other Hazards

Decomposition : Decomposition products are hazardous. This material can be decomposed by high temperatures (open flames, glowing metal surfaces, etc.) forming hydrofluoric acid, and possibly carbonyl halides.

TOXICOLOGICAL INFORMATION

Animal Data

The blend is untested.

HFC-125

Inhalation 4-hour ALC: >709,000 ppm in rats

Single, high inhalation exposures caused decreased activity, labored breathing and weight loss. Cardiac sensitization occurred in dogs exposed to concentrations of 10-30% in air and given an intravenous epinephrine challenge; no cardiac sensitization occurred at a concentration of 7.5%.

No animal data are available to define carcinogenic or reproductive hazards. HFC-125 did not cause developmental toxicity in rats or rabbits at inhalation concentrations of up to 50,000 ppm. HFC-125 does not produce genetic damage in bacterial or mammalian cell cultures or when been tested in animals.

HFC-32

Inhalation 4 hour-ALC: > 520,000 ppm in rats

Single exposure caused: Lethargy. Spasms. Loss of mobility in the hind limbs. Other effects include weak cardiac sensitization, a potentially fatal disturbance of heart rhythm caused by a heightened sensitivity to the action of epinephrine. 250,000 ppm.

Repeated exposure caused pathological changes of the lungs, liver, spleen, kidneys. In more recent studies repeated exposure caused: No significant toxicological effects. No-Observed-Effect-Level (NOEL): 49,100 ppm.

No animal data are available to define the following effects of this material: carcinogenicity, reproductive toxicity.

(Continued)

TOXICOLOGICAL INFORMATION (Continued)

Animal data show slight fetotoxicity but only at exposure levels producing other toxic effects in the adult animal. Tests have shown that this material does not cause genetic damage in bacterial or mammalian cell cultures, or in animals. This material has not been tested for its ability to cause permanent genetic damage in reproductive cells of mammals (not tested for heritable genetic damage).

DISPOSAL CONSIDERATIONS

Waste Disposal

Comply with Federal, State, and local regulations. Reclaim by distillation or remove to a permitted waste disposal facility.

TRANSPORTATION INFORMATION

Shipping Information

DOT/IMO

Proper Shipping Name	LIQUIFIED GAS, N.O.S. (CONTAINS DIFLUOROMETHANE AND PENTAFLUOROETHANE)
Hazard Class	2.2
UN No.	UN1956 Air freight: UN3163
DOT/IMO Label	NONFLAMMABLE GAS

Shipping Containers

Tank Cars.

Cylinders
Ton Tanks

REGULATORY INFORMATION

U.S. Federal Regulations

TSCA Inventory Status Reported/Included.

TITLE III HAZARD CLASSIFICATIONS SECTIONS 311, 312

Acute : Yes
Chronic : Yes
Fire : No
Reactivity : No
Pressure : Yes

LISTS:

SARA Extremely Hazardous Substance	-No
CERCLA Hazardous Substance	-No
SARA Toxic Chemical	-No

(Continued)

OTHER INFORMATION

NFPA, NPCA-HMIS

NPCA-HMIS Rating

Health	1
Flammability	0
Reactivity	1

Personal Protection rating to be supplied by user depending on use conditions.

Additional Information

HFC-125 is TSCA listed, and controlled by a TSCA Section 5 Consent Order.

The data in this Material Safety Data Sheet relates only to the specific material designated herein and does not relate to use in combination with any other material or in any process.

Responsibility for MSDS : DuPont Chemicals
Address : Engineering & Product Safety
> : P.O. Box 80709, Chestnut Run
> : Wilmington, DE 19880-0709
Telephone : (302) 999-4946

# Indicates updated section.

End of MSDS

Du Pont Chemicals

6037FR

Revised 24-FEB-1995 Printed 19-APR-1995

"SUVA" 9000 (R407C)

CHEMICAL PRODUCT/COMPANY IDENTIFICATION

Material Identification
"SUVA" is a registered trademark of DuPont.

Corporate MSDS Number DU005999

Company Identification
MANUFACTURER/DISTRIBUTOR
DuPont
1007 Market Street
Wilmington, DE 19898

PHONE NUMBERS
Product Information 1-800-441-9442
Transport Emergency CHEMTREC: 1-800-424-9300
Medical Emergency 1-800-441-3637

COMPOSITION/INFORMATION ON INGREDIENTS

Components

Material	CAS Number	%
PENTAFLUOROETHANE (HFC-125)	354-33-6	25
	811-97-2	
ETHANE, 1,1,1,2-TETRAFLUORO- (HFC-134a)		52
DIFLUOROMETHANE (HFC-32)	75-10-5	23

HAZARDS IDENTIFICATION

Potential Health Effects

Inhalation of high concentrations of vapor is harmful and may cause heart irregularities, unconsciousness, or death. Intentional misuse or deliberate inhalation may cause death without warning. Vapor reduces oxygen available for breathing and is heavier than air. Liquid contact can cause

(Continued)

frostbite.

HUMAN HEALTH EFFECTS:

Overexposure to the vapors by inhalation may include temporary nervous system depression with anesthetic effects such as dizziness, headache, confusion, incoordination, and loss of consciousness. Higher exposures to the vapors may cause temporary alteration of the heart's electrical activity with irregular pulse, palpitations, or inadequate circulation. Gross overexposure may be fatal. Skin contact with the liquid may cause frostbite.

Individuals with preexisting diseases of the central nervous or cardiovascular system may have increased susceptibility to the toxicity of increased exposures.

Carcinogenicity Information

None of the components present in this material at concentrations equal to or greater than 0.1% are listed by IARC, NTP, OSHA or ACGIH as a carcinogen.

FIRST AID MEASURES

First Aid

INHALATION

If inhaled, immediately remove to fresh air. Keep person calm. If not breathing, give artificial respiration. If breathing is difficult, give oxygen. Call a physician.

SKIN CONTACT

Flush area with lukewarm water. Do not use hot water. If frostbite has occurred, call a physician.

EYE CONTACT

In case of contact, immediately flush eyes with plenty of water for at least 15 minutes. Call a physician.

INGESTION

Not a probable route. However, in case of accidental ingestion, call a physician.

Notes to Physicians

THIS MATERIAL MAY MAKE THE HEART MORE SUSCEPTIBLE TO ARRHYTHMIAS. Catecholamines such as adrenaline, and other compounds having similar effects, should be reserved for emergencies and then used only with special caution.

(Continued)

FIRE FIGHTING MEASURES

Flammable Properties

Flash Point	Will not burn
Flammable limits in Air, % by Volume	
LEL	Not applicable
UEL	Not applicable
Autoignition	Not determined

Fire and Explosion Hazards:

Cylinders may rupture under fire conditions. Decomposition may occur.

Potential Combustibility:

"SUVA" 9000 is not flammable at temperatures up to 100 deg C (212 deg F) and at atmospheric pressure. Data are not available at higher temperatures and pressures. However, one of the components, HFC-32 is flammable. Another, HFC-134a, has been shown in tests to be combustible at pressures as low as 5.5 psig at 177 deg C (351 deg F) when mixed with air at concentrations of generally more than 60 volume % air. At lower temperatures, higher pressures are required for combustibility. Therefore, "SUVA" 9000 should not be mixed with air for leak testing. In general, it should not be use or allowed to be present with high concentrations of air above atmospheric pressure. Experimental data have also been reported which indicate combustibility of HFC-134a in the presence of certain concentrations of chlorine.

Extinguishing Media
As appropriate for combustibles in area.

Fire Fighting Instructions
Cool cylinder with water spray or fog. Self-contained breathing apparatus (SCBA) is required if cylinders rupture and contents are released under fire conditions.

ACCIDENTAL RELEASE MEASURES

Safeguards (Personnel)
NOTE: Review FIRE FIGHTING MEASURES and HANDLING (PERSONNEL) sections before proceeding with clean-up. Use appropriate PERSONAL PROTECTIVE EQUIPMENT during clean-up.

Accidental Release Measures
Ventilate area, especially low or enclosed places where heavy vapors might collect. Remove open flames. Use self-contained breathing apparatus (SCBA) for large spills or releases.

(Continued)

HANDLING AND STORAGE

Handling (Personnel)

Avoid breathing vapor. Avoid liquid contact with eyes and skin. Use with sufficient ventilation to keep employee exposure below recommended limits. Contact with chlorine or other strong oxidizing agents should also be avoided. See Fire and Explosion Data section.

Storage

Clean, dry area. Do not heat above 52 deg C (125 deg F).

EXPOSURE CONTROLS/PERSONAL PROTECTION

Engineering Controls

Avoid breathing vapors. Avoid contact with skin or eyes. Use with sufficient ventilation to keep employee exposure below the recommended exposure limit. Local exhaust should be used if large amounts are released. Mechanical ventilation should be used in low or enclosed places.

Personal Protective Equipment

Impervious gloves should be used to avoid prolonged or repeated exposure. Chemical splash goggles should be available for use as needed to prevent eye contact. Under normal manufacturing conditions, no respiratory protection is required when using this product. Self-contained breathing apparatus (SCBA) is required if a large release occurs.

 # Exposure Guidelines

Applicable Exposure Limits

PENTAFLUOROETHANE (HFC-125)

PEL (OSHA)	None Established
TLV (ACGIH)	None Established
AEL * (Du Pont)	1000 ppm, 8 & 12 Hr. TWA

ETHANE, 1,1,1,2-TETRAFLUORO- (HFC-134a)

PEL (OSHA)	None Established
TLV (ACGIH)	None Established
AEL * (Du Pont)	1000 ppm, 8 & 12 Hr. TWA
WEEL (AIHA)	1000 ppm, 8 Hr. TWA

DIFLUOROMETHANE (HFC-32)

AEL * (Du Pont)	1000 ppm, 8 & 12 Hr. TWA
WEEL (AIHA)	1000 ppm, 8 Hr. TWA

* AEL is Du Pont's Acceptable Exposure Limit. Where governmentally imposed occupational exposure limits which are lower than the AEL are in effect, such limits shall take precedence.

(Continued)

PHYSICAL AND CHEMICAL PROPERTIES

Physical Data

Boiling Point	-43.9 C (-47 F) Average
Vapor Pressure	171.8 psia 25 C (77 F)
% Volatiles	100 WT%
Evaporation Rate	(Cl4 = 1) Greater than 1
Solubility in Water	Not determined
Odor	Slight ethereal
Form	Liquefied gas
Color	Clear, colorless
Specific Gravity	1.136 @ 25 C (77 F)

STABILITY AND REACTIVITY

Chemical Stability

Material is stable. However, avoid open flames and high temperatures.

Incompatibility with Other Materials

Incompatible with active metals, alkali or alkaline earth metals--powdered Al, Zn, Be, etc.

Polymerization

Polymerization will not occur.

Other Hazards

Decomposition : Decomposition products are hazardous. "SUVA" 9000 can be decomposed by high temperatures (open flames, glowing metal surfaces, etc.) forming hydrofluoric acid, and possibly carbonyl halides.

TOXICOLOGICAL INFORMATION

Animal Data

The blend is untested.

HFC-125

Inhalation 4 hour ALC: > 709,000 ppm in rats

Single, high inhalation exposures caused lethargy, decreased activity, labored breathing and weight loss. Weak cardiac sensitization effect, a potentially fatal disturbance of heart rhythm caused by a heightened sensitivity to the action of epinephrine.

No animal data are available to define carcinogenic, developmental or reproductive hazards. In animal testing this material has not caused developmental toxicity. HFC-125 does not produce genetic damage in bacterial or mammalian cell cultures or when tested in animals (not

(Continued)

tested for heritable genetic damage).

HFC-134a

Inhalation 4-hour LC50: 567,000 ppm in rats

A 5 or 10 second spray of vapor produced very slight eye irritation and a 24-hour occlusive application produced slight skin irritation in rabbits. The compound is not a skin sensitizer in animals. No toxic effects were seen in animals from exposures by inhalation to concentrations up to 81,000 ppm. Lethargy and rapid respiration were observed at a vapor concentration of 305,000 ppm and pulmonary congestion, edema, and central nervous system effects occurred at a vapor concentration of 750,000 ppm. Cardiac sensitization occurred in dogs at 75,000 ppm following an epinephrine challenge. No effects in animals occurred from repeated inhalation exposures to 99,000 ppm for two weeks or to 50,000 ppm for three months. Repeated exposures to higher concentrations caused transient tremors, incoordination and some organ weight changes. Long-term exposures produced increased testes weights and increased urinary fluoride levels. No adverse effects were observed in male and female rats fed 300 mg/kg/day of HFC-134a for 52 weeks. Animal testing indicates that this compound does not have carcinogenic or mutagenic effects. Inhalation of 50,000 ppm for two years caused an increase in benign testicular tumors in male rats. No effects were observed at lower concentrations. The tumors were late-occurring and were judged not to be life-threatening. Embryotoxic activity has been observed in some animal tests but only at maternally toxic levels.

HFC-32

Inhalation: 4 hour-ALC: > 520,000 ppm in rats

Single exposure caused: Lethargy. Spasms. Loss of mobility in the hind limbs. Other effects include weak cardiac sensitization, a potentially fatal disturbance of heart rhythm caused by a heightened sensitivity to the action of epinephrine. 250,000 ppm.

Repeated exposure caused pathological changes of the lungs, liver, spleen, kidneys. In more recent studies repeated exposure caused: No significant toxicological effects. No-Observed-Effect-Level (NOEL): 49,100 ppm.

No animal data are available to define the following effects of this material: carcinogenicity, reproductive toxicity. Animal data show slight fetotoxicity but only at exposure levels producing other toxic effects in the adult animal. Tests have shown that this material does not cause genetic damage in bacterial or mammalian cell cultures, or in animals. This material has not been tested for its ability to cause permanent genetic damage in reproductive cells of mammals (not tested for heritable genetic damage).

(Continued)

DISPOSAL CONSIDERATIONS

Waste Disposal

Comply with Federal, State, and local regulations. Reclaim by distillation or remove to a permitted waste disposal facility.

TRANSPORTATION INFORMATION

Shipping Information

DOT/IMO

Proper Shipping Name	LIQUIFIED GAS, N.O.S. (CONTAINS DIFLUOROMETHANE AND PENTAFLUOROETHANE)
Hazard Class	2.2
UN No.	1956
DOT/IMO Label	NONFLAMMABLE GAS

Shipping Containers

Tank Cars.

Cylinders
Ton Tanks

REGULATORY INFORMATION

U.S. Federal Regulations

TSCA Inventory Status   Reported/Included.

TITLE III HAZARD CLASSIFICATIONS SECTIONS 311, 312

Acute : Yes
Chronic : Yes
Fire : No
Reactivity : No
Pressure : Yes

LISTS:

SARA Extremely Hazardous Substance	-No
CERCLA Hazardous Substance	-No
SARA Toxic Chemical	-No

OTHER INFORMATION

NFPA, NPCA-HMIS

NPCA-HMIS Rating

Health	1
Flammability	0
Reactivity	1

Personal Protection rating to be supplied by user depending on use

(Continued)

conditions.

Additional Information

MEDICAL USE: CAUTION: Do not use in medical applications involving permanent implantation in the human body. For other medical applications see DuPont CAUTION Bulletin No. H-50102.

HFC-125 is TSCA listed, and controlled by a TSCA Section 5 Consent Order.

The data in this Material Safety Data Sheet relates only to the specific material designated herein and does not relate to use in combination with any other material or in any process.

Responsibility for MSDS : DuPont Chemicals
Address : Engineering & Product Safety
> : P.O. Box 80709, Chestnut Run
> : Wilmington, DE 19880-0709
Telephone : (302) 999-4946

# Indicates updated section.

End of MSDS

Du Pont Chemicals

6087FR

Revised 14-FEB-1995 Printed 19-APR-1995

"SUVA" 95

CHEMICAL PRODUCT/COMPANY IDENTIFICATION

Material Identification

Corporate MSDS Number DU008080

Company Identification

MANUFACTURER/DISTRIBUTOR

DuPont
1007 MARKET STREET
WILMINGTON, DE 19898

PHONE NUMBERS

Product Information 1-800-441-7515
Transport Emergency CHEMTREC 1-800-424-9300
Medical Emergency 1-800-441-3637

COMPOSITION/INFORMATION ON INGREDIENTS

Components

Material	CAS Number	%
NJ TRADE SECRET REGISTRY #00850201001-5519P		30-50
NJ TRADE SECRET REGISTRY #00850201001-5520P		50-70

HAZARDS IDENTIFICATION

Potential Health Effects

Inhalation of high concentrations of vapor is harmful and may cause heart irregularities, unconsciousness, or death. Intentional misuse can be fatal. Vapor reduces oxygen available for breathing and is heavier than air. Liquid contact can cause frostbite.

HUMAN HEALTH EFFECTS:

Human health effects of overexposure by inhalation may include nonspecific discomfort such as nausea, headache, or

(Continued)

HAZARDS IDENTIFICATION (Continued)

weakness; temporary nervous system depression with anaesthetic effects such as dizziness, headache, confusion, incoordination, and loss of consciousness; or with gross overexposure, possibly temporary alteration of the heart's electrical activity with irregular pulse, palpitations, or inadequate circulation. Individuals with preexisting diseases of the central nervous or cardiovascular system may have increased susceptibility to the toxicity of excessive exposures. Eye or skin contact with the liquid may cause frostbite.

NOTE: DuPont has established an (Acceptable Exposure Limit) AEL of 1,000 ppm, 8 & 12 Hr. TWA for each of the components listed.

Carcinogenicity Information

None of the components present in this material at concentrations equal to or greater than 0.1% are listed by IARC, NTP, OSHA or ACGIH as a carcinogen.

FIRST AID MEASURES

First Aid

IF HIGH CONCENTRATIONS ARE INHALED: Immediately remove to fresh air. Keep persons calm. Call a physician. If not breathing, give artificial respiration. If breathing is difficult, give oxygen.

IN CASE OF SKIN CONTACT: Flush with water. Treat for frostbite if necessary.

IN CASE OF EYE CONTACT: Flush with water. Call a physician if frostbite occurs.

IF SWALLOWED: Ingestion is not considered a potential route of exposure.

Notes to Physicians

Because of possible disturbances of cardiac rhythm, catecholamine drugs, such a epinephrine, should be considered only as a last resort in life-threatening emergencies.

FIRE FIGHTING MEASURES

Flammable Properties

Will not burn.

(Continued)

FIRE FIGHTING MEASURES (Continued)

Fire and Explosion Hazards:

Use water spray or fog to cool containers. Cylinders are equipped with temperature and pressure relief devices but may still rupture under fire conditions. Decomposition may occur, producing HF, CO and possibly COF2.

Extinguishing Media
Use media appropriate for surrounding material.

Fire Fighting Instructions
Self-contained breathing apparatus (SCBA) is required if cylinders rupture or release under fire conditions.

ACCIDENTAL RELEASE MEASURES

Safeguards (Personnel)
NOTE: Review FIRE FIGHTING MEASURES and HANDLING (PERSONNEL) sections before proceeding with clean-up. Use appropriate PERSONAL PROTECTIVE EQUIPMENT during clean-up.

Accidental Release Measures
Material evaporates at atmospheric pressure (vaporizes). Ventilate area - especially low places where heavy vapors might collect. Remove open flames.

HANDLING AND STORAGE

Handling (Personnel)
Avoid contact of liquid with eyes and prolonged skin exposure. Use with sufficient ventilation to keep employee exposure below recommended limits.

Storage
Clean, dry area. Do not heat above 51.7 deg. C (125 deg. F)

EXPOSURE CONTROLS/PERSONAL PROTECTION

Engineering Controls
Normal ventilation for standard manufacturing procedures is generally adequate. Local exhaust should be used when large amounts are released. Mechanical ventilation should be used in low places.

Personal Protective Equipment
Neoprene rubber or leather gloves should be used when handling liquid. Chemical splash goggles should be worn when handling liquid. Under normal manufacturing conditions, no respiratory protection is required when using this product. Self-contained breathing apparatus (SCBA) is required if a large spill or release occurs.

(Continued)

EXPOSURE CONTROLS/PERSONAL PROTECTION(Continued)

Exposure Guidelines
Exposure Limits

"SUVA" 95

PEL (OSHA)	None Established
TLV (ACGIH)	None Established

PHYSICAL AND CHEMICAL PROPERTIES

Physical Data

Boiling Point	-88 C (-126 F)
Vapor Density	(Air = 1)
% Volatiles	100 WT%
Odor	Slight ethereal
Form	Compressed Gas
Color	Clear, colorless

STABILITY AND REACTIVITY

Chemical Stability

Material is stable. However, avoid open flames and high temperatures.

Polymerization

Polymerization will not occur.

 # Other Hazards

Incompatibility : No data available.

Decomposition : This product can be decomposed by high temperatures (open flames, glowing metal surfaces, etc.) forming HF, COF2, or CO.

TOXICOLOGICAL INFORMATION

Animal Data

NJ REGISTERY # 00850201001-5519P

Inhalation 1 hour LC50: >900,000 ppm (species unknown)

Toxic effects described in animals from exposure by inhalation include anaesthetic effects and nonspecific effects such as weight loss at concentrations >22%. No cardiac sensitization was observed in dogs after breathing 800,000 ppm for periods of 5-10 minutes following an epinephrine challenge. No animal test reports are available to define carcinogenic, embryotoxic, or reproductive hazards. Tests in bacterial or mammalian cell cultures demonstrate no mutagenic activity.

NJ REGISTERY # 00850201001-5520P

Inhalation 4-hour LC50: >800,000 ppm in rats

(Continued)

TOXICOLOGICAL INFORMATION (Continued)

Effects observed in animals by inhalation include decreased growth rate, pulmonary changes, irregular respiration, increased urine volume and creatinine, reversible pathological changes in the kidneys, and increased urinary fluoride concentration. One study showed no arrhythmogenic effects in dogs at a concentration of 20%, while another study did show some arrhythmogenic effects in both guinea pigs and dogs. Long-term inhalation exposures resulted in an initial decrease in growth rate, but no other adverse changes were noted. No animal test reports are available to define carcinogenic, developmental, or reproductive hazards. The compound does not produce genetic damage in bacterial cell cultures but has not been tested in animals.

DISPOSAL CONSIDERATIONS

Waste Disposal

Reclaim by distillation or remove to a permitted waste disposal facility. Dispose in accordance with all Federal, State and local regulations.

TRANSPORTATION INFORMATION

Shipping Information

DOT/IMO

Proper Shipping Name	COMPRESSED GAS, N.O.S. (FLUORINATED HYDROCARBONS)
Hazard Class	2.2
UN No.	1956
DOT/IMO Label	Nonflammable Gas

Shipping Containers

Cylinders and ton tanks.

REGULATORY INFORMATION

U.S. Federal Regulations

TSCA Inventory Status Reported/Included.

TITLE III HAZARD CLASSIFICATIONS SECTIONS 311, 312

Acute : Yes
Chronic : No
Fire : No
Reactivity : No
Pressure : Yes

(Continued)

REGULATORY INFORMATION(Continued)

LISTS:

SARA Extremely Hazardous Substance - No
CERCLA Hazardous Substance - No
SARA Toxic Chemicals - No

OTHER INFORMATION

NFPA, NPCA-HMIS

NPCA-HMIS Rating

Health	1
Flammability	0
Reactivity	1

Personal Protection rating to be supplied by user depending on use conditions.

The data in this Material Safety Data Sheet relates only to the specific material designated herein and does not relate to use in combination with any other material or in any process.

Responsibility for MSDS : DuPont Chemicals
Address : Engineering & Product Safety
> : P.O. Box 80709, Chestnut Run
> : Wilmington, DE 19880-0709
Telephone : (302) 999-4946

# Indicates updated section.

End of MSDS

DuPont Chemicals

2200FR Revised 15-NOV-1993 Printed 19-APR-1995

"SUVA" 124

CHEMICAL PRODUCT/COMPANY IDENTIFICATION

Material Identification
"SUVA" is a pending trademark of DuPont.

Corporate MSDS Number	DU002790
CAS Number	2837-89-0
Formula	CHClF-CF3
Molecular Weight	136.48
CAS Name	2-CHLORO-1,1,1,2-TETRAFLUOROETHANE

Tradenames and Synonyms
1-Chloro-1,2,2,2-Tetrafluoroethane

Company Identification
MANUFACTURER/DISTRIBUTOR
DuPont
1007 Market Street
Wilmington, DE 19898

PHONE NUMBERS
Product Information 1-800-441-9442
Transport Emergency CHEMTREC: 1-800-424-9300
Medical Emergency 1-800-441-3637

COMPOSITION/INFORMATION ON INGREDIENTS

 # Components

Material	CAS Number	%
*ETHANE, 2-CHLORO-1,1,1,2-TETRAFLUORO-	2837-89-0	94.7
(HCFC-124)		
*ETHANE, 1-CHLORO-1,1,2,2-TETRAFLUORO-	354-25-6	5
(HCFC-124a)		

* Regulated as a Toxic Chemical under Section 313 of Title III of the Superfund Amendments and Reauthorization Act of 1986 and 40 CFR part 372.

(Continued)

HAZARDS IDENTIFICATION

Potential Health Effects

Inhalation of high concentrations of vapor is harmful and may cause heart irregularities, unconsciousness, or death. Intentional misuse or deliberate inhalation may cause death without warning. Vapor reduces oxygen available for breathing and is heavier than air. Liquid contact causes frostbite.

HUMAN HEALTH EFFECTS:

Skin contact may cause frostbite from exposure to the liquid.

Inhalation may include nonspecific discomfort, such as nausea, headache, or weakness; or temporary nervous system depression with anesthetic effects such as dizziness, headache, confusion, incoordination, and loss of consciousness.

Higher exposures (>20%) may lead to these effects: temporary lung irritation effects with cough, discomfort, difficulty breathing, or shortness of breath; temporary alteration of the heart's electrical activity with irregular pulse, palpitations, or inadequate circulation; abnormal kidney function as detected by laboratory tests; or fatality from gross overexposure.

Individuals with preexisting diseases of the central nervous system, cardiovascular system, lungs or kidneys may have increased susceptibility to the toxicity of excessive exposures.

Carcinogenicity Information

None of the components present in this material at concentrations equal to or greater than 0.1% are listed by IARC, NTP, OSHA or ACGIH as a carcinogen.

FIRST AID MEASURES

First Aid

INHALATION

If high concentrations are inhaled, immediately remove to fresh air. Keep person calm. If not breathing, give artificial respiration. If breathing is difficult, give oxygen. Call a physician.

SKIN CONTACT

Flush skin with water for at least 15 minutes after excessive contact. Seek medical assistance if irritation is present. Wash

(Continued)

FIRST AID MEASURES (Continued)

contaminated clothing before reuse. Treat for frostbite if necessary by gently warming affected area.

EYE CONTACT

In case of contact, immediately flush eyes with plenty of water for at least 15 minutes. Call a physician.

INGESTION

Ingestion is not considered a potential route of exposure.

Notes to Physicians
Because of possible disturbances of cardiac rhythm, catecholamine drugs, such as epinephrine, should only be used with special caution in situations of emergency life support.

FIRE FIGHTING MEASURES

Flammable Properties
Autoignition 715 C (1319 F)

Will not burn.

Fire and Explosion Hazards:

Cylinders may rupture under fire conditions. Decomposition may occur.

Extinguishing Media
Use media appropriate for surrounding material.

Fire Fighting Instructions
Cool tank/container with water spray. Self-contained breathing apparatus (SCBA) may be required if cylinders rupture or release under fire conditions.

ACCIDENTAL RELEASE MEASURES

Safeguards (Personnel)
NOTE: Review FIRE FIGHTING MEASURES and HANDLING (PERSONNEL) sections before proceeding with clean-up. Use appropriate PERSONAL PROTECTIVE EQUIPMENT during clean-up.

Ventilate area, especially low or enclosed places where heavy vapors might collect. Remove open flames. Use self-contained breathing apparatus (SCBA) if large spill or leak occurs.

Spill Clean Up
Comply with Federal, State, and local regulations for reporting releases.

(Continued)

HANDLING AND STORAGE

Handling (Personnel)

Avoid breathing vapors or mist. Avoid contact with eyes or skin. Use with sufficient ventilation to keep employee exposure below recommended limits.

Storage

Store in a clean, dry place. Do not heat above 52 C (126 F).

EXPOSURE CONTROLS/PERSONAL PROTECTION

Engineering Controls

Use sufficient ventilation to keep employee exposure below recommended limits. Local exhaust should be used when large amounts are released. Mechanical ventilation should be used in low or enclosed places.

Personal Protective Equipment

Lined butyl gloves should be used to avoid prolonged or repeated exposure.

Chemical splash goggles should be available for use as needed to prevent eye contact.

Under normal manufacturing conditions, no respiratory protection is required when using this product.

Self-contained breathing apparatus (SCBA) is required if a large release occurs.

Exposure Guidelines

Exposure Limits

"SUVA" 124

PEL (OSHA)	None Established
TLV (ACGIH)	None Established
AEL * (DuPont)	500 ppm, 8 & 12 Hr. TWA

* AEL is DuPont's Acceptable Exposure Limit. Where governmentally imposed occupational exposure limits which are lower than the AEL are in effect, such limits shall take precedence.

PHYSICAL AND CHEMICAL PROPERTIES

Physical Data

Boiling Point	-11 C (12 F) @ 760 mm Hg
Vapor Pressure	61 psia @ 25 C (77 F)
Freezing Point	-199 C (-326 F)
% Volatiles	100 WT%
Solubility in Water	1.71 WT% @ 24 C (75 F)
Odor	Ether (slight).
Form	Liquified Gas.
Color	Clear, Colorless.
Density	1.364 g/cm3 @ 25 C (77 F)
Critical temperature	122.2 C (252 F)
Critical pressure	518.3 psia
Saturated Vapor Density	6.882 g/L at boiling point
Critical volume	246.4 cc/g mol
Critical density	0.554 g/cm3

(Continued)

STABILITY AND REACTIVITY

Chemical Stability
Stable.

Conditions to Avoid
Avoid open flames and high temperatures.

Incompatibility with Other Materials
Incompatible with alkali or alkaline earth metals - powdered Al, Zn, Be, etc.

Decomposition
Decomposition products are hazardous. This material can be decomposed by high temperatures (open flames, glowing metal surfaces, etc.) forming hydrochloric and hydrofluoric acids, and possibly carbonyl halides.

Polymerization
Polymerization will not occur.

TOXICOLOGICAL INFORMATION

 # Animal Data
HCFC-124

Inhalation 4-hour ALC: >230,000 ppm in rats

The effects in animals from single inhalation exposures by inhalation include central nervous system effects, anesthesia and decreased blood pressure. Cardiac sensitization occurred in dogs exposed to a concentration of 2.5% in air and given an intravenous epinephrine challenge. Repeated exposures produced increased liver weights, anesthetic effects, irregular respiration, poor coordination and nonspecific effects such as decreased body weight gain, however, no irreversible effects were seen as evidenced by histopathologic evaluation.

Tests in animals suggest no developmental toxicity potential. HCFC-124 was not mutagenic in bacterial and mammalian cell cultures or whole animal studies.

HCFC-124a

Inhalation 2-hour ALC: >200,000 ppm in guinea pigs

Single inhalation exposure to very high concentrations caused weakness. Repeated inhalation exposure at lower concentrations was without effect.

(Continued)

DISPOSAL CONSIDERATIONS

Waste Disposal

Treatment, storage, transportation, and disposal must be in accordance with applicable Federal, State/Provincial, and Local regulations. Recover by distillation or remove to a permitted waste disposal facility.

TRANSPORTATION INFORMATION

Shipping Information

DOT/IMO

Proper Shipping Name	CHLOROTETRAFLUOROETHANE
Hazard Class	2.2
UN No.	1021
DOT/IMO Label	NONFLAMMABLE GAS

Shipping Containers

Tank Cars.
Cylinders.
Ton Tanks.

REGULATORY INFORMATION

U.S. Federal Regulations

TSCA Inventory Status   Reported/Included.

TITLE III HAZARD CLASSIFICATIONS SECTIONS 311, 312

Acute : Yes
Chronic : No
Fire : No
Reactivity : No
Pressure : Yes

HAZARDOUS CHEMICAL LISTS

SARA Extremely Hazardous Substance: No
CERCLA Hazardous Substance : No
SARA Toxic Chemical : No

OTHER INFORMATION

NFPA, NPCA-HMIS

NPCA-HMIS Rating

Health	1
Flammability	0
Reactivity	1

Personal Protection rating to be supplied by user depending on use conditions.

(Continued)

OTHER INFORMATION(Continued)

Additional Information

HCFC-124 is TSCA-listed but its use is controlled by a TSCA Section 5, Significant New Use Rule (SNUR); 40 CFR 721.3180. The SNUR prohibits the commercial use of HCFC-124 as a blowing agent in the manufacture of structural insulation foams for commercial or consumer purposes. Activity related to this application is therefore limited to technical research and development conducted in accordance with the requirements of the R&D Exemption of the TSCA PMN regulations. Refer to 40 CFR 720.36 for further details on the requirements of this Exemption. All other uses of HCFC-124 are permitted.

The data in this Material Safety Data Sheet relates only to the specific material designated herein and does not relate to use in combination with any other material or in any process.

Responsibility for MSDS : DuPont Chemicals
Address : Engineering & Product Safety
> : P.O. Box 80709, Chestnut Run
> : Wilmington, DE 19880-0709
Telephone : (302) 999-4946

# Indicates updated section.

End of MSDS

DuPont Chemicals

2191FR | Revised 12-MAR-1994 | Printed 19-APR-1995

"SUVA"-123 REFRIGERANT

CHEMICAL PRODUCT/COMPANY IDENTIFICATION

Material Identification

"SUVA" is a pending trademark of DuPont.

Corporate MSDS Number	DU002798
CAS Number	306-83-2
Formula	CHCl2CF3
CAS Name	2,2-dichloro-1,1,1-trifluoroethane (HCFC-123)

Company Identification

MANUFACTURER/DISTRIBUTOR
DuPont
1007 Market Street
Wilmington, DE 19898

PHONE NUMBERS

Product Information	1-800-441-9442
Transport Emergency	CHEMTREC: 1-800-424-9300
Medical Emergency	1-800-441-3637

COMPOSITION/INFORMATION ON INGREDIENTS

Components

Material	CAS Number	%
*ETHANE, 2,2-DICHLORO-1,1,1-TRIFLUORO- (HCFC 123)	306-83-2	100

* Regulated as a Toxic Chemical under Section 313 of Title III of the Superfund Amendments and Reauthorization Act of 1986 and 40 CFR part 372.

(Continued)

HAZARDS IDENTIFICATION

Potential Health Effects

Inhalation of high concentrations of vapor is harmful and may cause heart irregularities, unconsciousness, or death. Intentional misuse or deliberate inhalation may cause death without warning. Vapor reduces oxygen available for breathing and is heavier than air. Product causes mild eye irritation. Decomposition products are hazardous.

HUMAN HEALTH EFFECTS:

Human health effects of overexposure by eye contact may include eye irritation with discomfort, tearing, or blurring of vision. Overexposure by inhalation to the vapors may cause temporary nervous system depression with anesthetic effects such as dizziness, headache, confusion, incoordination, and loss of consciousness; or with gross overexposure (>20%), possibly temporary alteration of the heart's electrical activity with irregular pulse, palpitations, or inadequate circulation.

Individuals with preexisting diseases of the central nervous or cardiovascular system may have increased susceptibility to the toxicity of excessive exposures.

Carcinogenicity Information

None of the components present in this material at concentrations equal to or greater than 0.1% are listed by IARC, NTP, OSHA or ACGIH as a carcinogen.

FIRST AID MEASURES

First Aid

INHALATION

If high concentrations are inhaled, immediately remove to fresh air. Keep person calm. If not breathing, give artificial respiration. If breathing is difficult, give oxygen. Call a physician.

SKIN CONTACT

In case of contact, flush with water. Get medical attention if irritation is present.

EYE CONTACT

In case of contact, immediately flush eyes with plenty of water for at least 15 minutes. Call a physician.

INGESTION

(Continued)

FIRST AID MEASURES (Continued)

No specific intervention is indicated as compound is not likely to be hazardous by ingestion. Consult a physician if necessary.

Do not induce vomiting because the hazard of aspirating the material into the lungs is considered greater than swallowing it.

Notes to Physicians

Because of possible disturbances of cardiac rhythm, catecholamine drugs, such as epinephrine, should only be used with special caution in situations of emergency life support.

FIRE FIGHTING MEASURES

Flammable Properties

Flash Point : Will not burn

HCFC-123 is not flammable at ambient temperatures and atmospheric pressure, but materials with similar chemical structure have been shown to be combustible at pressure as low as 5.5 psig (at 177 C) when mixed with air at concentrations of more than 60 volume % air. At lower temperatures higher pressures were required for combustibility.

Fire and Explosion Hazards:

Containers may rupture under fire conditions. Decomposition may occur.

Extinguishing Media

Use media appropriate for surrounding material.

Fire Fighting Instructions

Cool tank/container with water spray. Self-contained breathing apparatus (SCBA) is required if drums rupture and contents are spilled under fire conditions.

ACCIDENTAL RELEASE MEASURES

Safeguards (Personnel)

NOTE: Review FIRE FIGHTING MEASURES and HANDLING (PERSONNEL) sections before proceeding with clean-up. Use appropriate PERSONAL PROTECTIVE EQUIPMENT during clean-up.

Ventilate spill area.

DuPont Emergency Exposure Limits (EEL) are established to facilitate site or plant emergency evacuation and specify airborne concentrations of brief durations which should not result in permanent adverse health effects or interfere with escape. EEL's are expressed as airborne concentration multiplied by time (CxT) for up to a maximum of 60 minutes and as a ceiling airborne concentration. These limits are used in conjunction with engineering controls/monitoring and as an aid in planning for

(Continued)

episodic releases and spills. For more information on the applicability of EEL's, contact DuPont.

The DuPont Emergency Exposure Limit (EEL) for HCFC-123 is 1000 ppm for up to 60 minutes with a 1 minute not-to-exceed ceiling of 2500 ppm.

Initial Containment

Dike spill. Prevent material from entering sewers, waterways, or low areas.

Spill Clean Up

Collect on absorbent material and transfer to steel drums for recovery/disposal. Comply with Federal, State, and local regulations for reporting releases.

HANDLING AND STORAGE

Handling (Personnel)

Avoid breathing high concentrations of vapor. Provide adequate ventilation for storage, handling, and use, especially for enclosed or low spaces. Avoid contact of liquid with eyes and prolonged skin exposure.

Handling (Physical Aspects)

Do not allow product to contact open flame or electrical heating elements because dangerous decomposition products may form.

Storage

Store in a clean, dry place. Do not heat above 52 C (126 F).

EXPOSURE CONTROLS/PERSONAL PROTECTION

Engineering Controls

Normal ventilation for standard manufacturing procedures is generally adequate. Local exhaust should be used when large amounts are released. Mechanical ventilation should be used in low or enclosed places.

Personal Protective Equipment

Impervious gloves should be used to avoid prolonged or repeated exposure.

Chemical splash goggles should be available for use as needed to prevent eye contact.

Use NIOSH approved respiratory protection if exposure limits may be exceeded.

Self-contained breathing apparatus (SCBA) is required if a large release occurs.

(Continued)

EXPOSURE CONTROLS/PERSONAL PROTECTION (Continued)

 # Exposure Guidelines

Exposure Limits

"SUVA"-123 REFRIGERANT

PEL (OSHA)	None Established
TLV (ACGIH)	None Established
AEL * (DuPont)	30 ppm, 8 & 12 Hr. TWA

* AEL is DuPont's Acceptable Exposure Limit. Where governmentally imposed occupational exposure limits which are lower than the AEL are in effect, such limits shall take precedence.

PHYSICAL AND CHEMICAL PROPERTIES

Physical Data

Boiling Point	27.6 C (81.7 F) @ 760 mm Hg
Vapor Pressure	13 psia @ 25 C (77 F)
Vapor Density	5.3 (Air=1.0)
% Volatiles	100 WT%
Evaporation Rate	<1 (CCl4=1.0)
Solubility in Water	0.39 WT% @ 25 C (77 F)
pH	Neutral
Odor	Ether (slight).
Form	Liquid.
Color	Clear, Colorless.
Liquid Density	1.46 g/cm3 @ 25 C (77 F)

STABILITY AND REACTIVITY

Chemical Stability

Stable.

Conditions to Avoid

Avoid open flames and high temperatures.

Incompatibility with Other Materials

Incompatible with alkali or alkaline earth metals - powdered Al, Zn, Be, etc.

Decomposition

Decomposition products are hazardous. This material can be decomposed by high temperatures (open flames, glowing metal surfaces, etc.) forming hydrochloric and hydrofluoric acids, and possibly carbonyl halides.

Polymerization

Polymerization will not occur.

(Continued)

TOXICOLOGICAL INFORMATION

Animal Data

Inhalation 4-hour LC50: 32,000 ppm in rats
Oral ALD : 9000 mg/kg in rats
Skin Absorption LD50 : >2000 mg/kg in rabbits

The compound is not a skin irritant, is a mild to moderate eye irritant, and is not a skin sensitizer in animals. Single applications of high doses to the skin caused nonspecific effects such as weight loss and irritation. Toxic effects noted in animals from single exposure by inhalation at concentrations of 5000 ppm or greater include effects on unconditioned reflexes, locomotor activity and coordination, suggesting anesthetic effects. Single inhalation exposures of concentrations above 18,900 caused central nervous system effects, such as anesthesia, and nonspecific effects associated with lethality. Cardiac sensitization occurred in dogs at concentrations of 20,000 ppm and greater. Repeated exposures to 300 ppm resulted in alterations in blood chemistry; higher doses caused anesthetic effects, reduced lymphocyte counts, increased liver weight and enzyme alterations, and decreased body weight gain. Long-term exposure caused decreased body weight, altered clinical chemistry, and increased urinary fluoride concentration in rats; dogs demonstrated slight liver damage. HCFC-123 was not neurotoxic in animals repeatedly exposed by inhalation at concentrations up to 5,000 ppm, but did cause a slight decrease in arousal at this concentration.

Inhalation of 300, 1000 or 5000 ppm for two years caused an increase in benign testicular and benign pancreatic tumors in male rats; an increase in benign pancreatic tumors was observed in female rats exposed to 5000 ppm. In the same study, male and female rats exposed to 5000 ppm showed an increased incidence in benign liver tumors. Smaller increases in the incidence of these benign liver tumors were observed in females at 300 and 1000 ppm. The tumors were late-occurring and none were judged to be life-threatening. The biological significance of these tumors to man is considered to be limited. Additionally, evidence of retinal atrophy was observed in this two-year study in both treated and control animals, although the toxicological significance is undetermined.

HCFC-123 did not affect reproductive performance in rats. Animal data indicate that this material does not specifically harm the unborn animal. The compound does not produce genetic damage in bacterial cell cultures or in animals; however, in one study genetic damage was produced in mammalian cell cultures.

(Continued)

ECOLOGICAL INFORMATION

Ecotoxicological Information

AQUATIC TOXICITY:
Slightly toxic.
96 hour LC50 - Fathead minnows: > 77 mg/L

DISPOSAL CONSIDERATIONS

Waste Disposal

Recover by distillation or remove to a permitted waste disposal facility. Treatment, storage, transportation, and disposal must be in accordance with applicable Federal, State/Provincial, and Local regulations.

TRANSPORTATION INFORMATION

Shipping Information

Not regulated as a hazardous material by DOT or IMO.

Shipping Containers

Tank Cars.
Tank Trucks.
Pails.
Drums.

REGULATORY INFORMATION

U.S. Federal Regulations

TSCA Inventory Status   Reported/Included.

TITLE III HAZARD CLASSIFICATIONS SECTIONS 311, 312

Acute : Yes
Chronic : Yes
Fire : No
Reactivity : No
Pressure : No

HAZARDOUS CHEMICAL LISTS

SARA Extremely
Hazardous Substance - No
CERCLA Hazardous Substance - No
SARA Toxic Chemical - See Components Section

(Continued)

OTHER INFORMATION

NFPA, NPCA-HMIS

NPCA-HMIS Rating

Health	1
Flammability	0
Reactivity	1

Personal Protection rating to be supplied by user depending on use conditions.

The data in this Material Safety Data Sheet relates only to the specific material designated herein and does not relate to use in combination with any other material or in any process.

Responsibility for MSDS	: DuPont Chemicals
Address	: Engineering & Product Safety
>	: P.O. Box 80709, Chestnut Run
>	: Wilmington, DE 19880-0709
Telephone	: (302) 999-4946

# Indicates updated section.

End of MSDS

Du Pont Chemicals

MSDS — MATERIAL SAFETY DATA SHEET

6000FR Revised 19-APR-1994 Printed 18-APR-1995

"SUVA" HP81 (R402B)

CHEMICAL PRODUCT/COMPANY IDENTIFICATION

Material Identification

"SUVA" is a registered trademark of DuPont.

Corporate MSDS Number DU005603

Company Identification

MANUFACTURER/DISTRIBUTOR

DuPont
1007 Market Street
Wilmington, DE 19898

PHONE NUMBERS

Product Information	1-800-441-9442
Transport Emergency	CHEMTREC: 1-800-424-9300
Medical Emergency	1-800-441-3637

COMPOSITION/INFORMATION ON INGREDIENTS

Components

Material	CAS Number	%
ETHANE, PENTAFLUORO- (HFC-125)	354-33-6	38
*METHANE, CHLORODIFLUORO- (HCFC-22)	75-45-6	60
PROPANE	74-98-6	2

* Regulated as a Toxic Chemical under Section 313 of Title III of the Superfund Amendments and Reauthorization Act of 1986 and 40 CFR part 372.

HAZARDS IDENTIFICATION

Potential Health Effects

Inhalation of high concentrations of vapor is harmful and may cause heart irregularities, unconsciousness, or death. Intentional misuse or deliberate inhalation may cause death without warning. Vapor reduces oxygen available for

(Continued)

HAZARDS IDENTIFICATION (Continued)

breathing and is heavier than air. Liquid contact can cause frostbite.

HUMAN HEALTH EFFECTS:

Overexposure to the vapors by inhalation may include temporary nervous system depression with anesthetic effects such as dizziness, headache, confusion, incoordination, and loss of consciousness. Higher exposures to the vapors may cause temporary alteration of the heart's electrical activity with irregular pulse, palpitations, or inadequate circulation. Fatality may occur from gross overexposure. Skin contact with the liquid may cause frostbite.

Individuals with preexisting diseases of the central nervous or cardiovascular system may have increased susceptibility to the toxicity of increased exposures.

Carcinogenicity Information

None of the components present in this material at concentrations equal to or greater than 0.1% are listed by IARC, NTP, OSHA or ACGIH as a carcinogen.

FIRST AID MEASURES

First Aid

INHALATION

If inhaled, immediately remove to fresh air. Keep person calm. If not breathing, give artificial respiration. If breathing is difficult, give oxygen. Call a physician.

SKIN CONTACT

Flush area with lukewarm water. Do not use hot water. If frostbite has occurred, call a physician.

EYE CONTACT

In case of contact, immediately flush eyes with plenty of water for at least 15 minutes. Call a physician.

INGESTION

Not a probable route. However, in case of accidental ingestion, call a physician.

Notes to Physicians

THIS MATERIAL MAY MAKE THE HEART MORE SUSCEPTIBLE TO ARRHYTHMIAS. Catecholamines such as adrenaline, and other compounds having similar effects, should be reserved for emergencies and then used only with special caution.

(Continued)

FIRE FIGHTING MEASURES

 # Flammable Properties

Flammable limits in Air, % by Volume

LEL	Not determined
UEL	Not determined

Fire and Explosion Hazards:

Cylinders may rupture under fire conditions. Decomposition may occur.

"SUVA" HP81 is not flammable at temperatures up to 100 deg C (212 deg F) and at atmospheric pressure. Data are not available at higher temperatures and pressures. However, one of the components, propane, is flammable. HCFC-22 has been shown in tests to be combustible at pressures as low as 60 psig at ambient temperature when mixed with air at concentrations of 65 volume % air. Therefore, "SUVA" HP81 should not be mixed with air for leak testing. In general, it should not be used or allowed to be present with high concentrations of air above atmospheric pressure.

Extinguishing Media

As appropriate for combustibles in area.

Fire Fighting Instructions

Keep cylinders cool with water spray or fog. Self-contained breathing apparatus (SCBA) is required if cylinders rupture and contents are released under fire conditions.

ACCIDENTAL RELEASE MEASURES

Safeguards (Personnel)

NOTE: Review FIRE FIGHTING MEASURES and HANDLING (PERSONNEL) sections before proceeding with clean-up. Use appropriate PERSONAL PROTECTIVE EQUIPMENT during clean-up.

Accidental Release Measures

Ventilate area, especially low or enclosed places where heavy vapors might collect. Remove open flames. Use self-contained breathing apparatus (SCBA) for large spills or releases.

HANDLING AND STORAGE

Handling (Personnel)

Avoid breathing vapors. Avoid liquid contact with skin or eyes. Use with sufficient ventilation to keep employee exposure below the recommended limits. Avoid prolonged or repeated exposure. Wash thoroughly after handling.

Storage

Clean, dry area. Do not heat above 52 deg C (125 deg F).

(Continued)

EXPOSURE CONTROLS/PERSONAL PROTECTION

Engineering Controls

Use with sufficient ventilation to keep employee exposure below the recommended exposure limit. Local exhaust should be used if large amounts are released. Mechanical ventilation should be used in low or enclosed places.

Personal Protective Equipment

Impervious gloves should be used to avoid prolonged or repeated exposure. Chemical splash goggles should be available for use as needed to prevent eye contact. Under normal manufacturing conditions, no respiratory protection is required when using this product. Self-contained breathing apparatus (SCBA) is required if a large release occurs.

Exposure Guidelines

Applicable Exposure Limits

ETHANE, PENTAFLUORO- (HFC-125)

PEL (OSHA)	None Established
TLV (ACGIH)	None Established
AEL * (Du Pont)	1000 ppm, 8 & 12 Hr. TWA

METHANE, CHLORODIFLUORO- (HCFC-22)

PEL (OSHA)	None Established
TLV (ACGIH)	1,000 ppm, 3,540 mg/m3, 8 Hr. TWA
AEL * (Du Pont)	None Established

PROPANE

PEL (OSHA)	1,000 ppm, 1,800 mg/m3, 8 Hr. TWA
TLV (ACGIH)	Simple Asphyxiant
AEL * (Du Pont)	None Established

* AEL is Du Pont's Acceptable Exposure Limit. Where governmentally imposed occupational exposure limits which are lower than the AEL are in effect, such limits shall take precedence.

PHYSICAL AND CHEMICAL PROPERTIES

Physical Data

Boiling Point	-47.4 C (-53.3 F) Average
Vapor Pressure	179.6 psia at 25 deg C (77 deg F)
% Volatiles	100 WT%
Evaporation Rate	(CCl4 = 1) Greater than 1
Solubility in Water	Not determined
Odor	Slight ethereal
Form	Liquefied gas
Color	Clear, colorless
Density	1.14 gm/cc at 25 deg C (77 deg F) - Liquid

(Continued)

STABILITY AND REACTIVITY

Chemical Stability

Material is stable. However, avoid open flames and high temperatures.

Incompatibility with Other Materials

Incompatible with alkali or alkaline earth metals - powdered Al, Zn, Be, etc.

Polymerization

Polymerization will not occur.

Other Hazards

Decomposition : Decomposition products are hazardous. "SUVA" HP81 can be decomposed by high temperatures (open flames, glowing metal surfaces, etc.) forming hydrochloric and hydrofluoric acids, and possibly carbonyl halides.

TOXICOLOGICAL INFORMATION

Animal Data

The blend is untested.

ETHANE, PENTAFLUORO

Inhalation 4 hour ALC: > 709,000 ppm in rats

Single, high inhalation exposures caused lethargy, decreased activity, labored breathing and weight loss. Weak cardiac sensitization effect, a potentially fatal disturbance of heart rhythm caused by a heightened sensitivity to the action of epinephrine.

No animal data are available to define carcinogenic, developmental or reproductive hazards. In animal testing this material has not caused developmental toxicity. HFC-125 does not produce genetic damage in bacterial or mammalian cell cultures or when tested in animals (not tested for heritable genetic damage).

METHANE, CHLORODIFLUORO

Inhalation 4-hour LC50: 220,000 ppm in rats

The compound is a skin irritant and a slight eye irritant, but is not a skin sensitizer in animals.

Effects from single high exposures include central nervous system depression, anesthesia, rapid breathing, lung congestion and microscopic liver changes. Cardiac sensitization occurred in dogs at 50,000 ppm or greater from the action of exogenous epinephrine.

(Continued)

No toxic effects or abnormal histopathological observations occurred in rats repeatedly exposed to concentrations ranging from 10,000 to 50,000 ppm (v/v). Long-term exposures to 50,000 ppm (v/v) of vapors produced organ weight increases and a decrease in body weight gain, but no increased mortality or adverse hematological effects.

In chronic inhalation studies, HCFC-22, at a concentration of 50,000 ppm (v/v), produced a small, but statistically significant increase of late-occurring tumors involving salivary glands in male rats, but not female rats or male or female mice. In the same studies, no increased incidence of tumors was seen in either species at concentrations of 10,000 ppm or 1000 ppm (v/v).

Long-term administration in corn oil produced no effects on body weight or mortality.

HCFC-22 was mutagenic in some strains of bacteria in bacterial cell cultures, but not mammalian cell cultures or animals. It did not cause heritable genetic damage in mammals.

A slight, but significant increase in developmental toxicity was observed at high concentrations (50,000 ppm) of HCFC-22, a concentration which also produced toxic effects in the adult animal. Based on these findings, and other negative developmental studies, HCFC-22 is not considered a unique hazard to the conceptus. Studies of the effects of HCFC-22 on male reproductive performance have been negative. Specific studies to evaluate the effect on female reproductive performance have not been conducted, however, limited information obtained from studies on developmental toxicity do not indicate adverse effects on female reproductive performance at concentrations up to 50,000 ppm.

PROPANE

Toxicity in animals occurring only with inhalation exposures at high concentrations (10% or greater) include cardiac sensitization, analgesia, irregular respiration and hypotension. No animal test reports are available to define carcinogenic, developmental, or reproductive hazards. Tests in bacteria cell cultures demonstrate no mutagenic activity.

(Continued)

DISPOSAL CONSIDERATIONS

Waste Disposal

Comply with Federal, State, and local regulations. Reclaim by distillation or remove to a permitted waste disposal facility.

TRANSPORTATION INFORMATION

Shipping Information

DOT/IMO

Proper Shipping Name	LIQUEFIED GAS, N.O.S. (CONTAINS CHLORODIFLUOROMETHANE AND PENTAFLUOROETHANE)
Hazard Class	2.2
UN No.	1956
DOT/IMO Label	NONFLAMMABLE GAS

Shipping Containers

Tank Cars.

Cylinders
Ton Tanks

REGULATORY INFORMATION

U.S. Federal Regulations

TSCA Inventory Status   Reported/Included.

TITLE III HAZARD CLASSIFICATIONS SECTIONS 311, 312

Acute	: Yes
Chronic	: No
Fire	: No
Reactivity	: No
Pressure	: Yes

HAZARDOUS CHEMICAL LISTS

SARA Extremely Hazardous Substance: No
CERCLA Hazardous Substance : No
SARA Toxic Chemical - See Components Section

OTHER INFORMATION

NFPA, NPCA-HMIS

NPCA-HMIS Rating

Health	1
Flammability	0
Reactivity	1

Personal Protection rating to be supplied by user depending on use

(Continued)

conditions.

Additional Information

MEDICAL USE: CAUTION: Do not use in medical applications involving permanent implantation in the human body. For other medical applications see DuPont CAUTION Bulletin No. H-50102.

HFC-125 is TSCA listed, and is controlled by a TSCA Section 5 Consent Order.

The data in this Material Safety Data Sheet relates only to the specific material designated herein and does not relate to use in combination with any other material or in any process.

Responsibility for MSDS : DuPont Chemicals
Address : Engineering & Product Safety
> : P.O. Box 80709, Chestnut Run
> : Wilmington, DE 19880-0709
Telephone : (302) 999-4946

# Indicates updated section.

End of MSDS

MSDS — MATERIAL SAFETY DATA SHEET

DuPont Chemicals

3030FR — Revised 13-APR-1995 — Printed 18-APR-1995

"SUVA" MP39 (R401A) and "SUVA" MP66 (R401B)

CHEMICAL PRODUCT/COMPANY IDENTIFICATION

Material Identification

"SUVA" is a registered trademark of DuPont.

Corporate MSDS Number	DU004507
Formula	CHClF2/CH3CHF2/CHClFCF3

Company Identification

MANUFACTURER/DISTRIBUTOR

DuPont
1007 Market Street
Wilmington, DE 19898

PHONE NUMBERS

Product Information	1-800-441-9442
Transport Emergency	CHEMTREC: 1-800-424-9300
Medical Emergency	1-800-441-3637

COMPOSITION/INFORMATION ON INGREDIENTS

Components

Material	CAS Number	%
"SUVA" MP39 (R-401A)		
* METHANE, CHLORODIFLUORO- (HCFC-22)	75-45-6	53
ETHANE, 1,1-DIFLUORO- (HFC-152a)	75-37-6	13
* ETHANE, 2-CHLORO-1,1,1,2-TETRAFLUORO (HCFC-124)	2837-89-0	34
"SUVA" MP66 (R401B)		
* METHANE, CHLORODIFLUORO- (HCFC-22)	75-45-6	61

(Continued)

COMPOSITION/INFORMATION ON INGREDIENTS (Continued)

ETHANE, 1,1-DIFLUORO- (HFC-152a)	75-37-6	11
* ETHANE, 2-CHLORO-1,1,1,2-TETRAFLUORO (HCFC-124)	2837-89-0	28

* Regulated as a Toxic Chemical under Section 313 of Title III of the Superfund Amendments and Reauthorization Act of 1986 and 40 CFR part 372.

HAZARDS IDENTIFICATION

Potential Health Effects

Inhalation of high concentrations of vapor is harmful and may cause heart irregularities, unconsciousness, or death. Intentional misuse or deliberate inhalation may cause death without warning. Vapor reduces oxygen available for breathing and is heavier than air. Liquid contact can cause frostbite.

HUMAN HEALTH EFFECTS:

Skin contact may cause frostbite from exposure to the liquid.

Inhalation may include nonspecific discomfort, such as nausea, headache, or weakness; or temporary nervous system depression with anesthetic effects such as dizziness, headache, confusion, incoordination, and loss of consciousness.

Higher exposures (>20%) may lead to these effects: temporary lung irritation effects with cough, discomfort, difficulty breathing, or shortness of breath; temporary alteration of the heart's electrical activity with irregular pulse, palpitations, or inadequate circulation; abnormal kidney function as detected by laboratory tests; or fatality from gross overexposure.

Individuals with preexisting diseases of the central nervous system, cardiovascular system, lungs or kidneys may have increased susceptibility to the toxicity of excessive exposures.

Carcinogenicity Information

None of the components present in this material at concentrations equal to or greater than 0.1% are listed by IARC, NTP, OSHA or ACGIH as a carcinogen.

(Continued)

FIRST AID MEASURES

First Aid

INHALATION

If high concentrations are inhaled, immediately remove to fresh air. Keep person calm. If not breathing, give artificial respiration. If breathing is difficult, give oxygen. Call a physician.

SKIN CONTACT

Flush skin with water after excessive contact. Treat for frostbite if necessary by gently warming affected area. Seek medical assistance if irritation is present. Wash contaminated clothing before reuse.

EYE CONTACT

In case of contact, immediately flush eyes with plenty of water for at least 15 minutes. Call a physician.

INGESTION

Ingestion is not considered a potential route of exposure.

Notes to Physicians

Because of possible disturbances of cardiac rhythm, catecholamine drugs, such as epinephrine, should only be used with special caution in situations of emergency life support.

FIRE FIGHTING MEASURES

Flammable Properties

Flash Point	Will not burn
Method	TOC
Flammable limits in Air, % by Volume	
LEL	Not applicable
UEL	Not applicable
Autoignition	681 C (1258 F) 0 "SUVA" MP39 (R-401A)
	685 C (1265 F) 0 "SUVA" MP66 (R-401B)

Fire and Explosion Hazards:

Cylinders may rupture under fire conditions. Decomposition may occur.

Potential Combustibility:

"SUVA" MP39 is not flammable at temperatures up to 80 deg C (176 deg F) and at atmospheric pressure. Data are not available at higher temperatures and pressures. However, one of the components, HFC-152a, is flammable. Another, HCFC-22, has been shown in tests to be combustible at pressures as low as 60 psig at ambient temperature when mixed with air at concentrations of 65 volume % air. Therefore, "SUVA" MP39 should not be mixed with air for leak

(Continued)

FIRE FIGHTING MEASURES (Continued)

testing. In general, it should not be used or allowed to be present with high concentrations of air above atmospheric pressure.

Extinguishing Media

As appropriate for combustibles in area.

Fire Fighting Instructions

Cool tank/container with water spray.

Self-contained breathing apparatus (SCBA) is required if cylinders rupture and contents are released under fire conditions.

ACCIDENTAL RELEASE MEASURES

Safeguards (Personnel)

NOTE: Review FIRE FIGHTING MEASURES and HANDLING (PERSONNEL) sections before proceeding with clean-up. Use appropriate PERSONAL PROTECTIVE EQUIPMENT during clean-up.

Accidental Release Measures

Ventilate area, especially low or enclosed places where heavy vapors might collect. Remove open flames. Wear self-contained breathing apparatus (SCBA) for large spills or when a release occurs. Comply with Federal, State, and local regulations for reporting releases.

HANDLING AND STORAGE

Handling (Personnel)

Avoid breathing vapors. Avoid liquid contact with skin or eyes. Use with sufficient ventilation to keep employee exposure below the recommended limit.

Storage

Clean, dry area. Do not heat above 52 deg C (125 deg F).

EXPOSURE CONTROLS/PERSONAL PROTECTION

Engineering Controls

Use with sufficient ventilation to keep employee exposure below recommended exposure limit. Local exhaust should be used if large amounts are released. Mechanical ventilation should be used in low or enclosed places.

Personal Protective Equipment

Lined butyl gloves should be used to avoid prolonged or repeated exposure. Chemical splash goggles should be available for use as needed to prevent eye contact. Under normal manufacturing conditions, no respiratory protection

(Continued)

EXPOSURE CONTROLS/PERSONAL PROTECTION (Continued)

is required when using this product. Self-contained breathing apparatus (SCBA) is required if a large release occurs.

 # Exposure Guidelines

Applicable Exposure Limits

METHANE, CHLORODIFLUORO- (HCFC-22)

PEL (OSHA)	None Established
TLV (ACGIH)	1,000 ppm, 3,540 mg/m3, 8 Hr. TWA
AEL * (DuPont)	None Established

ETHANE, 1,1-DIFLUORO- (HFC-152a)

PEL (OSHA)	None Established
TLV (ACGIH)	None Established
AEL * (DuPont)	1000 ppm, 8 Hr. TWA
WEEL (AIHA)	1000 ppm, 8 Hr. TWA

ETHANE, 2-CHLORO-1,1,1,2-TETRAFLUORO

PEL (OSHA)	None Established
TLV (ACGIH)	None Established
AEL * (DuPont)	500 ppm, 8 & 12 Hr. TWA

* AEL is DuPont's Acceptable Exposure Limit. Where governmentally imposed occupational exposure limits which are lower than the AEL are in effect, such limits shall take precedence.

PHYSICAL AND CHEMICAL PROPERTIES

Physical Data

Boiling Point	-33 C (-27 F) Average
Vapor Pressure	111.2 psia at 25 deg C (77 deg F)
% Volatiles	100 WT%
Evaporation Rate	(CCl4 = 1) Greater than 1
Solubility in Water	0.1 WT% @ 25 C (77 F)
Odor	Slight ethereal
Form	Liquefied gas
Color	Clear, colorless
Density	25 C (77 F) 1.188 g/cc

STABILITY AND REACTIVITY

Chemical Stability

Material is stable. However, avoid open flames and high temperatures.

Incompatibility with Other Materials

Incompatible with alkali or alkaline earth metals- powdered Al, Zn, Be, etc.

Polymerization

Polymerization will not occur.

(Continued)

STABILITY AND REACTIVITY (Continued)

Other Hazards

Decomposition : Decomposition products are hazardous. "SUVA" MP39 can be decomposed by high temperature (open flames, glowing metal surfaces, etc.) forming hydrochloric and hydrofluoric acids, and possibly carbonyl halides.

TOXICOLOGICAL INFORMATION

Animal Data

The blend is untested.

CHLORODIFLUOROMETHANE

Inhalation 4-hour LC50: 220,000 ppm in rats

The compound is a skin irritant and a slight eye irritant, but is not a skin sensitizer in animals.

Effects from single high exposures include central nervous system depression, anesthesia, rapid breathing, lung congestion and microscopic liver changes. Cardiac sensitization occurred in dogs at 50,000 ppm or greater from the action of exogenous epinephrine.

No toxic effects or abnormal histopathological observations occurred in rats repeatedly exposed to concentrations ranging from 10,000 to 50,000 ppm (v/v). Long-term exposures to 50,000 ppm (v/v) of vapors produced organ weight increases and a decrease in body weight gain, but no increased mortality or adverse hematological effects.

In chronic inhalation studies, HCFC-22, at a concentration of 50,000 ppm (v/v), produced a small, but statistically significant increase of late-occurring tumors involving salivary glands in male rats, but not female rats or male or female mice. In the same studies, no increased incidence of tumors was seen in either species at concentrations of 10,000 ppm or 1000 ppm (v/v).

Long-term administration in corn oil produced no effects on body weight or mortality.

HCFC-22 was mutagenic in some strains of bacteria in bacterial cell cultures, but no mammalian cell cultures or animals. It did not cause heritable genetic damage in mammals.

A slight, but significant increase in developmental toxicity was observed at high concentrations (50,000 ppm) of HCFC-22, a concentration which also produced toxic effects in the adult animal. Based on these findings, and other negative

(Continued)

developmental studies, HCFC-22 is not considered a unique hazard to the conceptus. Studies of the effects of HCFC-22 on male reproductive performance have been negative. Specific studies to evaluate the effect on female reproductive performance have not been conducted, however, limited information obtained from studies on developmental toxicity do not indicate adverse effects on female reproductive performance at concentrations up to 50,000 ppm.

DIFLUOROETHANE

Inhalation 4-hour ALC: 383,000 ppm in rats
Oral ALD : >1,500 mg/kg in rats

Effects of a single exposure to high levels include labored breathing, lung irritation, lethargy, incoordination and loss of consciousness. Cardiac sensitization occurred in dogs exposed to a concentration of 150,000 ppm in air and given an intravenous epinephrine challenge. Effects of repeated exposure include increased urinary fluoride, reduced kidney weight, and reversible kidney changes.

Effects of a single high oral dose include weight loss and lethargy.

Tests in animals demonstrate no carcinogenic activity or developmental effects. Tests in animals for reproductive effects have not been performed. This compound does not produce genetic damage in bacterial cell cultures but has not been tested in animals.

CHLOROTETRAFLUOROETHANE

Inhalation 4-hour ALC: >230,000 ppm in rats

The effects in animals from single inhalation exposures by inhalation include central nervous system effects, anesthesia and decreased blood pressure. Cardiac sensitization occurred in dogs exposed to a concentration of 2.5% in air and given an intravenous epinephrine challenge. Repeated exposures produced increased liver weights, anesthetic effects, irregular respiration, poor coordination and nonspecific effects such as decreased body weight gain. However, no irreversible effects were seen as evidenced by histopathologic evaluation.

Tests in animals suggest no developmental toxicity potential. HCFC-124 was not mutagenic in bacterial and mammalian cell cultures or whole animal studies.

(Continued)

DISPOSAL CONSIDERATIONS

Waste Disposal

Comply with Federal, State, and local regulations. Reclaim by distillation or remove to a permitted waste disposal facility.

TRANSPORTATION INFORMATION

Shipping Information

DOT/IMO

Proper Shipping Name	LIQUEFIED GAS, N.O.S. (CONTAINS CHLORODIFLUOROMETHANE AND CHLOROTETRAFLUOROETHANE)
Hazard Class	2.2
UN No.	1956
DOT/IMO Label	NONFLAMMABLE GAS

Shipping Containers

Tank Cars.

Cylinders
Ton Tanks

REGULATORY INFORMATION

U.S. Federal Regulations

TSCA Inventory Status Reported/Included.

TITLE III HAZARD CLASSIFICATIONS SECTIONS 311, 312

Acute : Yes
Chronic : No
Fire : No
Reactivity : No
Pressure : Yes

HAZARDOUS CHEMICAL LISTS

SARA Extremely Hazardous Substance: No
CERCLA Hazardous Substance : No
SARA Toxic Chemical - See Components Section

OTHER INFORMATION

NFPA, NPCA-HMIS

NPCA-HMIS Rating

Health	1
Flammability	0
Reactivity	1

(Continued)

The data in this Material Safety Data Sheet relates only to the specific material designated herein and does not relate to use in combination with any other material or in any process.

Responsibility for MSDS : DuPont Chemicals
Address : Engineering & Product Safety
> : P.O. Box 80709, Chestnut Run
> : Wilmington, DE 19880-0709
Telephone : (302) 999-4946

# Indicates updated section.

End of MSDS

Du Pont Chemicals

6002FR Revised 24-FEB-1995 Printed 18-APR-1995

"SUVA" HP62 (R404A)

CHEMICAL PRODUCT/COMPANY IDENTIFICATION

Material Identification

"SUVA" is a registered trademark of DuPont.

Corporate MSDS Number DU005612

Company Identification

MANUFACTURER/DISTRIBUTOR
DuPont
1007 Market Street
Wilmington, DE 19898

PHONE NUMBERS

Product Information	1-800-441-9442
Transport Emergency	CHEMTREC: 1-800-424-9300
Medical Emergency	1-800-441-3637

COMPOSITION/INFORMATION ON INGREDIENTS

Components

Material	CAS Number	%
PENTAFLUOROETHANE (HFC-125)	354-33-6	44
ETHANE, 1,1,1-TRIFLUORO- (HFC-143a)	420-46-2	52
	811-97-2	
ETHANE, 1,1,1,2-TETRAFLUORO- (HFC-134a)		4

HAZARDS IDENTIFICATION

Potential Health Effects

Inhalation of high concentrations of vapor is harmful and may cause heart irregularities, unconsciousness, or death. Intentional misuse or deliberate inhalation may cause death without warning. Vapor reduces oxygen available for breathing and is heavier than air. Liquid contact can cause

(Continued)

HAZARDS IDENTIFICATION (Continued)

frostbite.

HUMAN HEALTH EFFECTS:

Overexposure to the vapors by inhalation may include temporary nervous system depression with anesthetic effects such as dizziness, headache, confusion, incoordination, and loss of consciousness. Higher exposures to the vapors may cause temporary alteration of the heart's electrical activity with irregular pulse, palpitations, or inadequate circulation; or fatality from gross overexposure. Contact with the liquid may cause frostbite.

Individuals with preexisting diseases of the central nervous or cardiovascular system may have increased susceptibility to the toxicity of increased exposures.

Carcinogenicity Information

None of the components present in this material at concentrations equal to or greater than 0.1% are listed by IARC, NTP, OSHA or ACGIH as a carcinogen.

FIRST AID MEASURES

First Aid

INHALATION

If inhaled, immediately remove to fresh air. Keep person calm. If not breathing, give artificial respiration. If breathing is difficult, give oxygen. Call a physician.

SKIN CONTACT

Flush area with lukewarm water. Do not use hot water. If frostbite has occurred, call a physician.

EYE CONTACT

In case of contact, immediately flush eyes with plenty of water for at least 15 minutes. Call a physician.

INGESTION

Not a probable route. However, in case of accidental ingestion, call a physician.

Notes to Physicians

THIS MATERIAL MAY MAKE THE HEART MORE SUSCEPTIBLE TO ARRHYTHMIAS. Catecholamines such as adrenaline, and other compounds having similar effects, should be reserved for emergencies and then used only with special caution.

(Continued)

FIRE FIGHTING MEASURES

Flammable Properties

Flash Point	Will not burn
Method	TOC
Flammable limits in Air, % by Volume	
LEL	Not applicable
UEL	Not applicable
Autoignition	Not determined

Fire and Explosion Hazards:

Cylinders may rupture under fire conditions. Decomposition may occur.

Potential Combustibility:

"SUVA" HP62 is not flammable at temperatures up to 80 deg C (176 deg F) and at atmospheric pressure. Data are not available at higher temperatures and pressures. However, one of the components, HFC-143a is flammable. Another, HFC-134a, has been shown in tests to be combustible at pressures as low as 60 psig at ambient temperature when mixed with air at concentrations of 65 volume % air. Therefore, "SUVA" HP62 should not be mixed with air for leak testing. In general, it should not be used or allowed to be present with high concentrations of air above atmospheric pressure. Experimental data have also been reported which indicate combustibility of HFC-134a in the presence of certain concentrations of chlorine.

Extinguishing Media

As appropriate for combustibles in area.

Fire Fighting Instructions

Cool cylinder with water spray or fog. Self-contained breathing apparatus (SCBA) is required if cylinders rupture and contents are released under fire conditions.

ACCIDENTAL RELEASE MEASURES

Safeguards (Personnel)

NOTE: Review FIRE FIGHTING MEASURES and HANDLING (PERSONNEL) sections before proceeding with clean-up. Use appropriate PERSONAL PROTECTIVE EQUIPMENT during clean-up.

Accidental Release Measures

Ventilate area, especially low or enclosed places where heavy vapors might collect. Remove open flames. Use self-contained breathing apparatus (SCBA) for large spills or releases.

(Continued)

HANDLING AND STORAGE

Handling (Personnel)

Avoid breathing vapor. Avoid liquid contact with eyes and skin. Use with sufficient ventilation to keep employee exposure below recommended limits. Contact with chlorine or other strong oxidizing agents should also be avoided. See Fire and Explosion Data section.

Storage

Clean, dry area. Do not heat above 52 deg C (125 deg F).

EXPOSURE CONTROLS/PERSONAL PROTECTION

Engineering Controls

Avoid breathing vapors. Avoid contact with skin or eyes. Use with sufficient ventilation to keep employee exposure below the recommended exposure limit. Local exhaust should be used if large amounts are released. Mechanical ventilation should be used in low or enclosed places.

Personal Protective Equipment

Impervious gloves should be used to avoid prolonged or repeated exposure. Chemical splash goggles should be available for use as needed to prevent eye contact. Under normal manufacturing conditions, no respiratory protection is required when using this product. Self-contained breathing apparatus (SCBA) is required if a large release occurs.

 # Exposure Guidelines

Applicable Exposure Limits

PENTAFLUOROETHANE (HFC-125)

PEL (OSHA)	None Established
TLV (ACGIH)	None Established
AEL * (Du Pont)	1000 ppm, 8 & 12 Hr. TWA

ETHANE, 1,1,1-TRIFLUORO- (HFC-143a)

PEL (OSHA)	None Established
TLV (ACGIH)	None Established
AEL * (Du Pont)	1000 ppm, 8 & 12 Hr. TWA
WEEL (AIHA)	1000 ppm, 8 Hr. TWA

ETHANE, 1,1,1,2-TETRAFLUORO- (HFC-134a)

PEL (OSHA)	None Established
TLV (ACGIH)	None Established
AEL * (Du Pont)	1000 ppm, 8 & 12 Hr. TWA
WEEL (AIHA)	1000 ppm, 8 Hr. TWA

* AEL is Du Pont's Acceptable Exposure Limit. Where governmentally imposed occupational exposure limits which are lower than the AEL are in effect, such limits shall take precedence.

(Continued)

PHYSICAL AND CHEMICAL PROPERTIES

Physical Data

Boiling Point	-46.7 C (-52.1 F) Average
Vapor Pressure	182.1 psia at 25 deg C (77 deg F)
% Volatiles	100 WT%
Evaporation Rate	(CL4 = 1) Greater than 1
Solubility in Water	Not determined
Odor	Slight ethereal
Form	Liquefied gas
Color	Clear, colorless
Specific Gravity	1.05 @ 25C (77F)

STABILITY AND REACTIVITY

Chemical Stability

Material is stable. However, avoid open flames and high temperatures.

Incompatibility with Other Materials

Incompatible with active metals, alkali or alkaline earth metals--powdered Al, Zn, Be, etc.

Decomposition

Decomposition products are hazardous. This material can be decomposed by high temperatures (open flames, glowing metal surfaces, etc.) forming hydrofluoric acid and possibly carbonyl fluoride.

Polymerization

Polymerization will not occur.

TOXICOLOGICAL INFORMATION

Animal Data

The blend is untested.

HFC-125

Inhalation 4 hour ALC: > 709,000 ppm in rats

Single, high inhalation exposures caused lethargy, decreased activity, labored breathing and weight loss. Weak cardiac sensitization effect, a potentially fatal disturbance of heart rhythm caused by a heightened sensitivity to the action of epinephrine.

No animal data are available to define carcinogenic, developmental or reproductive hazards. In animal testing this material has not caused developmental toxicity. HFC-125 does not produce genetic damage in bacterial or mammalian cell cultures or when tested in animals (not tested for heritable genetic damage).

(Continued)

HFC-134a

Inhalation 4-hour LC50: 567,000 ppm in rats

A 5 or 10 second spray of vapor produced very slight eye irritation and a 24-hour occlusive application produced slight skin irritation in rabbits. The compound is not a skin sensitizer in animals. No toxic effects were seen in animals from exposures by inhalation to concentrations up to 81,000 ppm. Lethargy and rapid respiration were observed at a vapor concentration of 305,000 ppm and pulmonary congestion, edema, and central nervous system effects occurred at a vapor concentration of 750,000 ppm. Cardiac sensitization occurred in dogs at 75,000 ppm following an epinephrine challenge. No effects in animals occurred from repeated inhalation exposures to 99,000 ppm for two weeks or up to 50,000 ppm for three months. Repeated exposures to higher concentrations caused transient tremors, incoordination and some organ weight changes. Long-term exposures produced increased testes weights and increased urinary fluoride levels. No adverse effects were observed in male and female rats fed diets containing 300 mg/kg/day of HFC-134a for 52 weeks. Animal testing indicates that this compound does not have carcinogenic or mutagenic effects. Inhalation of 50,000 ppm for two years caused an increase in benign testicular tumors in male rats. No effects were observed at lower concentrations. The tumors were late-occurring and were judged not to be life-threatening. Embryotoxic activity has been observed in some animal tests but only at high concentrations that were also maternally toxic.

HFC-143a

Inhalation 4-hour LC50: >540,000 ppm in rats

Single exposures by inhalation to 500,000 ppm caused anesthesia but no mortality at 540,000 ppm. Cardiac sensitization occurred in dogs at 300,000 ppm following an intravenous challenge with epinephrine. Two, 4-week inhalation have been conducted. In the first study, pathological changes in the testes were observed at all exposure concentrations; no effects were observed in females. The testicular effect was considered related to the method used to expose the rats to HFC-143a. In the second study using the same exposure concentrations, no effects were noted in males at any concentration. Data from a 90-day study revealed no effects in male or female rats at exposures up to 40,000 ppm. Long-term exposure caused significantly decreased body weights in male rats fed 300 mg/kg for 52 weeks, but there was no effect on mortality. Tests in rats demonstrated no carcinogenic activity when administered orally 300 mg/kg/day for 52 weeks and observed

(Continued)

TOXICOLOGICAL INFORMATION (Continued)

for an additional 73 weeks. Tests in bacterial cell cultures demonstrated mutagenic activity, but the compound did not induce transformation of mammalian cells in culture or in the whole animal. Tests in animals demonstrate no developmental toxicity.

ECOLOGICAL INFORMATION

Ecotoxicological Information

Aquatic Toxicity

HFC 143a
96-hour LC50, rainbow trout: >40 mg/L

DISPOSAL CONSIDERATIONS

Waste Disposal

Comply with Federal, State, and local regulations. Reclaim by distillation or remove to a permitted waste disposal facility.

TRANSPORTATION INFORMATION

Shipping Information

DOT/IMO

Proper Shipping Name	LIQUIFIED GAS, N.O.S. (CONTAINS PENTAFLUOROETHANE AND TETRAFLUOROETHANE)
Hazard Class	2.2
UN No.	1956
DOT/IMO Label	NONFLAMMABLE GAS

Shipping Containers

Tank Cars.

Cylinders
Ton Tanks

REGULATORY INFORMATION

U.S. Federal Regulations

TSCA Inventory Status   Reported/Included.

TITLE III HAZARD CLASSIFICATIONS SECTIONS 311, 312

Acute : No
Chronic : No

(Continued)

REGULATORY INFORMATION(Continued)

Fire : No
Reactivity : No
Pressure : Yes

LISTS:

SARA Extremely Hazardous Substance -No
CERCLA Hazardous Material -No
SARA Toxic Chemicals -No

OTHER INFORMATION

NFPA, NPCA-HMIS

NPCA-HMIS Rating

Health	1
Flammability	0
Reactivity	1

Personal Protection rating to be supplied by user depending on use conditions.

Additional Information

HFC-125 and HFC-143a are TSCA listed, and are controlled by a TSCA Section 5 Consent Order.

The data in this Material Safety Data Sheet relates only to the specific material designated herein and does not relate to use in combination with any other material or in any process.

Responsibility for MSDS	DuPont Chemicals
Address	Engineering & Product Safety P. O. Box 80709, Chestnut Run Wilmington, DE 19880-0709
Telephone	302-999-4946

# Indicates updated section.

End of MSDS

Du Pont Chemicals

MSDS MATERIAL SAFETY DATA SHEET

3034FR   Revised 31-AUG-1993   Printed 19-APR-1995

"SUVA" MP66 (R401B)

CHEMICAL PRODUCT/COMPANY IDENTIFICATION

Material Identification
"SUVA" is a registered trademark of DuPont.

Corporate MSDS Number	DU005356
Formula	CHClF2/CH3CHF2/CHClFCF3

Company Identification
MANUFACTURER/DISTRIBUTOR
DuPont
1007 Market Street
Wilmington, DE 19898

PHONE NUMBERS

Product Information	1-800-441-9442
Transport Emergency	CHEMTREC: 1-800-424-9300
Medical Emergency	1-800-441-3637

COMPOSITION/INFORMATION ON INGREDIENTS

Components

Material	CAS Number	%
*METHANE, CHLORODIFLUORO- (HCFC-22)	75-45-6	61
*ETHANE, 2-CHLORO-1,1,1,2-TETRAFLUORO- (HCFC-124)	2837-89-0	28
ETHANE, 1,1-DIFLUORO- (HFC-152a)	75-37-6	11

* Regulated as a Toxic Chemical under Section 313 of Title III of the Superfund Amendments and Reauthorization Act of 1986 and 40 CFR part 372.

(Continued)

HAZARDS IDENTIFICATION

Potential Health Effects

Inhalation of high concentrations of vapor is harmful and may cause heart irregularities, unconsciousness, or death. Intentional misuse or deliberate inhalation may cause death without warning. Vapor reduces oxygen available for breathing and is heavier than air. Liquid contact can cause frostbite.

HUMAN HEALTH EFFECTS:

Skin contact may cause frostbite from exposure to the liquid.

Inhalation may include nonspecific discomfort, such as nausea, headache, or weakness; or temporary nervous system depression with anesthetic effects such as dizziness, headache, confusion, incoordination, and loss of consciousness.

Higher exposures (>20%) may lead to these effects: temporary lung irritation effects with cough, discomfort, difficulty breathing, or shortness of breath; temporary alteration of the heart's electrical activity with irregular pulse, palpitations, or inadequate circulation; abnormal kidney function as detected by laboratory tests; or fatality from gross overexposure.

Individuals with preexisting diseases of the central nervous system, cardiovascular system, lungs or kidneys may have increased susceptibility to the toxicity of excessive exposures.

Carcinogenicity Information

None of the components present in this material at concentrations equal to or greater than 0.1% are listed by IARC, NTP, OSHA or ACGIH as a carcinogen.

FIRST AID MEASURES

First Aid

INHALATION

If high concentrations are inhaled, immediately remove to fresh air. Keep person calm. If not breathing, give artificial respiration. If breathing is difficult, give oxygen. Call a physician.

SKIN CONTACT

Flush skin with water after excessive contact. Treat for frostbite if necessary by gently warming affected area. Seek

(Continued)

FIRST AID MEASURES(Continued)

medical assistance if irritation is present. Wash contaminated clothing before reuse.

EYE CONTACT

In case of contact, immediately flush eyes with plenty of water for at least 15 minutes. Call a physician.

INGESTION

Ingestion is not considered a potential route of exposure.

Notes to Physicians

Because of possible disturbances of cardiac rhythm, catecholamine drugs, such as epinephrine, should only be used with special caution in situations of emergency life support.

FIRE FIGHTING MEASURES

Flammable Properties

Will not burn.

Fire and Explosion Hazards:

Cylinders may rupture under fire conditions. Decomposition may occur.

Potential Combustibility:

"SUVA" MP66 is not flammable at temperatures up to 80 C (176 F) and at atmospheric pressure. Data are not available at higher temperatures and pressures. However, one of the components, HFC-152a, is flammable. Another, HCFC-22, has been shown in tests to be combustible at pressures as low as 60 psig at ambient temperature when mixed with air at concentrations of 65 volume % air. Therefore, "SUVA" MP66 should not be mixed with air for leak testing. In general, it should not be used or allowed to be present with high concentrations of air above atmospheric pressure.

Extinguishing Media

As appropriate for combustibles in area.

Fire Fighting Instructions

Use water spray or fog to cool containers. Self-contained breathing apparatus (SCBA) is required if cylinders rupture and contents are released under fire conditions.

(Continued)

ACCIDENTAL RELEASE MEASURES

Safeguards (Personnel)

NOTE: Review FIRE FIGHTING MEASURES and HANDLING (PERSONNEL) sections before proceeding with clean-up. Use appropriate PERSONAL PROTECTIVE EQUIPMENT during clean-up.

Accidental Release Measures

Ventilate area, especially low or enclosed places where heavy vapors might collect. Remove open flames. Wear self-contained breathing apparatus (SCBA) for large spills or when a release occurs. Comply with Federal, State, and local regulations for reporting releases.

HANDLING AND STORAGE

Handling (Personnel)

Avoid breathing vapors. Avoid liquid contact with skin or eyes. Use with sufficient ventilation to keep employee exposure below the recommended limit.

Storage

Clean, dry area. Do not heat above 52 C (125 F).

EXPOSURE CONTROLS/PERSONAL PROTECTION

Engineering Controls

Normal ventilation for standard manufacturing procedures is generally adequate. Local exhaust should be used if large amounts are released. Mechanical ventilation should be used in low or enclosed places.

Personal Protective Equipment

Lined butyl gloves should be used to avoid prolonged or repeated exposure. Chemical splash goggles should be available for use as needed to prevent eye contact. Under normal manufacturing conditions, no respiratory protection is required when using this product. Self-contained breathing apparatus (SCBA) is required if a large release occurs.

 # Exposure Guidelines

Applicable Exposure Limits

METHANE, CHLORODIFLUORO- (HCFC-22)

PEL (OSHA)	None Established
TLV (ACGIH)	1,000 ppm, 3,540 mg/m3, 8 Hr. TWA
AEL * (Du Pont)	None Established

ETHANE, 2-CHLORO-1,1,1,2-TETRAFLUORO-

PEL (OSHA)	None Established
TLV (ACGIH)	None Established
AEL * (Du Pont)	500 ppm, 8 & 12 Hr. TWA

(Continued)

EXPOSURE CONTROLS/PERSONAL PROTECTION(Continued)

ETHANE, 1,1-DIFLUORO- (HFC-152a)

PEL (OSHA)	None Established
TLV (ACGIH)	None Established
AEL * (Du Pont)	1000 ppm, 8 Hr. TWA
WEEL (AIHA)	1000 ppm, 8 Hr. TWA

* AEL is Du Pont's Acceptable Exposure Limit. Where governmentally imposed occupational exposure limits which are lower than the AEL are in effect, such limits shall take precedence.

PHYSICAL AND CHEMICAL PROPERTIES

Physical Data

Boiling Point	-34.7 C (-30.5 F) Average
Vapor Pressure	100.4 psia @ 25 C (77 F)
% Volatiles	100 WT%
Evaporation Rate	>1 (CCl_4=1.0)
Solubility in Water	0.1 WT% @ 25 C (77 F)
Odor	Slight ethereal
Form	Liquified Gas.
Color	Clear, Colorless.
Density	1.186 g/cm3 @ 25 C (77 F)

STABILITY AND REACTIVITY

Chemical Stability

Material is stable. However, avoid open flames and high temperatures.

Incompatibility with Other Materials

Incompatible with alkali or alkaline earth metals - powdered Al, Zn, Be, etc.

Decomposition

Decomposition products are hazardous. "SUVA" MP66 can be decomposed by high temperature (open flames, glowing metal surfaces, etc.) forming hydrochloric and hydrofluoric acids, and possibly carbonyl halides.

Polymerization

Polymerization will not occur.

TOXICOLOGICAL INFORMATION

Animal Data

The blend is untested.

CHLORODIFLUOROMETHANE

Inhalation 4-hour LC50: 220,000 ppm in rats

The compound is a skin irritant and a slight eye irritant, but is not a skin sensitizer in animals.

(Continued)

Effects from single high exposures include central nervous system depression, anesthesia, rapid breathing, lung congestion and microscopic liver changes. Cardiac sensitization occurred in dogs at 50,000 ppm or greater from the action of exogenous epinephrine.

No toxic effects or abnormal histopathological observations occurred in rats repeatedly exposed to concentrations ranging from 10,000 to 50,000 ppm (v/v). Long-term exposures to 50,000 ppm (v/v) of vapors produced organ weight increases and a decrease in body weight gain, but no increased mortality or adverse hematological effects.

In chronic inhalation studies, HCFC-22, at a concentration of 50,000 ppm (v/v), produced a small, but statistically significant increase of late-occurring tumors involving salivary glands in male rats, but not female rats or male or female mice. In the same studies, no increased incidence of tumors was seen in either species at concentrations of 10,000 ppm or 1000 ppm (v/v).

Long-term administration in corn oil produced no effects on body weight or mortality.

HCFC-22 was mutagenic in some strains of bacteria in bacterial cell cultures, but not mammalian cell cultures or animals. It did not cause heritable genetic damage in mammals.

A slight, but significant increase in developmental toxicity was observed at high concentrations (50,000 ppm) of HCFC-22, a concentration which also produced toxic effects in the adult animal. Based on these findings, and other negative developmental studies, HCFC-22 is not considered a unique hazard to the conceptus. Studies of the effects of HCFC-22 on male reproductive performance have been negative. Specific studies to evaluate the effect on female reproductive performance have not been conducted, however, limited information obtained from studies on developmental toxicity do not indicate adverse effects on female reproductive performance at concentrations up to 50,000 ppm.

DIFLUOROETHANE

Inhalation 4-hour ALC: 383,000 ppm in rats
Oral ALD : >1,500 mg/kg in rats

Effects of a single exposure to high levels include labored breathing, lung irritation, lethargy, incoordination and loss of consciousness. Cardiac sensitization occurred in dogs exposed to a concentration of 150,000 ppm in air and given an intravenous epinephrine challenge. Effects of

(Continued)

TOXICOLOGICAL INFORMATION (Continued)

repeated exposure include increased urinary fluoride, reduced kidney weight, and reversible kidney changes.

Effects of a single high oral dose include weight loss and lethargy.

Tests in animals demonstrate no carcinogenic activity or developmental effects. Tests in animals for reproductive effects have not been performed. This compound does not produce genetic damage in bacterial cell cultures but has not been tested in animals.

CHLOROTETRAFLUOROETHANE

Inhalation 4-hour ALC: >230,000 ppm in rats

The effects in animals from single inhalation exposures by inhalation include central nervous system effects, anesthesia and decreased blood pressure. Cardiac sensitization occurred in dogs exposed to a concentration of 2.5% in air and given an intravenous epinephrine challenge. Repeated exposures produced increased liver weights, anesthetic effects, irregular respiration, poor coordination and nonspecific effects such as decreased body weight gain. However, no irreversible effects were seen as evidenced by histopathologic evaluation.

Tests in animals suggest no developmental toxicity potential. HCFC-124 was not mutagenic in bacterial and mammalian cell cultures or whole animal studies.

DISPOSAL CONSIDERATIONS

Waste Disposal

Comply with Federal, State, and local regulations. Reclaim by distillation or remove to a permitted waste disposal facility.

TRANSPORTATION INFORMATION

Shipping Information

DOT/IMO

Proper Shipping Name	LIQUEFIED GAS, N.O.S. (CONTAINS CHLORODIFLUOROMETHANE AND CHLOROTETRAFLUOROETHANE)
Hazard Class	2.2
UN No.	1956
DOT/IMO Label	NONFLAMMABLE GAS

Shipping Containers

Tank Cars
Cylinders
Ton Tanks

(Continued)

REGULATORY INFORMATION

U.S. Federal Regulations

TSCA Inventory Status   Reported/Included.

TITLE III HAZARD CLASSIFICATIONS SECTIONS 311, 312

Acute : Yes
Chronic : No
Fire : No
Reactivity : No
Pressure : Yes

HAZARDOUS CHEMICAL LISTS

SARA Extremely Hazardous Substance: No
CERCLA Hazardous Substance : No
SARA Toxic Chemical - See Components Section

OTHER INFORMATION

NFPA, NPCA-HMIS

NPCA-HMIS Rating

Health	1
Flammability	0
Reactivity	1

The data in this Material Safety Data Sheet relates only to the specific material designated herein and does not relate to use in combination with any other material or in any process.

Responsibility for MSDS : DuPont Chemicals
Address : Engineering & Product Safety
> : P.O. Box 80709, Chestnut Run
> : Wilmington, DE 19880-0709
Telephone : (302) 999-4946

# Indicates updated section.

End of MSDS

Du Pont Chemicals

MATERIAL SAFETY DATA SHEET

6003FR

Revised 19-APR-1994 Printed 18-APR-1995

"SUVA" HP80 (R402A)

CHEMICAL PRODUCT/COMPANY IDENTIFICATION

Material Identification
"SUVA" is a registered trademark of DuPont.

Corporate MSDS Number DU005613

Company Identification
MANUFACTURER/DISTRIBUTOR
DuPont
1007 Market Street
Wilmington, DE 19898

PHONE NUMBERS
Product Information 1-800-441-9442
Transport Emergency CHEMTREC: 1-800-424-9300
Medical Emergency 1-800-441-3637

COMPOSITION/INFORMATION ON INGREDIENTS

Components

Material	CAS Number	%
ETHANE, PENTAFLUORO- (HFC-125)	354-33-6	60
*METHANE, CHLORODIFLUORO- (HCFC-22)	75-45-6	38
PROPANE	74-98-6	2

* Regulated as a Toxic Chemical under Section 313 of Title III of the Superfund Amendments and Reauthorization Act of 1986 and 40 CFR part 372.

HAZARDS IDENTIFICATION

Potential Health Effects

Inhalation of high concentrations of vapor is harmful and may cause heart irregularities, unconsciousness, or death. Intentional misuse or deliberate inhalation may cause death without warning. Vapor reduces oxygen available for

(Continued)

HAZARDS IDENTIFICATION (Continued)

breathing and is heavier than air. Liquid contact can cause frostbite.

HUMAN HEALTH EFFECTS:

Overexposure to the vapors by inhalation may include temporary nervous system depression with anesthetic effects such as dizziness, headache, confusion, incoordination, and loss of consciousness. Higher exposures to the vapors may cause temporary alteration of the heart's electrical activity with irregular pulse, palpitations, or inadequate circulation. Fatality may occur from gross overexposure. Skin contact with the liquid may cause frostbite.

Individuals with preexisting diseases of the central nervous or cardiovascular system may have increased susceptibility to the toxicity of increased exposures.

Carcinogenicity Information

None of the components present in this material at concentrations equal to or greater than 0.1% are listed by IARC, NTP, OSHA or ACGIH as a carcinogen.

FIRST AID MEASURES

First Aid

INHALATION

If inhaled, immediately remove to fresh air. Keep person calm. If not breathing, give artificial respiration. If breathing is difficult, give oxygen. Call a physician.

SKIN CONTACT

Flush area with lukewarm water. Do not use hot water. If frostbite has occurred, call a physician.

EYE CONTACT

In case of contact, immediately flush eyes with plenty of water for at least 15 minutes. Call a physician.

INGESTION

Not a probable route. However, in case of accidental ingestion, call a physician.

Notes to Physicians

THIS MATERIAL MAY MAKE THE HEART MORE SUSCEPTIBLE TO ARRHYTHMIAS. Catecholamines such as adrenaline, and other compounds having similar effects, should be reserved for emergencies and then used only with special caution.

(Continued)

FIRE FIGHTING MEASURES

 # Flammable Properties

Flammable limits in Air, % by Volume

LEL	Not determined
UEL	Not determined

Fire and Explosion Hazards:

Cylinders may rupture under fire conditions. Decomposition may occur.

"SUVA" HP80 is not flammable at temperatures up to 100 deg C (212 deg F) and at atmospheric pressure. Data are not available at higher temperatures and pressures. However, one of the components, propane, is flammable. HCFC-22 has been shown in tests to be combustible at pressures as low as 60 psig at ambient temperature when mixed with air at concentrations of 65 volume % air. Therefore, "SUVA" HP80 should not be mixed with air for leak testing. In general, it should not be used or allowed to be present with high concentrations of air above atmospheric pressure.

Extinguishing Media

As appropriate for combustibles in area.

Fire Fighting Instructions

Keep cylinders cool with water spray or fog. Self-contained breathing apparatus (SCBA) is required if cylinders rupture and contents are released under fire conditions.

ACCIDENTAL RELEASE MEASURES

Safeguards (Personnel)

NOTE: Review FIRE FIGHTING MEASURES and HANDLING (PERSONNEL) sections before proceeding with clean-up. Use appropriate PERSONAL PROTECTIVE EQUIPMENT during clean-up.

Accidental Release Measures

Ventilate area, especially low or enclosed places where heavy vapors might collect. Remove open flames. Use self-contained breathing apparatus (SCBA) for large spills or releases.

HANDLING AND STORAGE

Handling (Personnel)

Avoid breathing vapors. Avoid liquid contact with skin or eyes. Use with sufficient ventilation to keep employee exposure below the recommended limits. Avoid prolonged or repeated exposure. Wash thoroughly after handling.

Storage

Clean, dry area. Do not heat above 52 deg C (125 deg F).

(Continued)

EXPOSURE CONTROLS/PERSONAL PROTECTION

Engineering Controls

Use with sufficient ventilation to keep employee exposure below the recommended exposure limit. Local exhaust should be used if large amounts are released. Mechanical ventilation should be used in low or enclosed places.

Personal Protective Equipment

Impervious gloves should be used to avoid prolonged or repeated exposure. Chemical splash goggles should be available for use as needed to prevent eye contact. Under normal manufacturing conditions, no respiratory protection is required when using this product. Self-contained breathing apparatus (SCBA) is required if a large release occurs.

Exposure Guidelines

Applicable Exposure Limits

ETHANE, PENTAFLUORO- (HFC-125)

PEL (OSHA)	None Established
TLV (ACGIH)	None Established
AEL * (Du Pont)	1000 ppm, 8 & 12 Hr. TWA

METHANE, CHLORODIFLUORO- (HCFC-22)

PEL (OSHA)	None Established
TLV (ACGIH)	1,000 ppm, 3,540 mg/m3, 8 Hr. TWA
AEL * (Du Pont)	None Established

PROPANE

PEL (OSHA)	1,000 ppm, 1,800 mg/m3, 8 Hr. TWA
TLV (ACGIH)	Simple Asphyxiant
AEL * (Du Pont)	None Established

* AEL is Du Pont's Acceptable Exposure Limit. Where governmentally imposed occupational exposure limits which are lower than the AEL are in effect, such limits shall take precedence.

PHYSICAL AND CHEMICAL PROPERTIES

Physical Data

Boiling Point	-49.2 C (-56.6 F)
Vapor Pressure	193.6 psia at 25 deg C (77 deg F)
% Volatiles	100 WT%
Evaporation Rate	(CCl4 = 1) Greater than 1
Solubility in Water	Not determined
Odor	Slight ethereal
Form	Liquefied gas
Color	Clear, colorless
Density	1.152 gm/cc at 25 deg C (77 deg F) - Liquid

(Continued)

STABILITY AND REACTIVITY

Chemical Stability

Material is stable. However, avoid open flames and high temperatures.

Incompatibility with Other Materials

Incompatible with alkali or alkaline earth metals - powdered Al, Zn, Be, etc.

Polymerization

Polymerization will not occur.

Other Hazards

Decomposition : Decomposition products are hazardous. "SUVA" HP80 can be decomposed by high temperatures (open flames, glowing metal surfaces, etc.) forming hydrochloric and hydrofluoric acids, and possibly carbonyl halides.

TOXICOLOGICAL INFORMATION

Animal Data

The blend is untested.

ETHANE, PENTAFLUORO

Inhalation 4 hour ALC: > 709,000 ppm in rats

Single, high inhalation exposures caused lethargy, decreased activity, labored breathing and weight loss. Weak cardiac sensitization effect, a potentially fatal disturbance of heart rhythm caused by a heightened sensitivity to the action of epinephrine.

No animal data are available to define carcinogenic, developmental or reproductive hazards. In animal testing this material has not caused developmental toxicity. HFC-125 does not produce genetic damage in bacterial or mammalian cell cultures or when tested in animals (not tested for heritable genetic damage).

METHANE, CHLORODIFLUORO

Inhalation 4-hour LC50: 220,000 ppm in rats

The compound is a skin irritant and a slight eye irritant, but is not a skin sensitizer in animals.

Effects from single high exposures include central nervous system depression, anesthesia, rapid breathing, lung congestion and microscopic liver changes. Cardiac sensitization occurred in dogs at 50,000 ppm or greater from the action of exogenous epinephrine.

(Continued)

No toxic effects or abnormal histopathological observations occurred in rats repeatedly exposed to concentrations ranging from 10,000 to 50,000 ppm (v/v). Long-term exposures to 50,000 ppm (v/v) of vapors produced organ weight increases and a decrease in body weight gain, but no increased mortality or adverse hematological effects.

In chronic inhalation studies, HCFC-22, at a concentration of 50,000 ppm (v/v), produced a small, but statistically significant increase of late-occurring tumors involving salivary glands in male rats, but not female rats or male or female mice. In the same studies, no increased incidence of tumors was seen in either species at concentrations of 10,000 ppm or 1000 ppm (v/v).

Long-term administration in corn oil produced no effects on body weight or mortality.

HCFC-22 was mutagenic in some strains of bacteria in bacterial cell cultures, but not mammalian cell cultures or animals. It did not cause heritable genetic damage in mammals.

A slight, but significant increase in developmental toxicity was observed at high concentrations (50,000 ppm) of HCFC-22, a concentration which also produced toxic effects in the adult animal. Based on these findings, and other negative developmental studies, HCFC-22 is not considered a unique hazard to the conceptus. Studies of the effects of HCFC-22 on male reproductive performance have been negative. Specific studies to evaluate the effect on female reproductive performance have not been conducted, however, limited information obtained from studies on developmental toxicity do not indicate adverse effects on female reproductive performance at concentrations up to 50,000 ppm.

PROPANE

Toxicity in animals occurring only with inhalation exposures at high concentrations (10% or greater) include cardiac sensitization, analgesia, irregular respiration and hypotension. No animal test reports are available to define carcinogenic, developmental, or reproductive hazards. Tests in bacteria cell cultures demonstrate no mutagenic activity.

(Continued)

DISPOSAL CONSIDERATIONS

Waste Disposal

Comply with Federal, State, and local regulations. Reclaim by distillation or remove to a permitted waste disposal facility.

TRANSPORTATION INFORMATION

Shipping Information

DOT/IMO

Proper Shipping Name	LIQUEFIED GAS, N.O.S. (CONTAINS CHLORODIFLUOROMETHANE AND PENTAFLUOROETHANE)
Hazard Class	2.2
UN No.	1956
DOT/IMO Label	NONFLAMMABLE GAS

Shipping Containers

Tank Cars.

Cylinders
Ton Tanks

REGULATORY INFORMATION

U.S. Federal Regulations

TSCA Inventory Status Reported/Included.

TITLE III HAZARD CLASSIFICATIONS SECTIONS 311, 312

Acute : Yes
Chronic : No
Fire : No
Reactivity : No
Pressure : Yes

HAZARDOUS CHEMICAL LISTS

SARA Extremely Hazardous Substance: No
CERCLA Hazardous Substance : No
SARA Toxic Chemical - See Components Section

OTHER INFORMATION

NFPA, NPCA-HMIS

NPCA-HMIS Rating

Health	1
Flammability	0
Reactivity	1

Personal Protection rating to be supplied by user depending on use

(Continued)

OTHER INFORMATION(Continued)

conditions.

Additional Information

MEDICAL USE: CAUTION: Do not use in medical applications involving permanent implantation in the human body. For other medical applications see DuPont CAUTION Bulletin No. H-50102.

HFC-125 is TSCA listed, and is controlled by a TSCA Section 5 Consent Order.

The data in this Material Safety Data Sheet relates only to the specific material designated herein and does not relate to use in combination with any other material or in any process.

Responsibility for MSDS : DuPont Chemicals
Address : Engineering & Product Safety
> : P.O. Box 80709, Chestnut Run
> : Wilmington, DE 19880-0709
Telephone : (302) 999-4946

# Indicates updated section.

End of MSDS

DuPont Chemicals

2187FR | Revised 12-MAR-1994 | Printed 18-APR-1995

"SUVA" 134a

CHEMICAL PRODUCT/COMPANY IDENTIFICATION

Material Identification

"SUVA" is a pending trademark of DuPont.

Corporate MSDS Number	DU000693
CAS Number	811-97-2
Formula	CH2FCF3
CAS Name	1,1,1,2-TETRAFLUOROETHANE

Tradenames and Synonyms

"SUVA" 134a
HFC 134a
VT1505

Company Identification

MANUFACTURER/DISTRIBUTOR
DuPont
1007 Market Street
Wilmington, DE 19898

PHONE NUMBERS

Product Information	1-800-441-7515
Transport Emergency	CHEMTREC: 1-800-424-9300
Medical Emergency	1-800-441-3637

COMPOSITION/INFORMATION ON INGREDIENTS

Components

Material	CAS Number	%
ETHANE, 1,1,1,2-TETRAFLUORO-	811-97-2	100
(HFC-134a)		

(Continued)

HAZARDS IDENTIFICATION

Potential Health Effects

Inhalation of high concentrations of vapor is harmful and may cause heart irregularities, unconsciousness or death. Intentional misuse or deliberate inhalation may cause death without warning. Vapor reduces oxygen available for breathing and is heavier than air. Liquid contact can cause frostbite.

HUMAN HEALTH EFFECTS:

Overexposure by inhalation to very high concentrations may cause temporary alteration of the heart's electrical activity with irregular pulse, palpitations, or inadequate circulation. Skin contact with the liquid may cause frostbite.

Individuals with preexisting diseases of the central nervous or cardiovascular system may have increased susceptibility to the toxicity of excessive exposures.

Carcinogenicity Information

None of the components present in this material at concentrations equal to or greater than 0.1% are listed by IARC, NTP, OSHA or ACGIH as a carcinogen.

FIRST AID MEASURES

First Aid

INHALATION

If high concentrations are inhaled, immediately remove to fresh air. Keep person calm. If not breathing, give artificial respiration. If breathing is difficult, give oxygen. Call a physician.

SKIN CONTACT

In case of contact, immediately flush skin with plenty of water for at least 15 minutes, while removing contaminated clothing and shoes. Call a physician. Wash contaminated clothing before reuse. Treat for frostbite if necessary by gently warming affected area.

EYE CONTACT

In case of contact, immediately flush eyes with plenty of water for at least 15 minutes. Call a physician.

INGESTION

(Continued)

FIRST AID MEASURES (Continued)

Ingestion is not considered a potential route of exposure.

Notes to Physicians

Because of possible disturbances of cardiac rhythm, catecholamine drugs, such as epinephrine, should only be used with special caution in situations of emergency life support.

FIRE FIGHTING MEASURES

Flammable Properties

Flash Point : Will not burn

Flammable limits in Air, % by Volume

LEL	Not Applicable
UEL	Not Applicable
Autoignition	>743 C (>1369 F)

HFC-134a is not flammable at ambient temperatures and atmospheric pressure. However, HFC-134a has been shown in tests to be combustible at pressure as low as 5.5 psig at 177 C (351 F) when mixed with air at concentrations of generally more than 60 volume % air. At lower temperatures, higher pressures are required for combustibility. Experimental data have also been reported which indicate combustibility of HFC-134a in the presence of certain concentrations of chlorine.

Fire and Explosion Hazards:

Cylinders may rupture under fire conditions. Decomposition may occur.

Extinguishing Media

Use media appropriate for surrounding material.

Fire Fighting Instructions

Cool tank/container with water spray. Self-contained breathing apparatus (SCBA) may be required if cylinders rupture or release under fire conditions.

ACCIDENTAL RELEASE MEASURES

Safeguards (Personnel)

NOTE: Review FIRE FIGHTING MEASURES and HANDLING (PERSONNEL) sections before proceeding with clean-up. Use appropriate PERSONAL PROTECTIVE EQUIPMENT during clean-up.

Ventilate area, especially low or enclosed places where heavy vapors might collect. Remove open flames. Use self-contained breathing apparatus (SCBA) if large spill or leak occurs.

(Continued)

HANDLING AND STORAGE

Handling (Personnel)
Use with sufficient ventilation to keep employee exposure below recommended limits.

Handling (Physical Aspects)
HFC-134a should not be mixed with air for leak testing or used for any other purpose above atmospheric pressure. See Flammable Properties section. Contact with chlorine or other strong oxidizing agents should also be avoided.

Storage
Store in a clean, dry place. Do not heat above 52 C (126 F).

EXPOSURE CONTROLS/PERSONAL PROTECTION

Engineering Controls
Normal ventilation for standard manufacturing procedures is generally adequate. Local exhaust should be used when large amounts are released. Mechanical ventilation should be used in low or enclosed places.

Personal Protective Equipment
Impervious gloves and chemical splash goggles should be used when handling liquid.

Under normal manufacturing conditions, no respiratory protection is required when using this product.

Self-contained breathing apparatus (SCBA) is required if a large release occurs.

\# **Exposure Guidelines**

Exposure Limits

"SUVA" 134a

PEL (OSHA)	None Established
TLV (ACGIH)	None Established
AEL * (DuPont)	1000 ppm, 8 & 12 Hr. TWA
WEEL (AIHA)	1000 ppm, 8 Hr. TWA

* AEL is DuPont's Acceptable Exposure Limit. Where governmentally imposed occupational exposure limits which are lower than the AEL are in effect, such limits shall take precedence.

PHYSICAL AND CHEMICAL PROPERTIES

Physical Data

Boiling Point	-26.5 C (-15.7 F) @ 736 mm Hg
Vapor Pressure	96 psia @ 25 C (77 F)
Vapor Density	3.6 (Air=1.0) @ 25 C (77 F)
% Volatiles	100 WT%
Solubility in Water	0.15 WT% @ 25 C (77 F) @ 14.7 psia
Odor	Ether (slight).
Form	Liquified Gas.
Color	Colorless.
Liquid Density	1.21 g/cm3 @ 25 C (77 F)

(Continued)

STABILITY AND REACTIVITY

Chemical Stability

Stable.

Conditions to Avoid

Avoid open flames and high temperatures.

Incompatibility with Other Materials

Incompatible with alkali or alkaline earth metals - powdered Al, Zn, Be, etc.

Decomposition

Decomposition products are hazardous. This material can be decomposed by high temperatures (open flames, glowing metal surfaces, etc.) forming hydrofluoric acid and possibly carbonyl fluoride.

Polymerization

Polymerization will not occur.

TOXICOLOGICAL INFORMATION

Animal Data

Inhalation 4-hour ALC: 567,000 ppm in rats

A 5 or 10 second spray of vapor produced very slight eye irritation and a 24-hour occlusive application produced slight skin irritation in rabbits. The compound is not a skin sensitizer in animals. No toxic effects were seen in animals from exposures by inhalation to concentrations up to 81,000 ppm. Lethargy and rapid respiration were observed at a vapor concentration of 305,000 ppm and pulmonary congestion, edema, and central nervous system effects occurred at a vapor concentration of 750,000 ppm. Cardiac sensitization occurred in dogs at 75,000 ppm from the action of exogenous epinephrine. No effects in animals occurred from repeated inhalation exposures to 99,000 ppm for two weeks or to 50,000 ppm for three months. Repeated exposures to higher concentations caused transient tremors, incoordination and some organ weight changes. Long-term exposure produced increased testes weights and increased urinary fluoride levels. No adverse effects were observed in male and female rats fed 300 mg/kg/day of HFC-134a for 52 weeks. Animal testing indicates that this compound does not have carcinogenic or mutagenic effects. Inhalation of 50,000 ppm for two years caused an increase in benign testicular tumors in male rats. No effects were observed at lower concentrations. The tumors were late-occurring and were judged not to be life-threatening. Embryotoxic activity has been observed in some animal tests but only at maternally toxic dose levels.

(Continued)

DISPOSAL CONSIDERATIONS

Waste Disposal

Contaminated HFC-134a can be recovered by distillation or removed to a permitted waste disposal facility. Comply with Federal, State, and local regulations.

TRANSPORTATION INFORMATION

Shipping Information

DOT/IMO

Proper Shipping Name	LIQUEFIED GAS, N.O.S. (TETRAFLUOROETHANE)
Hazard Class	2.2
UN No.	1956
DOT/IMO Label	NONFLAMMABLE GAS

Shipping Containers

Tank Cars.
Tank Trucks.
Ton Tanks.
Cylinders.

REGULATORY INFORMATION

U.S. Federal Regulations

TSCA Inventory Status   Reported/Included.

TITLE III HAZARD CLASSIFICATIONS SECTIONS 311, 312

Acute : Yes
Chronic : Yes
Fire : No
Reactivity : No
Pressure : Yes

HAZARDOUS CHEMICAL LISTS

SARA Extremely Hazardous Substance: No
CERCLA Hazardous Substance : No
SARA Toxic Chemical : No

OTHER INFORMATION

NFPA, NPCA-HMIS

NPCA-HMIS Rating

Health	1
Flammability	0
Reactivity	1

Personal Protection rating to be supplied by user depending on use conditions.

Additional Information

MEDICAL USE: CAUTION: Do not use in medical applications involving permanent implantation in the human body. For other medical applications see DuPont CAUTION Bulletin No. H-50102.

(Continued)

The data in this Material Safety Data Sheet relates only to the specific material designated herein and does not relate to use in combination with any other material or in any process.

Responsibility for MSDS : DuPont Chemicals
Address : Engineering & Product Safety
> : P.O. Box 80709, Chestnut Run
> : Wilmington, DE 19880-0709
Telephone : (302) 999-4946

# Indicates updated section.

End of MSDS

Suva®

alternative refrigerants

AS-1

Safety of Suva Refrigerants

DuPont Answers Your Questions about the Safe Handling and Use of Suva Refrigerants

DuPont Suva Refrigerants

Suva refrigerants, which are composed of hydrochlorofluorocarbon (HCFC) and hydrofluorocarbon (HFC) compounds were developed as safe, effective alternatives to existing chlorofluorocarbon (CFC) refrigerants.

Suva Centri-LP and Suva 123 are the DuPont brand names for its HCFC-123 refrigerant, which is targeted as a replacement for CFC-11. Suva 124 is the DuPont brand name for its HCFC-124 refrigerant, which may have application in some CFC-114 systems and is also a component of Suva MP blends. Suva 125 is the DuPont brand name for its HFC-125 refrigerant, which is used alone and as a component of Suva HP refrigerants. Suva Cold-MP, Suva Trans A/C, and Suva 134a are the DuPont brand names for its HFC-134a refrigerant, which is a primary alternative for CFC-12.

The table below provides a quick overview of these refrigerants, including chemical formula, boiling point, and Acceptable Exposure Limit (AEL) information.

Introduction

For many years, chlorofluorocarbons (CFCs) have been used successfully as refrigerants. CFCs seemed to be the ideal choice due to their unique combination of properties; however, the exceptional stability of these compounds, coupled with their chlorine content, has linked them to the depletion of the earth's protective ozone layer.

As a result, many companies, including DuPont, have developed alternative refrigerants to replace CFCs. The DuPont series of alternatives are based on hydrochlorofluorocarbon (HCFC) and hydrofluorocarbon (HFC) compounds. Unlike CFCs, HFCs contain no chlorine and, therefore, have zero ozone-depletion potential (ODP); HCFCs do contain chlorine but have up to 98 percent less ODP than CFCs. The presence of one or more hydrogen atoms in HCFC molecules allows them to break apart faster in the lower atmosphere so that fewer harmful chlorine molecules reach the ozone layer.

These alternative refrigerants have similar performance characteristics to CFCs, but with greatly

Physical Properties of Suva Refrigerants

Product	Formula	Boiling Point °C	Boiling Point °F	AEL,[1] ppm (v/v)	EEL,[2] ppm (v/v)
HCFC-123	CF_3CHCl_2	27.9	82.0	30	1000 up to 1 hr 2500 up to 1 min
HCFC-124	$CHClFCF_3$	–12.1	10.3	500	Not established
HFC-125	CHF_2CF_3	–48.1	–54.7	1000	Not established
HFC-134a	CH_2FCF_3	–26.1	–14.9	1000	Not established

[1]AEL (Acceptable Exposure Limit) is an airborne exposure limit established by DuPont which specifies time-weighted average (TWA) airborne concentrations to which nearly all workers may be repeatedly exposed without adverse effects during an 8- or 12-hour day or 40-hour work week.

[2]EEL (Emergency Exposure Limit) is an airborne concentration of brief duration which should not result in permanent adverse health effects or interfere with escape in the event of a major release or spill.

reduced environmental impact. Suva refrigerants are nonflammable and offer in-use stability and zero or reduced ozone-depletion and global-warming potential. Although they are not drop-in replacements, HCFC- and HFC-based refrigerants require minimal changes to equipment when compared to other alternative products. For detailed discussions about retrofitting equipment with alternatives, refer to DuPont Bulletins ART-5, ART-9, ART-15, and ART-16.

The Program for Alternative Fluorocarbon Toxicity Testing (PAFT), an international consortium of leading CFC producers, is currently evaluating seven of the possible alternative products: HFC-134a, HCFC-123, HCFC-124, HFC-125, HFC-32, HCFC-141b, and HCFC-225ca/cb. PAFT integrates past and present toxicological information to perform a careful hazard assessment of the proposed alternatives.

The PAFT I program for HCFC-123 is nearly complete. Results from all testing indicate that HCFC-123, an alternative to CFC-11, has low toxicity and is not genotoxic or a developmental toxicant. Although some test data resulted in a lower occupational exposure limit compared to other refrigerants, there is nothing to preclude the safe use of HCFC-123 in general industrial areas, provided that it is handled according to well-established recommendations.

The PAFT I program for HFC-134a is nearly complete. Results from all testing indicate that HFC-134a, an alternative to CFC-12, has low acute and chronic toxicity and is not genotoxic or a developmental toxicant. Test data indicate that HFC-134a can be safely used if it is handled according to well-established recommendations. All available results show that HFC-134a will be at least as safe in use as CFC-12.

The PAFT III program for HCFC-124 is complete except for a lifetime inhalation study with rats still in progress. Results from this study are not expected until 1995. However, results from all other testing indicate that HCFC-124, an alternative to CFC-114, has low toxicity and is not genotoxic or a developmental toxicant. Test data indicate that HCFC-124 can be safely used provided that it is handled according to well-established recommendations.

The PAFT III program for HFC-125 is in progress. Results from testing completed so far indicate that HFC-125 has very low acute and subchronic inhalation toxicity, and is not mutagenic or a developmental toxicant. Test data indicate that HFC-125 can be safely used provided that it is handled according to well-established recommendations.

This bulletin answers common safety-related questions, discusses potential symptoms of overexposure, and provides first aid and medical advice for effects of overexposure that may occur from improper use or handling of Suva refrigerants. Users must read and understand the Material Safety Data Sheets (MSDSs) before handling or using Suva refrigerants. MSDSs can be obtained from the DuPont locations listed on the last page of this bulletin or from any DuPont authorized distributor.

Flammability

Are Suva refrigerants flammable?

Suva refrigerants are nonflammable and nonexplosive. However, mixing Suva refrigerants with flammable gases or liquids can result in a flammable solution. Therefore, Suva refrigerants should never be mixed with any flammable gas or liquid.

Also, Suva refrigerants should not be exposed to open flames or electrical heating elements.

HFC-134a is not flammable at ambient temperatures and atmospheric pressure. However, tests have shown HFC-134a to be combustible at pressures as low as 5.5 psig (139.3 kPa absolute) at 177°C (350°F) when mixed with air at concentrations of generally more than 60 volume percent air. At lower temperatures, higher pressures are required for combustibility. HCFC-22 is also combustible at pressures above atmospheric in the presence of high air concentrations. *Suva refrigerants should not be mixed with air for leak testing.* In general, they should not be used or allowed to be present with high concentrations of air above atmospheric pressure. Detailed procedures for handling HFC-134a are given in DuPont Bulletin P-134a.

Inhalation Toxicity/Suffocation

Are Suva refrigerants toxic?

Suva refrigerants pose no acute or chronic hazard when they are handled in accordance with DuPont recommendations and when exposures are maintained at or below recommended exposure limits, such as the DuPont Acceptable Exposure Limit (AEL).

What is an AEL?

An Acceptable Exposure Limit (AEL) is an airborne exposure limit established by DuPont that specifies Time-Weighted Average (TWA) airborne concentrations to which nearly all workers may be repeatedly exposed without adverse effects during an 8- or 12-hour day or 40-hour work week. In practice, short-term exposures should not exceed three times the established exposure limit for more than a total of 30 minutes during a workday, provided that the TWA is not exceeded. *Under no circumstances* should exposures exceed five times the AEL. If a process displays this variability in airborne exposures, efforts should be made to restore control.

What are EELs?

Emergency Exposure Limits (EELs) are set for emergency situations, such as a spill or accidental release of a chemical. An EEL is an airborne concentration of brief duration which should not result in permanent adverse health effects or interfere with escape in the event of a major release or spill.

What are the symptoms of overexposure?

Inhaling high concentrations of Suva refrigerant vapor may cause temporary central nervous system depression with narcosis (sleepiness), lethargy, and weakness. Other effects that may occur include dizziness, a feeling of intoxication, and a loss of coordination. Continued breathing of high concentrations of Suva vapors may produce cardiac irregularities (cardiac sensitization), unconsciousness, and, with gross overexposure, death. A person experiencing *any* of the initial symptoms should be moved to fresh air and kept calm. If not breathing, give artificial respiration. If breathing is difficult, give oxygen. Call a physician.

What is cardiac sensitization?

As with many other halocarbons or hydrocarbons, inhalation of high concentrations of Suva refrigerants in the presence of high blood levels of the body's own epinephrine (adrenaline) may result in serious heart irregularities and possibly death, a condition known as cardiac sensitization. In experimental screening studies in dogs, inhalation of HCFC-123, HFC-134a, HCFC-124, or HFC-125 followed by injection of epinephrine to simulate human stress reactions, results respectively in a cardiac sensitization response at levels of approximately 20,000 ppm, 75,000 ppm, 25,000 ppm, and 100,000 ppm and higher, well above expected exposures. By comparison, a cardiac sensitization response is observed with CFC-11 and CFC-12 at, respectively, approximately 5,000 and 50,000 ppm and higher.

Because of possible disturbances of cardiac rhythm, catecholamine drugs, such as epinephrine, should be considered only as a last resort in life-threatening emergencies.

Can inhaling Suva refrigerant vapors cause suffocation?

If a large release occurs, vapors may concentrate near the floor or low spots and displace oxygen available for breathing, causing suffocation. In the event of a large spill or leak, always wear appropriate respiratory and other personal protective equipment. Use self-contained breathing apparatus or an air-line mask when entering tanks or other areas where vapors might exist. Station a second employee outside the tank, and use a lifeline.

How can I work safely on systems in enclosed areas?

First, route relief and purge vent piping outdoors, away from air intakes. Second, make certain the area is well ventilated, using auxiliary ventilation if necessary to move refrigerant vapors. Third, make sure the area is clear of vapors prior to beginning work. And finally, install air-monitoring equipment to detect leaks. For a complete discussion about leak detection, refer to DuPont Bulletin ARTD-27. Also, refer to ASHRAE Standard 15, "Safety Code for Mechanical Refrigeration" for ventilation requirements.

Is the deliberate inhalation of Suva refrigerant vapors dangerous?

Intentional misuse or deliberate inhalation of Suva refrigerants may cause death without warning. This practice is extremely dangerous.

Can I smell Suva refrigerants?

Some Suva refrigerants have a slightly sweet odor that can be difficult to detect. Others, such as HCFC-123, have such a faint odor that they cannot be detected by smell at levels that are considered safe for exposure. Therefore, frequent leak checks and the installation of permanent leak detectors may be necessary for enclosed areas used by personnel.

What should I do if a large spill or leak occurs?

Evacuate *everyone* until the area has been ventilated. Use blowers or fans to circulate the air at floor level. Do not re-enter the affected area unless you are equipped with a self-contained breathing apparatus.

Special Requirements for HCFC-123

- Install an air monitor capable of detecting HCFC-123 in concentrations of 0 to 150 ppm.
- Install suitable alarms that activate at, or below, the AEL of 30 ppm and alert persons inside and outside of the equipment room that a leak condition exists.
- Route relief valve discharge headers and purge units outdoors, away from all air intakes.
- Install local exhaust to ventilate the workplace in the event that the air monitor alarm point is exceeded.
- Follow minimum standards for safety group B1 refrigerants as required by ASHRAE Standard 15.
- When filling and handling drums of HCFC-123, wear eye protection, gloves of an impervious material like butyl rubber, and safety shoes. Nitrile, PVC-coated nitrile, and PVC protective equipment are not recommended.

Refer to DuPont Bulletin AS-5 for more detailed guidelines for using HCFC-123 in refrigeration and air conditioning applications.

Skin and Eye Contact

Is skin or eye contact with Suva refrigerants hazardous?

At room temperature, Suva refrigerant *vapors* have little or no effect on the skin or eyes. However, Suva refrigerants that are liquid at room temperature tend to affect the skin's protective fat, causing dryness and irritation, particularly after prolonged or repeated contact.

Always wear protective clothing when there is a risk of exposure to liquid Suva refrigerants. Where splashing is possible, *always* wear eye protection and a face shield. If your eyes are splashed, flush them with plenty of water.

Frostbite

Is frostbite a possible hazard?

In liquid form, low- and medium-temperature Suva refrigerants can freeze skin on contact, causing frostbite. If contact with liquid does occur, soak the exposed areas in lukewarm water, not cold or hot. In all cases, seek medical attention immediately.

Pressure

Can pressure ever cause a hazard?

Yes. Some of the potential hazards are:

- An overfilled container, vessel, or pipeline whose temperature is increased. This may make the container "liquid full" and immediately cause a dangerous increase in hydrostatic pressure.

  DuPont owns returnable refrigerant cylinders and ton tanks. No containers may be refilled without DuPont consent. DOT regulations forbid transportation of returnable cylinders refilled without DuPont authorization.
- A correctly filled returnable or disposable cylinder that is heated above the recommended maximum temperature of 52°C (125°F) could result in dangerously high pressures, in excess of the cylinder design pressure.
- A returnable or disposable refrigerant cylinder connected to the discharge side of refrigeration or air conditioning systems. Pressure may increase beyond the capacity of the relief devices, causing the cylinder to rupture or shatter.

What are the do's and don'ts for handling disposable and returnable cylinders?

- Do verify proper hookup.
- Do open valves slowly.
- Do protect from rusting during storage.
- Do verify that the label matches the color code.
- Don't tamper with the pressure relief devices.
- Don't drop, dent, or mechanically abuse containers.
- Don't use disposable cylinders as air tanks.
- Don't reuse disposable cylinders.
- Don't *ever* force connections.
- Don't heat above 52°C (125°F).

How should I braze or weld pipes on air conditioning or refrigeration systems?

- Make certain there is adequate ventilation in the area. Provide auxiliary ventilation if necessary.
- Evacuate Suva refrigerant from the refrigeration or air conditioning system. Make sure that refrigerant is not vented to the workspace.

- Purge system with nitrogen.
- Leave system open before beginning welding or brazing. This will prevent a dangerous increase in the hydrostatic pressure in the system and potential refrigerant decomposition.

Decomposition

What causes decomposition?

Suva refrigerants will decompose when exposed to high temperatures from flames or electric resistance heaters. Decomposition may produce toxic and irritating compounds, such as hydrogen chloride and hydrogen fluoride.

How can I tell if Suva refrigerant has decomposed?

The pungent odors released will irritate your nose and throat. The irritating nature of the fumes released from decomposition will generally force people to evacuate the area. Therefore, it is important to prevent decomposition by following DuPont recommendations for handling and use.

Are decomposition products hazardous?

Yes, the acidic vapors produced are dangerous and the area should be evacuated and ventilated to prevent exposure to personnel. Anyone exposed to the decomposition products should be taken to fresh air and given medical treatment immediately. In fact, the irritating nature of the fumes will generally *force* people to leave the area well before hazardous effects can occur.

Caution!

- *Never* pressurize Suva refrigerants with air for leak testing or any other purpose.
- *Never* heat cylinders above 52°C (125°F).
- *Never* tamper with valves or pressure relief devices.
- *Never* refill disposable cylinders with anything.

  Disposable cylinders should never be refilled or converted for use as compressed air tanks. Empty cylinders should be vented and discarded.

  Reuse of these cylinders can result in a serious hazard because of the possibility of corrosion and subsequent weakening of the container walls. The hazard is particularly great when corrosion is caused by water vapor in the gas or compressed air with which the cylinder is refilled; there may be no visible evidence of the damage to the cylinder until the walls are seriously weakened and the cylinder ruptures violently.

  The shipment of refilled disposable cylinders is prohibited by DOT regulations.
- *Always* store disposable cylinders in a dry area. Storage in dampness can permit rusting to occur, which will weaken the cylinder over a period of time.

For Sales Information:

DuPont Fluorochemicals
Customer Service Center, B-15305
Wilmington, DE 19898
U.S.A.
(302) 774-2099
800-441-9442

For Technical Information:

Fluorochemicals Laboratory
Wilmington, DE 19898
U.S.A.
(302) 999-3129
800-582-5606

Europe

DuPont de Nemours
International S.A.
2 Chemin du Pavillon
P.O. Box 50
CH-1218 Le Grand-Saconnex
Geneva, Switzerland
41-22-717-5111

Canada

DuPont Canada, Inc.
P.O. Box 2200, Streetsville
Mississauga, Ontario
Canada
L5M 2H3
(905) 821-3300

Mexico

DuPont, S.A. de C.V.
Homero 206
Col. Chapultepec Morales
C.P. 11570 Mexico, D.F.
52-5-250-8000

South America

DuPont do Brasil S.A.
Alameda Itapecuru, 506
Alphaville 06400 Barueri
São Paulo, Brazil
55-11-421-8509

DuPont Argentina S.A.
Casilla Correo 1888
Correo Central
1000 Buenos Aires, Argentina
54-1-311-8167

Pacific

DuPont Australia
P.O. Box 930
North Sydney, NSW 2060
Australia
61-2-923-6165

Japan

Mitsui DuPont Fluorochemicals
Co., Ltd.
Mitsui Seimei Bldg.
2-3, 1-Chome Ohtemachi
Chiyoda-Ku, Tokyo 100 Japan
81-3-3216-8451

Asia

DuPont Taiwan
P.O. Box 81-777
Taipei, Taiwan
886-2-514-4400

DuPont Asia Pacific Limited
P.O. Box TST 98851
Tsim Sha Tsui
Kowloon, Hong Kong
852-734-5345

DuPont Thailand
P.O. Box 2398
Bangkok 10501, Thailand
66-2-238-4361

DuPont China Ltd.
Rm. 1704, Union Bldg.
100 Yenan Rd. East
Shanghai, PR China 200 002
Phone: 86-21-328-3738
Telex: 33448 DCLSH CN
Fax: 86-21-320-2304

DuPont Far East Inc.
P.O. Box 12396
50776 Kuala Lumpur, Malaysia
Phone: 60-3-232-3522
Telex: (784) 30391 DUFE M
Fax: 60-3-238-7250

DuPont Korea Ltd.
C.P.O. Box 5972
Seoul, Korea
82-2-721-5114

DuPont Singapore Pte. Ltd.
1 Maritime Square #07 01
World Trade Centre
Singapore 0409
65-273-2244

DuPont Far East, Philippines
5th Floor, Solid Bank Bldg.
777 Paseo de Roxas
Makati, Metro Manila
Philippines
63-2-818-9911

DuPont Far East Inc.
7A Murray's Gate Road
Alwarpet
Madras, 600 018, India
91-44-454-029

DuPont Far East Inc.—Pakistan
9 Khayaban-E-Shaheen
Defence Phase 5
Karachi, Pakistan
92-21-533-350

DuPont Far East Inc.
P.O. Box 2553/Jkt
Jakarta 10001, Indonesia
62-21-517-800

(1/94) 240879A Printed in U.S.A.
[Replaces: H-27350-2]
Reorder No.: H-27350-3

P134a

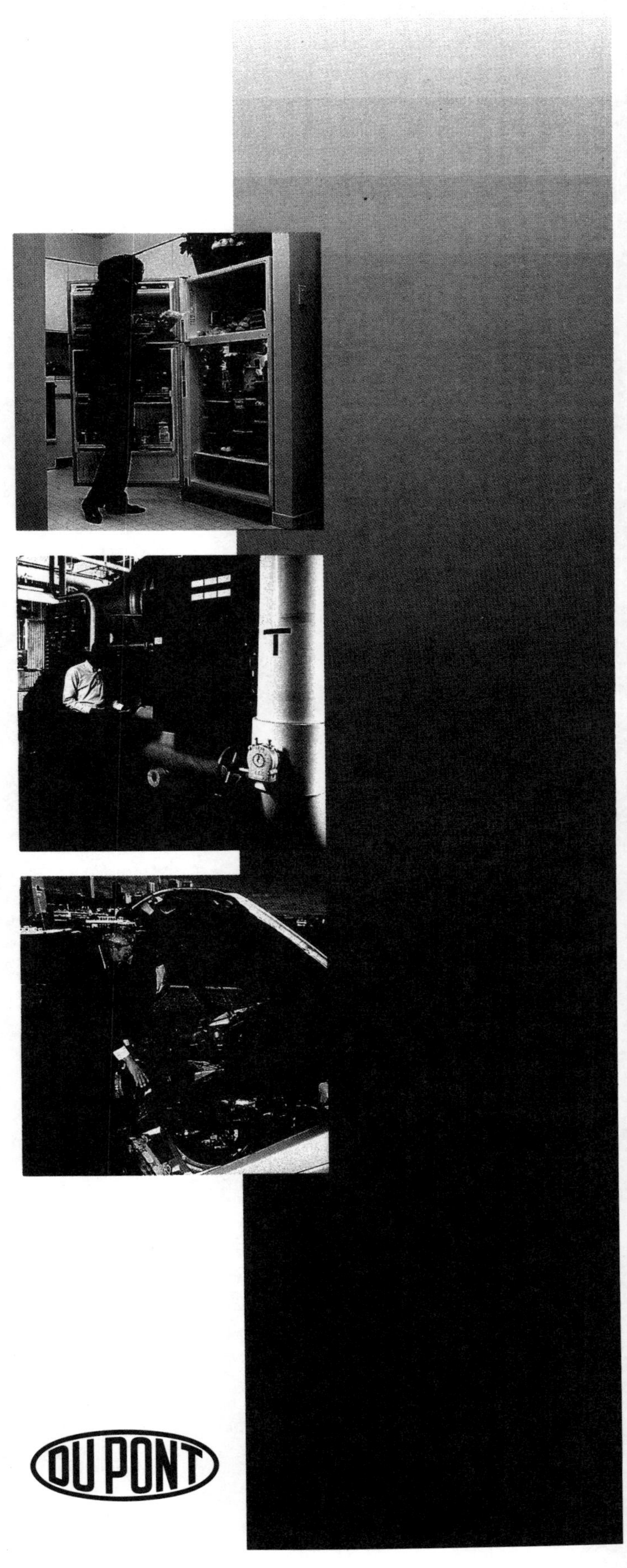

DuPont HFC-134a

Properties, Uses, Storage and Handling

SUVA® 134a refrigerant

SUVA® *Cold-MP* refrigerant

SUVA® *Trans A/C* refrigerant

FORMACEL® Z•4 foam expansion agent

DYMEL® 134a aerosol propellant

DYMEL® 134a/P aerosol propellant

HFC-134a

Properties, Uses, Storage and Handling

Table of Contents

INTRODUCTION

BACKGROUND

HFC-134a has been introduced by DuPont as a replacement for chlorofluorocarbons (CFCs) in many applications. CFCs, which were developed over 60 years ago, have many unique properties. They are low in toxicity, nonflammable, noncorrosive and compatible with other materials. In addition, they offer the thermodynamic and physical properties that make them ideal for a variety of uses. CFCs are used as refrigerants; as blowing agents in the manufacture of insulation, packaging and cushioning foams; as cleaning agents for metal and electronic components; and in many other applications.

However, the stability of these compounds, coupled with their chlorine content, has linked them to depletion of the earth's protective ozone layer. As a result, DuPont plans to phase out production of CFCs and introduce environmentally acceptable alternatives, such as hydrofluorocarbon (HFC) 134a.

HFC-134a—AN ENVIRONMENTALLY ACCEPTABLE ALTERNATIVE

HFC-134a does not contain chlorine; therefore, it has an ozone depletion potential (ODP) of zero. Listed below are all generic and DuPont trade names:

- Hydrofluorocarbon-134a
- HFC-134a
- HFA-134a
- SUVA® 134a
- SUVA® Trans A/C (automotive market)
- SUVA® Cold MP (stationary refrigeration/air conditioning market)
- FORMACEL® Z-4 (foam blowing agent market)
- DYMEL® 134a /P (aerosol pharmaceutical market)
- DYMEL® 134a (general aerosol market)

The chemical properties of HFC-134a are listed below.

HFC-134a

Chemical Name	1,1,1, 2-tetrafluoroethane
Molecular Formula	CH_2FCF_3
CAS Registry Number	811-97-2
Molecular Weight	102.0
Chemical Structure	F F / F—C—C—H / F H

Figure 1. Infrared Spectrum of HFC-134a Vapor at 400 mm Hg Pressure (53.3 kPa) in a 10-cm Cell.

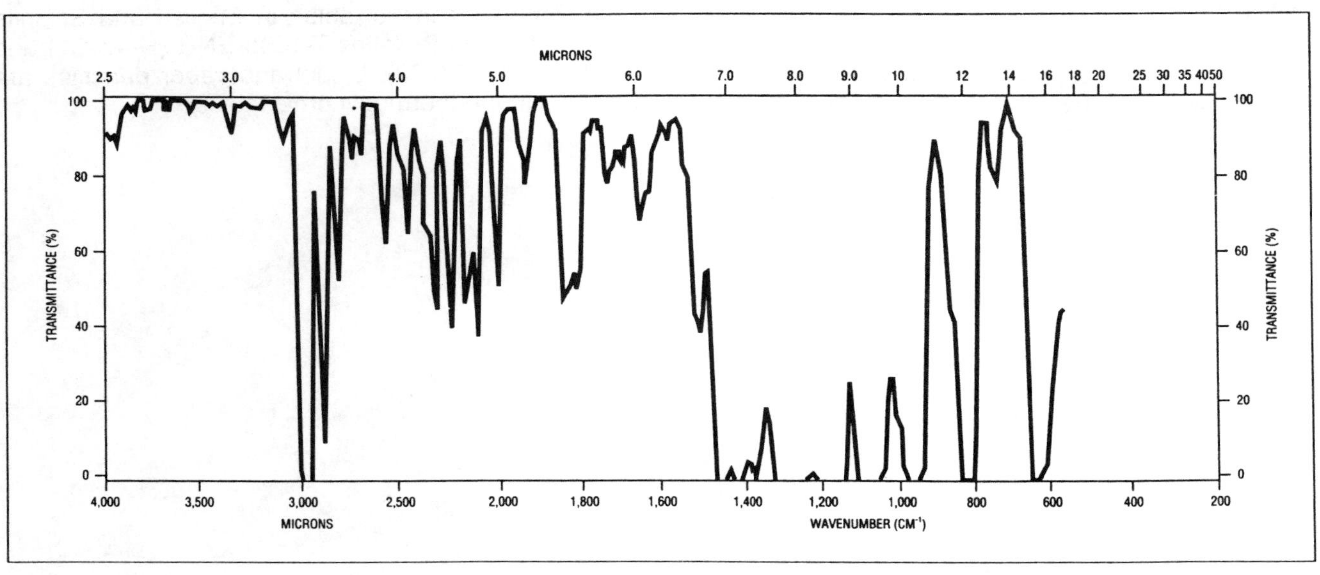

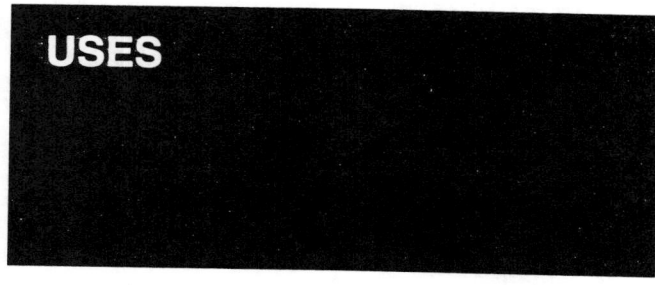

HFC-134a can be used in many applications that currently use dichlorodifluoromethane (CFC-12). These include refrigeration, polymer foam blowing and aerosol products. However, equipment design changes are sometimes required to optimize the performance of HFC-134a in these applications.

The thermodynamic and physical properties of HFC-134a, coupled with its low toxicity, make it a very efficient and safe replacement refrigerant for CFC-12 in many segments of the refrigeration industry, most notably in automotive air conditioning, appliances, small stationary equipment, medium-temperature supermarket cases and industrial and commercial chillers. *Table 1* provides a comparison of the theoretical performance of CFC-12 and HFC-134a at medium-temperature conditions.

TABLE 1
Theoretical Cycle Comparison of CFC-12 and HFC-134a*

	CFC-12	HFC-134a
Capacity (as % CFC-12)	100	99.7
Coefficient of Performance (COP)	3.55	3.43
Compressor		
Exit Temperature, °C (°F)	86.8 (188.2)	83.1 (181.5)
Exit Pressure, kPa (psia)	1349 (195.6)	1473 (213.7)
Compression Ratio	4.1	4.7

* Temperatures were as follows: Condenser, 54.4°C (130.0°F); Evaporator, 1.7°C (35.0°F); Compressor Suction, 26.7°C (80.0°F); Expansion Device, 51.7°C (125.0°F).

As a blowing agent in polymer foams, HFC-134a can be used to replace CFC-12 in many thermoplastic foam applications. Recent developments, however, are also providing new technology that uses HFC-134a as a replacement for CFC-12 in thermoset foams. HFC-134a features properties that are advantageous for high value-in-use products and meets the requirements of safety/environmental issues. HFC-134a is nonflammable, has negligible photochemical reactivity and low vapor thermal conductivity.

HFC-134a is also being developed for use in pharmaceutical inhalers because of its low toxicity and nonflammability. Other aerosol applications may use HFC-134a where these properties are critical. See DuPont DYMEL® Bulletin ATB-30 (H-44691) for additional information on aerosol applications of HFC-134a.

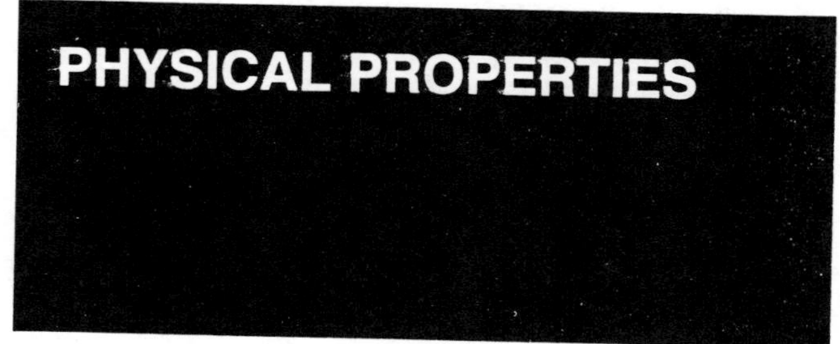

Physical properties of HFC-134a are given in *Table 2* and *Figures 2* to *8*. Additional physical property data may be found in other DuPont publications. Bulletin ART-1 (H-43855-1) contains viscosity, thermal conductivity and heat capacity data for saturated liquid and vapor in addition to heat capacity data and heat capacity ratios for both saturated and superheated vapors. Thermodynamic tables in English and SI units are available in Bulletins T-134a-ENG (H-47751) and T-134a-SI (H-47752). Liquid and vapor densities are included in the thermodynamic tables.

TABLE 2
Physical Properties of HFC-134a

Physical Properties	Units	HFC-134a
Chemical Name	—	Ethane, 1,1,1,2-Tetrafluoro
Chemical Formula	—	CH_2FCF_3
Molecular Weight	—	102.03
Boiling Point at 1 atm (101.3 kPa or 1.013 bar)	°C °F	–26.1 –14.9
Freezing Point	°C °F	–103.0 –153.9
Critical Temperature	°C °F	101.1 213.9
Critical Pressure	kPa lb/in.² abs	4060 588.9
Critical Volume	m³/kg ft³/lb	1.94×10^{-3} 0.0311
Critical Density	kg/m³ lb/ft³	515.3 32.17
Density (Liquid) at 25°C (77°F)	kg/m³ lb/ft³	1206 75.28
Density (Saturated Vapor) at Boiling Point	kg/m³ lb/ft³	5.26 0.328
Heat Capacity (Liquid) at 25°C (77°F)	kJ/kg·K or Btu/(lb) (°F)	1.44 0.340
Heat Capacity (Vapor at Constant Pressure) at 25°C (77°F) and 1 atm (101.3 kPa or 1.013 bar)	kJ/kg·K or Btu/(lb) (°F)	0.852 0.204
Vapor Pressure at 25°C (77°F)	kPa bar psia	666.1 6.661 96.61
Heat of Vaporization at Boiling Point	kJ/kg Btu/lb	217.1 93.4
Thermal Conductivity at 25°C (77°F)		
Liquid	W/m·K Btu/hr·ft°F	0.0824 0.0478
Vapor at 1 atm (101.3 kPa or 1.013 bar)	W/m·K Btu/hr·ft°F	0.0145 0.00836
Viscosity at 25°C (77°F)		
Liquid	mPa·S (cP)	0.202
Vapor at 1 atm (101.3 kPa or 1.013 bar)	mPa·S (cP)	0.012
Solubility of HFC-134a in Water at 25°C (77°F) and 1 atm (101.3 kPa or 1.013 bar)	wt %	0.15
Solubility of Water in HFC-134a at 25°C (77°F)	wt %	0.11
Flammability Limits in Air at 1 atm (101.3 kPa or 1.013 bar)	vol %	None
Autoignition Temperature	°C °F	770 1418
Ozone Depletion Potential	—	0
Halocarbon Global Warming Potential (HGWP) (For CFC-11, HGWP = 1)	—	0.28
Global Warming Potential (GWP) (100 yr. ITH. For CO_2, GWP = 1)	—	1200
TSCA Inventory Status	—	Reported/Included
Toxicity AEL[a] (8- and 12-hr TWA)	ppm (v/v)	1,000

[a] AEL (Acceptable Exposure Limit) is an airborne exposure limit established by DuPont scientists for substances to ensure the safe handling and use of that substance.

Note: kPa is absolute pressure.

Figure 2. Solubility of Water in HFC-134a.

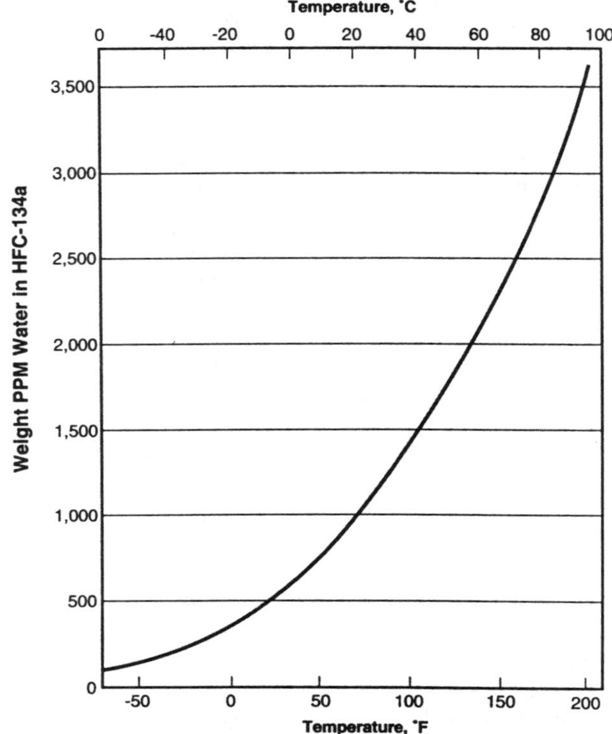

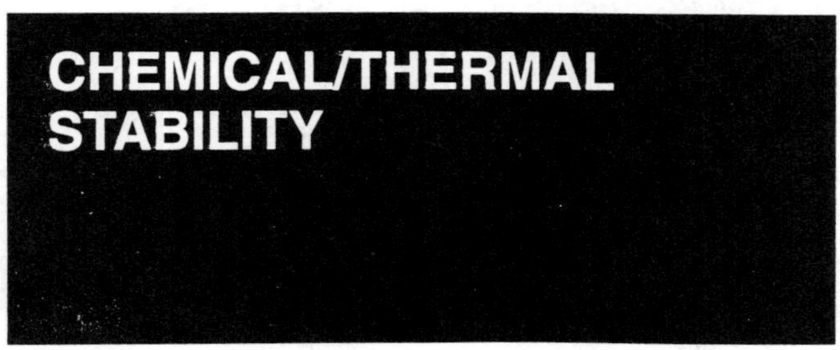

CHEMICAL/THERMAL STABILITY

THERMAL DECOMPOSITION

HFC-134a vapors will decompose when exposed to high temperatures from flames or electric resistance heaters. Decomposition may produce toxic and irritating compounds, such as hydrogen fluoride. The pungent odors released will irritate the nose and throat and generally force people to evacuate the area. Therefore, it is important to prevent decomposition by avoiding exposure to high temperatures.

STABILITY WITH METALS AND REFRIGERATION LUBRICANTS

Stability tests for refrigerants with metals are typically performed in the presence of refrigeration oils. The results of sealed tube stability tests are available for CFC-12/mineral oil combinations, which have shown long-term stability in contact with copper, steel and aluminum in actual refrigeration systems. Polyalkylene glycol (PAG) and polyol ester (POE) lubricants will most likely be used with HFC-134a. Sealed tube tests were, therefore, run to determine the relative long-term stability of HFC-134a/metals in the presence of these lubricants.

The method followed was generally the same as ASHRAE 97 with several minor modifications. A 3-mL volume of refrigerant/lubricant solution was heated in the presence of copper, steel and aluminum strips in an oven for 14 days at 175°C (347°F). Both the neat lubricant and a mixture of lubricant and refrigerant (50/50 volume ratio) were tested. Visual ratings were obtained on both the liquid solutions and the metal coupons after the designated exposure time. The visual ratings ranged from 0 to 5, with 0 being the best and 5 being the worst.

After the visual ratings were obtained, sample tubes were opened and the lubricant and refrigerant (if present) were analyzed. The lubricant was typically checked for halide content and viscosity, while the refrigerant was examined for the presence of decomposition products. *Table 3* summarizes typical data for both HFC-134a and CFC-12. Visual ratings are listed for the neat lubricant, the lubricant/refrigerant solution and the three metals that were present in the lubricant/refrigerant solutions. Viscosity was determined on the unused lubricant, the tested neat lubricant and the lubricant tested in the presence of refrigerant. A percent change was calculated for the two tested lubricants. The decomposition products listed are HFC-143a (the predominant decomposition product for HFC-134a) and fluoride ion. Both species are typically measured in the low parts per million (ppm) range.

As the CFC-12/mineral oil combinations have been proven in actual service, these tests indicate that HFC-134a/PAG and HFC-134a/POE solutions have acceptable chemical stability. In several other tests, results have confirmed that the HFC-134a molecule is as chemically stable as CFC-12.

Figure 3. Pressure vs. Temperature (English Units).

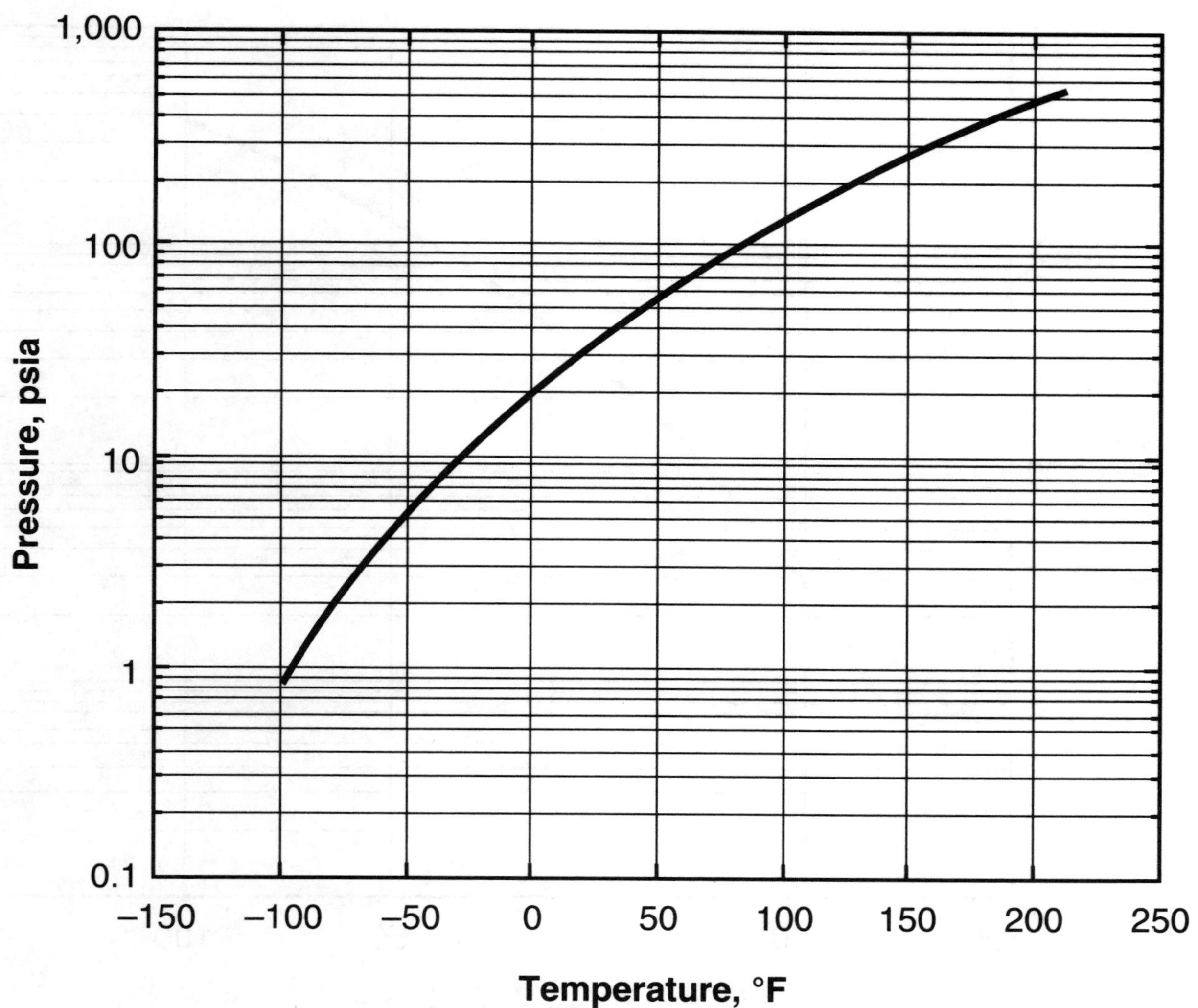

Figure 4. Pressure vs. Temperature (SI Units).

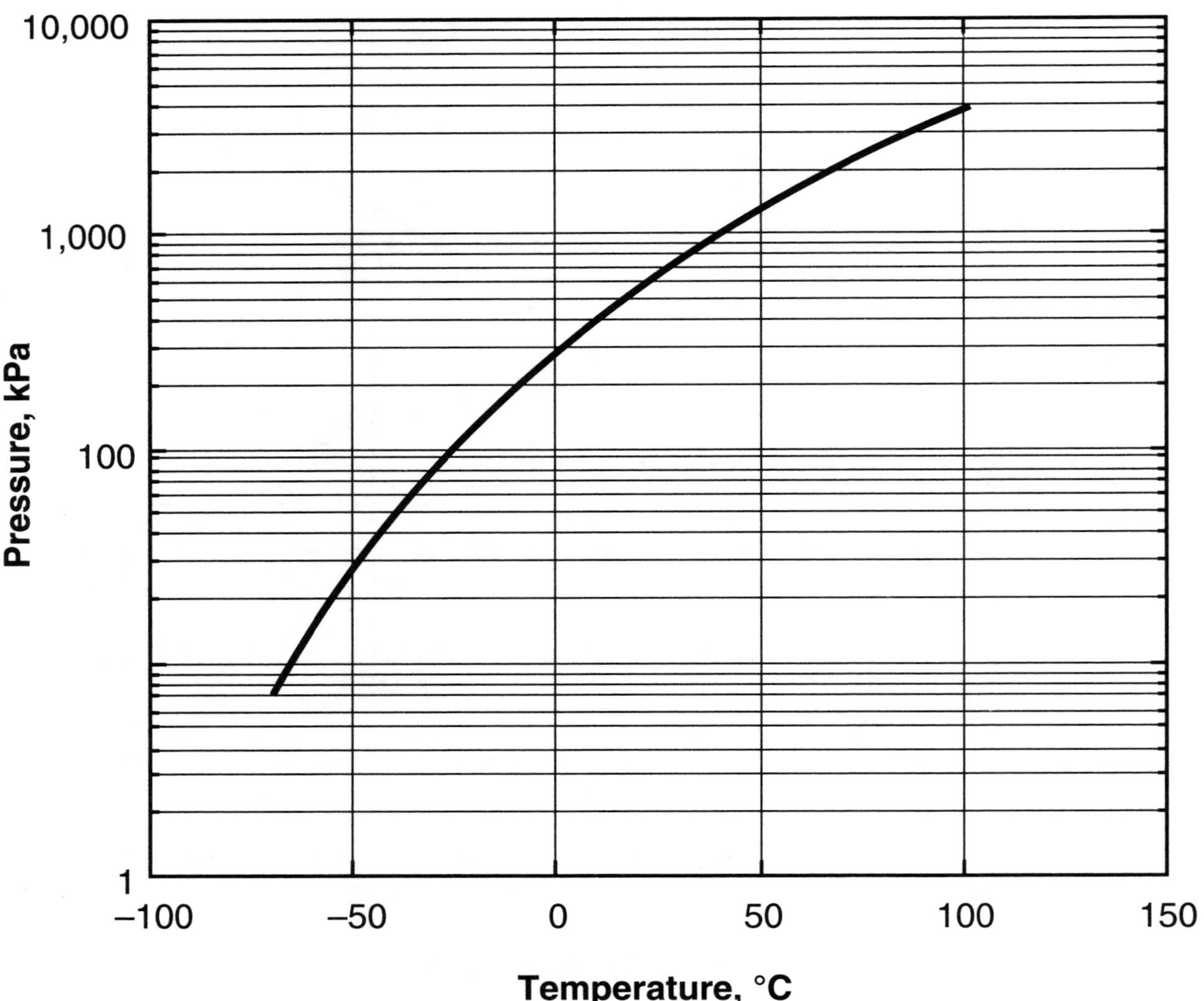

Figure 5. Vapor Thermal Conductivity of HFC-134a at Atmospheric Pressure (English Units).

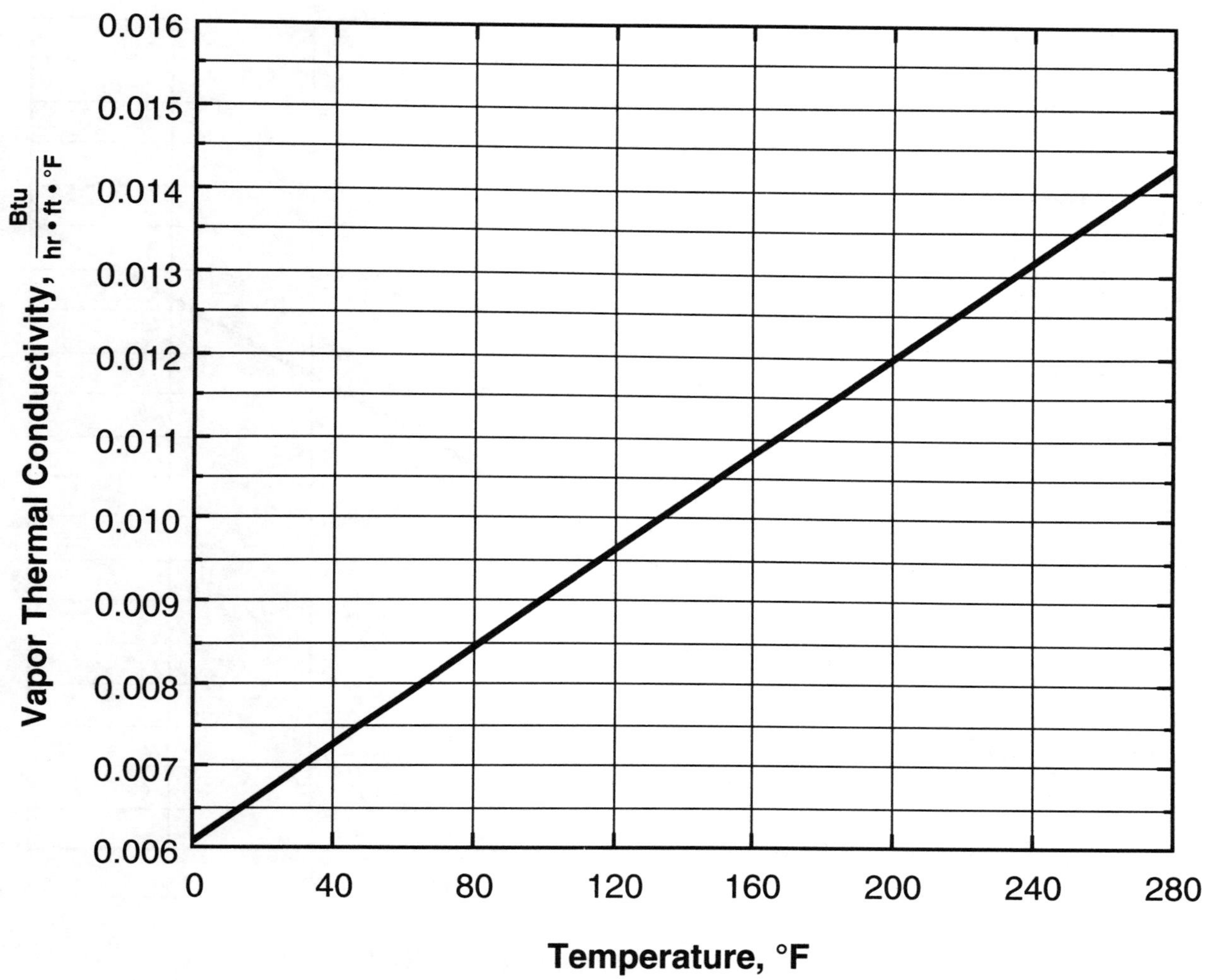

Figure 6. Vapor Thermal Conductivity of HFC-134a at Atmospheric Pressure (SI Units).

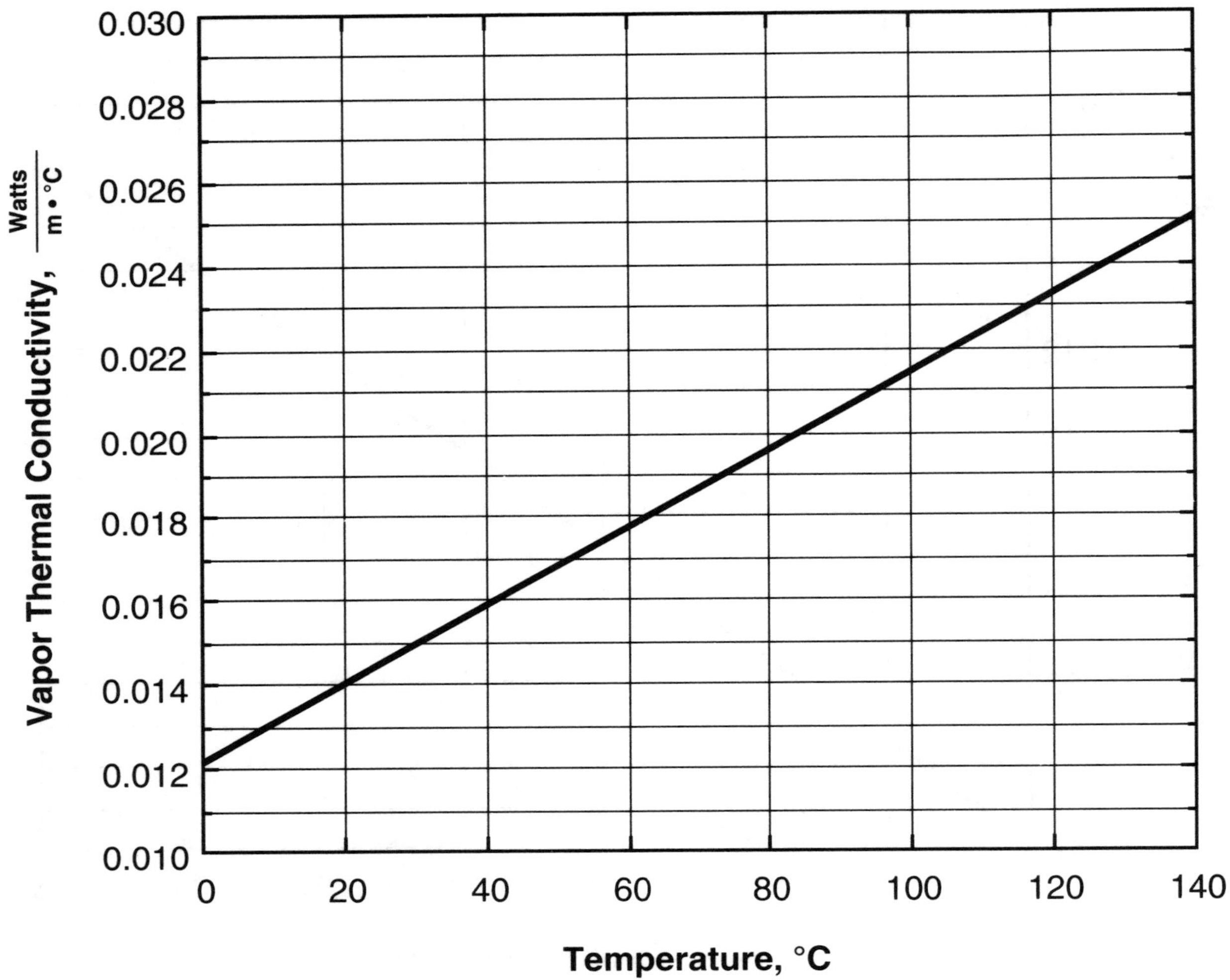

TABLE 3
Stability of HFC-134a with Metals and Lubricating Oils

Oil	Mineral Oil	Mineral Oil	UCON RO-W-6602[a]	Mobil EAL Arctic 32[b]	Castrol Icematic SW 100[b]
Oil Viscosity, cSt at 40°C (104°F)	30.7	125	134	29.4	108.8
Refrigerant	R-12	R-12	HFC-134a	HFC-134a	HFC-134a
Ratings					
Neat Oil	—	—	0	0	0
Oil/Refrigerant	4	4	0	0	0
Copper	2	2	0	0	0
Iron	3	3	0	0	0
Aluminum	2	2	0	0	0
Viscosity Change					
% Change Neat	ND	ND	<1	–3.1	4.3
% Change with Refrigerant	ND	ND	–12.7	–36.2	–27.1
Decomposition Analysis					
HFC-143a, ppm	ND	ND	<7	<3	<0.3
Fluoride, ppm	ND	420	<0.7	—	<7

[a] Polyalkylene glycol lubricant.
[b] Polyol ester lubricant.
ND = Not determined.

Stability Ratings: 0 to 5
0 = Best
3 = Failed
5 = Coked

STABILITY WITH FOAM CHEMICALS

As with other alternative blowing agents, the stability of HFC-134a in foam chemicals (B-side systems) is being studied. The first tests evaluated HFC-134a stability in a sucrose-amine polyether polyol with either an amine catalyst, a potassium catalyst, a tin catalyst or an amine catalyst neutralized with an organic acid. The initial tests, which included analysis of the volatile components, showed no degradation of HFC-134a in any of the systems, even at elevated temperatures. The results are summarized in *Table 4*.

TABLE 4
Stability of HFC-134a with Foam Chemicals

Catalyst	Degradation, %
Amine	<0.001
Potassium	<0.001
Tin	<0.001
Neutralized Amine	<0.001

Test Conditions:
Six weeks at 60°C (140°F).
25% (wt.) HFC-134a.
Two parts catalyst per 100 parts polyol by weight.
One part water per 100 parts polyol by weight.
Type 1010 steel test coupon.

COMPATIBILITY CONCERNS IF HFC-134a AND CFC-12 ARE MIXED

HFC-134a and CFC-12 are chemically compatible with each other; this means that they do NOT react with each other and form other compounds. However, when the two materials are mixed together, they form what is known as an "azeotrope." An azeotrope is a mixture of two components that acts like a single compound, but has physical and chemical properties different than either of the two components. An example of this is FREON® 502, which is an azeotrope of HCFC-22 and CFC-115. When HFC-134a and CFC-12 are mixed in certain concentrations, they form a high-pressure (low boiling) azeotrope. This means that the vapor pressure of the azeotrope is higher than that of either of the two components by themselves. At 109 psia (752 kPa absolute) the azeotrope contains 46 weight percent HFC-134a. In general, compressor discharge pressures will be undesirably high if refrigeration equipment is operated with a mixture of HFC-134a and CFC-12.

Another characteristic of an azeotrope is that it is very difficult to separate the components once they are mixed together. Therefore, a mixture of HFC-134a and CFC-12 cannot be separated in an on-site recycle machine or in the typical facilities of an off-site reclaimer. Mixtures of HFC-134a and CFC-12 will usually have to be disposed of by incineration.

Figure 7. Pressure-Enthalpy Diagram for HFC-134a (English Units).

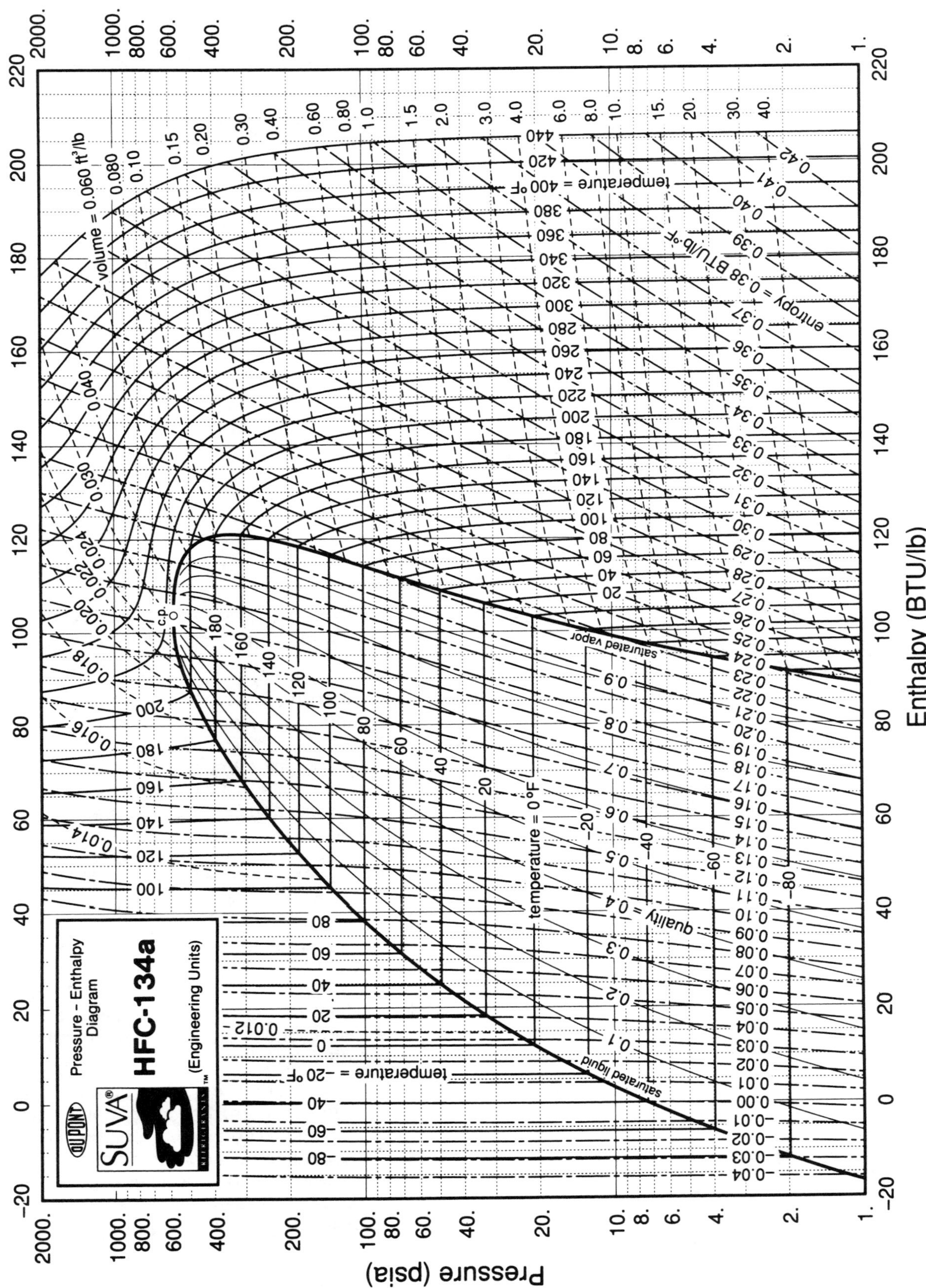

Figure 8. Pressure-Enthalpy Diagram for HFC-134a (SI Units).

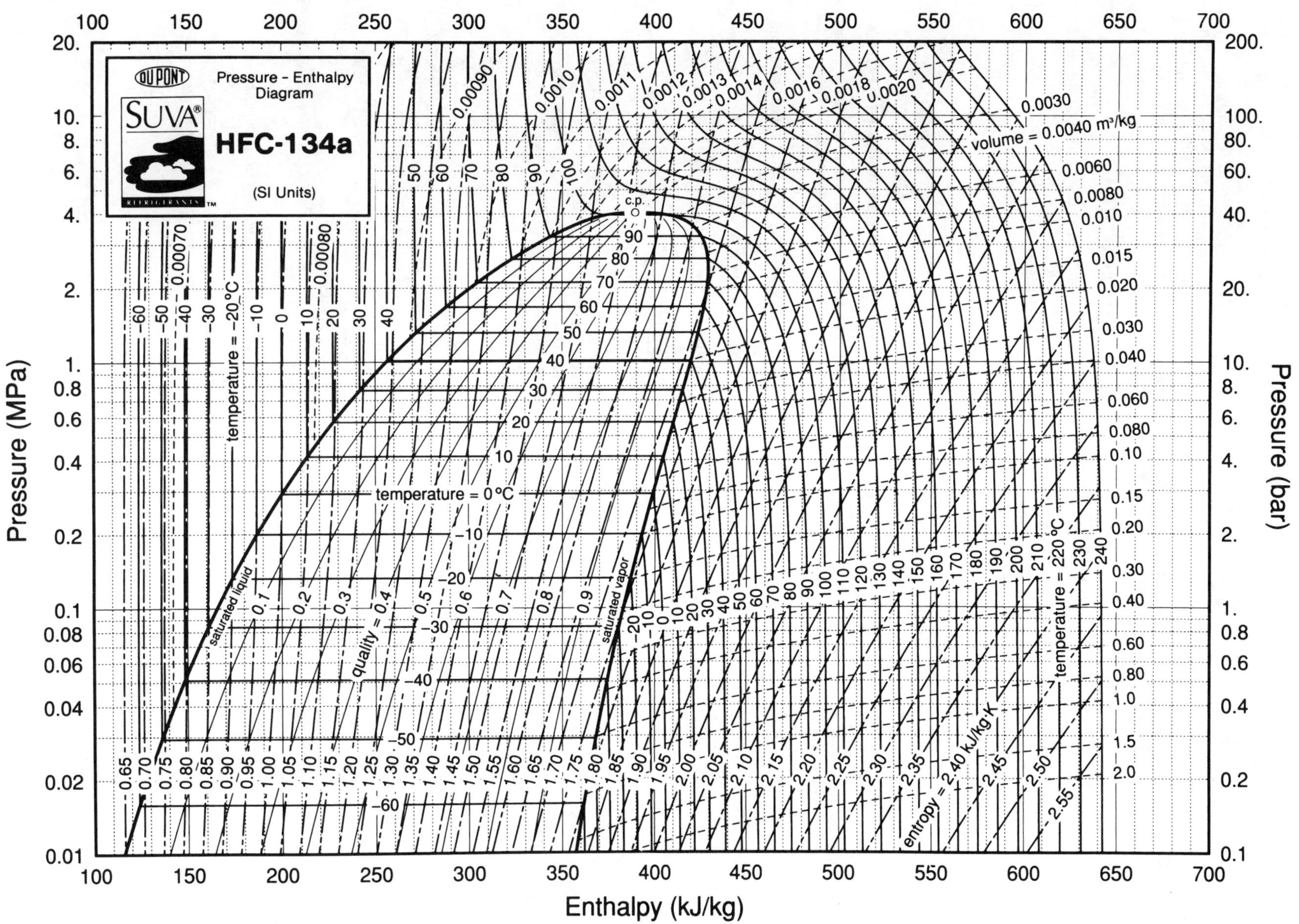

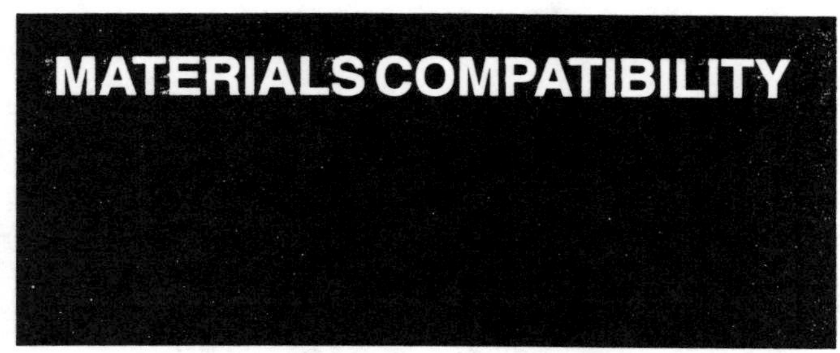

Because HFC-134a is used in many applications, it is important to review materials of construction for compatibility when designing new equipment, retrofitting existing equipment or preparing storage and handling facilities.

PLASTICS

Customary industry screening tests, in which twenty-three typical plastic materials were exposed to liquid HFC-134a in sealed glass tubes at room temperature, are summarized in *Table 5.* Observations of weight gain and physical change were used to separate materials meriting further laboratory and/or field testing from materials which appeared unacceptable. The majority of the materials tested merit further evaluation.

Since the performance of plastic materials is affected by polymer variations, compounding agents, fillers, and molding processes, verifying compatibility using actual fabricated parts under end-use conditions is advised.

ELASTOMERS

Compatibility results for HFC-134a and CFC-12 are compared for 11 typical elastomers in *Tables 6* through *17.* It should be recognized, however, that effects on specific elastomers depend on the nature of the polymer, the compounding formulation used and the curing or vulcanizing conditions. Actual samples should be tested under end-use conditions before specifying elastomers for critical components.

Recommendations, based on the detailed data in *Tables 7* through *17*, are given in *Table 6.* Data on "temporary" elastomer swell and hardness changes were used as the prime determinants of compatibility. The subsequent "final" data were used as a guide to indicate if the seals in a refrigeration system should be replaced after equipment tear down.

Most polymeric materials used in refrigeration equipment are exposed to a mixture of refrigerant and refrigeration oil. Data on the compatibility of elastomers and motor materials with HFC-134a in combination with mineral oils and a PAG lubricant are available in Bulletins ARTD-18 (H-26845) and ARTD-30 (H-32123). Data for nylon and for graphite-filled TEFLON® fluorocarbon resin are included in ARTD-30. Additional data are being developed by equipment manufacturers.

HOSE PERMEATION

Elastomeric hoses are used in mobile air conditioning systems and for transferring HFC-134a in other applications. The permeation rates of HFC-134a and CFC-12 through several automotive A/C hoses were measured as a guide to hose selection.

TABLE 5
Plastics Compatibility of HFC-134a

Test Conditions: Plastic specimens exposed to liquid HFC-134a (no lubricant) in sealed glass tubes for two weeks at room temperature.

Chemical Type	Trade Name
Plastic materials meriting further testing:	
ABS	KRALASTIC®
Acetal	DELRIN®
Epoxy	
Fluorocarbons	
PTFE	TEFLON®
ETFE	TEFZEL®
PVDF	
Ionomer	SURLYN®
Polyamide	
6/6 Nylon	ZYTEL®
Polyarylate	ARYLON®
Polycarbonate	TUFFAK®
Polyester	
PBT	VALOX®
PET	RYNITE®
Polyetherimide	ULTEM®
Polyethylene-HD	ALATHON®
Polyphenylene Oxide	NORYL®
Polyphenylene Sulfide	RYTON®
Polypropylene	
Polystyrene	STYRON®
Polysulfone	POLYSUFONE®
Polyvinyl Chloride	
PVC	
CPVC	
Plastic materials exhibiting unacceptable change:	
Acrylic	LUCITE®
Cellulosic	ETHOCEL®

TABLE 6
Elastomer Compatibility of HFC-134a

	Ratings					
	CFC-12			HFC-134a		
	25°C (77°F)	80°C (176°F)	141°C (285°F)	25°C (77°F)	80°C (176°F)	141°C (285°F)
ADIPRENE® L	1	5		2	5	
Buna N	1*	0*	2*	1	0*	1
Buna S	3	4		3	2	
Butyl Rubber	2	4		0	3	
HYPALON® 48	1	0	0	1*	0	0
Natural Rubber	4	5		0	2	
Neoprene W	0*	1*		0	2	
NORDEL® Elastomer	2*	2*		1	1	
Silicone	5	5		2	2	
THIOKOL® FA	1	1		1*	0	
VITON® A	5	5		5	5	

*Recommend elastomer replacement after equipment teardown.

HYPALON®, NORDEL® and VITON® are DuPont registered trademarks.
ADIPRENE® is a Uniroyal registered trademark.
THIOKOL® FA is a Morton Thiokol registered trademark.

Codes:
0 = No change.
1 = Acceptable change.
2 = Borderline change.
3 = Slightly unacceptable change.
4 = Moderately unacceptable change.
5 = Severely unacceptable change.

The studies were run at 80°C (176°F) with an initial 80 volume percent liquid loading of HFC-134a in 76-cm (30-in.) lengths of 15.9-mm (5/8-in.) inside diameter automotive air conditioning hose. Hose construction and permeation rates are summarized in *Table 18*. Based on these tests, hoses lined with nylon, as well as those made of HYPALON® 48, appear to be suitable for use with HFC-134a. Note, however, that these rate measurements provide a comparison of the various hoses at a single temperature and should not be used as an indication of actual permeation losses from an operating system.

DESICCANTS

Dryers filled with desiccant are typically used in refrigeration systems and bulk storage facilities. A common molecular sieve desiccant used with CFC-12, UOP's (formerly Union Carbide Molecular Sieve) 4A-XH-5, is not compatible with HFC-134a; however, UOP has developed other molecular sieve desiccants, such as XH-7 and XH-9, which perform well in HFC-134a service. In addition, several other manufacturers offer loose-fill and molded-core desiccants that are compatible with HFC-134a and lubricants. Be sure to indicate your specific HFC-134a application when ordering a dryer or desiccant.

REFRIGERATION LUBRICANTS

Most compressors require a lubricant to protect internal moving parts. The compressor manufacturer usually recommends the type of lubricant and viscosity that should be used to ensure proper operation and equipment durability. Recommendations are based on several criteria, such as lubricity, compatibility with materials of construction, thermal stability and refrigerant/oil miscibility. To ensure efficient operation and long equipment life, it is important to follow the manufacturer's recommendations.

Current lubricants used with CFC-12 are fully miscible over the range of expected operating conditions, easing the problem of getting the lubricant to flow back to the compressor. Refrigeration systems using CFC-12 take advantage of this full miscibility when considering lubricant return. Refrigerants such as HFC-134a, with little or no chlorine, may exhibit less solubility with many existing mineral oil or alkylbenzene lubricants.

The search for lubricants for use with HFC-134a started with commercially available products. *Table 19* shows solubilities of various refrigerant/lubricant combinations. Current naphthenic, paraffinic and alkylbenzene lubricants have very poor solubility with HFC-134a. PAGs with low viscosity show good solubility but, as viscosity increases, they become less soluble. Ester lubricants, of which there are many types, generally show good solubility with HFC-134a. When compared to PAGs, ester lubricants are more compatible with hermetic motor components and are less sensitive to mineral oil and CFC-12 remaining in a refrigeration system.

Although HFC-134a and CFC-12 are chemically compatible with each other, such is not the case with CFC-12 and PAG lubricants. Specifically, the chlorine contained in CFC-12 or other chlorinated compounds can react with the PAG and cause lubricant degradation. CFC-11, which is often used as a cleaning or flushing agent, is also incompatible with PAGs. At contaminant levels of 1 percent CFC-11 or 2 to 10 percent residual mineral oil (saturated with CFC-12), the stability of the system is affected enough to cause possible degradation. Lubricant degradation can result in poor lubrication and premature failure. In addition, sludge will be formed that can plug orifice tubes and other small openings.

TABLE 7
Compatibility of Refrigerants with ADIPRENE® L

Test Conditions: 27 days immersion of the polymer at 25°C (77°F) and 80°C (176°F) in liquid (temporary) plus two weeks drying in air at about 25°C (77°F) (final).

	25°C (77°F)		80°C (176°F)	
	CFC-12	HFC-134a	CFC-12	HFC-134a
Length Change (%)				
Temporary	1.8	5.5	2.1	5.0
Final	0.3	0.1	(a)	–0.5
Weight Change (%)				
Temporary	8.5	20	5.2	20
Final	1.2	0.3	(a)	–0.5
Shore A Hardness				
Original	60	61	60	63
Temporary, Δ SH	–2	–4	(a)	–28
Final, Δ SH	0	1	—	–19
Elasticity Rating				
Temporary	0	0	5(a)	4(b)
Final	0	0	5(a)	5(c)
Visual Rating				
Liquid	0	0	0	0
Polymer				
Temporary	0	0	0	1(d)
Final	0	0	5(a)	2(d)

(a) Sample disintegrated
(b) More elastic
(c) Broke when stretched
(d) Sticky

TABLE 8
Compatibility of Refrigerants with Buna N

Test Conditions: 27 days immersion of the polymer at 25°C (77°F), 80°C (176°F) and 141°C (285°F)in liquid (temporary) plus two weeks drying in air at about 25°C (77°F) (final).

	CFC-12			HFC-134a		
	25°C (77°F)	80°C (176°F)	141°C (285°F)	25°C (77°F)	80°C (176°F)	141°C (285°F)
Length Change (%) (±0.5)						
Temporary	2	1	2	2	2	3
Final	0	–1	0	0	0	0
Weight Change (%) (±0.5)						
Temporary	7	6	8	8	8	8
Final	0	–1	2	0	0	0
Shore A Hardness						
Original	77	76	72	77	74	75
Temporary, Δ SH	–6	–1	9	–5	–1	–3
Final, Δ SH	7	9	14	5	7	4
Elasticity Rating						
Temporary	0	1	1(a)	0	1	1
Final	0	0	0	0	0	0
Visual Rating						
Liquid	0	0	0	0	0	0
Polymer						
Temporary	0	1	1(b)	0	0	0
Final	0	1	1(b)	0	0	0

(a) More elastic
(b) Surface dulled

TABLE 9
Compatibility of Refrigerants with Buna S

Test Conditions: 27 days immersion of the polymer at 25°C (77°F) and 80°C (176°F) in liquid (temporary) plus two weeks drying in air at about 25°C (77°F) (final).

	25°C (77°F)		80°C (176°F)	
	CFC-12	**HFC-134a**	**CFC-12**	**HFC-134a**
Length Change (%)				
Temporary	–0.1	1.1	0.7	0.8
Final	–2.5	<0.1	–2.6	0.3
Weight Change (%)				
Temporary	2.8	1.9	2.9	2.5
Final	–6.2	–0.1	–6.2	–0.1
Shore A Hardness				
Original	85	84	83	81
Temporary, Δ SH	–12	–12	–16	–9
Final, Δ SH	8	–2	–9	–2
Elasticity Rating				
Temporary	0	0	0	1[a]
Final	3[b]	1[b]	3[b]	0
Visual Rating				
Liquid	0	0	0	0
Polymer				
Temporary	0	0	0	0
Final	0	0	0	0

[a] More elastic
[b] Less elastic

TABLE 10
Compatibility of Refrigerants with Butyl Rubber

Test Conditions: 27 days immersion of the polymer at 25°C (77°F) and 80°C (176°F) in liquid (temporary) plus two weeks drying in air at about 25°C (77°F) (final).

	25°C (77°F)		80°C (176°F)	
	CFC-12	**HFC-134a**	**CFC-12**	**HFC-134a**
Length Change (%)				
Temporary	6.3	0.2	7.6	1.3
Final	–1.2	0	–0.8	0.4
Weight Change (%)				
Temporary	34	2.0	36	3.7
Final	–2.6	–0.1	–1.2	0.6
Shore A Hardness				
Original	54	54	57	58
Temporary, Δ SH	–8	–1	–14	–4
Final, Δ SH	–1	–2	–10	–3
Elasticity Rating				
Temporary	1[a]	1[a]	3[a]	0
Final	0	0	2[a]	0
Visual Rating				
Liquid	0	0	3[b]	0
Polymer				
Temporary	0	0	3[c]	4[c]
Final	0	0	1[d]	2[d]

[a] More elastic
[b] White solids in liquid
[c] White deposit on elastomer
[d] White film on elastomer

TABLE 11
Compatibility of Refrigerants with HYPALON® 48

Test Conditions: 27 days immersion of the polymer at 25°C (77°F), 80°C (176°F) and 141°C (285°F) in liquid (temporary) plus two weeks drying in air at about 25°C (77°F) (final).

	CFC-12			HFC-134a		
	25°C (77°F)	80°C (176°F)	141°C (285°F)	25°C (77°F)	80°C (176°F)	141°C (285°F)
Length Change (%) (±0.5)						
Temporary	1	0	1	0	0	1
Final		0	0	0	0	0
Weight Change (%) (±0.5)						
Temporary	7	5	9	0	1	2
Final	2	1	4	0	0	1
Shore A Hardness						
Original	79	81	81	76	82	82
Temporary, Δ SH	–4	0	0	3	1	1
Final, Δ SH	4	2	2	8	1	4
Elasticity Rating						
Temporary	0	0	0	0	0	0
Final	0	0	0	0	0	0
Visual Rating						
Liquid	0	0	0	0	0	0
Polymer						
Temporary	0	1	1[(a)]	0	0	0
Final	0	1	1[(a)]	0	0	0

[(a)] Surface dulled

TABLE 12
Compatibility of Refrigerants with Natural Rubber

Test Conditions: 27 days immersion of the polymer at 25°C (77°F) and 80°C (176°F) in liquid (temporary) plus two weeks drying in air at about 25°C (77°F) (final).

	25°C (77°F)		80°C (176°F)	
	CFC-12	HFC-134a	CFC-12	HFC-134a
Length Change (%)				
Temporary	14	1.3	14	2.0
Final	–1.1	–0.3	–0.8	0.4
Weight Change (%)				
Temporary	51	4.5	55	5.8
Final	–2.6	–0.5	–2.6	–0.6
Shore A Hardness				
Original	55	56	56	57
Temporary, Δ SH	–9	–1	–17	–8
Final, Δ SH	–5	–4	–8	–4
Elasticity Rating				
Temporary	0	0	1[(a)]	1[(a)]
Final	0	0	2[(a)]	0
Visual Rating				
Liquid	0	0	0	0
Polymer				
Temporary	0	0	0	0
Final	0	0	0	0

[(a)] More elastic

TABLE 13
Compatibility of Refrigerants with Neoprene W

Test Conditions: 27 days immersion of the polymer at 25°C (77°F) and 80°C (176°F) in liquid (temporary) plus two weeks drying in air at about 25°C (77°F) (final).

	25°C (77°F)		80°C (176°F)	
	CFC-12	HFC-134a	CFC-12	HFC-134a
Length Change (%)				
Temporary	0.2	0.7	0.9	1.4
Final	–7.6	–0.5	–7.3	–0.3
Weight Change (%)				
Temporary	6.6	2.3	6.8	2.9
Final	–12	–0.6	–13	–1.8
Shore A Hardness				
Original	73	73	73	72
Temporary, Δ SH	–1	0	–5	–7
Final, Δ SH	–10	0	5	–5
Elasticity Rating				
Temporary	2[(a)]	0	1[(b)]	0
Final	2[(a)]	0	2[(b)]	0
Visual Rating				
Liquid	1[(c)]	0	1[(d)]	0
Polymer				
Temporary	0	0	1[(e)]	0
Final	0	0	0	0

(a) Less elastic
(b) More elastic
(c) Clear, yellow
(d) Hazy
(e) White film

TABLE 14
Compatibility of Refrigerants with NORDEL® Elastomer

Test Conditions: 27 days immersion of the polymer at 25°C (77°F) and 80°C (176°F) in liquid (temporary) plus two weeks drying in air at about 25°C (77°F) (final).

	25°C (77°F)		80°C (176°F)	
	CFC-12	HFC-134a	CFC-12	HFC-134a
Length Change (%)				
Temporary	–0.6	0.5	–0.4	0.7
Final	–8.2	–0.2	–8.4	0.4
Weight Change (%)				
Temporary	5.5	2.8	6.1	4.4
Final	–22	<0.1	–22	–0.2
Shore A Hardness				
Original	66	66	65	63
Temporary, Δ SH	–4	–3	0	–6
Final, Δ SH	19	–4	20	0
Elasticity Rating				
Temporary	2[(a)]	0	2[(b)]	1[(b)]
Final	2[(a)]	0	2[(b)]	0
Visual Rating				
Liquid	0	0	0	1[(d)]
Polymer				
Temporary	0	0	0	0
Final	0	0	1[(c)]	0

(a) Less elastic
(b) More elastic
(c) White film
(d) Hazy

TABLE 15
Compatibility of Refrigerants with Silicone

Test Conditions: 27 days immersion of the polymer at 25°C (77°F) and 80°C (176°F) in liquid (temporary) plus two weeks drying in air at about 25°C (77°F) (final).

	25°C (77°F)		80°C (176°F)	
	CFC-12	HFC-134a	CFC-12	HFC-134a
Length Change (%)				
Temporary	41	6.1	44	5.5
Final	–0.1	0.1	–0.2	–0.2
Weight Change (%)				
Temporary	173	20	187	20.3
Final	0.7	–0.1	–0.7	–0.3
Shore A Hardness				
Original	60	61	60	58
Temporary, Δ SH	–13	–8	–15	–6
Final, Δ SH	–7	–4	–7	–2
Elasticity Rating				
Temporary	0	1[a]	1[a]	0
Final	0	0	0	0
Visual Rating				
Liquid	0	0	0	0
Polymer				
Temporary	5[b]	0	4[b]	0
Final	0	0	0	0

[a] Less elastic

[b] Swollen

TABLE 16
Compatibility of Refrigerants with THIOKOL® FA

Test Conditions: 27 days immersion of the polymer at 25°C (77°F) and 80°C (176°F) in liquid (temporary) plus two weeks drying in air at about 25°C (77°F) (final).

	25°C (77°F)		80°C (176°F)	
	CFC-12	HFC-134a	CFC-12	HFC-134a
Length Change (%)				
Temporary	1.3	0.8	1.4	–0.2
Final	–0.5	–0.2	–0.5	–0.9
Weight Change (%)				
Temporary	1.9	1.0	3.7	1.9
Final	–0.2	–0.1	–0.8	–0.8
Shore A Hardness				
Original	70	69	74	74
Temporary, Δ SH	–6	–4	–6	0
Final, Δ SH	–5	–6	–1	0
Elasticity Rating				
Temporary	1[b]	1[b]	0	1[b]
Final	0	0	1[a]	2[a]
Visual Rating				
Liquid	0	0	0	0
Polymer				
Temporary	0	0	0	0
Final	0	0	0	0

[a] Less elastic

[b] More elastic

TABLE 17
Compatibility of Refrigerants with VITON® A

Test Conditions: 27 days immersion of the polymer at 25°C (77°F) and 80°C (176°F) in liquid (temporary) plus two weeks drying in air at about 25°C (77°F) (final).

	25°C (77°F)		80°C (176°F)	
	CFC-12	**HFC-134a**	**CFC-12**	**HFC-134a**
Length Change (%)				
Temporary	5.5	13	4.9	12
Final	0.7	–0.1	1.2	0.3
Weight Change (%)				
Temporary	19	48	20	49
Final	1.8	0.7	2.5	1.2
Shore A Hardness				
Original	74	74	73	73
Temporary, Δ SH	–19	–30	–23	–31
Final, Δ SH	–7	–8	–10	–6
Elasticity Rating				
Temporary	2[(b)]	2[(b)]	3[(a)]	3[(a)]
Final	0	0	0	0
Visual Rating				
Liquid	0	0	0	0
Polymer				
Temporary	0	1[(c)]	0	0
Final	0	1[(d)]	0	5[(e)]

(a) Less elastic
(b) More elastic
(c) Very slightly tacky
(d) Oily sheen
(e) Puffed mounds—5% of surface

TABLE 18
HFC-134a Permeation Through Elastomeric Hoses

	Permeation Rate, gm/cm-yr (lb/ft-yr)			
	Nylon	**HYPALON® 48**	**Nitrile #1**	**Nitrile #2**
CFC-12	4.5 (0.3)	14.9 (1.0)	22.3 (1.5)	28.3 (1.9)
HFC-134a	3.0 (0.2)	3.0 (0.2)	26.8 (1.8)	40.2 (2.7)
Hose Construction:				
Inner Liner	Nylon	HYPALON® 48	Nitrile (NBR)	
Second Layer	—	Rayon	Rayon	
Reinforcement	Nylon	2 Braids	2 Braids	
Outer Cover	Chlorobutyl	EPDM	EPDM	

TABLE 19
Solubilities of HFC-134a in Lubricants

Temperature Range: –50°C to 93°C (–58°F to 199°F)

Oil Type	Percent Refrigerant in Mixture 30%	60%	90%
500 SUS Naphthenic	2 phase	2 phase	2 phase
500 SUS Paraffinic	2 phase	2 phase	2 phase
125 SUS Dialkylbenzene	2 phase	2 phase	2 phase
300 SUS Alkylbenzene	2 phase	2 phase	2 phase
165 SUS PAG	–50 to >93[a]	–50 to >93	–50 to +73
525 SUS PAG	–50 to >93	–40 to +35	–23 to –7
100 SUS Ester	–40 to >93	–35 to >93	–35 to >93
150 SUS Ester	–50 to >93	–50 to >93	–50 to >93
300 SUS Ester	–50 to >93	–50 to >93	–50 to >93
500 SUS Ester	–40 to >93	–35 to >93	–35 to >93

[a] One phase in this temperature range, °C.

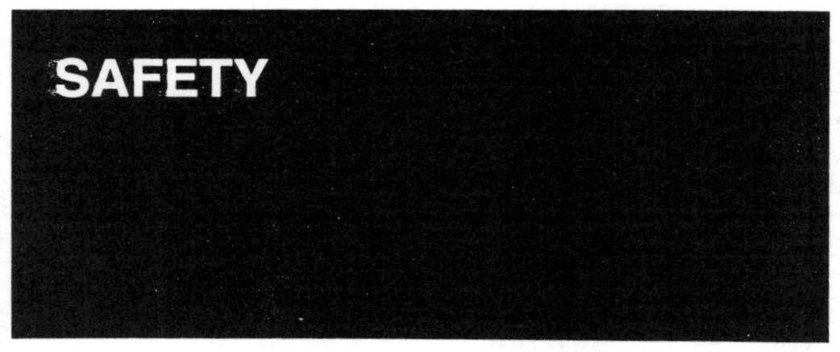

INHALATION TOXICITY

HFC-134a poses no acute or chronic hazard when it is handled in accordance with DuPont recommendations and when exposures are maintained at or below the DuPont Acceptable Exposure Limit (AEL) of 1,000 ppm (8- and 12-hour Time-Weighted Average or TWA).

An AEL is an airborne exposure limit established by DuPont scientists that specifies time-weighted average (TWA) airborne concentrations to which nearly all workers may be repeatedly exposed without adverse effects. The AEL for HFC-134a has the same value as the Threshold Limit Values (TLVs) established for CFC-12 and HCFC-22. TLVs are established by the American Conference of Governmental and Industrial Hygienists (ACGIH).

However, inhaling high concentrations of HFC-134a vapor may cause temporary central nervous system depression with narcosis, lethargy and anesthetic effects. Other effects that may occur include dizziness, a feeling of intoxication and a loss of coordination. Continued breathing of high concentrations of HFC-134a vapors may produce cardiac irregularities (cardiac sensitization), unconsciousness and, with gross overexposure, death. Intentional misuse or deliberate inhalation of HFC-134a may cause death without warning. This practice is *extremely dangerous.*

If you experience *any* of the initial symptoms, move to fresh air and seek medical attention.

CARDIAC SENSITIZATION

If vapors are inhaled at a concentration of 75,000 ppm, which is well above the AEL, the heart may become sensitized to adrenaline, leading to cardiac irregularities and, possibly, to cardiac arrest. The likelihood of these cardiac problems increases if you are under physical or emotional stress.

Medical attention must be given immediately if exposed to high concentrations of HFC-134a. Do ***not*** treat with adrenaline (epinephrine) or similar drugs. These drugs may *increase* the risk of cardiac arrhythmias and cardiac arrest. If the person is having difficulty breathing, administer oxygen. If breathing has stopped, give artificial respiration.

SPILLS OR LEAKS

If a large release of vapor occurs, such as from a large spill or leak, the vapors may concentrate near the floor or low spots and displace the oxygen available for breathing, causing suffocation.

Evacuate *everyone* until the area has been ventilated. Use blowers or fans to circulate the air at floor level. Do not reenter the affected area unless you are equipped with a self-contained breathing apparatus or unless an area monitor indicates that the concentration of HFC-134a vapors in the area is below the AEL.

Always use self-contained breathing apparatus or an air-line mask when entering tanks or other areas where vapors might exist. Use the buddy system *and* a lifeline. Refer to the Material Safety Data Sheet (MSDS) for HFC-134a for more information.

HFC-134a vapors have a slightly sweet odor that can be difficult to detect. Therefore, frequent leak checks and the installation of permanent area monitors may be necessary in enclosed spaces. Refer to ASHRAE Standards 15 and 34 for refrigeration machinery rooms.

To ensure safety when working with HFC-134a in enclosed areas:

1. Route relief and purge vent piping (if present) outdoors, away from air intakes.
2. Make certain the area is well ventilated, using auxiliary ventilation, if necessary, to move vapors.
3. Make sure the area is clear of vapors prior to beginning work.
4. Install air monitoring equipment to detect leaks. (Monitors are discussed in the next section, Monitors and Leak Detection.)

SKIN AND EYE CONTACT

At room temperature, HFC-134a vapors have little or no effect on the skin or eyes. However, in liquid form, HFC-134a can freeze skin or eyes on contact, causing frostbite. Following contact, soak the exposed area in lukewarm water, not cold or hot. If medical treatment cannot begin immediately, apply a light coat of a nonmedicated ointment, such as petroleum jelly. If the exposed area is in a location where the presence of the ointment would be awkward, such as on the eye, apply a light bandage. In *all* cases of frostbite, seek medical attention as soon as possible.

Always wear protective clothing when there is a risk of exposure to liquid HFC-134a. Where splashing is possible, *always* wear eye protection and a face shield.

COMBUSTIBILITY OF HFC-134a

HFC-134a is *nonflammable* at ambient temperatures and atmospheric pressure. However, tests have shown HFC-134a to be combustible at pressures as low as 5.5 psig (139.3 kPa absolute) at 177°C (350°F) when mixed with air at concentrations generally greater than 60 volume % air. At lower temperatures, higher pressures are required for combustibility. (HCFC-22 is also combustible at pressures above atmospheric in the presence of high air concentrations.) Test results and calculations have shown:

- At ambient temperature, all concentrations of HFC-134a in air are nonflammable at pressures below 15 psig (205 kPa absolute).
- Combustible mixtures of air and HFC-134a will not form when liquid HFC-134a is pumped into a closed vessel if the initial air pressure in the vessel is limited to one atmosphere absolute and the final pressure is limited to 300 psig (2,170 kPa absolute). If the initial air pressure is greater than one atmosphere, combustible mixtures may form as the tank is filled.

Based on the above information, the following operating practices are recommended:

- **Leak Testing**
  - Equipment should **never** be leak tested with a pressurized mixture of HFC-134a and air. HFC-134a may be safely pressured with dry nitrogen.
- **Bulk Delivery and Storage**
  - Tanks should normally be evacuated at the start of filling, and should never be filled while under positive air pressure.
  - Tank pressure should never be allowed to exceed 300 psig (2,170 kPa) when filling with HFC-134a. Relief devices on either the tanks or the HFC-134a supply system usually prevent this.
  - Tank pressures should be monitored routinely.
  - Air lines should never be connected to storage tanks.
- **Filling and Charging Operations**
  - Before evacuating cylinders or refrigeration equipment, any remaining refrigerant should be removed by a recovery system.
  - Vacuum pump discharge lines should be free of restrictions that could increase discharge pressures above 15 psig (205 kPa) and result in the formation of combustible mixtures.
  - Cylinders or refrigeration equipment should normally be evacuated at the start of filling, and should never be filled while under positive air pressure.
  - Final pressures should not exceed 300 psig (2,170 kPa).
  - Filled cylinders should periodically be analyzed for air (nonabsorbable gas or NAG).

- **Refrigerant Recovery Systems**

  Efficient recovery of refrigerant from equipment or containers requires evacuation at the end of the recovery cycle. Suction lines to a recovery compressor should be periodically checked for leaks to prevent compressing air into the recovery cylinder during evacuation. In addition, the recovery cylinder pressure should be monitored, and evacuation stopped in the event of a rapid pressure rise indicating the presence of noncondensable air. The recovery cylinder contents should then be analyzed for NAG, and the recovery system leak checked if air is present. Do not continue to evacuate a refrigeration system that has a major leak.

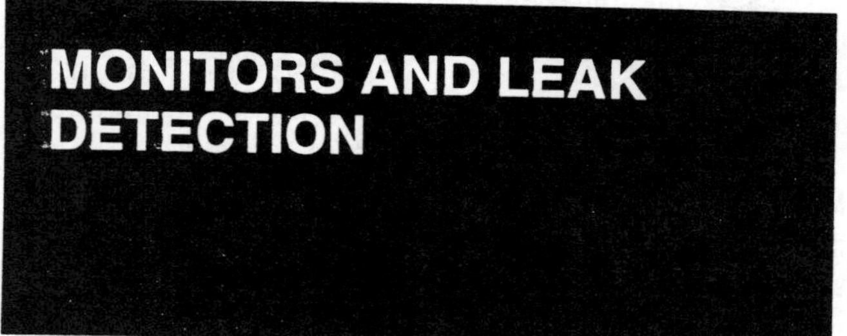

MONITORS AND LEAK DETECTION

Service personnel have used leak detection equipment for years when servicing equipment. Leak detectors exist not only for pinpointing specific leaks, but also for monitoring an entire room on a continual basis. There are several reasons for leak pinpointing or area monitoring, including: conservation of HFCs, protection of valuable equipment, reduction of fugitive emissions and protection of employees.

Leak detectors can be placed into two broad categories: leak pinpointers and area monitors. Before purchasing a monitor or pinpointer, several instrumental criteria should be considered, including sensitivity, detection limits and selectivity.

TYPES OF DETECTORS

Using selectivity as a criterion, leak detectors can be placed into one of three categories: nonselective, halogen-selective or compound-specific. In general, as the specificity of the monitor increases, so does the complexity and cost. Another method used to find leaks is to add fluorescent dyes to the system.

A detailed discussion of leak detection, along with a list of manufacturers of leak detection equipment, is given in Bulletin ARTD-27 (H-31753-2).

NONSELECTIVE DETECTORS

Nonselective detectors are those that will detect any type of emission or vapor present, regardless of its chemical composition. These detectors are typically quite simple to use, very rugged, inexpensive and almost always portable. However, their inability to be calibrated, long-term drift, lack of selectivity and lack of sensitivity limit their use for area monitoring.

Some nonselective detectors designed for use with CFC-12 may have a much lower sensitivity when used with HFC-134a. However, newly designed detectors with good HFC-134a sensitivity are now available. Be sure to consult with the manufacturer before selecting or using a nonselective detector with HFC-134a.

HALOGEN-SELECTIVE DETECTORS

Halogen-selective detectors use a specialized sensor that allows the monitor to detect compounds containing fluorine, chlorine, bromine and iodine without interference from other species. The major advantage of such a detector is a reduction in the number of "nuisance alarms"—false alarms caused by the presence of some compound in the area other than the target compound.

These detectors are typically easy to use, feature higher sensitivity than the nonselective detectors (detection limits are typically <5 ppm when used as an area monitor and <0.05 oz/yr (<1.4 gm/yr) when used as a leak pinpointer), and are very durable. In addition, due to the partial specificity of the detector, these instruments can be calibrated easily.

COMPOUND-SPECIFIC DETECTORS

The most complex detectors, which are also the most expensive, are compound-specific detectors. These units are typically capable of detecting the presence of a single compound without interference from other compounds.

FLUORESCENT DYES

Fluorescent dyes have been used in refrigeration systems for several years. These dyes, invisible under ordinary lighting, but visible under ultraviolet (UV) light, are used to pinpoint leaks in systems. The dyes are typically placed into the refrigeration lubricant when the system is serviced. Leaks are detected by using a UV light to search for dye that has escaped from the system.

Recent innovations in dye technology have allowed fluorescent dyes to be used with HFC-134a. However, before adding dyes to a system, the compatibility of the specific dye with the lubricant and refrigerant should be tested.

DuPont has formed a partnership with Spectronics Corporation to supply refrigerant mixed with fluorescent additives and to assist in developing additives that are compatible with new alternative refrigerants. For additional information, contact DuPont.

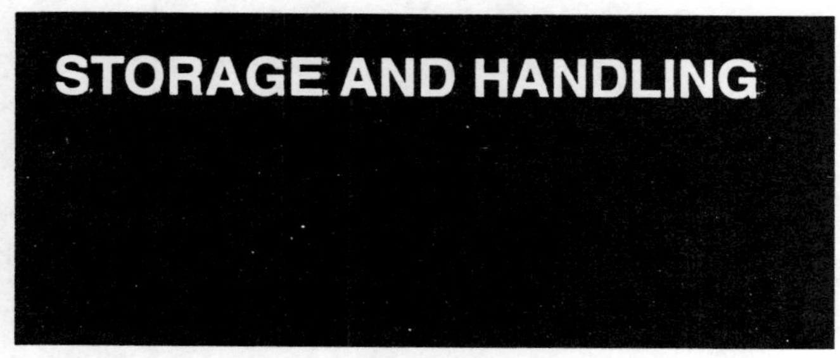

SHIPPING CONTAINERS IN THE U.S.

HFC-134a is a liquefied compressed gas. According to the U.S. Department of Transportation (DOT), a nonflammable compressed gas is defined as a nonflammable material having an absolute pressure greater than 40 psi at 21°C (70°F) and/or an absolute pressure greater than 104 psi at 54°C (130°F).

The appropriate DOT designations are as follows:

Proper shipping name: Refrigerant Gas, N.O.S. (Tetrafluoroethane)

Hazard class: Nonflammable Gas

UN/NA No.: UN 1078

A list of the different types of containers that can be used to ship HFC-134a in the United States, along with their water capacities, dimensions, DOT specifications and the net weights of HFC-134a, are provided in *Table 20*. All pressure relief devices used on the containers must be in compliance with the corresponding Compressed Gas Association (CGA) Standards for compressed gas cylinders, cargo and portable tanks.

The 30-lb and 123-lb cylinders designed for refrigerant applications are a light blue color with labels that bear the name of the product in light blue. The color designation is "Light Blue (Sky)," PMS 2975.

The 30-lb cylinder, known as a "Dispose A Can®" (D.A.C.) fits into a box that measures 10 in. x 10 in. x 17 in. Dispose A Can is DuPont's registered trade name for this type of single-use container. When used to ship SUVA® Cold-MP for the stationary refrigeration market, these 30-lb cylinders have the same outlet fittings as cylinders of CFC-12. However, when used for SUVA® Trans A/C for the automotive industry, these cylinders have a CGA-167 valve outlet. This fitting was specified by the Society of Automotive Engineers (SAE) to avoid mixing CFC-12 and HFC-134a when servicing mobile air conditioning systems. Additional unique fittings used with HFC-134a in automotive service applications are discussed in Bulletin ART-12 (H-45948).

The 123-lb cylinders are equipped with a nonrefillable liquid vapor CGA-660 valve. With this two-way valve, HFC-134a can be removed from the cylinder as either a vapor or as a liquid, without inverting the cylinder. The vapor handwheel is located on the top. The liquid wheel is on the side of the valve and attached to a dip tube extending to the bottom of the cylinder. Each is clearly identified as vapor or liquid.

The 4,400-gal cylinder is known as an ISO tank. The dimensions referenced in *Table 20* represent the frame in which the container is shipped. The tank itself has the same length of 20 ft and an outside diameter of approximately 86 in. ISO tanks are used for export shipments of HFC-134a from the United States.

The general construction of a one-ton returnable container is shown in *Figure 9*. Notice that one end of the container is fitted with two valves. When the container is turned so that the valves are lined up vertically, the top valve will discharge vapor and the bottom valve will discharge liquid. The valves are protected by a dome cover.

TABLE 20
Specifications of Shipping Containers for HFC-134a

Water Capacity	Dimensions	DOT Specification	Net Weight (lb) HFC-134a
30 lb Dispose A Can®*	10" x 10" x 17" (box)	39	30
123 lb	55" H x 10" OD	4BA300	125
1,682 lb	82" L x 30" OD	110A500W	1,750
5,000 gal	Tank Truck	MC-330 or -331	40,000
4,400 gal ISO	8' x 8.5' x 20' (frame)	51	30,865
170,000 lb	Tank Rail Car	114A340W	—

*Dispose A Can® is a registered trademark of the DuPont Company.

Figure 9. One-Ton Returnable Container.

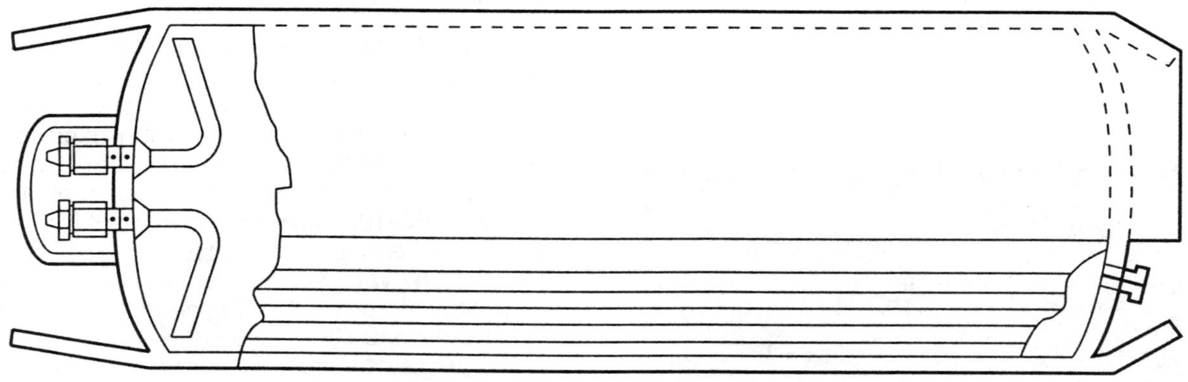

Ton containers are equipped with two fusible plugs in each end. The fusible metal in the plugs is designed to start melting at 69°C (157°F) and completely melt at 74°C (165°F). Containers should never be heated to temperatures higher than 52°C (125°F). One spring-loaded pressure relief valve is also located in each end of the ton container.

BULK STORAGE SYSTEMS

DuPont sells storage systems, at cost, to its HFC-134a customers. The systems are prefabricated, tested and ready to install on site. The units are designed to optimize economy, efficiency and safety in the storage and dispensing of HFC-134a. The delivered systems include all components, such as storage tanks, pumps, piping, valves, motors and gauges, as an integrated unit. All systems are equipped with the DuPont F.E.E.D. (Fluorochemical Emission Elimination Delivery) system to prevent emissions during deliveries, and with dual pumps to provide an installed spare. The units are skid-mounted and require only placement on a concrete pad and connection to electrical and process systems.

A typical bulk storage system is shown in *Figure 10.*

Your DuPont Marketing Representative can arrange for guidance on site selection, purchase, installation, start-up and maintenance.

CONVERTING BULK STORAGE TANKS FROM CFC-12 TO HFC-134a

Before switching from CFC-12 to HFC-134a, the existing storage equipment must be checked to verify that it is adequate. Storage tanks built to the specifications of the American Society of Mechanical Engineers (ASME) Pressure Vessel Code are required to have a metal nameplate indicating each tank's maximum allowable working pressure (MAWP). This rating must be 185 psig (1377 kPa absolute) or higher for HFC-134a service. In most cases, existing storage tanks that have been properly designed to contain CFC-12 will have an adequate pressure rating for HFC-134a. The set pressure of the relief devices on the top of the tanks must also be verified and changed, if necessary.

We recommend that storage tanks be **completely** emptied of all CFC-12 liquid and vapor before introducing HFC-134a. In general, converting a storage tank from CFC-12 to HFC-134a requires:

1. Removing CFC-12 from the storage tank, lines and equipment.
2. Evacuating the storage tank to 25 inches of mercury vacuum (16.7 kPa absolute pressure) and purging with compressed dry nitrogen gas.
3. Making necessary repairs to the tank after initial evacuation and purging.
4. Repeating step 2 until CFC-12 and moisture analyses are within acceptable limits.
5. Refilling system with HFC-134a.

The above is a simplified outline of what is actually a lengthy procedure. Your DuPont Marketing Representative can assist in obtaining the equipment, instrumentation and technical assistance to safely and effectively make the conversion.

MATERIAL COMPATIBILITY CONCERNS

Most metal components suitable for use with CFC-12 are also compatible with HFC-134a, including standard types of carbon steel, aluminum and copper. Some elastomeric or nonmetallic components suitable for CFC-12 may not be adequate. Therefore, all elastomeric or nonmetallic components throughout the system must be identified and their compatibility with HFC-134a verified. See Materials Compatibility section. For complete reliability, any component that cannot be properly identified should be replaced.

In a fluorocarbon storage system, elastomers are most commonly found in:

- Packing and seats of manual valves
- Pressure-relief device seats
- Flange and manway gaskets
- Mechanical pump seals
- Wet-end pump gaskets and O-rings
- Filter O-rings
- Sight-flow indicator gaskets
- Back-pressure regulator diaphragms and O-rings.

HANDLING PRECAUTIONS FOR HFC-134a SHIPPING CONTAINERS

The following rules for handling HFC-134a containers are strongly recommended:

- Use personal protective equipment, such as side shield glasses, gloves and safety shoes when handling HFC-134a containers.
- Avoid skin contact with liquid HFC-134a, since it may cause frostbite.
- Never heat a container to a temperature higher than 52°C (125°F).
- Never apply direct flame or live steam to a container or valve.
- Never refill disposable cylinders with anything. The shipment of refilled disposable cylinders is prohibited by DOT regulations.
- Never refill returnable cylinders without DuPont consent. DOT regulations forbid transportation of returnable cylinders refilled without DuPont's authorization.
- Never use a lifting magnet or sling (rope or chain) when handling containers. A crane may be used when a safe cradle or platform is used to hold the container.

Figure 10. Typical Bulk Storage System.

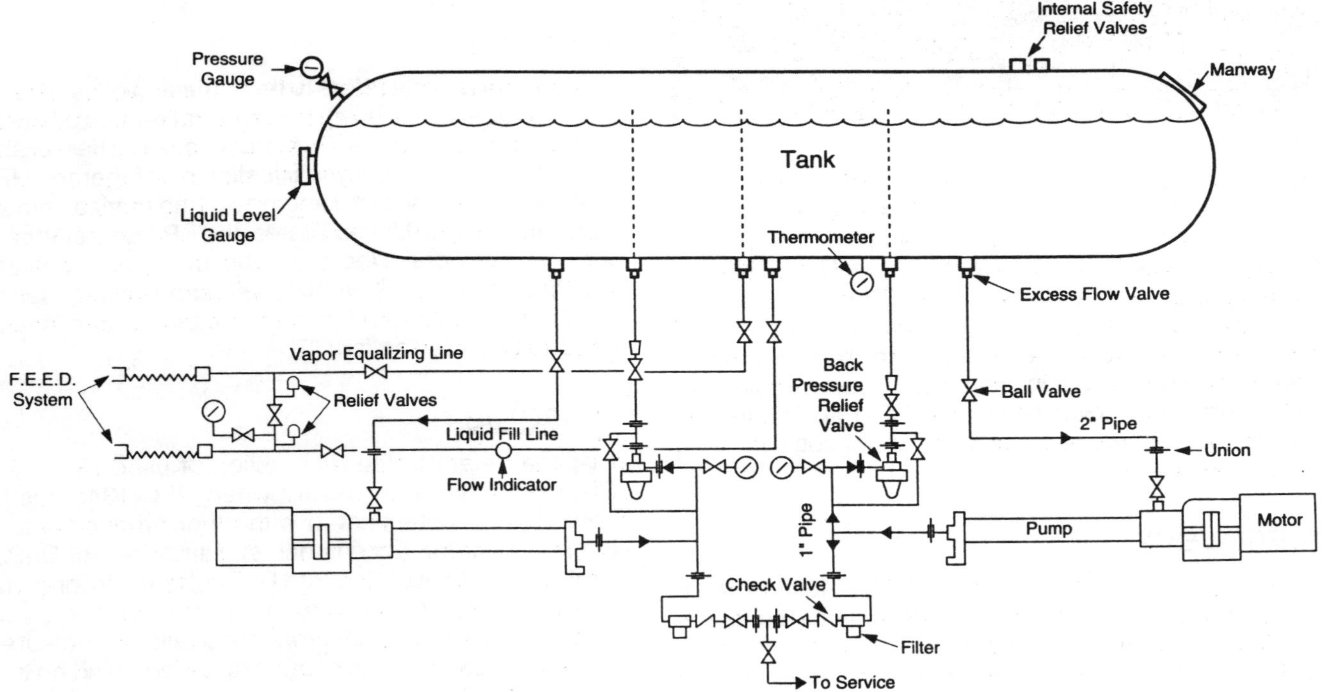

- Never use containers as rollers, supports or for any purpose other than to carry HFC-134a.
- Protect containers from any object that will result in a cut or other abrasion in the surface of the metal.
- Never tamper with the safety devices in the valves or containers.
- Never attempt to repair or alter containers or valves.
- Never force connections that do not fit. Make sure the threads on the regulators or other auxiliary equipment are the same as those on the container valve outlets.
- Keep valves tightly closed and valve caps and hoods in place when the containers are not in use.
- Store containers under a roof to protect them from weather extremes.
- Use a vapor recovery system to collect HFC-134a vapors from lines after unloading.

RECOVERY, RECLAMATION, RECYCLE AND DISPOSAL

Responsible use of HFC-134a requires that the product be recovered for reuse or disposal whenever possible. DuPont purchases used refrigerants for reclamation through its distributor networks in the United States, Canada and Europe. In the United States, used HFC-134a is accepted as part of this program. Recovery and reuse of HFC-134a makes sense from an environmental and economic standpoint. In addition, the U.S. Clean Air Act will prohibit known venting of HFC-134a in late 1995 during the maintenance, servicing or disposal of refrigeration equipment.

RECOVERY

Recovery refers to the removal of HFC-134a from equipment and collection in an appropriate external container. As defined by the Air Conditioning and Refrigeration Institute (ARI), a U.S. organization, recovery does not involve processing or analytical testing. HFC-134a may be recovered from refrigeration equipment using permanent on-site equipment or one of the portable recovery devices now on the market. The portable devices contain a small compressor and an air cooled condenser, and may be used for vapor or liquid recovery. At the end of the recovery cycle, the system is evacuated to remove vapors. In the United States, the Environmental Protection Agency (EPA) sets standards for recovery equipment. Before purchasing a specific recovery unit, check with the manufacturer to be sure that it contains elastomeric seals and a compressor oil compatible with HFC-134a.

RECLAMATION

Reclamation refers to the reprocessing of used HFC-134a to new product specifications. Quality of reclaimed product is verified by chemical analysis. In the United States, HFC-134a is included in DuPont's refrigerant reclamation program. Contact DuPont or one of its authorized distributors for further information.

Reclamation offers advantages over on-site refrigerant recycling procedures because these systems cannot guarantee complete removal of contaminants. Putting refrigerants that do not meet new product specifications back into expensive equipment may cause damage.

RECYCLE

Refrigerant recycle refers to the reduction of used refrigerant contaminants using devices that reduce oil, water, acidity and particulates. Recycle is usually a field or shop procedure with no analytical testing of refrigerant. HFC-134a may be recycled using one of the devices now on the market. In the United States, the EPA sets standards for these devices. Recycle is becoming the accepted practice in the U.S. mobile air conditioning service industry. Consult with the manufacturer before specifying a recycle device for HFC-134a.

DISPOSAL

Disposal refers to the destruction of used HFC-134a. Disposal may be necessary when HFC-134a has become badly contaminated with other products and no longer meets the acceptance specifications of DuPont or other reclaimers. Although DuPont does not presently accept severely contaminated refrigerants for disposal, licensed waste disposal firms are available. Be sure to check the qualifications of any firm before sending them used HFC-134a.

H-45945-1 3/93

Printed in U.S.A.

233264A

DuPont Chemicals
Fluorochemicals Customer Service Center
Wilmington, DE 19898

For sales information:
1-800-441-9442
In Delaware (302) 774-2099

For technical information:
1-800-582-5606
In Delaware (302) 999-3129

Europe
DuPont de Nemours
International S.A.
2 Chemin du Pavillon
P.O. Box 50
CH-1218 Le Grand-Saconnex
Geneva, Switzerland
41-22-717-5111

Canada
DuPont Canada, Inc.
P.O. Box 2200, Streetsville
Mississauga, Ontario
L5M 2H3
(416) 821-3300

Mexico
DuPont, S.A. de C.V.
Homero 206
Col. Chapultepec Morales
C.P. 11570 Mexico, D.F.
52-5-250-8000

South America
DuPont do Brasil S.A.
Alameda Itapicuru, 506
Alphaville 06400 Barueri
São Paulo, Brazil
55-11-421-8509

DuPont Argentina S.A.
Casilla Correo 1888
Correo Central
1000 Buenos Aires, Argentina
54-1-311-8167

Pacific
DuPont Australia
P.O. Box 930
North Sydney, NSW 2060
Australia
61-2-923-6165

Japan
Mitsui DuPont Fluoro-chemicals Company, Ltd.
Mitsui Seimei Building
2-3, 1-Chome Ohtemachi
Chiyoda-Ku, Tokyo 100 Japan
81-3-3216-8451

Asia
DuPont Taiwan
P.O. Box 81-777
Taipei, Taiwan
886-2-514-4400

DuPont Asia Pacific Limited
P.O. Box TST 98851
Tsim Sha Tsui
Kowloon, Hong Kong
852-734-5345

DuPont Thailand
P.O. Box 2398
Bangkok 10501, Thailand
66-2-238-4361

DuPont China Ltd.
Room 1704, Union Bldg.
100 Yanan Rd. East
Shanghai, PR China 200 002
Phone: 86-21-328-3738
Telex: 33448 DCLSH CN
Fax: 86-21-320-2304

DuPont Far East Inc.
P.O. Box 12396
50776 Kuala Lumpur,
Malaysia
Phone: 60-3-232-3522
Telex: (784) 30391 DUFE M
Fax: 60-3-238-7250

DuPont Korea Ltd.
C.P.O. Box 5972
Seoul, Korea
82-2-721-5114

DuPont Singapore Pte. Ltd.
1 Maritime Square #07 01
World Trade Centre
Singapore 0409
65-273-2244

DuPont Far East, Philippines
5th Floor, Solid Bank Building
777 Paseo de Roxas
Makati, Metro Manila
Philippines
63-2-818-9911

DuPont Far East Inc.
7A Murray's Gate Road
Alwarpet
Madras, 600 018 India
91-44-454-029

DuPont Far East Inc.—
Pakistan
9 Khayaban-E-Shaheen
Defence Phase 5
Karachi, Pakistan
92-21-533-350

DuPont Far East Inc.
P.O. Box 2553/Jkt
Jakarta 10001
Indonesia
62-21-517-800

(Stock number on last page of text)

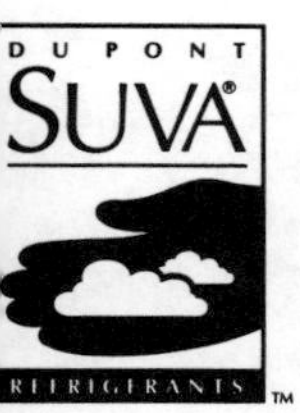

SUVA®

REFRIGERANTS

ART - 1

PRODUCT INFORMATION

Transport Properties of SUVA® Refrigerants:

SUVA® COLD - MP (HFC - 134a)
SUVA® TRANS A/C (HFC - 134a)
SUVA® CENTRI - LP (HCFC - 123)

Viscosity
Thermal Conductivity
and
Heat Capacity
for the
Liquid and Vapor

DUPONT

Transport Properties of SUVA® Refrigerants

SUVA® COLD - MP[1] • SUVA® TRANS A/C[1] • SUVA® CENTRI LP[2]

TABLE OF CONTENTS

1. HFC - 134a (1,1,1,2 - TETRAFLUOROETHANE; CH_2FCF_3)
2. HCFC - 123 (2,2 - DICHLORO - 1,1,1 - TRIFLUOROETHANE; $CHCl_2CF_3$)

Liquid Viscosity

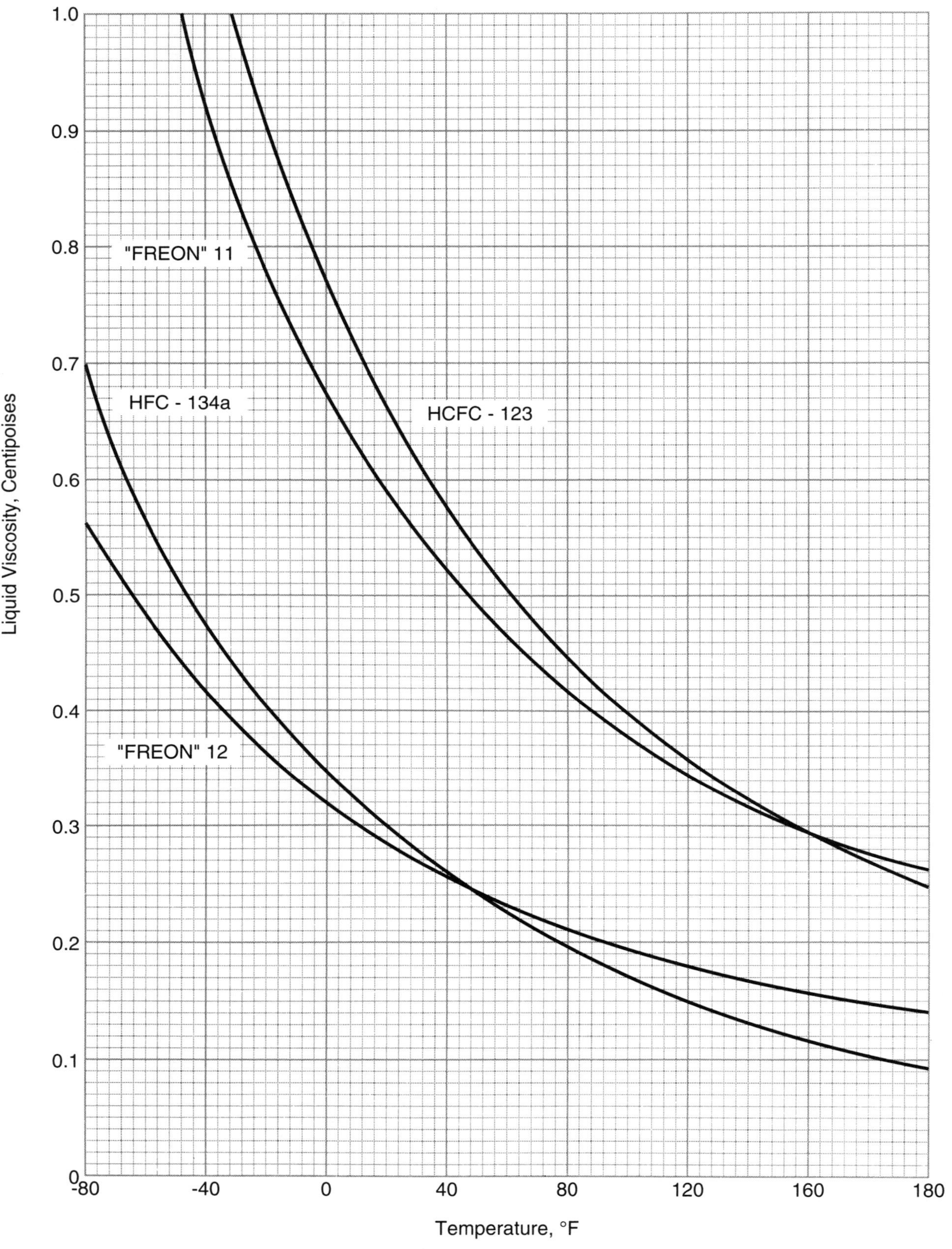

Liquid Thermal Conductivity

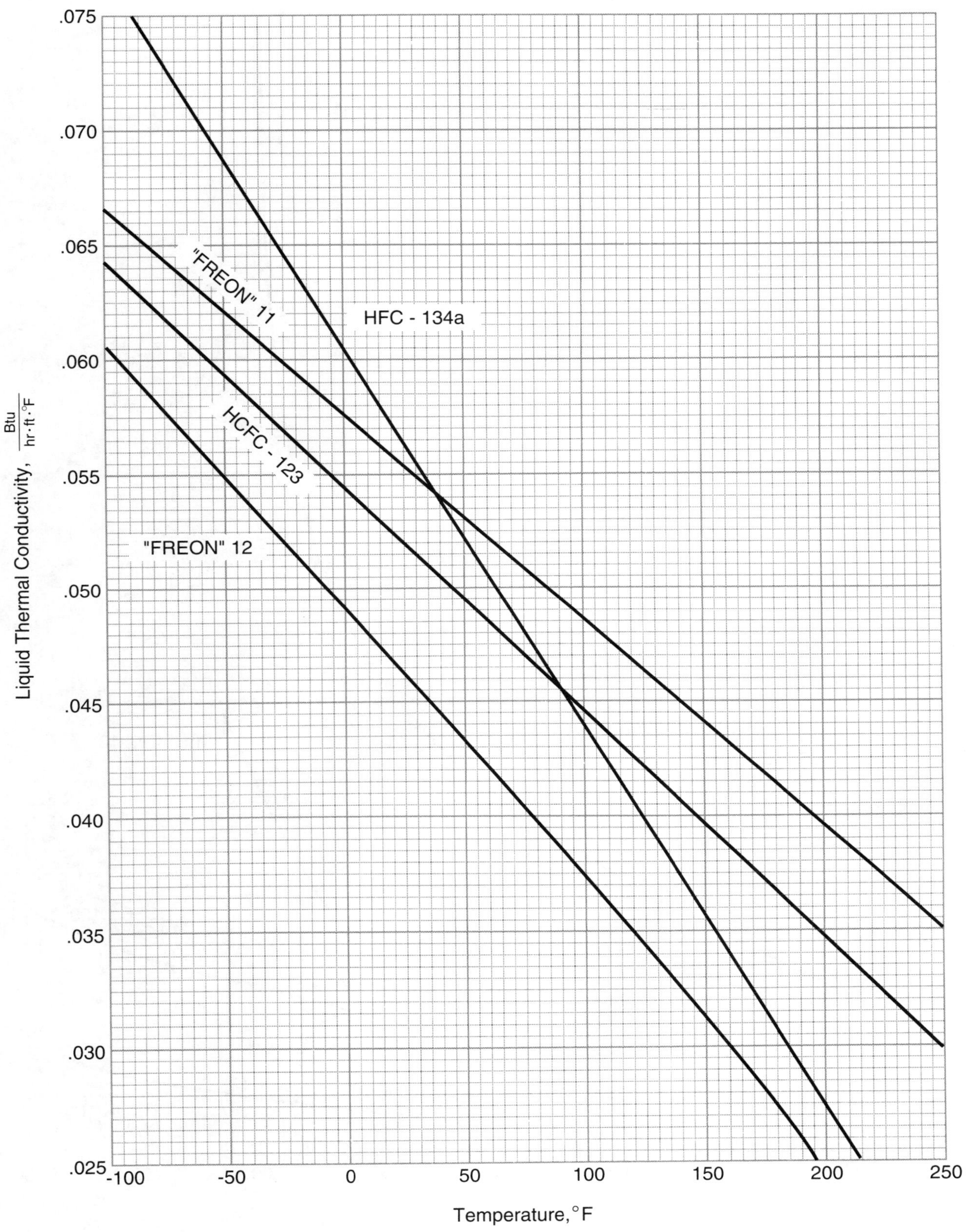

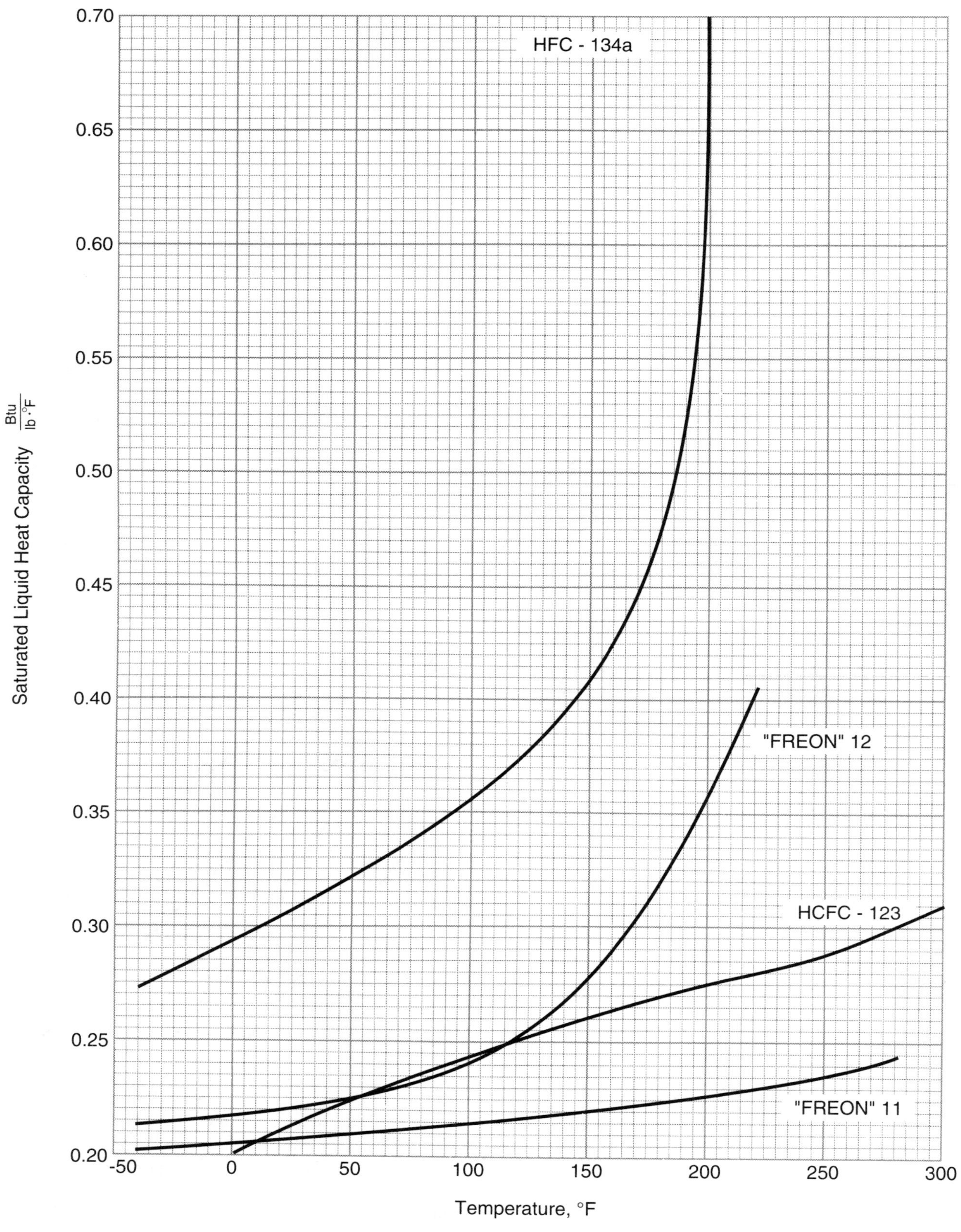

Saturated Liquid Heat Capacity
HFC - 134a
"FREON" 12
HCFC - 123
"FREON" 11
Saturated Liquid Heat Capacity Btu/lb·°F
0.70
0.65
0.60
0.55
0.50
0.45
0.40
0.35
0.30
0.25
0.20
-50
0
50
100
150
200
250
300
Temperature, °F

Vapor Viscosity at Atmospheric Pressure

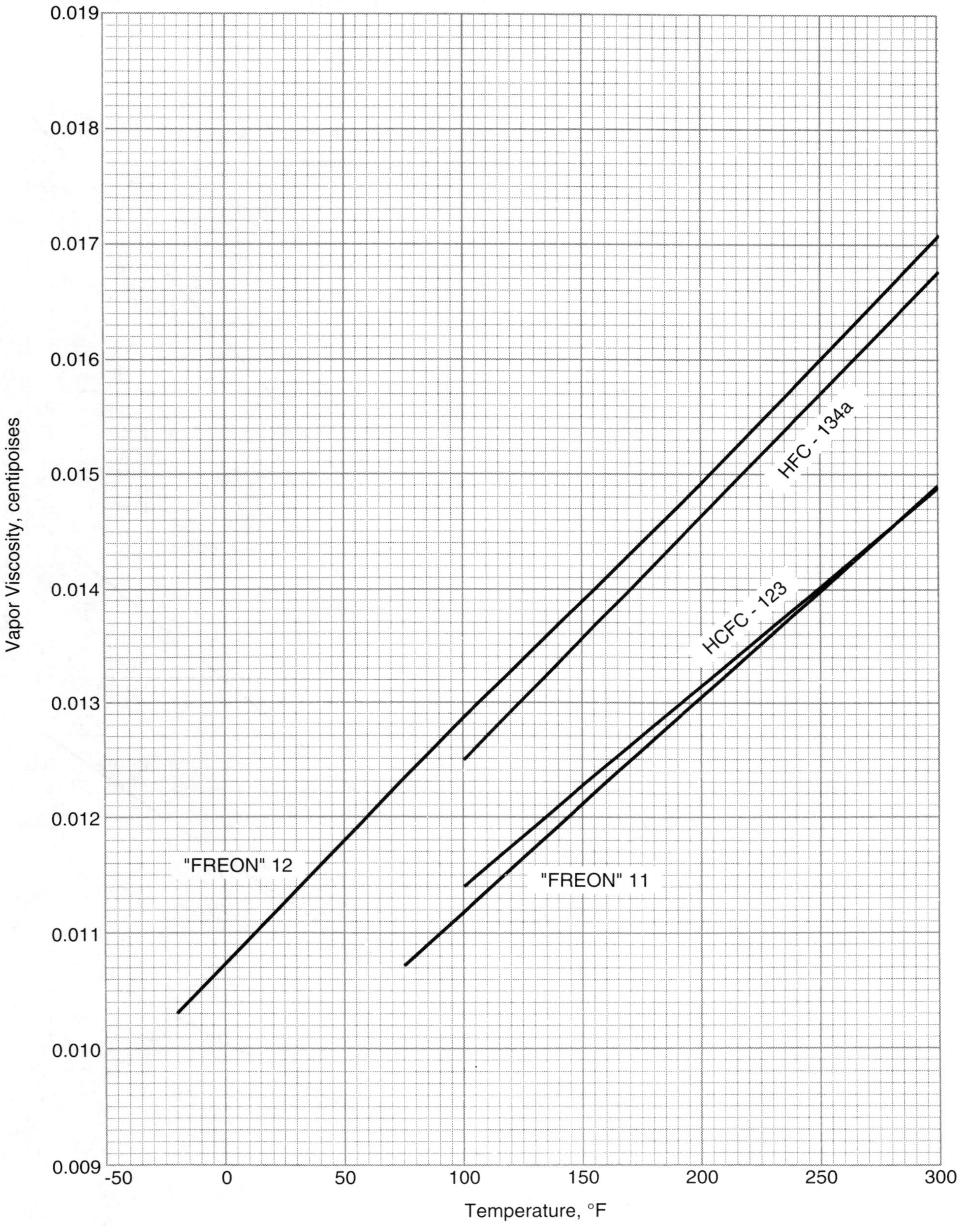

Vapor Thermal Conductivity at Atmospheric Pressure

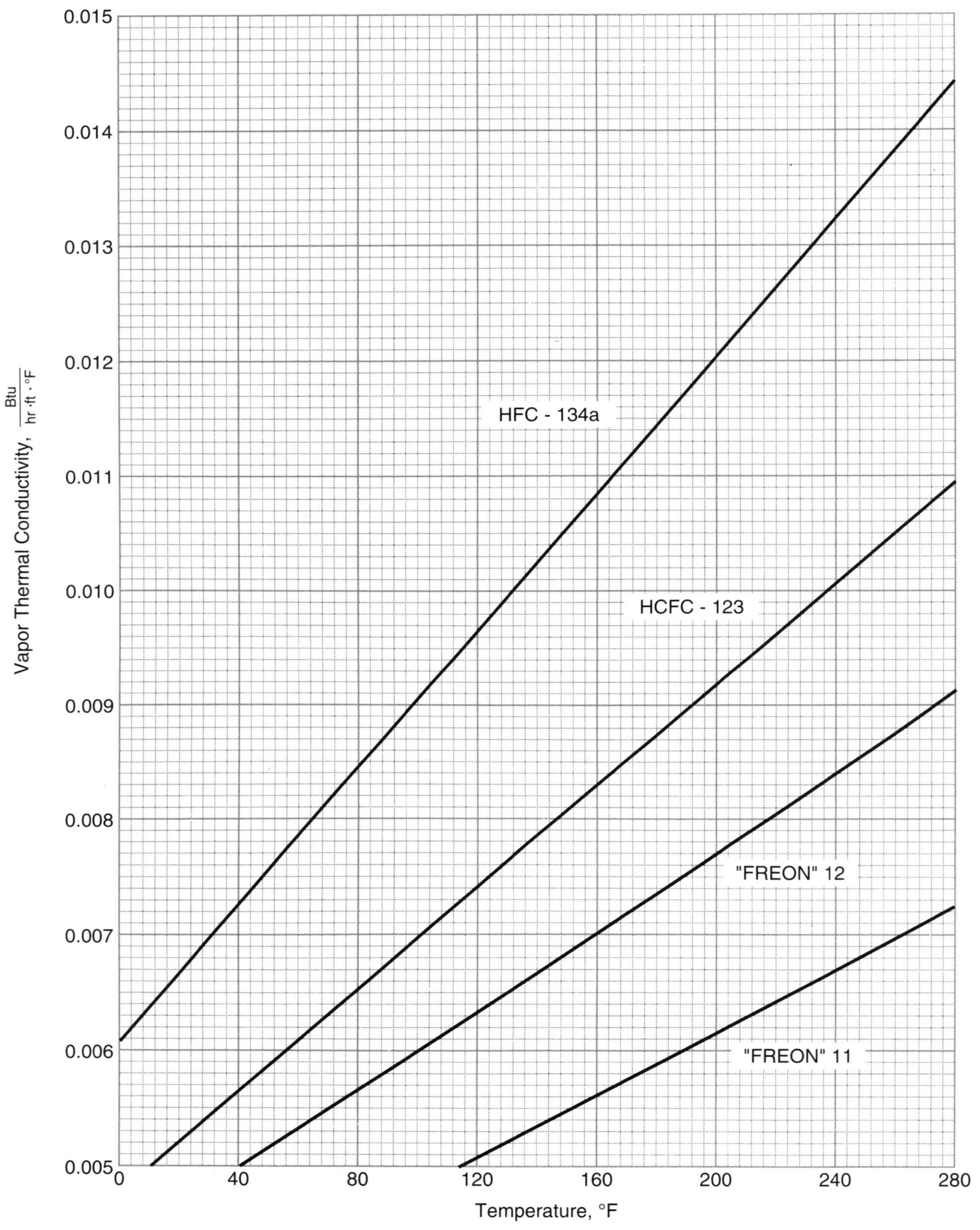

HFC - 134a Vapor Heat Capacity

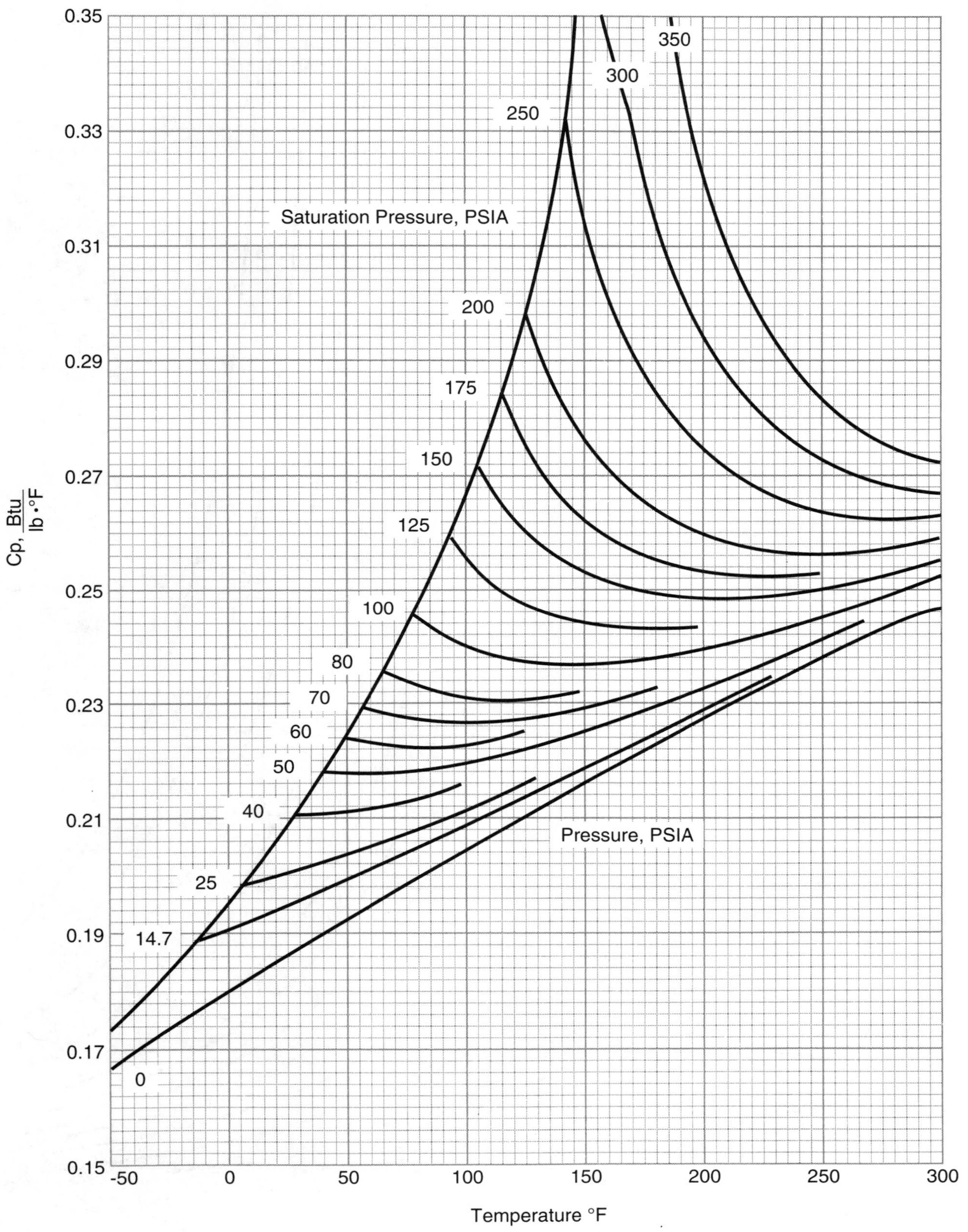

HFC - 134a Vapor Heat Capacity Ratio

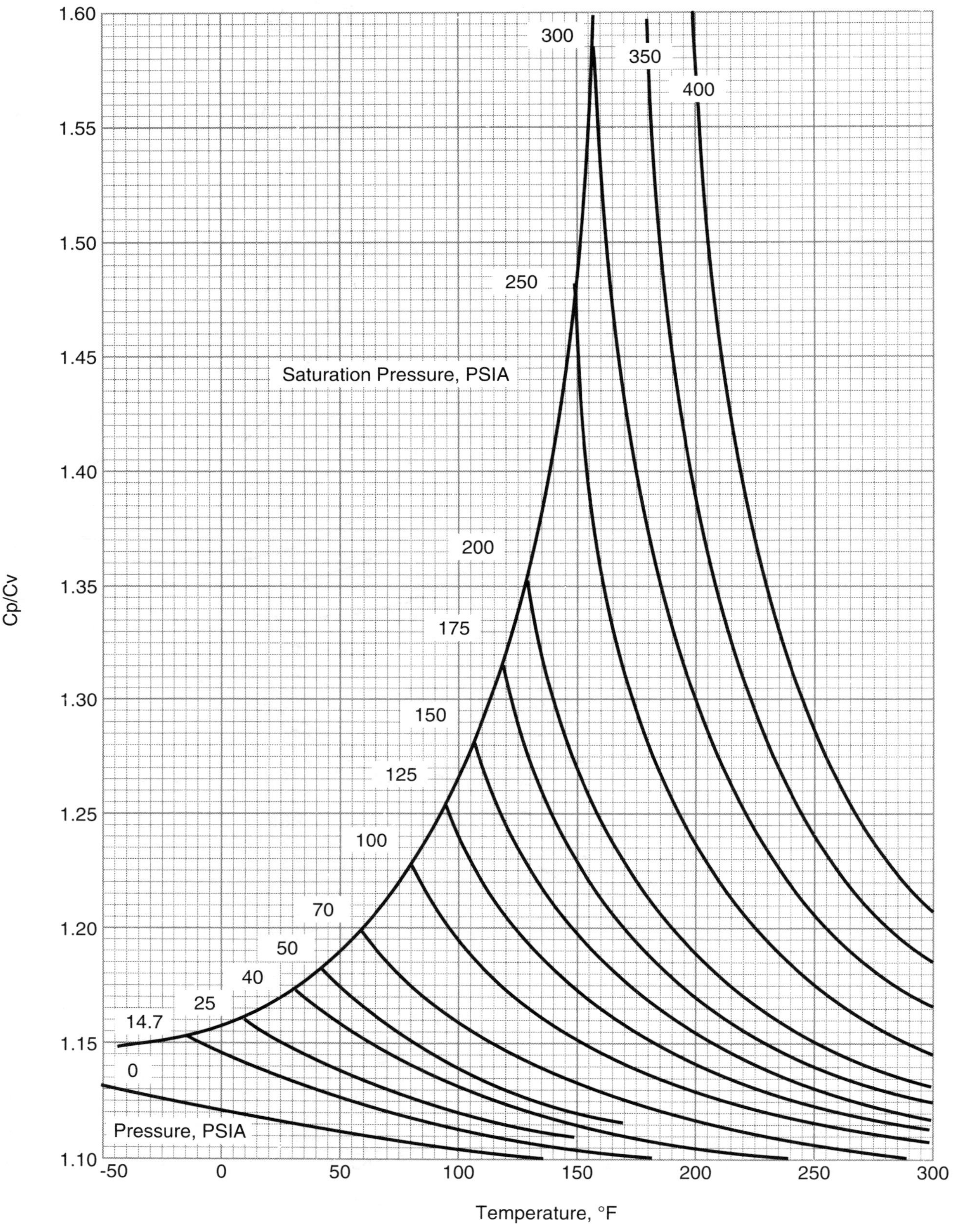

HCFC - 123 Vapor Heat Capacity

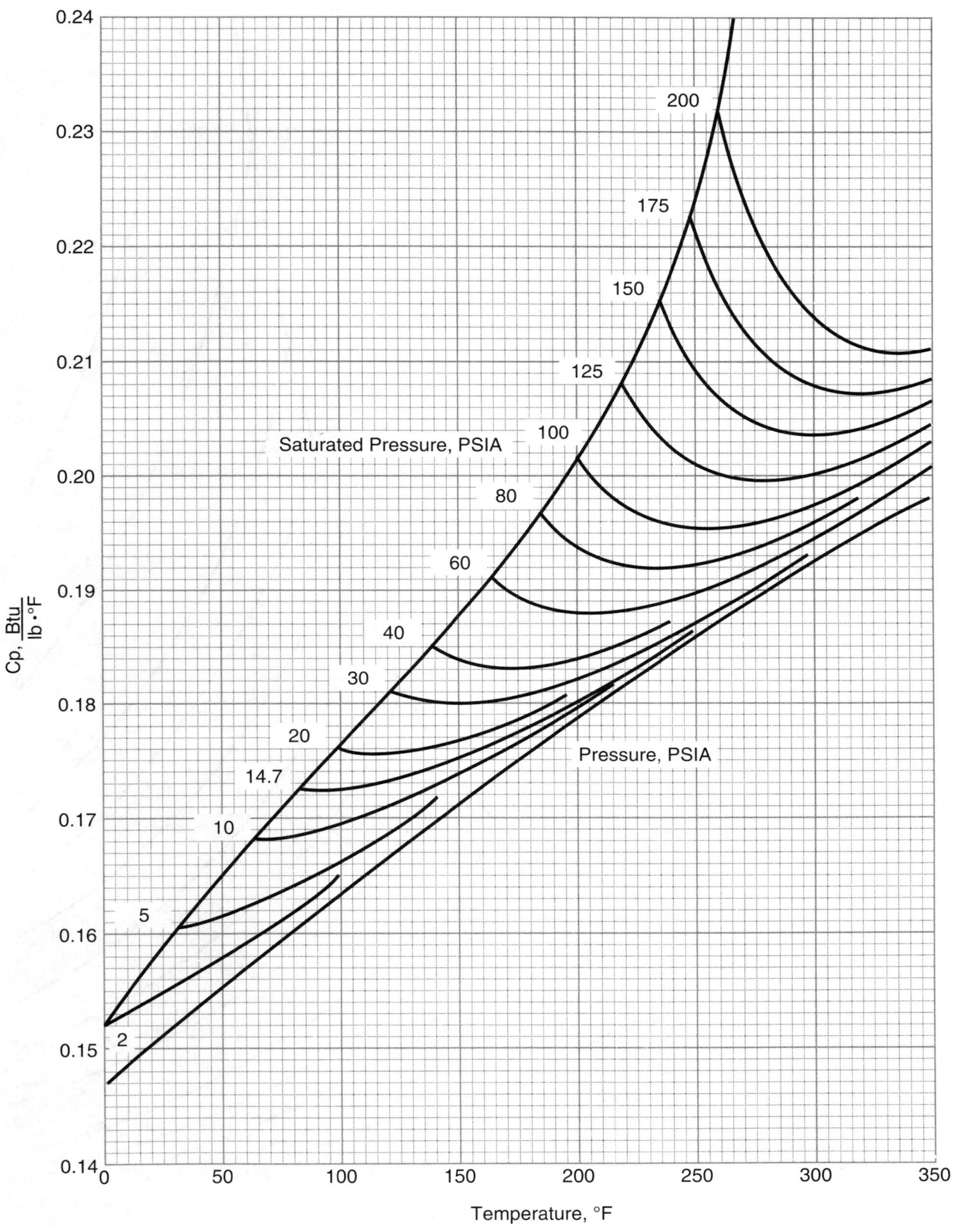

HCFC - 123 Vapor Heat Capacity Ratio

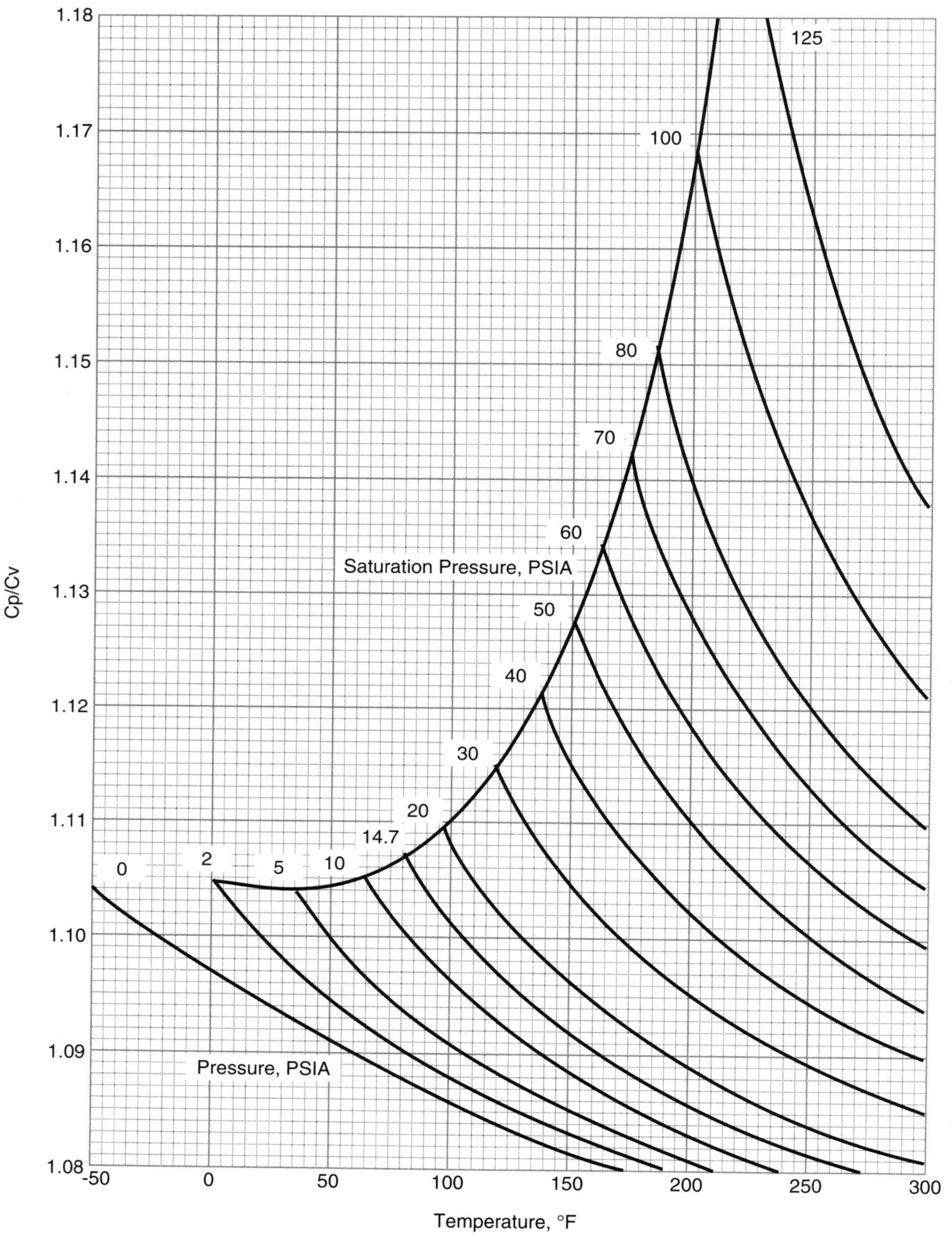

EQUATIONS FOR PROPERTY ESTIMATION

English Units

The measured data has been curve-fitted to obtain the following equations for estimation of properties within the ranges specified.

Liquid Viscosity in cP

HCFC-123: $\mu_l = -0.000000133T^3 + 0.00005259T^2 - 0.007978T + 0.79566$

HFC-134a: $\mu_l = -0.0000000376T^3 + 0.00001575T^2 - 0.00292T + 0.346317$

$(-70 \leq T \leq 200°F)$

Liquid Thermal Conductivity in Btu/hr ft °F

HCFC-123: $k_l = 0.0548 - 0.000104\ T$ $(-76 \leq T \leq 248°F)$

HFC-134a: $k_l = 0.06041 - 0.000166\ T$ $(-76 \leq T \leq 140°F)$

Liquid Heat Capacity in Btu/lbm °F

HCFC-123: $c_p = 0.2016 + 0.0004125\ T$ (for $T < 160°F$)

$$c_p = \exp\left[-580.035 + 119.419 \ln T + \frac{8262.6}{T} - 0.5637\ T + 0.000437\ T^2\right]$$

(for $160 \leq T \leq 350°F$)

HFC-134a: $c_p = 0.2935 + 0.000729\ T$ (for $T < 170$)

$$c_p = \exp\left[9776.1 - 1887.24 \ln T - \frac{168763}{T} + 5.40\ T - 0.000334\ T^2\right]$$

(for $170°F \leq T \leq 210°F$)

Vapor Viscosity in cP

HCFC-123: $\mu_v = 0.00956 + 0.0000179T$

HFC-134a: $\mu_v = 0.010338 + 0.0000214T$

$(100 \leq T \leq 300°F)$

Vapor Thermal Conductivity in Btu/Lb ft °F

HCFC-123: $k_v = 0.004465 + 0.000025\ T$ $(104 \leq T \leq 248°F)$

HFC-134a: $k_v = 0.006006 + 0.000031\ T$ $(32 \leq T \leq 248°F)$

Liquid Viscosity

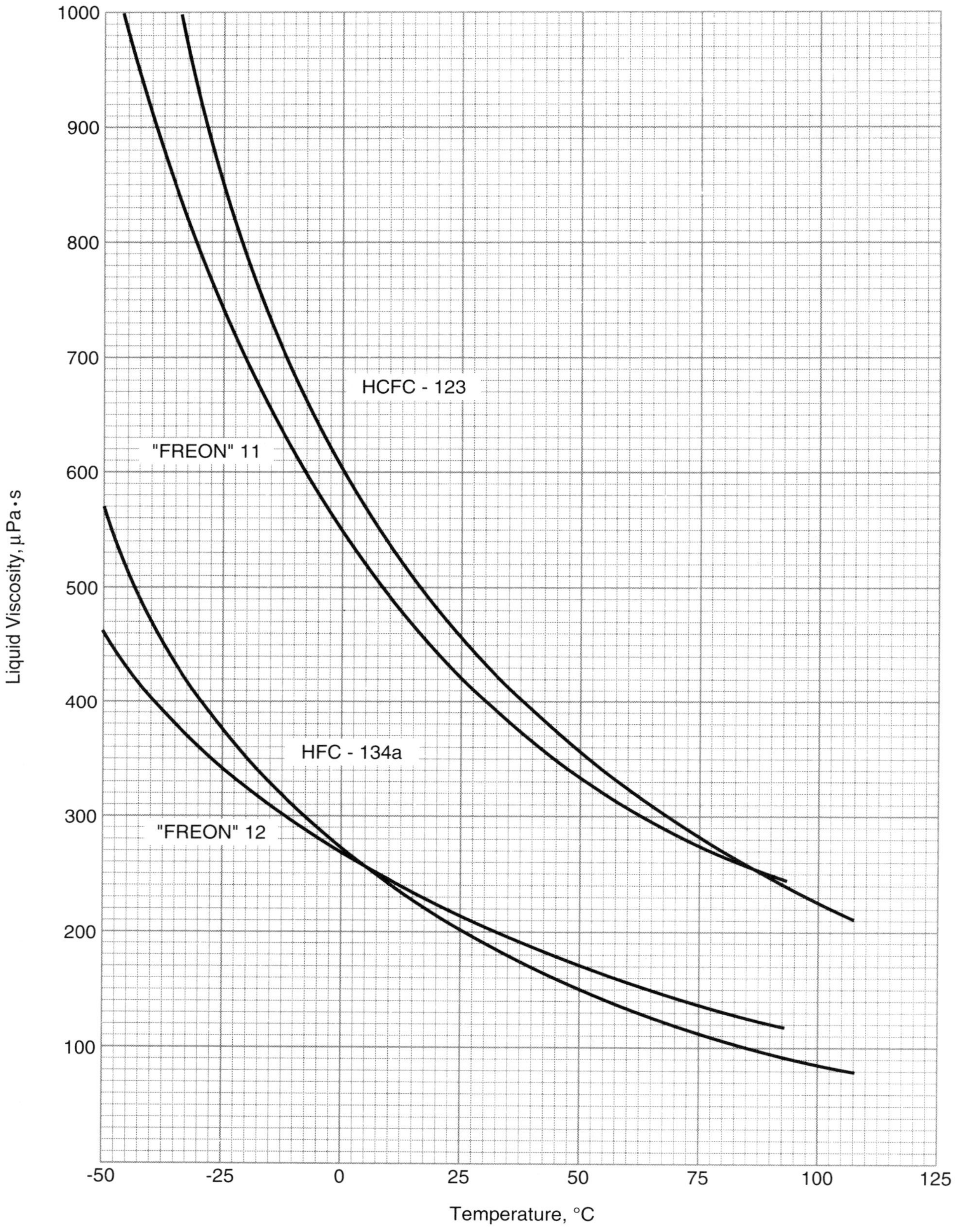

Liquid Thermal Conductivity

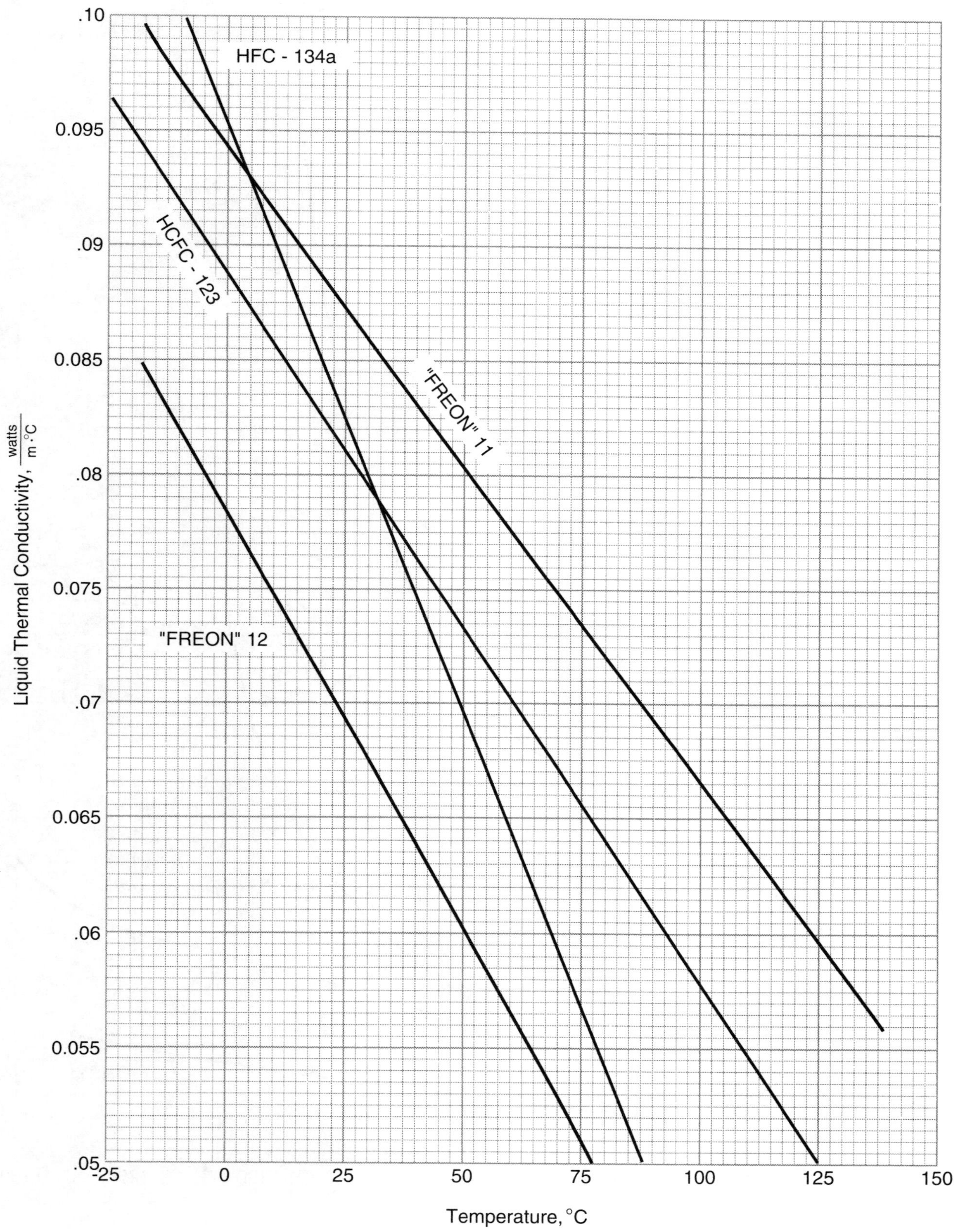

Saturated Liquid Heat Capacity

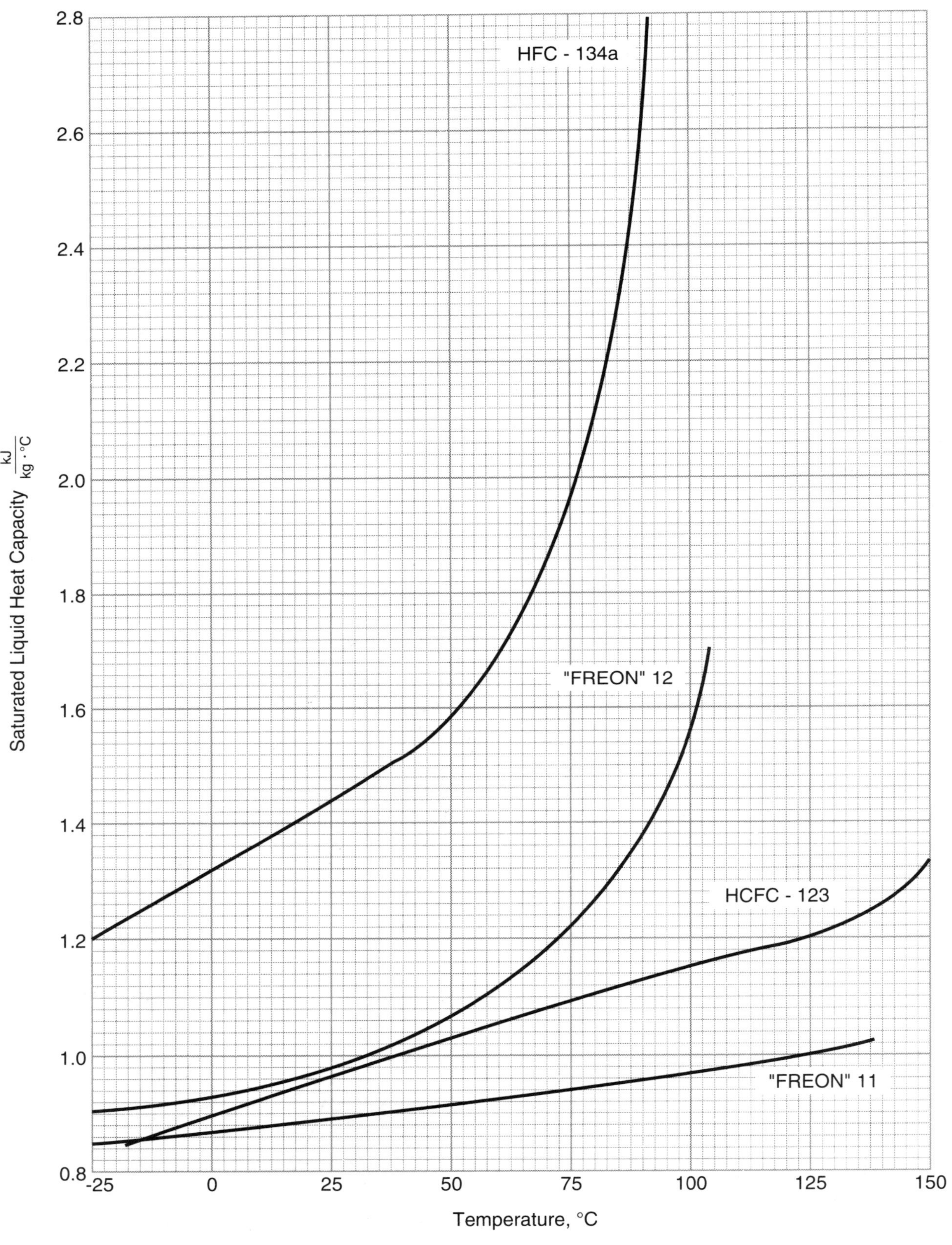

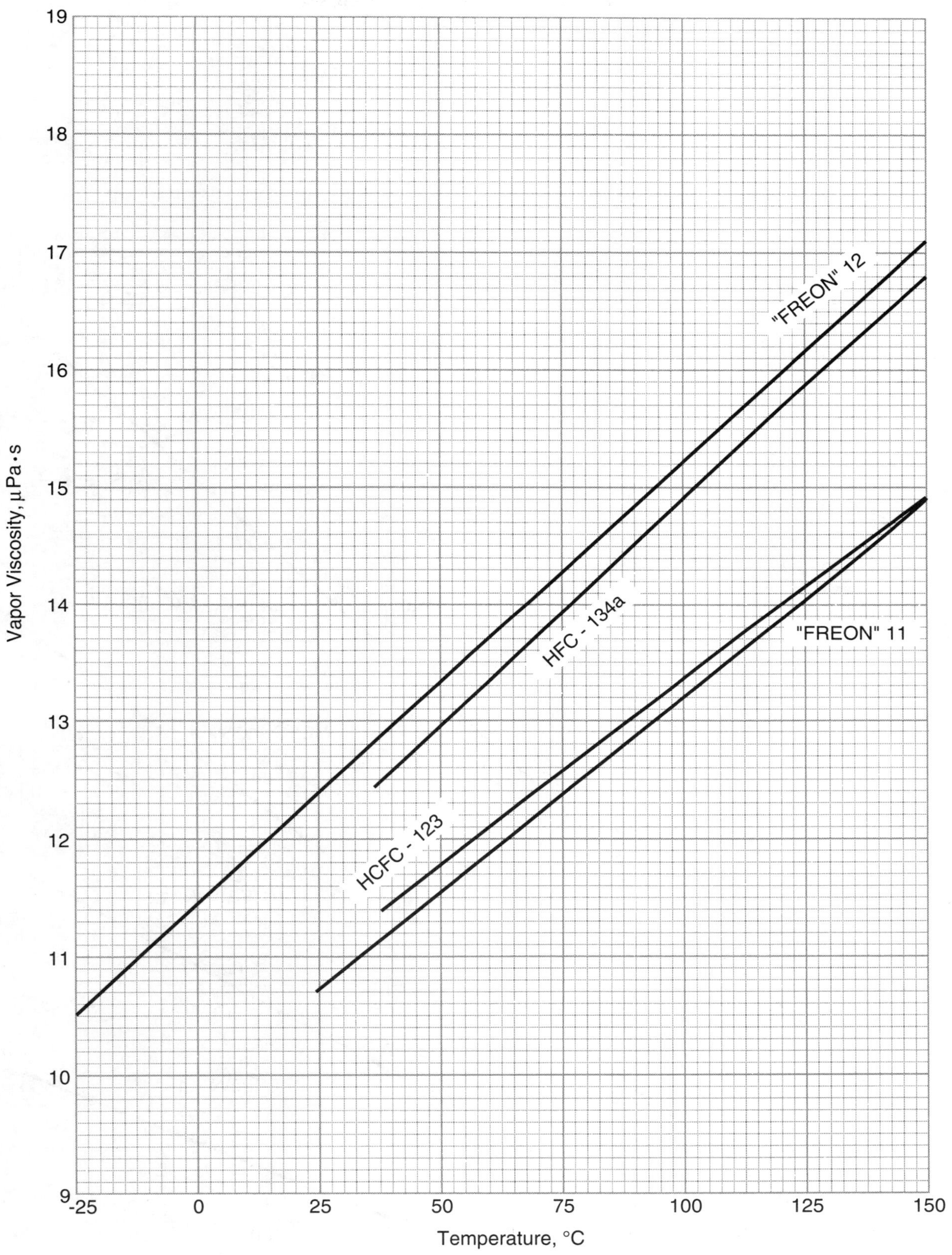
Vapor Viscosity at Atmospheric Pressure
19
18
17
16
15
14
13
12
11
10
9
-25
0
25
50
75
100
125
150
Temperature, °C
Vapor Viscosity, μPa•s
"FREON" 12
HFC - 134a
"FREON" 11
HCFC - 123

Vapor Thermal Conductivity at Atmospheric Pressure

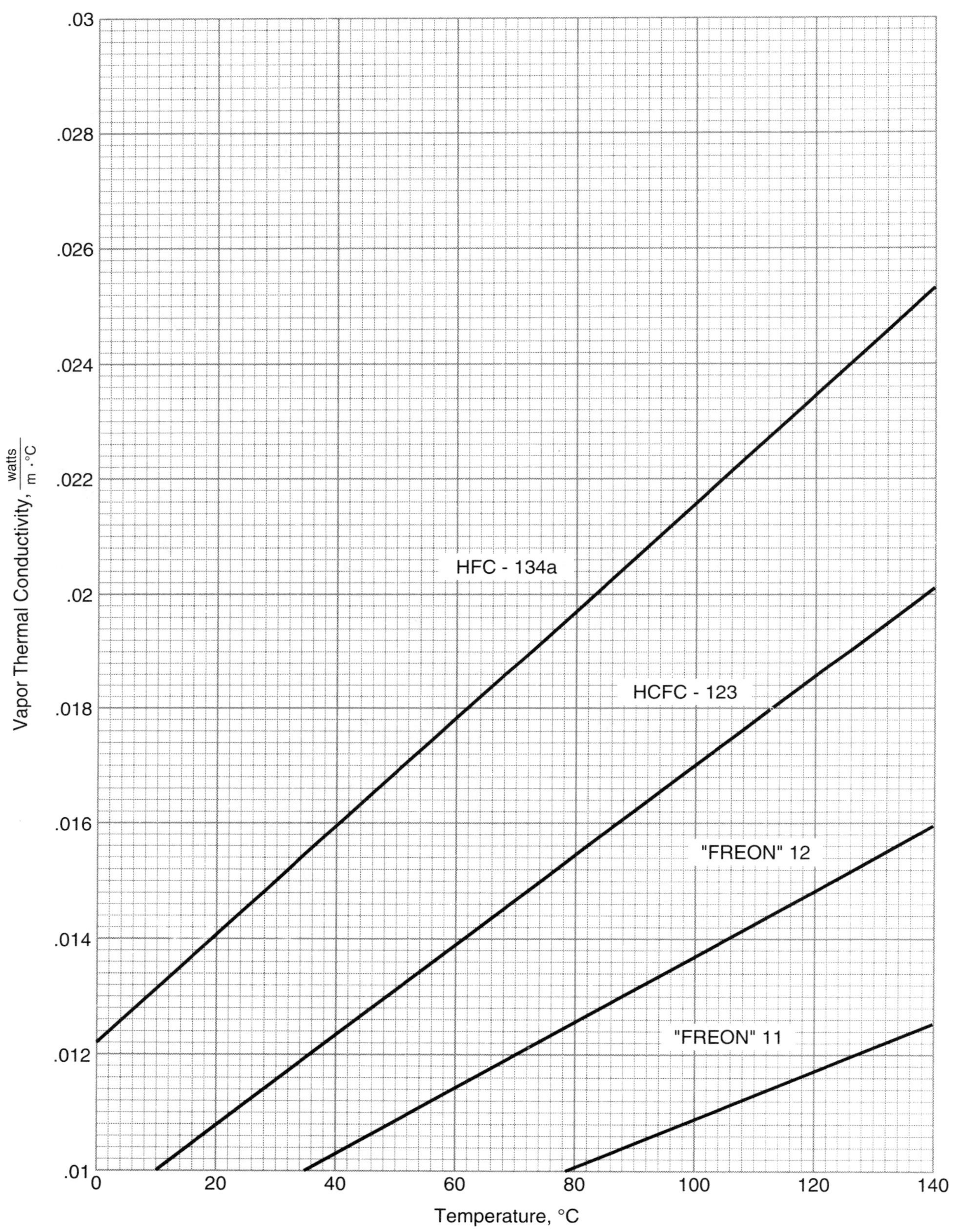

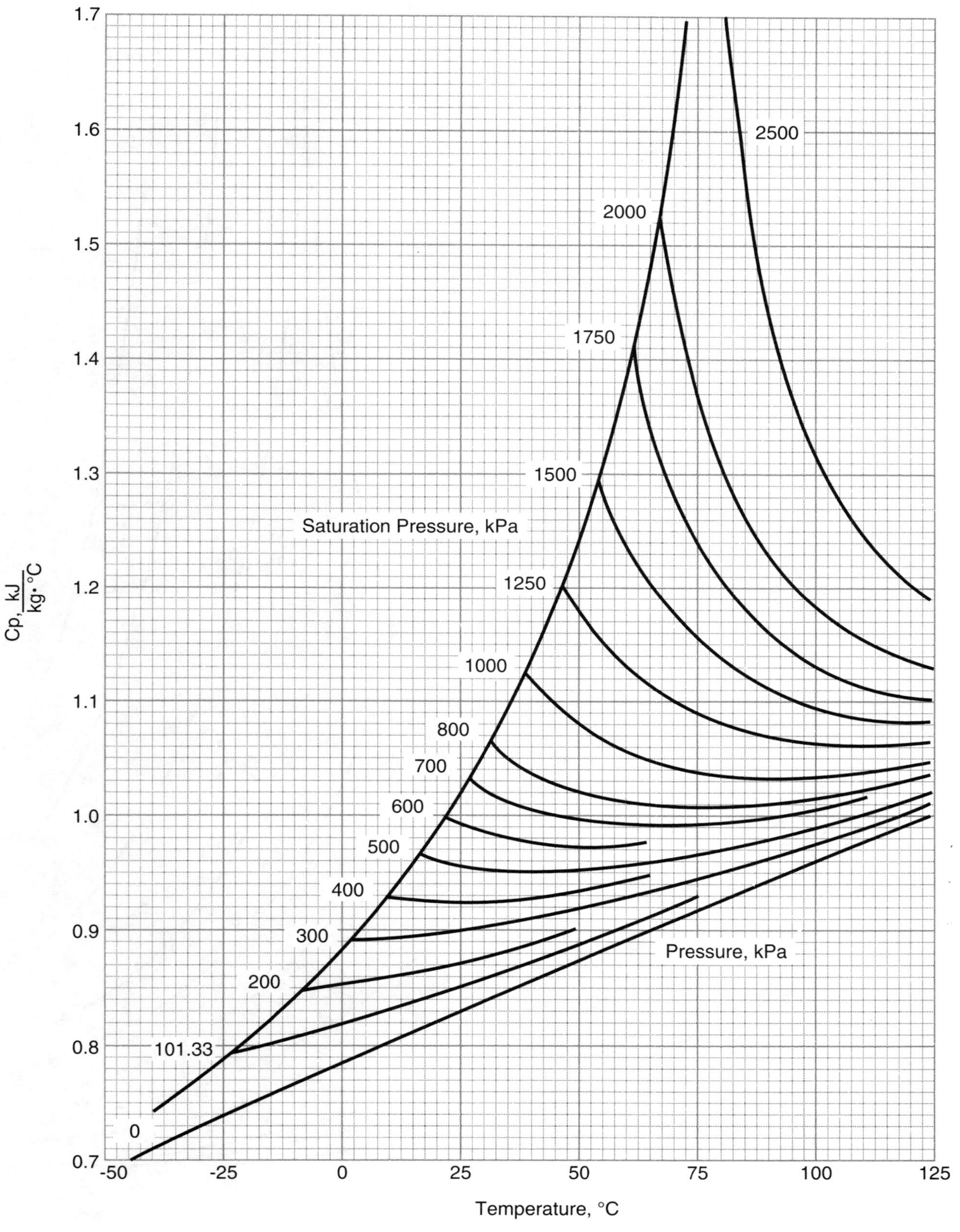

HFC - 134a Vapor Heat Capacity
1.7
1.6
1.5
1.4
1.3
1.2
1.1
1.0
0.9
0.8
0.7
Cp, kJ/kg·°C
-50
-25
0
25
50
75
100
125
Temperature, °C
Saturation Pressure, kPa
Pressure, kPa
2500
2000
1750
1500
1250
1000
800
700
600
500
400
300
200
101.33
0

HFC - 134a Vapor Heat Capacity Ratio

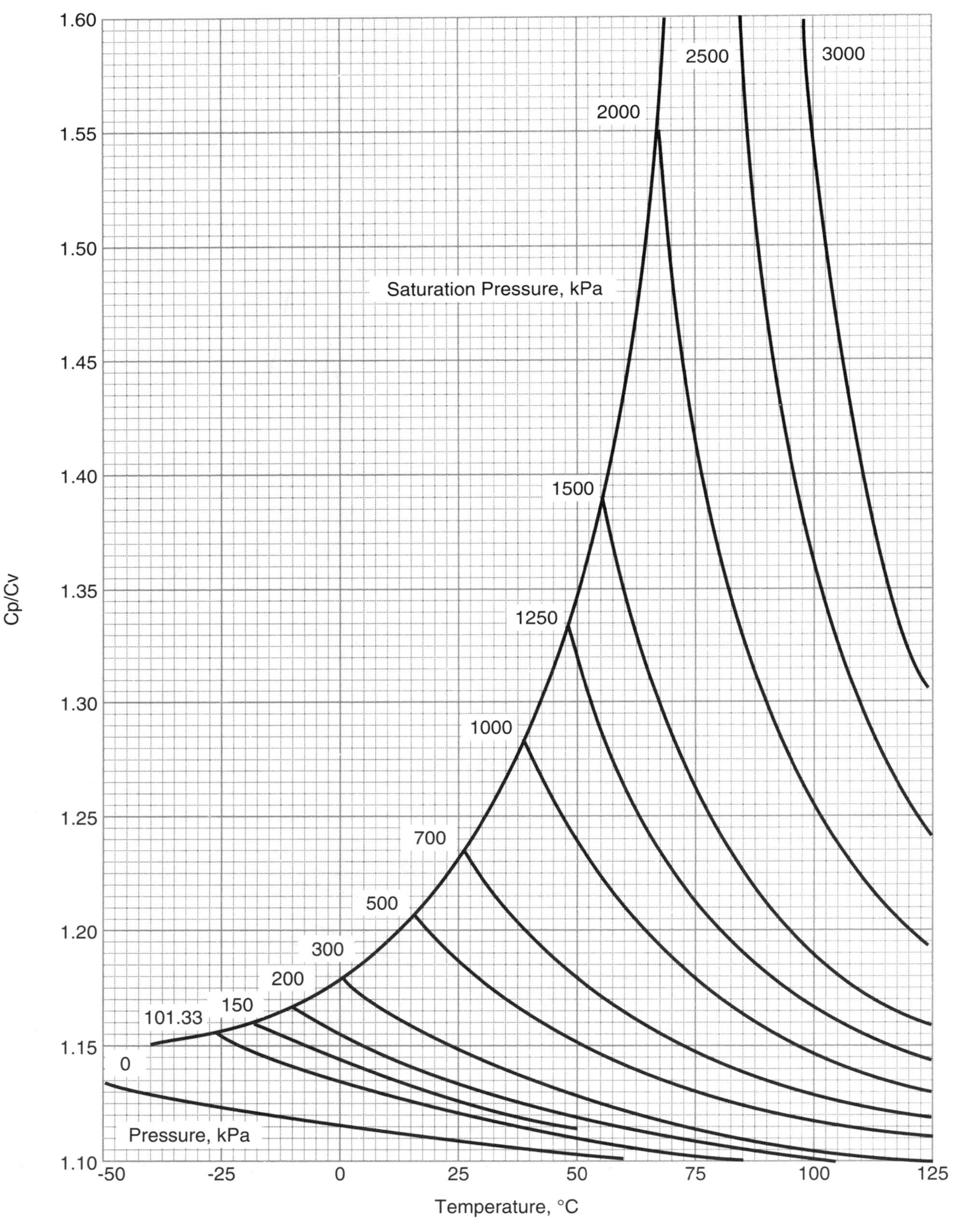

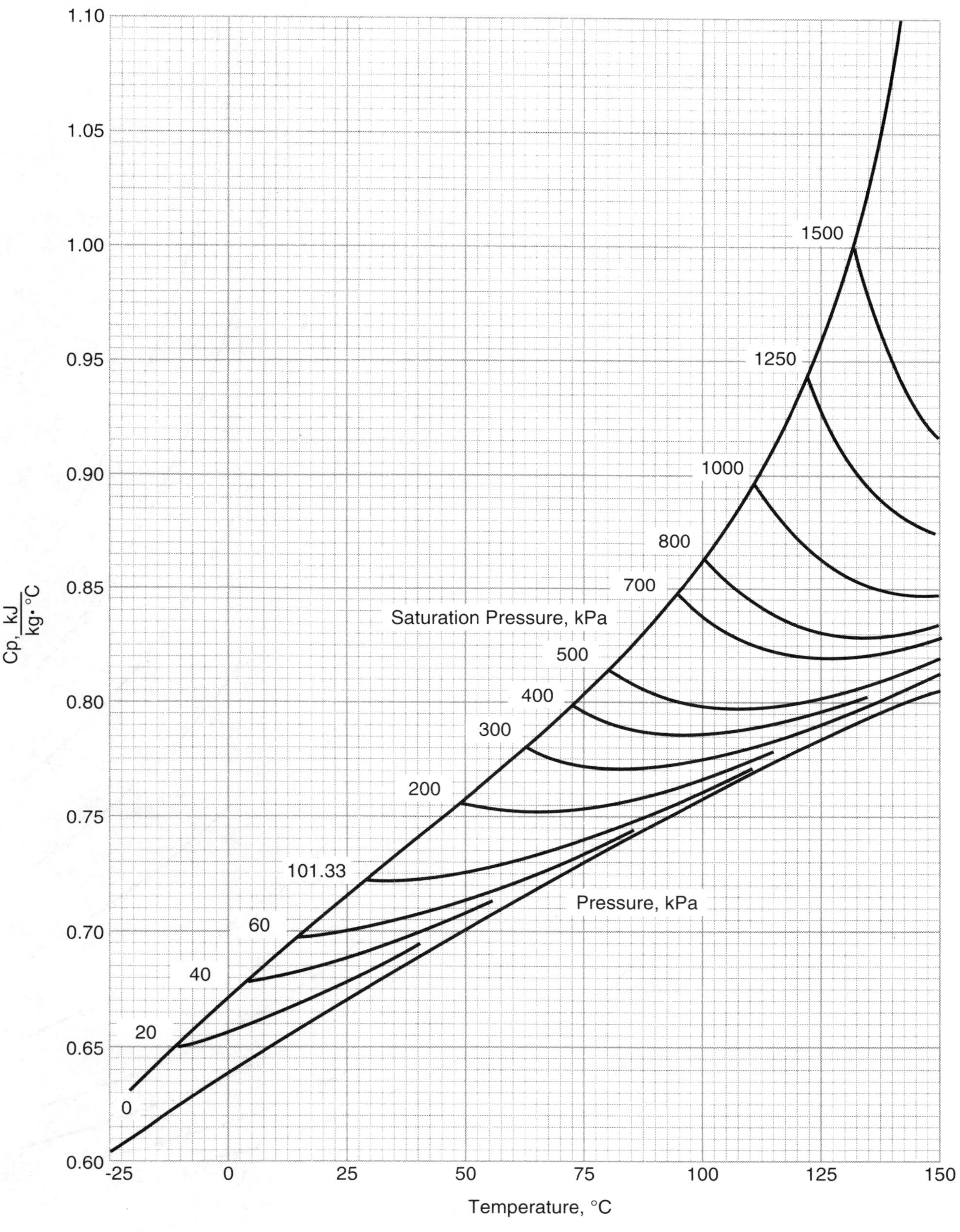
HCFC - 123 Vapor Heat Capacity
Cp, kJ/kg·°C
1.10
1.05
1.00
0.95
0.90
0.85
0.80
0.75
0.70
0.65
0.60
-25
0
25
50
75
100
125
150
Temperature, °C
Saturation Pressure, kPa
Pressure, kPa
0
20
40
60
101.33
200
300
400
500
700
800
1000
1250
1500

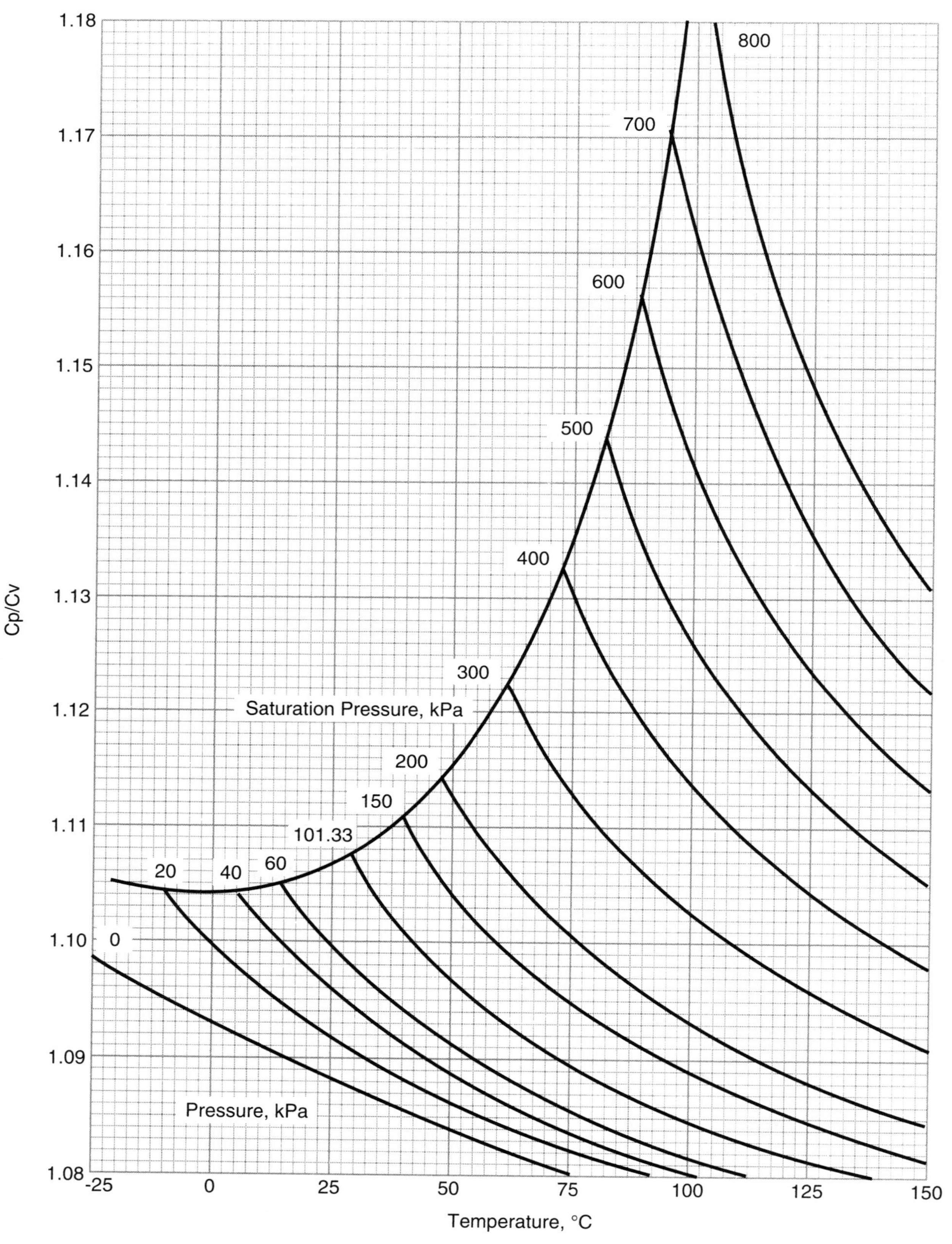
HCFC - 123 Vapor Heat Capacity Ratio
Cp/Cv
1.18
1.17
1.16
1.15
1.14
1.13
1.12
1.11
1.10
1.09
1.08
-25
0
25
50
75
100
125
150
Temperature, °C
Saturation Pressure, kPa
Pressure, kPa
0
20
40
60
101.33
150
200
300
400
500
600
700
800

EQUATIONS FOR PROPERTY ESTIMATION

Metric Units

The measured data has been curve-fitted to obtain the following equations for estimation of properties within the ranges specified.

Liquid Viscosity in μPa's

HCFC-123: $\mu_l = -0.0007765T^3 + 0.12886T^2 - 9.0295T + 589.72$

HFC-134a: $\mu_l = -0.0002191T^3 + 0.039304T^2 - 3.6494T + 267.67$

$(-57 \leq T \leq 93°C)$

Liquid Thermal Conductivity in W/m°C

HCFC-123: $k_l = 0.08908 - 0.000324\ T$ $(-60 \leq T \leq 120°C)$

HFC-134a: $k_l = 0.09537 - 0.000517\ T$ $(-60 \leq T \leq 60°C)$

Liquid Heat Capacity in kJ/kg °C

HCFC-123: $c_p = 0.9104 + 0.00257\ T$ (for $T < 90°C$)

$$c_p = \exp\left[-1515.07 + 354.086 \ln T + \frac{13952.48}{T} - 2.95702T + 0.004074T^2\right]$$

(for $90 \leq T \leq 176.7°C$)

HFC-134a: $c_p = 1.327 + 0.005509T$ (for $T \leq 75°C$)

$$c_p = \exp\left[1979.525 - 374.95752 \ln T - \frac{24459.904}{T} - 1.62846T + 0.015674T^2\right]$$

(for $75°C < T \leq 100°C$)

Vapor Viscosity in μ Pa's

HCFC-123: $\mu_V = 10.131 + 0.03224T$

HFC-134a: $\mu_V = 11.021 + 0.038599T$

$(38 \leq T \leq 149°C)$

Vapor Thermal Conductivity in W/m°C

HCFC-123: $k_V = 0.009171 + 0.000077\ T$ $(40 \leq T \leq 120°C)$

HFC-134a: $k_V = 0.01212 + 0.000096\ T$ $(0 \leq T \leq 120°C)$

Data Sources

All data on 134a and 123 were measured and provided by an independent source.

Data for 11 and 12 were taken from "Thermophysical Properties of Refrigerants" as published by:
American Society of Heating, Refrigerating and Air-Conditioning Engineers, Inc.
345 East 47th Street
New York, NY 10017

Contacts for Further Information

Du Pont Chemicals
Customer Service Center, B15305
Wilmington, DE 19898
1-800-441-9450
In Delaware: 774-2099

Europe
Du Pont de Nemours International S.A.
2 Chemin du Pavillon
PO Box 50
CH 1218 Le Grand-Saconnex
Geneva, Switzerland
41-22-717-5111

Canada
Du Pont Canada, Inc.
PO Box 2200, Streetsville
Mississauga, Ontario
L5M 2H3
(416) 821-3300

Mexico
Du Pont, S.A. de C.V. DUPSA
Homero 206
Col. Chapultepec Morales
C.P. 11570 Mexico, D.F.
52-5-250-8000

South America
Du Pont do Brasil S.A.
Alameda Itapicuru, 506
Alphaville 06454 Barueri
Sao Paulo, Brazil
55-11-421-8005

Du Pont Argentina S.A.
Casilla Correo 1888
Correo Central
1000 Buenos Aires, Argentina
54-1-311-8167

Australia
Du Pont Australia
PO Box 930
North Sydney, NSW, 2060
Australia
61-2-923-6111

Japan
Du Pont Mitsui Fluorochemicals Company Ltd.
Mitsui Seimei Building
2-3, Ohtemachi, 1-Chome
Chiyoda-Ku, Tokyo 100 Japan
81-03-3216-8471

Asia Pacific
Du Pont Taiwan
13th Floor, Hung Kuo Building
167 Tun Hwa North Road, Taipei
Taiwan 10590, R.O.C.
886-2-514-4400

Du Pont China Limited
PO Box TST 98851
1122 New World Office Building
(East Wing)
Salisbury Road
Tsim Sha Tsui
Kowloon, Hong Kong
852-734-5345

Du Pont Thailand
PO Box 2398
Bangkok 10501, Thailand
66-2-238-4361

Du Pont Korea
CPO Box 5972
9th Floor Kyobo Building
1,1-KA, Chong-Ro, Chongro-Ku
Seoul, Korea
82-2-734-3661

Du Pont Far East, Singapore
1 Maritime Square #07 01
World Trade Centre
Singapore, 0409
65-273-2244

Du Pont Far East, Phillippines
5th Floor, Solid Bank Building
777 Paseo de Roxas
Makati, Metro Manila
Phillippines
63-2-818-9911

Du Pont Far East, India
U 50 Hyatt Regency Delhi
Bhikaiji Cama Place, Ring Road
New Delhi, 110066
India
91-11-607-665/674-443

Printed in the U.S.A.

H-43855-1 9-92

alternative refrigerants

ART-16

Retrofit Guidelines for Suva 134a (Suva Cold MP) in Stationary Equipment

Introduction

As production of chlorofluorocarbon CFC-12 is reduced and ultimately phased out, environmentally acceptable replacement compounds are needed for use in existing CFC-12 medium-temperature refrigeration applications.

Suva Cold MP and Suva 134a are the DuPont brand names for HFC-134a, a commercially available hydrofluorocarbon (HFC) refrigerant for use as a long-term replacement for CFC-12 in new equipment and for retrofitting medium-temperature CFC-12 systems.

Using the retrofit guidelines summarized below, many CFC-12 systems using positive displacement compressors, i.e., reciprocating, rotary, screw, and scroll, can be retrofitted for use with HFC-134a. This allows the existing equipment to continue to operate safely and efficiently for the remainder of its useful life, even after CFC-12 is no longer available.

Properties and Safety

HFC-134a offers improved environmental properties versus CFC-12, with zero ozone depletion potential (ODP) and a significantly lower global warming potential (GWP). The properties of HFC-134a are summarized in *Table 1*. Like CFC-12, HFC-134a is nonflammable and has a low degree of toxicity.

Table 1
HFC-134a Physical Properties

Physical Property	Units	HFC-134a	CFC-12
Boiling Point at 1 atm	°C °F	–26.1 –14.9	–29.8 –21.6
Vapor Pressure Saturated Liquid at 25°C (77°F)	kPa psia	666.1 96.61	651.6 94.51
Liquid Density at 25°C (77°F)	kg/m^3 lb/ft^3	1206 72.28	1311 81.84
Density Saturated Vapor at 25°C (77°F)	kg/m^3 lb/ft^3	32.4 2.02	37.2 2.32
Ozone Depletion Potential as compared to CFC-12	CFC-12 = 1	0	1
Halocarbon Global Warming Potential as compared to CFC-11	CFC-11 = 1	0.28	3.1
Capacity as compared to CFC-12*	R-12 = 100%	99.7	100
Energy Efficiency as compared to CFC-12 (COP)*	R-12 = 100%	96.6	100

*Conditions: 1.7°C (35°F) evaporator; 54.4°C (130°F) condenser; 26.7°C (80°F) suction temperature

Tests have shown, however, that HFC-134a is combustible at pressures as low as 5.5 psig (139.3 kPa absolute) at 177°C (350°F) when mixed with air at concentrations generally greater than 60 volume percent air. At lower temperatures, higher pressures are required for combustibility. Equipment should **never** be leak tested with a pressurized mixture of HFC-134a and air. HFC-134a may be safely pressured with dry nitrogen.

Refer to DuPont Bulletin P-134a (H-45945-1) for more detailed information on properties, uses, storage, and handling. Refer to the Material Safety Data Sheet (MSDS) for additional safety information.

Selection of Refrigerant

HFC-134a is recommended for use as a retrofit refrigerant for CFC-12 applications having evaporator temperatures of –7°C (20°F) and above, making it suitable for use in such applications as:

- Dairy and produce cases
- Commercial refrigeration
- Air conditioning
- Medium-temperature appliances
- Chillers

HFC-134a may be used in existing equipment at lower evaporator temperatures, but may exhibit reduced capacity versus CFC-12 without modifications to the compressor.

Other alternative refrigerants are available for retrofitting over the entire temperature range of CFC-12 refrigeration applications. For CFC-12 evaporator temperatures from –43° to –23°C (–45° to –10°F), Suva MP66 is recommended. For –23°C (–10°F) and above, Suva MP39 is preferred.

Retrofitting with Suva MP refrigerants is cost effective in many situations because flushing is usually not required to remove residual mineral oil. Refer to DuPont Bulletin ART-5 (H-42446-2) for information on retrofitting with Suva MP39 and MP66 and Bulletin P-MP (H-45944-2) for more detailed information on their uses and properties. For chiller retrofits using HFC-134a, refer to DuPont Bulletin ART-3 (H-42444-1).

For assistance in determining which alternative is right for your application, contact the compressor manufacturer, equipment manufacturer, or a DuPont distributor.

Lubricants

Lubricant selection is based upon many factors, including compressor wear characteristics, material compatibility, and oil return to the compressor (lubricant/refrigerant miscibility). In order to maintain the same miscibility as CFC-12/mineral oil, a lubricant change is required when retrofitting to HFC-134a because HFC-134a is not miscible with mineral oil. Polyol ester lubricants are recommended for use in most HFC-134a systems and are available through DuPont distributors. There are many polyol ester lubricant manufacturers; contact the compressor manufacturer or equipment manufacturer for specific lubricant recommendations for your system.

Special care should be taken when handling polyol ester lubricants because of their tendency to absorb water. Contact with air should be minimized and the lubricant should be stored in a sealed container.

To achieve equivalent miscibility when retrofitting CFC-12/mineral oil systems to HFC-134a/polyol ester, the residual mineral oil should constitute no more than about 5 weight percent of the total lubricant in the system. Allowable residual mineral oil is highly dependent on system configuration and operating conditions. If the retrofitted system shows signs of poor heat transfer in the evaporator or poor oil return to the compressor, it may be necessary to further reduce the residual mineral oil. A series of successive lubricant changes using polyol esters can normally reduce the mineral oil concentration to low levels. Lubricant manufacturers are developing field test methods to determine the concentration of mineral oil in polyol ester lubricant. Contact the lubricant manufacturer for the recommended test method.

Filter Drier

It is recommended that the filter drier be changed during the retrofit, as is routine practice following system maintenance. There are three types of filter driers commonly used in CFC-12 equipment:

- Solid core driers, in which the molecular sieve desiccant is dispersed within a solid core binder.
- Loose filled driers, which contain only the molecular sieve desiccant.
- Compacted bead driers, which also contain only the molecular sieve desiccant, but where the desiccant is compacted in the drier by mechanical pressure, usually a spring.

For solid core driers, consult the drier manufacturer for their recommended drier for use with HFC-134a. Some existing models of solid core driers, such as the Sporlan Catch All® or Alco ADK, are compatible with HFC-134a.

The XH-7 or XH-9 molecular sieve desiccants manufactured by UOP or the MS 592 or MS 594 molecular sieves manufactured by Grace are recommended for use in loose filled driers with HFC-134a. Equivalent molecular sieves produced by other manufacturers may also be used.

Compacted bead driers may use either XH-6, XH-7, or XH-9 desiccants or MS 592 or MS 594. Consult the drier manufacturer for their recommendations.

System Modification

HFC-134a provides similar energy efficiency and capacity to CFC-12 with a lower discharge temperature and slightly higher discharge pressure. As a result, minimal system modifications are anticipated when retrofitting CFC-12 systems with HFC-134a.

The chemical compatibility of plastics and elastomers should be considered before retrofitting to HFC-134a and polyol ester. Testing shows that there will be no one family of elastomers or plastics that will work with all the alternative refrigerants. It is recommnednded that gaskets, shaft seals, and o-rings be reviewed with the equipment manufacturer before retrofit. In the absence of other information, it is recommended that Buna-N, Hypalon® 48 synthetic rubber, neoprene, or Nordel® hydrocarbon rubber be used. See Bulletin P-134a for more information on the compatibility of elastomers and plastics with HFC-134a.

It is also important to note that HFC-134a was not designed for use in conjunction with other refrigerants. Adding HFC-134a to an existing CFC-12 charge can form a high-pressure azeotrope, which could cause system damage as well as undesirable performance.

Overview of Retrofit Process

Retrofit of an existing CFC-12 system with HFC-134a can be accomplished using service practices and equipment commonly used by trained mechanics or service contractors in the field.

The key steps involved in the retrofit are:

- Isolate the compressor from the system, remove the mineral oil, and replace with polyol ester lubricant. Run system with CFC-12 for 48 to 72 hours. Repeat these steps at least two more times. (In systems where the compressor cannot be isolated, the refrigerant charge will have to be recovered before each lubricant change.)
- Recover CFC-12 charge from the system.
- Replace filter/drier with new drier compatible with HFC-134a.
- Charge system with HFC-134a.
- Start system and adjust charge and/or controls to achieve desired operation.

For the majority of systems, the compressor lubricant change, a filter/drier change, and a possible adjustment to the superheat setting (in systems with expansion valves) will be the only system modifications required in a retrofit to HFC-134a. For systems that are still under warranty, we recommend contacting the equipment or compressor manufacturer prior to performing the retrofit. Some equipment or compressor warranties may be impacted by a change from the refrigerant or lubricant originally specified for the system or compressor.

Equipment and Supplies Needed for Retrofit

- Safety equipment (gloves, glasses)
- Manifold gauges
- Thermocouples to read line temperatures
- Vacuum pump
- Leak detection equipment
- Scale
- Recovery unit (RRU30 by Refrigerant Recovery Technologies, Inc. is recommended. See your DuPont authorized distributor.)
- Recovery cylinder
- Container for recovered lubricant
- Replacement lubricant
- Replacement refrigerant
- Replacement filter/drier
- Labels indicating the refrigerant and lubricant charged to the system

Retrofit Procedure

Summarized below is a more detailed discussion of the recommended procedures for retrofitting a CFC-12 system to HFC-134a:

1. **Baseline Data with CFC-12.** For service contractors performing their initial retrofits with HFC-134a, it is recommended that system performance data be collected while CFC-12 remains in the system. Check for correct refrigerant charge and operating conditions. The baseline of temperatures and pressures with the correct

charge of CFC-12 at various points in the system (evaporator, condenser, compressor suction and discharge, expansion device, etc.) will be useful when optimizing operation of the system with HFC-134a. A **System Data Sheet** is attached for recording these baseline data.

2. **Drain/Charge System Lubricant.** Where mineral oil is the existing lubricant in the system, it will have to be drained. This may require removing the compressor from the system, particularly with small hermetic compressors that have no oil drain. In this case, the lubricant can be drained from the suction line of the compressor. In most small systems, 90–95% of the lubricant can be removed from the compressor in this manner. Larger systems may require drainage from additional points in the system, particularly low spots around the evaporator, to remove the majority of the lubricant. In systems with an oil separator, any lubricant present in the separator should also be drained.

   In all cases, *measure* the volume of lubricant removed from the system. Compare to the compressor/system specifications to ensure that the majority of lubricant has been removed. Polyol ester lubricant is recommended for use with HFC-134a. In order to achieve equivalent miscibility to CFC-12/mineral oil, the residual mineral oil should be about 5 weight percent or less of the total lubricant used in the system. In larger systems, the amount of residual mineral oil can be reduced by using a flushing technique. Three to five lubricant flushes may be required. Lubricant flushes involve:

   - Draining existing lubricant from the system, as described above.
   - Selecting a polyol ester lubricant with similar viscosity to the existing lubricant.
   - Charging an amount of polyol ester equal to the amount of lubricant removed.
   - Running the system with CFC-12 to mix the polyol ester and existing lubricant. A total of 48 to 72 hours of operation may be required.

   Repeat these steps two more times. DuPont experience is that three lubricant flushes are usually sufficient to ensure satisfactory system operation. If poor evaporator heat transfer or oil return are noted on start-up, an additional lubricant flush should correct the situation. If complete draining of lubricant from the system is difficult, it may be desirable to sample the lubricant in the system after three flushes and test it for percent mineral oil.

3. **Remove CFC-12 Charge.** CFC-12 should be removed from the system and collected in a recovery cylinder using a recovery device capable of pulling 10–20 in. Hg vacuum (34–67 kPa, 0.34–0.67 bar). If the correct CFC-12 charge size for the system is not known, weigh the amount of refrigerant removed, as the initial quantity of HFC-134a charged to the system will be determined from this figure.

4. **Reinstall Compressor.** (If removed from system in Step 2.) Use normal service practices.

5. **Replace Filter Drier.** It is routine practice to replace the filter drier following system maintenance. Replacement driers that are compatible with HFC-134a are available.

   For loose filled driers, the XH-7 or XH-9 molecular sieve desiccant manufactured by UOP are recommended for use with HFC-134a. Compacted bead driers may use either XH-6, XH-7, or XH-9 desiccant. Equivalent molecular sieves produced by other manufacturers, such as MS 592 or MS 594 by Grace, may be used.

   For solid core driers, consult the drier manufacturer for their recommendations. Some models of solid-core driers manufactured in the U.S., such as the Sporlan Catch All® or Alco ADK, are compatible with HFC-134a.

6. **Reconnect System and Evacuate.** Use normal service practices. To remove air or other non-condensables from the system, evacuate the system to near full vacuum (29.9 in. Hg vacuum/500 microns/0.14 kPa/0.0014 bar).

   Leak Check System. Use normal service practices. If a leak detector is used consult the leak detector manufacturer for unit's sensitivity to HFC-134a. Reevacuate system following leak check if necessary.

7. **Charge System with HFC-134a.** HFC-134a can be charged to the system from either the vapor or liquid phase of the cylinder (the same as CFC-12). Returnable cylinders of HFC-134a are equipped with dip tubes allowing liquid to be removed from the cylinder when the cylinder is in the upright position; 13.6 kg (30 lb) **Dispos-a-Can**® cylinders are **not equipped with dip tubes.** *Liquid and vapor charging positions are indicated by arrows on the cylinder or cylinder box.*

   The refrigerant system will require less weight of HFC-134a than CFC-12. The optimum charge will vary depending on the operating conditions, size of the evaporator and condenser, size of the receiver (if present), and the length of pipe or tubing runs in the system. For most systems, the optimum charge will be 90–95% by weight of the original equipment manufacturer CFC-12 charge.

It is recommended that the system be initially charged with about 90% by weight of the correct CFC-12 charge. Add the initial charge to the high-pressure side of the system (compressor **not** running). When the system and cylinder pressures equilibrate, load the remainder of the refrigerant to the suction side of the system (compressor running). Liquid refrigerant should never enter the suction side of the compressor as this can damage the compressor. If removing liquid from the cylinder and charging to the suction of the compressor, a throttling valve can be used to ensure that the liquid is converted to vapor prior to entering the system.

8. **Start Up System and Adjust Charge.** Start up the system, and let conditions stabilize. If the system is undercharged, add additional HFC-134a in small amounts until the system conditions reach the desired levels. Refer to the HFC-134a Pressure-Temperature Chart (*Table 2*) to compare system suction pressure and evaporator temperature with the suction pressure and evaporator temperature for CFC-12. In general, the suction pressure for HFC-134a will run from 1 psi (7 kPa/0.07 bar) to 3 psi (21 kPa/0.21 bar) lower than the suction pressure for CFC-12. HFC-134a will have higher discharge pressures and lower discharge temperatures when compared to CFC-12 operation. A typical increase in discharge pressure would be from 15 to 30 psi (103–207 kPa/1.03–2.07 bar); a typical decrease in discharge temperature would be 3°C (5°F).

   Label Components and System. After retrofitting the system with HFC-134a, label the system components to identify the type of refrigerant (HFC-134a) and lubricant in the system so that the proper refrigerant and lubricant will be used to service the equipment in the future. Suva refrigerant identification labels are available from DuPont.

Summary

With the phaseout of CFCs, existing refrigeration equipment will need to be replaced with new equipment or retrofitted with alternative refrigerants. Using the procedures described above, existing CFC-12 refrigeration systems can be retrofitted for use with HFC-134a, allowing them to continue in service for the remainder of their useful life.

Attached is a **Retrofit Checklist, System Data Sheet**, and **Pressure-Temperature Chart** for HFC-134a to assist you in the retrofit process.

Table 2
Pressure-Temperature Chart
HFC-134a Saturation Properties
(Engineering and SI Units)

Pressure (psig)	HFC-134a Saturation Temperature (°F)	Pressure (kPa)	HFC-134a Saturation Temperature (°C)
15*	–40	25	–53
10*	–30	50	–40
5*	–22	75	–32
0	–15	100	–26
5	–3	125	–21
10	7	150	–17
15	15	175	–13
20	22	200	–10
25	29	225	–7
30	35	250	–4
35	40	275	–2
40	45	300	1
45	50	325	3
50	54	350	5
55	58	375	7
60	62	400	9
65	66	450	12
70	69	500	16
75	73	550	19
80	76	600	22
85	79	650	24
90	82	700	27
95	85	750	29
100	88	800	31
110	93	900	36
120	98	1000	39
130	103	1200	46
140	107	1400	52
150	112	1600	58
165	118	1800	63
180	123	2000	67
195	129	2200	72
210	134	2400	76
225	139	2600	79
240	143	2800	83
255	148	3000	86
270	152	3200	89
285	156	3400	93
300	160	3600	95

*Inches of Hg, vacuum

Checklist for Suva HFC-134a Retrofit

________ Establish baseline performance with CFC-12. (See data sheet for recommended data.)

________ Consult the original equipment manufacturer of the system components for their recommendation on the following:
- – Plastics compatibility.
- – Elastomers compatibility.
- – Lubricant (viscosity, manufacturer, additives).
- – Retrofit procedure to sustain warranty.

________ Drain lubricant charge from the refrigerant system (unless polyol ester lubricant is already in the system).*
- – Remove 90–95% of lubricant from the system.
- – Measure amount of lubricant removed and record. ____________

________ Charge polyol ester lubricant using amount equivalent to amount of mineral oil removed. Run system with CFC-12 for 48–72 hours minimum.

________ Repeat lubricant drain and ester charging two more times or until mineral oil content is less than 5%.

________ Remove CFC-12 charge from system. (Need 10–20 in. Hg vacuum [34–67 kPa/0.34–0.67 bar] to remove charge.)

________ Replace filter drier with new drier approved for use with HFC-134a.

________ Reconnect system and evacuate with vacuum pump. (Evacuate to full vacuum [29.9 in. Hg vacuum/0.14 kPa/0.0014 bar].)

________ Leak check system. (Reevacuate system following leak check.)

________ Charge system with HFC-134a.
- – Initially charge 90% by weight of original equipment manufacturer specified CFC-12 charge.
- – Amount of refrigerant charged: ______________

________ Start up equipment and adjust charge until desired operating conditions are achieved.
- – If low in charge, add in increments of 2–3% of original CFC-12 charge.
- – Amount of refrigerant charged: ______________

Total Refrigerant Charged: ______________

________ Label components and system for type of refrigerant (HFC-134a) and lubricant (polyol ester).

Conversion is complete!!

*CFC-12 charge should only be removed if compressor cannot be isolated from the rest of the system.

System Data Sheet

Type of System/Location: ____________________

Equipment Mfg.: ____________________
Model No.: ____________________
Serial No.: ____________________
CFC-12 Charge Size: ____________________

Compressor Mfg.: ____________________
Model No.: ____________________
Serial No.: ____________________
Original Lubricant:
Type/Mfg.: ____________________
Charge Size: ____________________
New Lubricant:
Type/Mfg.: ____________________
1st Charge Size: ____________________
2nd Charge Size: ____________________
Additional Charge Size: ____________________

Drier Mfg.: ____________________
Model No.: ____________________

Drier Type (check one):
Loose Fill: ____________________
Solid Core: ____________________

Condenser Cooling Medium (Air/Water): ____________________

Expansion Device (check one): Capillary Tube: ____________________
Expansion Valve: ____________________

If Expansion Valve:
Manufacturer: ____________________
Model No.: ____________________
Control/Set Point: ____________________
Location of Sensor: ____________________

Other System Controls (e.g., head pressure control), Describe: ____________________

____

(Circle units used where applicable)

Date/Time				
Refrigerant				
Charge Size (lb, oz/g)				
Ambient Temp. (°F/°C)				
Relative Humidity				
Compressor:				
Suction T (°F/°C)				
Suction P (psig, psia/kPa, bar)				
Discharge T (°F/°C)				
Discharge P (psig, psia/kPa, bar)				
Box/CaseT (°F/°C)				
Evaporator:				
Refrigerant Inlet T (°F/°C)				
Refrigerant Outlet T (°F/°C)				
Coil Air/H_2O In T (°F/°C)				
Coil Air/H_2O Out T (°F/°C)				
Refrigerant T at Superht. Ctl. Pt. (°F/°C)				
Condenser:				
Refrigerant Inlet T (°F/°C)				
Refrigerant Outlet T (°F/°C)				
Coil Air/H_2O In T (°F/°C)				
Coil Air/H_2O Out T (°F/°C)				
Exp. Device Inlet T (°F/°C)				
Motor Amps				
Run/Cycle Time				

Comments: ____________________

____

For Sales Information:

DuPont Fluorochemicals
Customer Service Center, B-15305
Wilmington, DE 19898
U.S.A.
(302) 774-2099
800-441-9442

For Technical Information:

Fluorochemicals Laboratory
Wilmington, DE 19898
U.S.A.
(302) 999-3129
800-582-5606

Europe

DuPont de Nemours
International S.A.
2 Chemin du Pavillon
P.O. Box 50
CH-1218 Le Grand-Saconnex
Geneva, Switzerland
41-22-717-5111

Canada

DuPont Canada, Inc.
P.O. Box 2200, Streetsville
Mississauga, Ontario
Canada
L5M 2H3
(905) 821-3300

Mexico

DuPont, S.A. de C.V.
Homero 206
Col. Chapultepec Morales
C.P 11570 Mexico, D.F.
52-5-250-8000

South America

DuPont do Brasil S.A.
Alameda Itapecuru, 506
Alphaville 06400 Barueri
São Paulo, Brazil
55-11-421-8509

DuPont Argentina S.A.
Casilla Correo 1888
Correo Central
1000 Buenos Aires, Argentina
54-1-311-8167

Pacific

DuPont Australia
P.O. Box 930
North Sydney, NSW 2060
Australia
61-2-923-6165

Japan

Mitsui DuPont Fluorochemicals
Co., Ltd.
Mitsui Seimei Bldg.
2-3, 1-Chome Ohtemachi
Chiyoda-Ku, Tokyo 100 Japan
81-3-3216-8451

Asia

DuPont Taiwan
P.O. Box 81-777
Taipei, Taiwan
886-2-514-4400

DuPont Asia Pacific Limited
P.O. Box TST 98851
Tsim Sha Tsui
Kowloon, Hong Kong
852-734-5345

DuPont Thailand
P.O. Box 2398
Bangkok 10501, Thailand
66-2-238-4361

DuPont China Ltd.
Rm. 1704, Union Bldg.
100 Yenan Rd. East
Shanghai, PR China 200 002
Phone: 86-21-328-3738
Telex: 33448 DCLSH CN
Fax: 86-21-320-2304

DuPont Far East Inc.
P.O. Box 12396
50776 Kuala Lumpur, Malaysia
Phone: 60-3-232-3522
Telex: (784) 30391 DUFE M
Fax: 60-3-238-7250

DuPont Korea Ltd.
C.P.O. Box 5972
Seoul, Korea
82-2-721-5114

DuPont Singapore Pte. Ltd.
1 Maritime Square #07 01
World Trade Centre
Singapore 0409
65-273-2244

DuPont Far East, Philippines
5th Floor, Solid Bank Bldg.
777 Paseo de Roxas
Makati, Metro Manila
Philippines
63-2-818-9911

DuPont Far East Inc.
7A Murray's Gate Road
Alwarpet
Madras, 600 018, India
91-44-454-029

DuPont Far East Inc.—Pakistan
9 Khayaban-E-Shaheen
Defence Phase 5
Karachi, Pakistan
92-21-533-350

DuPont Far East Inc.
P.O. Box 2553/Jkt
Jakarta 10001, Indonesia
62-21-517-800

(4/94) 235703B Printed in U.S.A.
[Replaces: H-47761-1]
Reorder No.: H-47761-2

P-123

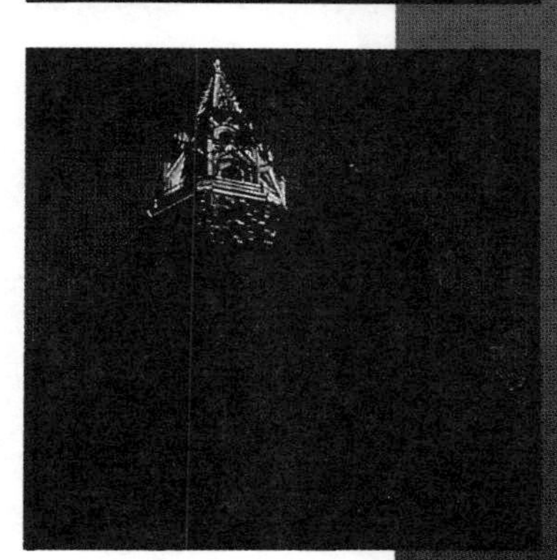

DuPont HCFC-123

Properties, Uses, Storage and Handling

SUVA® 123 refrigerant

SUVA® *Centri-LP* refrigerant

HCFC-123

Properties, Uses, Storage and Handling

Table of Contents

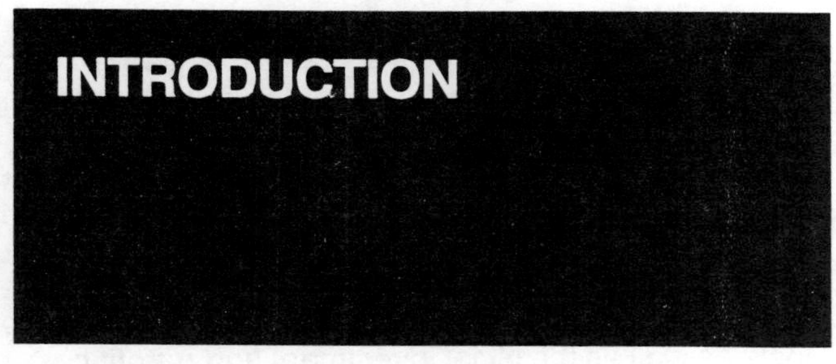

INTRODUCTION

BACKGROUND

HCFC-123 has been introduced by DuPont as an environmentally acceptable, nonflammable replacement for chlorofluorocarbon (CFC) 11 in refrigeration and heat-transfer applications. CFCs, which were developed over 60 years ago, have many unique properties. CFCs are low in toxicity, nonflammable, noncorrosive, and compatible with other materials. In addition, they offer the thermodynamic and physical properties that make them ideal for a variety of uses. CFCs are used as refrigerants; as blowing agents in the manufacture of insulation, packaging, and cushioning foams; as cleaning agents for metal and electronic components; and in many other applications.

However, the stability of these compounds, coupled with their chlorine content, has linked them to depletion of the earth's protective ozone layer. As a result, DuPont plans to phase out production of CFCs and introduce environmentally acceptable alternatives, such as hydrochlorofluorocarbon (HCFC) 123.

HCFC-123—AN ENVIRONMENTALLY ACCEPTABLE ALTERNATIVE

Although HCFC-123 contains chlorine, its hydrogen containing molecules decompose primarily in the lower atmosphere before they can reach the ozone layer. Because the chlorine is dissipated at lower altitudes, HCFCs have relatively short atmospheric lifetimes and much lower ozone depletion potentials (ODPs) than CFCs. The ODP of HCFC-123 is 0.02 compared to 1.00 for CFC-11. The list below gives generic and DuPont trade names for HCFC-123:

- SUVA® Centri-LP
- SUVA® 123
- Hydrochlorofluorocarbon 123
- HCFC-123

The chemical properties of HCFC-123 are listed below.

Chemical Name	2,2-dichloro-1,1,1-trifluoroethane
Molecular Formula	CF_3CHCl_2
Molecular Weight	152.93
CAS Registry Number	306-83-2

Chemical Structure

```
   F   Cl
   |   |
F—C —C —H
   |   |
   F   Cl
```

The infrared spectrum of HCFC-123 is shown in *Figure 1.*

Figure 1. Infrared Spectrum of HCFC-123 Liquid.

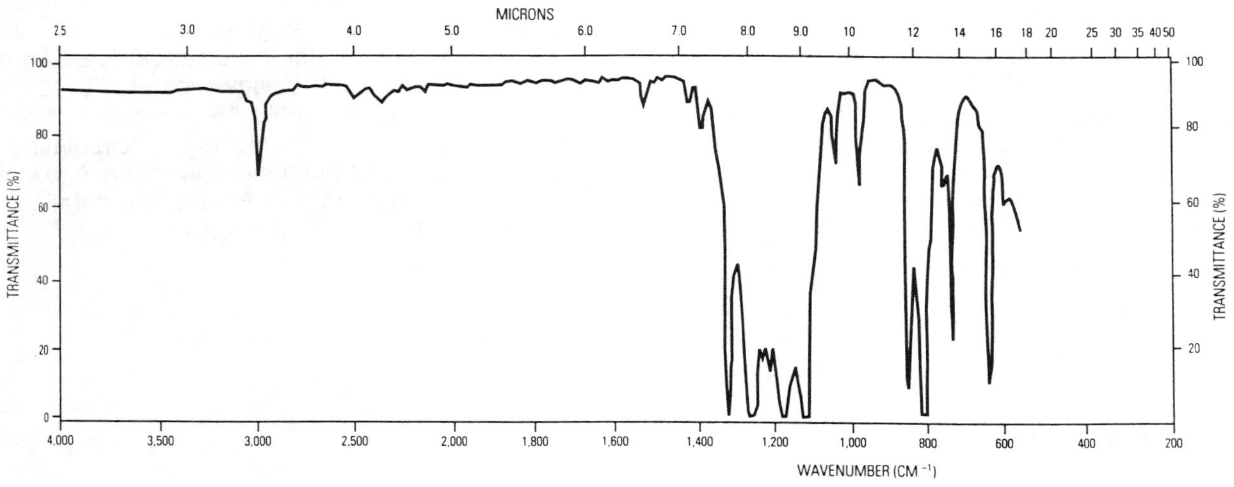

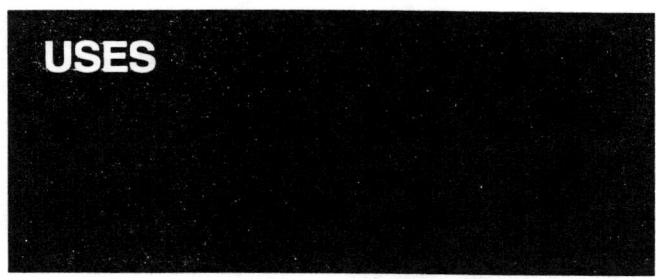

HCFC-123 is a viable replacement for CFC-11 as a refrigerant and as a heat-transfer fluid. Since HCFC-123 has an Allowable Exposure Limit (AEL) of 30 ppm, its use is limited to applications where it can be effectively contained within the operating equipment. DuPont does not sell HCFC-123 for use as blowing agents for polymer foams or aerosol propellants. See later sections of this Bulletin for discussions of toxicity and recommendations for safe handling.

REFRIGERANT

The thermodynamic and physical properties of HCFC-123, coupled with its nonflammability, make it an efficient and safe replacement refrigerant for CFC-11 in centrifugal chillers. In fact, HCFC-123 offers the best theoretical efficiency of the several alternatives for use in chillers. DuPont is now producing HCFC-123, and making it available to chiller manufacturers for use in new and existing equipment. DuPont is also converting most of its own CFC-11 chillers to HCFC-123.

HCFC-123 was selected as a replacement for CFC-11 because the two compounds will produce roughly the same operating pressures and temperatures in a chiller. However, an unmodified chiller will produce less cooling capacity and an equivalent or lower efficiency with HCFC-123 than it did with CFC-11. The differences in capacity and efficiency will depend on the original system component selection and operating conditions. *Table 1* gives performance ranges to be expected based on actual retrofit experience.

TABLE 1
Retrofit Experience with Unmodified Chillers
HCFC-123 vs. CFC-11

Capacity	–5 to –20%
Coefficient of Performance	0 to –5%
Evaporator Pressure	–2 to –3 psi –14 to –21 kPa
Condenser Pressure	–2 to –3 psi –14 to –21 kPa
Discharge Temperature	–2 to –6°F –1 to –3°C

The industry has developed mechanical components optimized for HCFC-123 which can be installed in existing equipment to maintain full capacity in a retrofit application. In addition, new equipment designed specifically for HCFC-123 will have equivalent or better capacity and efficiency than the equipment it is designed to replace. When considering whether to retrofit or replace existing systems, one should compare, on a life-cycle basis, the difference in operating and maintenance costs as well as the initial investment and retrofit costs. Newly designed and optimized refrigeration equipment may provide very much lower operating costs than existing equipment.

In general, alternative refrigerants cannot be simply "dropped into" systems designed to use CFCs. Alternatives are similar but not the same as the CFCs they are targeted to replace. The differences in physical properties and in compatibilities with construction materials must be carefully considered. Applications Bulletins are available from DuPont giving more details on the use of HCFC-123 as a refrigerant.

HEAT-TRANSFER FLUID

In many applications, refrigeration equipment is located in a service facility separate from an industrial process. The process heat is transferred to the refrigeration equipment by means of a circulating heat-transfer fluid, known as a "brine" or secondary refrigerant. A typical brine system is shown in *Figure 2.* The most common brines are water based solutions of salts, glycols, or alcohols. However, for low temperatures or in situations where chemical inertness is important, chlorinated organic solvents (methylene chloride, trichloroethylene) or CFCs (CFC-11, CFC-113) have been widely used. These compounds are no longer acceptable from an environmental or, in the case of the chlorinated solvents, an occupational health standpoint.

Table 2 compares pertinent physical properties of HCFC-123 with those of typical brines. When planning to retrofit a brine system to HCFC-123, it is important to check heat-transfer design calculations for the system. Rates will be similar if the retrofit is being made from CFC-11 or CFC-113. However, HCFC-123 has a specific heat approximately 15 per cent lower than methylene chloride, requiring higher circulating flow rates and increased pumping power. An Applications Bulletin is available from DuPont giving details on the use of HCFC-123 as a heat-transfer brine.

Figure 2. Schematic Diagram of Typical Brine System.

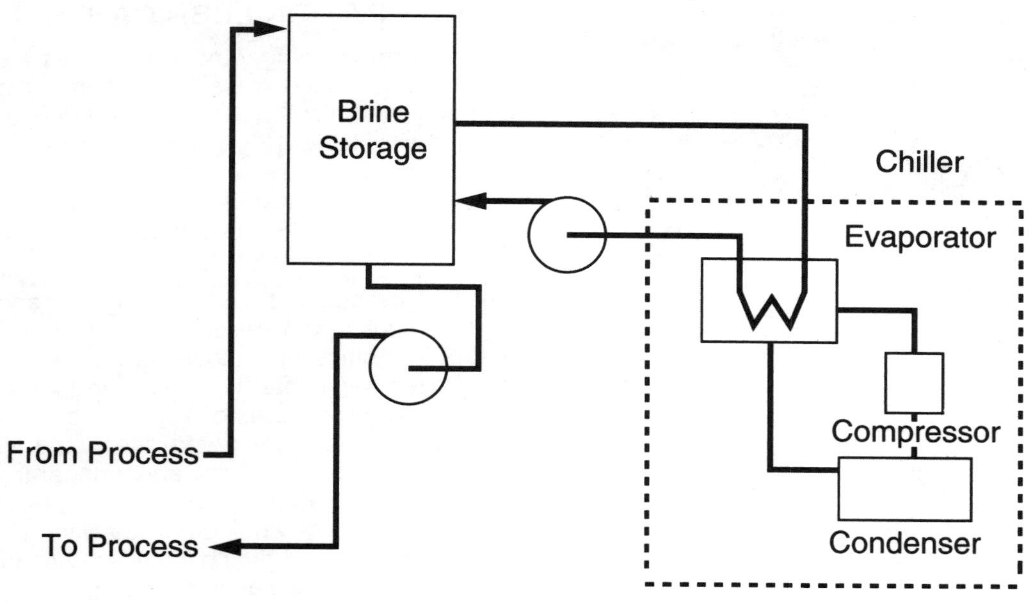

TABLE 2
Measured Properties of Heat-Transfer Brines

Property	Aqueous Calcium Chloride (25%)	Methylene Chloride	CFC-11	CFC-113	HCFC-123
Boiling Point					
°C	>100	40	24	48	28
°F	>212	104	75	118	82
Freezing Point					
°C	–29	–97	–111	–35	–107
°F	–20	–143	–168	–31	–161
Vapor Pressure @ 25°C					
kPa	NA	57	106	45	91
psig	NA	–6.4	0.7	–8.2	–1.5
Viscosity					
mPa·sec (cP)	12	0.70	0.73	1.49	0.82
Specific Heat					
kJ/kg·°K	2.81	1.13	0.84	0.88	0.90
Btu/lb·°F	0.67	0.26	0.20	0.21	0.22
Thermal Conductivity					
W/m·°K	0.50	0.19	0.10	0.08	0.096
Btu/hr·ft·°F	0.29	0.11	0.06	0.05	0.056
Density					
kg/m^3	1260	1400	1560	1650	1578
lb/ft^3	78.8	87.5	97.5	103.0	98.5

Note: Properties other than vapor pressure are given at –24°C (–11°F).
NA = not available.

PHYSICAL PROPERTIES

Physical properties of HCFC-123 are given in *Table 3* and *Figures 3* to *7.* Additional physical property data may be found in other DuPont publications. Bulletin ART-1 (H-43855-1) contains viscosity, thermal conductivity and heat capacity data for saturated liquid and vapor in addition to heat capacity data and heat capacity ratios for both saturated and superheated vapors. Thermodynamic tables in English and SI units are available in Bulletins T-123-ENG (H-47753) and T-123-SI (H-47754). Liquid and vapor densities are included in the thermodynamic tables.

CHEMICAL/THERMAL STABILITY

THERMAL DECOMPOSITION

HCFC-123 vapors will decompose when exposed to high temperatures from flames or electric resistance heaters. Decomposition may produce toxic and irritating compounds, such as hydrogen fluoride and hydrogen chloride. The pungent odors released will irritate the nose and throat and generally force people to evacuate the area. Therefore, it is important to prevent decomposition by avoiding exposure to high temperatures.

STABILITY WITH METALS AND REFRIGERATION LUBRICANTS

Stability tests for refrigerants with metals are typically performed in sealed glass tubes in the presence of refrigeration lubricants. Since existing refrigeration oils are used with HCFC-123, stability tests were performed in the presence of several mineral oils. Results are presented here for two series of tests in which the stability of HCFC-123 was compared to CFC-11 under identical test conditions.

In the first test series, 1.0 mL of refrigerant and an equal weight of lubricant were added to glass tubes in the presence of strips of Sandvik valve steel. The tubes were frozen, evacuated, sealed, and then heated for 14 days at temperatures of 105°C and 150°C (221°F and 302°F). Aged tubes were inspected visually for insoluble reaction products and appearance of the metal surfaces. Exposed tubes were opened and the chloride contents determined by analysis. The amount of refrigerant reacted during each test was then calculated from the amount of chloride formed.

The results from the first test series are summarized in *Table 4.* HCFC-123 appeared approximately ten times more stable than CFC-11 in these tests.

In the second test series, 3.0 mL of refrigerant and 0.52 mL of lubricant were added to glass tubes in the presence of steel, copper, and aluminum coupons. The tubes were frozen, evacuated, sealed, and then heated for 2.95 days at 151°C (304°F). After exposure, visual ratings were obtained on both the liquid and the metal coupons. Visual ratings ranged from 0 to 5, with 0 being the best and 5 being the worst. The sample tubes were then opened and the lubricant/refrigerant solutions analyzed for chloride and fluoride ions to indicate the extent of refrigerant decomposition.

The results of the second test series are in *Table 5.* The HCFC-123 again exhibited improved stability versus CFC-11.

Since CFC-11/metal/mineral oil combinations have given good results in actual refrigeration service, these tests indicate that replacement of CFC-11 by HCFC-123 will give satisfactory performance from a compatibility standpoint.

Note that the tests described here were accelerated tests. HCFC-123 and CFC-11 are low-pressure refrigerants and would seldom be exposed to temperatures as high as the upper test temperature (150°C or 302°F).

TABLE 3
Physical Properties of HCFC-123

Physical Properties	Units	HCFC-123
Chemical Name	—	2,2-dichloro-1,1,1-trifluoroethane
Chemical Formula	—	CF_3-$CHCl_2$
Molecular Weight	—	152.93
Boiling Point at 1 atm (101.3 kPa/1.013 bar)	°C °F	27.85 82.0
Freezing Point	°C °F	–107.0 –161.0
Critical Temperature	°C °F	183.68 362.63
Critical Pressure	kPa lb/in^2 abs	3668 532.0
Critical Volume	m^3/kg ft^3/lb	1.82×10^{-3} 0.0291
Critical Density	kg/m^3 lb/ft^3	550.0 34.34
Density (Liquid) at 25°C (77°F)	kg/m^3 lb/ft^3	1463 91.3
Density (Saturated Vapor) at Boiling Point	kg/m^3 lb/ft^3	6.47 0.403
Heat Capacity (Liquid) at 25°C (77°F)	kJ/kg·K Btu/(lb) (°F)	0.965 0.235
Heat Capacity (Vapor at Constant Pressure) at 25°C (77°F) and 1 atm (101.3 kPa/1.013 bar)	kJ/kg·K Btu/(lb) (°F)	0.721 0.172
Vapor Pressure at 25°C (77°F)	kPa bar lb/in^2 abs	91.29 0.9129 13.241
Heat of Vaporization at Boiling Point	kJ/kg Btu/lb	170 73.3
Thermal Conductivity at 25°C (77°F)		
Liquid	W/m·K Btu/hr·ft·°F	0.0810 0.0471
Vapor at 1 atm (101.3 kPa/1.013 bar)	W/m·K Btu/hr·ft·°F	0.0112 0.0064
Viscosity at 25°C (77°F)		
Liquid	mPa·s (cP)	0.456
Vapor at 1 atm (101.3 kPa/1.013 bar)	mPa·s (cP)	0.0110
Solubility of HCFC-123 in Water at 25°C (77°F) and 1 atm (101.3 kPa/1.013 bar)	wt %	0.39
Solubility of Water in HCFC-123 at 25°C (77°F)	wt %	0.08
Flammability Limits in Air at 1 atm (101.3 kPa/1.013 bar)	vol %	None
Ozone Depletion Potential (ODP) (For CFC-11, ODP = 1)	—	0.02
Halocarbon Global Warming Potential (HGWP) (For CFC-11, HGWP = 1)	—	0.02
Global Warming Potential (GWP) (100 yr. ITH. For CO_2, GWP = 1)	—	93
TSCA Inventory Status	—	Listed
Inhalation Exposure Limit (AEL[a])	ppm (v/v) 8- and 12-hr TWA	30
Emergency Exposure Limits (EEL[b])	ppm (v/v)	1000 for 1 hour 2500 for 1 minute

[(a)] AEL (Acceptable Exposure Limit) is an airborne exposure limit established by DuPont which specifies time-weighted average concentrations to which nearly all workers may be repeatedly exposed without adverse effects.

[(b)] EEL (Emergency Exposure Limit) is an airborne exposure limit established by DuPont to which workers may be exposed during an emergency occurring rarely in a lifetime without harmful effects.

Note: kPa is absolute pressure.

Figure 3. Solubility of Water in HCFC-123.

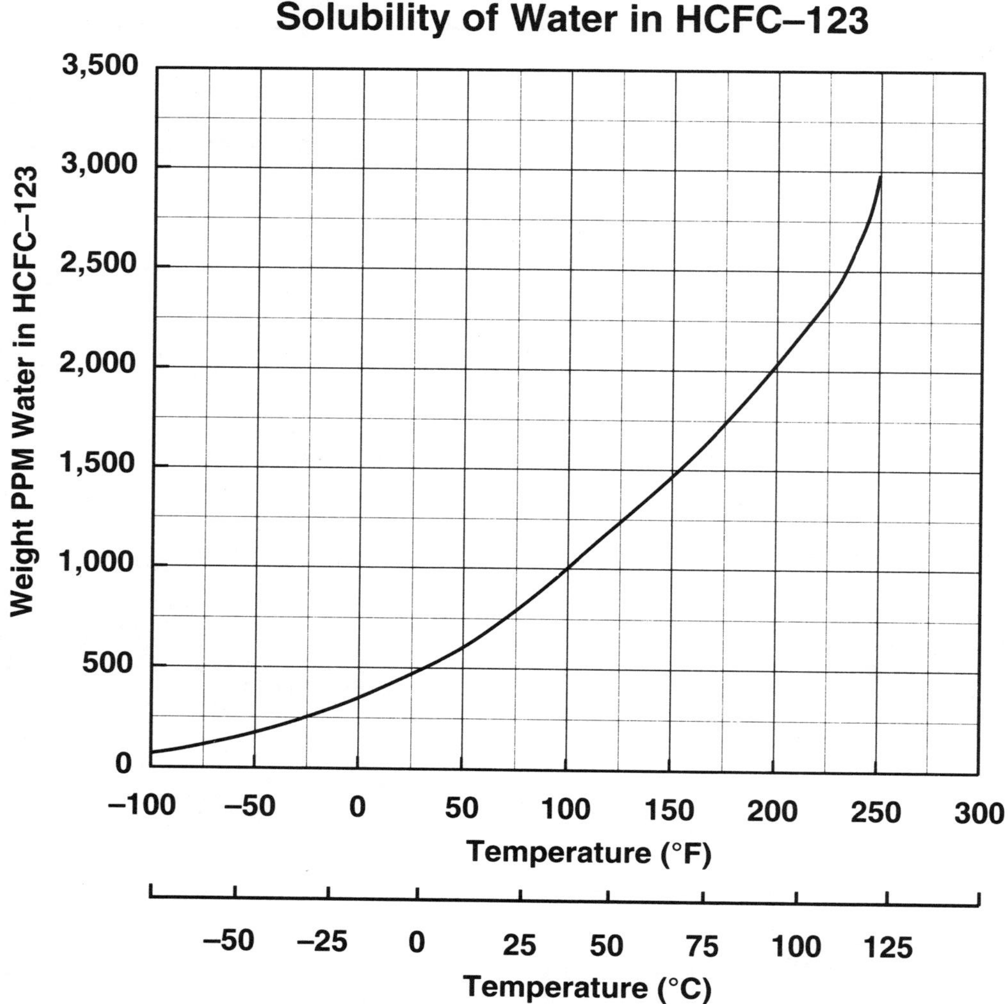

Figure 4. Vapor Pressure of HCFC-123 vs. Temperature (English Units)

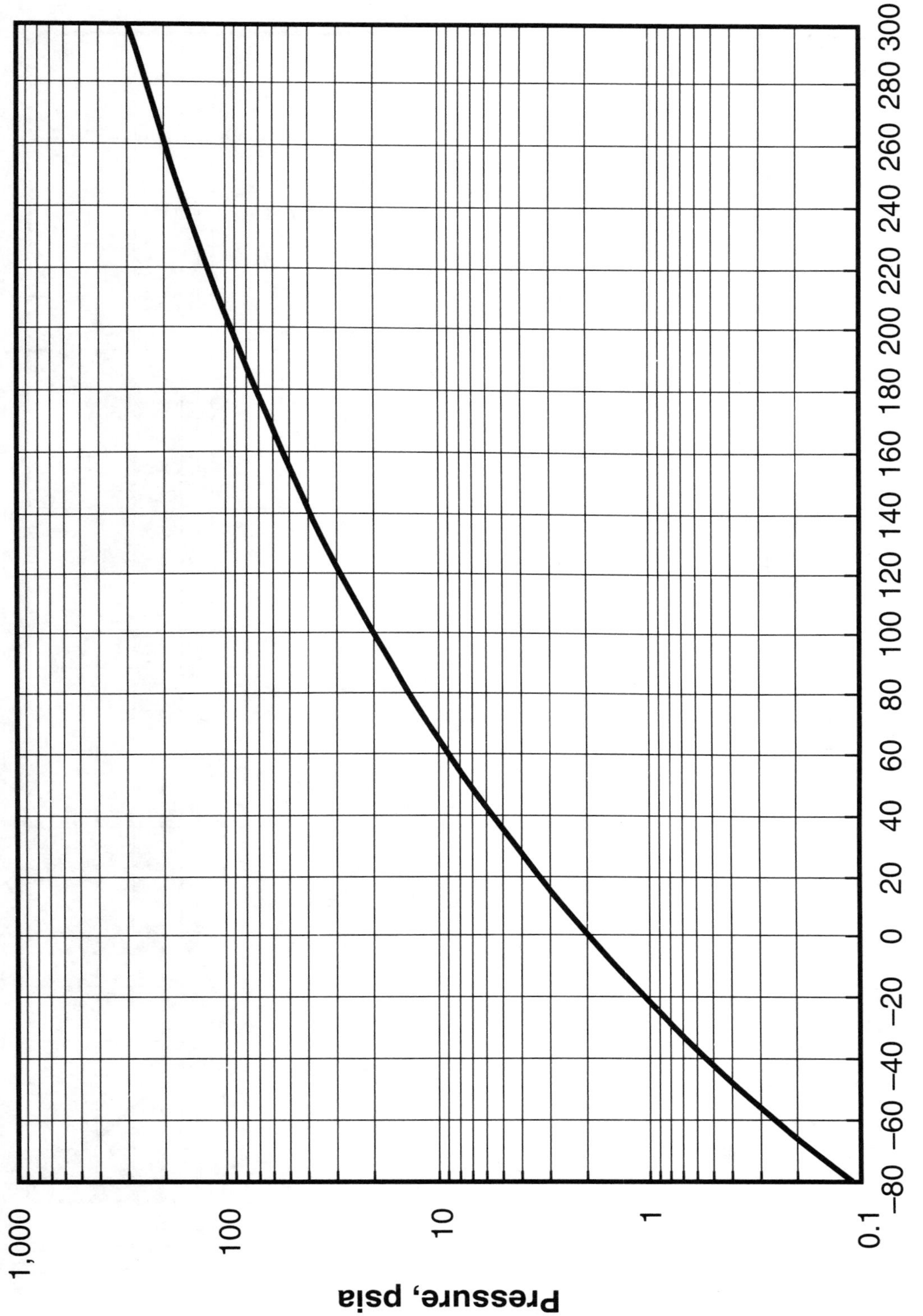

Figure 5. Vapor Pressure of HCFC-123 vs. Temperature (SI Units)

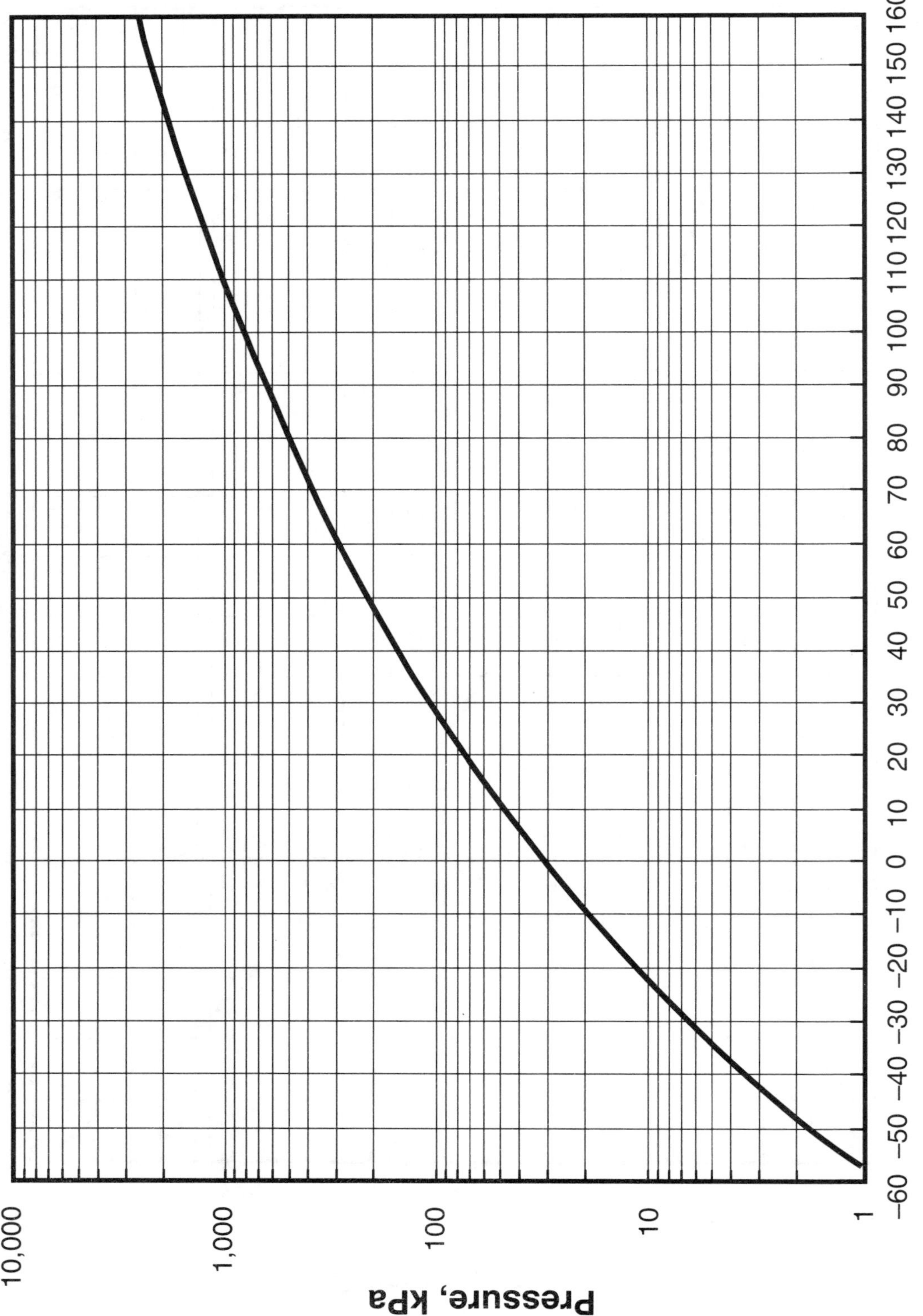

Figure 6. Pressure-Enthalpy Diagram for HCFC-123 (English Units)

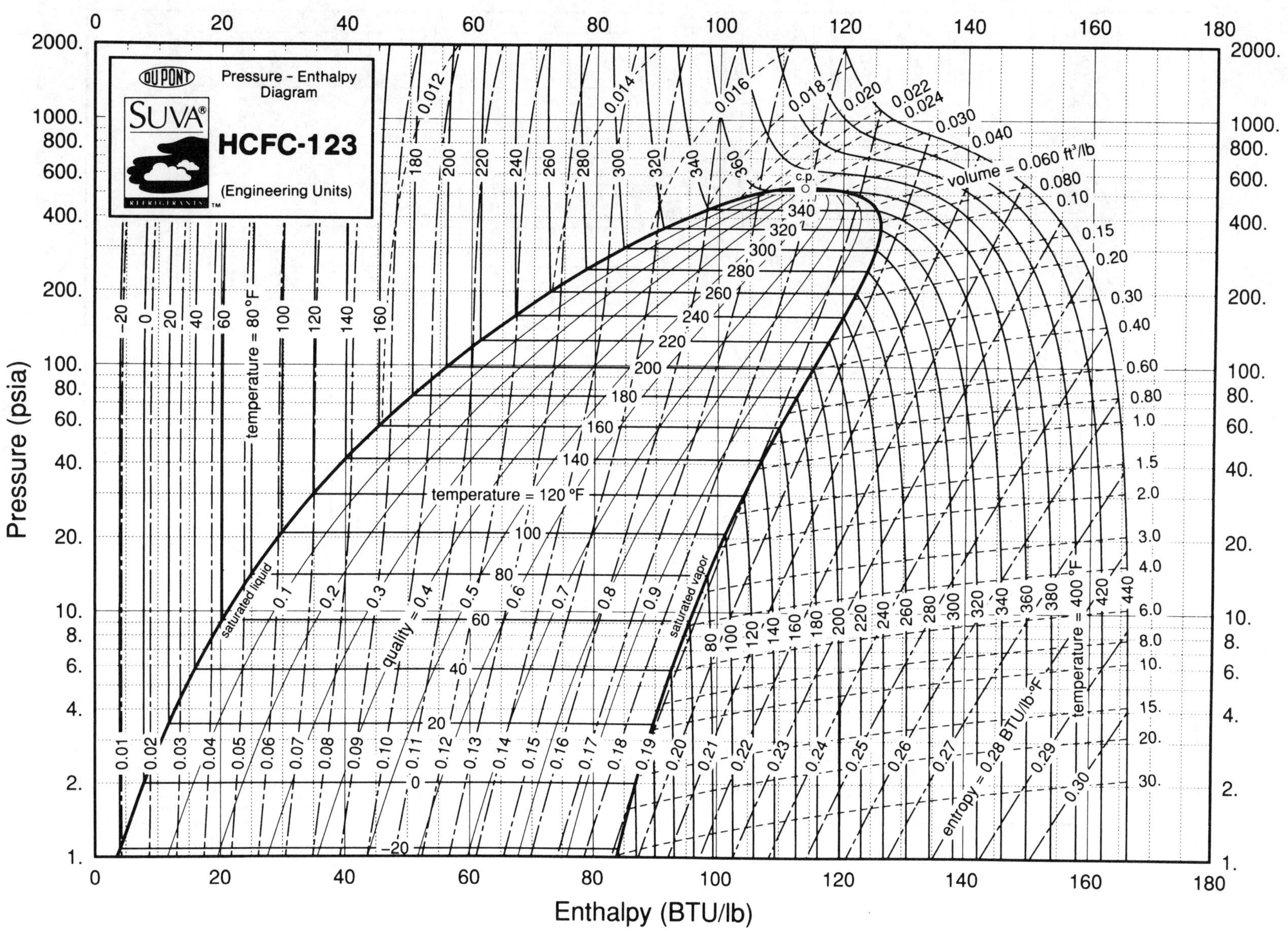

Figure 7. Pressure-Enthalpy Diagram for HCFC-123 (SI Units)

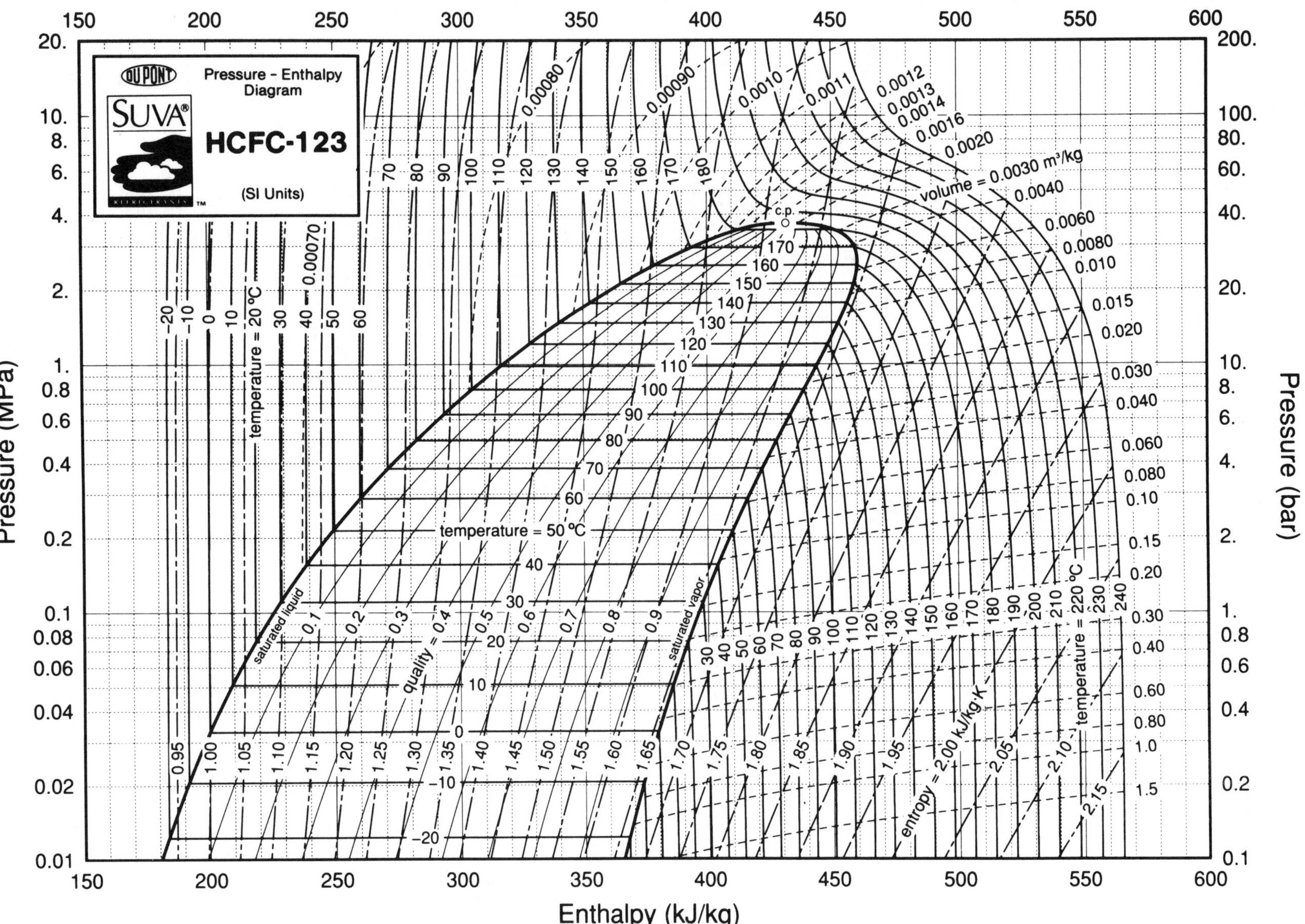

TABLE 4
Stability of HCFC-123 with Steel and Lubricating Oils

Oil	Mineral Oil ISO VG32				White Naphthenic Oil ISO VG46			
Temperature	105°C 221°C		150°C 302°F		105°C 221°F		150°C 302°F	
Refrigerant	R-11	R-123	R-11	R-123	R-11	R-123	R-11	R-123
Chloride, mg	1.06	0.099 0.066	225	3.26 5.66	0.033	0.048	94.5	12.2
Percent Refrigerant Reacted from Chloride	0.46	0.045 0.032	72.0	1.56 2.71	0.014	0.002	45.2	5.84
Appearance of Steel	Light Stains	Brown Stain	Heavy Sludge	Light Sludge	Slight Color	No Change	Etched	Light Deposits

Source of Data: D. F. Huttenlocher (Spauchus Associates), "Chemical and Thermal Stability of Refrigerant-Lubricant Mixtures with Metals," Report DOE/CE/23810-3B, Air Conditioning and Refrigeration Technology Institute, Arlington, VA, July 10, 1992.

Test Conditions:

Sealed tubes containing 0.9 g refrigerant + 0.9 g lubricant

Metal specimen: 1/4″ (6.4 mm) × 1-1/4″ (3.18 cm) strip of valve steel (Sandvik Steel Company)

Exposure: 14 days at indicated temperature

TABLE 5
Stability of HCFC-123 with Steel, Copper, Aluminum, and Heavy Naphthenic Oil

Metals: steel 1010
copper
aluminum 1100

Oil: Witco Freezene®, heavy white naphthenic mineral oil, 255 SUS [approx. 55 cSt at 100°F (38°C)]

Refrigerant	R-11	HCFC-123 Sample 1	HCFC-123 Sample 2
Visual Ratings			
Liquid	3	0+	2
Steel	1	1+	2
Copper	3	2	2
Aluminum	1	0	0
Decomposition Analyses			
Chloride, wt. %	1.7	0.08	0.13
Fluoride, wt. %	0.42	0.003	0.004

Source of Data: DuPont Tests

Test Conditions:

Sealed tubes containing 3.0 mL refrigerant + 0.52 mL lubricant

Metal specimens: 2-3/8″ (6.0 cm) × 1/4″ (6.4 mm) × 1/16″ (1.6 mm)

Exposure: 2.95 days at 151°C (304°F)

Visual Ratings: 0 to 5

Rating	Metal	Liquid
0	Bright, shiny	Clear, colorless
3	Darkening	Clear, brown
5	Severe deposits	Black, coke present

(Ratings of 3 and higher considered unacceptable).

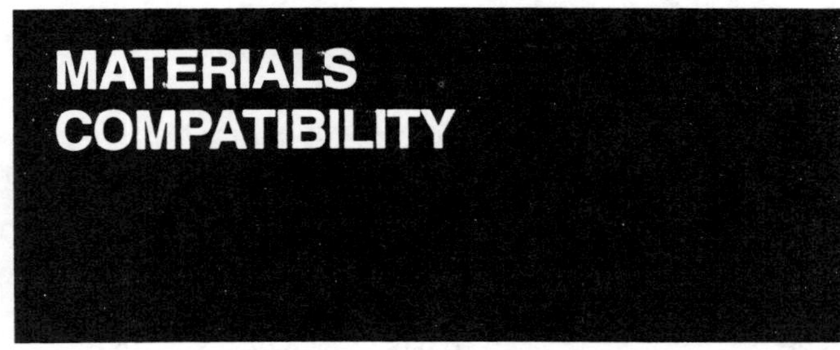

It is important to review materials of construction for compatibility when designing new equipment, retrofitting existing equipment, or preparing storage and handling facilities. Since HCFC-123 will be used primarily as a refrigerant or heat-transfer fluid, the compatibility data summarized below include materials commonly used in refrigeration applications.

PLASTICS

Compatibility results for HCFC-123 and CFC-11 are compared for 10 typical plastic materials in *Table 6.* The table summarizes screening tests in which these materials were exposed to liquid refrigerant in sealed glass tubes at two temperatures. The ratings given are based on observations of length, weight, and appearance changes. The presence of a hydrogen atom on the HCFC-123 molecule makes it a stronger solvent than CFC-11 and, therefore, more aggressive toward plastics. Several plastics used with CFC-11 are also compatible with HCFC-123. As its use becomes more common, other materials will be approved for use with HCFC-123.

Since the performance of plastic materials is affected by polymer variations, compounding agents, fillers, and molding processes, verifying compatibility using actual fabricated parts under end-use conditions is advised.

Refrigerant contacts the motor windings in a hermetic compressor. Equipment manufacturers have developed specially cured epoxy wire insulation which has performed well in hermetic compressors handling HCFC-123. Be sure to check with the manufacturer before using any hermetic compressor with HCFC-123.

ELASTOMERS

Compatibility results for HCFC-123 and CFC-11 are compared for 11 typical elastomers in *Table 7.* The table lists linear swell immediately after exposure and weight change measured after drying. As in the case of plastics, HCFC-123 may affect some elastomers more than CFC-11. Low swelling and extraction are not sufficient by themselves to qualify an elastomer. Elastomers that show limited effects must still be tested for changes in mechanical properties, such as hardness, tensile strength, and compression set. Some of the elastomers listed here, such as polysulfide, show limited swelling and weight change, but significant differences in properties after exposure to HCFC-123.

Although they contain elastomeric binders, compressed sheet gasketing can be used with HCFC-123 since elastomers are not the major components of these materials. Manufacturers have successfully formulated sheet gasketing based on neoprene and other elastomers. Chiller manufacturers consider many of these formulations to be proprietary. Garlock, Inc. recommends their Style 3300 compressed sheet gasketing, which utilizes a neoprene binder, for HCFC-123 service. Filled PTFE gasketing should also be satisfactory.

The original equipment manufacturer should always be consulted before specifying gasketing material to be used in a chiller with HCFC-123.

Effects on specific elastomers depend on the nature of the polymer, the compounding formulation and the curing or vulcanizing conditions. Actual samples should be tested under end-use conditions before specifying elastomers for critical components.

DESICCANTS

Driers filled with desiccant are typically used in refrigeration systems and bulk storage facilities. Actual field experience has shown that HCFC-123 is compatible with solid-core driers used with established refrigerants such as R-11, R-12, and R-22.

REFRIGERATION LUBRICANTS

Most compressors require a lubricant to protect internal moving parts. The compressor manufacturer usually recommends the type of lubricant and viscosity that should be used to ensure proper operation and equipment durability. Recommendations are based on several criteria, such as lubricity, compatibility with materials of construction, thermal stability, and refrigerant/oil miscibility. To ensure efficient operation and long equipment life, it is important to follow the manufacturer's recommendations.

In refrigeration and air conditioning systems, some lubricant escapes from the compressor discharge area and circulates through the system with the refrigerant. Current lubricants used with CFC-11 are fully miscible over the range of expected operating conditions, easing the problem of getting the lubricant to flow back to the compressor. Refrigeration systems using CFC-11 take advantage of this full miscibility when considering lubricant return.

Several families of lubricants that have acceptable miscibility with HCFC-123 have been identified. Although most applications for HCFC-123 will not involve high discharge temperatures or evaporator temperatures below 0°C (32°F), the candidate lubricants were tested over the broad temperature range shown in *Table 8.* All the lubricants listed in the table were miscible over the entire temperature range in the proportions listed.

In summary, lubricants used with CFC-11 are giving satisfactory performance with HCFC-123 in operating systems.

TABLE 6
Plastics Compatibility of CFC-11 versus HCFC-123

Screening Test Conditions: Plastic specimens exposed to liquid in sealed glass tubes at temperatures and exposure times given below.

Plastic		Compatibility Ratings			
		4 Hours at 75°F (24°C)		100 Hours at 130°F (54°C)	
Chemical Type	**Trade Name**	**CFC-11**	**HCFC-123**	**CFC-11**	**HCFC-123**
ABS	KRALASTIC®	0	4	0	4
Acetal	DELRIN®	0	0	0	1
Acrylic	LUCITE®	0	4	0	4
Fluorocarbon PTFE	TEFLON®	0	0	0	1
Polyamide 6/6 nylon	ZYTEL®	0	0	0	0
Polycarbonate	LEXAN®	0	4	0	4
Polyethylene-HD	ALATHON®	0	0	1	1
Polypropylene	ALATHON®	0	0	2	2
Polystyrene	STYRON®	0	4	4	4
Polyvinyl Chloride		0	0	1	1

Ratings: 0 = Suitable for use
1 = Probably suitable for use
2 = Probably not suitable for use
3 = Not suitable
4 = Plastic disintegrated or dissolved in liquid

Ratings Based On: Specimen dimensional, weight, and surface changes.

TABLE 7
Elastomer Compatibility of CFC-11 versus HCFC-123

Test Conditions: Exposure to liquid in sealed tubes for 7 days at 130°F (54°C), then ambient air drying for 21 days.

Elastomer		Length Change at End of Exposure, %		Weight Change After Drying, %	
Chemical Type	**Trade Name**	**CFC-11**	**HCFC-123**	**CFC-11**	**HCFC-123**
Butyl Rubber		16	11	–4	–2
Chlorosulfonated Polyethylene (CSM)	HYPALON®	2	12	–2	–5
Fluoroelastomer	VITON® A	2	23	0	5
Hydrocarbon Rubber (EPDM)	NORDEL®	12	13	–9	–6
Natural Rubber		31	39	–4	–4
Neoprene		2	10	–8	–9
Nitrile Rubber					
Buna N (NBR)		1	50	0	–4
Buna S (SBR)		13	26	–8	–9
Polysulfide	THIOKOL® FA	0	7	–1	–2
Silicone		33	28	–2	–2
Urethane	ADIPRENE® C	7	56	–3	–5

TABLE 8
Mutual Solubility Tests with HCFC-123 and Lubricants

Refrigeration oils determined to be miscible from –10°C to 93°C (14°F to 199°F) in mixtures containing 30, 60, and 90 weight percent HCFC-123:

Lubricant
500 SUS Alkylbenzene Lubricant
500 SUS Paraffinic Lubricant
500 SUS Naphthenic Lubricant
125 SUS Alkylbenzene Lubricant

Note: 500 SUS (Saybolt Universal Seconds) viscosity is equivalent to approximately 110 cSt at 38°C; 125 SUS viscosity is equivalent to approximately 27 cSt at 38°C.

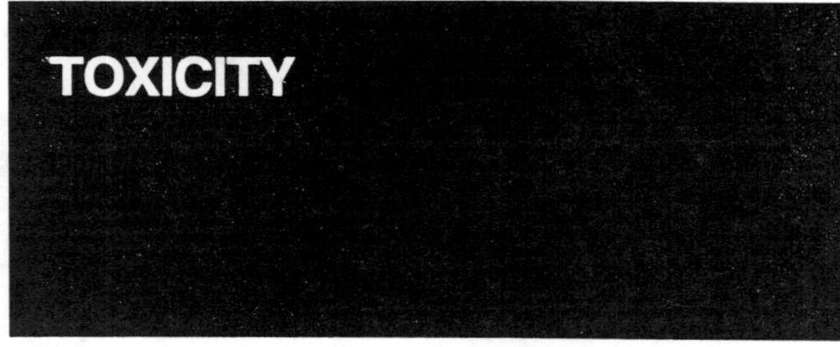

Users must implement a program to inform employees of the hazards of HCFC-123 and the protective measures to be taken to protect against overexposure during routine operations and emergencies. Users must read and understand the HCFC-123 Material Safety Data Sheet (MSDS).

INHALATION TOXICITY

DuPont has concluded that HCFC-123 poses no acute or chronic hazard when it is handled in accordance with recommendations and when exposures are maintained at or below the DuPont Acceptable Exposure Limit (AEL) of 30 ppm (8- and 12-hour Time-Weighted Average or TWA).

An AEL is an airborne exposure limit established by DuPont that specifies time-weighted average (TWA) airborne concentrations to which nearly all workers may be repeatedly exposed without adverse effects during an 8- or 12-hour day or 40-hour work week.

DuPont has also set an Emergency Exposure Limit (EEL) of 1000 ppm for up to one hour with a one-minute ceiling of 2500 ppm based on the acute or short-term effects of HCFC-123. During an emergency, occurring rarely in a lifetime, workers may be exposed to these concentrations without harmful effects. The short-term (or acute) effects of CFC-11 and HCFC-123 are similar, and any necessary response to emergency situations involving either would be essentially the same. The American Conference of Governmental Industrial Hygienists (ACGIH) has set a ceiling Threshold Limit Value (TLV) of 1000 ppm for CFC-11.

Prolonged inhalation of high concentrations of HCFC-123 vapor may cause temporary nervous system depression with anesthetic effects such as dizziness, headache, confusion, incoordination, and loss of consciousness. With gross overexposure (greater than 20 per cent concentration), a temporary alteration of the heart's electrical activity with irregular pulse, palpitations, or inadequate circulation may occur. Similar effects are observed in overexposure to CFC-11. Intentional misuse or deliberate inhalation of HCFC-123 may cause death without warning. This practice is *extremely dangerous*. A person experiencing any of the initial symptoms should be moved to fresh air and kept calm. If not breathing, give artificial respiration. If breathing is difficult, give oxygen. Call a physician.

CARDIAC SENSITIZATION

If HCFC-123 vapors are inhaled at a concentration of 20,000 ppm or greater, the heart may become sensitized to adrenaline leading to cardiac irregularities and, possibly, to cardiac arrest. Similar effects are observed with CFC-11 at concentrations in air of 3500 ppm or greater. The likelihood of these cardiac problems increases if you are under physical or emotional stress.

Because of possible disturbances of cardiac rhythm, catecholamine drugs, such as epinephrine, should be considered only as a last resort in life-threatening emergencies.

SKIN AND EYE CONTACT

HCFC-123 is not a skin irritant or skin sensitizer, but is a mild to moderate eye irritant. Overexposure by eye contact may include eye irritation with discomfort, tearing, or blurring of vision.

In case of skin contact, flush with water for 15 minutes. Get medical attention if irritation is present. In case of eye contact, immediately flush eyes with plenty of water for 15 minutes. Call a physician.

MONITORS AND LEAK DETECTION

Service personnel have used leak detection equipment for years when servicing equipment. Leak detectors exist not only for pinpointing specific leaks, but also for monitoring an entire room on a continual basis. There are several reasons for leak pinpointing or area monitoring, including: conservation of refrigerants, protection of valuable equipment, reduction of fugitive emissions, and protection of employees. ASHRAE (American Society of Heating, Refrigerating, and Air Conditioning Engineers) Standard 15 requires area monitors in refrigeration Machinery Rooms as defined in the standard. In conformance with the Standard, an air monitor capable of measuring 0 to 150 ppm of HCFC-123 is required for indoor applications.

Leak detectors can be placed into two broad categories: leak pinpointers and area monitors. Before purchasing a monitor or pinpointer, several instrumental criteria should be considered, including sensitivity, detection limits and selectivity.

TYPES OF DETECTORS

Using selectivity as a criterion, leak detectors can be placed into one of three categories: nonselective, halogen-selective, or compound-specific. In general, as the specificity of the monitor increases, so does the complexity and cost.

A detailed discussion of leak detection, along with a list of manufacturers of leak detection equipment, is given in Bulletin ARTD-27 (H-31753-2).

NONSELECTIVE DETECTORS

Nonselective detectors are those that will detect any type of emission or vapor present, regardless of its chemical composition. These detectors are typically quite simple to use, very rugged, inexpensive and almost always portable. However, their inability to be calibrated, long-term drift, lack of selectivity, and lack of sensitivity limit their use for area monitoring.

Non-selective detectors will respond to chlorine containing soaps commonly used in leak testing.

Although nonselective detectors designed for use with CFCs will respond well to HCFC-123, the low AEL of HCFC-123 requires detection of very small leaks. Recently new detectors with greatly improved sensitivity to HCFC-123 have become available. Be sure to consult with the manufacturer before selecting or using a nonselective detector with HCFC-123.

HALOGEN-SELECTIVE DETECTORS

Halogen-selective detectors use a specialized sensor that allows the monitor to detect compounds containing fluorine, chlorine, bromine and iodine without interference from other species. The major advantage of such a detector is a reduction in the number of "nuisance alarms"—false alarms caused by the presence of some compound in the area other than the target compound.

These detectors are typically easy to use, feature higher sensitivity than the nonselective detectors (detection limits are typically <5 ppm when used as an area monitor and <0.05 oz/yr (<1.4 gm/yr) when used as a leak pinpointer), and are very durable. In addition, due to the partial specificity of the detector, these instruments can be calibrated easily.

Halogen-selective detectors should not be used as area monitors for HCFC-123 unless it is extremely unlikely that other halogen compounds will be present in the area.

COMPOUND-SPECIFIC DETECTORS

The most complex detectors, which are also the most expensive, are compound-specific detectors. These units are typically capable of detecting the presence of a single compound without interference from other compounds. Compound-specific detectors are preferred for monitoring HCFC-123.

STORAGE AND HANDLING

SHIPPING CONTAINERS IN THE U.S.

HCFC-123 is a nonflammable liquid. It is not regulated by the U.S. Department of Transportation and therefore does not have a proper shipping name or hazard class.

A list of the different types of containers that can be used to ship HCFC-123 in the United States, along with their water capacities, dimensions, DOT specifications, and the net weights of HCFC-123, are provided in *Table 9*. Any pressure relief devices used on the containers must be in compliance with the corresponding Compressed Gas Association (CGA) Standards for cargo and portable tanks.

The drums used for HCFC-123 are painted "Light Grey," PMS 428. Drums have 2-inch and 3/4-inch openings diametrically opposite on the top heads. The 2-inch opening is fitted with a 2-inch steel plated flange with

TABLE 9
Specifications of Shipping Containers for HCFC-123

Nominal Size	Dimensions	DOT Specification	Color Code	Net Weight (lb) HCFC-123
10-gal tight head drum	14-5/8″ OD × 17-3/4″ H	17E	PMS 428	100
20-gal tight head drum	16-1/4″ OD × 28-5/16″ H	17E	PMS 428	200
55-gal tight head drum	23-1/2″ OD × 34″ H	17C	PMS 428	625
5,000 gal	Tank Truck	MC-307 MC-330 MC-331		40,000 Maximum
20,000 gal	Tank Rail Car	105A100W		—

white neoprene gasket and containing 2-inch and 3/4-inch zinc die cast combination plugs with bottle cap and irradiated polyethylene gasket beneath the 3/4-inch plug. The "bottle cap" provides a seal and is ruptured upon initial opening of the drum as described under "Handling" in the section on STORAGE, HANDLING, AND USE RECOMMENDATIONS.

BULK STORAGE SYSTEMS

DuPont sells storage systems, at cost, to its refrigerant customers. The systems are prefabricated, tested and ready to install on site. Although most HCFC-123 customers receive product in drums and do not require storage facilities on site, bulk tanks can be provided if desired.

The delivered systems include all components, such as storage tanks, pumps, piping, valves, motors and gauges, as an integrated unit. Units are skid-mounted and require only placement on a concrete pad and connection to electrical and process systems. Your DuPont Marketing Representative can arrange for guidance on site selection, purchase, installation, start-up and maintenance.

STORAGE, HANDLING, AND USE RECOMMENDATIONS

An HCFC-123 specific air monitor with 0 to 150 ppm range is required for all indoor applications. Sensors should be located so that samples are representative of worker exposure. Appropriate respiratory protection should be available for immediate use in the event of a large release or leak. ASHRAE (American Society of Heating, Refrigerating, and Air Conditioning Engineers) Standard 15, "Safety Code for Mechanical Refrigeration" provides additional guidance on system and room design.

PROHIBITED USES

HCFC-123, or mixtures containing HCFC-123, should not be used as an uncontained flushing fluid in refrigeration work or as a general cleaning solvent.

PERSONAL PROTECTIVE EQUIPMENT

Respiratory protection should be worn when performing all operations during which there is potential for exposure in excess of an average of 30 ppm, for an entire 8- or 12-hour work day. DuPont recommends the use of NIOSH approved respiratory protection, as shown in *Table 10.* **Note: Cartridge performance is affected by humidity. Cartridges should be changed after two hours of continuous use unless it is determined that the humidity is less than 75 percent, in which case, cartridges can be used for four hours. Used cartridges should be discarded daily, regardless of the length of time used.** People who will work with HCFC-123 should be trained on the proper use of respirators, and should be fit-tested annually to ensure respirator fit is adequate.

Industrial hygiene evaluations of workplace conditions may justify less stringent repirator program recommendations.

Eye protection, gloves of butyl rubber or other impervious material, and safety shoes should be used when filling and handling drums. Nitrile, PVC-coated nitrile, and PVC protective equipment are not recommended. Directed mechanical ventilation or localized exhaust may facilitate controlling airborne HCFC-123 concentrations.

Coverall chemical goggles and a face shield should be used when making first breaks into a system if liquid splash is a potential problem and full-face respiratory protection is not worn. Eyewash fountains or water hoses with quick opening valves should be accessible to HCFC-123 work areas.

TABLE 10
Minimum Respirator Protection

Concentration of HCFC-123 in Air	Exposure Time	Minimum Respirator Protection
Less than 30 ppm* as a Time Weighted Average (TWA)	8–12 hours per day	None
30–90 ppm*	Less than 30 minutes per workshift	None

When performing tasks which monitoring data indicate may result in concentrations exceeding the above or when performing non-routine or unusual tasks, the following protection is recommended:

Concentration of HCFC-123 in Air, ppm	Minimum Respirator Protection
30–300	Half Mask, Organic Vapor Cartridge or Canister Or Full Mask, Organic Vapor Cartridge or Canister
300 or greater	Full Face Air Line or Self Contained Breathing Apparatus (SCBA)

* Instantaneous spikes may occur during operations such as disconnecting charging lines or tapping drums. When factored into the Time Weighted Average, existing monitoring data on excursions have not resulted in exceeding the AEL during typical routine servicing.

STORAGE

Drums of HCFC-123 should be stored upright, at a temperature below 125°F (52°C), and out of direct sunlight. All drum bungs should be leak tight (at a minimum sealed with TFE tape). Storage of factory sealed drums does not require a continuously operating air monitor. A monitor is, however, required if liquid transfer or drumming operations are being performed in an indoor storage location. Quantities stored should be limited to that needed for reasonable maintenance requirements. Empty drums should be stored outside.

No storage of HCFC-123 should be permitted in areas containing alkali or alkaline earth metals such as powdered aluminum, zinc, or beryllium.

HANDLING

When moving drums of HCFC-123, the use of gloves, safety glasses with side shields, and steel-toe shoes is recommended. Use either a hand truck or forklift when moving drums, since filled units can weigh as much as 309 kg (680 lb). When using a forklift truck, always follow the manufacturer's recommended weight capacity.

The larger bung on HCFC-123 drums loaded in the United States contains a smaller built-in opening for hose/piping connections. This smaller opening has a metal seal to minimize vapors released to the atmosphere on initial opening of the drum. **On initial opening of a drum, it is recommended that a combination 3/4-inch screwed brass ball valve with TEFLON® packing and seat and a 3/4 × 2-inch pipe nipple be screwed into the threaded bung.** This will rupture the seal and allow for fluid transfer.

This operation should be performed outdoors; if indoors, use directed mechanical ventilation or localized exhaust equipment. Appropriate refrigeration fittings can be connected to the valve for transfer into the machine. This procedure minimizes emissions of refrigerant during drum opening.

CHARGING, MAINTENANCE, AND SAMPLING

When making first breaks into the system, wear appropriate respiratory protection unless the room air monitoring data indicates that HCFC-123 concentration in air can reasonably be expected to remain below the 30 ppm AEL during the work in progress. See *Table 10*. Directed mechanical ventilation or localized exhaust may facilitate controlling airborne concentrations.

When charging refrigerant into or drawing it out of a chiller, connect the drum to the chiller with both a liquid transfer line and a vent line in order to avoid a vacuum or overpressure condition in the drum and to minimize venting of HCFC-123 vapor into the workspace during liquid transfer. The transfer and vent lines should be compatible with HCFC-123. Minimize HCFC-123 emission to atmosphere from transfer lines during connection and disconnection. If possible use the previously recommended drum connection device (valve and nipple) and charge refrigerant under cool ambient conditions.

Good work place practices should be utilized to avoid spills, drippage, exposed contaminated equipment, or open containers of HCFC-123.

When working on a chiller, de-inventory into drums through a recovery device or into a receiver (if provided) and evacuate the system to 29 inches of mercury (absolute pressure of 3.4 kPa). Break the vacuum with nitrogen, re-evacuate, and break vacuum again with nitrogen. Waste oil should be disposed of in accordance with appropriate regulatory requirements. Waste oil will contain significant quantities of dissolved HCFC-123.

LEAKS AND SPILLS

Major leaks or spills will not evaporate readily due to the high boiling point of HCFC-123, forcing recovery as a liquid. Self-Contained Breathing Air (SCBA) is required until levels are reduced sufficiently to permit other or no respiratory protection. Spill control measures should be preplanned, and all washes should be disposed of in accordance with applicable government regulations. If splash potential exists, wear protective equipment fabricated from an impervious material such as butyl rubber.

RECOVERY, RECLAMATION, RECYCLE AND DISPOSAL

Responsible use of HCFC-123 requires that the product be recovered for reuse or disposal. DuPont purchases used refrigerants for reclamation through its distributor networks in the United States, Canada and Europe. In the United States, used HCFC-123 is accepted as part of this program. Recovery and reuse of HCFC-123 makes sense from an environmental and economic standpoint. In addition, the U.S. Clean Air Act prohibits known venting of HCFC refrigerants during the maintenance, servicing or disposal of refrigeration equipment.

RECOVERY

Recovery refers to the removal of HCFC-123 from equipment and collection in an appropriate external container. As defined by the Air Conditioning and Refrigeration Institute (ARI, a U.S. organization), recovery does not involve processing or analytical testing.

HCFC-123 may be recovered from refrigeration equipment using recovery equipment available from chiller manufacturers and from refrigeration contractors. These recovery units are often mounted on a base with casters and have provision for storage of a limited amount of refrigerant during chiller maintenance. Recovery units may be purchased or leased. These devices contain a vacuum pump and water cooled condenser and may be used for liquid and vapor recovery. At the end of the recovery cycle, the system must be evacuated to remove vapors. In the U.S., the Environmental Protection Agency (EPA) sets standards for recovery equipment. Before purchasing a specific recovery unit, check with the manufacturer to be sure that it is compatible with HCFC-123.

RECLAMATION

Reclamation refers to the reprocessing of used HCFC-123 to new product specifications. Quality of reclaimed product is verified by chemical analysis. In the U.S., HCFC-123 is included in DuPont's refrigerant reclamation program. Contact DuPont or one of its authorized distributors for further information.

Reclamation offers advantages over on-site refrigerant recycling procedures because these systems cannot guarantee complete removal of contaminants. Putting refrigerants that do not meet new product specifications back into expensive equipment may cause damage.

RECYCLE

Refrigerant recycle refers to the reduction of used refrigerant contaminants using devices that reduce oil, water, acidity, and particulates. Recycle is usually a field procedure with no analytical testing of refrigerant. HCFC-123 may be recycled using recycle/recovery systems now on the market. In the U.S., the EPA sets standards for these devices. Consult with the manufacturer before specifying a recycle device for HCFC-123.

DISPOSAL

Disposal refers to the destruction of used HCFC-123. Disposal may be necessary when HCFC-123 has become badly contaminated with other products and no longer meets the acceptance specifications of DuPont or other reclaimers. Although DuPont does not presently accept severely contaminated refrigerants for disposal, licensed waste disposal firms are available. Be sure to check the qualifications of any firm before sending them used HCFC-123.

H-52157 (11/93)

Printed in U.S.A.

204132A

DuPont Chemicals
Fluorochemicals Customer Service Center
Wilmington, DE 19898

For sales information:
1-800-441-9442
In Delaware (302) 774-2099

For technical information:
1-800-582-5606
In Delaware (302) 999-3129

Europe
DuPont de Nemours
International S.A.
2 Chemin du Pavillon
P.O. Box 50
CH-1218 Le Grand-Saconnex
Geneva, Switzerland
41-22-717-5111

Canada
DuPont Canada, Inc.
P.O. Box 2200, Streetsville
Mississauga, Ontario
L5M 2H3
(905) 821-3300

Mexico
DuPont, S.A. de C.V.
Homero 206
Col. Chapultepec Morales
C.P. 11570 Mexico, D.F.
52-5-250-8000

South America
DuPont do Brasil S.A.
Alameda Itapicuru, 506
Alphaville 06400 Barueri
São Paulo, Brazil
55-11-421-8509

DuPont Argentina S.A.
Casilla Correo 1888
Correo Central
1000 Buenos Aires, Argentina
54-1-311-8167

Pacific
DuPont Australia
P.O. Box 930
North Sydney, NSW 2060
Australia
61-2-923-6165

Japan
Mitsui DuPont Fluoro-
chemicals Company, Ltd.
Mitsui Seimei Building
2-3, 1-Chome Ohtemachi
Chiyoda-Ku, Tokyo 100 Japan
81-3-3216-8451

Asia
DuPont Taiwan
P.O. Box 81-777
Taipei, Taiwan
886-2-514-4400

DuPont Asia Pacific Limited
P.O. Box TST 98851
Tsim Sha Tsui
Kowloon, Hong Kong
852-734-5345

DuPont Thailand
P.O. Box 2398
Bangkok 10501, Thailand
66-2-238-4361

DuPont China Ltd.
Room 1704, Union Bldg.
100 Yanan Rd. East
Shanghai, PR China 200 002
Phone: 86-21-328-3738
Telex: 33448 DCLSH CN
Fax: 86-21-320-2304

DuPont Far East Inc.
P.O. Box 12396
50776 Kuala Lumpur,
Malaysia
Phone: 60-3-232-3522
Telex: (784) 30391 DUFE M
Fax: 60-3-238-7250

DuPont Korea Ltd.
C.P.O. Box 5972
Seoul, Korea
82-2-721-5114

DuPont Singapore Pte. Ltd.
1 Maritime Square #07 01
World Trade Centre
Singapore 0409
65-273-2244

DuPont Far East, Philippines
5th Floor, Solid Bank Building
777 Paseo de Roxas
Makati, Metro Manila
Philippines
63-2-818-9911

DuPont Far East Inc.
7A Murray's Gate Road
Alwarpet
Madras, 600 018 India
91-44-454-029

DuPont Far East Inc.—
Pakistan
9 Khayaban-E-Shaheen
Defence Phase 5
Karachi, Pakistan
92-21-533-350

DuPont Far East Inc.
P.O. Box 2553/Jkt
Jakarta 10001
Indonesia
62-21-517-800

(Stock number on last page of text)

P-HP

DuPont SUVA® HP Refrigerants

Properties, Uses, Storage and Handling

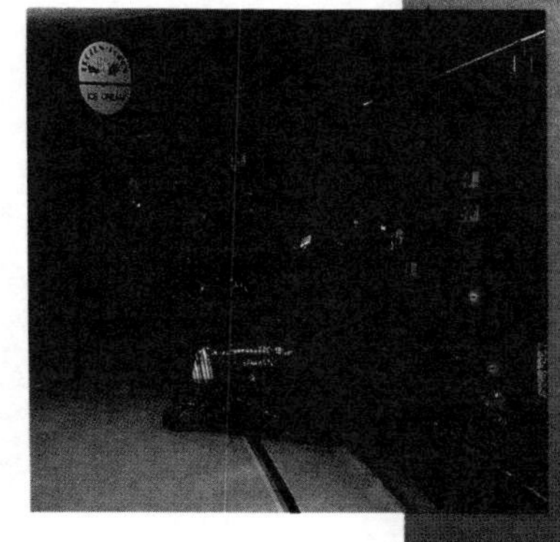

SUVA® HP80 refrigerant

SUVA® HP81 refrigerant

SUVA® HP62 refrigerant

SUVA® HP Refrigerants

Properties, Uses, Storage and Handling

Table of Contents

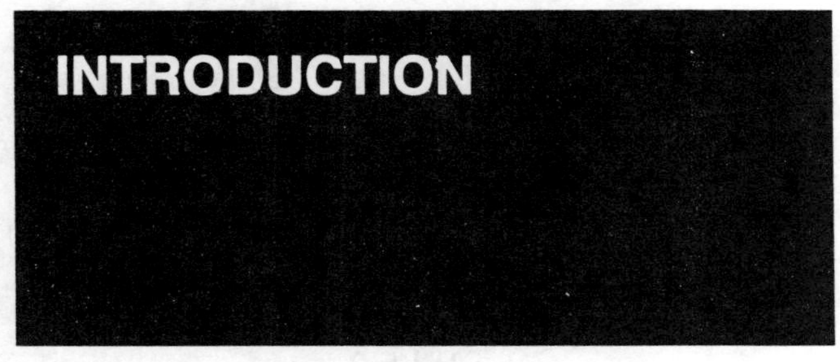

INTRODUCTION

BACKGROUND

Chlorofluorocarbons (CFCs), which were developed over 60 years ago, have many unique properties. They are low in toxicity, nonflammable, non-corrosive and compatible with other materials. In addition, they offer the thermodynamic and physical properties that make them ideal for a variety of uses. CFCs are used as refrigerants; as blowing agents in the manufacture of insulation, packaging and cushioning foams; as cleaning agents for metal and electronic components; and in many other applications.

However, the stability of these compounds, coupled with their chlorine content, has linked them to depletion of the earth's protective ozone layer. As a result, DuPont is phasing out production of CFCs and introducing environmentally acceptable alternatives, such as the SUVA® HP refrigerant family.

SUVA® HP REFRIGERANTS

The products designated as SUVA® HP refrigerants are intended as replacements for R-502 in medium and low temperature refrigeration systems. The SUVA® HP refrigerant family contains two different types of refrigerants. Both types involve the use of refrigerant blends to achieve alternatives that will act very much like R-502 in refrigeration systems.

The first type of blends incorporate the following refrigerants in two compositions to optimize different performance characteristics:

	HCFC-22	HFC-125	Propane
SUVA® HP80	38 wt%	60%	2%
SUVA® HP81	60%	38%	2%

In addition, DuPont has formulated a mixture based on all-HFC refrigerants, which results in no ozone depletion factor. This refrigerant is called SUVA® HP62, and its composition is:

	HFC-125	HFC-143a	HFC-134a
SUVA® HP62	44 wt.%	52%	4%

The individual components of the three mixtures are listed in *Table 1* to show their chemical names and formulae. In addition, the physical properties of the SUVA® HP refrigerants are listed in *Table 3*.

TABLE 1
Refrigerant Information

Refrigerant	Chemical Name	Formula	CAS No.	Molecular Wt.
HCFC-22	Chlorodifluoromethane	CF_2HCl	75-45-6	86.47
HFC-125	Pentafluoroethane	CF_3CHF_2	354-33-6	120.02
HFC-134a	1,1,1,2-Tetrafluoroethane	CF_3CH_2F	811-97-2	102.0
HFC-143a	1,1,1-Trifluoroethane	CF_3CH_3	420-46-2	84.08
HC-290	Propane	C_3H_8	74-98-6	44.1

USES

The SUVA® HP refrigerants will be used in virtually all R-502 based applications, either as a result of retrofit of existing equipment that uses R-502, or following development of new equipment designed to utilize the SUVA® HP products.

R-502 currently serves a wide range of applications in the refrigeration industry. It is used widely in supermarket applications, in food service and warehousing, for transport refrigeration, in cascade systems for very low temperatures, and other assorted applications. It offers good capacity and efficiency without suffering from the high compressor discharge temperatures that can be seen with HCFC-22 single-stage equipment.

SUVA® HP80 and HP81, which contain HCFC-22, are each formulated to optimize different performance characteristics.

SUVA® HP80 offers compressor discharge temperatures equivalent to R-502, with improved capacity versus R-502, and slightly lower theoretical efficiency.

SUVA® HP81 offers the highest efficiency versus R-502, with slightly better capacity. However, the higher HCFC-22 content results in compressor discharge temperatures in the range of 14°C (25°F) higher than that of R-502, which makes HP81 most suited for medium temperature systems such as ice machines.

SUVA® HP62 offers the best overall properties when compared to R-502. Capacity and efficiency values should be equivalent to R-502, and compressor discharge temperatures may be up to 9°C (14°F) lower than R-502, which may equate to longer compressor life and better lubricant stability.

In addition, the heat transfer characteristics of all the SUVA® HP products appear to be better than R-502, so any loss of compression efficiency may be offset by improvements in heat transfer.

Due to the differences in operating characteristics described above, there will be some market differentiation of SUVA® HP80 and HP81, in that HP81 will be targeted only for systems where the higher discharge temperatures will not create operating difficulties. Both SUVA® HP80 and HP62 will be full-range R-502 replacements, with HP80 targeted for retrofitting of existing systems, and possibly some new equipment designs, and HP62 for new equipment designs starting in 1993. *Table 2* shows some markets that are expected to utilize each of these refrigerants.

TABLE 2
SUVA® HP Refrigerant Market Applications

Product	Medium Temperature	Low Temperature
SUVA® HP81	Ice Machines Food Service Vending Supermarket	To Be Determined
SUVA® HP80	Supermarket Transport	Supermarket Transport Food Service
SUVA® HP62	All	

PHYSICAL PROPERTIES

General physical properties of the SUVA® HP refrigerants are shown in *Table 3*. Pressure-enthalpy diagrams for the SUVA® HP refrigerants are shown in *Figures 1–6*.

Additional physical property data may be found in other DuPont publications. Bulletin ART-18 (H-49740) contains viscosity, thermal conductivity, and heat capacity data for saturated liquid and both saturated and superheated vapor. ART-18 also contains heat capacity ratios for saturated and superheated vapor.

Thermodynamic tables in English and SI units are available in Bulletins T-HP80-ENG (H-47766), T-HP80-SI (H-47767-1), T-HP81-ENG (H-47757), T-HP81-SI (H-47758), T-HP62-ENG (H-49744-1), and T-HP62-SI (H-49745) for SUVA® HP80, SUVA® HP81, and SUVA® HP62.

TABLE 3
General Property Information

Physical Property	Units	HP80	HP81	HP62
Molecular Wt.	(avg.)	101.55	94.71	97.6
Boiling Point (1 atm)	°C °F	–49.2 –56.5	–47.4 –53.2	–46.5 –51.6
Freezing Point	°C °F	n/a	n/a	n/a
Critical Temp.	°C °F	75.5 167.9	82.6 180.7	72.1 161.7
Critical Pressure	kPa psia	4135 599.7	4445 644.8	3732 541.2
Critical Density	kg/cu m lb/cu ft	541.7 33.82	530.7 33.13	484.5 30.23
Liquid Density at 25°C (77°F)	kg/cu m lb/cu ft	1151 71.86	1156 72.14	1048 65.45
Density, Satd. Vapor at –15°C	kg/cu m lb/cu ft	19.93 1.24	16.90 1.05	18.20 1.14
Specific Heat Liquid, 25°C	kJ/kg K Btu/lb °F	1.37 0.328	1.34 0.320	1.53 0.367
Specific Heat Vapor, 25°C & 1 atm	kJ/kg K Btu/lb °F	0.755 0.181	0.725 0.173	0.870 0.207
Vapor Pressure, at 25°C	kPa psia	1337 194.0	1254 181.9	1255 182.0
Heat of Vaporization, at B.P.	kJ/kg Btu/lb	194.0 83.5	210.0 90.3	202.1 87.0
Thermal Conductivity, at 25°C				
Liquid	W/m K Btu/hr ft. °F	6.91E-2 4.00E-2	7.35E-2 4.25E-2	6.83E-2 3.94E-2
Vapor (1 atm)	W/m K Btu/hr ft. °F	1.266E-2 7.32E-3	1.205E-2 6.96E-3	1.346E-2 7.78E-3
Viscosity, 25°C				
liquid	Pa s	1.38E-4	1.45E-4	1.28E-4
vapor (1 atm)	Pa s	1.29E-5	1.28E-5	1.22E-5
Flammability Limit in Air (1 atm)	vol %	none	none	none
Ozone Depletion Potential	(CFC-12 = 1)	0.02	0.03	0.0
Halocarbon Global Warming Potential	(CFC-11 = 1)	0.63	0.52	0.94
TSCA Inventory Status	Reported/Included?	yes	yes	yes
Inhalation Exposure Limit	AEL* ppm (8 and 12 hr. TWA)	1000	1000	1000

* AEL (Acceptable Exposure Limit) is an airborne inhalation exposure limit established by DuPont which specifies time-weighted average concentrations to which nearly all workers may be repeatedly exposed without adverse effects.

Figure 1. Pressure–Enthalpy Diagram for SUVA® HP80 (English Units).

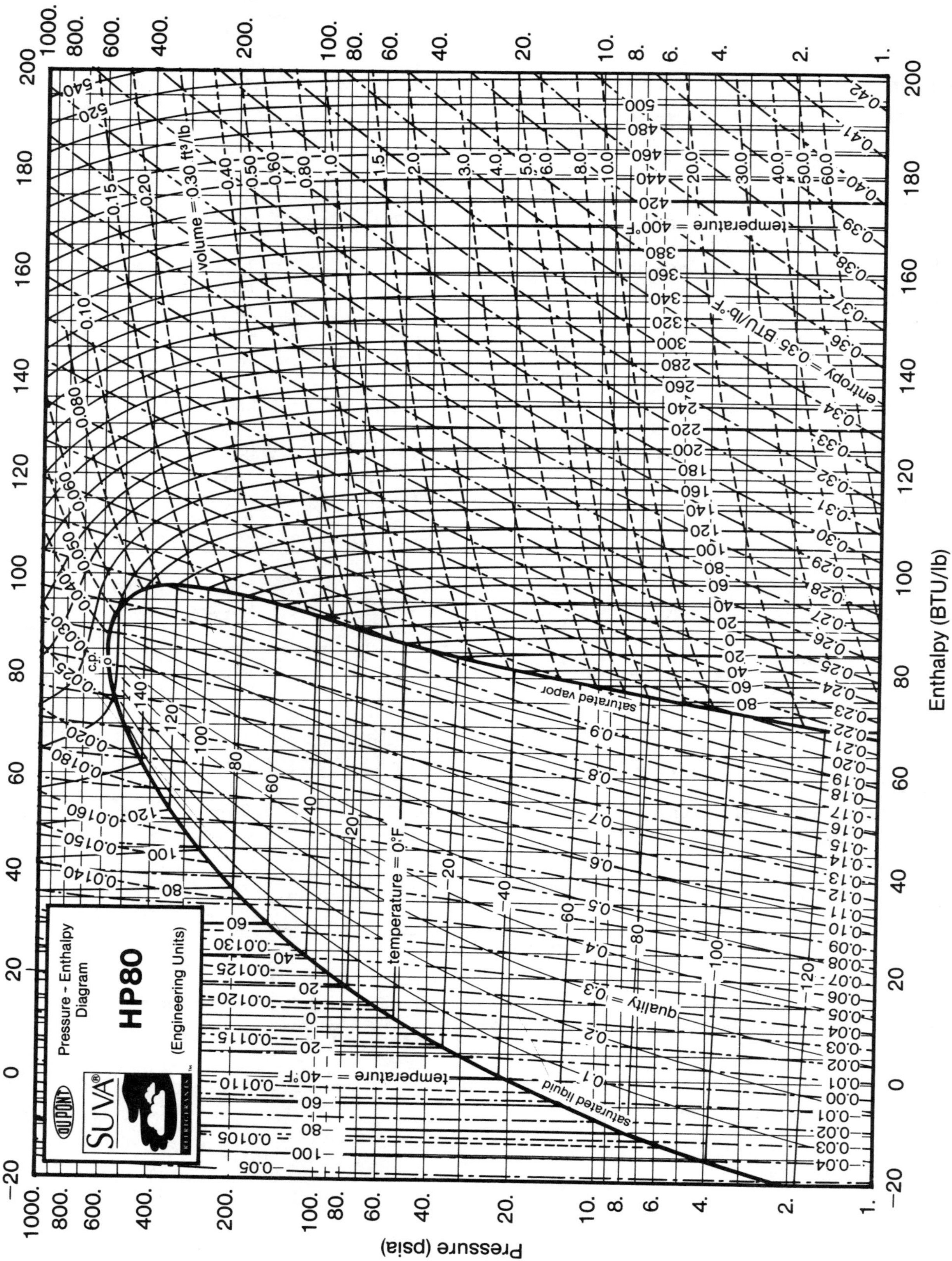

Figure 2. Pressure–Enthalpy Diagram for SUVA® HP80 (SI Units).

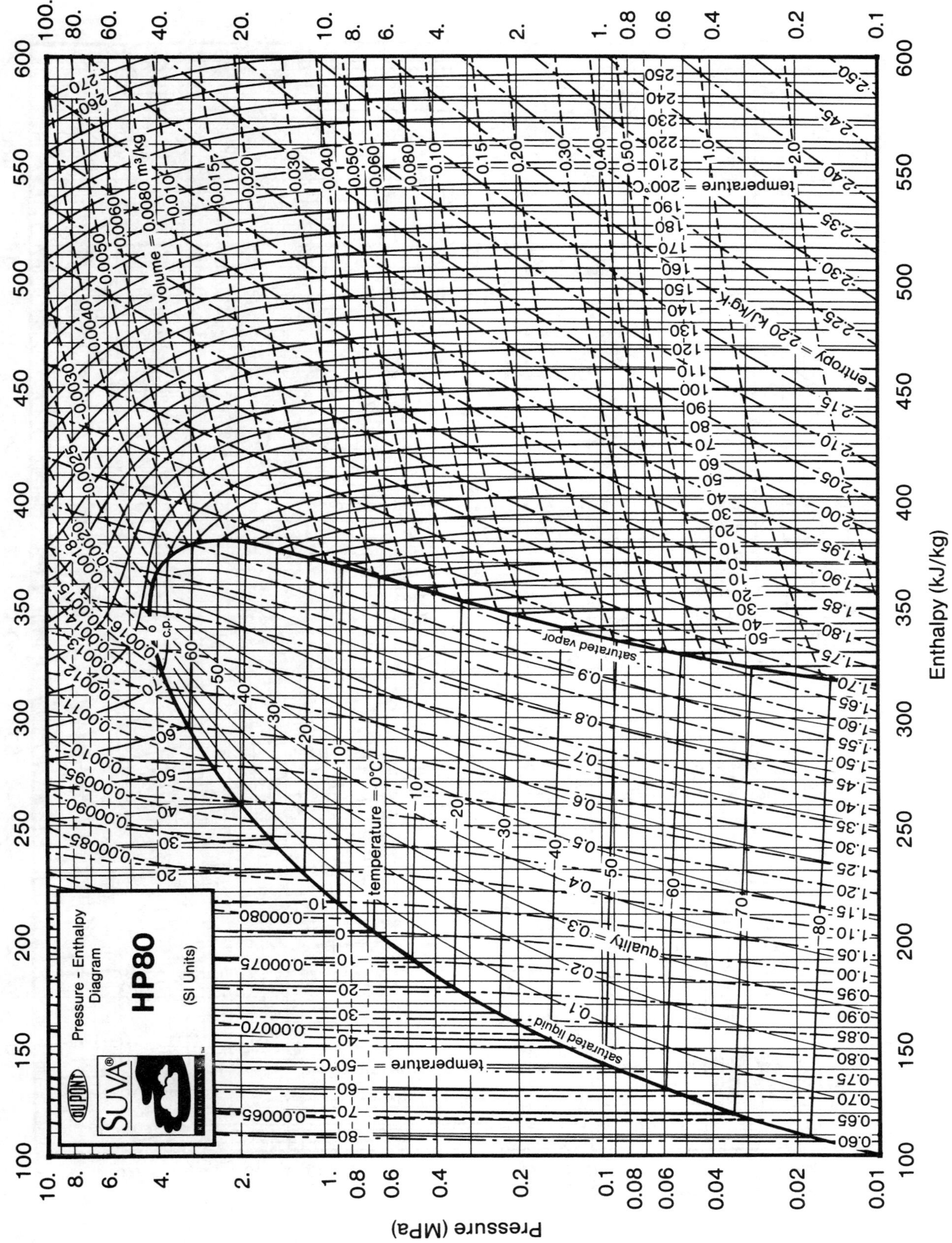

Figure 3. Pressure–Enthalpy Diagram for SUVA® HP81 (English Units).

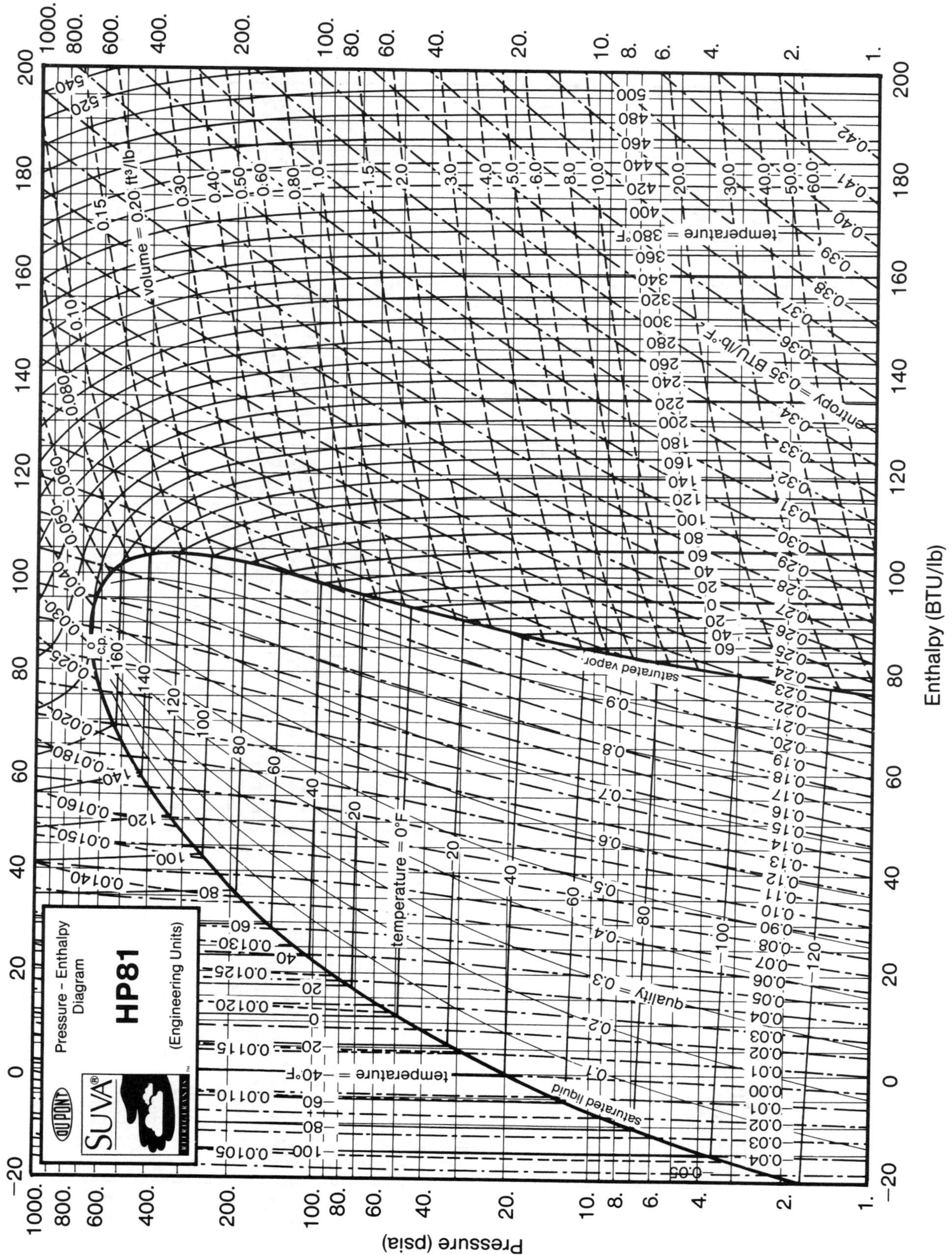

Figure 4. Pressure–Enthalpy Diagram for SUVA® HP81 (SI Units).

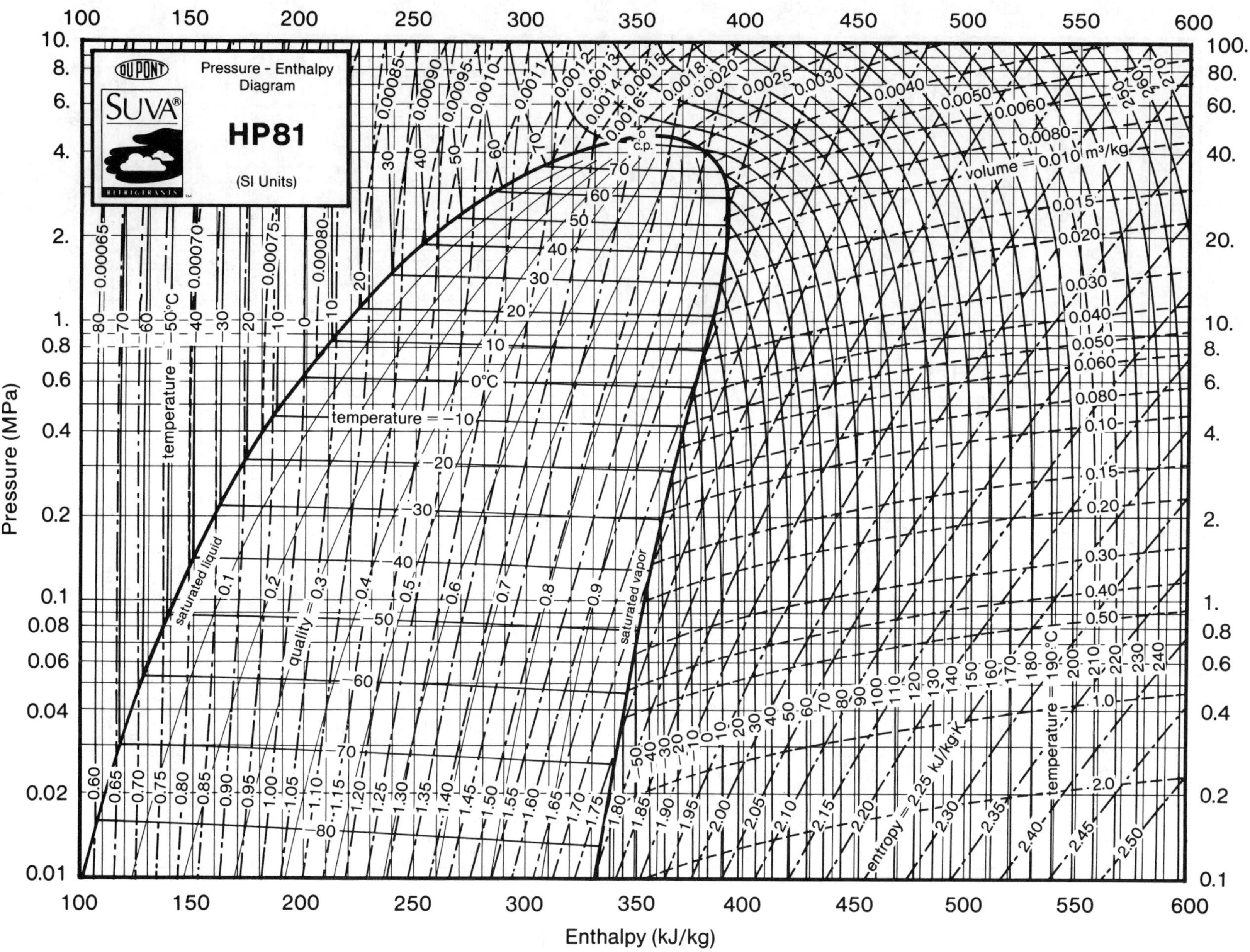

Figure 5. Pressure–Enthalpy Diagram for SUVA® HP62 (English Units).

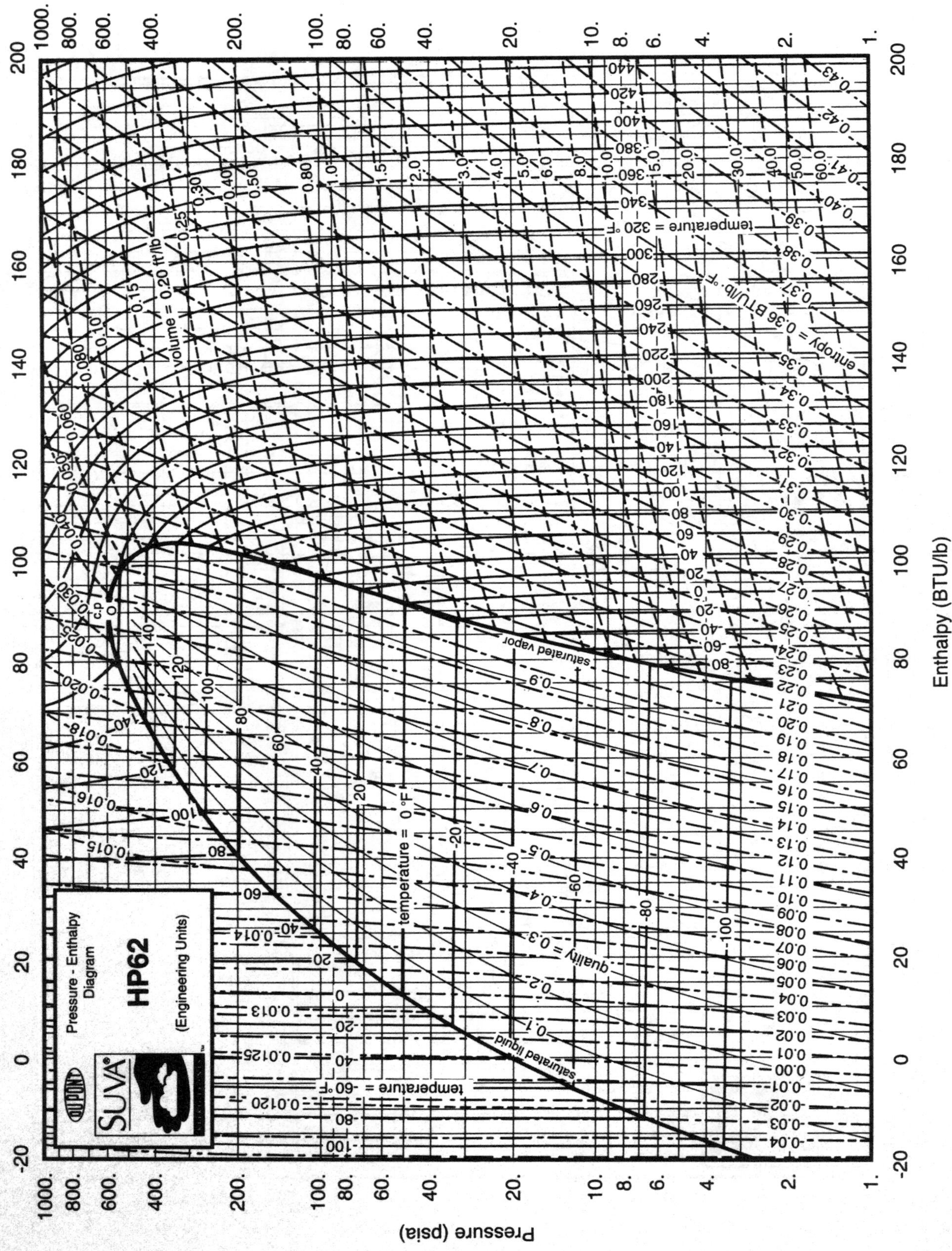

Figure 6. Pressure–Enthalpy Diagram for SUVA® HP62 (SI Units).

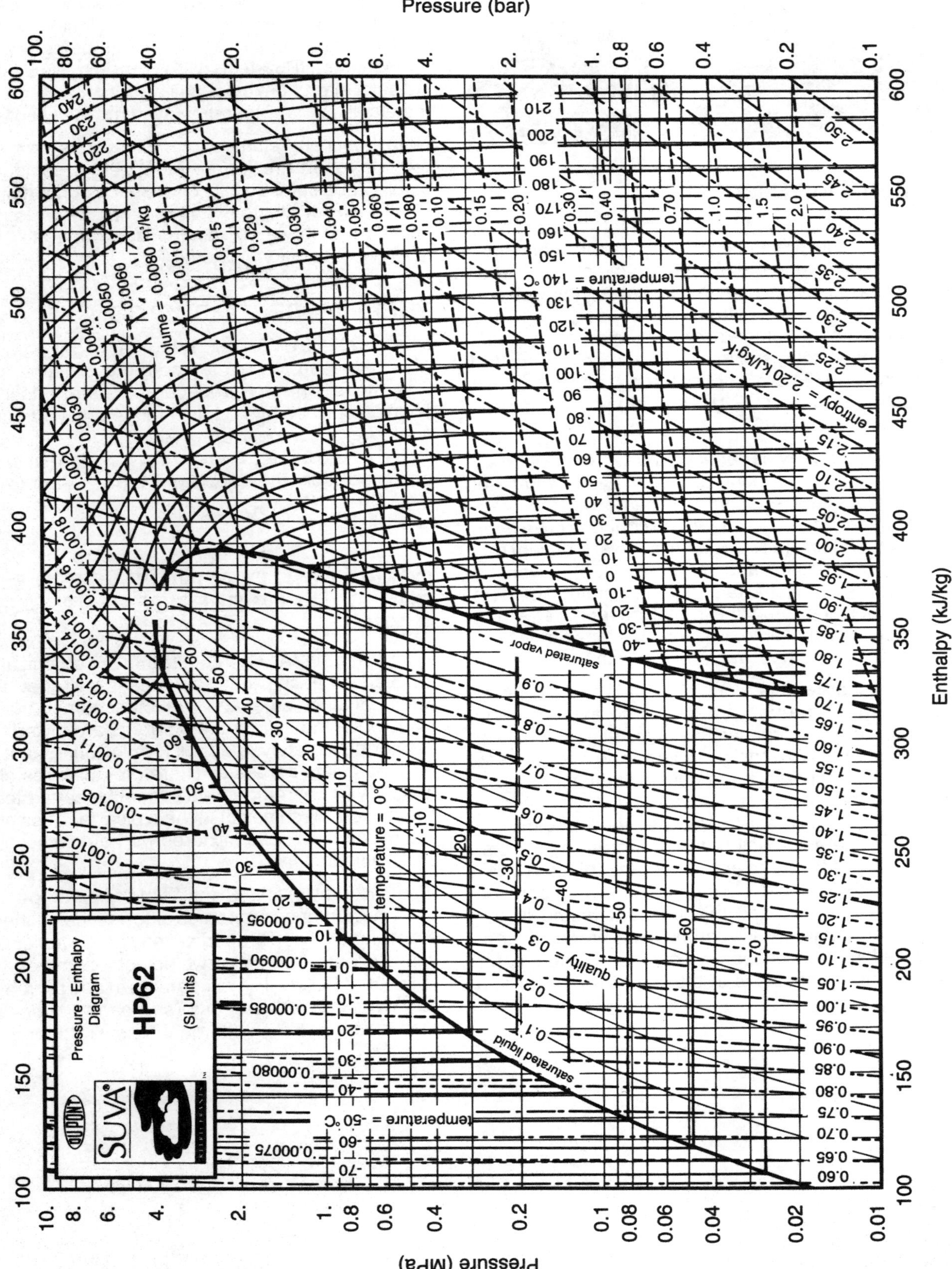

CHEMICAL/THERMAL STABILITY

STABILITY WITH METALS

Stability tests for refrigerant with metals are typically performed in the presence of refrigeration lubricants. Results of sealed tube stability tests available for R-502/ mineral oil and alkylbenzene lubricants have shown long-term stability in contact with copper, steel and aluminum in actual refrigeration systems. Mineral oils, alkylbenzene, mixtures of mineral oil/alkylbenzene and polyol esters (POE) are all possible candidates for use with SUVA® HP80 and HP81; POE are proposed lubricants for use with HP62.

The method followed was generally the same as ASHRAE 97 with several minor modifications. A 3-mL volume of refrigerant/lubricant solution was heated in the presence of copper, steel and aluminum coupons in an oven for 14 days at 175°C (347°F). Both the neat lubricant and a mixture of lubricant and refrigerant (50/50 volume ratio) were tested. Visual ratings were obtained on both the liquid solutions and the metal coupons after the designated exposure time. The visual ratings range from 0 to 5, with 0 being best and 5 being worst.

After the visual ratings were obtained, sample tubes were opened and the lubricant and refrigerant (if present) were analyzed. The lubricant was typically checked for halide content and viscosity, while the refrigerant was examined for the presence of decomposition products. *Table 4* summarizes typical data for SUVA® HP refrigerants. Visual ratings are listed for the neat lubricant, the lubricant/refrigerant solution and the three metals that were present in the lubricant/refrigerant solutions. Viscosity was determined on the unused lubricant, the tested neat lubricant and the lubricant tested in the presence of refrigerant. Decomposition products were determined in some cases. Typical measurements for decomposition products is in the low parts per million (ppm) range.

SUVA® HP81 tests with various lubricants indicate it has adequate chemical stability with these lubricants. In addition, we believe that HP80 will have similar behavior due to the same refrigerants being used in the formulation. HP62 tests with common POE lubricants indicate that chemical stability of HP62 with common metals used in refrigeration systems is acceptable.

Note: Lubricant/refrigerant combinations shown throughout this report are for the purposes of comparing the stability and compatibility of different lubricants with the SUVA® HP products. No recommendation is made or implied that these combinations will operate successfully in refrigeration systems.

THERMAL DECOMPOSITION

Like R-502, SUVA® HP refrigerants will decompose when exposed to high temperature or flame sources. Decomposition may produce toxic and irritating compounds, such as hydrogen chloride and hydrogen fluoride. The decomposition products released will irritate the nose and throat. Therefore, it is important to prevent decomposition by following DuPont Material Safety Data Sheet (MSDS) recommendations for handling and use.

COMPATIBILITY CONCERNS IF R-502 AND SUVA® HP REFRIGERANTS ARE MIXED

R-502 and SUVA® HP refrigerants are chemically compatible with each other; this means that they do NOT react with each other and form other compounds. However, when the different refrigerants are mixed by accident or deliberately, they will form mixtures that can be very difficult to separate. Therefore, mixtures of R-502 and SUVA® HP refrigerants cannot be separated in on-site recycle machines or in the typical facilities of an off-site reclaimer. These mixtures will have to be disposed of by incineration.

Also, mixtures of R-502 and SUVA® HP refrigerants will have performance properties different than either refrigerant alone. These properties may not be acceptable for your systems. Therefore, we do not recommend mixing R-502 and SUVA® HP refrigerants in any systems. First remove the R-502 properly (*see page 21 for recovery discussion*) and then charge the new refrigerant.

TABLE 4
Stability of HP Refrigerants with Metals and Lubricants

SUVA® HP81 with various lubricants

Property	HP81 w/ Min. Oil SUNISO 3GS	HP81 w/ Alkylbenzene ZEROL 150 TD	HP81 w/ Polyol Ester Castrol "Icematic" SW32
Viscosity of Neat Oil at 40°C (104°F), $(mm)^2/s$ (cSt)	ND	ND	29.6
Stability Tests			
Visual Ratings			
Neat Oil	0	ND	1,H
Oil/Refrig.	1,G,H	2,P	0
Copper	0	2,T	0
Iron	0	0	1,T
Aluminum	0	0	0
Viscosity Change			
% Change Neat	ND	ND	5.0
% Change w/ Refrig.	ND	ND	–13.3
Decomposition Analysis			
[F-], ppm	ND	ND	7
[Cl-], ppm	ND	ND	7

(values for SUVA® HP80 assumed to be comparable)

SUVA® HP62 with various lubricants

Property	HP62 w/ Min. Oil SUNISO 3GS	HP62 w/ Alkylbenzene ZEROL 150 TD	HP62 w/ Polyol Ester Castrol "Icematic" SW 32	HP62 w/ Polyol Ester Mobil "Arctic" EAL 22
Viscosity of Neat Oil at 40°C (104°F), $(mm)^2/s$ (cSt)	ND	ND	29.6	23.7
Stability Tests				
Visual Ratings				
Neat Oil	0	0	1,H	0
Oil/Refrig.	1,G	2,P,G,H	0,G	1,G
Copper	0	2,T	0	0
Iron·	0	1,T	1,T,P	0
Aluminum	0	0	0	0
Viscosity Change				
% Change Neat	ND	ND	5.0	ND
% Change w/ Refrig.	ND	ND	ND	ND

Visual Ratings:
ND = Not Determined
G = Gel
T = Tarnish
H = Haze
P = Precipitate

Stability Ratings: 0 to 5
0 = Best
3 = Failed
5 = Coked

MATERIALS COMPATIBILITY

Because the SUVA® HP refrigerants will be used in many different applications, it is important to review materials of construction for compatibility when designing new equipment, retrofitting existing equipment or preparing storage and handling facilities. Since the SUVA® HP products have been designed as refrigerants, the compatibility data summarized here will include materials commonly used in refrigeration applications.

ELASTOMERS

Compatibility results for SUVA® HP81 and SUVA® HP62 were developed with five (5) different polymer and lubricant combinations. It was assumed that SUVA® HP80 compatibility would be similar to HP81.

It should be recognized that these data reflect compatibility in sealed tube tests, and that refrigerant compatibility in real systems can be influenced by the actual operating conditions, the nature of the polymers used, compounding formulations of the polymers, and the curing or vulcanization processes used to create the polymer. Polymers should always be tested under actual operating conditions before reaching final conclusions about their suitability.

The rankings shown in *Table 5* are based on duplicate samples of each polymer subjected to aging at 150°C for 30 days in various lubricant/refrigerant combinations. Physical properties of the test samples were determined before and after aging. The resulting ratings are based on one (1) being best and five (5) being worst for the purposes of comparison. The factors included in the overall assessment of compatibility included:

- visual observations of material changes due to aging
- changes in weight and volume of the samples due to aging
- changes in hardness of the samples due to aging
- changes in flexural properties of the samples due to aging
- recovery of weight and flexural properties after refrigerant evaporation

The compounds tested were:

- PTFE (TEFLON®, commercial grade skived sheet, from Tex-O-Lon Mfg. Co.)
- Neoprene W (from Precision Rubber Co.)
- HNBR (hydrogenated nitrile butadiene, N1195 from Parker Seal Co.)
- EPDM (ethylene propylene diene, commercial grade, Kirkhill Rubber Co.)
- NBR ("BUNA" N, nitrile butadiene, from Parker Seal Co.)

Lubricants tested:

- Mineral Oil, "SUNISO" 3GS, Witco Corporation
- Alkylbenzene, "ZEROL" 150 TD, Shrieve Chemical Products Inc.
- Polyol Ester, "ICEMATIC" SW32, Castrol
- Polyol Ester, "ARCTIC" EAL 22, Mobil Chemical

TABLE 5
Relative Ranking of Polymer/Refrigerant/Lubricant Compatibility

Refrig./Lubricant	Polymer				
	PTFE	HNBR	Neoprene W	EPDM	NBR
R-502 neat	2	4	2	2	1
R-502/Min. Oil	2	4	4	5	2
R-502/Alkylbenzene	2	4	2	5	2
HP81 neat	2	4	2	2	2
HP81/Min. Oil	2	4	4	5	2
HP81/Alkylbenzene	2	4	2	5	2
HP81/Castrol Ester	2	4	2	2	5
HP81/Mobil Ester	2	4	2	1	5
HP62 neat	2	1	1	2	1
HP62/Min. Oil	2	2	4	5	2
HP62/Alkylbenzene	2	2	3	5	2
HP62/Castrol Ester	2	4	2	1	5
HP62/Mobil Ester	2	4	2	1	5

(1 → 5, best → worst)

MOTOR MATERIALS

In hermetic and semi-hermetic compressors, the compressor motor is normally cooled by direct contact with refrigerant returning from the evaporator. As a result, the motor must be compatible with the refrigerants and lubricants used in the refrigeration system.

Accelerated aging tests were conducted with combinations of refrigerants, lubricants and motor materials using sealed tube tests prepared according to ANSI/ASHRAE 97-1989. After aging, the materials in the tubes were inspected visually and microscopically and tested physically and chemically to determine property changes.

Materials tested, and a summary of test results, were:

PET (polyethylene terephthalate, MYLAR®)

PET film is used as phase and slot insulation in hermetic motors. Visual inspection of sealed tubes after aging in refrigerant environments revealed no extracts with refrigerant alone (R-502, SUVA® HP81 or SUVA® HP62), but varying degrees of cloudiness and light precipitates when lubricants were present.

PET weight change on aging was small (< 5%) and occurred with R-502/lubricant and HP81/lubricant combinations. Weight gain with HP62/ester lubricants was 2 percent or less.

PET flexibility after aging was determined by a bend test. The results show excellent retention of flexibility on aging at 135°C. There is definite loss of flexibility when PET is aged in R-502/Mineral oil or R-502/alkylbenzene at 150°C. This loss of flexibility does not occur when PET is aged in HP81 or HP62 with ester lubricants at 150°C.

Polyesterimide Enameled Motor Wire, amide-imide overcoated (NEMA NW 35C)

No extracts or precipitates were observed on aging the enameled wire in any of the lubricant/refrigerant combinations. No blistering, crazing or cracking was observed after aging. Retention of flexibility was confirmed by 1x bend tests of the wire after aging.

DACRON®/MYLAR®/DACRON® lead wire (Belden 14 AWG)

After aging of D-M-D samples in refrigerant/lubricant environments, contents of the tubes were inspected for particulates, the tubes were cooled and opened and the lead wire samples were subjected to bend tests. Minimal particulates or extracts were observed after aging. PET embrittlement, ranging from slight loss of flexibility to shattering, was observed when specimens were bent 135 degrees. The degree of embrittlement appeared to be a factor of the lubricant, rather than the refrigerant. All D-M-D samples were embrittled in the presence of mineral oil or alkylbenzene lubricants. Good flexibility was seen after aging with polyol esters in the presence of all refrigerants.

Summary

In summary, ester-based lubricants appear to cause much less effect on common motor materials than mineral oils or alkylbenzene lubricants. In all cases, the results appeared to be better than R-502 with lubricants commonly used with 502.

DESICCANTS

In refrigeration systems, keeping the refrigerant and lubricant free of moisture is very important. Dryers filled with moisture-absorbing desiccant are typically used to prevent moisture accumulation. A desiccant used with R-502, UOP's (formerly Union Carbide Molecular Sieve) 4A-XH-5, is not generally compatible with highly fluorinated refrigerants, such as the SUVA® HP products. However, compatible molecular sieve desiccants, such as XH-9, have been developed. For loose-filled and solid core dryers, new desiccants are available which are also compatible with the new refrigerants and lubricants. Be sure to tell your parts wholesaler what refrigerants you plan to use when specifying the dryer for your system.

REFRIGERATION LUBRICANTS

Most compressors require a lubricant to protect internal moving parts. The compressor manufacturer usually recommends the type of lubricant(s) and proper viscosity that should be used to ensure acceptable operation and equipment durability. Recommendations are based on several criteria, which can include lubricity, miscibility, compatibility with materials of construction, thermal stability and compatibility with other lubricants. It is important to follow the manufacturers' recommendations for lubricants to be used with their equipment.

Current lubricants used with R-502 have at least partial miscibility with R-502, which eases the problems of designing systems to allow lubricant return back to the compressor. Many refrigeration systems take advantage of this miscibility when considering lubricant return.

Refrigerants such as the SUVA® HP products, with little or no chlorine present in them, may exhibit less miscibility with common lubricants used with R-502. Although many R-502 systems operating at low temperatures allow for reduced miscibility with the lubricant, it is important to know that the lubricants used with the SUVA® HP refrigerants will return to the compressor using existing equipment designs.

Different compressor and equipment manufacturers will recommend lubricants to use with their equipment and the SUVA® HP products. It would be difficult to summarize all possible lubricant candidates that may be screened by various equipment manufacturers. In addition, there will be continuing research and development of new lubricants that we may not have tested, since the market for alternative refrigerants continues to stimulate other market areas. Review your system needs with the equipment manufacturer, DuPont Distributor, certified refrigeration service contractor, or other qualified party. NEVER assume the current lubricant in your refrigeration system will be acceptable with the SUVA® HP refrigerant you intend to use. ALWAYS review system components for compatibility with the new refrigerant and possibly a new lubricant.

Table 6 shows a summary of miscibility tests done with a 50/50 volume mixture of refrigerant and lubricant over a wide range of temperatures, with visual inspection for phase separation as the tubes are slowly warmed. This table does not show that any refrigerant/lubricant combination is acceptable, only whether the two appear to be miscible at the conditions shown.

TABLE 6
Miscibility Summary

	Range	Phases	Range	Phases
R-502				
w/mineral oil	–60	2 phases	+73 to +80	2 phases (inversion)
w/alkylbenzene	–60 to –27	2 phases	+80	1 phase
SUVA® HP81				
w/mineral oil	–60	2 phases	+68 to +80	2 phases (inversion)
w/alkylbenzene	–60	2 phases	+16 to +80	1 phase
w/polyol ester	–60 to +80	1 phase		
SUVA® HP80				
w/mineral oil	–50	2 phases	+65 to +72	2 phases (inversion)
w/alkylbenzene	–50	2 phases	+66 to +72	2 phases (inversion)
w/polyol ester	–50 to +72	1 phase		
SUVA® HP62				
w/mineral oil	–60	2 phases	+52 to +80	2 phases (inversion)
w/alkylbenzene	–60	2 phases	+57 to +80	2 phases (inversion)
w/polyol ester	–60 to +80	1 phase		

(All temperatures in °C)

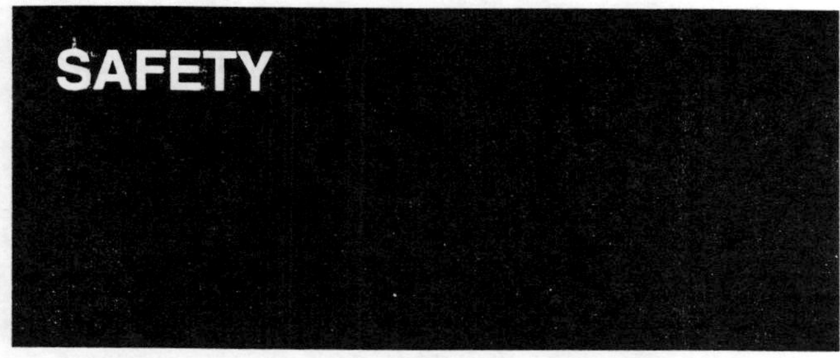

Users must have and understand the applicable SUVA® HP refrigerant Material Safety Data Sheets (MSDS).

INHALATION TOXICITY

SUVA® HP refrigerants pose no acute or chronic hazard when they are handled in accordance with DuPont recommendations and when exposures are maintained below recommended exposure limits, such as the DuPont Acceptable Exposure Limit (AEL) of 1,000 ppm, 8 or 12 hour time weighted average (TWA).

An AEL is an airborne exposure limit established by DuPont which specifies time-weighted average airborne concentrations to which nearly all workers may be repeatedly exposed without adverse effects. The AEL for the SUVA® HP refrigerants is the same level as the Threshold Limit Value (TLV) established for HCFC-22 and calculated for R-502 based on the TLVs for the components.

However, like R-502, exposure above the recommended exposure limit to the vapors of SUVA® HP refrigerants by inhalation may cause human health effects that can include temporary nervous system depression with anesthetic effects such as dizziness, headache, confusion, loss of coordination and even loss of consciousness. Higher exposures to the vapors may cause temporary alteration of the heart's electrical activity with irregular pulse, palpitations, or inadequate circulation. Death can occur from gross overexposure. Intentional misuse or deliberate inhalation of SUVA® HP refrigerant vapors may cause death without warning. This practice is extremely dangerous.

A person experiencing any of the initial symptoms should be moved to fresh air and kept calm. If not breathing, give artificial respiration. If breathing is difficult, give oxygen. Call a physician.

CARDIAC SENSITIZATION

As with many other halocarbons and hydrocarbons, inhalation of SUVA® HP refrigerants followed by intravenous injection of epinephrine, to simulate human stress reactions, results in a cardiac sensitization response. In humans, this can lead to cardiac irregularities and even cardiac arrest. The likelihood of these cardiac problems increases if you are under physical or emotional stress. The SUVA® HP refrigerants can cause these responses well above the AEL, but the effect level varies with people, and has not been fully determined.

If you are exposed to very high concentrations of SUVA® HP refrigerants, move immediately from the area, and seek medical attention as a precaution. DO NOT attempt to remain in the area to fix a leak or perform other duties—the effects of overexposure can be very sudden.

Medical attention must be given immediately if someone is having symptoms of overexposure to SUVA® HP refrigerants. DO NOT treat the patient with drugs such as epinephrine, since these drugs could increase the risk of cardiac problems. If the person is having trouble breathing, administer oxygen. If breathing has stopped, give artificial respiration immediately.

SKIN AND EYE CONTACT

At room temperature, SUVA® HP refrigerant vapors have little or no effect on the skin or eyes. However, in liquid form, they can freeze skin or eyes on contact, causing frostbite. If contact with liquid does occur, soak the exposed areas in lukewarm water, not cold or hot. In all cases, seek medical attention immediately.

Always wear protective clothing when there is a risk of exposure to liquid refrigerants. Where splashing of refrigerant may occur, always wear eye protection and a face shield.

SPILLS OR LEAKS

If a large release of vapor occurs, such as from a large spill or leak, the vapors may concentrate near the floor or in low elevation areas, which can displace the oxygen needed for life, resulting in suffocation.

Evacuate everyone until the area has been well ventilated. Re-enter the area only while using self-contained breathing apparatus. Use blowers or fans to circulate the air at floor or low levels.

Always use self-contained breathing apparatus or an air-line respirator when entering tanks or other areas where vapors might exist. Use the buddy system (a second employee stationed outside the tank) and a lifeline. Refer to the Material Safety Data Sheet (MSDS) for the specific SUVA® HP refrigerant you plan to use.

SUVA® HP refrigerants have virtually no odor, and therefore can be extremely difficult to detect in enclosed areas. Frequent leak checks and the installation of permanent leak detectors may be necessary for enclosed areas or machinery rooms. Refer to ASHRAE Standards 15 and 34 for machinery room requirements.

To ensure safety when using SUVA® HP refrigerants in enclosed areas:

1) route relief and purge vent piping outdoors, away from air intakes

2) make certain the area is well ventilated at all times; use auxiliary ventilation, if necessary, to remove vapors
3) make sure the work area is free of vapors prior to beginning any work
4) install air monitoring equipment to detect leaks.

COMBUSTIBILITY OF SUVA® HP REFRIGERANTS

All SUVA® HP refrigerants have been confirmed as nonflammable at atmospheric pressure with temperatures up to 80°C (176°F). However, tests show that HCFC-22 can become combustible at pressures as low as 60 psig (515 kPa) at ambient temperature when mixed with air at concentrations of 65 volume percent or greater. Therefore, SUVA® HP80 and HP81 should not be mixed with air for leak testing. In general, they should not be used or allowed to be present with high concentrations of air above atmospheric pressure.

In addition, HFC-143a as a pure compound is flammable. Also, HFC-134a has been shown in tests to be combustible at pressures as low as 5.5 psig (139 kPa) at 177°C (350°F) when mixed with air at concentrations generally in excess of 60 volume percent. At lower temperatures, higher pressures are required for combustibility. Therefore, SUVA® HP62 should not be mixed with air for leak testing, or used or allowed to be present with high concentrations of air above atmospheric pressure or at high temperatures.

Based on the above information, the following operating practices are recommended:

LEAK TESTING

- Equipment should NEVER be leak tested with a pressurized mixture of air and SUVA® HP refrigerants.

STORAGE TANKS

- Bulk storage tanks should be evacuated prior to initial filling, and should NEVER be under positive air pressure.
- Tanks should not be pressurized above 1.5 times the normal working pressure with SUVA® HP refrigerants. Relief devices on either the tanks or refrigerant supply system should be verified to be set below this pressure.
- Tank pressures should be monitored routinely to look for accumulation of air.
- Air lines should NEVER be connected to refrigerant storage tanks.

FILLING AND CHARGING OPERATIONS

- Before starting work, read the DuPont Material Safety Data Sheet (MSDS) for the SUVA® HP refrigerant you are using.
- Before evacuating cylinders or refrigeration equipment, any remaining refrigerant should be removed using a recovery system.
- Vacuum pump discharge lines should be free of restrictions that could increase discharge pressures and result in the formation of combustible mixtures.
- Cylinders or refrigeration equipment should normally be evacuated at the start of filling, and never be under positive air pressure.
- Filled cylinders should periodically be analyzed for air (non-absorbable gases or NAGs).

REFRIGERANT RECOVERY SYSTEMS

Efficient recovery of refrigerant from equipment or containers requires evacuation at the end of the recovery cycle. Suction lines to a recovery compressor should be periodically checked for leaks to prevent compressing air into the recovery cylinder during evacuation. In addition, the recovery cylinder pressure should be monitored, and evacuation stopped in the event of a rapid pressure rise indicating the presence of non-condensible air. The recovery cylinder contents should then be analyzed for NAG, and the recovery system leak checked if air is present. Do not continue to evacuate a refrigeration system that has a major leak.

AIR MONITORS AND LEAK DETECTION

Service personnel have used leak detection equipment for years when servicing equipment. Leak detectors exist not only for pinpointing specific leaks, but also for monitoring an entire room on a continual basis. There are several reasons for leak pinpointing or area monitoring, including:

- conservation of refrigerant
- protection of employees
- detection of fugitive or small emissions
- protection of equipment

Leak detectors can be placed into two broad categories: leak pinpointers and area monitors. Before purchasing a monitor or pinpointer, several criteria should be considered, which include sensitivity, detection limits and selectivity.

TYPES OF DETECTORS

Using selectivity as a criterion, leak detectors can be placed into one of three categories: nonselective, halogen selective or compound specific. In general, as the specificity of the monitor increases, so will the complexity and cost.

A different technology that can be employed to find leaks is by using a dye or other additive that is placed in the refrigeration system and is emitted with the leaking refrigerant and lubricant.

A detailed discussion of leak detection, along with a list of manufacturers of leak detection equipment, can be found in DuPont Bulletin ARTD-27 (H-31753-2).

NONSELECTIVE DETECTORS

Nonselective detectors are those that will detect any type of emission or vapor present, regardless of its chemical composition. These detectors are typically quite simple to use, very rugged, inexpensive and almost always portable. However, their inability to be calibrated, long-term drift, lack of selectivity and lack of sensitivity limit their use for area monitoring.

Some nonselective detectors designed for use with R-502 may have a much lower sensitivity when used with SUVA® HP refrigerants. However, newly designed detectors with good sensitivity for HFCs are now available. Be sure to consult with the manufacturer before selecting or using a nonselective detector with SUVA® HP refrigerants.

HALOGEN-SELECTIVE DETECTORS

Halogen-selective detectors use a specialized sensor that allows the monitor to detect compounds containing fluorine, chlorine, bromine and iodine without interference from other species. The major advantage of such a detector is a reduction in the number of "nuisance alarms"—false alarms caused by the presence of some compound in the area other than the target compound.

These detectors are typically easy to use, feature higher sensitivity than the non-selective detectors (detection limits are typically <5 ppm when used as an area monitor and < 0.05 oz./yr. (< 1.4 gm./yr.) when used as a leak pinpointer) and are very durable. In addition, due to the partial specificity of the detector, these instruments can be easily calibrated.

COMPOUND-SPECIFIC DETECTORS

The most complex detectors, which are also the most expensive, are compound-specific detectors. These units are typically capable of detecting the presence of a single compound without interference from other compounds.

With SUVA® HP refrigerants, using compound-specific detectors may be difficult, since the different mixtures often contain similar types of compounds. In an area where different refrigerant mixtures are used, these detectors may offer more specificity than is needed for normal leak management. Discuss these issues with the equipment manufacturers before making a purchase decision.

FLUORESCENT ADDITIVES

Fluorescent additives have been used in refrigeration systems for several years. These additives, invisible under ordinary lighting, but visible under ultraviolet (UV) light, are used to pinpoint leaks in systems. The additives are typically placed into the refrigeration lubricant when the system is serviced or charged. Leaks are detected by using a UV light to search for additive that has escaped from the system.

Recent innovations in dye technology have allowed fluorescent additives to be used with HFCs and new refrigerant mixtures. However, before adding additives to a system, the compatibility of the specific dye with the lubricant and refrigerant should be tested.

DuPont has formed a partnership in the U.S. with Spectronics Corporation to supply refrigerants mixed with fluorescent additives and to assist in developing additives that are compatible with new alternative refrigerants. For additional information, contact DuPont.

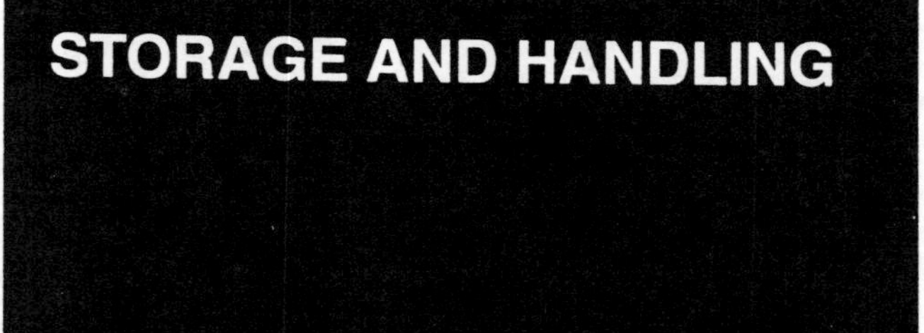

STORAGE AND HANDLING

SHIPPING CONTAINERS IN THE U.S.

SUVA® HP refrigerants are liquefied compressed gases. According to the U.S. Department of Transportation (DOT) a nonflammable compressed gas is defined as a nonflammable material having an absolute pressure greater than 40 psia at 21°C (70°F) and/or an absolute pressure greater than 104 psia at 54°C (130°F).

The appropriate DOT designations are as follows:

DOT Proper Shipping Name	(HP80/81)	COMPRESSED GAS N.O.S. (CONTAINS PENTAFLUOROETHANE AND CHLORODIFLUOROMETHANE)
	(HP62)	COMPRESSED GAS N.O.S. (CONTAINS PENTAFLUOROETHANE AND TRIFLUOROETHANE)
Hazard Class	(ALL)	NONFLAMMABLE GAS
DOT/IMO Hazard Class	(HP80/81)	2
	(HP62)	2.2
UN/NA Number	(ALL)	UN 1956
DOT Labels	(ALL)	NONFLAMMABLE GAS
DOT Placard	(ALL)	NONFLAMMABLE GAS

A list of the different types of containers that can be used to ship SUVA® HP refrigerants in the United States, along with their water capacities, dimensions, DOT specifications and net weights, are provided in *Table 7* below. All pressure relief devices used on the containers must be in compliance with the corresponding Compressed Gas Association (CGA) Standards for compressed gas cylinders, cargo and portable tanks.

TABLE 7
Specifications of Shipping Containers for SUVA® HP Refrigerants

Container	Dimensions	DOT Spec.	Net Weight (lb)		Color Code
15 lb Dispose A Can®*	7.5″×7.5″×14.5″	39	(HP81 Only)	13	PMS 385
30 lb Dispose A Can®	10″×10″×17″	39	(HP80) (HP62)	27 24	PMS 461 PMS 021
123 lb Cylinder	55″H×10″OD	4BA300 4BA400	(HP81) (HP62) (HP80)	110 100 110	
1,682 lb ton Cylinder	82″L×30″OD	110A500W			
5,000 gal	Tank Truck	MC-330 or -331	40,000		
4,400 gal ISO	8′×8.5′×20′ (frame)	51			
170,000 lb	Rail Car	114A340W			

* Dispose A Can is a registered trademark of the DuPont Company.

The 15-lb., 30-lb. and 123-lb. cylinders designed for refrigerant applications will be painted the colors shown above, with labels that bear the name of the product in the same color. For clarification, the colors are:

SUVA® HP80	PMS 461	Light brown
SUVA® HP81	PMS 385	Green brown
SUVA® HP62	PMS 021	Orange

Disposable cylinders, known as a "Dispose A Can" or DAC, fit into a box with the measurements given in *Table 7*. "Dispose A Can" is DuPont's registered trade name for this type of container. When used to ship SUVA® HP refrigerants to the stationary refrigeration market, the cylinders will have the same outlet fittings as cylinders of R-502.

The 123-lb. cylinders are equipped with a non-refillable liquid vapor CGA-660 valve. With this two-way valve, refrigerant can be removed from the cylinder as either vapor or liquid, without inverting the cylinder. The vapor valve handwheel is located on the top of the valve assembly. The liquid handwheel is on the side of the valve and attached to a dip tube extending to the bottom of the cylinder. Each is clearly identified as vapor or liquid.

The 4,400-gal. cylinder is known as an ISO tank. The dimensions referenced in *Table 7* represent the frame in which the container is shipped. The tank itself has the same length of 20 feet and an outside diameter of approximately 86 inches. ISO tanks are used for export shipments of refrigerants from the United States.

The general construction of a one-ton returnable container is shown in *Figure 7* below. Note that one end of the container is fitted with two valves. When the container is turned so that the valves are lined up vertically, the top valve will discharge vapor and the bottom valve will discharge liquid. The valves are protected by a dome cover. The valves are Superior Type 660-X1-B1.

Ton containers are equipped with two fusible plugs in each end. The fusible metal in the plugs is designed to start melting at 69°C (157°F) and completely melt at 74°C (165°F). Containers should never be heated to temperatures higher than 52°C (125°F). One spring-loaded pressure relief valve is also located in each end of the container.

BULK STORAGE SYSTEMS

DuPont sells storage systems, at cost, to their refrigeration customers. The systems are prefabricated, tested and ready to install on site. The units are designed to optimize economy, efficiency and safety in the storage and dispensing of DuPont refrigerants. The delivered systems include all components, such as storage tank, pumps, piping, valves, motors and instrumentation as an integrated unit. All systems are equipped with dual pumps to provide an installed spare. The units are skid-mounted and require only placement on a concrete pad and connection to electrical and process systems.

Figure 7. One-Ton Returnable Container

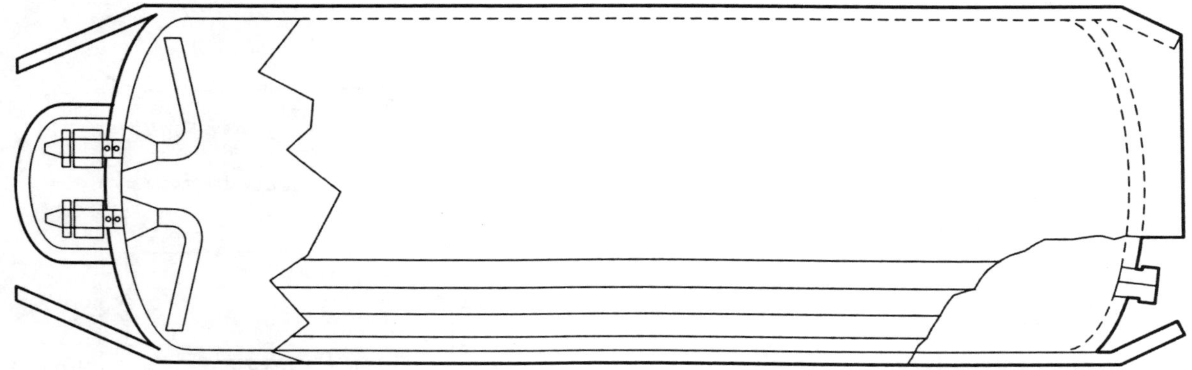

A typical bulk storage system is shown in *Figure 8.* Your DuPont Marketing Representative can arrange for guidance on site selection, purchase, installation, start-up and maintenance.

CONVERTING BULK STORAGE TANKS FROM R-502 TO SUVA® HP REFRIGERANTS

Before switching any R-502 storage system to SUVA® HP refrigerants, the existing storage equipment must be checked to verify that it is adequate. Storage tanks built to the specifications of the American Society of Mechanical Engineers (ASME) Pressure Vessel Code are required to have a metal nameplate indicating each tank's maximum allowable working pressure (MAWP). This rating must be 320 psig or higher for use with all SUVA® HP refrigerants. In addition, the set pressure of the tank relief device must also be checked and changed if necessary. This relief setting cannot be higher than the maximum working pressure listed on the nameplate, however.

We recommend that storage tanks be completely emptied of all R-502 liquid and vapor before introducing the HP refrigerant. In general, converting a storage tank to HP refrigerant requires:

1. Removing all R-502 from the storage tank, lines and equipment.
2. Evacuating the storage tank to 25–29 inches of vacuum and purging with compressed dry nitrogen gas.
3. Making necessary repairs to the tank after initial evacuation and purging.
4. Repeating step 2 until R-502 and moisture levels are within acceptable limits.
5. Refilling the system with SUVA® HP refrigerant.

The above is a simplified outline of what is actually a lengthy procedure. Your DuPont Marketing Representative can assist in obtaining the equipment, instrumentation and technical assistance to safely and effectively make the conversion.

MATERIAL COMPATIBILITY CONCERNS

Most metal components suitable for use with R-502 are also compatible with SUVA® HP refrigerants. These include standard grades of carbon steel, aluminum and copper. Some elastomeric or nonmetallic components suitable for R-502 may not be adequate with the new refrigerants. Therefore, all elastomeric or nonmetallic components throughout the system must be identified and their compatibility with SUVA® HP refrigerants verified. For complete reliability, any component that cannot be properly identified should be replaced.

Figure 8. Typical Bulk Storage System

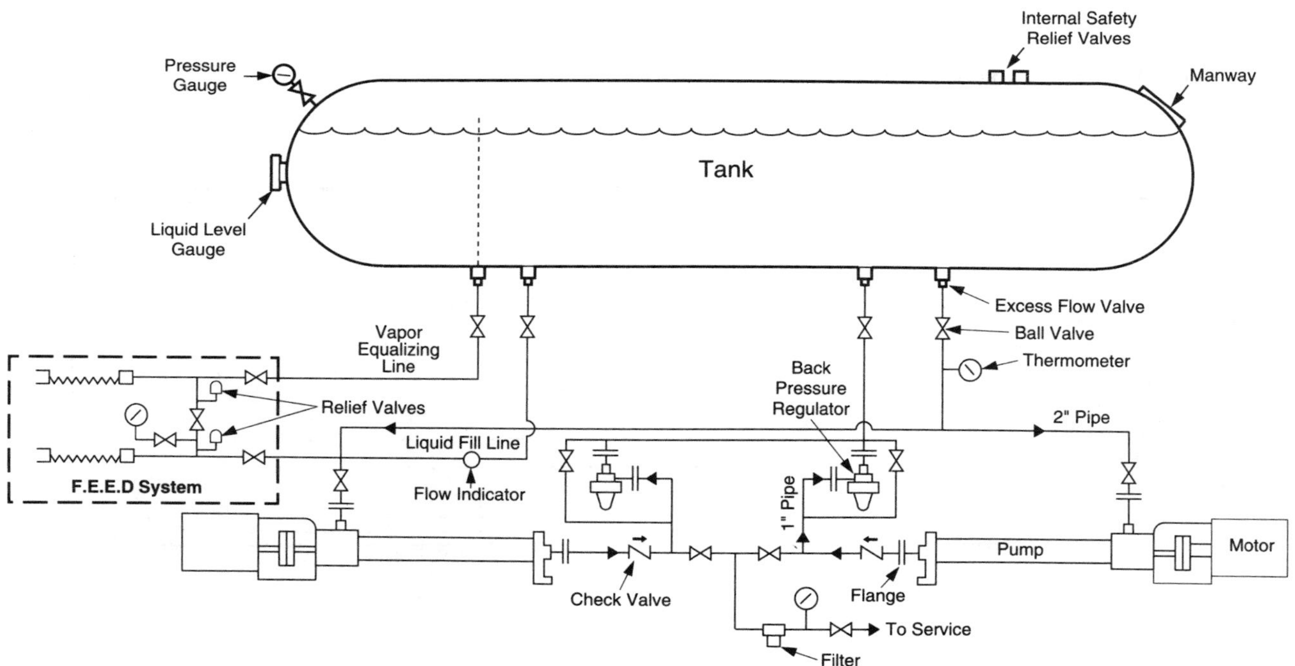

In a fluorocarbon storage system, elastomers are most commonly found in:

- Packing and seats of manual valves
- Pressure relief device seats
- Flange and manway gaskets
- Mechanical pump seals
- Wet-end pump gaskets and O-rings
- Filter O-rings
- Sight-glass gaskets
- Back-pressure regulator diaphragms and O-rings.

HANDLING PRECAUTIONS FOR SUVA® HP REFRIGERANT SHIPPING CONTAINERS

The following rules for handling HP refrigerant containers are strongly recommended:

- Use personal protective equipment, such as side shield safety glasses, gloves and safety shoes when handling refrigerant containers.
- Avoid skin contact with refrigerants, as they may cause frostbite.
- Never heat a container to temperatures higher than 52°C (125°F).
- Never apply direct flame or live steam to a container or valve.
- Never refill disposable cylinders with anything. The shipment of refilled disposable cylinders is prohibited by DOT regulations.
- Never refill returnable cylinders without DuPont consent. DOT regulations forbid transportation of returnable cylinders refilled without DuPont authorization.
- Never use a lifting magnet or sling (rope or chain) when handling containers. A crane may be used when a safe cradle or platform is used to hold the container.
- Never use containers as rollers, supports or for any purpose other than to carry refrigerant.
- Protect containers from any object that will result in a cut or other abrasion in the surface of the metal.
- Never tamper with the safety devices in the valves or containers.
- Never attempt to repair or alter containers or valves.
- Never force connections that do not fit. Make sure the threads on the regulators or other auxiliary equipment are the same as those on the container valve outlets.
- Keep valves tightly closed and valve caps and hoods in place when the containers are not in use.
- Store containers under a roof to protect them from weather extremes.
- Use a vapor recovery system to collect refrigerant vapors from lines after unloading.

RECOVERY, RECYCLE, RECLAMATION AND DISPOSAL

Responsible use of SUVA® HP refrigerants requires that the product be recovered for re-use or disposal whenever possible. DuPont purchases used refrigerant for reclamation through its distributor networks in the United States, Canada and Europe. In the United States, all SUVA® HP products will be accepted as part of this program. Recovery and re-use of refrigerant makes sense from an environmental and economic standpoint. In addition, the U.S. Clean Air Act and other global regulations prohibit venting of refrigerants now (in the case of CFCs and HCFCs) or in the near future for all refrigerants.

RECOVERY

Recovery refers to the removal of refrigerant from equipment and collection in an appropriate container. As defined by the Air Conditioning and Refrigeration Institute (ARI), recovery does not involve processing or analysis of the refrigerants. SUVA® HP refrigerants may be recovered from refrigeration equipment using permanent on-site equipment or many of the portable recovery devices now available in the marketplace. The portable devices contain a small compressor and an air-cooled condenser, and may be used for vapor (and in some cases, liquid) recovery. At the end of the recovery cycle, the system is evacuated thoroughly to remove vapors. In the United States, the Environmental Protection Agency (EPA) sets standards for recovery equipment. Before purchasing a specific recovery unit, check with the manufacturer to be sure that it contains proper materials of construction and lubricant for the refrigerants you intend to recover.

Due to the fact that SUVA® HP products are not azeotropes, it is important that all refrigerant is removed from a system during recovery or recycle. It is always recommended that refrigerant transfers be made liquid phase whenever possible to minimize composition changes in the products.

RECYCLE

Refrigerant recycle refers to reducing the contaminant levels in used refrigerants by passing the refrigerants through devices that separate out or reduce the amount of lubricant, water, acidity and particulates. Recycle is usually a field or shop procedure with no analytical testing of refrigerant. SUVA® HP refrigerants may be recycled using many of the devices now available. In the United States, the EPA sets standards for these devices. Recycle is already standard practice in many portions of the commercial refrigeration industry. Consult with the manufacturer before specifying a recycle device for any refrigerant.

If you routinely recycle SUVA® HP refrigerants through several cycles, we recommend that you have the composition of the refrigerant checked periodically. This will prevent loss of performance in the unlikely event that the composition has shifted.

RECLAMATION

Reclamation refers to the reprocessing of used refrigerant to new product specifications. Quality of the reclaimed product is verified by chemical analysis. In the United States, SUVA® HP refrigerants are included in DuPont's refrigerant reclamation program. Contact DuPont or one of our authorized distributors for further information.

Reclamation offers advantages over on-site refrigerant recycling procedures because recycling systems cannot guarantee complete removal of all contaminants. Putting refrigerants that do not meet new product specifications into expensive equipment may cause damage.

DISPOSAL

Disposal refers to the destruction of used refrigerant. Disposal may be necessary when the refrigerant has become badly contaminated with other products and no longer meets the acceptance specifications of DuPont or other reclaimers. Although DuPont does not presently accept severely contaminated refrigerant for disposal, licensed waste disposal firms are available. Be sure to check the qualifications of any firm before sending them used refrigerants.

H-47122-2 (2/94) Printed in U.S.A. 235091C

DuPont Chemicals
Fluorochemicals Customer Service Center
Wilmington, DE 19898

For sales information:
1-800-441-9442
In Delaware (302) 774-2099

For technical information:
1-800-582-5606
In Delaware (302) 999-3129

Europe
DuPont de Nemours
International S.A.
2 Chemin du Pavillon
P.O. Box 50
CH-1218 Le Grand-Saconnex
Geneva, Switzerland
41-22-717-5111

Canada
DuPont Canada, Inc.
P.O. Box 2200, Streetsville
Mississauga, Ontario
L5M 2H3
(416) 821-3300

Mexico
DuPont, S.A. de C.V.
Homero 206
Col. Chapultepec Morales
C.P. 11570 Mexico, D.F.
52-5-250-8000

South America
DuPont do Brasil S.A.
Alameda Itapicuru, 506
Alphaville 06400 Barueri
São Paulo, Brazil
55-11-421-8509

DuPont Argentina S.A.
Casilla Correo 1888
Correo Central
1000 Buenos Aires, Argentina
54-1-311-8167

Pacific
DuPont Australia
P.O. Box 930
North Sydney, NSW 2060
Australia
61-2-923-6165

Japan
Mitsui DuPont Fluoro-
chemicals Company, Ltd.
Mitsui Seimei Building
2-3, 1-Chome Ohtemachi
Chiyoda-Ku, Tokyo 100 Japan
81-3-3216-8451

Asia
DuPont Taiwan
P.O. Box 81-777
Taipei, Taiwan
886-2-514-4400

DuPont Asia Pacific Limited
P.O. Box TST 98851
Tsim Sha Tsui
Kowloon, Hong Kong
852-734-5345

DuPont Thailand
P.O. Box 2398
Bangkok 10501, Thailand
66-2-238-4361

DuPont China Ltd.
Room 1704, Union Bldg.
100 Yanan Rd. East
Shanghai, PR China 200 002
Phone: 86-21-328-3738
Telex: 33448 DCLSH CN
Fax: 86-21-320-2304

DuPont Far East Inc.
P.O. Box 12396
50776 Kuala Lumpur,
Malaysia
Phone: 60-3-232-3522
Telex: (784) 30391 DUFE M
Fax: 60-3-238-7250

DuPont Korea Ltd.
C.P.O. Box 5972
Seoul, Korea
82-2-721-5114

DuPont Singapore Pte. Ltd.
1 Maritime Square #07 01
World Trade Centre
Singapore 0409
65-273-2244

DuPont Far East, Philippines
5th Floor, Solid Bank Building
777 Paseo de Roxas
Makati, Metro Manila
Philippines
63-2-818-9911

DuPont Far East Inc.
7A Murray's Gate Road
Alwarpet
Madras, 600 018 India
91-44-454-029

DuPont Far East Inc.—
Pakistan
9 Khayaban-E-Shaheen
Defence Phase 5
Karachi, Pakistan
92-21-533-350

DuPont Far East Inc.
P.O. Box 2553/Jkt
Jakarta 10001
Indonesia
62-21-517-800

(Stock number on last page of text)

SUVA®

REFRIGERANTS ART - 18

PRODUCT INFORMATION

Transport Properties of SUVA® Refrigerants:

SUVA® HP62
SUVA® HP80
SUVA® HP81

Viscosity
Thermal Conductivity
and
Heat Capacity
for the
Liquid and Vapor

DUPONT

Transport Properties of SUVA® Refrigerants

SUVA® MP39 **SUVA® MP52** **SUVA® MP66**

TABLE OF CONTENTS

English Units **Page**

Metric Units

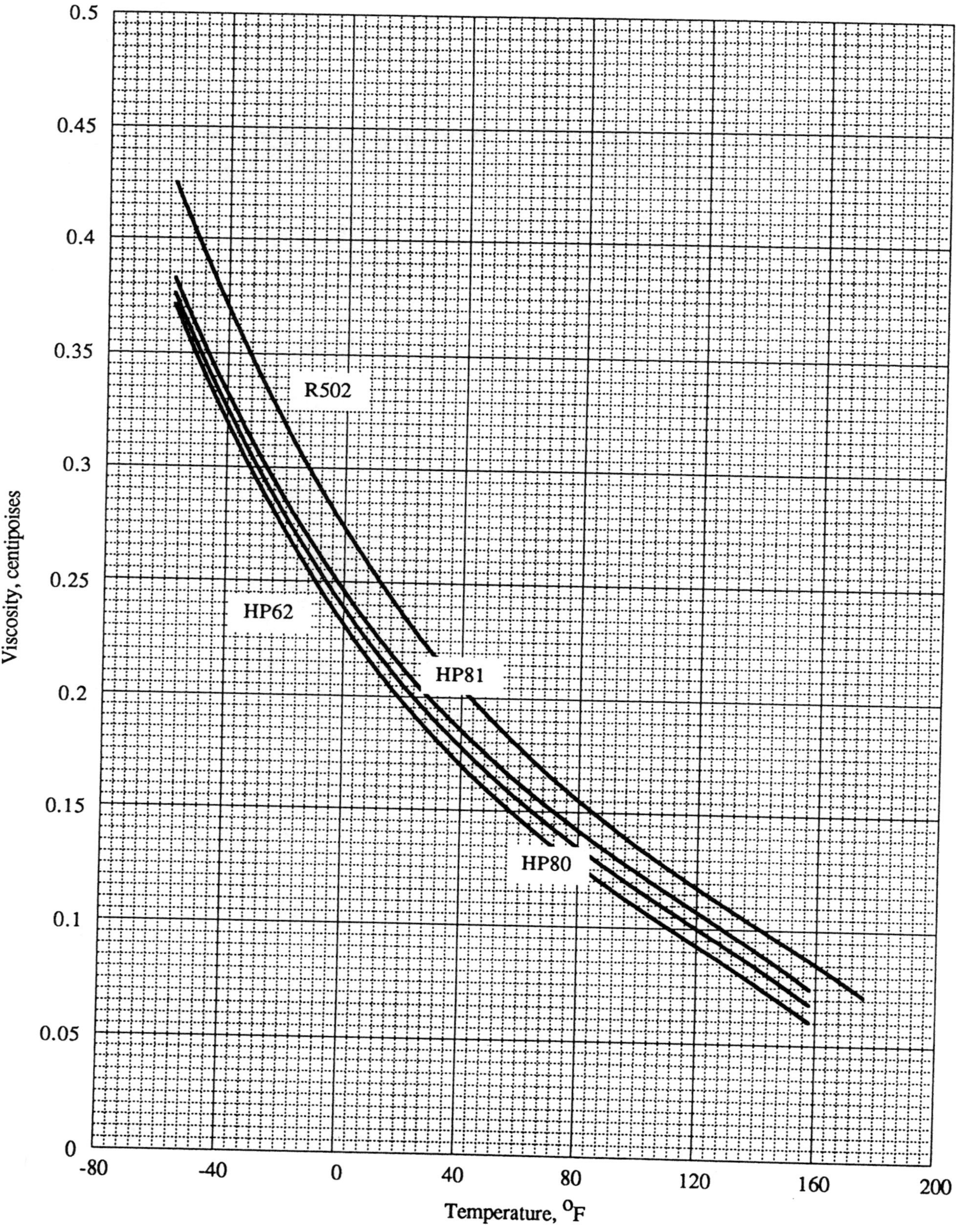

Saturated Liquid Viscosity
Viscosity, centipoises
0.5
0.45
0.4
0.35
0.3
0.25
0.2
0.15
0.1
0.05
0
R502
HP62
HP81
HP80
-80
-40
0
40
80
120
160
200
Temperature, °F

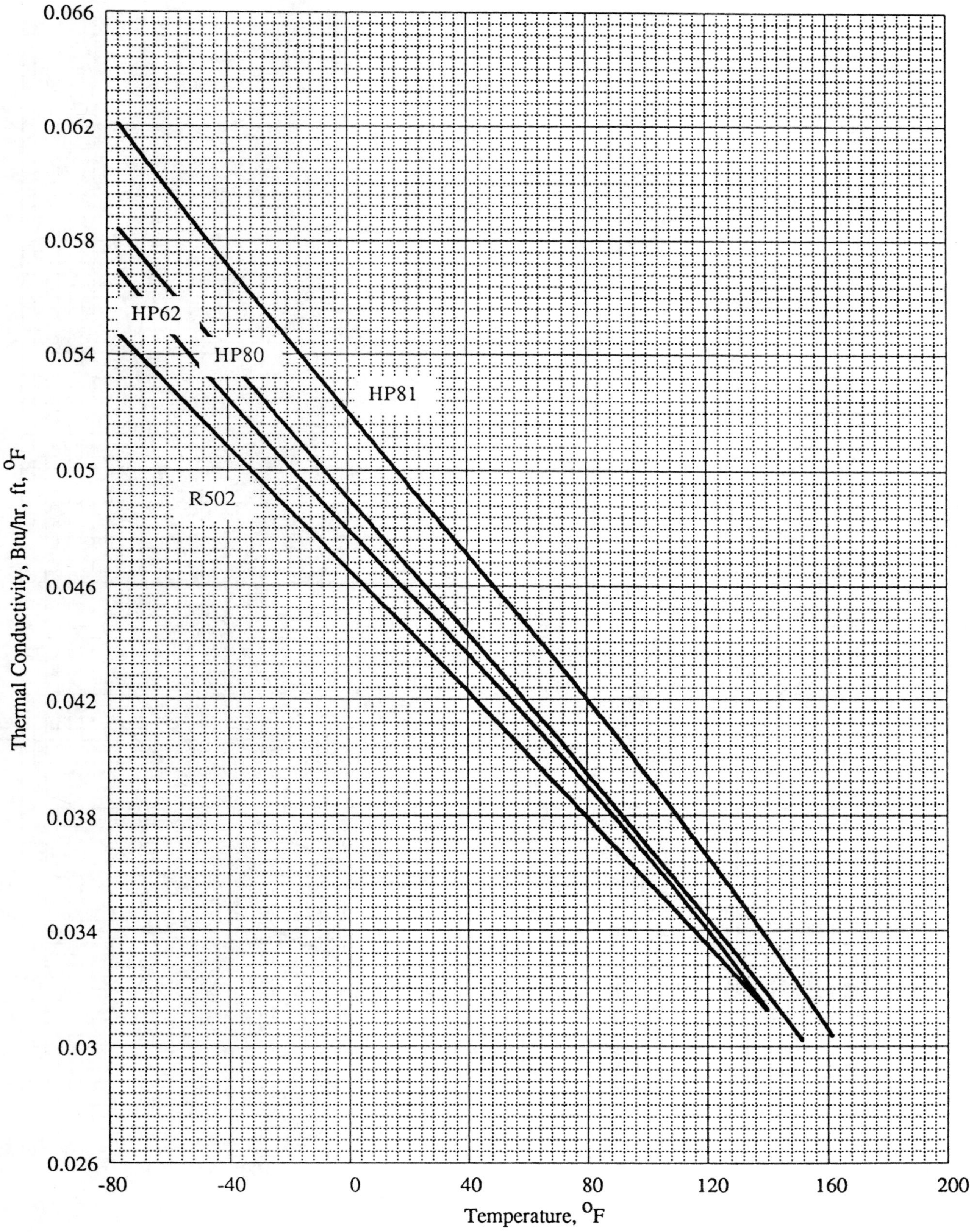
Saturated Liquid Thermal Conductivity
0.066
0.062
0.058
0.054
0.05
0.046
0.042
0.038
0.034
0.03
0.026
Thermal Conductivity, Btu/hr, ft, °F
HP62
HP80
HP81
R502
-80
-40
0
40
80
120
160
200
Temperature, °F

Saturated Liquid Heat Capacity

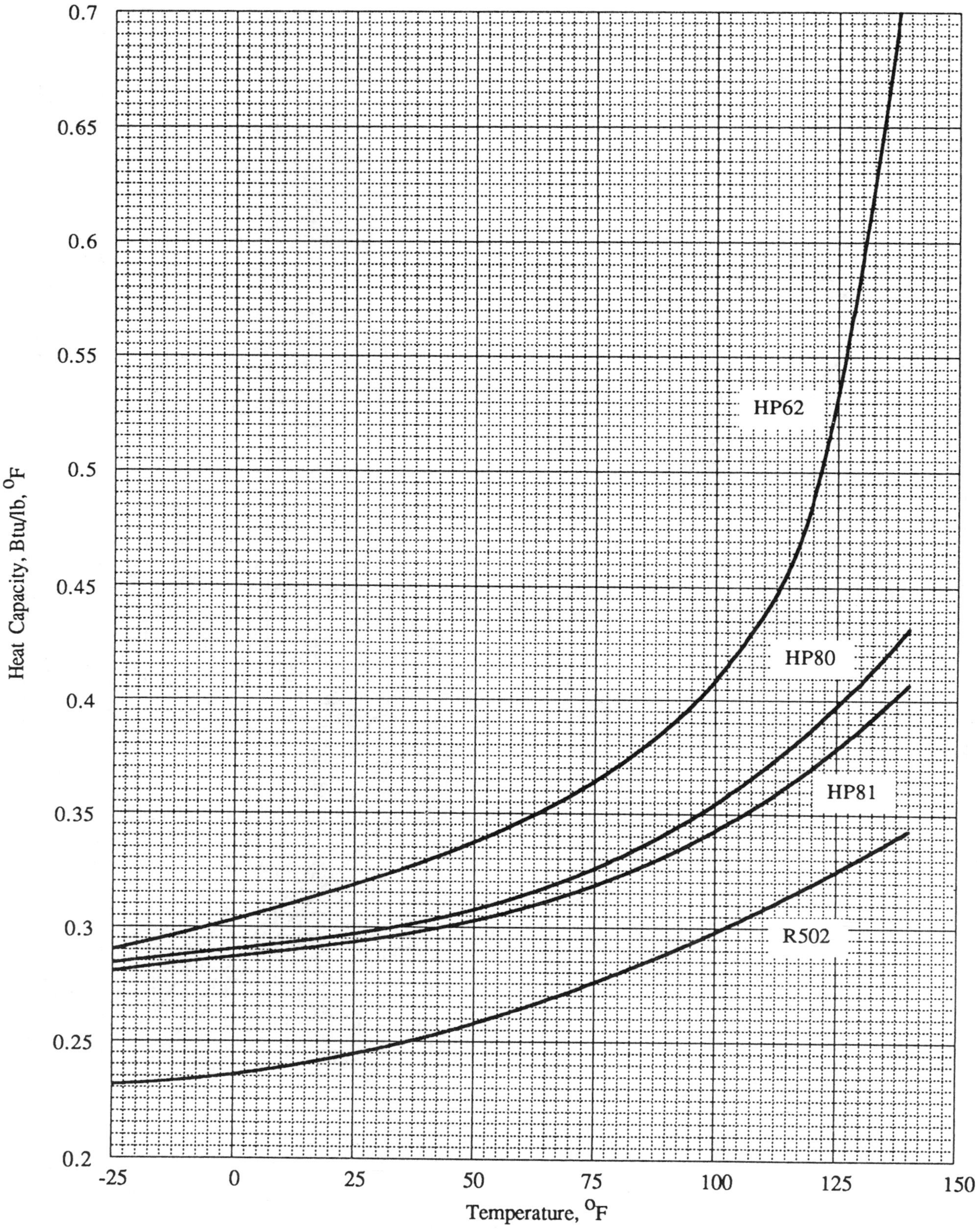

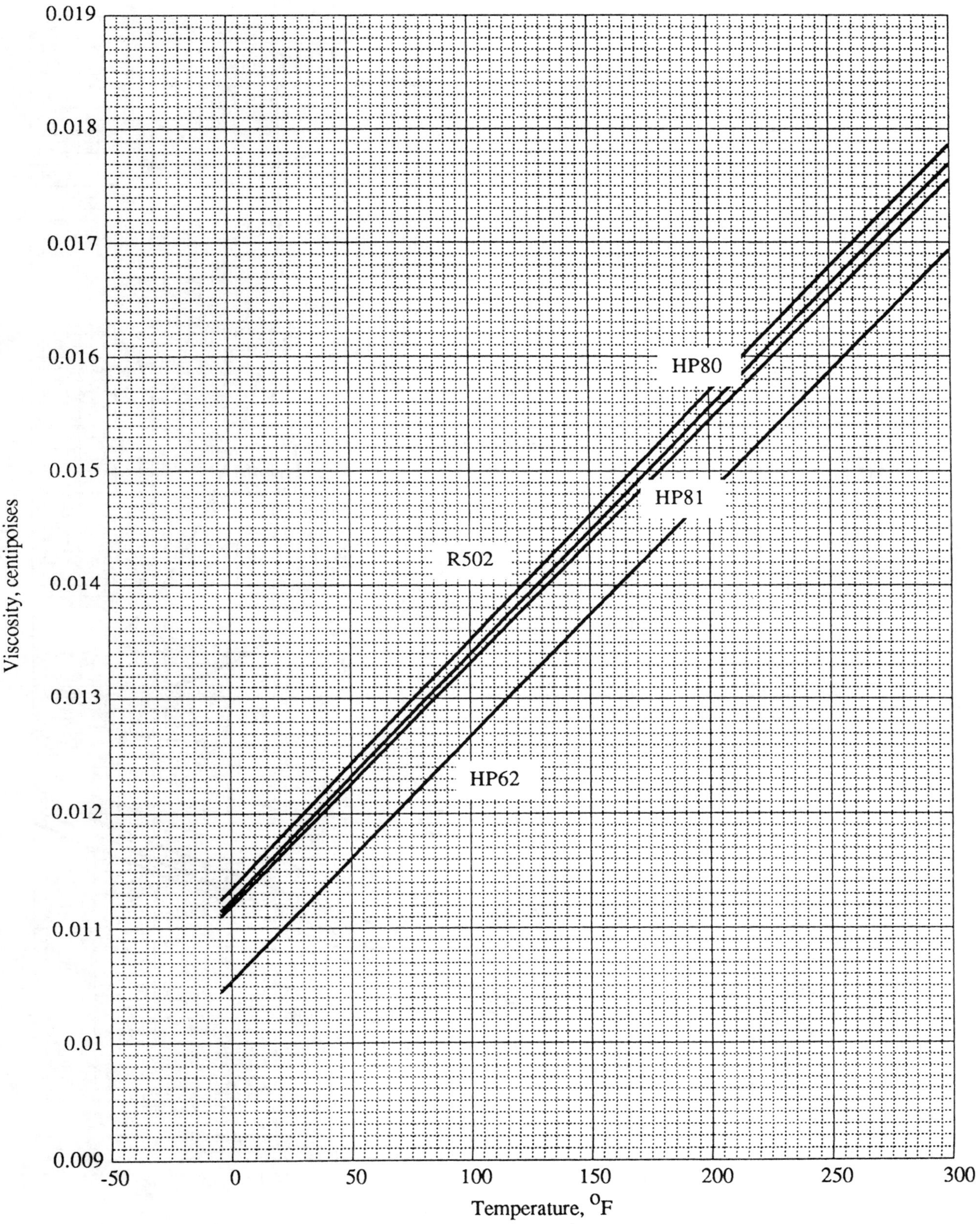
Vapor Viscosity at Atmospheric Pressure
0.019
0.018
0.017
0.016
0.015
0.014
0.013
0.012
0.011
0.01
0.009
Viscosity, centipoises
HP80
HP81
R502
HP62
-50
0
50
100
150
200
250
300
Temperature, °F

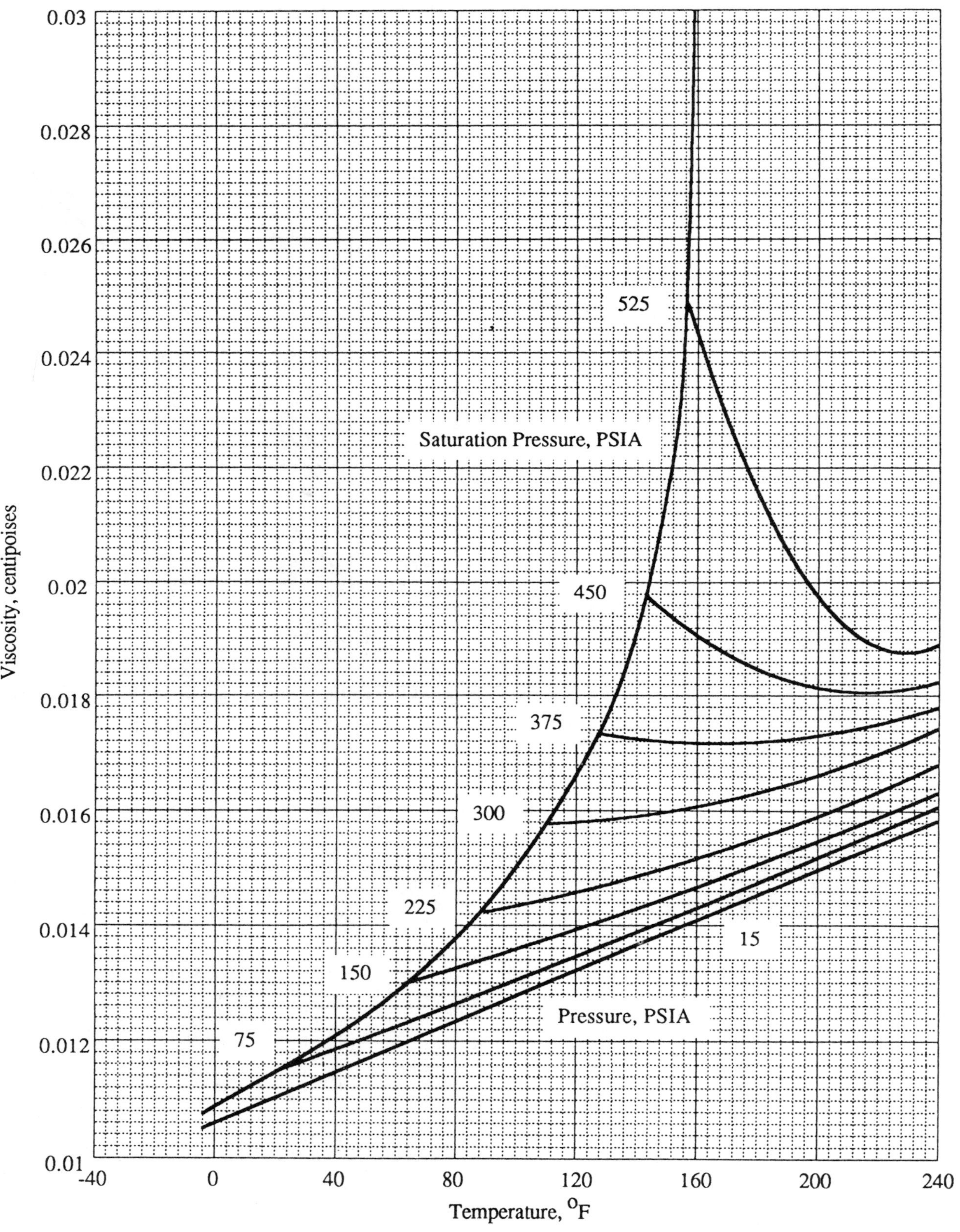
HP62 Vapor Viscosity
Viscosity, centipoises
0.03
0.028
0.026
0.024
0.022
0.02
0.018
0.016
0.014
0.012
0.01
-40
0
40
80
120
160
200
240
Temperature, °F
525
Saturation Pressure, PSIA
450
375
300
225
150
75
15
Pressure, PSIA

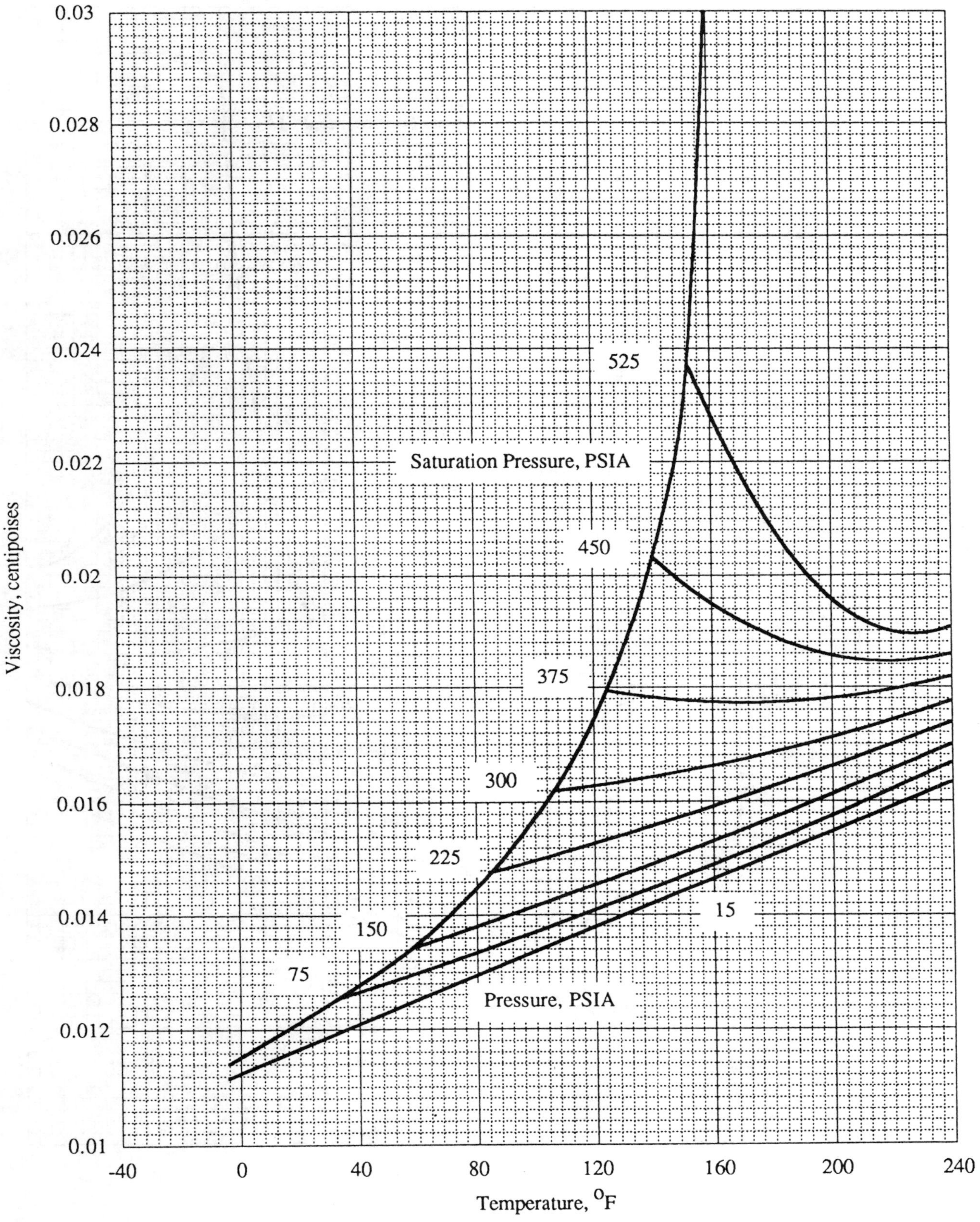
HP80 Vapor Viscosity
0.03
0.028
0.026
0.024
0.022
0.02
0.018
0.016
0.014
0.012
0.01
Viscosity, centipoises
-40
0
40
80
120
160
200
240
Temperature, °F
525
Saturation Pressure, PSIA
450
375
300
225
150
75
15
Pressure, PSIA

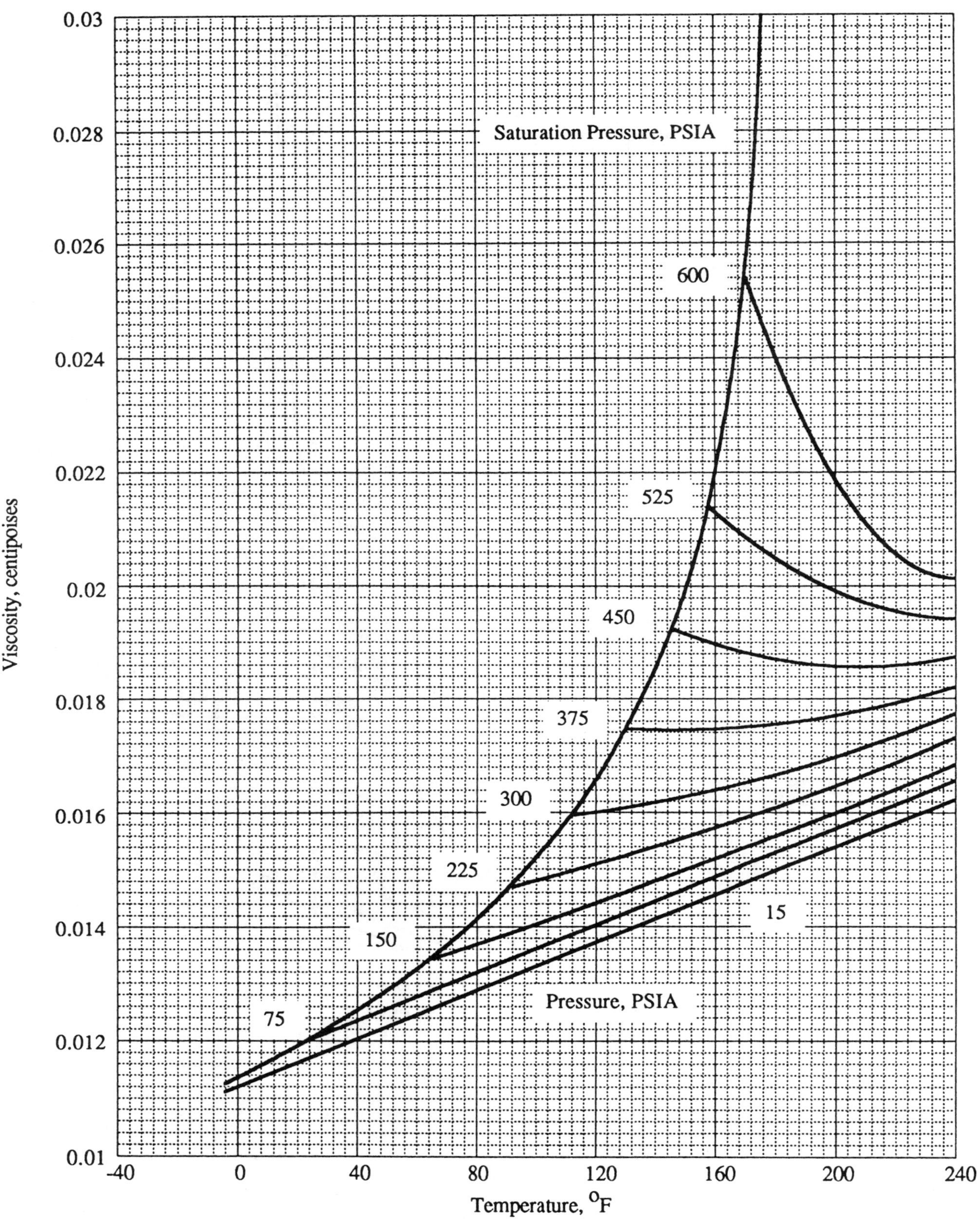
HP81 Vapor Viscosity
Saturation Pressure, PSIA
600
525
450
375
300
225
150
75
15
Pressure, PSIA
Viscosity, centipoises
0.03
0.028
0.026
0.024
0.022
0.02
0.018
0.016
0.014
0.012
0.01
-40
0
40
80
120
160
200
240
Temperature, °F

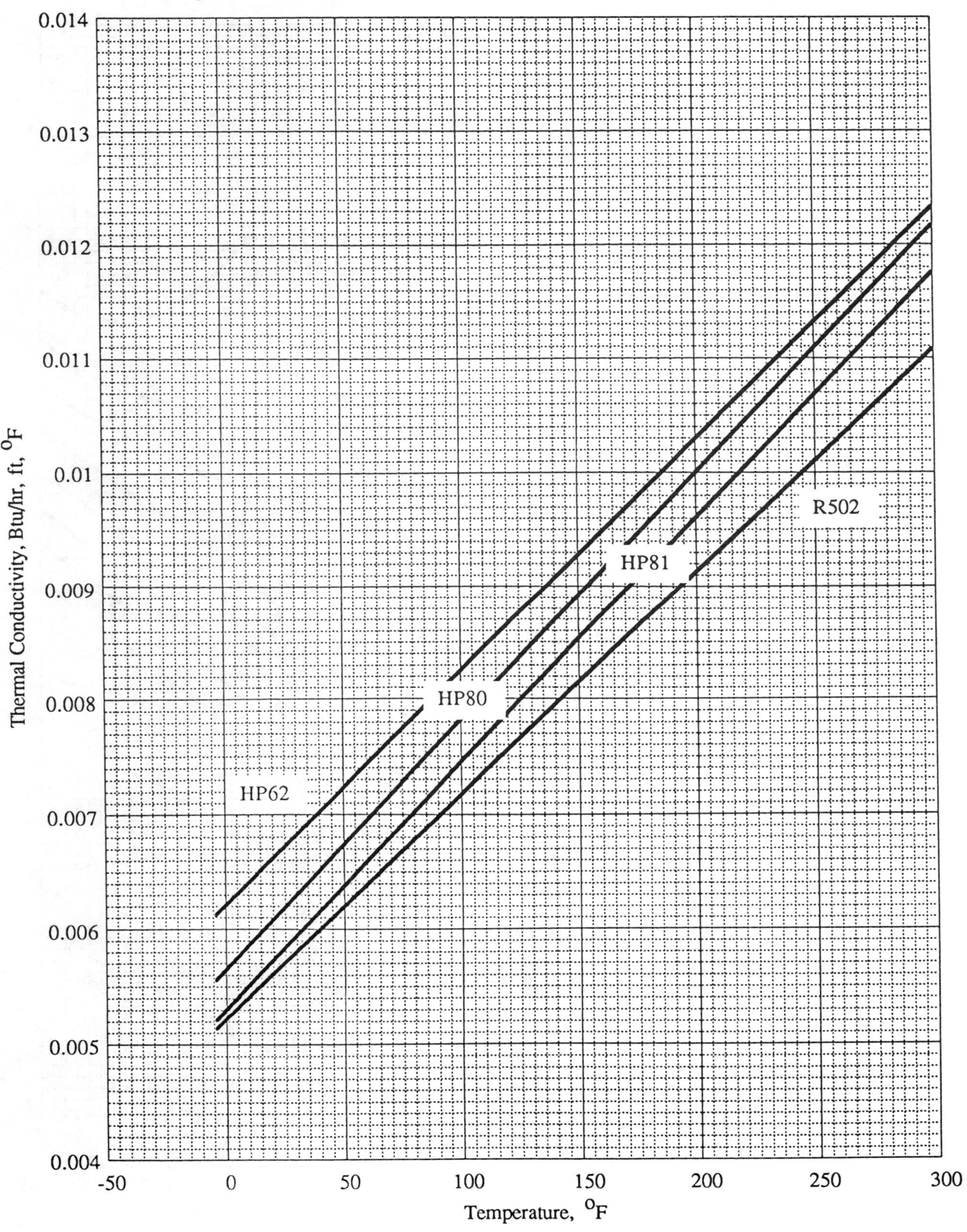

Vapor Thermal Conductivity at Atmospheric Pressure
0.014
0.013
0.012
0.011
0.01
0.009
0.008
0.007
0.006
0.005
0.004
Thermal Conductivity, Btu/hr, ft, °F
-50
0
50
100
150
200
250
300
Temperature, °F
HP62
HP80
HP81
R502

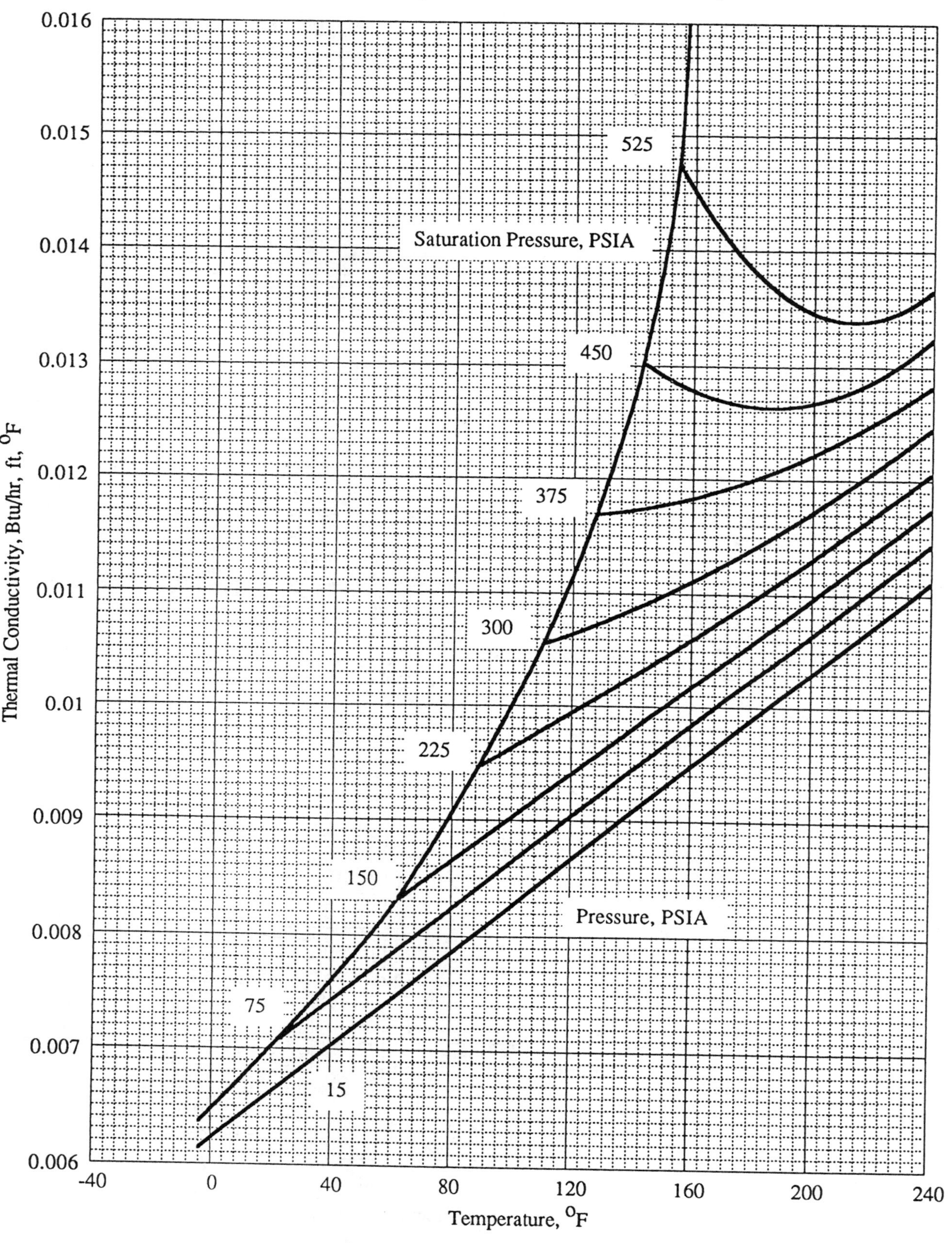
HP62 Vapor Thermal Conductivity
Thermal Conductivity, Btu/hr, ft, °F
Temperature, °F
0.016
0.015
0.014
0.013
0.012
0.011
0.01
0.009
0.008
0.007
0.006
-40
0
40
80
120
160
200
240
Saturation Pressure, PSIA
Pressure, PSIA
525
450
375
300
225
150
75
15

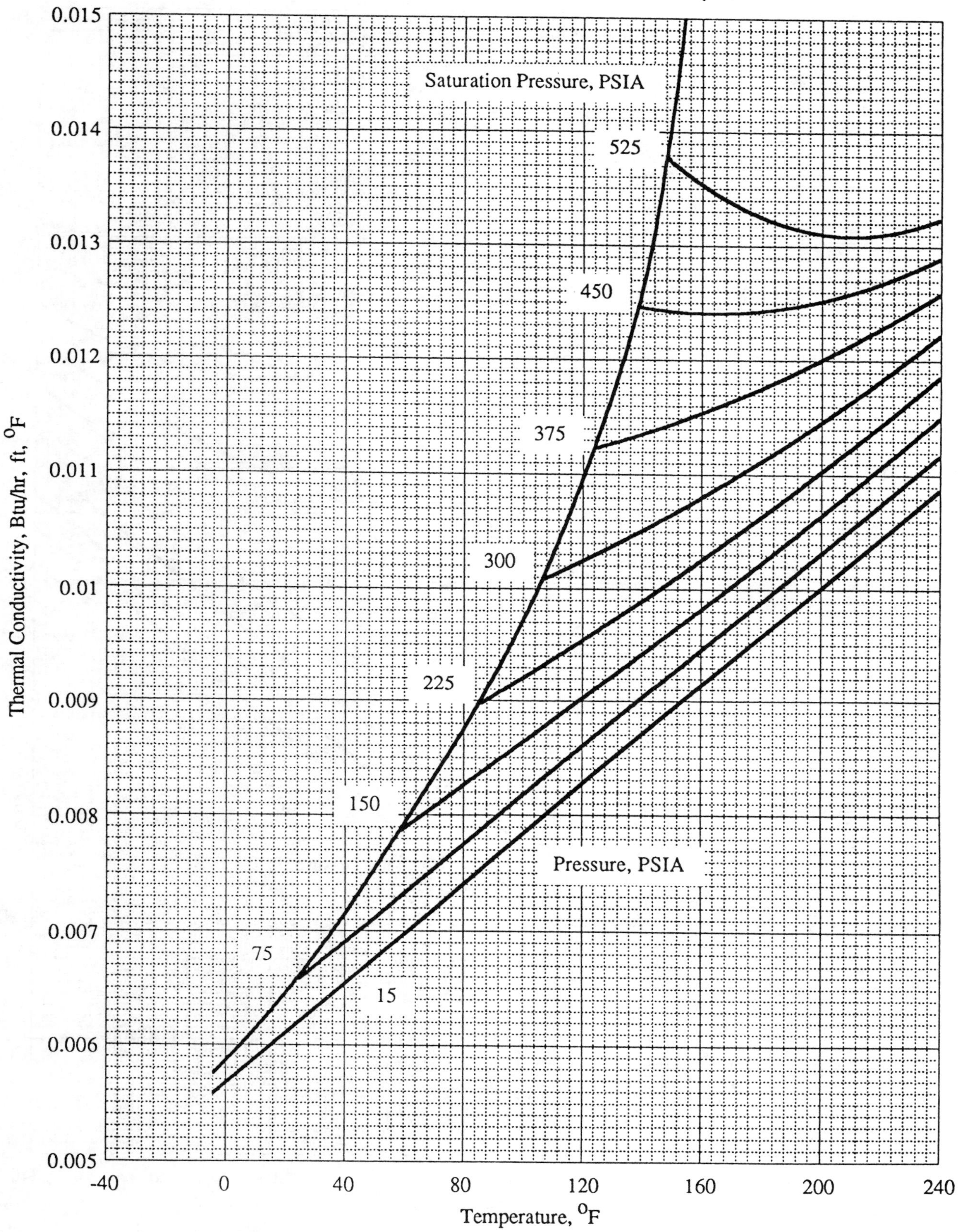
HP80 Vapor Thermal Conductivity
Saturation Pressure, PSIA
525
450
375
300
225
150
75
15
Pressure, PSIA
Thermal Conductivity, Btu/hr, ft, °F
Temperature, °F
0.015
0.014
0.013
0.012
0.011
0.01
0.009
0.008
0.007
0.006
0.005
-40
0
40
80
120
160
200
240

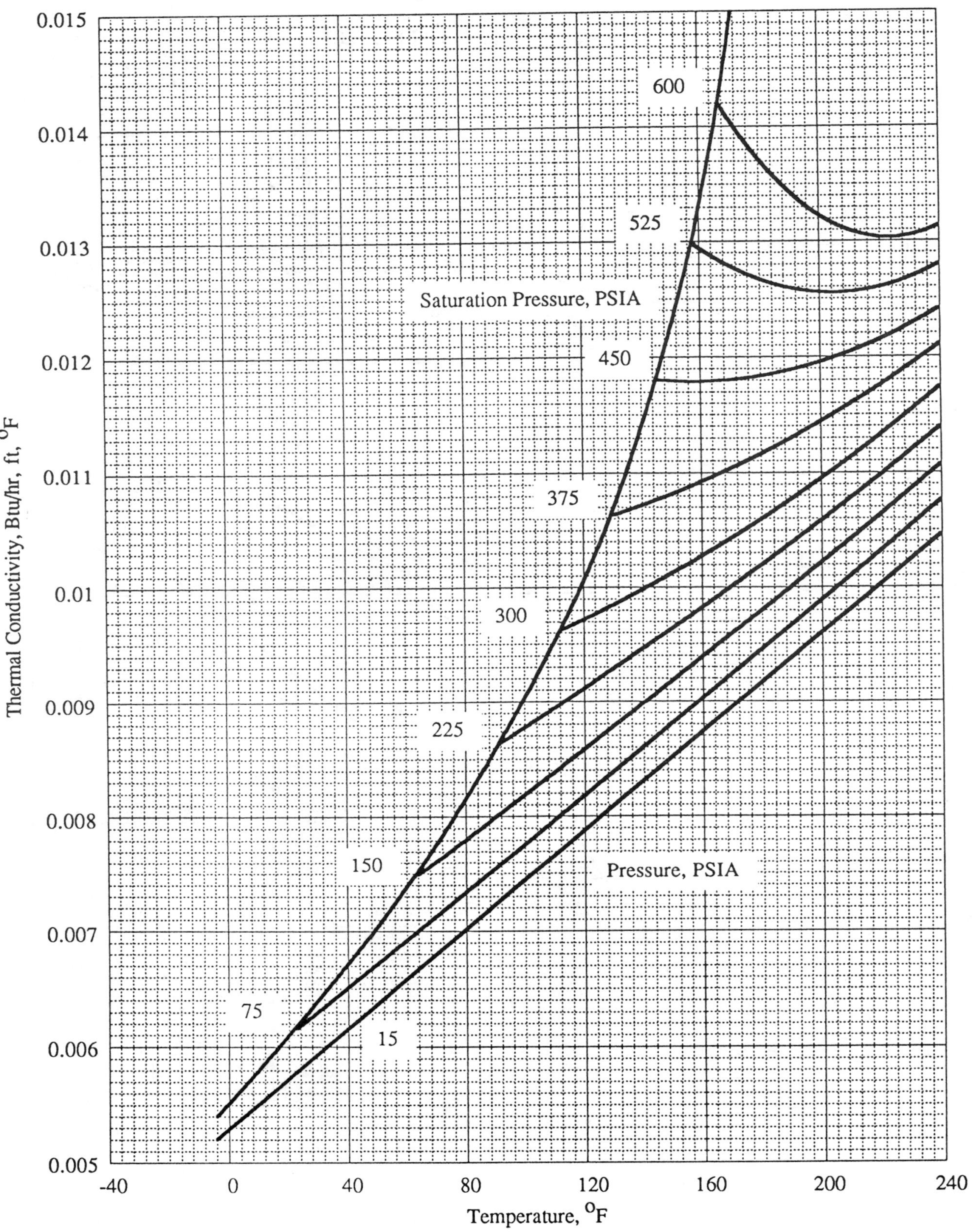
HP81 Vapor Thermal Conductivity
0.015
0.014
0.013
0.012
0.011
0.01
0.009
0.008
0.007
0.006
0.005
Thermal Conductivity, Btu/hr, ft, oF
-40
0
40
80
120
160
200
240
Temperature, oF
600
525
Saturation Pressure, PSIA
450
375
300
225
150
75
15
Pressure, PSIA

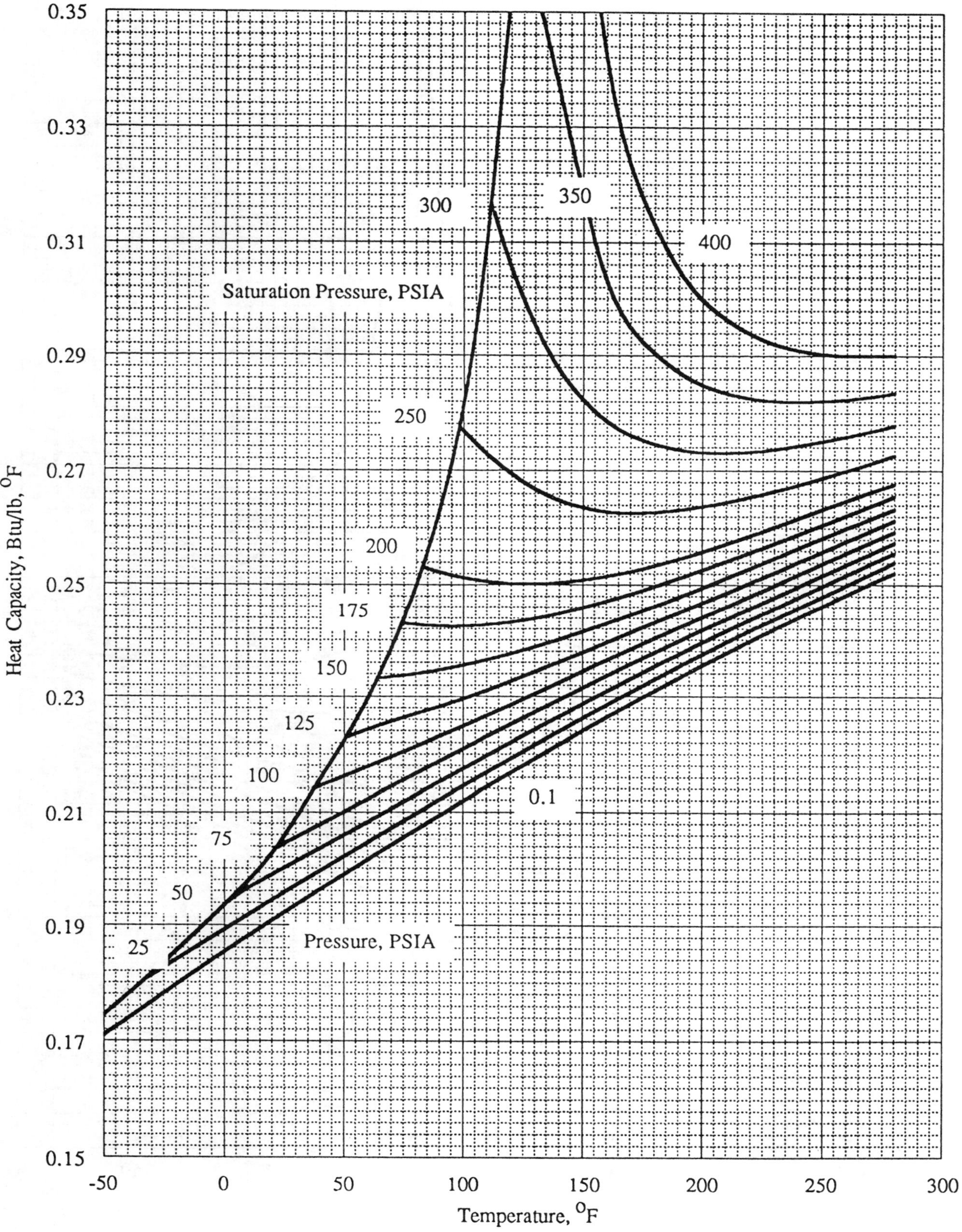
HP62 Vapor Heat Capacity
Heat Capacity, Btu/lb, °F
Temperature, °F
0.35
0.33
0.31
0.29
0.27
0.25
0.23
0.21
0.19
0.17
0.15
-50
0
50
100
150
200
250
300
Saturation Pressure, PSIA
Pressure, PSIA
300
350
400
250
200
175
150
125
100
75
50
25
0.1

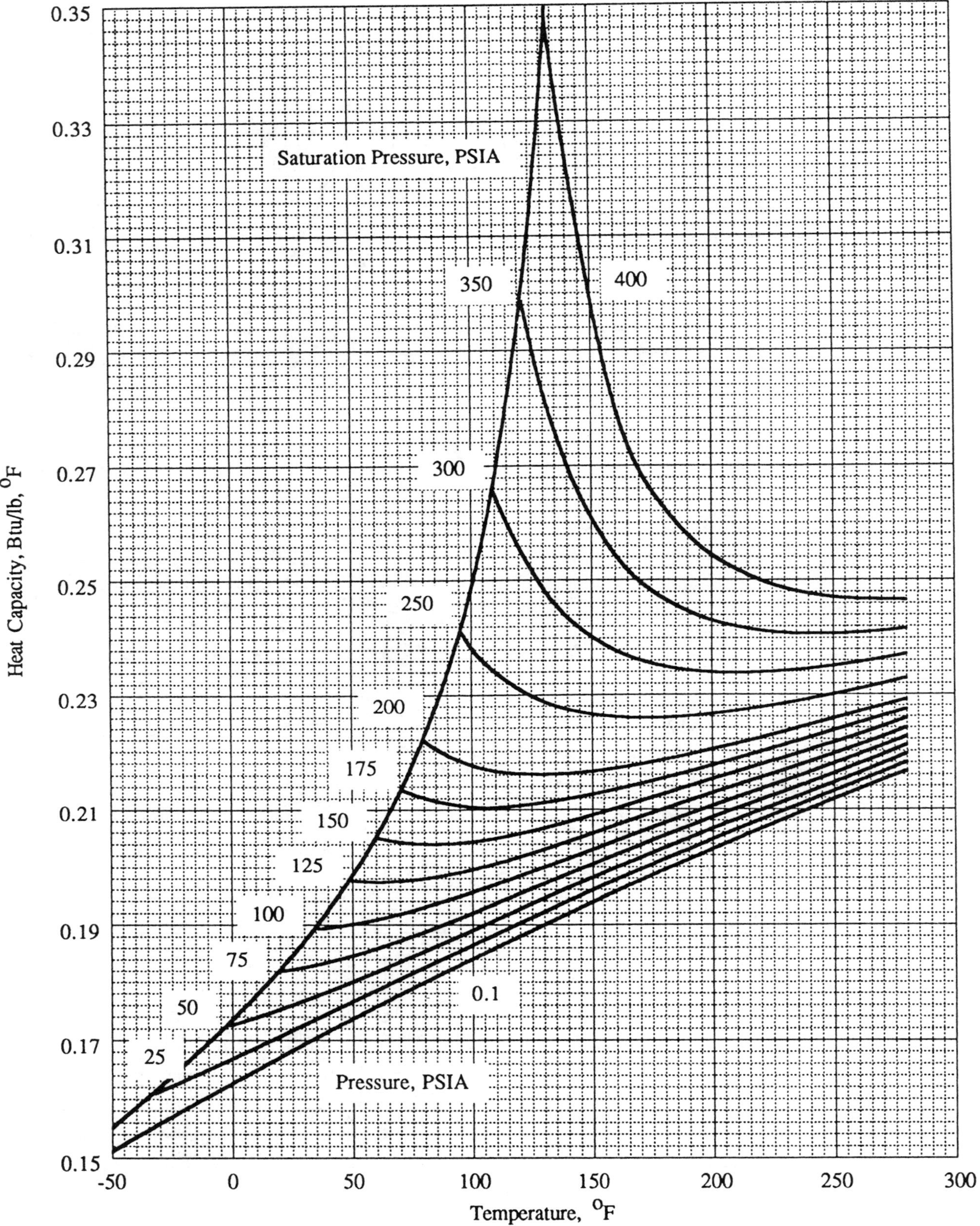
HP80 Vapor Heat Capacity
Saturation Pressure, PSIA
350
400
300
250
200
175
150
125
100
75
50
25
0.1
Pressure, PSIA
Heat Capacity, Btu/lb, °F
Temperature, °F
0.35
0.33
0.31
0.29
0.27
0.25
0.23
0.21
0.19
0.17
0.15
-50
0
50
100
150
200
250
300

HP81 Vapor Heat Capacity

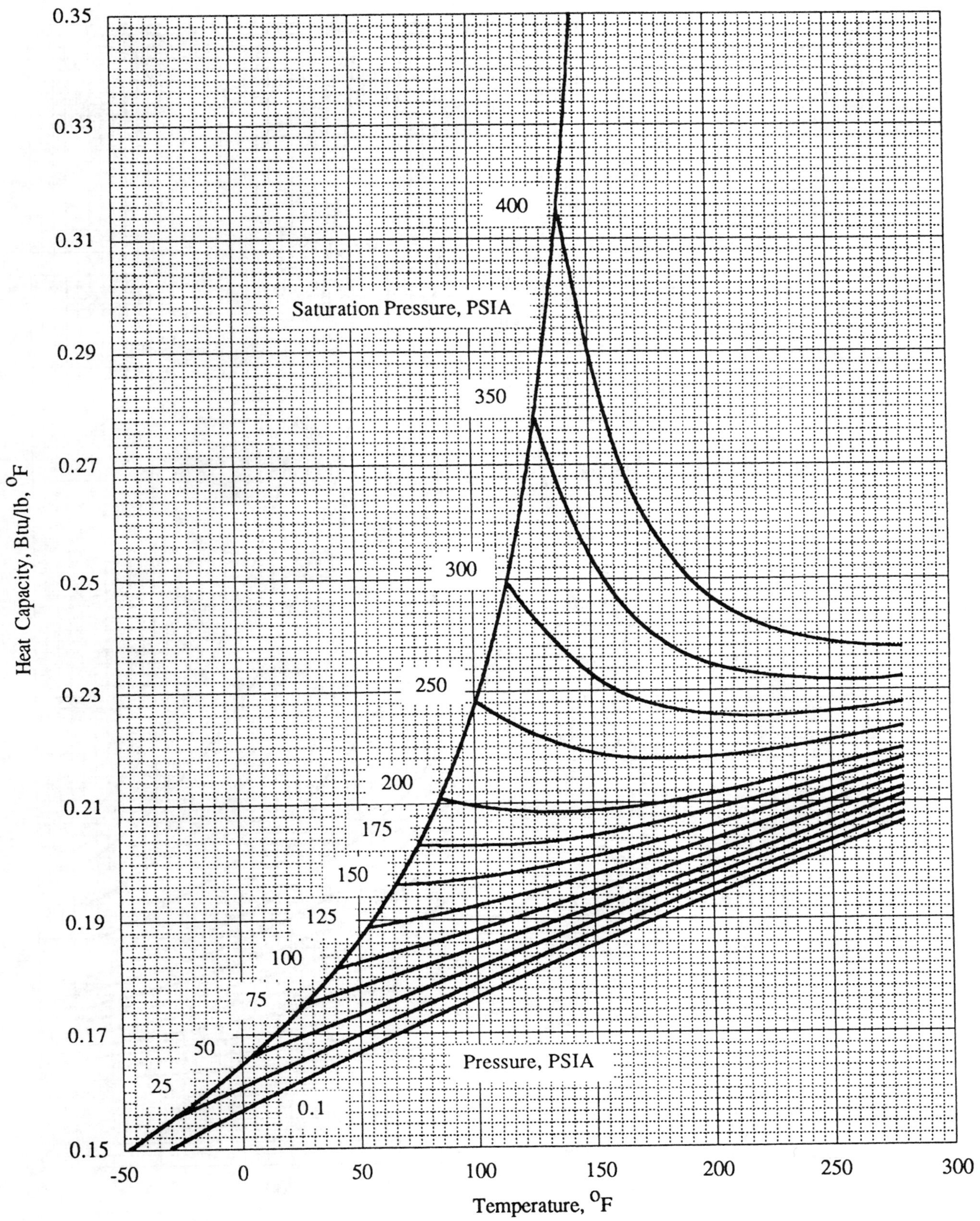

HP62 Vapor Heat Capacity Ratio

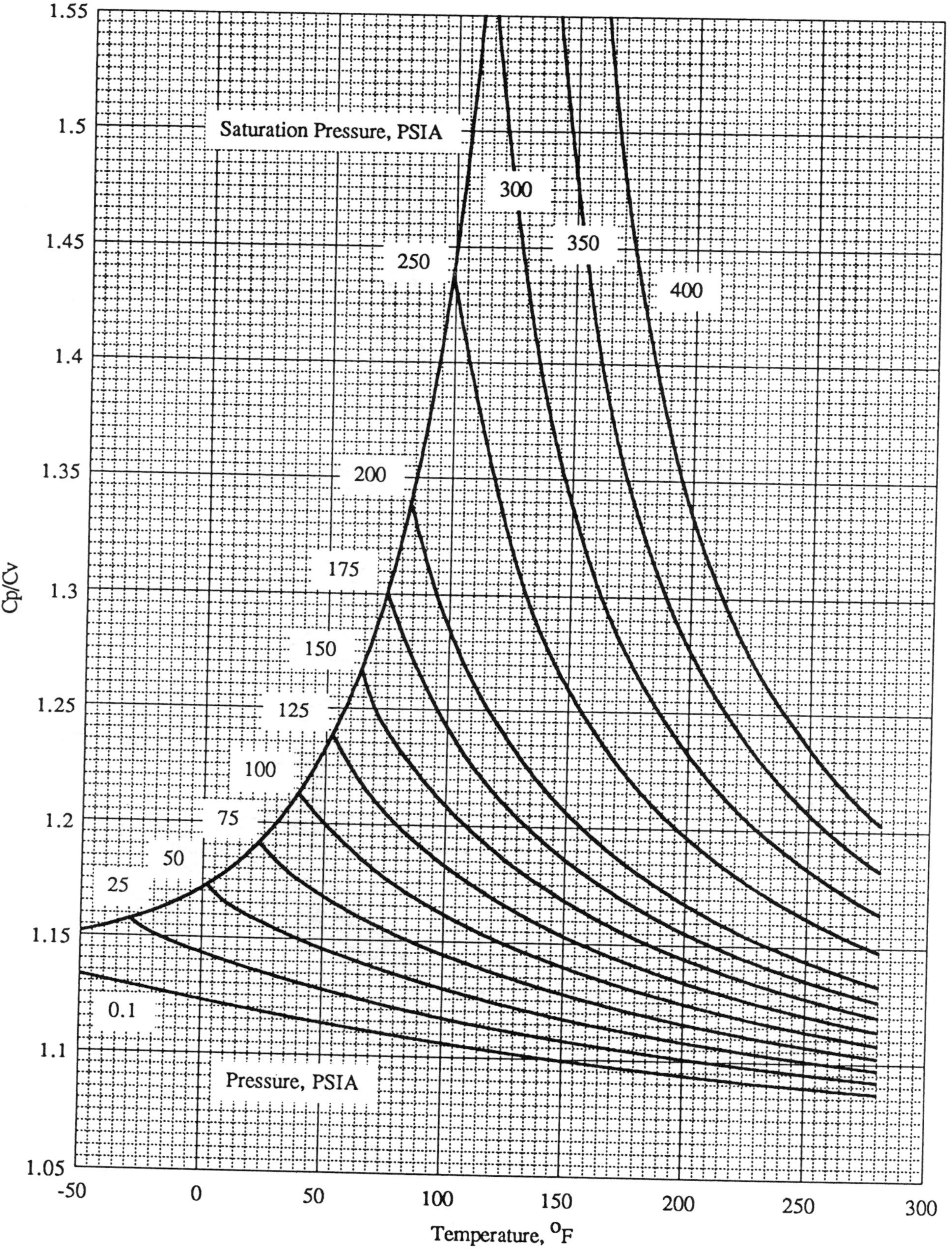

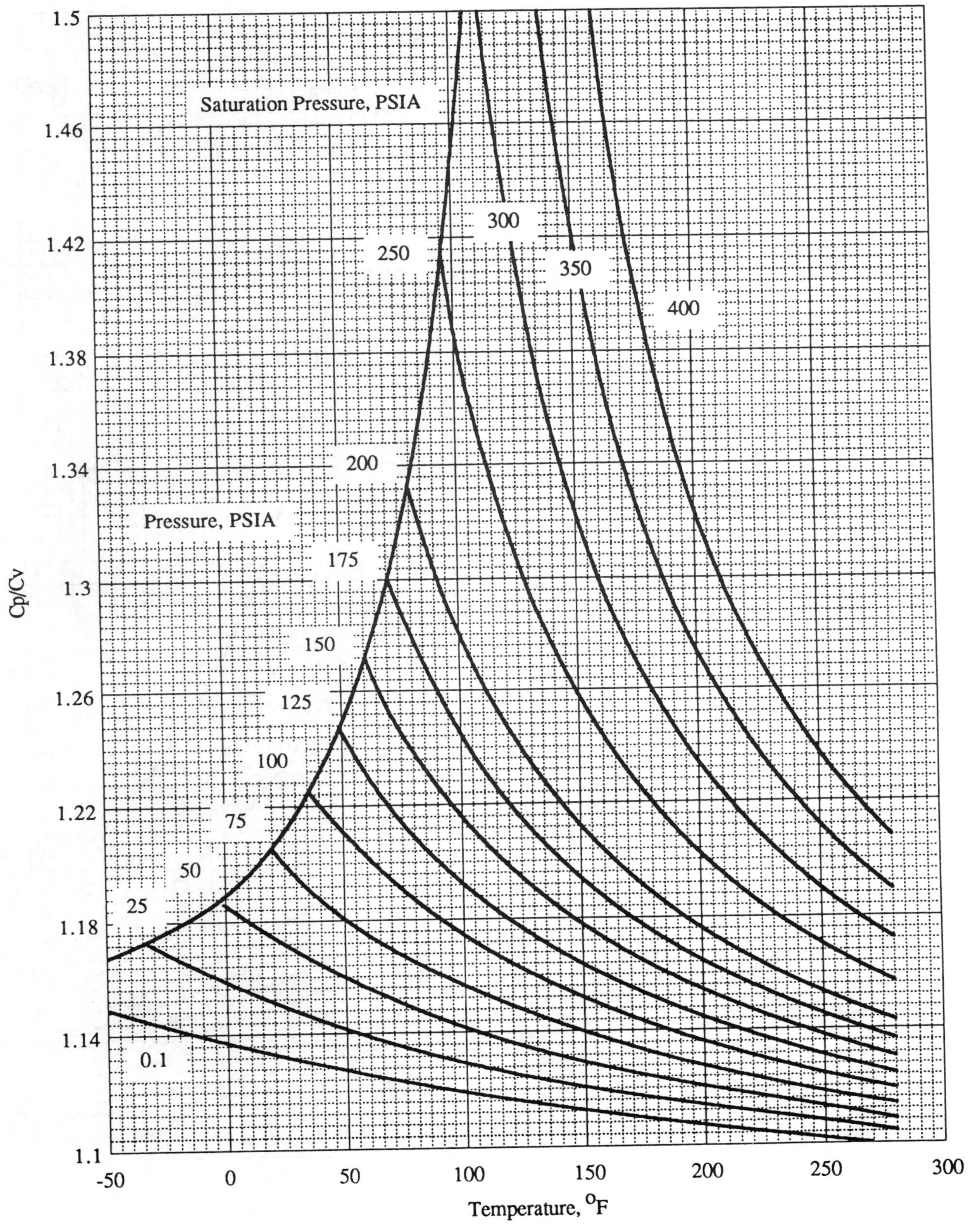
HP80 Vapor Heat Capacity Ratio
Saturation Pressure, PSIA
Pressure, PSIA
0.1
25
50
75
100
125
150
175
200
250
300
350
400
Cp/Cv
1.5
1.46
1.42
1.38
1.34
1.3
1.26
1.22
1.18
1.14
1.1
-50
0
50
100
150
200
250
300
Temperature, °F

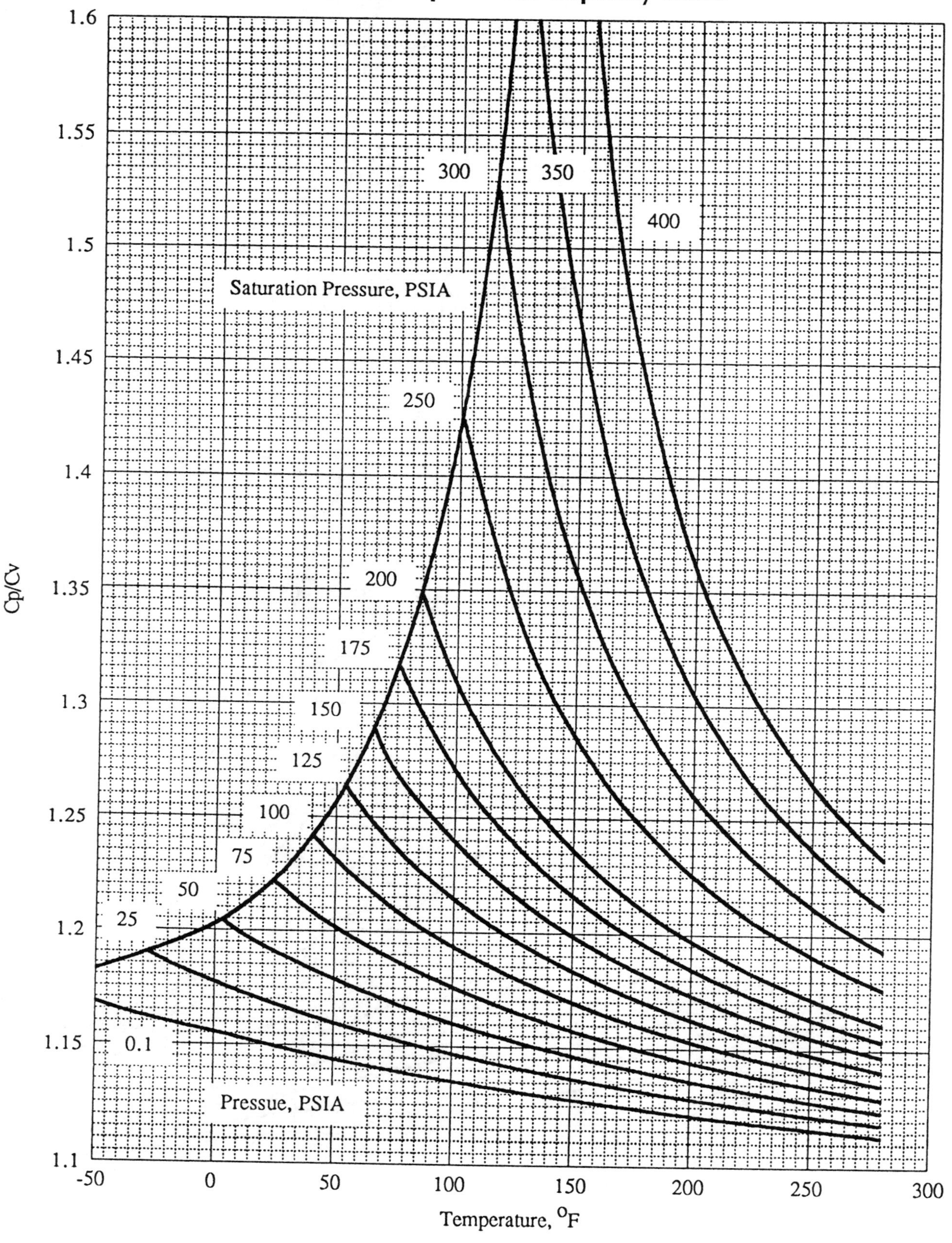
HP81 Vapor Heat Capacity Ratio
Saturation Pressure, PSIA
300
350
400
250
200
175
150
125
100
75
50
25
0.1
Pressue, PSIA
Cp/Cv
1.6
1.55
1.5
1.45
1.4
1.35
1.3
1.25
1.2
1.15
1.1
-50
0
50
100
150
200
250
300
Temperature, ^{o}F

EQUATIONS FOR PROPERTY ESTIMATION

English Units

Curves have been fitted to the measured data to obtain the following equations for estimation of properties within the ranges specified.

Liquid Viscosity in cP (–50°F to 160°F)

SUVA® HP62 $\mu = 0.231 - 1.838E\text{-}3\ T + 8.502E\text{-}6\ T^2 - 2.361E\text{-}8\ T^3$

SUVA® HP80 $\mu = 0.239 - 1.815E\text{-}3\ T + 8.207E\text{-}6\ T^2 - 2.259E\text{-}8\ T^3$

SUVA® HP81 $\mu = 0.246 - 1.807E\text{-}3\ T + 8.133E\text{-}6\ T^2 - 2.258E\text{-}8\ T^3$

Liquid Thermal Conductivity in Btu/hr ft °F (–80°F to 160°F)

SUVA® HP62 $k = 0.0480 - 1.102E\text{-}4\ T + 4.244E\text{-}8\ T^2 - 7.685E\text{-}10\ T^3$

SUVA® HP80 $k = 0.0491 - 1.199E\text{-}4\ T + 1.493E\text{-}8\ T^2 - 3.077E\text{-}10\ T^3$

SUVA® HP81 $k = 0.0521 - 1.248E\text{-}4\ T + 4.461E\text{-}8\ T^2 - 6.403E\text{-}10\ T^3$

Liquid Heat Capacity in Btu/lb °F (–40°F to 140°F)

SUVA® HP62 $C_p = 0.306 + 4.083E\text{-}4\ T - 1.194E\text{-}6\ T^2 + 8.056E\text{-}8\ T^3$

SUVA® HP80 $C_p = 0.290 + 2.362E\text{-}4\ T - 3.443E\text{-}7\ T^2 + 3.695E\text{-}8\ T^3$

SUVA® HP81 $C_p = 0.287 + 2.403E\text{-}4\ T - 3.045E\text{-}8\ T^2 + 3.179E\text{–}8\ T^3$

Vapor Viscosity at One Atmosphere in cP (–20°F to 300°F)

SUVA® HP62 $\mu = 0.01054 + 2.130E\text{-}5\ T$

SUVA® HP80 $\mu = 0.01124 + 2.154E\text{-}5\ T$

SUVA® HP81 $\mu = 0.01118 + 2.124E\text{-}5\ T$

Vapor Thermal Conductivity at One Atmosphere in Btu/lb ft °F (–20°F to 300°F)

SUVA® HP62 $k = 0.00620 + 2.046E\text{-}5\ T$

SUVA® HP80 $k = 0.00564 + 2.181E\text{-}5\ T$

SUVA® HP81 $k = 0.00530 + 2.155E\text{-}5\ T$

Where T = Temperature, °F

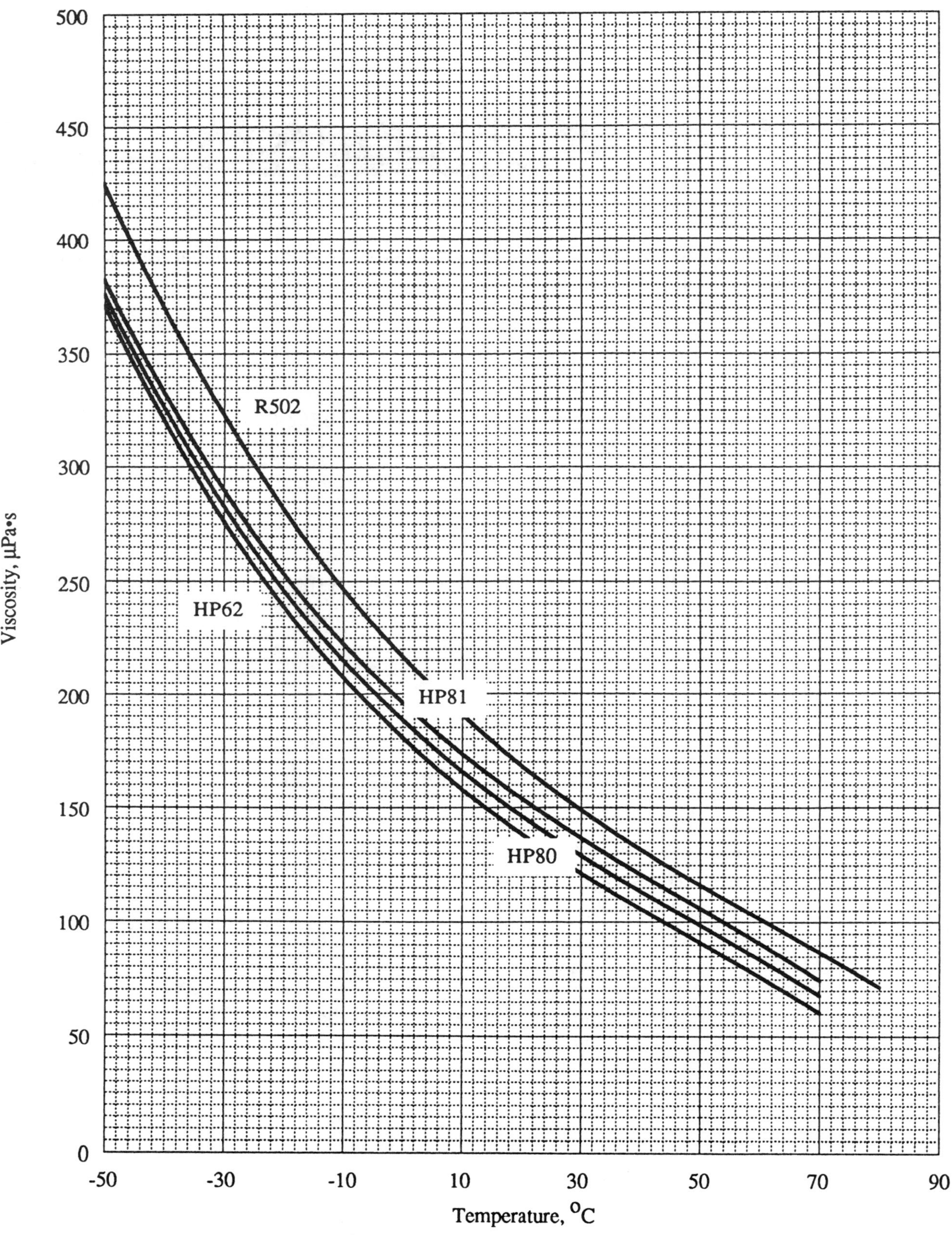
Saturated Liquid Viscosity
Viscosity, µPa•s
500
450
400
350
300
250
200
150
100
50
0
-50
-30
-10
10
30
50
70
90
Temperature, °C
R502
HP62
HP81
HP80

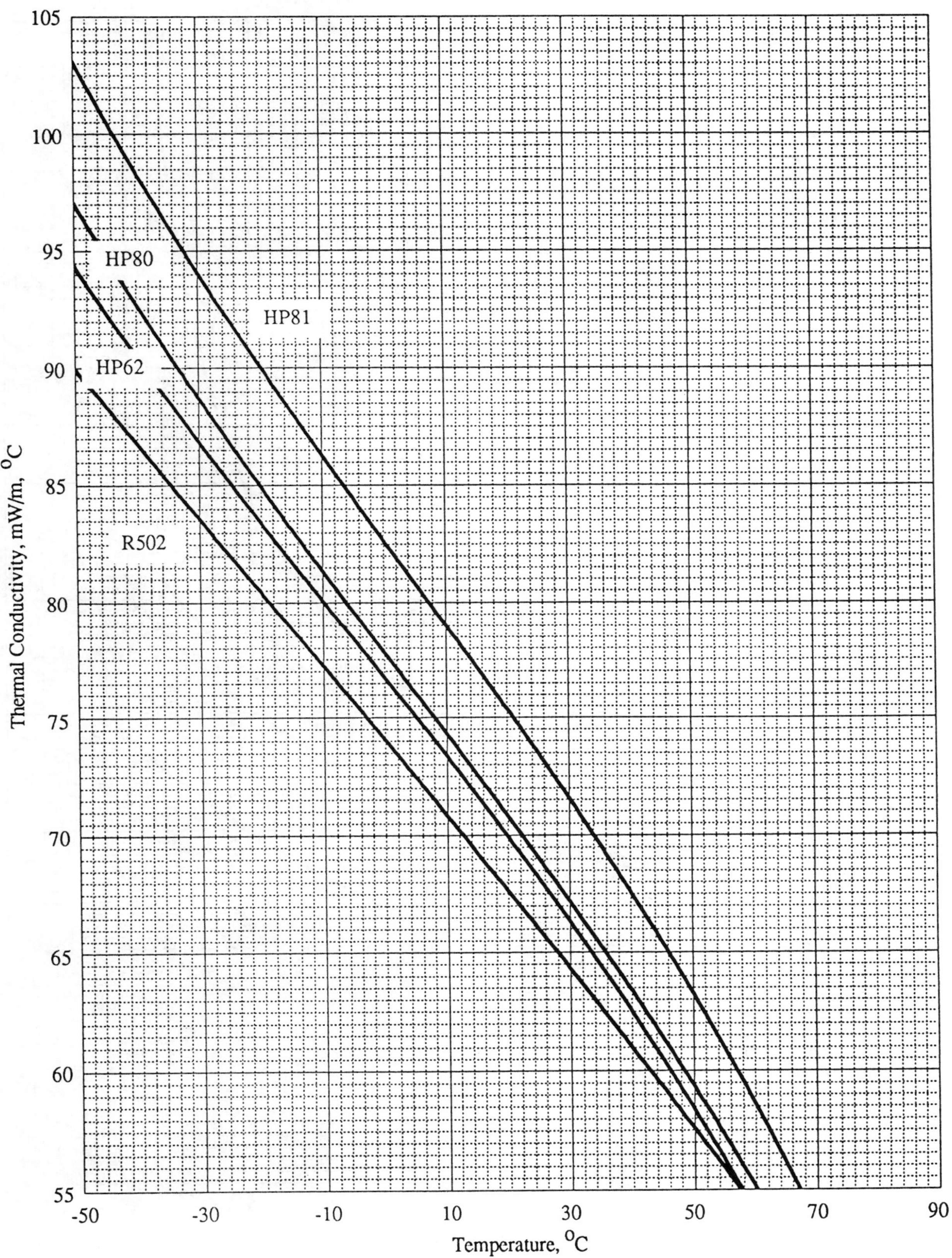
Saturated Liquid Thermal Conductivity
HP80
HP81
HP62
R502
Thermal Conductivity, mW/m, °C
Temperature, °C
105
100
95
90
85
80
75
70
65
60
55
-50
-30
-10
10
30
50
70
90

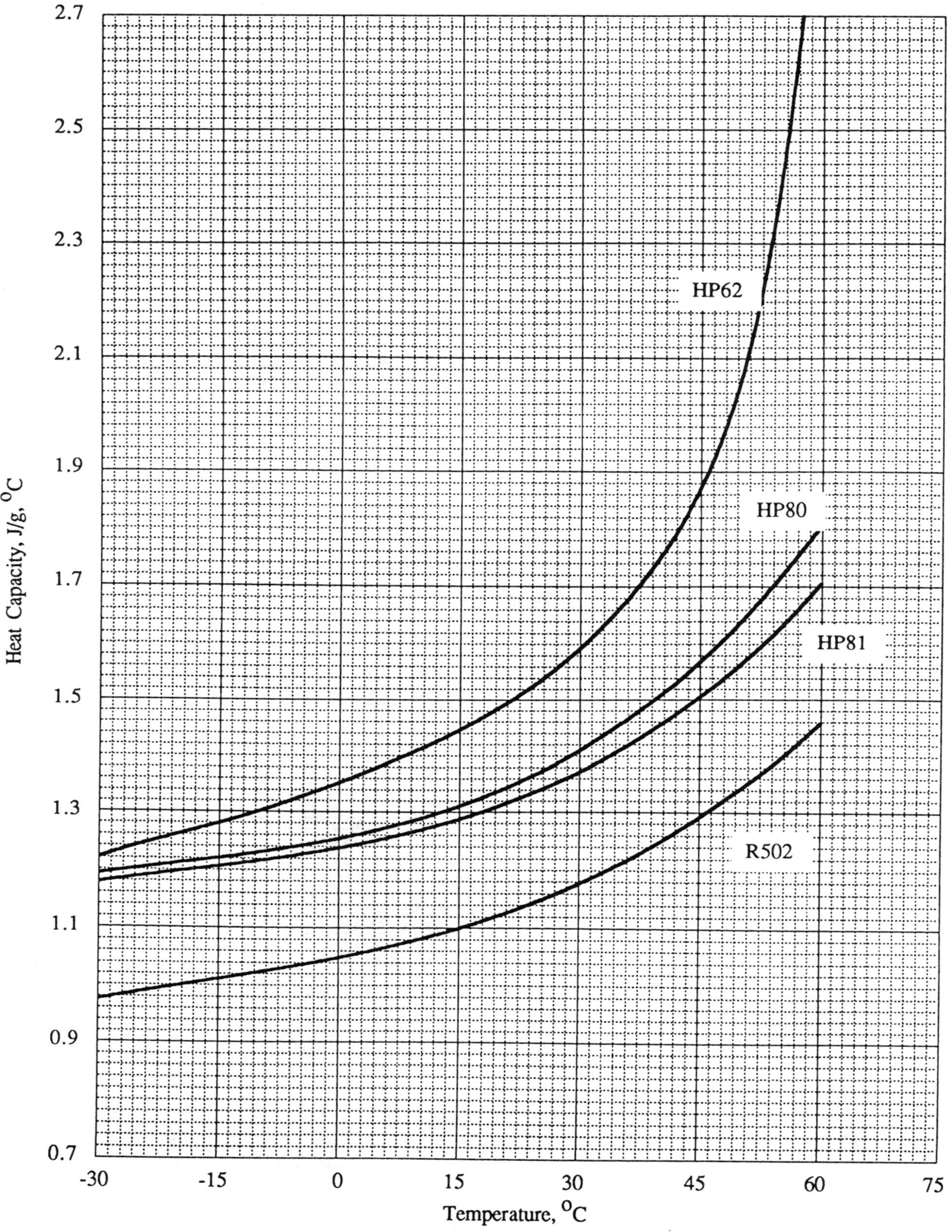
Saturated Liquid Heat Capacity
Heat Capacity, J/g, °C
Temperature, °C
2.7
2.5
2.3
2.1
1.9
1.7
1.5
1.3
1.1
0.9
0.7
-30
-15
0
15
30
45
60
75
HP62
HP80
HP81
R502

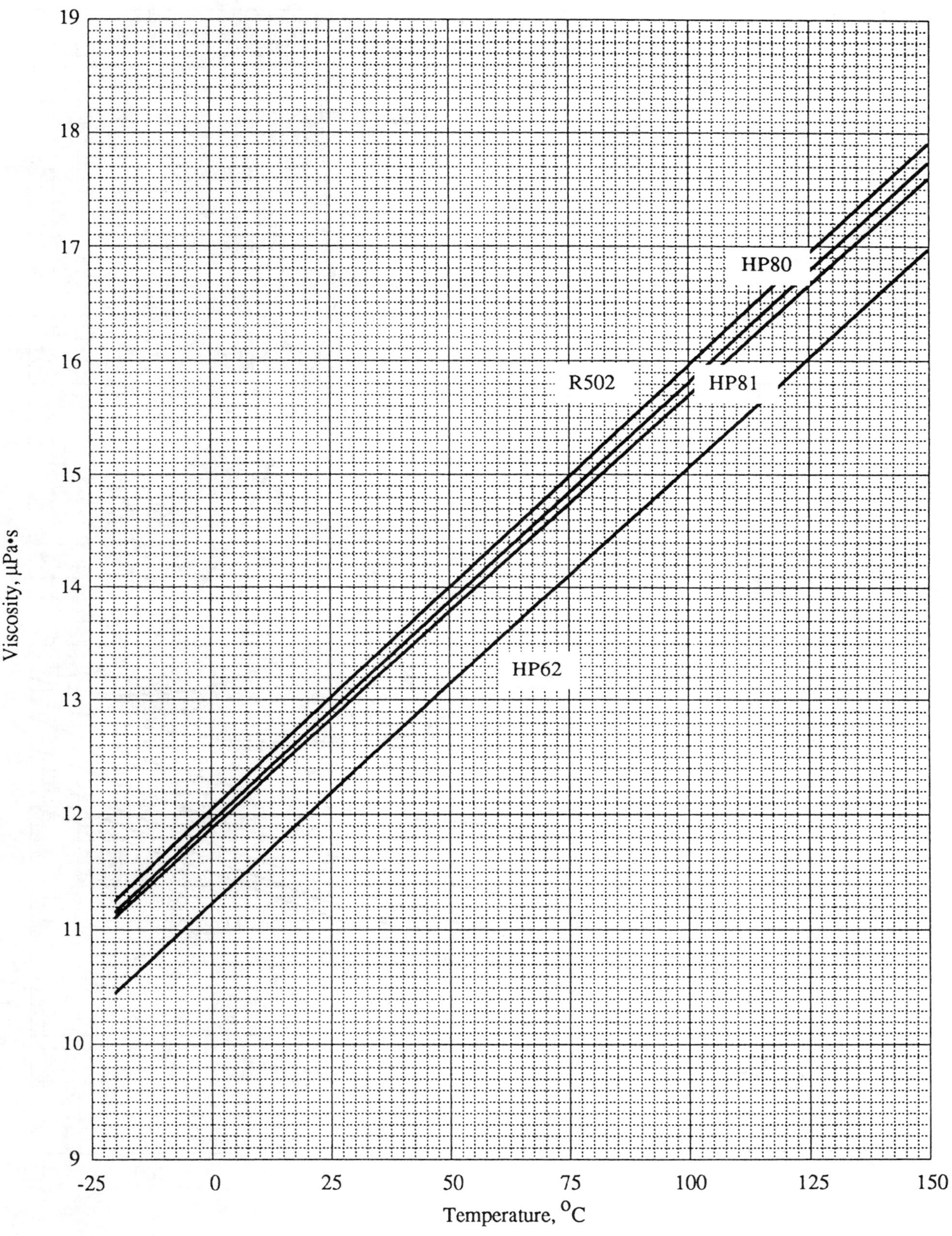
Vapor Viscosity at Atmospheric Pressure
19
18
17
16
15
14
13
12
11
10
9
Viscosity, µPa•s
-25
0
25
50
75
100
125
150
Temperature, °C
HP80
R502
HP81
HP62

HP62 Vapor Viscosity

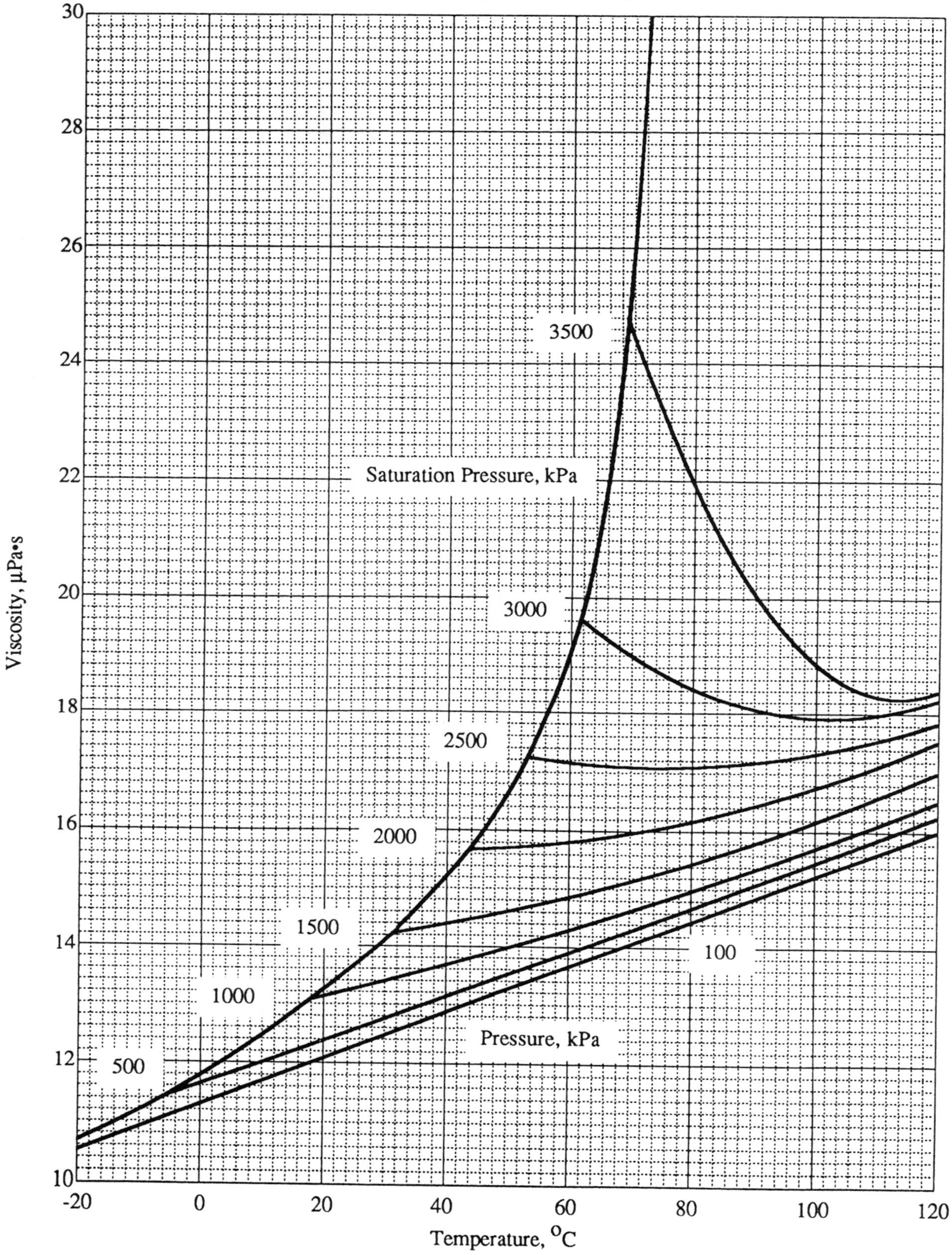

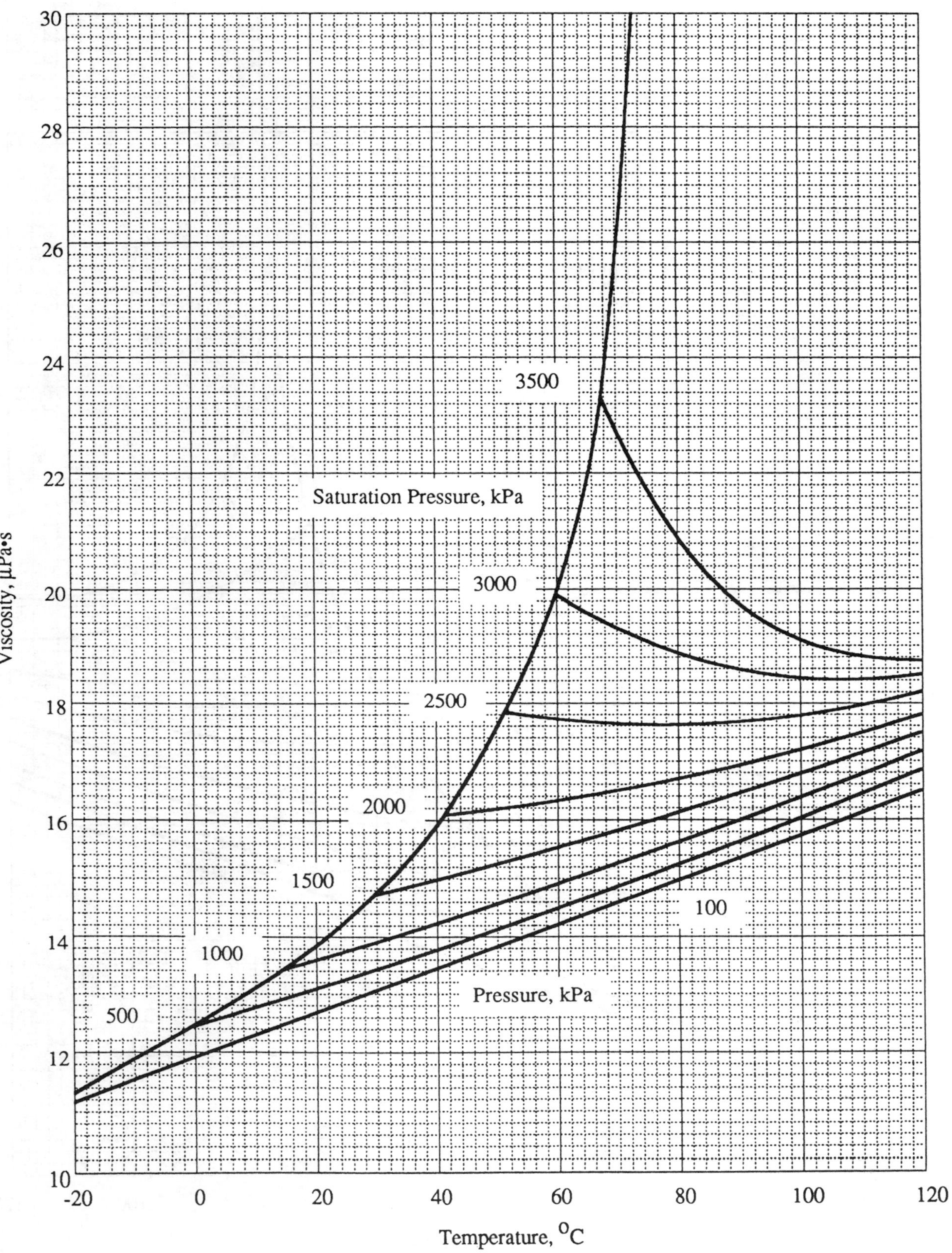
HP80 Vapor Viscosity
Saturation Pressure, kPa
3500
3000
2500
2000
1500
1000
500
100
Pressure, kPa
Viscosity, µPa•s
Temperature, °C
30
28
26
24
22
20
18
16
14
12
10
-20
0
20
40
60
80
100
120

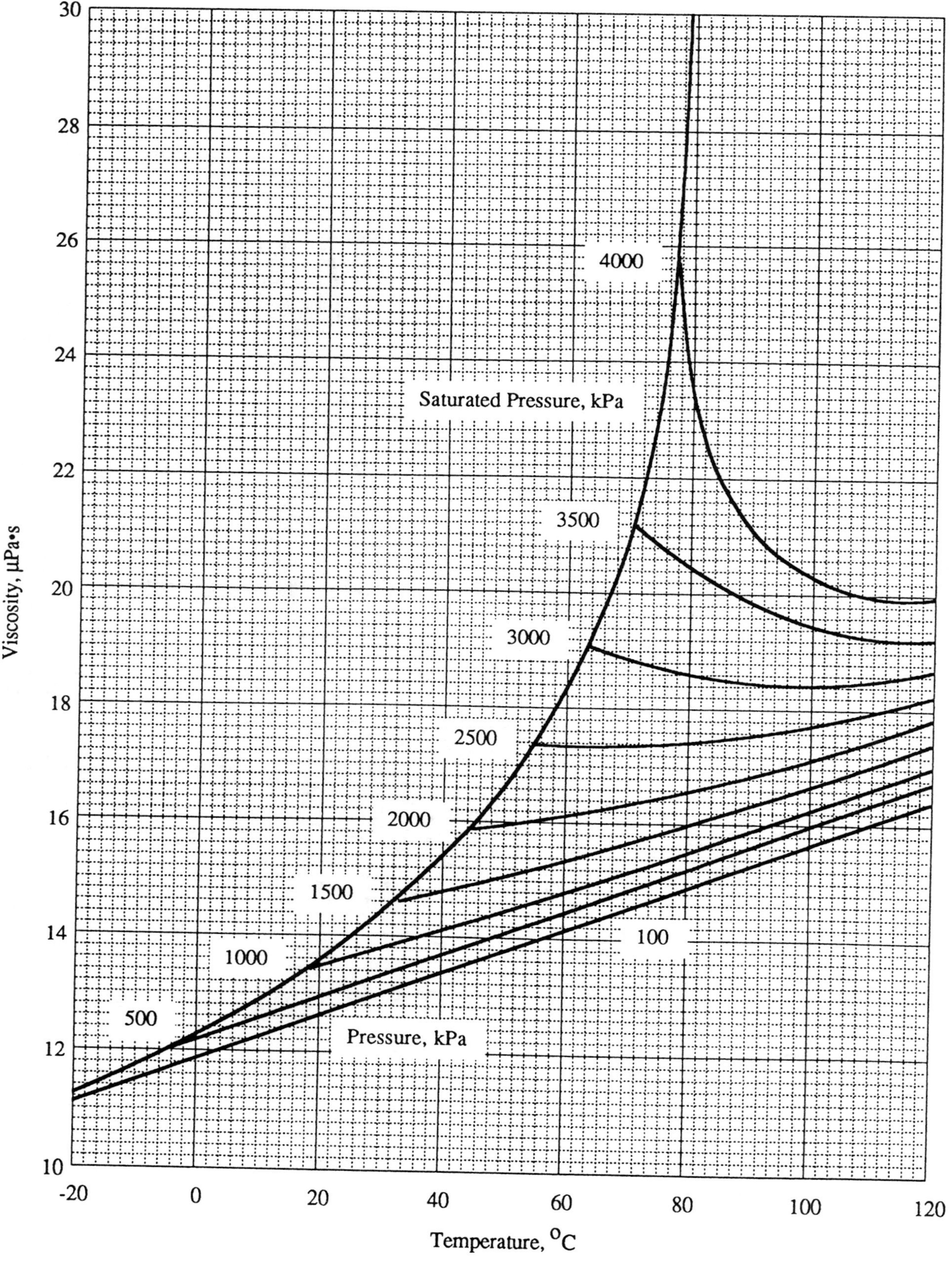

HP81 Vapor Viscosity
Viscosity, μPa•s
Temperature, °C
Saturated Pressure, kPa
Pressure, kPa
4000
3500
3000
2500
2000
1500
1000
500
100
30
28
26
24
22
20
18
16
14
12
10
-20
0
20
40
60
80
100
120

Vapor Thermal Conductivity at Atmospheric Pressure

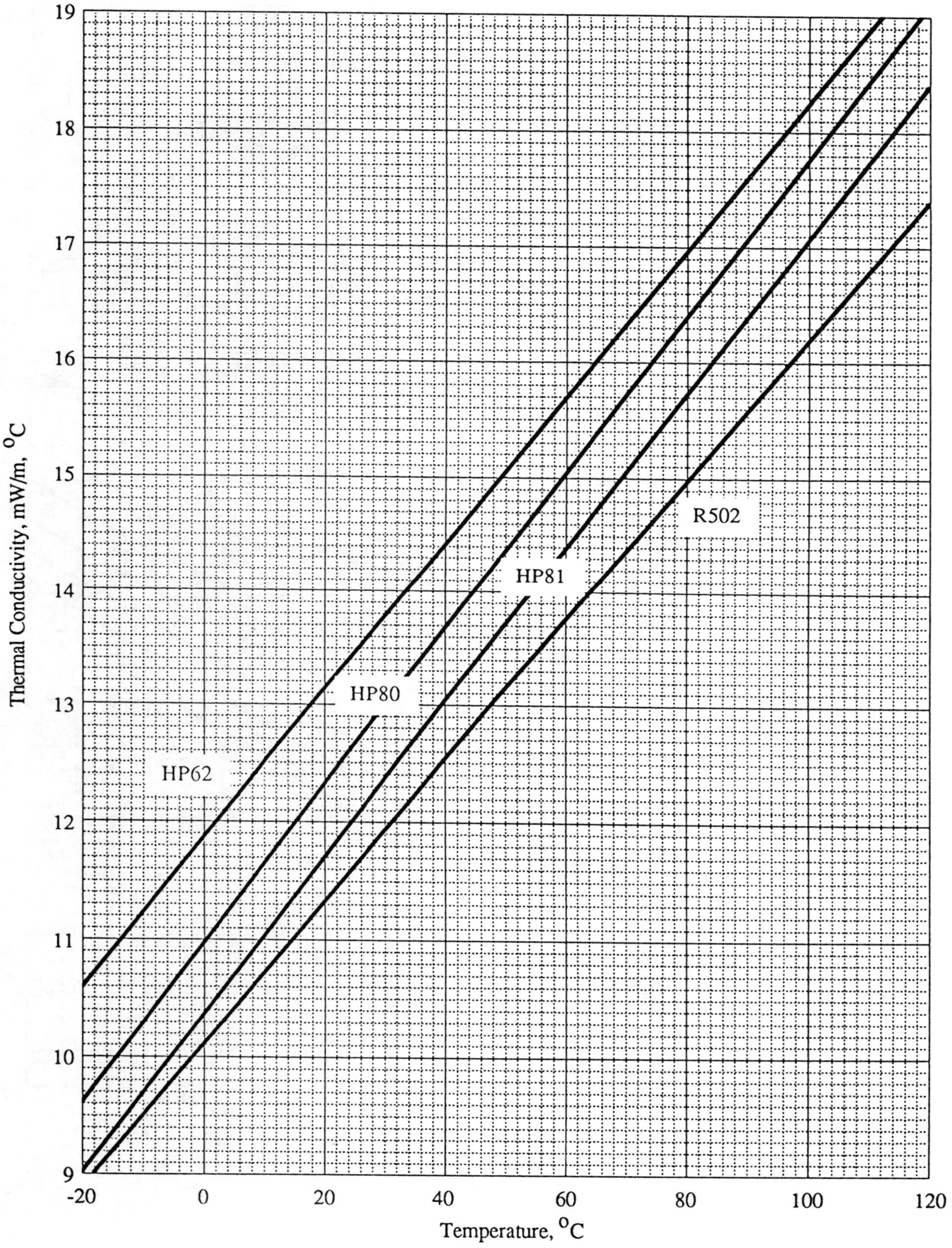

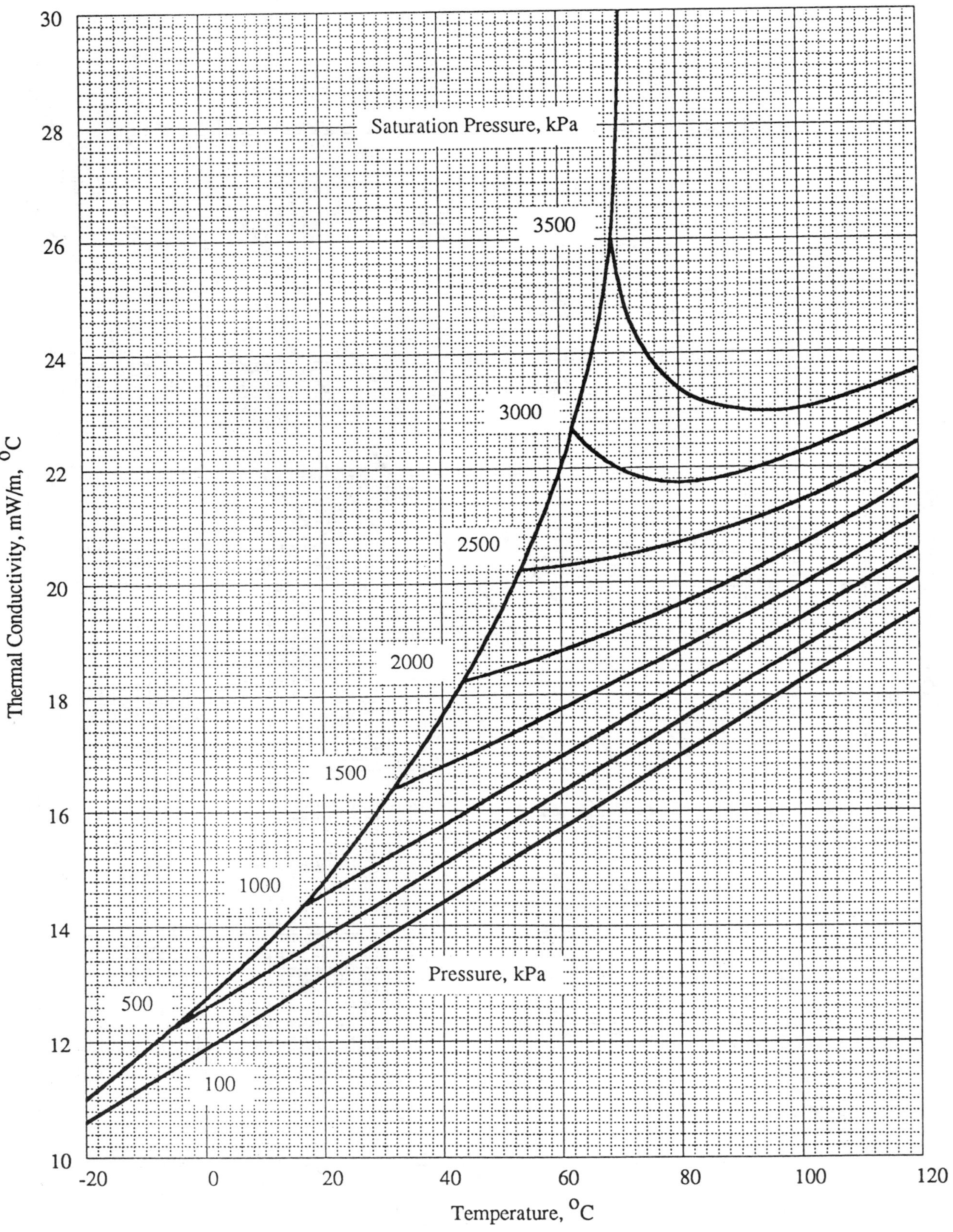
HP62 Vapor Thermal Conductivity
Saturation Pressure, kPa
3500
3000
2500
2000
1500
1000
500
100
Pressure, kPa
Thermal Conductivity, mW/m, °C
Temperature, °C
30
28
26
24
22
20
18
16
14
12
10
-20
0
20
40
60
80
100
120

HP80 Vapor Thermal Conductivity

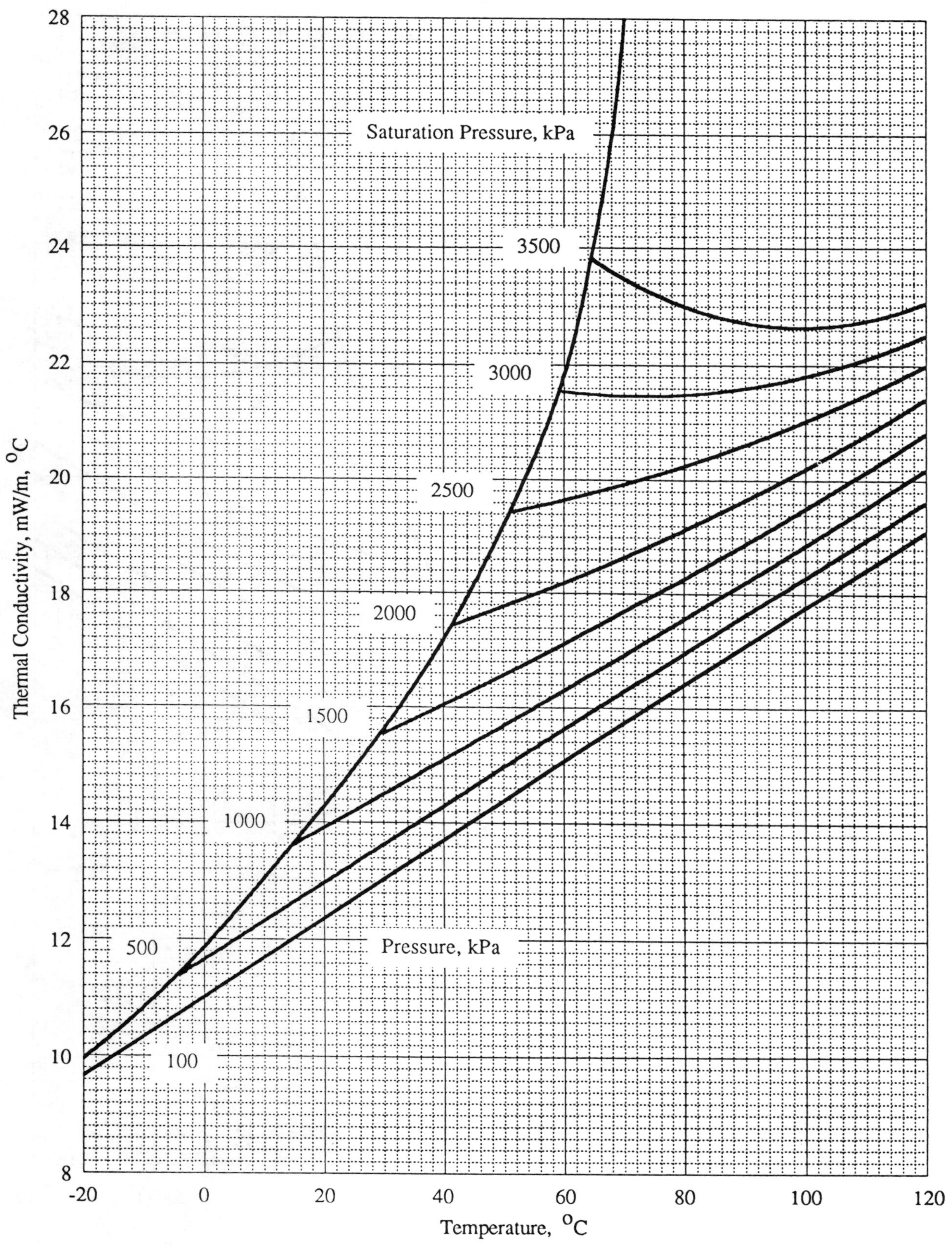

HP81 Vapor Thermal Conductivity

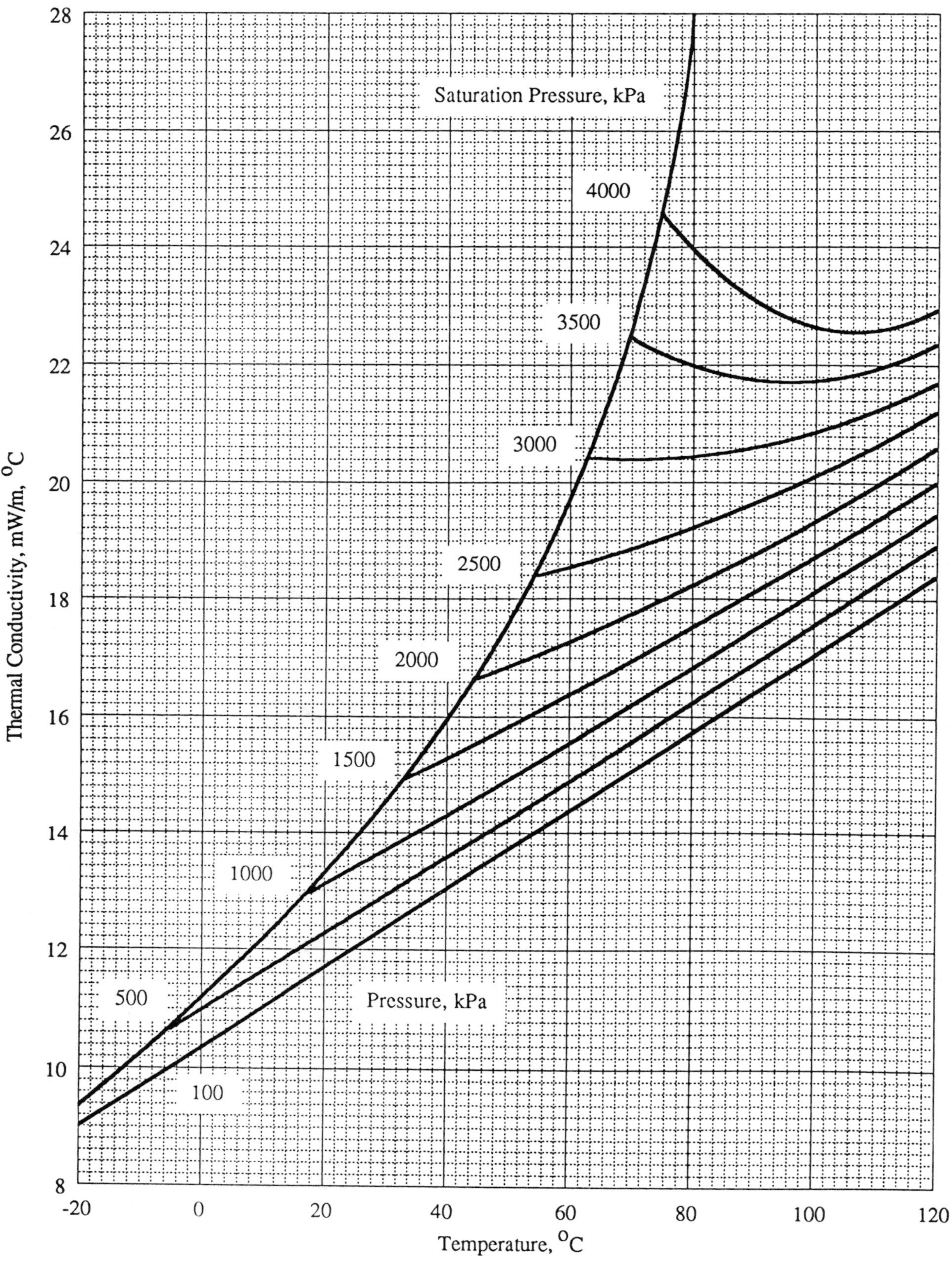

HP62 Vapor Heat Capacity

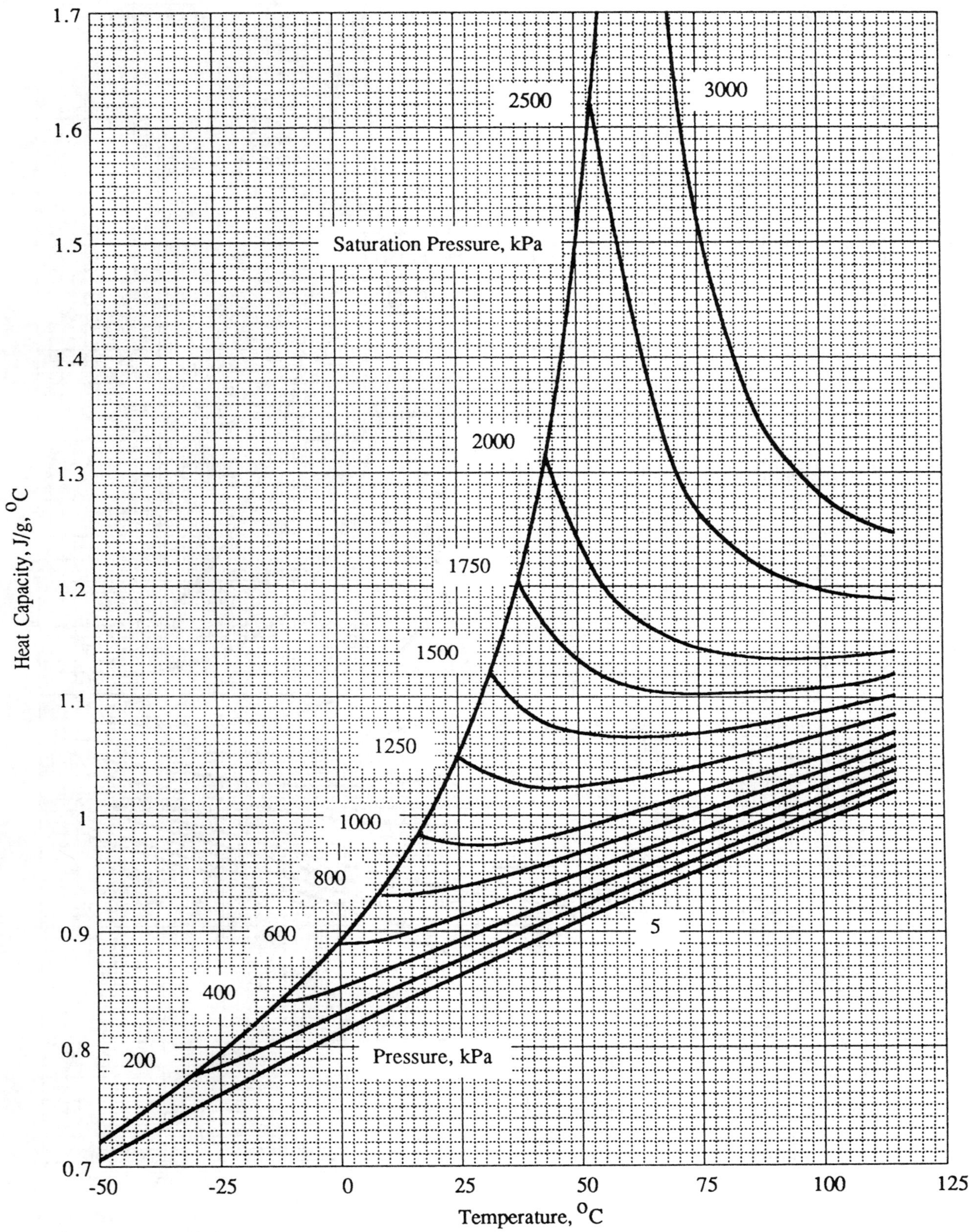

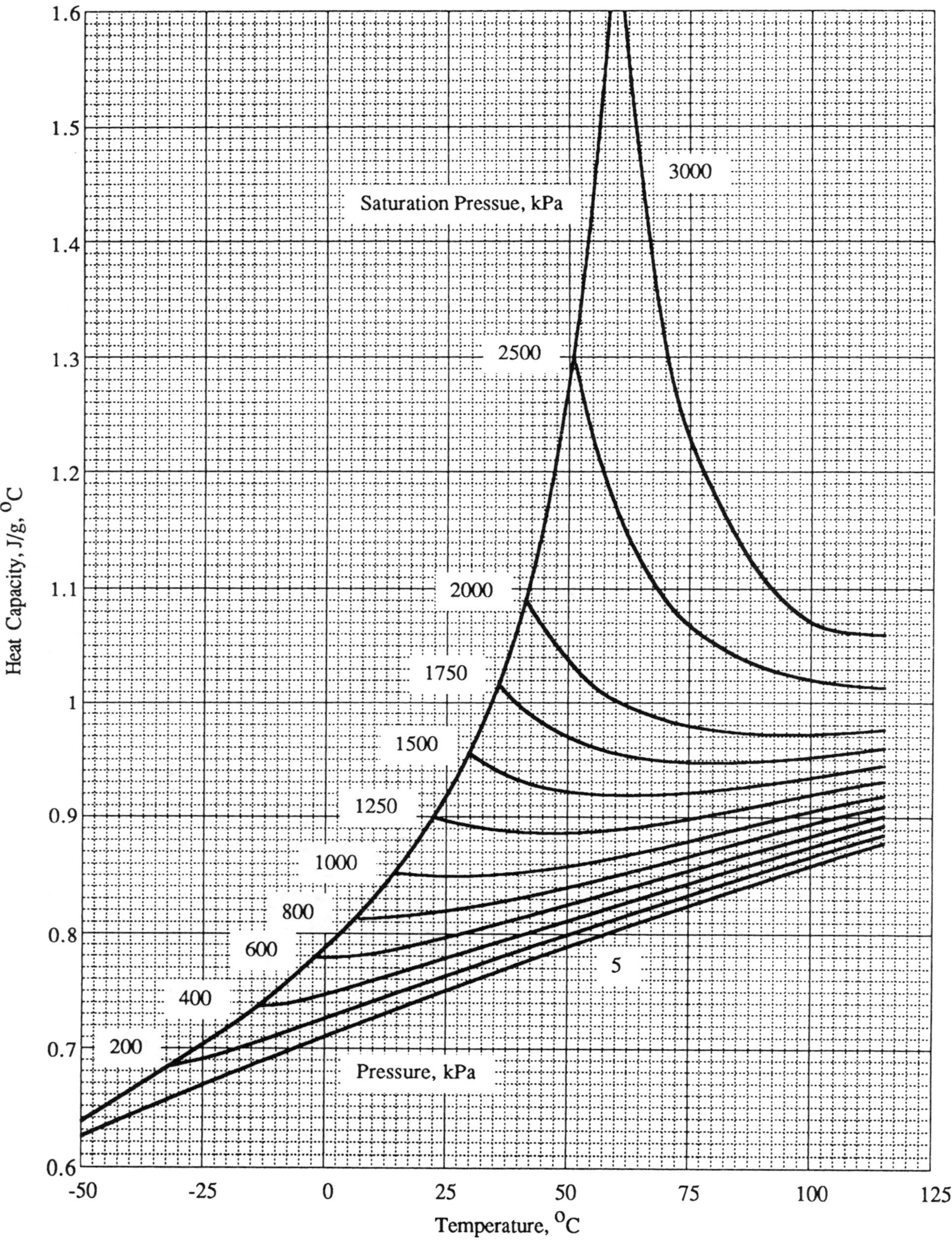

HP80 Vapor Heat Capacity
Heat Capacity, J/g, °C
Temperature, °C
Saturation Pressue, kPa
Pressure, kPa
3000
2500
2000
1750
1500
1250
1000
800
600
400
200
5
1.6
1.5
1.4
1.3
1.2
1.1
1
0.9
0.8
0.7
0.6
-50
-25
0
25
50
75
100
125

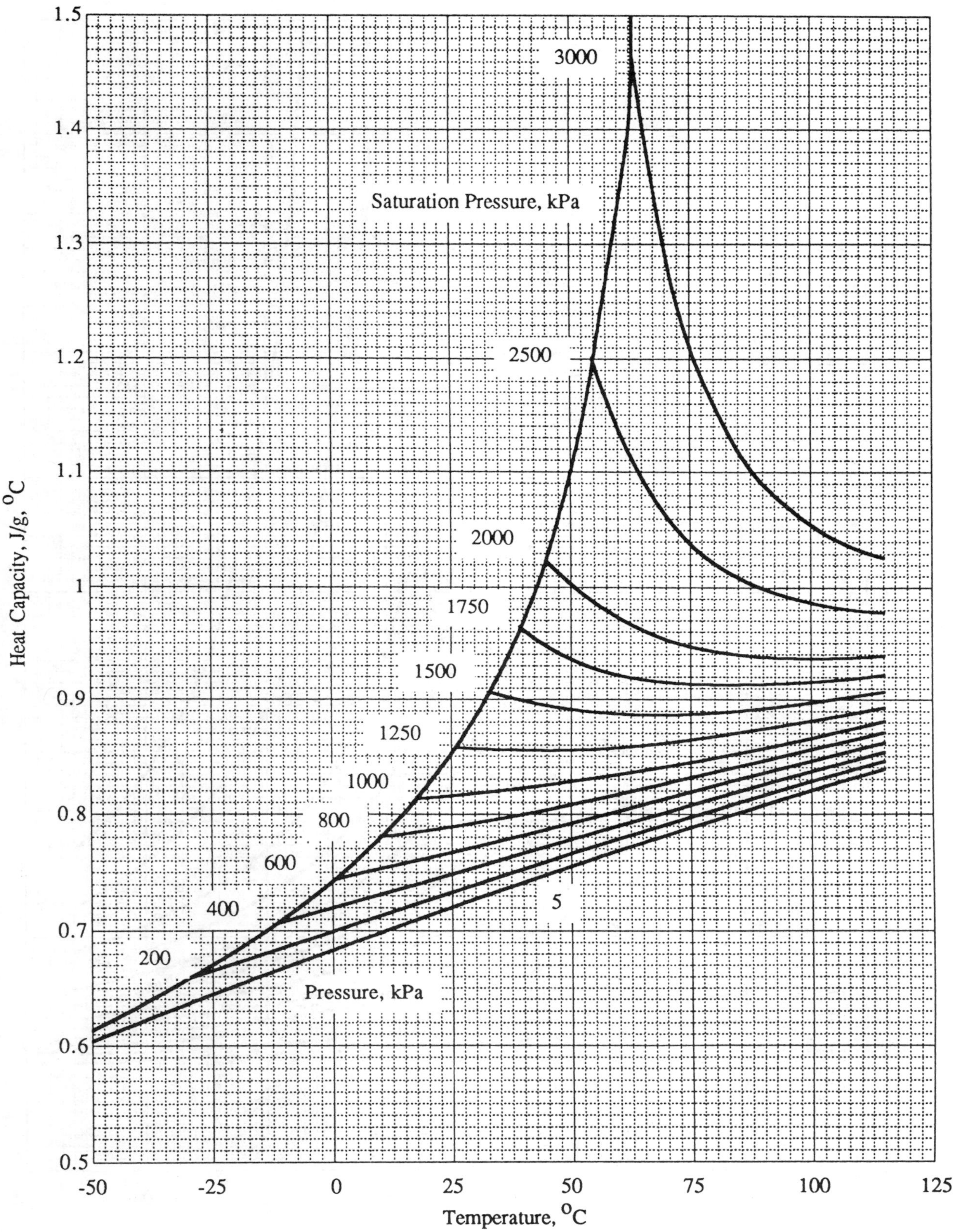

HP81 Vapor Heat Capacity
3000
Saturation Pressure, kPa
2500
2000
1750
1500
1250
1000
800
600
400
200
5
Pressure, kPa
Heat Capacity, J/g, °C
Temperature, °C
1.5
1.4
1.3
1.2
1.1
1
0.9
0.8
0.7
0.6
0.5
-50
-25
0
25
50
75
100
125

HP62 Vapor Heat Capacity Ratio

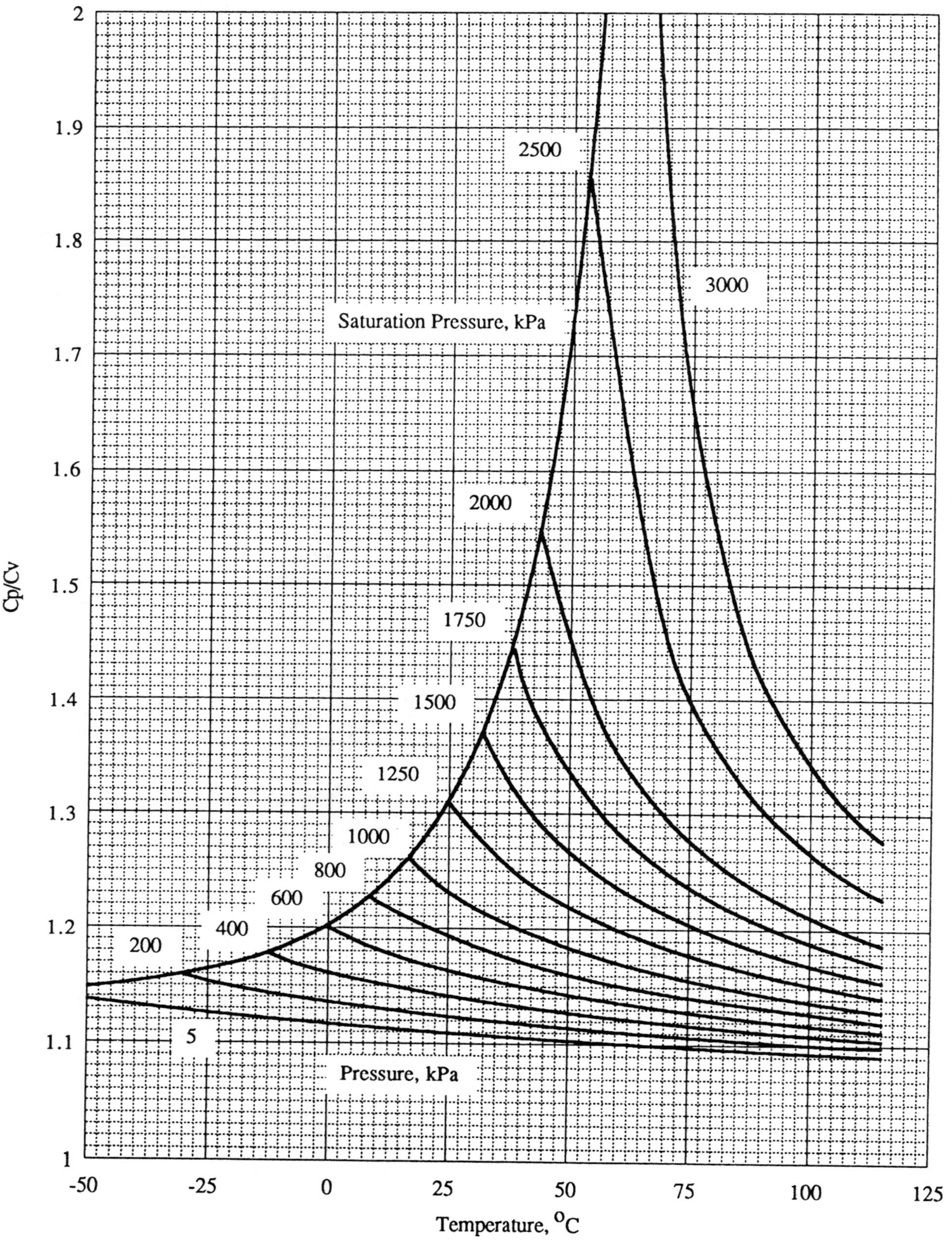

HP80 Vapor Heat Capacity Ratio

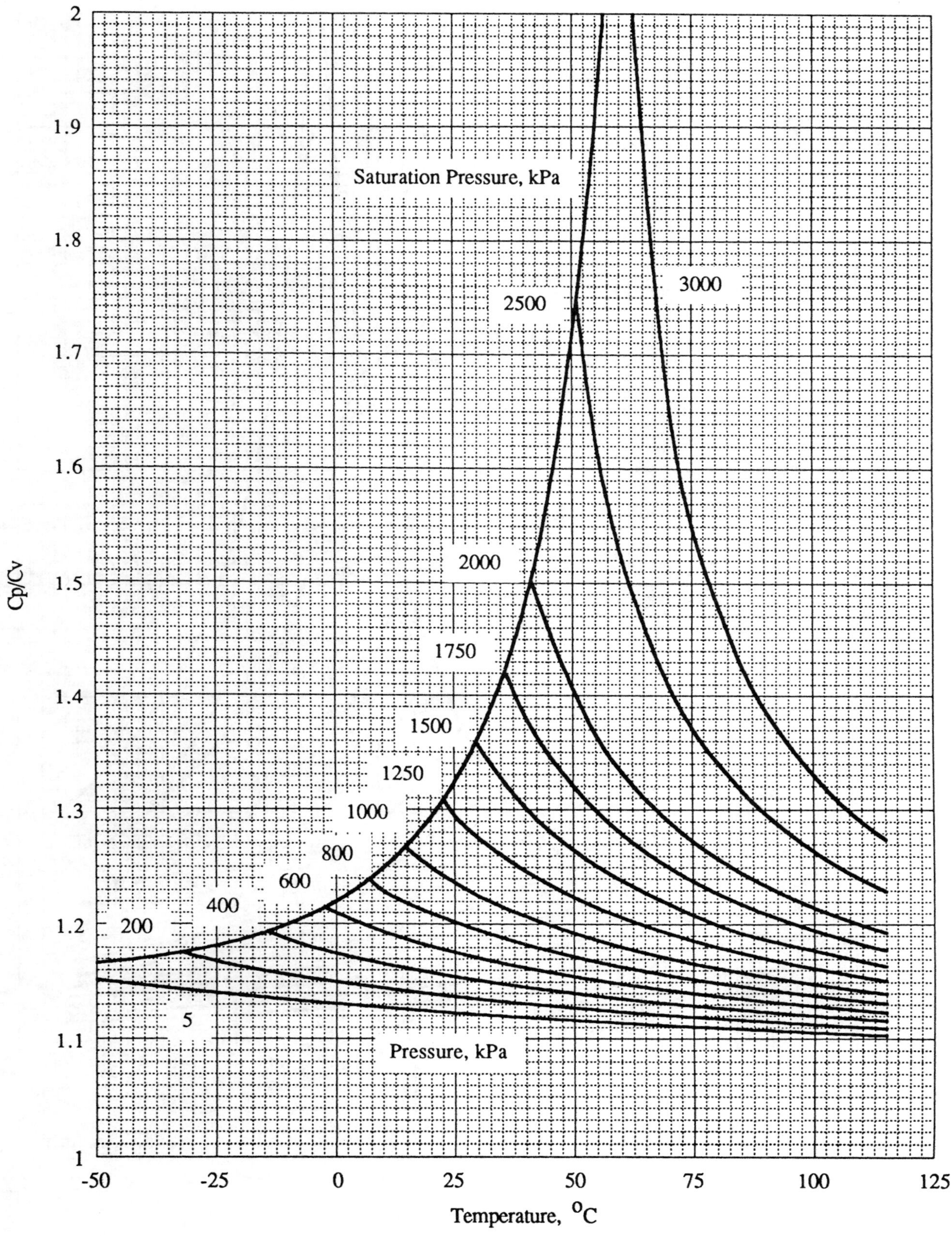

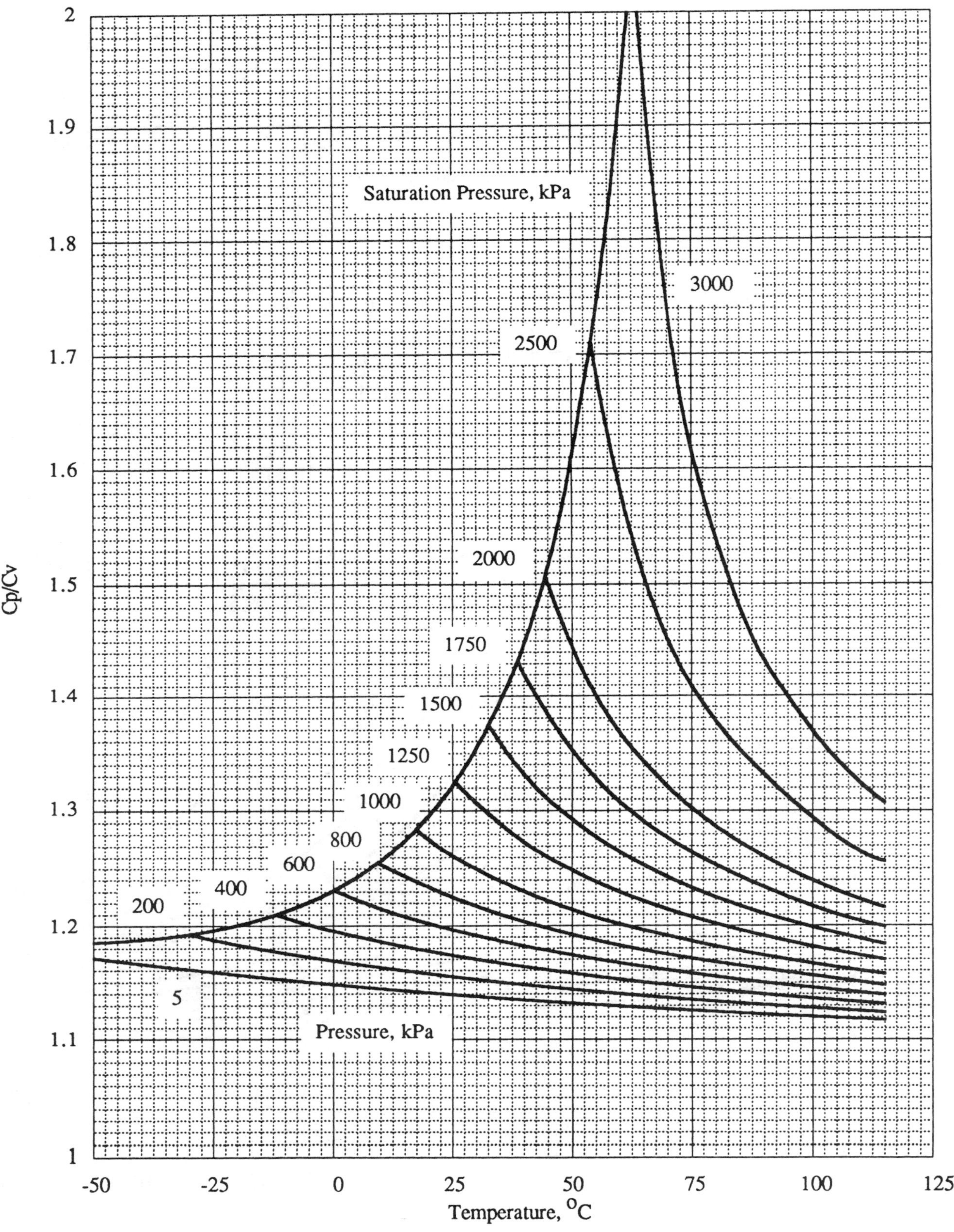
HP81 Vapor Heat Capacity Ratio
Saturation Pressure, kPa
3000
2500
2000
1750
1500
1250
1000
800
600
400
200
5
Pressure, kPa
Cp/Cv
2
1.9
1.8
1.7
1.6
1.5
1.4
1.3
1.2
1.1
1
-50
-25
0
25
50
75
100
125
Temperature, °C

EQUATIONS FOR PROPERTY ESTIMATION

Metric Units

Curves have been fitted to the measured data to obtain the following equations for estimation of properties within the ranges specified.

Liquid Viscosity in μPa·s (–50°C to 70°C)

SUVA® HP62 $\mu = 180.7 - 2.460\ T + 2.020E\text{-}2\ T^2 - 1.377E\text{-}4\ T^3$

SUVA® HP80 $\mu = 188.5 - 2.447\ T + 1.956E\text{-}2\ T^2 - 1.317E\text{-}4\ T^3$

SUVA® HP81 $\mu = 196.1 - 2.437\ T + 1.928E\text{-}2\ T^2 - 1.326E\text{-}4\ T^3$

Liquid Thermal Conductivity in mW/m °C (–50°C to 70°C)

SUVA® HP62 $k = 76.7 - 0.333\ T + 1.38E\text{-}4\ T^2 - 1.06E\text{-}5\ T^3$

SUVA® HP80 $k = 77.8 - 0.349\ T + 1.55E\text{-}4\ T^2 - 1.08E\text{-}5\ T^3$

SUVA® HP81 $k = 82.6 - 0.363\ T + 2.11E\text{-}4\ T^2 - 1.41E\text{-}5\ T^3$

Liquid Heat Capacity in J/g °C (–40°C to 60°C)

SUVA® HP62 $C_p = 1.345 + 4.435E\text{-}3\ T + 6.914E\text{-}5\ T^2 + 2.113E\text{-}6\ T^3$

SUVA® HP80 $C_p = 1.255 + 2.791E\text{-}3\ T + 5.556E\text{-}5\ T^2 + 8.231E\text{-}7\ T^3$

SUVA® HP81 $C_p = 1.238 + 2.280E\text{-}3\ T + 3.862E\text{-}5\ T^2 + 9.053E\text{-}7\ T^3$

Vapor Viscosity at One Atmosphere in μPa·s (–20°C to 150°C)

SUVA® HP62 $\mu = 11.22 + 3.835E\text{-}2\ T$

SUVA® HP80 $\mu = 11.93 + 3.876E\text{-}2\ T$

SUVA® HP81 $\mu = 11.86 + 3.823E\text{-}2\ T$

Vapor Thermal Conductivity at One Atmosphere in mW/m °C (–20°C to 150°C)

SUVA® HP62 $k = 11.86 + 6.36E\text{-}2\ T$

SUVA® HP80 $k = 10.97 + 6.78E\text{-}2\ T$

SUVA® HP81 $k = 10.36 + 6.70E\text{-}2\ T$

Where T = Temperature, °C

For Sales Information:

DuPont Chemicals
Customer Service Center, B-15305
Wilmington, DE 19898/U.S.A.
(302) 774-2099
1-800-441-9442

For Technical Information:

Fluorochemicals Laboratory
Wilmington, DE 19898/U.S.A.
(302) 999-3129
1-800-582-5606

Europe
DuPont de Nemours
International S.A.
2 Chemin du Pavillon
P.O. Box 50
CH-1218 Le Grand-Sacconex
Geneva, Switzerland
41-22-717-5111

Canada
DuPont Canada, Inc.
P.O. Box 2200, Streetsville
Mississauga, Ontario
L5M 2H3
(416) 821-3300

Mexico
DuPont, S.A. de C.V.
Homero 206
Col. Chapultepec Morales
C.P. 11570 Mexico, D.F.
52-5-250-8000

South America
DuPont do Brasil S.A.
Alameda Itapicuru, 506
Alphaville 06400 Barueri
Sao Paulo, Brazil
55-11-421-8509

DuPont Argentina S.A.
Casilla Correo 1888
Correo Central
1000 Buenos Aires, Argentina
54-1-311-8167

Pacific
DuPont Australia
P.O. Box 930
North Sydney, NSW 2060
Australia
61-2-923-6165

Japan
Mitsui DuPont Fluorochemicals
Company, Ltd.
Mitsui Seimei Building
2-3, 1-Chome Ohtemachi
Chiyoda-Ku, Tokyo 100 Japan
81-3-3216-8451

Asia
DuPont Taiwan
P.O. Box 81-777
Taipei, Taiwan
886-2-514-4400

DuPont Asia Pacific Limited
P.O. Box TST 98851
Tsim Sha Tsui
Kowloon, Hong Kong
852-734-5345

DuPont Thailand
P.O. Box 2398
Bangkok 10501, Thailand
66-2-238-4361

DuPont China Ltd.
Room 1704, Union Bldg.
100 Yanan Rd. East
Shanghai, PR China 200 002
Phone: 86-21-328-3738
Telex: 33448 DCLSH CN
Fax: 86-21-320-2304

DuPont Far East Inc.
P.O. Box 12396
50776 Kuala Lumpur, Malaysia
Phone: 60-3-232-3522
Telex: (784) 30391 DUFE M
Fax: 60-3-238-7250

DuPont Korea, Ltd.
C.P.O. Box 5972
Seoul, Korea
82-2-721-5114

DuPont Singapore Pte. Ltd.
1 Maritime Square #07 01
World Trade Centre
Singapore 0409
65-273-2244

DuPont Far East, Phillippines
5th Floor, Solid Bank Building
777 Paseo de Roxas
Makati, Metro Manila
Phillippines
63-2-818-9911

DuPont Far East Inc.
7A Murray's Gate Road
Alwarpet
Madras, 600 018 India
91-44-454-029

DuPont Far East Inc.-
Pakistan
9 Khayaban-E-Shaheen
Defence Phase 5
Karachi, Pakistan
92-21-533-350

DuPont Far East Inc.
P.O. Box 2553/Jkt
Jakarta 10001
Indonesia
62-21-517-800

H-49740 5/93

Printed in U.S.A.

235499A

ART-9

Retrofit Guidelines for Suva HP80

Introduction

Suva HP80 is a commercially available three component mixture of HCFC-22, HFC-125, and HC-290 developed as an alternative refrigerant to replace R-502. Using the retrofit guidelines summarized below, most R-502 systems using positive displacement compressors (i.e., reciprocating, rotary, screw, and scroll) can be *easily* and *economically* retrofitted for use with Suva HP80. This allows the existing equipment to continue to operate safely and efficiently even after R-502 is no longer available.

Properties and Safety

Suva HP80 offers improved environmental properties versus R-502, with significantly lower ozone depletion potential (ODP) and global warming potential (GWP). (See *Table 1*.) Suva HP80 requires the same safe handling procedures as R-502. Like R-502, Suva HP80 is nonflammable and has a low degree of toxicity. Refer to DuPont Technical Bulletin P-HP (H-47122-1) for more detailed information on the properties, uses, storage, and handling of Suva HP80. Refer to the Material Safety Data Sheets (MSDS) for more safety information on the use of Suva HP80.

Selection of Refrigerant

Suva HP80 is the recommended alternative for most existing R-502 systems. With Suva HP80, comparable discharge temperatures and efficiency to R-502 are expected. Suva HP80 has improved capacity versus R-502, making it suitable for use in such applications as walk-in coolers/freezers, frozen food and dairy display cases, ice cream dispensers, and beverage vending machines.

Lubricants

Lubricant selection is based upon many factors including oil return to the compressor (oil miscibility), lubricity, and materials compatibility. Because of the different miscibility characteristics of Suva HP80 when compared to R-502, the lubricant must be changed when retrofitting.

Several types of lubricants have successfully been tested with Suva HP80. They include refrigerant grade alkylbenzene (AB) lubricants and refrigerant grade polyol esters (POE). Most equipment manufacturers have found AB lubricants to be the first choice for retrofit with Suva HP80; however, POEs will also work well in some equipment.

Before a retrofit is started, it is recommended that the compressor manufacturer be consulted for specific lubricant recommendations. Other sources of lubricant information are the DuPont Authorized Distributor, lubricant manufacturers, system manufacturers.

Table 1
Suva HP80 Physical Properties

Property	Units	Suva HP80	R-502
Boiling Pt	°C	–49.2	–45.4
(1 atm)	°F	–56.5	–49.8
Vapor Pressure,	kPa	1337	1162
Sat'd Liquid at 25°C	psia	194	169
Liquid Density	kg/m³	1151	1217
at 25°C	lb/ft³	71.9	75.9
Density, Sat'd	kg/m³	69.2	66.7
Vapor at 25°C	lb/ft³	4.32	4.16
Ozone Depletion Potential as compared to R-12	R-12 = 1	0.02	0.23
Halocarbon Global Warming Potential as compared to R-11	R-11 = 1	0.63	3.75
Capacity as compared to R-502*	R-502 = 100%	107%	100%
Energy Eff. as compared to R-502 (COP)*	R-502 = 100%	96%	100%

*Conditions: –40°F evaporator/130°F condenser/65°F suction temperature

Filter Drier

It is recommended that the filter drier be changed during the retrofit, as is routine practice following system maintenance. There are three types of filter driers commonly used in R-502 equipment:

- Solid core driers, in which the molecular sieve desiccant is dispersed within a solid core binder.
- Loose filled driers, which contain only the molecular sieve desiccant.
- Compacted bead driers, which also contain only the molecular sieve desiccant, but where the desiccant is compacted in the drier by mechanical pressure, usually a spring.

For solid core driers, consult the drier manufacturer for their recommended drier for use with the Suva HP blends. Some existing models of solid core driers, such as the Sporlan Catch All® or Alco ADK, are compatible with the Suva HP blends.

The XH-9 molecular sieve desiccant (manufactured by UOP) or equivalent (such as MS 594 from Grace) is recommended for use in loose filled driers with the Suva HP blends.

Compacted bead driers may use either the XH-9 or XH-6 desiccant or equivalent. Consult the drier manufacturer for their recommendation.

System Modification

The composition of Suva HP80 has been selected to provide the lowest possible discharge temperature while also providing comparable performance to R-502 in terms of both capacity and energy efficiency. As a result, minimal system modifications are anticipated when retrofitting R-502 systems with Suva HP80.

Retrofits of R-502 systems with other alternative refrigerants, such as HCFC-22 or HFC-125, may require more extensive system modifications (compressor replacement to multistage compressor, use of liquid injection, etc.). For some systems, this cost may be prohibitive. Suva HP80 provides the service contractor and equipment owner with a cost-effective way to retrofit an existing R-502 system.

It is important to note, however, that Suva HP80 was not designed for use in conjunction with other refrigerants or additives which have not been clearly specified by DuPont (i.e., topping off an existing R-502 charge with Suva HP80). Mixing refrigerants may have negative effects on system performance and lead to equipment damage.

Overview of Retrofit Process

Retrofit of an existing R-502 system with Suva HP80 can be accomplished using service practices and service equipment commonly used by trained mechanics or service contractors in the field.

The key steps involved in the retrofit are:

1. Recover R-502 charge from system.
2. Remove mineral oil from compressor and replace with selected lubricant.
3. Replace filter drier with new drier compatible with Suva HP80.
4. Charge system with Suva HP80.
5. Start system and adjust charge and/or controls to achieve desired operation.

For the majority of systems, the compressor lubricant change, a filter drier change, and, in systems with expansion valves, a possible adjustment to the superheat setting will be the only system modifications required in a retrofit to Suva HP80. For systems which are still under warranty, we recommend contacting the equipment or compressor manufacturers prior to performing the retrofit. Some equipment or compressor warranties may be impacted by a change from the refrigerant originally specified for the system or compressor.

Copeland Corporation approves the use of Suva HP80 and HP62 in existing equipment, provided the following conditions are met:

- Retrofitting systems that employ compressors manufactured prior to 1973 is not recommended.
- You must follow Copeland retrofit guidelines, and use only Copeland-approved lubricants and other parts.
- Pressure safety controls may have to be reset, due to the higher operating pressures of the alternatives.
- Pressure relief devices MUST be added to the compressor crankcase set at a maximum of 375 psig on Discus 3D and 4D and all other semi-hermetic (non-Discus) models.

WARNING: It is possible that excess pressure build-up on models indicated could result in the compressor exploding unless the pressure relief valve specified has been properly installed on the originally built Copeland Compressor.

Equipment and Supplies Needed for Retrofit

- Safety equipment (gloves, glasses)
- Manifold gauges
- Thermocouples to read line temperatures
- Vacuum pump
- Leak detection equipment
- Scale
- Recovery unit (RRU30 by Refrigerant Recovery Technologies, Inc. is recommended. See your local DuPont Authorized Distributor)
- Recovery cylinder
- Container for recovered lubricant
- Replacement lubricant
- Replacement refrigerant
- Replacement drier
- Labels indicating the refrigerant and lubricant charged to the system

Retrofit Procedure

Summarized below is a more detailed discussion of the recommended procedures for retrofitting a R-502 system with Suva HP80. Prior to the retrofit, review the Material Safety Data Sheets for safety information on the use of Suva HP80.

1. **Baseline Data with R-502.** For service contractors performing their initial retrofits with Suva HP80, it is recommended that system performance data be collected while R-502 remains in the system. This baseline of temperatures and pressures at various points in the system (evaporator, condenser, compressor suction and discharge, expansion device, etc.) at normal operating conditions will be useful when optimizing operation of the system with Suva HP80. A **System Data Sheet** is attached for recording this baseline data.
2. **Remove R-502 Charge.** R-502 should be removed from the system and collected in a recovery cylinder using a recovery device capable of pulling 10–15 in. Hg vacuum (50–67 kPa, 0.50–0.67 bar). If the recommended R-502 charge size for the system is not known, weigh the amount of refrigerant removed, as the initial quantity of Suva HP80 charged in the system will be determined from this figure.
3. **Drain Lubricant from Compressor.** In the cases where mineral oil is the existing oil, the oil will have to be drained from the compressor. This may require removing the compressor from the system, particularly with small hermetic compressors which have no oil drain. In this case, the lubricant can be drained from the suction line of the compressor. In most small systems, 90–95% of the lubricant can be removed from the compressor in this manner. Larger systems may require drainage from additional points in the system, particularly low spots around the evaporator, to remove the majority of the lubricant. In systems with an oil separator, any lubricant present in the separator should also be drained.

   In all cases, *measure* the amount of lubricant removed from the compressor. Consult the equipment manufacturer for their recommendation on allowable residual mineral oil in AB or POE. DuPont experience has been that a lubricant mixture of more than 80% AB or POE with mineral oil ensures good system performance. If poor system performance is noted upon start-up, an additional lubricant change may be required. Record on the attached **Retrofit Checklist** the amount of lubricant removed, as this will be needed in the next step.
4. **Charge Compressor with Chosen Lubricant.** Charge the compressor with the same volume of new lubricant as the volume of mineral oil removed in step 3. If system was found to be undercharged with mineral oil, charge to the manufacturer's specified level (i.e., sight glass) with the new lubricant. If no manufacturer's recommendation is given, use a lubricant with similar viscosity to that of the oil previously used in the system (150 SUS or 32 cSt is typical for R-502 systems). An AB lubricant, such as Zerol® 150, is recommended. Refrigerant grade POEs may also be used.

   Reinstall Compressor (if removed from system in step 3). Use normal service practices.
5. **Replace Filter Drier.** It is routine practice to replace the filter drier following system maintenance.

   The XH-9 molecular sieve desiccant (manufactured by UOP) or equivalent is recommended for use in loose fill driers with Suva HP80. For solid core driers, consult the drier manufacturer for their recommended drier in use with Suva HP80. Some existing solid core driers, such as those produced by Sporlan® and Alco®, can be used with Suva HP80.
6. **Reconnect System and Evacuate.** Use normal service practices. To remove air or other noncondensibles in the system, it is recommended that the system be evacuated to full vacuum (29.9 in. Hg/500 microns/ 0.14 kPa/0.0014 bar).

   Leak Check System. Use normal service practices. Reevacuate system following leak check.
7. **Charge System with Suva HP80.** Suva HP80 is a near-azeotropic mixture; therefore the vapor composition in the refrigerant cylinder is different from the liquid composition. To ensure that the proper refrigerant composition is charged in the system, it is important that **LIQUID ONLY** be removed from the charging cylinder. **Cylinders of Suva HP80 are equipped with dip tubes, allowing liquid to be removed from the cylinder when the cylinder is in the upright position.** ***The proper position is indicated by arrows on the cylinder and cylinder box.*** Once removed from the cylinder as a liquid, Suva HP80 can be changed to the high side of a system as a liquid or flashed to the low side of a running system using a throttling valve or liquid dispensing device to protect the compressor. Suva HP80 should be removed from a cylinder as a vapor only if all of the refrigerant in the cylinder is transferred to the system.

   The refrigeration system will require less weight of Suva HP80 than R-502. The optimum charge will vary depending on the operating conditions and system design. For most systems, the optimum charge will be 90–95% by weight of the original R-502 charge. It is recommended that the system be initially charged with about 80% by weight of the original R-502 charge (ex: if original R-502 charge was 10 ounces [284 grams], initially charge about 8 ounces [227 grams] of HP80).

   Add the initial charge to the high pressure side of the system. When the system and cylinder pressures equilibrate, load the remainder of the refrigerant to the suction line of the system. In this step, the compressor will be running. Some compressors may be damaged if liquid refrigerant enters the suction side of the compressor. Since liquid must be removed from the charging cylinder, it is important to charge the refrigerant slowly into the suction line to allow it to flash before it enters the system. A throttling valve may also be used to cause the refrigerant to flash.

8. **Adjust Charge.** Let conditions stabilize. If the system is undercharged, add additional Suva HP80 in small amounts (still removing *liquid* from the charging cylinder) until the system conditions reach the desired levels.

   See "How to Determine Suction Pressure, Superheat, and Subcool" at the end of this guideline for optimizing system performance.

   For low temperature evaporator applications (–40°F or –40°C), the suction pressure with Suva HP80 will be approximately 1 psi (6.89 kPa, 0.069 bar) higher than R-502. At medium temperature evaporator conditions (10°F or –12.2°C), the suction pressure with Suva HP80 will be approximately 7 psi (48.2 kPa, 0.482 bar) higher than R-502. At high evaporator temperatures (40°F or 4.4°C), the suction pressure with Suva HP80 will be approximately 10 psi (68.0 kPa, 0.680 bar) higher than R-502. Suva HP80 will have comparable discharge temperatures and the discharge pressure will be 30–45 psi (207–310 kPa, 2.07–3.10 bar) higher than that for R-502.

NOTE: Sight glasses in the liquid line can be used for charging in most systems.

However, it is best to charge your system by measuring the operating conditions (discharge and suction pressures, suction line temperature, compressor amps, super heat, etc.) first, before using the liquid line sight glass as a guide.

However, if the sight glass is close to the exit of the condenser or there is very little subcooling prior to the sight glass, bubbles may still be observed in the sight glass when the system is properly charged. Attempting to charge until the sight glass is clear may result in overcharging of refrigerant.

NOTE: Label Components and System. After retrofitting the system with Suva HP80, label the system components to identify the type of refrigerant (Suva HP80) and lubricant in the system, so that the proper refrigerant and lubricant will be used to service the equipment in the future. Identification labels are available from DuPont Authorized Distributors.

Summary

With the phaseout of CFCs, existing refrigeration equipment will need to be replaced with new equipment or retrofitted with alternative refrigerants. Using the procedures described previously, existing R-502 refrigeration systems can be retrofitted for use with Suva HP80, allowing them to continue in service for the remainder of their useful life.

Attached is a **Retrofit Checklist**, **System Data Sheet,** and pressure–temperature charts including an explanation of pressure/temperature relationships for Suva HP80 to assist you in the retrofit process.

Pressure/Temperature Relationship of Suva HP80

Temperature Glide

Temperature glide occurs in both an evaporator and a condenser. In an evaporator at constant pressure, the refrigerant blend begins to boil at one temperature and finishes boiling at a higher temperature. The difference in these boiling temperatures is called temperature glide. This also occurs in a condenser, except the temperature decreases as the refrigerant vapor condenses. Temperature glide will not affect system performance.

How to Read the Tables

Tables 2a and *2b* show the pressure/temperature relationship of Suva HP80 compared to R-502. Two temperatures are shown for Suva HP80 at a given pressure:

Saturated Liquid Temperature—in the condenser, this is the temperature where the last bit of vapor has just condensed (all liquid). Below this temperature, the refrigerant will be subcooled.

Saturated Vapor Temperature—in the evaporator, this is the temperature where the last drop of liquid has just boiled (all vapor). Above this temperature, the refrigerant will be superheated.

How to Determine Suction Pressure, Superheat, and Subcool

Suction Pressure

1. Determine the expected evaporator temperature using the R-502 column (baseline data).
2. Find the same expected evaporator temperature in the column "Sat. Vapor Temp." and note the corresponding pressure for this temperature. This is the suction pressure at which the system should operate.
   Note: For Suva HP80 the average coil temperature is approximately equal to the "Sat. Vapor Temp."

Superheat

Using the "Saturated Vapor Temperature" column for Suva HP80, the amount of vapor superheat is calculated in the same manner as for R-502.

Subcool

Using the "Saturated Liquid Temperature" column for Suva HP80, the amount of liquid subcool is calculated in the same manner as for R-502.

Table 2a
Pressure–Temperature Chart
Suva HP80 (psig/°F)

Pressure (psig)	R-502 Temp. (°F)	Suva HP80 Sat'd Liquid Temp. (°F)	Suva HP80 Sat'd Vapor Temp. (°F)
20*	–88	–94	–89
18*	–82	–88	–84
16*	–77	–83	–79
14*	–73	–79	–75
12*	–69	–75	–71
10*	–65	–71	–67
8*	–61	–68	–64
6*	–58	–65	–61
4*	–55	–62	–58
2*	–52	–59	–55
0	–50	–57	–53
2	–45	–52	–48
4	–40	–47	–44
6	–36	–43	–40
8	–32	–39	–36
10	–29	–36	–33
12	–25	–33	–29
14	–22	–29	–26
16	–19	–26	–23
18	–16	–24	–21
20	–13	–21	–18
22	–11	–18	–15
24	–8	–16	–13
26	–6	–14	–11
28	–3	–11	–8
30	–1	–9	–6
32	1	–7	–4
34	3	–5	–2
36	5	–3	–0
38	7	–1	2
40	9	1	4
42	11	3	6
44	13	5	7
46	15	6	9
48	16	8	11
50	18	10	12
52	20	11	14
54	21	13	15
56	23	14	17
58	24	16	18
60	26	17	20
62	27	19	21
64	29	20	23
66	30	22	24
68	32	23	25
70	33	24	27
72	34	26	28
74	36	27	29
76	37	28	31
78	38	30	32
80	40	31	33
82	41	32	34
84	42	33	35
86	43	34	37
88	45	36	38
90	46	37	39
92	47	38	40
94	48	39	41
96	49	40	42
98	50	41	43
100	51	42	44
102	53	43	45
104	54	44	46
106	55	45	47
108	56	46	48

*inches of mercury below one atmosphere

Pressure (psig)	R-502 Temp. (°F)	Suva HP80 Sat'd Liquid Temp. (°F)	Suva HP80 Sat'd Vapor Temp. (°F)
110	57	47	49
115	60	50	52
120	62	52	54
125	64	54	56
130	67	57	59
135	69	59	61
140	71	61	63
145	73	63	65
150	75	65	67
155	78	67	69
160	80	69	71
165	82	71	73
170	84	73	75
175	85	75	77
180	87	77	78
185	89	78	80
190	91	80	82
195	93	82	84
200	95	83	85
205	96	85	87
210	98	87	88
215	100	88	90
220	101	90	92
225	103	91	93
230	105	93	95
235	106	94	96
240	108	96	97
245	109	97	99
250	111	99	100
255	112	100	102
260	114	102	103
265	115	103	104
270	117	104	106
275	118	106	107
280	119	107	108
285	121	108	110
290	122	110	111
295	123	111	112
300	125	112	114
305	126	113	115
310	127	115	116
315	129	116	117
320	130	117	118
325	131	118	120
330	132	119	121
335	134	121	122
340	135	122	123
345	136	123	124
350	137	124	125
355	138	125	126
360	139	126	127
365	141	127	128
370	142	128	130
375	143	130	131
380	144	131	132
385	145	132	133
390	146	133	134
395	147	134	135
400	148	135	136
405	149	136	137
410	150	137	138
415	151	138	139
420	152	139	140
425	153	140	141
430	154	141	142
435	155	142	143
440	156	143	144
445	157	144	144

Table 2b
Pressure–Temperature Chart
Suva HP80 (kPa/°C)

Pressure (kPa)	R-502 Temp. (°C)	Suva HP80 Sat'd Liquid Temp. (°C)	Suva HP80 Sat'd Vapor Temp. (°C)
10	–85.5	–88.5	–85.5
20	–75.0	–78.5	–75.5
30	–68.5	–72.0	–69.5
40	–63.5	–67.0	–64.5
50	–59.5	–63.0	–60.5
60	–56.0	–59.5	–57.5
70	–53.0	–56.5	–54.5
80	–50.5	–54.0	–52.0
90	–48.0	–51.5	–49.5
100	–45.5	–49.5	–47.5
110	–43.5	–47.5	–45.5
120	–41.5	–45.5	–43.5
130	–40.0	–44.0	–42.0
140	–38.5	–42.0	–40.5
150	–36.5	–40.5	–39.0
160	–35.0	–39.0	–37.5
170	–33.5	–37.5	–36.0
180	–32.5	–36.5	–34.5
190	–31.0	–35.0	–33.5
200	–29.5	–34.0	–32.0
210	–28.5	–32.5	–31.0
220	–27.5	–31.5	–30.0
230	–26.0	–30.5	–28.5
240	–25.0	–29.5	–27.5
250	–24.0	–28.5	–26.5
260	–23.0	–27.0	–25.5
270	–22.0	–26.5	–24.5
280	–21.0	–25.5	–23.5
290	–20.0	–24.5	–23.0
300	–19.0	–23.5	–22.0
310	–18.5	–22.5	–21.0
320	–17.5	–22.0	–20.0
330	–16.5	–21.0	–19.5
340	–15.5	–20.0	–18.5
350	–15.0	–19.5	–18.0
360	–14.0	–18.5	–17.0
370	–13.5	–18.0	–16.5
380	–12.5	–17.0	–15.5
390	–12.0	–16.5	–15.0
400	–11.0	–15.5	–14.0
410	–10.5	–15.0	–13.5
420	–9.5	–14.0	–12.5
430	–9.0	–13.5	–12.0
440	–8.0	–13.0	–11.5
450	–7.5	–12.0	–10.5
460	–7.0	–11.5	–10.0
470	–6.0	–11.0	–9.5
480	–5.5	–10.0	–9.0
490	–5.0	–9.5	–8.0
500	–4.5	–9.0	–7.5
510	–3.5	–8.5	–7.0
520	–3.0	–8.0	–6.5
530	–2.5	–7.0	–6.0
540	–2.0	–6.5	–5.5
550	–1.5	–6.0	–5.0
560	–0.5	–5.5	–4.0
570	0.0	–5.0	–3.5
580	0.5	–4.5	–3.0
590	1.0	–4.0	–2.5
600	1.5	–3.5	–2.0
610	2.0	–3.0	–1.5
620	2.5	–2.5	–1.0
630	3.0	–2.0	–0.5
640	3.5	–1.5	0.0
650	4.0	–1.0	0.5
660	4.5	–0.5	1.0
670	5.0	0.0	1.5
680	5.5	0.5	2.0
690	6.0	1.0	2.5
700	6.5	1.5	3.0
710	7.0	2.0	3.5
720	7.5	2.5	3.5
730	8.0	3.0	4.0
740	8.5	3.5	4.5
750	9.0	4.0	5.0
760	9.5	4.5	5.5
770	10.0	4.5	6.0
780	10.5	5.0	6.5
790	11.0	5.5	7.0
800	11.0	6.0	7.0
810	11.5	6.5	7.5
820	12.0	7.0	8.0
830	12.5	7.5	8.5
840	13.0	7.5	9.0
850	13.5	8.0	9.0
860	14.0	8.5	9.5
870	14.0	9.0	10.0
880	14.5	9.5	10.5
890	15.0	9.5	11.0
900	15.5	10.0	11.0
950	17.5	12.0	13.0
1000	19.5	14.0	15.0
1050	21.0	15.5	16.5
1100	23.0	17.0	18.5
1150	24.5	19.0	20.0
1200	26.0	20.5	21.5
1250	28.0	22.0	23.0
1300	29.5	23.5	24.5
1350	31.0	25.0	26.0
1400	32.5	26.5	27.5
1450	34.0	28.0	28.5
1500	35.5	29.0	30.0
1550	36.5	30.5	31.5
1600	38.0	31.5	32.5
1650	39.5	33.0	34.0
1700	40.5	34.0	35.0
1750	42.0	35.5	36.0
1800	43.0	36.5	37.5
1850	44.5	37.5	38.5
1900	45.5	39.0	39.5
1950	46.5	40.0	40.5
2000	48.0	41.0	42.0
2050	49.0	42.0	43.0
2100	50.0	43.0	44.0
2150	51.0	44.0	45.0
2200	52.0	45.0	46.0
2250	53.0	46.0	47.0
2300	54.0	47.0	48.0
2350	55.0	48.0	49.0
2400	56.0	49.0	49.5
2450	57.0	50.0	50.5
2500	58.0	51.0	51.5
2550	59.0	52.0	52.5
2600	60.0	52.5	53.5
2650	61.0	53.5	54.0
2700	62.0	54.5	55.0
2750	62.5	55.5	56.0
2800	63.5	56.0	56.5
2850	64.5	57.0	57.5
2900	65.5	58.0	58.5
2950	66.0	58.5	59.0
3000	67.0	59.5	60.0
3050	68.0	60.0	60.5
3100	68.5	61.0	61.5
3150	69.5	61.5	62.0
3200	70.0	62.5	63.0

Checklist for Suva HP80 Retrofit

_______ 1. Establish baseline performance with R-502. (See data sheet for recommended data.)

_______ 2. Remove R-502 charge from system.
(Need 10–15 in. Hg vacuum [50–67 kPa, 0.49–0.67 bar] to remove charge.)
- Use recovery cylinder/*Do Not Vent to Atmosphere*
- Weigh amount removed (if possible): _______

_______ 3. Drain lubricant charge from compressor (unless alkylbenzene or polyol ester lubricant is already in compressor).
- Measure amount of lubricant removed and record. _______

_______ 4. Charge alkylbenzene or polyol ester lubricant.
- Recharge with amount equivalent to amount removed in *Step 3*.
- Reinstall compressor (if removed).

_______ 5. Replace filter drier with new drier approved for use with Suva HP80.
- Solid core driers: check with drier manufacturer for recommendation
- Loose fill driers: use XH-9 desiccant
- Compacted bead driers: use XH-9 or XH-6 desiccant

_______ 6. Reconnect system and evacuate with vacuum pump. (Evacuate to full vacuum [29.9 in. Hg/500 microns/0.14 kPa/0.0014 bar]).
- Leak check system. (Reevacuate system following leak check).

_______ 7. Charge system with Suva HP80.
- Remove ***Liquid Only*** from cylinder
- Initial charge 80% by weight of original R-502 charge
- Amount of refrigerant charged: _______

_______ 8. Adjust charge until desired operating conditions are achieved.
- Remove ***Liquid Only*** from cylinder
- If low in charge, add in increments of 2–3% of original R-502 charge
- Amount of refrigerant charged: _______

Total Refrigerant Charged (add 7 and 8) _______

- Label components and system for type of refrigerant (Suva HP80) and lubricant (alkylbenzene or polyol ester).

Retrofit is complete!!

System Data Sheet

Type of System/Location: ______________________

Equipment Mfg.: ______________ Compressor Mfg.: ______________

Model No.: ______________ Model No.: ______________

Serial No.: ______________ Serial No.: ______________

R-502 charge size: ______________ Lubricant type: ______________

______________ Charge size: ______________

Drier Mfg.: ______________ Drier type (check one):

Model No.: ______________ Loose fill: ______________

______________ Solid core: ______________

Condenser cooling medium (air/water): ______________

Expansion Device (check one): Capillary tube: ________

Expansion valve: ________

If Expansion valve:

Manufacturer: ______________

Model No.: ______________

Control/set point: ______________

Location of sensor: ______________

Other System Controls (ex.: head press control), Describe: ______________

____

(circle units used where applicable)

Date/Time				
Refrigerant				
Charge Size (lb, oz/grams)				
Ambient Temp. (°F/°C)				
Relative Humidity				
Compressor:				
Suction T (°F/°C)				
Suction P (psig, psia/kPa, bar)				
Discharge T (°F/°C)				
Discharge P (psig, psia/kPa, bar)				
Box/Fixture T (°F/°C)				
Evaporator:				
Refrigerant Inlet T (°F/°C)				
Refrigerant Outlet T (°F/°C)				
Coil Air/H_2O In T (°F/°C)				
Coil Air/H_2O Out T (°F/°C)				
Refrigerant T at Superht. Ctl. Pt. (°F/°C)				
Condenser:				
Refrigerant Inlet T (°F/°C)				
Refrigerant Outlet T (°F/°C)				
Coil Air/H_2O In T (°F/°C)				
Coil Air/H_2O Out T (°F/°C)				
Exp. Device Inlet T (°F/°C)				
Motor Amps				
Run/Cycle Time				

Comments: ______________________

____

For Sales Information:

DuPont Fluorochemicals
Customer Service Center, B-15305
Wilmington, DE 19898
U.S.A.
(302) 774-2099
800-441-9442

For Technical Information:

Fluorochemicals Laboratory
Wilmington, DE 19898
U.S.A.
(302) 999-3129
800-582-5606

Europe

DuPont de Nemours
International S.A.
2 Chemin du Pavillon
P.O. Box 50
CH-1218 Le Grand-Saconnex
Geneva, Switzerland
41-22-717-5111

Canada

DuPont Canada, Inc.
P.O. Box 2200, Streetsville
Mississauga, Ontario
Canada
L5M 2H3
(905) 821-3300

Mexico

DuPont, S.A. de C.V.
Homero 206
Col. Chapultepec Morales
C.P. 11570 Mexico, D.F.
52-5-250-8000

South America

DuPont do Brasil S.A.
Alameda Itapecuru, 506
Alphaville 06400 Barueri
São Paulo, Brazil
55-11-421-8509

DuPont Argentina S.A.
Casilla Correo 1888
Correo Central
1000 Buenos Aires, Argentina
54-1-311-8167

Pacific

DuPont Australia
P.O. Box 930
North Sydney, NSW 2060
Australia
61-2-923-6165

Japan

Mitsui DuPont Fluorochemicals
Co., Ltd.
Mitsui Seimei Bldg.
2-3, 1-Chome Ohtemachi
Chiyoda-Ku, Tokyo 100 Japan
81-3-3216-8451

Asia

DuPont Taiwan
P.O. Box 81-777
Taipei, Taiwan
886-2-514-4400

DuPont Asia Pacific Limited
P.O. Box TST 98851
Tsim Sha Tsui
Kowloon, Hong Kong
852-734-5345

DuPont Thailand
P.O. Box 2398
Bangkok 10501, Thailand
66-2-238-4361

DuPont China Ltd.
Rm. 1704, Union Bldg.
100 Yenan Rd. East
Shanghai, PR China 200 002
Phone: 86-21-328-3738
Telex: 33448 DCLSH CN
Fax: 86-21-320-2304

DuPont Far East Inc.
P.O. Box 12396
50776 Kuala Lumpur, Malaysia
Phone: 60-3-232-3522
Telex: (784) 30391 DUFE M
Fax: 60-3-238-7250

DuPont Korea Ltd.
C.P.O. Box 5972
Seoul, Korea
82-2-721-5114

DuPont Singapore Pte. Ltd.
1 Maritime Square #07 01
World Trade Centre
Singapore 0409
65-273-2244

DuPont Far East, Philippines
5th Floor, Solid Bank Bldg.
777 Paseo de Roxas
Makati, Metro Manila
Philippines
63-2-818-9911

DuPont Far East Inc.
7A Murray's Gate Road
Alwarpet
Madras, 600 018, India
91-44-454-029

DuPont Far East Inc.—Pakistan
9 Khayaban-E-Shaheen
Defence Phase 5
Karachi, Pakistan
92-21-533-350

DuPont Far East Inc.
P.O. Box 2553/Jkt
Jakarta 10001, Indonesia
62-21-517-800

(12/93) 233260B Printed in U.S.A.
[Replaces: H-45947-1]
Reorder No.: H-45947-2

alternative refrigerants

ART-20

Properties and Applications of SUVA® HP62 Refrigerant

DuPont has developed a new hydrofluorocarbon (HFC) refrigerant, SUVA® HP62. SUVA® HP62 is the non-ozone depleting replacement for R-502 in refrigeration applications. Extensive laboratory and field tests have demonstrated that SUVA® HP62 is the closest match to R-502 among all alternatives. This document will discuss general properties of SUVA® HP62 and how it may be used in refrigeration applications.

PROPERTIES

SUVA® HP62 is a mixture of hydrofluorocarbon (HFC) refrigerants HFC-125, HFC-143a and HFC-134a. It is a near-azeotrope, nonflammable, and has no ozone depletion potential. These properties make it an ideal candidate refrigerant for applications where safety and consistency of performance are needed.

SUVA® HP62 will maintain a very consistent composition if leakage occurs in a refrigeration system, which means that operating performance will remain consistent following leakage/recharge cycles. As with all mixtures, we recommend that the liquid phase be removed from the storage cylinder to minimize composition changes when charging. SUVA® HP62 should not be mixed with any other refrigerant when charging, recycling, recovering or reclaiming.

Being nonflammable, SUVA® HP62 can be safely used in commercial systems such as supermarkets or transport refrigeration, where personnel and the public are in the vicinity of the refrigeration equipment. DuPont recommends the use of polyolester lubricants with SUVA® HP62; however, the compressor manufacturer should always be consulted for specific lubricant selection. HP62/polyolester mixtures have better miscibility than R-502/mineral oil at low temperatures which should aid in oil return for low temperature applications.

Table 1 lists the general properties of SUVA® HP62.

TABLE 1
General Properties of SUVA® HP62

Boiling Point (1 atm)	–46.5°C (–51.6°F)
Critical Temperature	72.1°C (161.7°F)
Critical Pressure	3732 kPa (541.2 psia)
Latent Heat of Vaporization at Boiling Point	202.1 kJ/kg (87.0 Btu/lb)
Saturated Vapor Density at –15°C	18.20 kg/cu m (1.14 lb/cu ft)
Ozone Depletion Potential	0
Global Warming Potential (HGWP; R-502 = 3.75)	0.94
DuPont AEL*	1,000 ppm (8 and 12-hour T.W.A.)
Flammability	None

*AEL (Acceptable Exposure Limit) is an airborne exposure limit established by DuPont toxicologists to which nearly all workers can be repeatedly exposed during a 40-hour work week, or 8-hour day, without adverse effects.

OPERATING CHARACTERISTICS

SUVA® HP62 is a long term replacement for R-502 and offers excellent operating characteristics when compared to R-502. Capacity and efficiency values should be nearly equivalent to R-502. The compressor discharge temperature may be as much as 7.4°C (13.3°F) lower than with R-502, which may equate to longer compressor life and better lubricant stability. For example, if a system were operated at –17.8°C (0°F) evaporation and 32.2°C (90°F) condensing, with a 18.3°C (65°F) suction gas temperature, estimated values of performance (with R-502 equal to 1.0) are:

Capacity	1.02
Theoretical Efficiency	0.97
Discharge Temperature	7.4°C (13.3°F) lower than R-502
Discharge Pressure	114.2 kPa (16.56 psia) higher than R-502
Suction Pressure	15.6 kPa (2.26 psia) higher than R-502

COMMERCIAL AVAILABILITY

SUVA® HP62 components are TSCA (U.S.A.) and EINECS (Europe) listed; also, SUVA® HP62 has been recognized by Underwriters Laboratories (UL).

Commercial quantities of SUVA® HP62 will be available by late 1993. Contact DuPont at locations shown on the back page, or contact any DuPont authorized distributor for more information.

For Sales Information:

DuPont Fluorochemicals
Customer Service Center, B-15305
Wilmington, DE 19898/U.S.A.
(302) 774-2099
1-800-441-9442

For Technical Information:

Fluorochemicals Laboratory
Wilmington, DE/U.S.A.
(302) 999-3129
1-800-582-5606

Europe
DuPont de Nemours
International S.A.
2 Chemin du Pavillon
P.O. Box 50
CH-1218 Le Grand-Saconnex
Geneva, Switzerland
41-22-717-5111

Canada
DuPont Canada, Inc.
P.O. Box 2200, Streetsville
Mississauga, Ontario
L5M 2H3
(416) 821-3300

Mexico
DuPont, S.A. de C.V.
Homero 206
Col. Chapultepec Morales
C.P. 11570 Mexico, D.F.
52-5-250-8000

South America
DuPont do Brasil S.A.
Alameda Itapicuru, 506
Alphaville 06400 Barueri
Sao Paulo, Brazil
55-11-421-8509

DuPont Argentina S.A.
Casilla Correo 1888
Correo Central
1000 Buenos Aires, Argentina
54-1-311-8167

Pacific
DuPont Australia
P.O. Box 930
North Sydney, NSW 2060
Australia
61-2-923-6165

Japan
Mitsui DuPont Fluorochemicals
Company, Ltd.
Mitsui Seimei Building
2-3, 1-Chome Ohtemachi
Chiyoda-Ku, Tokyo 100 Japan
81-3-3216-8451

Asia
DuPont Taiwan
P.O. Box 81-777
Taipei, Taiwan
886-2-514-4400

DuPont Asia Pacific Limited
P.O. Box TST 98851
Tsim Sha Tsui
Kowloon, Hong Kong
852-734-5345

DuPont Thailand
P.O. Box 2398
Bangkok 10501, Thailand
66-2-238-4361

DuPont China Ltd.
Room 1704, Union Bldg.
100 Yanan Rd. East
Shanghai, PR China 200 002
Phone: 86-21-328-3738
Telex: 33448 DCLSH CN
Fax: 86-21-320-2304

DuPont Far East, Inc.
P.O. Box 12396
50776 Kuala Lumpur, Malaysia
Phone: 60-3-232-3522
Telex: (784) 30391 DUFE M
Fax: 60-3-238-7250

DuPont Korea Ltd.
C.P.O. Box 5972
Seoul, Korea
82-2-721-5114

DuPont Singapore Pte. Ltd.
1 Maritime Square #07 01
World Trade Centre
Singapore 0409
65-273-2244

DuPont Far East, Philippines
5th Floor, Solid Bank Building
777 Paseo de Roxas
Makati, Metro Manila
Philippines
63-2-818-9911

DuPont Far East Inc.
7A Murray's Gate Road
Alwarpet
Madras, 600 018 India
91-44-454-029

DuPont Far East Inc.–
Pakistan
9 Khayaban-E-Shaheen
Defence Phase 5
Karachi, Pakistan
92-21-533-350

DuPont Far East Inc.
P.O. Box 2553/Jkt
Jakarta 10001
Indonesia
62-21-517-800

H-52162 (9/93) Printed in U.S.A. 204141A

P-MP

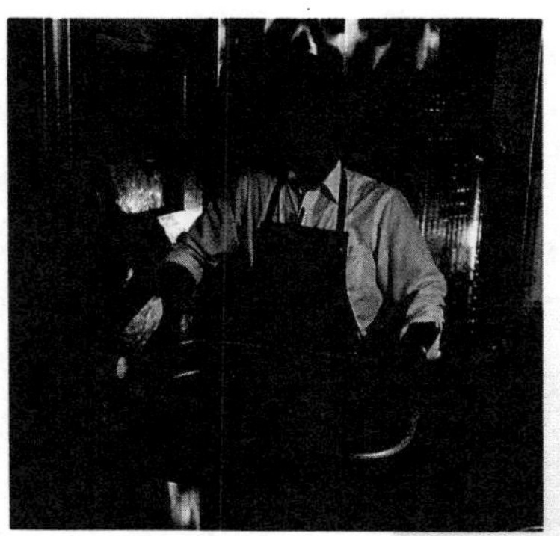

DuPont SUVA® MP Refrigerant Blends

Properties, Uses, Storage and Handling

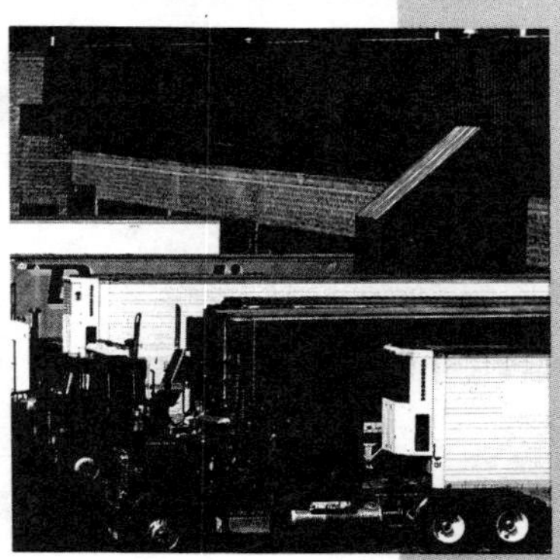

SUVA® MP39 refrigerant
SUVA® MP66 refrigerant
SUVA® MP52 refrigerant

SUVA® MP Refrigerant Blends

Properties, Uses, Storage and Handling

Table of Contents

BACKGROUND

Chlorofluorocarbons (CFCs), which were developed over 60 years ago, have many unique properties. They are low in toxicity, nonflammable, noncorrosive and compatible with other materials. In addition, they offer the thermodynamic and physical properties that make them ideal for a variety of uses. CFCs are used as refrigerants; as blowing agents in the manufacture of insulation, packaging and cushioning foams; as cleaning agents for metal and electronic components; and in many other applications.

However, the stability of these compounds, coupled with their chlorine content, has linked them to depletion of the earth's protective ozone layer. As a result, DuPont is phasing out production of CFCs and introducing environmentally acceptable alternatives, such as the SUVA® MP refrigerant blends family.

SUVA® MP REFRIGERANT BLENDS

DuPont has developed SUVA® MP series refriger-ants, ternary blends, as alternatives for CFC-12 in refrigeration and air conditioning applications. These refrigerants are intended to replace CFC-12 in existing refrigeration equipment.

This group of products contains three components: HCFC-22, HFC-152a and HCFC-124. *Table 1* shows their compositions.

TABLE 1
Composition of SUVA® MP Refrigerant Blends (in wt %)

	HCFC-22	HFC-152a	HCFC-124
SUVA® MP39	53	13	34
SUVA® MP52	33	15	52
SUVA® MP66	61	11	28

Table 2 shows the chemical names and formulae of the refrigerants above.

TABLE 2
Refrigerant Information

Refrigerant	Chemical Name	Formula	CAS No.*	Molecular Wt.
HCFC-22	Chlorodifluoromethane	$CHClF_2$	75-45-6	86.47
HFC-152a	1,1-Difluoroethane	CH_3CHF_2	75-37-6	66.00
HCFC-124	2-Chloro-1,1,1,2-Tetrafluoroethane	$CHClFCF_3$	2837-89-0	136.50

* CAS Chemical Abstract Service (American Chemical Society)

Some applications for SUVA® MP refrigerants are: mobile air conditioning, home refrigerators and freezers, reciprocating chillers, medium-temperature retail food refrigeration, refrigerated transportation equipment, dehumidifiers, ice machines, beverage vending machines, and water fountains.

SUVA® MP refrigerant blends are mixtures designed to replace CFC-12 in existing refrigeration systems:

SUVA® MP39 is an alternative for use in most medium temperature CFC-12 systems. With MP39, comparable capacities and efficiencies to CFC-12 are expected in systems operating at evaporator temperatures of −23°C (−10°F) and above, making it suitable for use in such applications as walk-in coolers, food and dairy display cases, beverage dispensers, beverage vending machines, and home refrigerators.

SUVA® MP66 provides comparable capacity to CFC-12 in retrofit CFC-12 systems operating at evaporator temperatures below −23°C (−10°F), making it suitable for use in transport refrigeration equipment and domestic and commercial freezers. SUVA® MP66 can also be used to replace R-500 in existing equipment.

SUVA® MP52 is intended as a retrofit replacement for CFC-12 in the mobile A/C service market.

The thermodynamic and physical properties of SUVA® MP refrigerants make them very efficient and safe replacement refrigerants for CFC-12.

Table 3 summarizes the theoretical performance characteristics of MP39 and MP66 at given evaporator conditions. Both MP39 and MP66 exhibit a slightly higher refrigeration capacity and equivalent coefficient of performance to CFC-12.

TABLE 3
Theoretical Cycle Comparison* of CFC-12, SUVA® MP39 and SUVA® MP66

	CFC-12	SUVA® MP39	SUVA® MP66
Refrigeration Capacity (Relative to CFC-12)	1.00	1.08	1.16
Coefficient of Performance	1.46	1.48	1.47
Compression Ratio	10.20	11.73	11.48
Compressor			
Discharge Temperature, °C	156	169	174
°F	313	336	345
Discharge Pressure, kPa (abs)	1340	1530	1620
psia	194	222	235
Temperature Glide			
Evaporator, °C (°F)	0	5.2 (9.3)	4.9 (8.8)
Condenser, °C (°F)	0	4.5 (8.2)	4.2 (7.6)

*−23°C (−10°F) evaporator/54°C (130°F) condenser/superheat and subcool to 32°C (90°F).

Table 4 shows the theoretical performance characteristics of SUVA® MP52 and CFC-12 at typical automotive conditions. SUVA® MP52 was specifically developed for this application and exhibits comparable refrigeration capacity and discharge pressure to CFC-12.

TABLE 4
Theoretical Cycle Comparison* of CFC-12 and SUVA® MP52

	CFC-12	SUVA® MP52
Refrigeration Capacity (Relative to CFC-12)	1.00	0.96
Coefficient of Performance	2.40	2.43
Compression Ratio	4.68	5.33
Compressor		
Discharge Temperature, °C	85	92
°F	185	197
Discharge Pressure, kPa (abs)	1530	1500
psia	222	218
Temperature Glide		
Evaporator, °C (°F)	0	4.7 (8.5)
Condenser, °C (°F)	0	4.5 (8.2)

* 2°C (35°F) evaporator/60°C (140°F) condenser/superheat and subcool of 2.8°C (5°F)

TEMPERATURE GLIDE

Since the SUVA® MP refrigerant blends are not true azeotropes their compositions change as they change state (boil or condense). This causes a change in temperature when they boil or condense at constant pressure. This phenomenon is seen in direct expansion evaporators and condensers and is called "temperature glide". In the evaporator, the boiling point increases 4–5°C (8–10°F) between the evaporator inlet and exit for the SUVA® MP refrigerants. In the condenser, the condensing temperature decreases 4–5°C (8–10°F) between the condenser inlet and exit. The actual amount of temperature glide will depend on system design, and may or may not have an effect on system performance. For a detailed description of temperature glide refer to technical bulletin ART-7 (H-45938-1).

EFFECT OF LEAKAGE ON PERFORMANCE

Although any leak in a refrigeration system should be repaired as soon as possible, it is advantageous that a refrigerant maintain its performance characteristics throughout a series of leaks and recharges. Theoretical calculations were made to simulate a realistic scenario in which a refrigeration system goes through a series of five vapor leaks and subsequent recharges with SUVA® MP39. Vapor leaks were induced in a static system (compressor not running). Each leak was 20% by weight of the original charge, and each recharge was made liquid phase. *Table 5* shows the performance characteristics of the refrigeration system after each recharge. Although the composition of the system refrigerant changes, its performance remains comparable to that of CFC-12, leveling off just below the capacity of CFC-12.

In field tests with continuously operating equipment (such as found in a supermarket), significant vapor leaks have been found to cause little change in refrigerant composition. The continuous operation keeps the refrigerant well mixed, resulting in a leakage of vapor with entrained liquid rather than exclusively vapor in the event of a leak in the two-phase region of the refrigeration system.

TABLE 5
Theoretical Effect of Leakage on SUVA® MP39 Performance

	Temperature Glide		Discharge	Discharge		
Leak No.	Condenser °C (°F)	Evaporator °C (°F)	Pressure kPa (psia)	Temperature °C (°F)	C.O.P.	Capacity W (BTU/min)
Initial	4.6 (8.2)	4.9 (8.8)	990 (144)	95.3 (204)	3.29	2619 (149)
1	4.6 (8.2)	4.9 (8.8)	967 (140)	94.9 (203)	3.28	2537 (144)
2	4.6 (8.2)	4.9 (8.8)	944 (137)	93.9 (201)	3.30	2491 (142)
3	4.5 (8.1)	4.8 (8.7)	928 (135)	93.5 (200)	3.30	2445 (139)
4	4.5 (8.1)	4.8 (8.6)	916 (133)	93.5 (200)	3.30	2409 (137)
5	4.5 (8.1)	4.8 (8.6)	905 (131)	92.9 (199)	3.30	2372 (135)
CFC-12	0.0	0.0	908 (132)	85.8 (186)	3.25	2391 (136)

Assumptions: –6.7°C (20°F) evaporator/37.8°C (100°F) condenser/ 18.3°C (65°F) suction gas/5.6°C (10°F) of subcooling

PHYSICAL PROPERTIES

General physical properties of the SUVA® MP refrigerant blends are shown in *Table 6*. Since these are blends of three different components, some of the properties shown are averages for the blend composition.

Additional physical property data may be found in other DuPont publications. Bulletin ART-10 (H-45949) contains viscosity, thermal conductivity, and heat capacity data for saturated liquid and vapor in addition to heat capacity data and heat capacity ratios for both saturated and superheated vapors. Thermodynamic tables in English and SI units are available for SUVA® MP39 in Bulletins T-MP39-ENG (H-47764) and T-MP39-SI (H-47765); for SUVA® MP52 in Bulletins T-MP52-ENG (H-47769) and T-MP52-SI (H-47770); and for SUVA® MP66 in Bulletins T-MP66-ENG (H-47759) and T-MP66-SI (H-47760).

Pressure/temperature relationships for the MP refrigerants are shown in *Figures 1* through *6*. Graphs are shown in both S.I. units and English units.

Note: Pressures shown are kPa (abs) and psia. The saturated liquid line (bubble point) and saturated vapor line (dew point) are indicated on each graph.

Pressure/enthalpy relationships for the MP refrigerants are shown in *Figures 7* through *12*.

Note: Isotherms shown within the 2-phase region slope due to the temperature glide of the MP refrigerants. See section on TEMPERATURE GLIDE for a more detailed explanation.

TABLE 6
General Property Information

Physical Property	Units	MP39	MP52	MP66
Composition (wt.%) (HCFC-22/HFC-152a/HCFC-124)	—	53/13/34	33/15/52	61/11/28
Molecular Wt.	g/mol (avg.)	94.4	101.0	92.8
Boiling Point (1 atm)	°C °F	–33.1 –27.6	–28.4 –19.0	–34.7 –30.4
Critical Temperature	°C °F	108 226	113 235	106 223
Critical Pressure	kPa (abs) psia	4604 668	4366 633	4682 679
Critical Volume	m^3/kg ft^3/lb	0.00196 0.0314	0.00195 0.0313	0.00195 0.0313
Critical Density	kg/m^3 lb/ft^3	510.6 31.9	512.3 32.0	512.7 32.0
Liquid Density at 25°C (77°F)	kg/m^3 lb/ft^3	1188 74.2	1207 75.4	1188 74.2
Density, Satd. Vapor at 25°C (77°F)	kg/m^3 lb/ft^3	29.0 1.81	25.9 1.61	30.7 1.92
Specific Heat Liquid, 25°C (77°F)	kJ/kg K BTU/lb °F	1.259 0.301	1.232 0.294	1.255 0.300
Specific Heat Vapor, 25°C (77°F) at 1 atm pressure	kJ/kg K BTU/lb °F	0.734 0.175	0.747 0.179	0.722 0.173
Vapor Pressure of Saturated Liquid at 25°C (77°F)	kPa (abs) psia	774.8 112.1	655.7 95.1	819.2 118.8
Heat of Vaporization at Normal Boiling Point	kJ/kg BTU/lb	234.3 100.8	221.7 95.4	235.7 101.4
Thermal Conductivity, at 25°C Liquid	W/m K BTU/hr ft °F	0.0840 0.0518	0.0799 0.0500	0.0850 0.0520
Vapor (1 atm)	W/m K BTU/hr ft °F	0.0101 0.00694	0.0102 0.00699	0.0101 0.00694
Viscosity, 25°C Liquid Vapor (1 atm)	mPa s (cP) micropoise	0.188 123	0.202 121	0.184 124
Solubility of Water in Refrigerant, 25°C	wt.%	0.10	0.10	0.10
Flammability Limit in Air (1 atm)	vol. %	none	none	none
Ozone Depletion Potential	CFC-12 = 1	0.03	0.03	0.035
Halocarbon Global Warming Potential	CFC-11 = 1	0.22	0.17	0.24
TSCA Inventory Status* Report/Included?		yes	yes	yes
Inhalation Exposure Limit	AEL* ppm (v/v)	800	720	840

*TSCA (U.S. Toxic Substance Control Act)

** AEL (Acceptable Exposure Limit) is a preliminary toxicity assessment established by DuPont; additional studies may be required.

Note: kPa is absolute pressure.

Figure 1. SUVA® MP39 Pressure vs. Temperature—SI Units

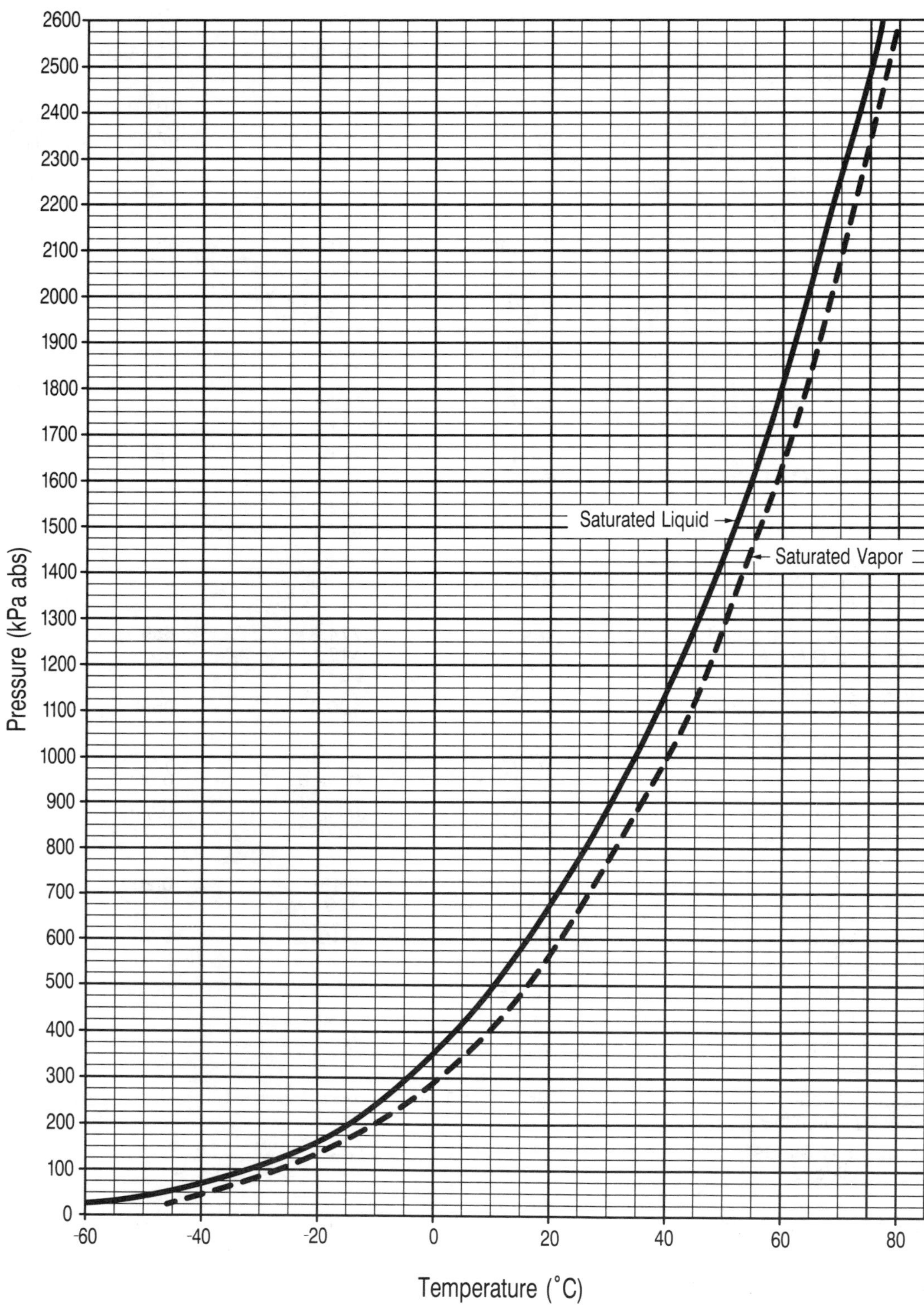

Figure 2. SUVA® MP39 Pressure vs. Temperature—English Units

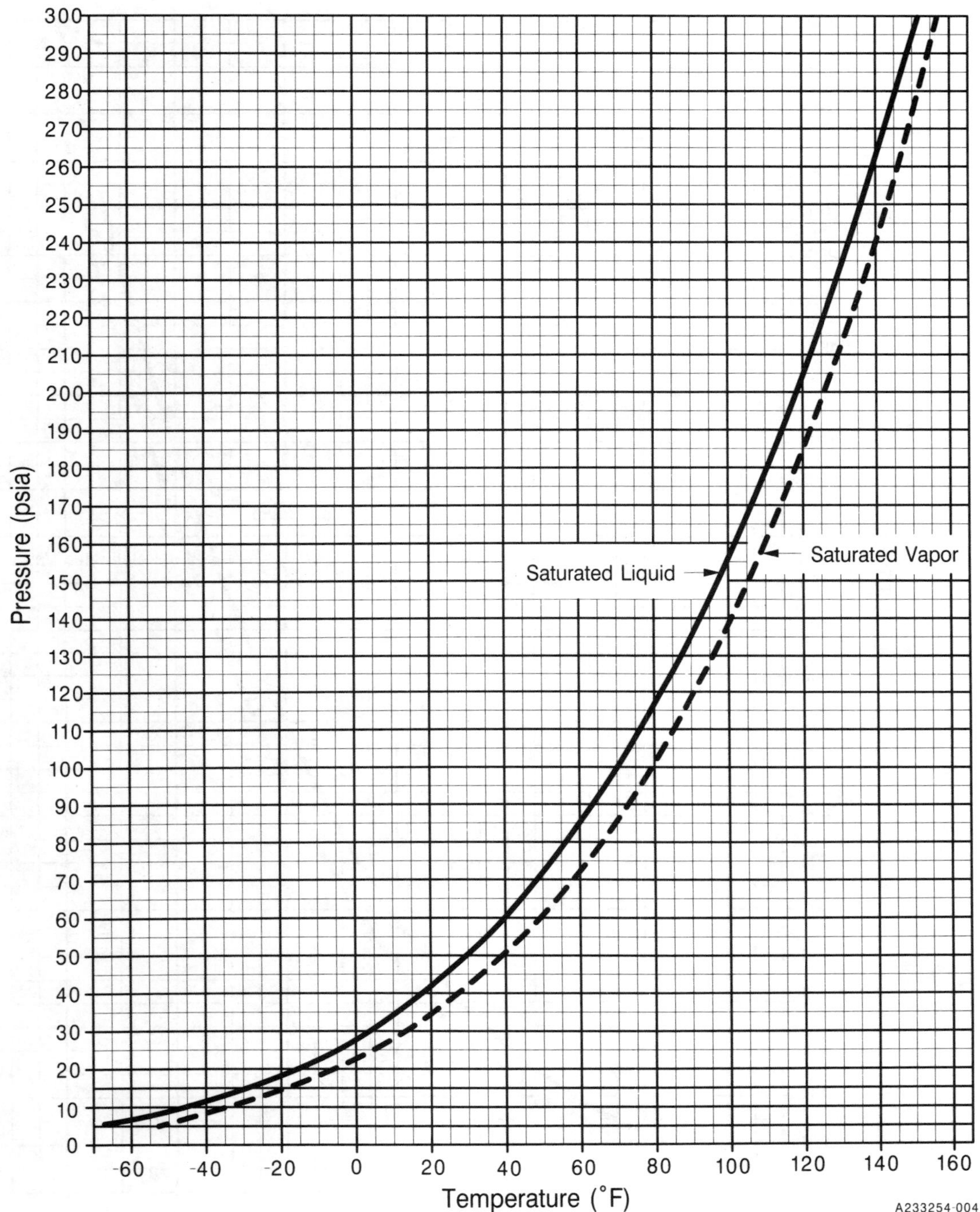

Figure 3. SUVA® MP52 Pressure vs. Temperature (SI Units)

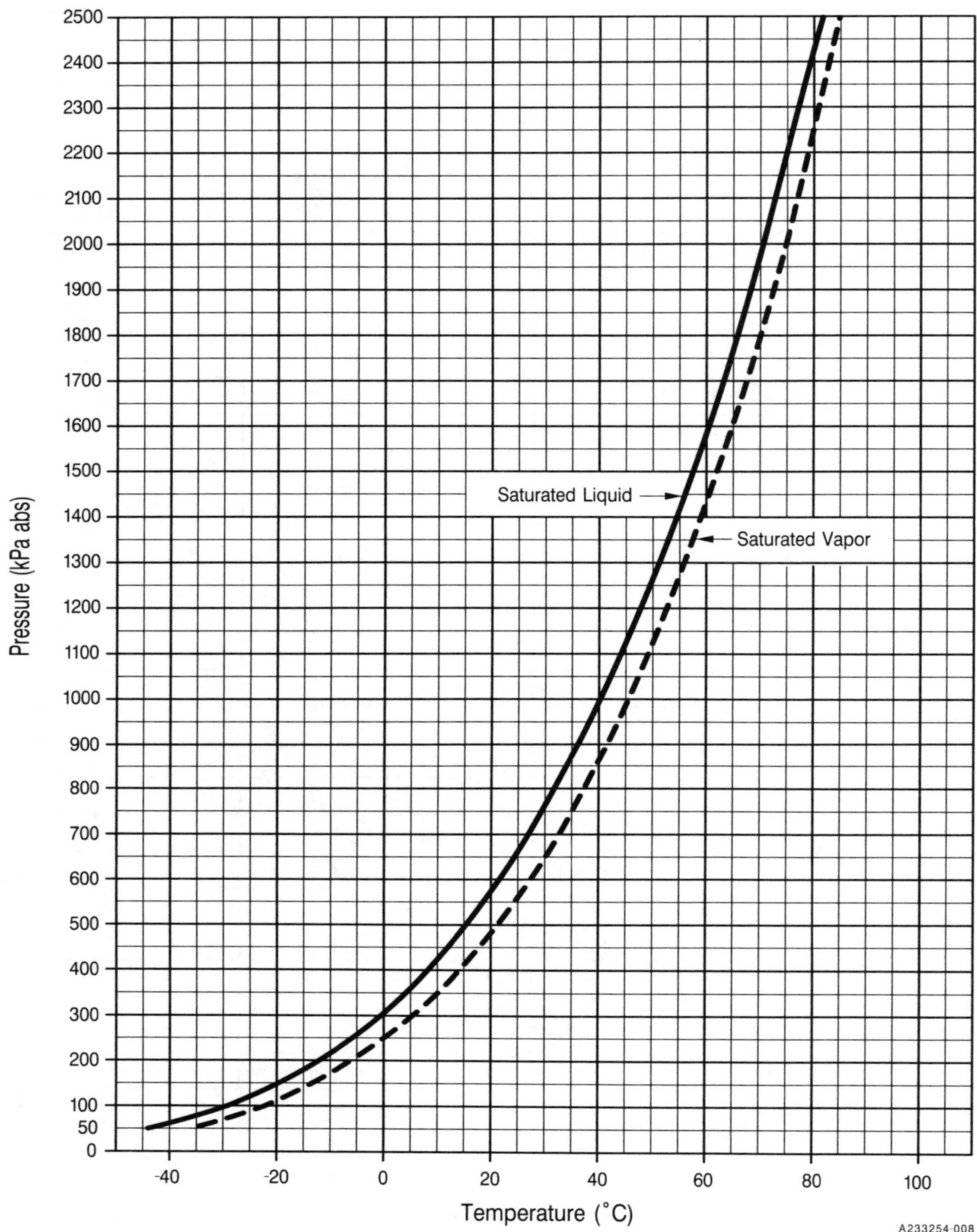

Figure 4. SUVA® MP52 Pressure vs. Temperature (English Units)

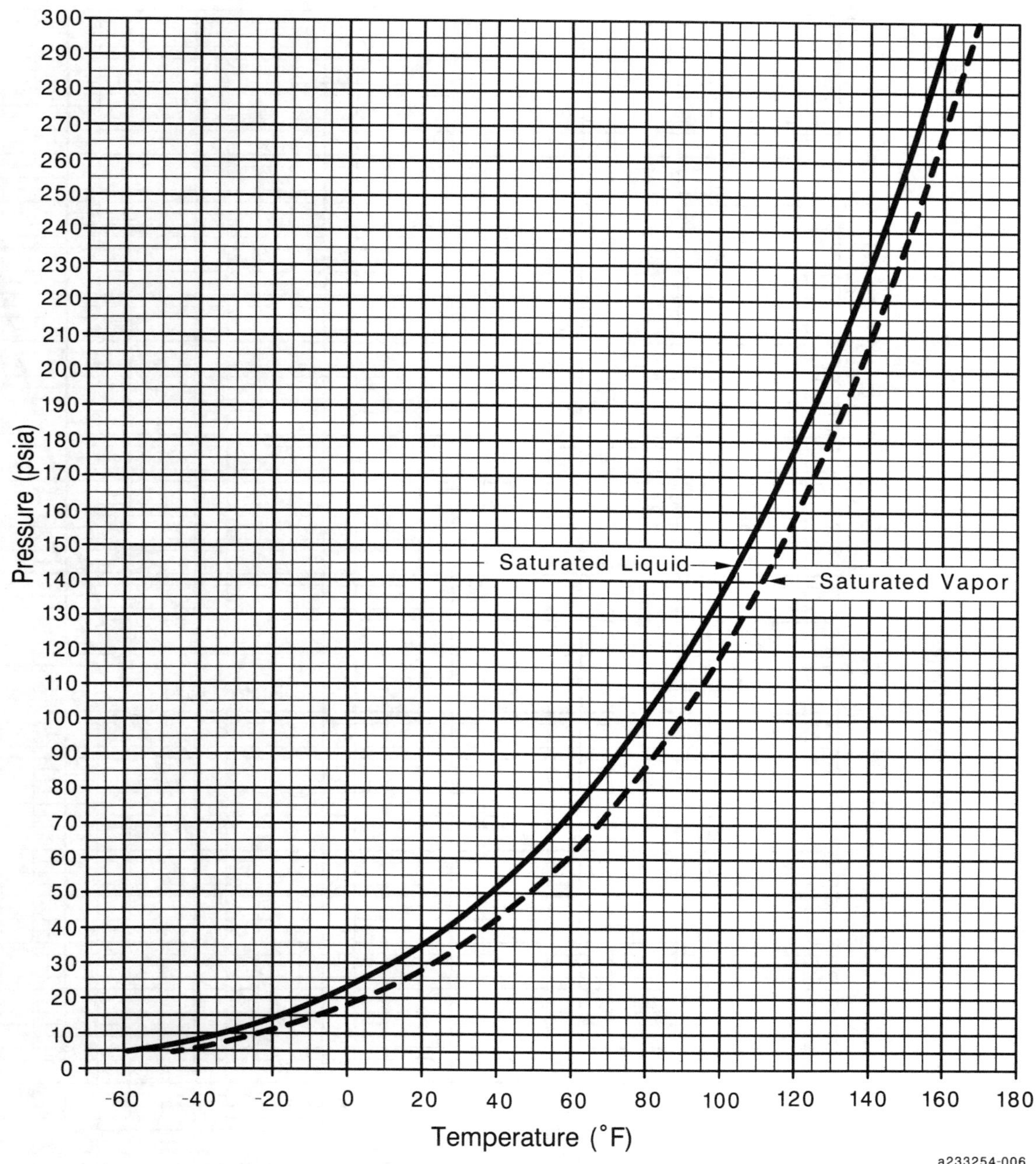

Figure 5. SUVA® MP66 Pressure vs. Temperature (SI Units)

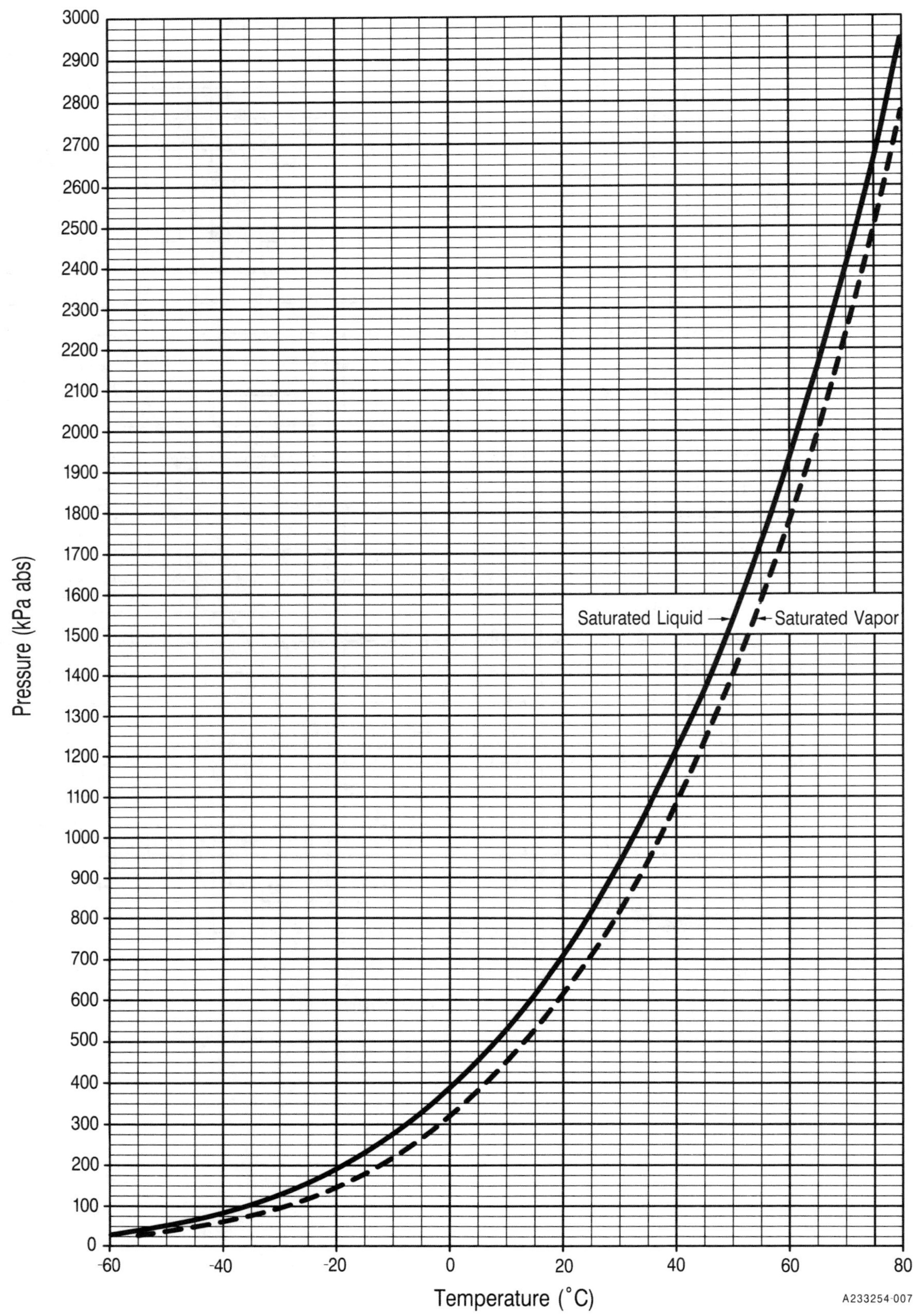

Figure 6. SUVA® MP66 Pressure vs. Temperature (English Units)

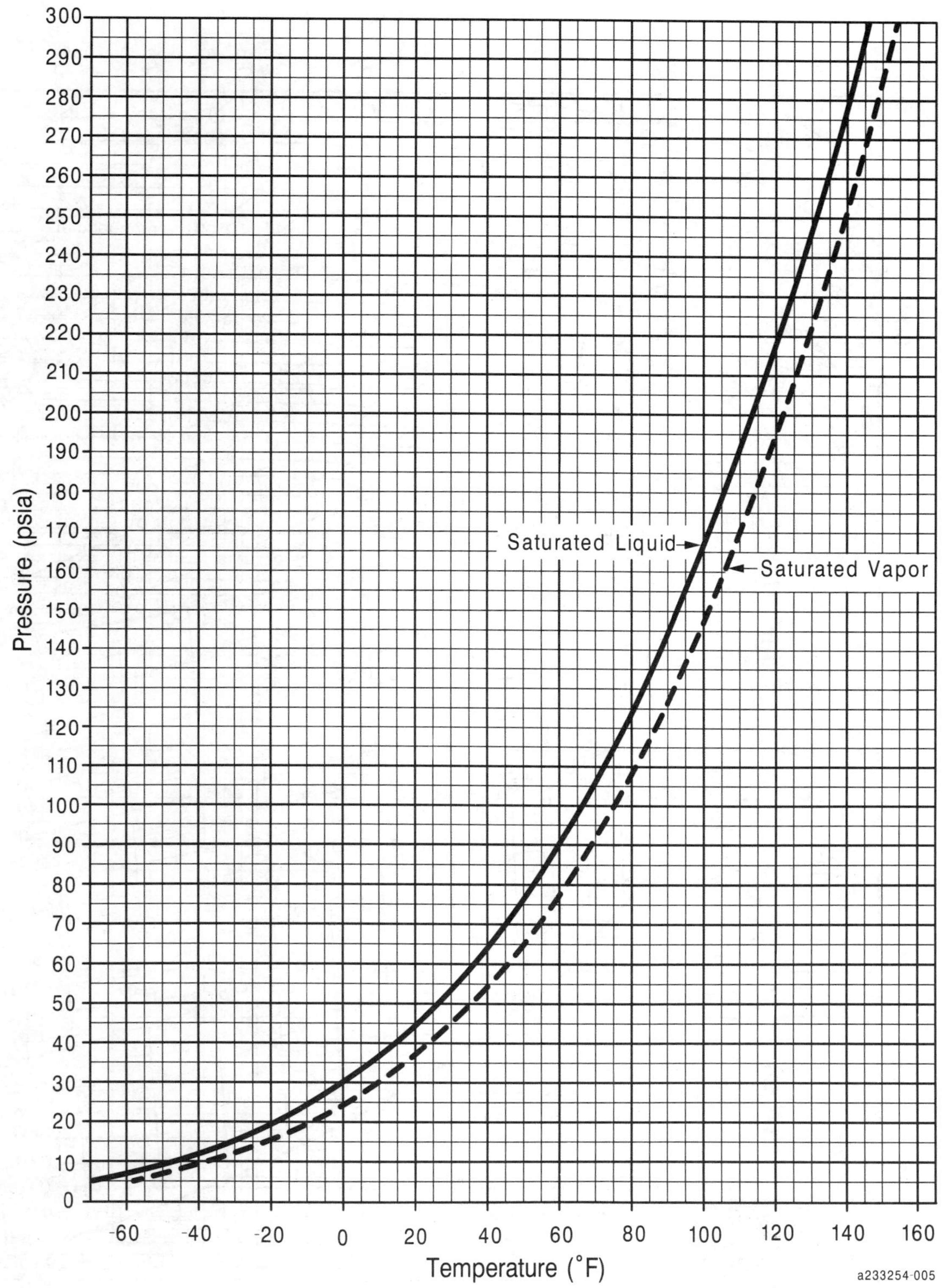

Figure 7. SUVA® MP39 Pressure vs. Enthalpy (SI Units)

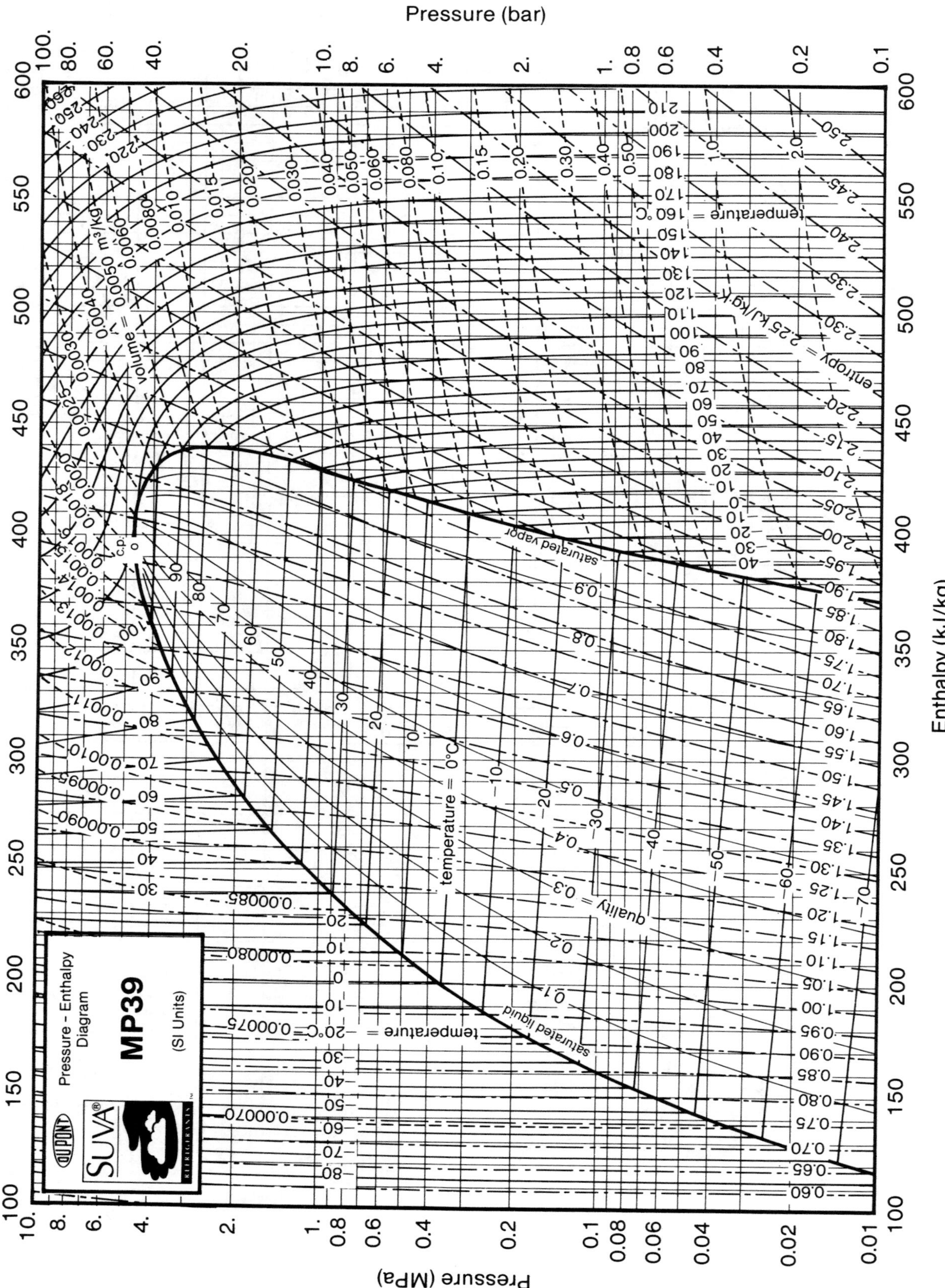

Figure 8. SUVA® MP39 Pressure vs. Enthalpy (Engineering Units)

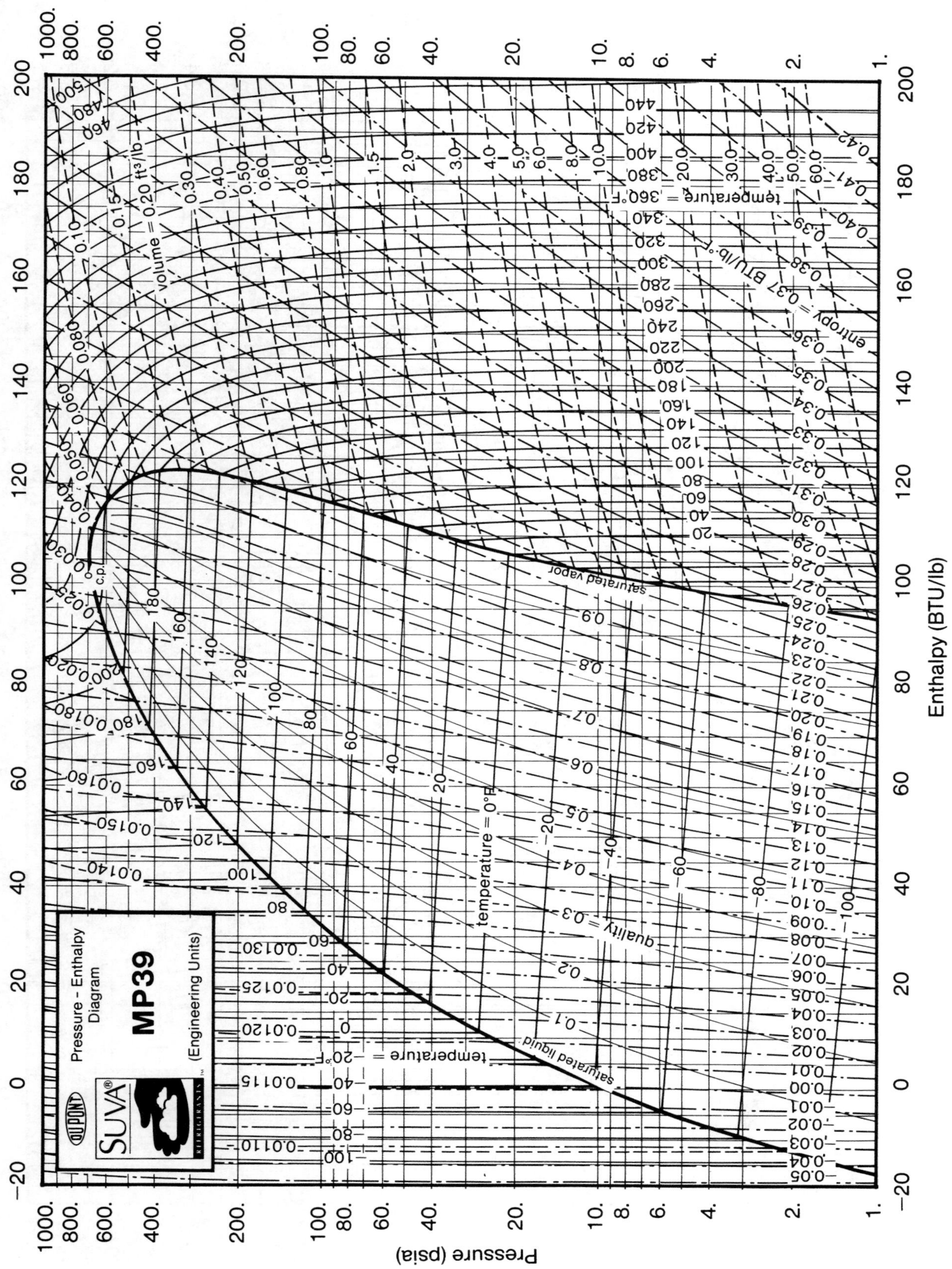

Figure 9. SUVA® MP52 Pressure vs. Enthalpy (SI Units)

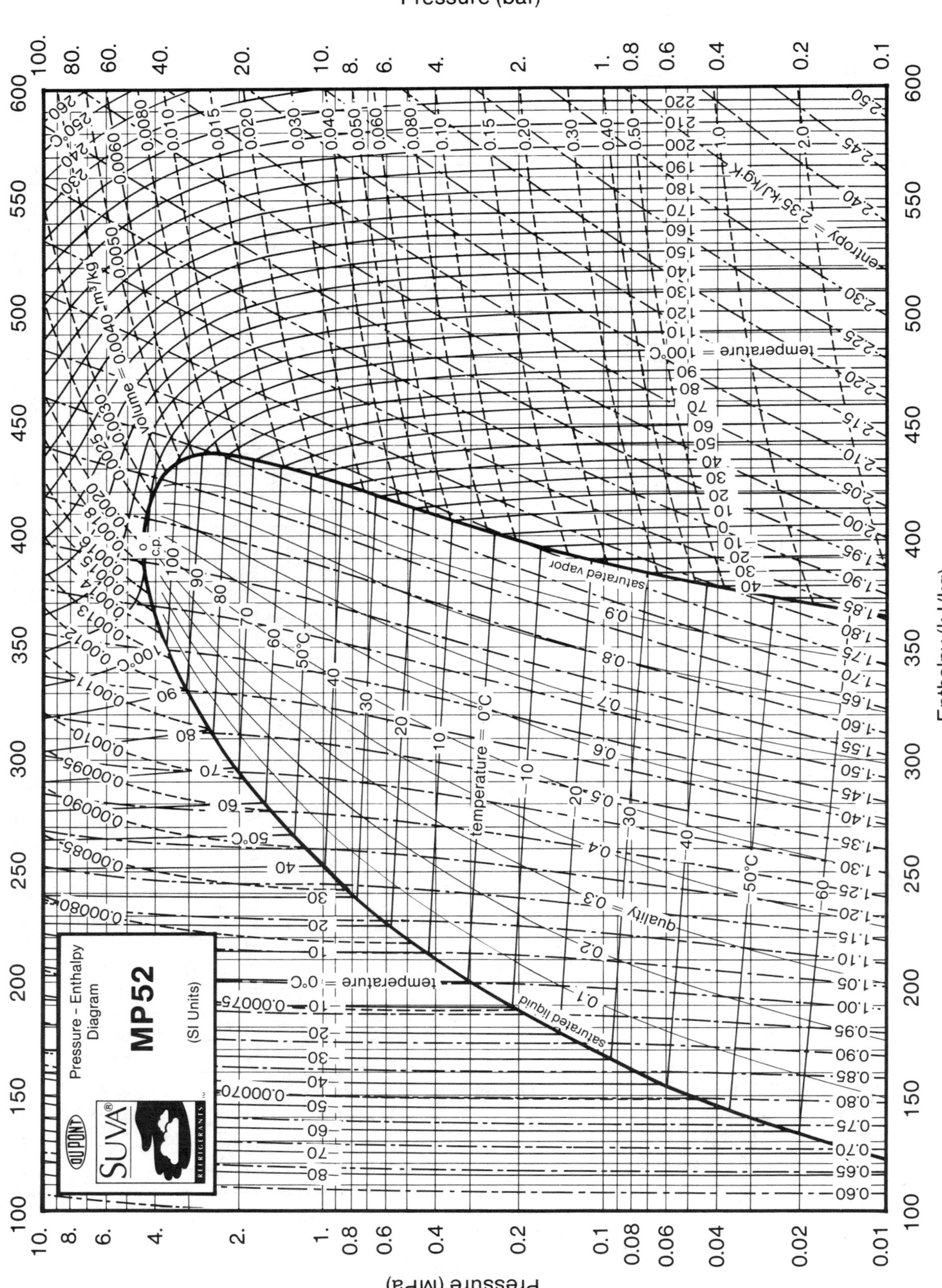

Figure 10. SUVA® MP52 Pressure vs. Enthalpy (Engineering Units)

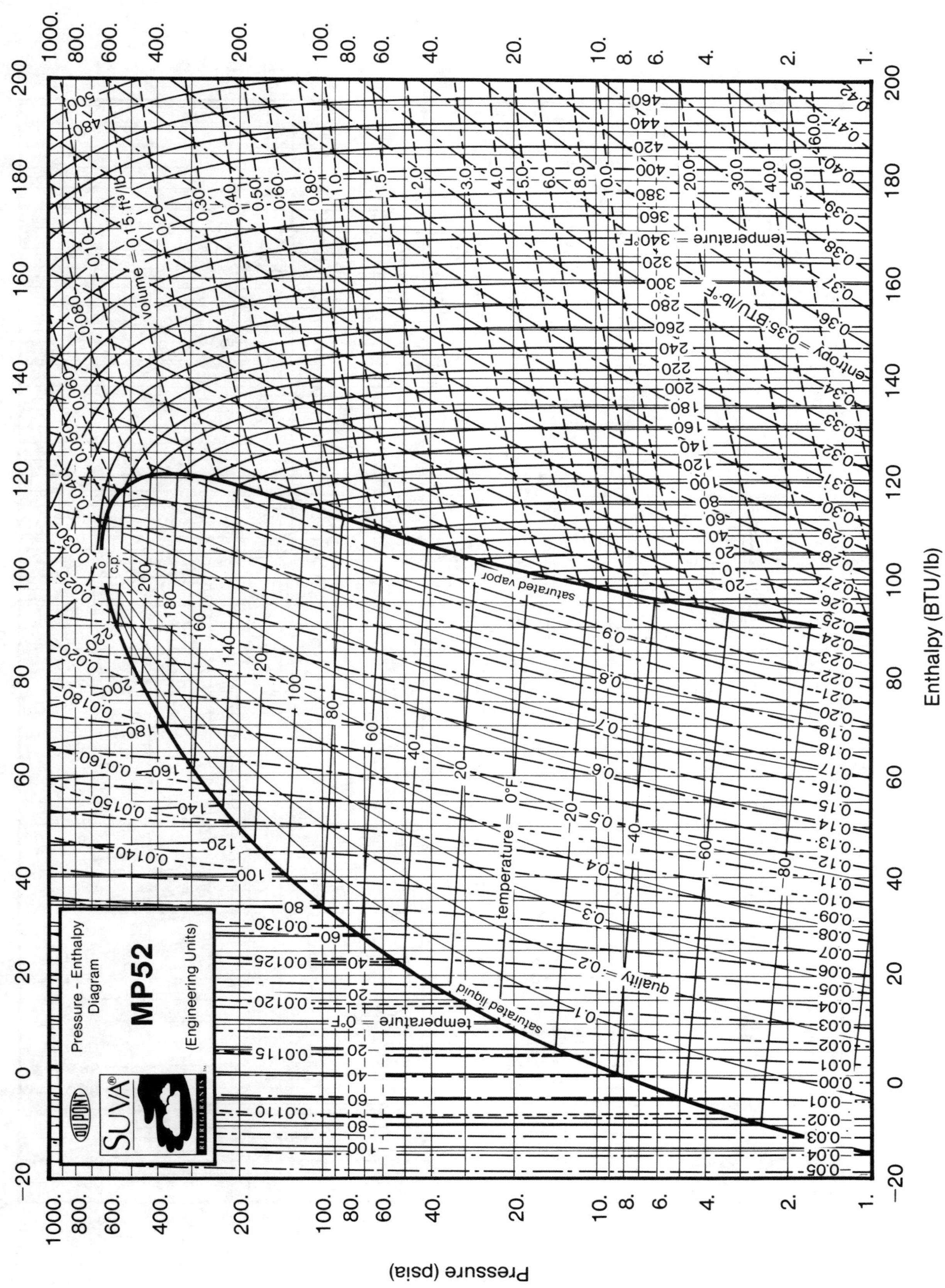

Figure 11. SUVA® MP66 Pressure vs. Enthalpy (SI Units)

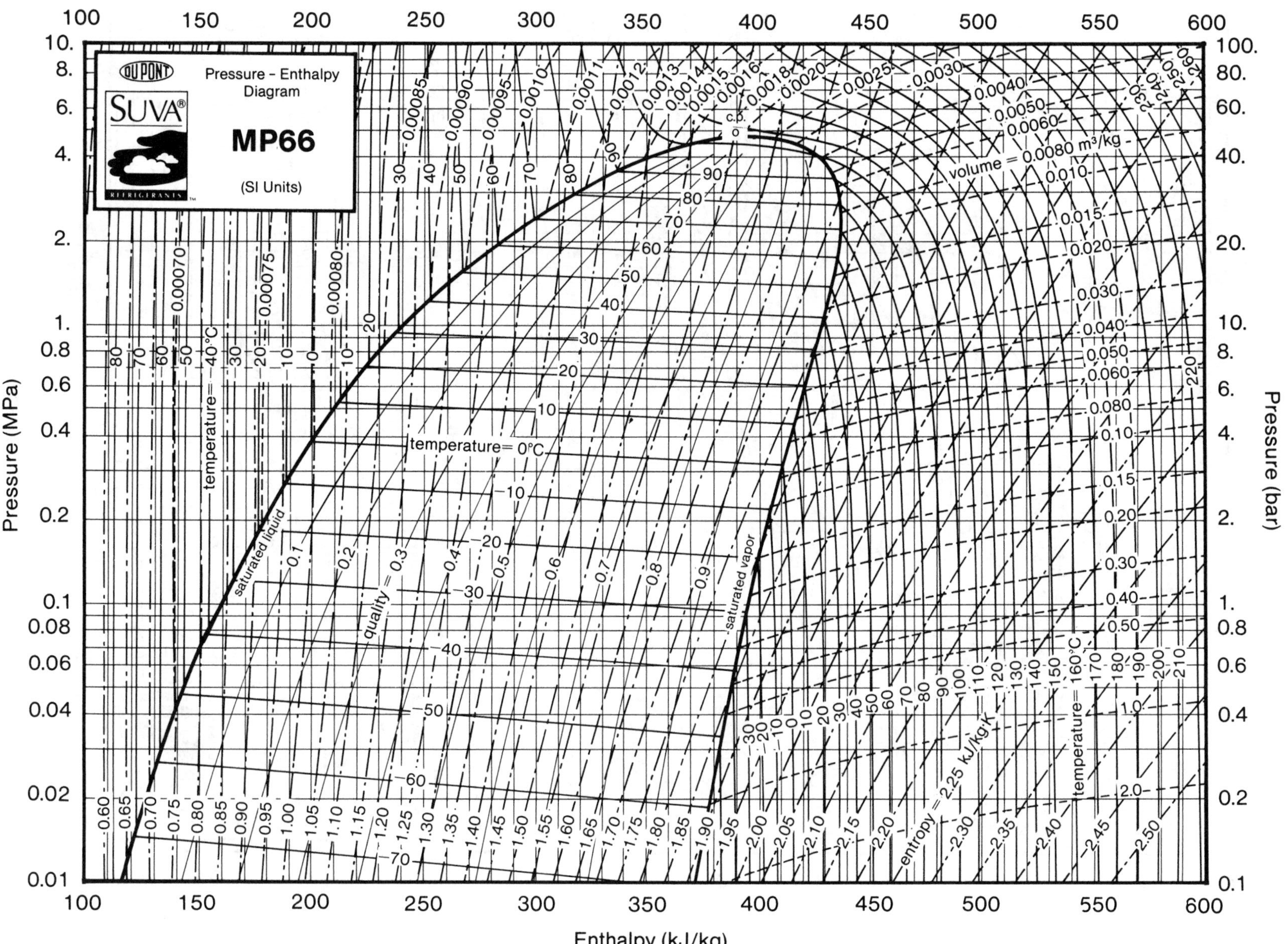

Figure 12. SUVA® MP66 Pressure vs. Enthalpy (Engineering Units)

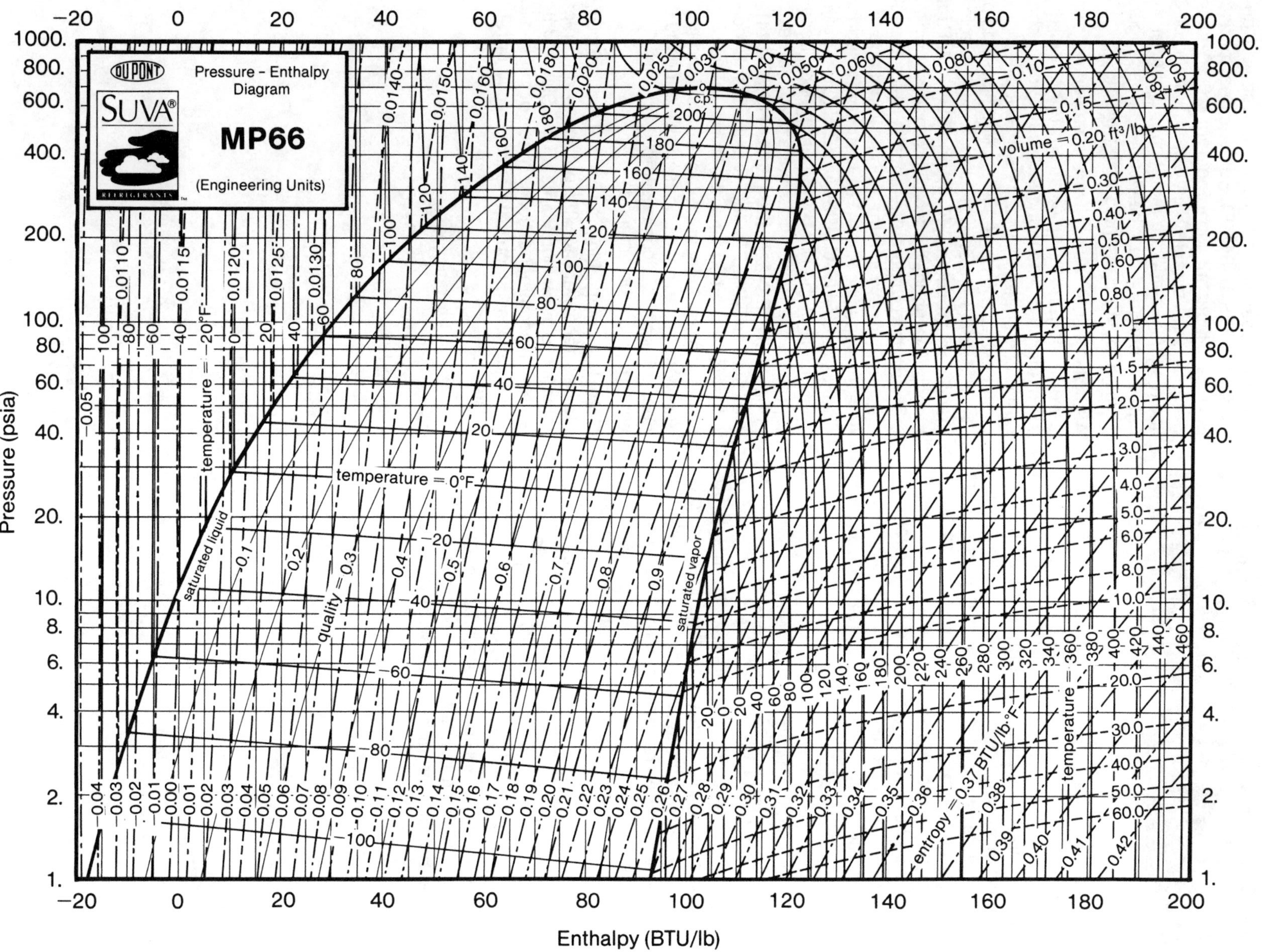

CHEMICAL/THERMAL STABILITY

THERMAL DECOMPOSITION

SUVA® MP refrigerant blends will decompose when exposed to high temperatures from sources such as open flames or electric resistance heaters. Decomposition may produce toxic and irritating compounds such as hydrochloric and hydrofluoric acid and possibly carbonyl halides. The pungent odors released will irritate the nose and throat and generally force people to evacuate the area. Therefore, it is important to prevent decomposition by following DuPont recommendations for handling and use.

STABILITY WITH METALS AND REFRIGERATION LUBRICANTS

Thermal stability tests for refrigerants with metals are typically performed in the presence of refrigeration oils. The results of sealed tube stability tests are available for CFC-12/mineral oil combinations, which have shown long term stability in contact with copper, steel, and aluminum in actual refrigeration systems. Alkylbenzene (AB), polyol ester (POE) and mixtures of AB/mineral oil or mixtures of POE/mineral oil are all possible candidates for use with SUVA® MP refrigerant blends. A summary of thermal stability tests performed with both AB and POE lubricants with MP refrigerant blends is shown in *Table 7*. **It should be noted that in all cases both AB and POE lubricants with MP refrigerants performed better than mineral oil with CFC-12.**

The sealed tube test method used for stability testing was generally the same as ASHRAE 97. A 3 ml volume of refrigerant/lubricant solution was heated in the presence of copper, steel, and aluminum strips in an oven for 14 days at 175°C (347°F). Both the neat lubricant and a mixture of lubricant and refrigerant (50/50 volume ratio) were tested. Visual ratings were obtained on both the liquid solutions and the metal coupons after the designated exposure time. The visual ratings range from 0 to 5, with 0 being best and 5 being worst.

After the visual ratings were obtained, sample tubes were opened and the lubricant and refrigerant (if present) were analyzed. The lubricant was typically checked for halide content and viscosity, while the refrigerant was examined for the presence of decomposition products. *Table 7* summarizes typical viscosity, miscibility, and stability data for both CFC-12 and SUVA® MP refrigerant blends. The lubricant miscibility range, shown in *Table 7*, indicates the temperature range in which the refrigerant and lubricant mix to form a single liquid phase. Stability data for a specific SUVA® MP refrigerant/lubricant combination (i.e., SUVA® MP39 with ZEROL® 150DL) should apply to all of the MP refrigerant blends because they represent different compositions of the same three components (HCFC-22, HFC-152a, HCFC-124). Ratings are listed in *Table 7* for the neat lubricant, the lubricant/refrigerant solution and the three metals that were present in the lubricant/refrigerant solutions. Viscosity was determined on the unused lubricant and the tested neat lubricant. Decomposition products (fluoride and chloride) were determined.

Note: Lubricant/refrigerant combinations shown throughout this report are for the purposes of comparing the effects of different lubricants on the SUVA® MP refrigerants. No recommendation is made or implied that these combinations will operate successfully in refrigeration systems.

TABLE 7
Stability of SUVA® MP Refrigerant Blends with Metals and Lubricants

Lubricant	Mineral Oil	Mineral Oil	ZEROL 150DL	ZEROL 300	ZEROL 500T	Castrol Icematic SW22	Castrol Icematic SW32	Castrol Icematic SW68	Castrol Icematic SW100	Mobil EAL Arctic 68	Emery ISO10 Refrigeration Lubricant	Emery ISO100 Refrigeration Lubricant	Lubrizol ISO 150
Lubricant Viscosity, cSt @ 40°C (104°F)	31	125	35	ND	94	22	32	68	100	62	10	100	140
Refrigerant	CFC-12	CFC-12	MP39	MP Blend***	MP Blend***	MP52	MP52	MP52	MP52	MP52	MP52	MP52	MP52
Lubricant Miscibility Range* 90% Refrigerant/10% Lubricant	–50°C to 93°C	–50°C to 93°C	–40°C to 85°C	ND	–10°C to 93°C	–50°C to 93°C	–50°C to 93°C	–50°C to 93°C	–50°C to 93°C	–50°C to 93°C	ND	–50°C to 93°C	ND
Thermal Stability Ratings													
Neat Lubricant	ND	ND	2, P	0	0	0	0	0	0	0	0	0	0
Lubricant/Refrigerant**	4	4	2, P	0	0	0	0	0	0	2	0	0	1, D
Copper	2	2	2, T	0	0	0	1	0	0	0	0	0	1, D
Iron	3	3	0, T	0	0	3	3	0	0	2, T, CP	3, T, CP	1, T	1, D, CP
Aluminum	2	2	0	0	0	0	2	0	0	0	0	0	0
% Viscosity Change of Neat Lubricant	ND	ND	ND	ND	ND	2.3	5.0	0.8	4.4	–2.0	1.3	0.1	ND
Decomposition Analysis													
Fluoride, ppm	ND	420	ND	10	10	80	60	<7	<7	113	ND	13	57
Chloride, ppm	ND	ND	ND	<10	<10	286	286	<7	<7	340	ND	7	57

ND = Not Determined

* Miscibility was tested in a sealed glass tube in the temperature range of –50°C to 93°C.

** Lubricant/refrigerant mixtures were all 50/50 ratios for sealed tube testing.

*** Representative MP refrigerant blend of HCFC-22/HFC-152a/HCFC-124 (36/24/40).

Stability Ratings: 0 to 5
0 = Best
3 = Failed
5 = Coked

Visual Ratings Key:
P = Precipitate present
CP= Copper plating
T = Tarnish
D = Dark colored liquid

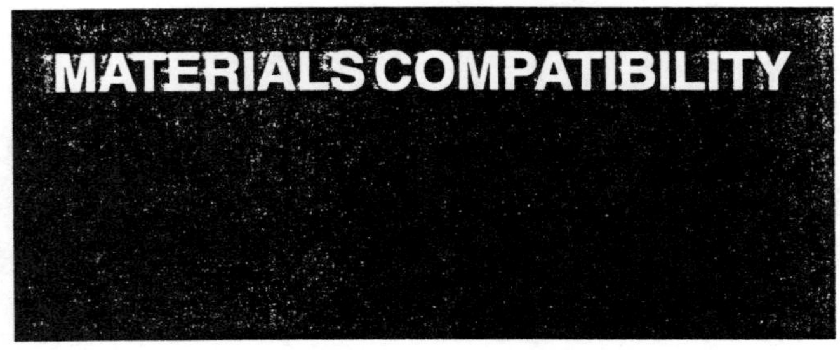

It is important to review materials of construction for compatibility when designing new equipment, retrofitting existing equipment or preparing storage and handling facilities. Since the SUVA® MP refrigerant blends have been designed as refrigerants, the compatibility data summarized below will include materials commonly used in refrigeration applications.

ELASTOMERS

Note: The data in *Tables 8* and *9* reflect compatibility in sealed tube tests. Actual refrigerant compatibility in real systems can be influenced by the operating conditions, the nature of the polymers used, compounding formulations of the polymers, and the curing or vulcanization processes used to create the polymer. Polymers should always be tested under actual operating conditions before reaching final conclusions about their suitability.

Sealed tube compatibility results for a representative SUVA® MP refrigerant blend (36% HCFC-22, 24% HFC-152a, 40% HCFC-124) were developed with eleven different polymers and ZEROL® 500 alkylbenzene lubricant (with additives). SUVA® MP39, SUVA® MP52, and SUVA® MP66 compatibilities are similar to the blend shown in *Table 8,* since the formulations are based on the same components. *Table 8* is a summary of these tests.

TABLE 8
Compatibility of SUVA® MP Refrigerant with Selected Elastomers

	Refrigerant/Lubricant (50/50%)			Refrigerant Only			Lubricant Only		
	Rating	Linear Swell (%)	ΔHardness (units)	Rating[a]	Linear Swell (%)	ΔHardness (units)	Rating	Linear Swell (%)	ΔHardness (units)
Natural Rubber	2	+48	–28	0 (2)	+5	–8	2	+56	–34[b]
Butyl Rubber	2	+20	–30	0 (0)	+1	–2	2	+30	–40
NORDEL® EPDM	2	+19	–19	0 (0)	<–1	–6	2	+31	–19
Neoprene W	0	+7	–3	1 (0)	<+1	–14	0	+7	–9
SBR	2	+22	–55[b]	1 (1)	+2	–15	2	+26	–46[b]
NBR Nitrile	1	+9	–15	2 (0)	+16	–6[c]	0	<–1	0
HYPALON® 48	0	+3	–6	0 (0)	<+1	–1	0	+3	–1
VITON®	2	+12	–11	2 (1)	+17	–33	0	–1	1
Silicone	2	+48	–27	2 (2)	+31	–14	2	+27	–29
ADIPRENE® Urethane	1	+11	–5	2 (2)	+29	–24	0	<+1	1
Thiokol FA®	2	+12	–21	0 (0)	+2	–7	2	+13	–12

NOTES:
Refrigerant Composition: 22/152a/124 (36/24/40%)
Lubricant: ZEROL® 500 (an alkyl benzene lubricant)
Ratings based on sealed tube tests at 80°C for 4 weeks.

		% Linear Swell		ΔHardness
Ratings:	0 = Compatible	≤10	and	≤10
	1 = Borderline	>10	or	>10
	2 = Incompatible	>10	and	≥10

[a] Ratings in ( ) are those of CFC-12; for comparisons.
[b] Gross loss of tensile strength (elastomer broke when stretched).
[c] Rating reflects Δhardness of –21 (at 25°C) and –11 (at 140°C).

In addition to the tests summarized in *Table 8*, compatibility tests were also run with SUVA® MP52, a mixture of lubricants (mineral oil and alkylbenzene), and selected polymers. The results of the tests are summarized in *Table 9. Table 10* shows a glossary of common elastomers.

TABLE 9
Compatibility of SUVA® MP52 with Selected Elastomers (With and Without Alkyl Benzene Lubricant)

	Refrigerant/Lubricant M (80/20%) (at 100°C)			Refrigerant Only (at 25°C)			Lubricant AB (at 60°C)		
	Rating[a]	**Linear Swell (%)**	**ΔHardness (units)**	**Rating[a]**	**Linear Swell (%)**	**ΔHardness (units)**	**Rating**	**Linear Swell (%)**	**ΔHardness (units)**
Neoprene CR	**0 (0)**	+4	−7	**0 (0)**	+1	−4	**0**	+5	−9
NBR Nitrile	**2 ( )[c]**	+11	−11	**2 (1)**	+13	−15	**0**	+0	−1
HNBR	**1 (0)**	+14	−4	**2 (0)**	+20	−12	**0**	+1	−5
Epichlorohydin Homopolymer	**0 (0)**	+3	−4	**1 (0)**	+4	−7	**0**	+1	−5
COPOLYMER	**0 (0)**	+8	−4	**2 (0)**	+12	−14	**0**	+0	−5

NOTES:

Refrigerant Composition: 22/152a/124 (33/15/52%)

Lubricant: M—Equal volume mixture of ZEROL® 500T (an alkyl benzene lubricant) and BVM 100N (a mineral oil)
AB—ZEROL® 500T

Ratings based on sealed tube tests done for 14 days.

		% Linear Swell		ΔHardness
Ratings:	0 = Compatible	≤10	and	≤10
	1 = Borderline	>10	or	>10
	2 = Incompatible	>10	and	≥10

[a] Ratings in (parenthesis) are those of CFC-12/mineral oil; for comparisons.
[b] Ratings in (parenthesis) are those of CFC-12; for comparisons.
[c] Not tested.

TABLE 10
Glossary of Elastomers

Common Name	ASTM D-1418	Chemical Description	Supplier Company Tradename
Natural Rubber	NR	Natural polyisoprene	
Butyl Rubber	IIR	Isobutylene/isoprene copolymer	
EPDM	EPDM	Ethylene/propylene/side-chain diene monomer terpolymer	DuPont NORDEL®
Neoprene; Chloroprene	CR	Polychloroprene	DuPont Neoprene
Buna-S	SBR	Styrene (25%)/butadiene copolymer	
Buna-N; Nitrile	NBR	Acrylonitrile/butadiene copolymer	Polysar KRYNAC®
HNBR	HNBR	Hydrogenated NBR	Polysar TORNAC®
HYPALON®	CSM	Chlorosulfonated polyethylene	DuPont HYPALON®
VITON®	FKM	Vinylidene fluoride/hexafluoropropylene copolymer	DuPont VITON®
Silicone	SI	Poly(dimethyl siloxane)	Dow SILASTIC®
Epichlorohydrin Homopolymer	CO	Polyepichlorohydrin	Goodrich HYDRIN® 100
Epichlorohydrin Copolymer	ECO	Epichlorohydrin/ethylene oxide copolymer	Goodrich HYDRIN® 200
Urethane	U	Reaction product of diisocyanates and polyalkylene ether glycols	Uniroyal ADIPRENE®
Thiokol FA®	T	Organic polysulfide	Thiokol FA®

MOTOR MATERIALS

Compatibility tests were performed on a representative SUVA® MP refrigerant blend with naphthenic and alkylbenzene lubricants in contact with a typical polyester insulation material used in hermetic motors. In this test, the polyester insulation was flexed and examined for cracks and splits to evaluate the level of embrittlement. The samples were rated according to a comparative scale, with zero as the best rating, indicating no change. The results shown in *Figure 13* show that this blend and alkylbenzene lubricant combination is very compatible, with no polyester embrittlement. In general, most modern (10–15 years old) compressor motors used in CFC-12 compressors are compatible with HCFC-22. Based on this, the SUVA® MP refrigerant blend should not have any gross effects on modern CFC-12 compressor motors.

Figure 13. Hermetic Motor Insulation Compatibility Test Conducted at 121°C (250°F) for 30 Days.

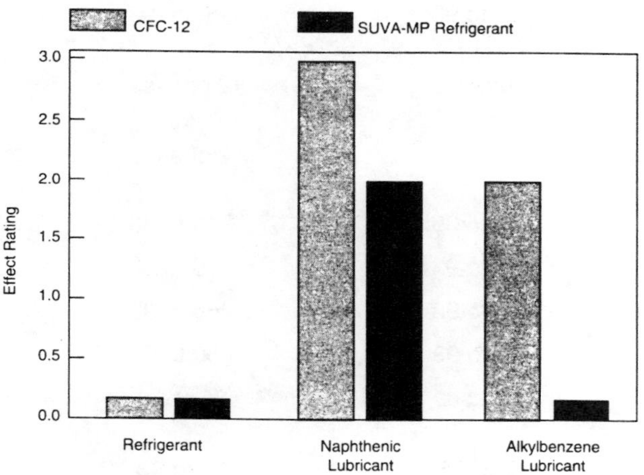

Note: SUVA® MP Refrigerant Composition: 22/152a/124 (36/24/40 wt %)

DESICCANTS

In refrigeration systems, keeping the refrigerant and lubricant free of moisture is very important. Dryers filled with moisture-absorbing desiccant are typically used to prevent moisture accumulation. For R-12, the 4A-XH-5 desiccant produced by UOP (a U.S. company—formerly Union Carbide Molecular Sieve) can be used for both loose-filled and solid core dryers. For SUVA® MP refrigerant blend, a new desiccant is needed for loose-filled dryers, since the HFC-152a contained in the blend is incompatible with loose-fill 4A-XH-5. UOP's XH-9 desiccant or equivalent is compatible with the SUVA® MP refrigerant blends, and is recommended for loose-filled dryers. For solid core dryers, some existing dryer models may be compatible. Consult dryer manufacturer or equipment manufacturer to determine a suitable dryer.

REFRIGERATION LUBRICANTS

Most compressors require a lubricant to protect internal moving parts. The compressor manufacturer usually recommends the type of lubricant(s) and proper viscosity that should be used to ensure acceptable operation and equipment durability. Recommendations are based on several criteria, which can include:

- lubricity
- lubricant/refrigerant solubility
- compatibility with materials of construction
- thermal stability and compatibility with other lubricants.

It is important to follow the manufacturers' recommendations for lubricants to be used with their equipment.

Lubricant return to the compressor is very important. One factor that affects this is the liquid-phase lubricant/refrigerant solubility, particularly at evaporator temperatures. Ideally the lubricant/refrigerant pair are completely soluble in each other (miscible, one phase forms), which allows the lubricant to flow with the liquid refrigerant and return to the compressor. Even if the lubricant/refrigerant pair are not miscible (two phases form) in the evaporator, they may still have some degree of solubility. Solubility of refrigerant in lubricant lowers lubricant viscosity which helps it flow through the evaporator and return to the compressor. This is why many refrigeration systems can operate properly even though the lubricant and refrigerant are immiscible (yet partially soluble) in the evaporator. Other factors, such as refrigerant vapor velocity, play a key role in lubricant return. Overall, it is important to note that lubricant/refrigerant miscibility is helpful, but not necessarily essential for proper system operation.

Naphthenic and paraffinic lubricants (mineral oils) are miscible (fully soluble) with CFC-12 over the range of expected operating conditions, which helps lubricant return to the compressor. SUVA® MP refrigerant blends are not miscible with mineral oils. Therefore, it is advantageous to use other lubricants that are more soluble with them, preferably fully soluble (miscible) at evaporator temperatures. *Table 11* shows the range of full solubility (miscibility) for selected SUVA® MP refrigerants, and for CFC-12 for comparison. Alkylbenzene and polyol ester lubricants offer excellent miscibility with the SUVA® MP refrigerant blends. Also, due to their similar compositions, all three SUVA® MP refrigerants, SUVA® MP39, MP52, and MP66, will have similar solubility characteristics with the various lubricants.

One important point is that residual mineral oil left in a refrigeration system after a retrofit is performed decreases lubricant/refrigerant solubility. *Table 11* shows that with 25% residual mineral oil in an alkylbenzene or a polyol ester lubricant miscibility is greatly reduced. For this reason, it is advantageous to minimize the amount of residual mineral oil, although the impact of the reduced solubility will depend on system design.

TABLE 11
Miscibility of SUVA® MP Refrigerant Blends/Lubricant Pairs in the Temperature Range –50° to 93°C (–58° to 199°F)

	Weight Percent of Lubricant		
Refrigerant/Lubricant Pair	**30%**	**60%**	**90%**
CFC-12/500 SUS paraffinic mineral oil	–50 to 93°C	–50 to 93°C	–50 to 93°C
CFC-12/500 SUS naphthenic mineral oil	–50 to 93	–50 to 93	–50 to 93
MP52/500 SUS paraffinic mineral oil	75 to 93	2 phases	2 phases
MP52/500 SUS naphthenic mineral oil	35 to 93	2 phases	2 phases
MP39/150 SUS alkylbenzene	–30 to 85	–20 to 35	–40 to 85
MP52/500 SUS alkylbenzene	–40 to 93	–10 to 93	–10 to 93
MP52/150 SUS polyol ester	–50 to 93	–50 to 93	–50 to 93
MP52/500 SUS polyol ester	–50 to 93	–50 to 93	–50 to 93
MP52/(75% alkylbenzene/ 25% paraffinic mineral oil)	10 to 93	2 phases	25 to 30
MP52/(75% alkylbenzene/ 25% naphthenic mineral oil)	–10 to 93	10 to 75	25 to 93
MP52/(75% polyol ester/ 25% paraffinic mineral oil)	20 to 93	2 phases	2 phases
MP52/(75% polyol ester/ 25% naphthenic mineral oil)	–10 to 93	20 to 93	20 to 93

Note: 100 SUS ≅ 20 cSt

HOSE PERMEATION

Tests have been run comparing hose permeation rates of CFC-12, HFC-134a, and SUVA® MP refrigerant blends through both nylon-lined and nitrile (all rubber) hoses as shown in *Table 12.* Permeation rates of SUVA® MP52 are much higher than those of CFC-12 or HFC-134a. More importantly, the permeation rates of SUVA® MP52 through nylon-lined hose are reduced by a factor of 8. For this reason, nylon-lined hose is recommended for use with SUVA® MP refrigerants.

TABLE 12

Permeation Rates of CFC-12, HFC-134a, and SUVA® MP Refrigerants Through Nylon-Lined and Nitrile Hoses (at 80°C [176°F])

	Permeation Rates, $g/cm^2 \cdot y$ ($lb/ft^2 \cdot y$)	
	Nylon-lined	Nitrile
CFC-12*	0.7 (1.5)	3.7 (7.5)
HFC-134a*	0.8 (1.6)	6.8 (14.0)
MP-52*	4.3 (8.7)	24.4 (50.0)

*Data supplied by Goodyear

Note: These tests are for comparison purposes only. Actual permeation will be less.

For MP52 use in automotive air conditioning retrofit, nylon hoses are recommended. Nylon hoses satisfy the proposed permeation criteria established by the U.S. Society of Automotive Engineers (SAE).

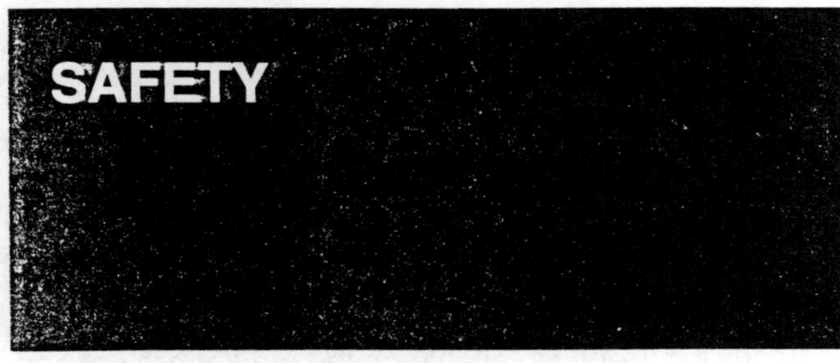

INHALATION TOXICITY

The SUVA® MP refrigerant blends pose no acute or chronic hazard when they are handled in accordance with DuPont recommendations, and when exposures are maintained at or below recommended exposure limits, such as the DuPont Acceptable Exposure Limit (AEL) of 800 ppm for SUVA® MP39, 720 ppm for SUVA® MP52 and 840 ppm for SUVA® MP66.

An AEL is an airborne exposure limit established by DuPont which specifies time-weighted average (TWA) airborne concentrations, usually eight hours, to which nearly all workers may be repeatedly exposed without adverse effects. In practice, short-term exposures should not exceed three times the established exposure limit for more than a total of 30 minutes during a workday, provided that the TWA is not exceeded.

Inhaling high concentrations of SUVA® MP refrigerant vapor may cause temporary central nervous system depression with narcosis, lethargy and anesthetic effects. Other effects that may occur include dizziness, a feeling of intoxication and a loss of coordination. Continued breathing of high concentrations of SUVA® MP vapors may produce cardiac irregularities (cardiac sensitization), unconsciousness, and with gross overexposure, death. If you experience any of the initial symptoms, move to fresh air and seek medical attention.

CARDIAC SENSITIZATION

An effect that occurs with most hydrocarbons and halocarbons at high concentrations is that the human heart can become sensitized to adrenalin, leading to cardiac irregularities and even cardiac arrest. The likelihood of these cardiac problems increases if you are under physical or emotional stress. The SUVA® MP refrigerant blends can cause these responses well above the AEL, but the effect level varies with people, and has not been fully determined.

If you are exposed to very high concentrations of SUVA® MP refrigerant blends, move immediately from the area, and seek medical attention as a precaution. DO NOT attempt to remain in the area to fix a leak or perform other duties—the effects of overexposure can be very sudden.

Medical attention must be given immediately if someone is having symptoms of overexposure to SUVA® MP refrigerant blends. DO NOT treat the patient with drugs such as epinephrine, since these drugs could increase the risk of cardiac problems. If the person is having trouble breathing, administer oxygen. If breathing has stopped, give artificial respiration immediately.

SPILLS OR LEAKS

If a large release of vapor occurs, such as from a large spill or leak, the vapors may concentrate near the floor or low spots and displace the oxygen available for breathing, causing suffocation. When a large spill or leak occurs, always wear appropriate respiratory and other personal protective equipment. Evacuate *everyone* until the area has been ventilated. Use blowers or fans to circulate the air at floor level. Do not reenter the affected area unless you are equipped with a self-contained breathing apparatus.

Always use a supplied air mask when entering tanks or other areas where vapor concentration might exist. Use the buddy system *and* a lifeline. Refer to the MSDS for SUVA® MP39, MP52 and MP66 for more information.

Some SUVA® refrigerants have a slightly sweet odor that can be difficult to detect. Therefore, frequent leak checks and the installation of permanent leak detectors may be necessary for enclosed areas used by personnel.

To ensure safety when working with SUVA® MP series, first, route relief and purge vent piping outdoors, away from air intakes. Second, make certain the area is well ventilated, using auxiliary ventilation if necessary to move refrigerant vapors. Third, make sure the area is clear of vapors prior to beginning work. And finally, install air monitoring equipment to detect leaks.

SKIN AND EYE CONTACT

Always wear protective clothing when there is a risk of exposure to liquid SUVA® MP refrigerant blends. Where splashing is possible, *always* wear eye protection and a face shield. If your eyes are splashed, flush them with plenty of water. (See the MSDS.) In liquid form, low- and medium-temperature SUVA® MP refrigerant blends can freeze skin on contact, causing frostbite.

Following contact, soak the exposed area in *lukewarm* water, *not* cold or hot.

If treatment cannot begin immediately, apply a light coat of a nonmedicated ointment, such as petroleum jelly. If the exposed area is in a location where the presence of the ointment would be awkward, such as on the eye, apply a light bandage.

In *all* cases of frostbite, seek medical attention as soon as possible.

NONFLAMMABILITY OF SUVA® MP SERIES

Nonflammability is an essential requirement for refrigeration and air conditioning applications. Although HFC-152a is a flammable compound, the SUVA® MP refrigerant blends are formulated so that they are nonflammable and will not reach a flammable composition during leakage from equipment. In addition, SUVA® MP refrigerant blends have been extensively tested for flammability by Underwriters Laboratories, Inc. (USA). SUVA® MP 39 and MP66 have been added to their list of recognized refrigerants.

MONITORS AND LEAK DETECTION

Service personnel have used leak detection equipment for years when servicing equipment. Leak detectors exist not only for pinpointing specific leaks, but also for monitoring an entire room on a continual basis. There are several reasons for leak pinpointing or area monitoring, including: conservation of refrigerants, protection of valuable equipment, reduction of fugitive emissions and protection of employees.

Leak detectors can be placed into two broad categories: leak pinpointers and area monitors. Before purchasing a monitor or pinpointer, several instrumental criteria should be considered, including: sensitivity, detection limits and selectivity.

TYPES OF DETECTORS

Using selectivity as a criteria, leak detectors can be placed into one of three categories: nonselective, halogen-selective or compound-specific. In general, as the specificity of the monitor increases, so does the complexity and cost. Another method used to find leaks is to add fluorescent additives to the system.

A detailed discussion of leak detection, along with a list of manufacturers of leak detection equipment, is given in Bulletin ARTD-27 (H-31753-2).

NONSELECTIVE DETECTORS

Nonselective detectors are those that will detect any type of emission or vapor present, regardless of its chemical composition. These detectors are typically quite simple to use, very durable, inexpensive and almost always portable. However, their inability to be calibrated, long-term drift, lack of selectivity and lack of sensitivity limit their use for area monitoring. Some detectors currently available on the market are not sensitive enough for use with the MP blend compositions.

Even detectors of SUVA® MP refrigerant components in the blends (i.e., HCFC-22) may not be sensitive to the blends.

HALOGEN-SELECTIVE DETECTORS

Halogen-selective detectors use a specialized sensor that allows the monitor to detect compounds containing fluorine, chlorine, bromine and iodine without interference from other species. The major advantage of such a detector is a reduction in the number of "nuisance alarms"—false alarms caused by the presence of some compound in the area other than the target compound.

These detectors are typically easy to use, feature higher sensitivity than the nonselective detectors (detection limits are typically <5 ppm when used as an area monitor and <0.05 oz/yr when used as a leak pinpointer), and are very durable. In addition, due to the partial specificity of the detector, these instruments can be calibrated easily. Contact the manufacturers of leak detectors for their current models.

COMPOUND-SPECIFIC DETECTORS

The most complex detectors, which are also the most expensive, are compound-specific detectors. These units are typically capable of detecting the presence of a single species without interference from other compounds.

FLUORESCENT ADDITIVES

Fluorescent additives have been used in refrigeration systems for several years. These additives, invisible under ordinary lighting, but visible under ultraviolet (UV) light, are used to pinpoint leaks in systems. The additives are typically placed into the refrigeration lubricant when the system is serviced. Leaks are detected by using a UV light to search for additive that has escaped from the system. The color of the additive when subjected to UV light is normally a bright green or yellow and is easily seen.

As a leak pinpointer, fluorescent additives work very well since large areas can be rapidly checked by a single individual. And, the recent introduction of battery-powered UV lights has made this task even simpler. Leak rates of less than 0.25 oz/year can be found with the additives. The only drawback to the use of additives is that some areas may be visually unobservable due to cramped spaces.

One cautionary note concerning the use of fluorescent additives: the compatibility of the specific additive with the lubricant and refrigerant should be tested prior to use. For detailed information about which lubricants and refrigerants have been tested with which additives, contact the fluorescent additive manufacturers.

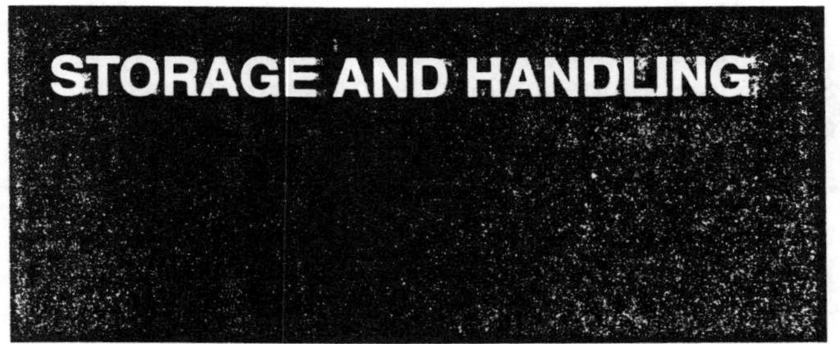

SHIPPING CONTAINERS IN U.S.

SUVA® MP refrigerant blends are liquefied compressed gases. According to the U.S. Department of Transportation (DOT), a nonflammable compressed gas is defined as a nonflammable material having an absolute pressure greater than 40 psi at 21°C (70°F) and/or an absolute pressure greater than 104 psi at 54°C (130°F).

The appropriate DOT designations are as follows:

Proper shipping name: Refrigerant Gas, N.O.S. (contains chlorotetrafluoroethane and chlorodifluoromethane)

Hazard class: Nonflammable Gas

UN/NA No.: UN 1078

Three different types of containers can be used to ship SUVA® MP; their water capacity, dimensions and DOT specifications are provided in *Table 13*. All pressure relief devices used on the containers must be in compliance with the corresponding Compressed Gas Association (CGA) Standards for compressed gas cylinders, cargo and portable tanks.

TABLE 13
Specifications of Shipping Containers for SUVA® MP Refrigerants

Water Capacity	Dimensions	DOT Specification
30 lb Dispose A Can®	10 × 10 × 17 in. (box)	39
125 lb	55 in. H × 10 in. OD	4BA300
1700 lb ton	82 in. L × 30 in. OD	110A500W

The 30-lb cylinder, known as a Dispose A Can® (DAC) fits into a box that measures 10 × 10 × 17 in. "Dispose A Can" is DuPont's registered trade name for this type of single-use container. The DAC valve will be standard valve **with dip tube** for SUVA® MP39 and SUVA® MP66 and **without dip tube** for SUVA® MP52.

The 125-lb cylinders are equipped with a nonrefillable liquid vapor CGA-660 valve. With this two-way valve, SUVA® MP refrigerant blends can be removed from the cylinder as either a vapor or as a liquid, without inverting the cylinder. The vapor handwheel is located on the top. The liquid wheel is on the side of the valve and attached to a dip tube extending to the bottom of the cylinder. Each is clearly identified as vapor or liquid.

The 30-lb and 125-lb cylinders designed for SUVA® MP use have the colors and weight/container as provided in *Table 14*.

The general construction of a one-ton returnable container is shown in *Figure 14*. Notice that one end of the container is fitted with two valves. When the container is turned so that the valves are lined up vertically, the top valve will discharge vapor and the bottom valve will discharge liquid. The valves are protected by a dome cover.

Ton containers are equipped with two fusible plugs in each end. The fusible metal in the plugs is designed to start melting at 69°C (157°F) and completely melt at 74°C (165°F). Containers should never be heated to temperatures higher than 52°C (125°F). One spring-loaded pressure relief valve is also located in each end of the ton container.

HANDLING PRECAUTIONS FOR SUVA® MP SHIPPING CONTAINERS

The following rules for handling SUVA® MP containers are strongly recommended:

- Use personal protective equipment, such as side shield glasses, gloves and safety shoes when handling containers.
- Avoid skin contact with SUVA® MP since it may cause frostbite.
- Never heat a container to a temperature higher than 52°C (125°F).
- Never apply direct flame or live steam to a container or valve.
- Never refill disposable cylinders with anything. The shipment of refilled disposable cylinders is prohibited by DOT regulations.
- Never refill returnable cylinders without DuPont consent. DOT regulations forbid transportation of returnable cylinders refilled without DuPont's authorization.
- Never use a lifting magnet or sling (rope or chain) when handling containers. A crane may be used when a safe cradle or platform is used to hold the container.
- Never use containers for rollers, supports or any purpose other than to carry SUVA® MP.
- Protect containers from any object that will result in a cut or other abrasion in the surface of the metal.
- Never tamper with the safety devices in the valves or containers.
- Never attempt to repair or alter containers or valves.
- Never force connections that do not fit. Make sure the threads on the regulators or other auxiliary equipment are the same as those on the container valve outlet.
- Keep valves tightly closed and valve caps and hoods in place when the containers are not in use.
- Store containers under a roof to protect them from weather extremes.
- Use a vapor recovery system to collect SUVA® MP vapors from lines after unloading a container.

TABLE 14
Color Codes and Fill Weights for SUVA® MP Refrigerants

Refrigerant	Color	PMS #	Net Weight (lb) MP Refrigerant: 30-lb Water Capacity	125-lb Water Capacity	Ton Cylinder
SUVA® MP39	Coral Red	177	30	125	1700
SUVA® MP66	Light Grey Green	413	30	125	1700
SUVA® MP52	Blue Green (Aqua)	3268	30	125	1750

Figure 14. One-Ton Returnable Container.

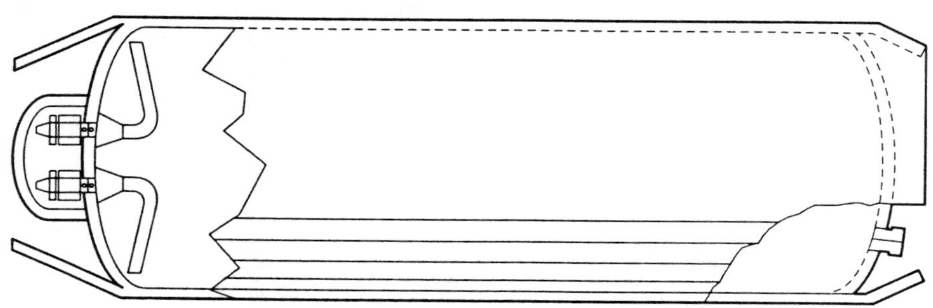

RECOVERY, RECLAMATION, RECYCLE AND DISPOSAL

Responsible use of SUVA® MP refrigerants requires that the product be recovered for re-use or disposal whenever possible. DuPont purchases used refrigerants for reclamation through its distributor networks in the United States, Canada and Europe. In the United States, used SUVA® MP refrigerants are accepted as part of this program. Recovery and re-use of SUVA® MP refrigerants makes sense from an environmental and economic standpoint. In addition, the U.S. Clean Air Act prohibits known venting of CFC and HCFC refrigerants during the maintenance, servicing or disposal of refrigeration equipment.

RECOVERY

Recovery refers to the removal of SUVA® MP refrigerants from equipment and collection in an appropriate external container. As defined by the Air Conditioning and Refrigeration Institute (ARI), a U.S. organization, recovery does not involve processing or analytical testing. SUVA® MP refrigerants may be recovered from refrigeration equipment using permanent on-site equipment or one of the portable recovery devices now on the market. The portable devices contain a small compressor and an air cooled condenser, and may be used for vapor or liquid recovery. At the end of the recovery cycle, the system is evacuated to remove vapors. In the United States, the Environmental Protection Agency (EPA) sets standards for recovery equipment. Before purchasing a specific recovery unit, check with the manufacturer to be sure that it contains elastomeric seals and a compressor oil compatible with SUVA® MP refrigerants.

RECLAMATION

Reclamation refers to the re-processing of used SUVA® MP refrigerants to new product specifications. Quality of reclaimed product is verified by chemical analysis. In the United States, SUVA® MP refrigerants are included in DuPont's refrigerant reclamation program. Contact DuPont or one of its authorized distributors for further information.

Reclamation offers advantages over on-site refrigerant recycling procedures because these systems cannot guarantee complete removal of contaminants. Putting refrigerants that do not meet new product specifications back into expensive equipment may cause damage.

RECYCLE

Refrigerant recycle refers to the reduction of used refrigerant contaminants using devices that reduce oil, water, acidity and particulates. Recycle is usually a field or shop procedure with no analytical testing of refrigerant. SUVA® MP refrigerants may be recycled using many of the devices now available providing that the entire charge is removed from the refrigeration equipment and recycled. If you routinely recycle SUVA® MP refrigerants through several cycles, we recommend that you have the composition of the refrigerant checked periodically. This will prevent loss of performance in the unlikely event that the composition has shifted.

In the United States the EPA sets standards for recycle equipment. Consult with the manufacturer before specifying a recycle device for any refrigerant.

DISPOSAL

Disposal refers to the destruction of used SUVA® MP refrigerants. Disposal may be necessary when SUVA® MP refrigerants has become badly contaminated with other products and no longer meet the acceptance specifications of DuPont or other reclaimers. Although DuPont does not presently accept severely contaminated refrigerants for disposal, licensed waste disposal firms are available. Be sure to check the qualifications of any firm before sending them used SUVA® MP refrigerants.

H-45944-2 (5/93) Printed in U.S.A. 233254C

DuPont Chemicals
Fluorochemicals Customer Service Center
Wilmington, DE 19898

For sales information:
1-800-441-9442
In Delaware (302) 774-2099

For technical information:
1-800-582-5606
In Delaware (302) 999-3129

Europe
DuPont de Nemours
International S.A.
2 Chemin du Pavillon
P.O. Box 50
CH-1218 Le Grand-Saconnex
Geneva, Switzerland
41-22-717-5111

Canada
DuPont Canada, Inc.
P.O. Box 2200, Streetsville
Mississauga, Ontario
L5M 2H3
(416) 821-3300

Mexico
DuPont, S.A. de C.V.
Homero 206
Col. Chapultepec Morales
C.P. 11570 Mexico, D.F.
52-5-250-8000

South America
DuPont do Brasil S.A.
Alameda Itapicuru, 506
Alphaville 06400 Barueri
São Paulo, Brazil
55-11-421-8509

DuPont Argentina S.A.
Casilla Correo 1888
Correo Central
1000 Buenos Aires, Argentina
54-1-311-8167

Pacific
DuPont Australia
P.O. Box 930
North Sydney, NSW 2060
Australia
61-2-923-6165

Japan
Mitsui DuPont Fluoro-
chemicals Company, Ltd.
Mitsui Seimei Building
2-3, 1-Chome Ohtemachi
Chiyoda-Ku, Tokyo 100 Japan
81-3-3216-8451

Asia
DuPont Taiwan
P.O. Box 81-777
Taipei, Taiwan
886-2-514-4400

DuPont Asia Pacific Limited
P.O. Box TST 98851
Tsim Sha Tsui
Kowloon, Hong Kong
852-734-5345

DuPont Thailand
P.O. Box 2398
Bangkok 10501, Thailand
66-2-238-4361

DuPont China Ltd.
Room 1704, Union Bldg.
100 Yanan Rd. East
Shanghai, PR China 200 002
Phone: 86-21-328-3738
Telex: 33448 DCLSH CN
Fax: 86-21-320-2304

DuPont Far East Inc.
P.O. Box 12396
50776 Kuala Lumpur,
Malaysia
Phone: 60-3-232-3522
Telex: (784) 30391 DUFE M
Fax: 60-3-238-7250

DuPont Korea Ltd.
C.P.O. Box 5972
Seoul, Korea
82-2-721-5114

DuPont Singapore Pte. Ltd.
1 Maritime Square #07 01
World Trade Centre
Singapore 0409
65-273-2244

DuPont Far East, Philippines
5th Floor, Solid Bank Building
777 Paseo de Roxas
Makati, Metro Manila
Philippines
63-2-818-9911

DuPont Far East Inc.
7A Murray's Gate Road
Alwarpet
Madras, 600 018 India
91-44-454-029

DuPont Far East Inc.—
Pakistan
9 Khayaban-E-Shaheen
Defence Phase 5
Karachi, Pakistan
92-21-533-350

DuPont Far East Inc.
P.O. Box 2553/Jkt
Jakarta 10001
Indonesia
62-21-517-800

(Stock number on last page of text)

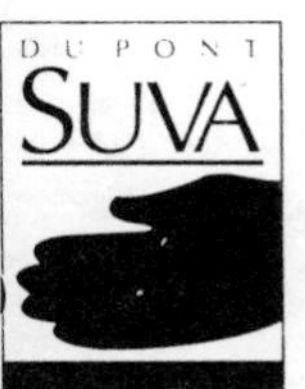

SUVA®

ART - 10

PRODUCT INFORMATION

Transport Properties of SUVA® Refrigerants:

SUVA® MP39
SUVA® MP52
SUVA® MP66

Viscosity
Thermal Conductivity
and
Heat Capacity
for the
Liquid and Vapor

Transport Properties of SUVA® Refrigerants

SUVA® MP39 SUVA® MP52 SUVA® MP66

TABLE OF CONTENTS

English Units **Page**

Metric Units

Saturated Liquid Viscosity

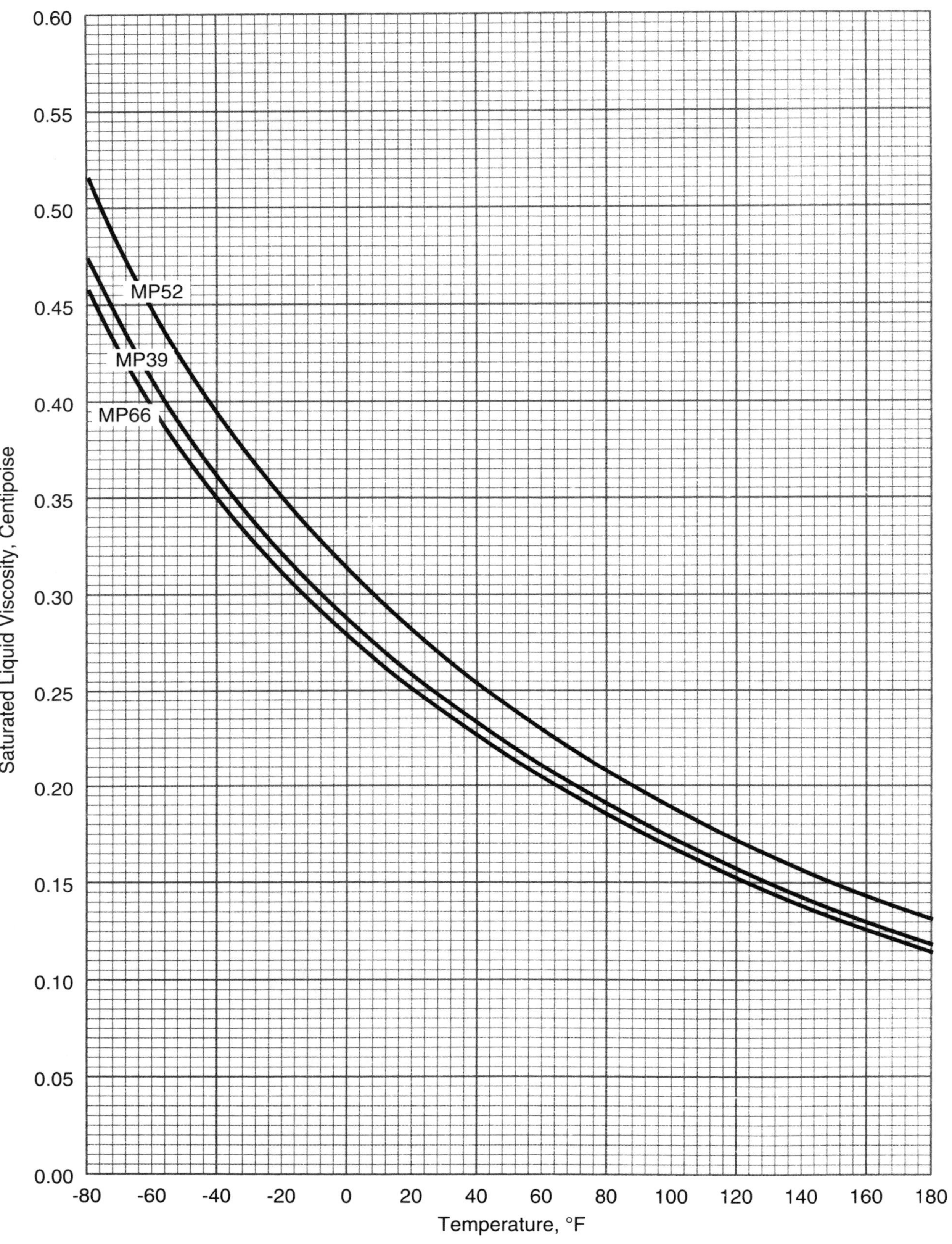

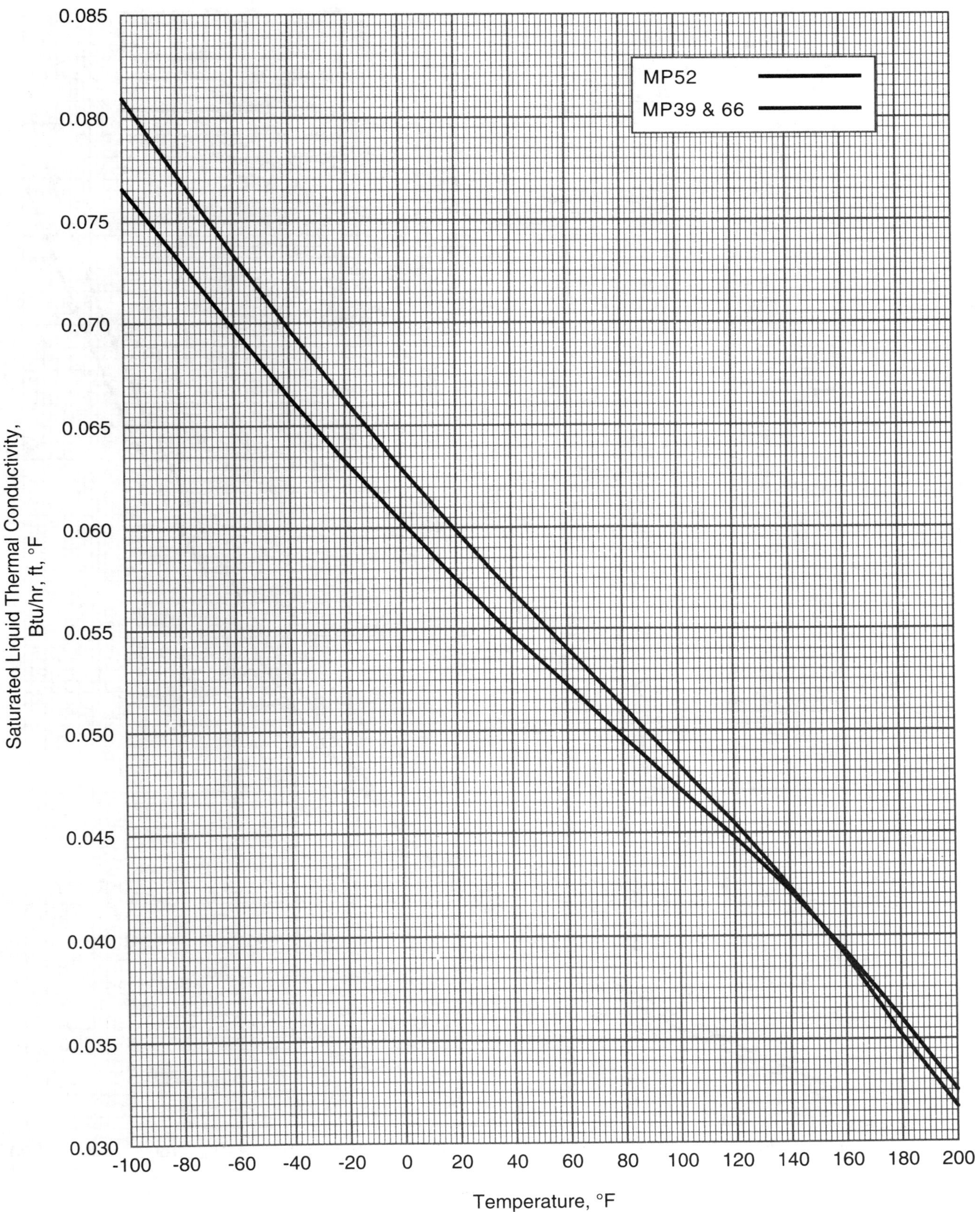
Saturated Liquid Thermal Conductivity
MP52
MP39 & 66
0.085
0.080
0.075
0.070
0.065
0.060
0.055
0.050
0.045
0.040
0.035
0.030
Saturated Liquid Thermal Conductivity,
Btu/hr, ft, °F
-100
-80
-60
-40
-20
0
20
40
60
80
100
120
140
160
180
200
Temperature, °F

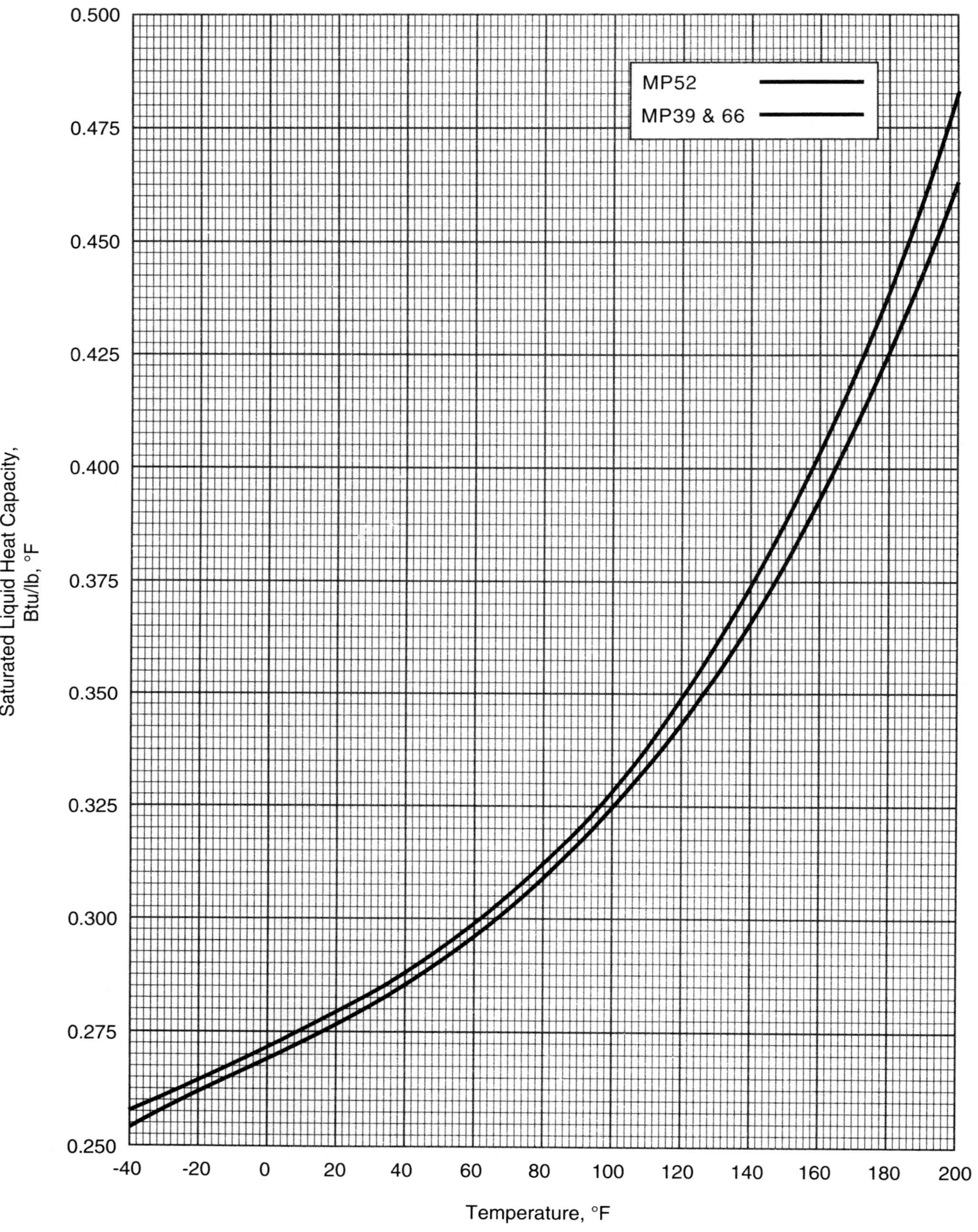
Saturated Liquid Heat Capacity
MP52
MP39 & 66
Saturated Liquid Heat Capacity, Btu/lb, °F
0.500
0.475
0.450
0.425
0.400
0.375
0.350
0.325
0.300
0.275
0.250
-40
-20
0
20
40
60
80
100
120
140
160
180
200
Temperature, °F

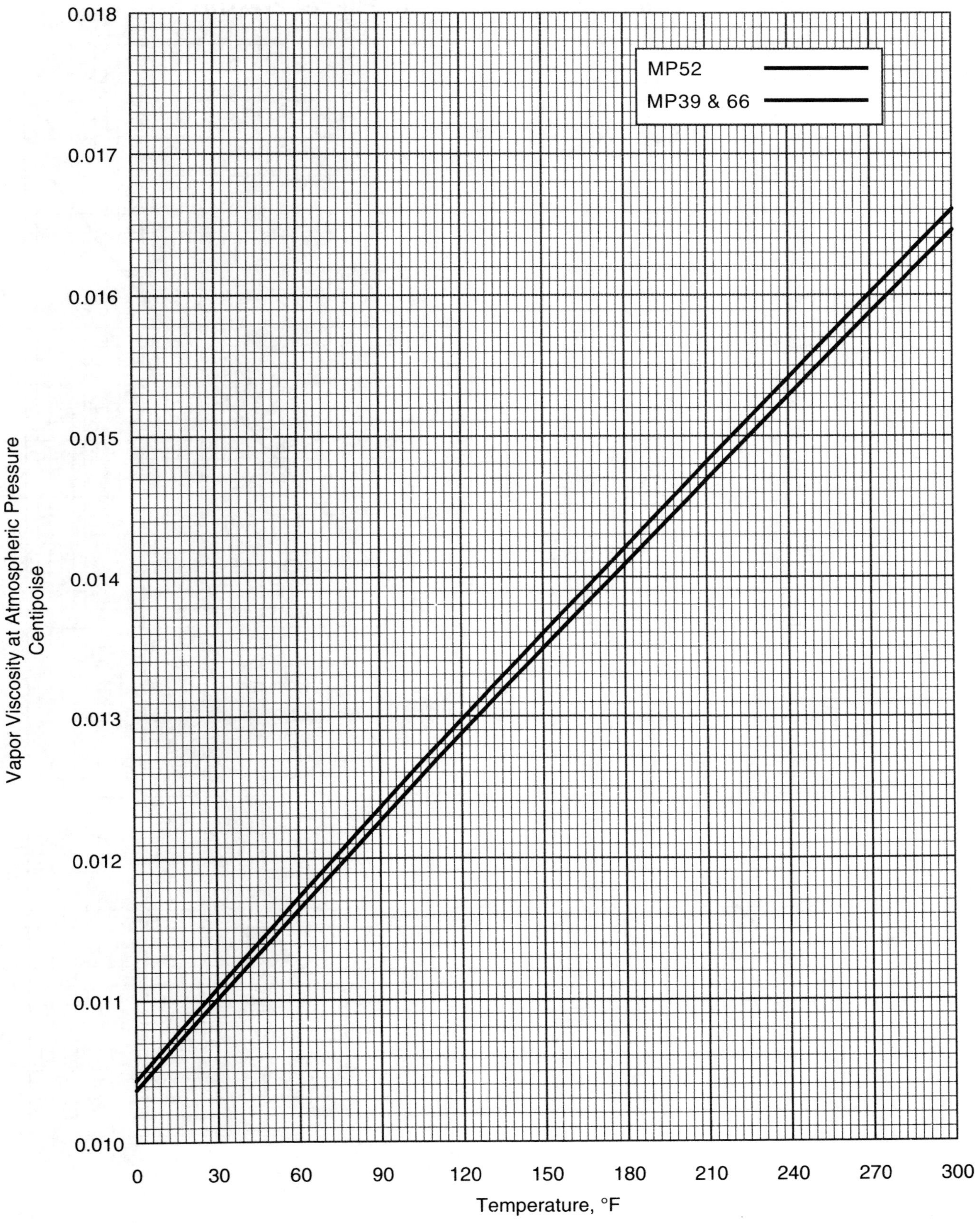

Vapor Viscosity at Atmospheric Pressure
MP52
MP39 & 66
0.018
0.017
0.016
0.015
0.014
0.013
0.012
0.011
0.010
Vapor Viscosity at Atmospheric Pressure
Centipoise
0
30
60
90
120
150
180
210
240
270
300
Temperature, °F

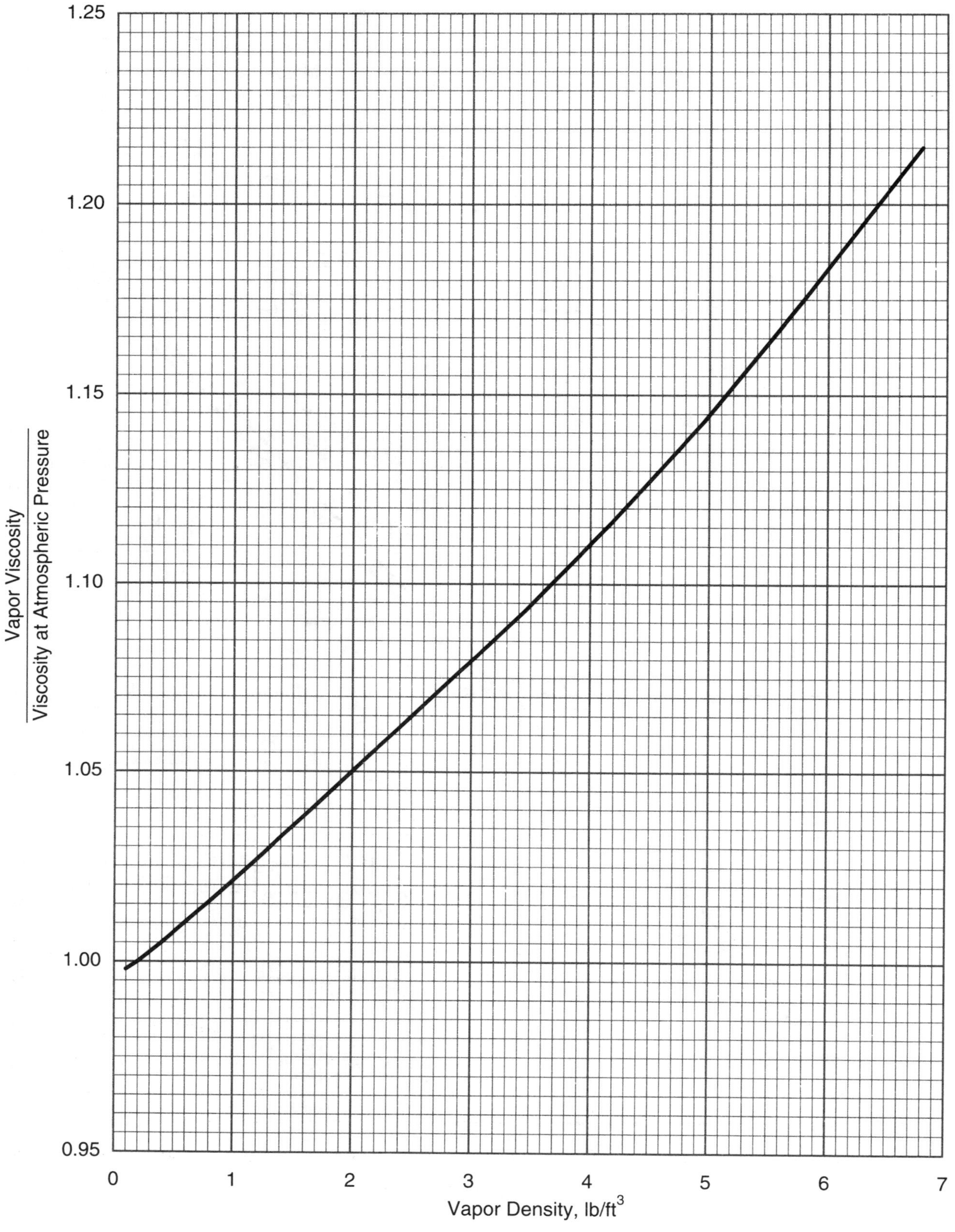

Correction of Vapor Viscosity at
Atmospheric Pressure to Higher Pressures
1.25
1.20
1.15
1.10
1.05
1.00
0.95
Vapor Viscosity / Viscosity at Atmospheric Pressure
0
1
2
3
4
5
6
7
Vapor Density, lb/ft3

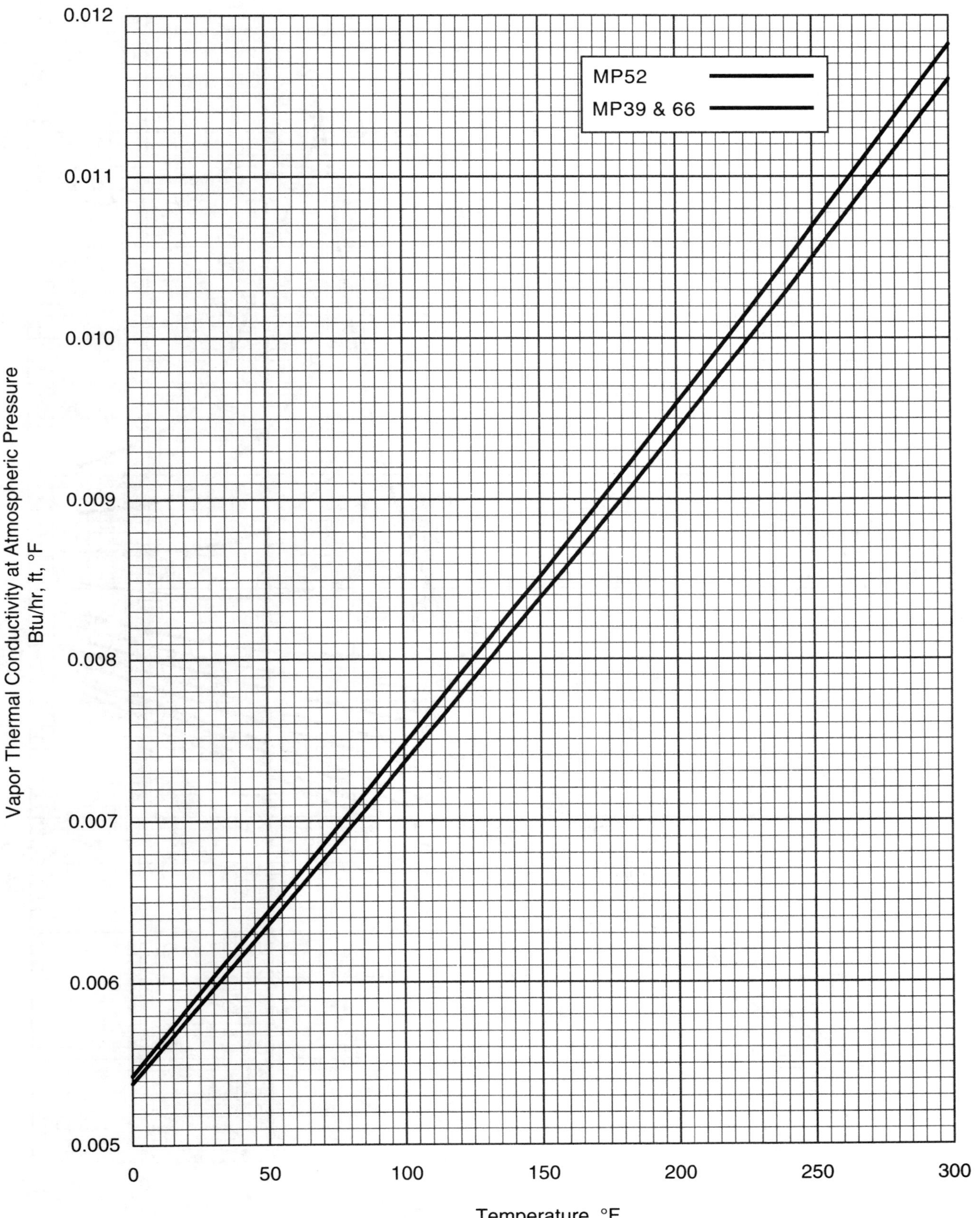

Vapor Thermal Conductivity at Atmospheric Pressure
MP52
MP39 & 66
Vapor Thermal Conductivity at Atmospheric Pressure
Btu/hr, ft, °F
0.012
0.011
0.010
0.009
0.008
0.007
0.006
0.005
0
50
100
150
200
250
300
Temperature, °F

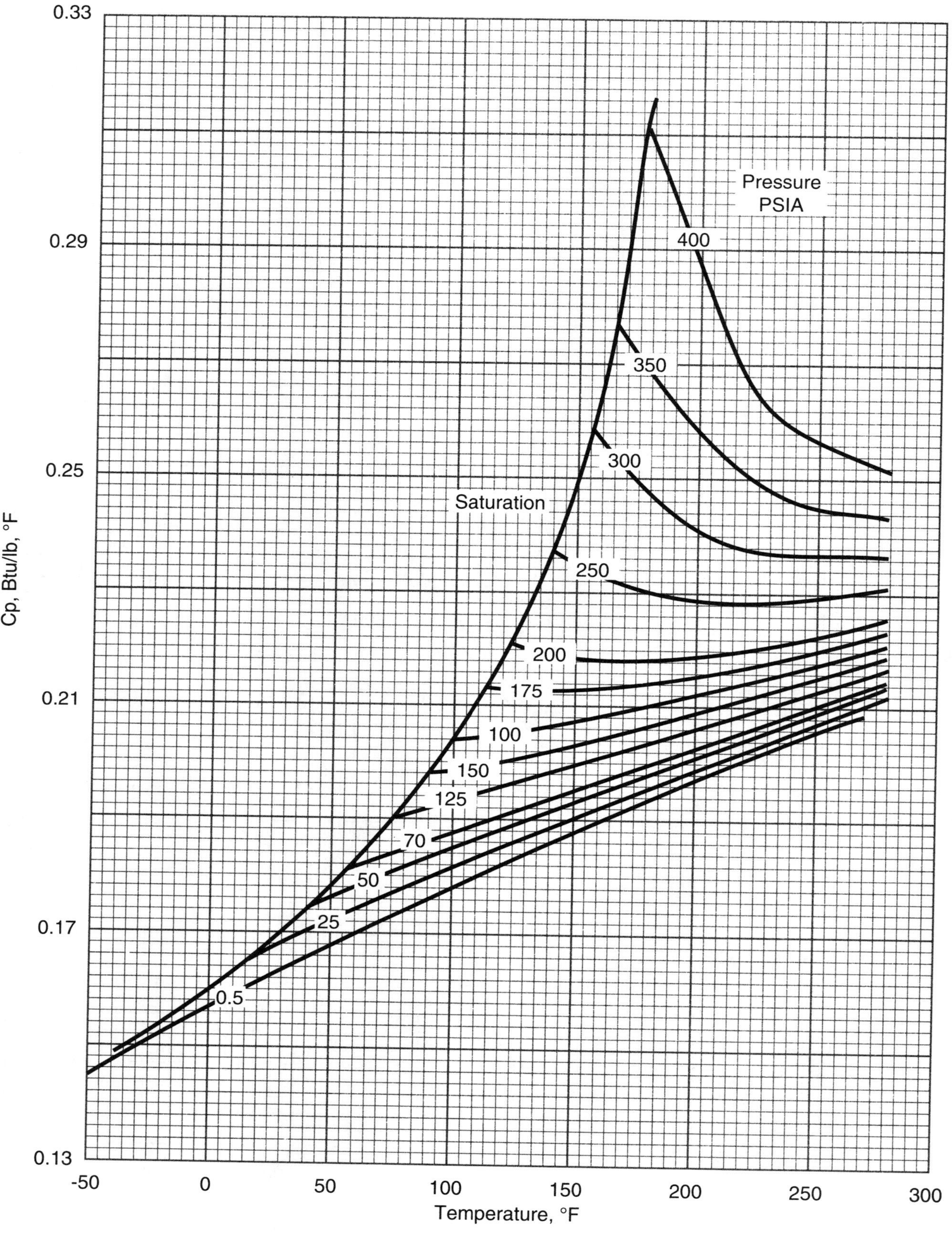
SUVA® MP39 Vapor Heat Capacity
Cp, Btu/lb, °F
Temperature, °F
0.33
0.29
0.25
0.21
0.17
0.13
-50
0
50
100
150
200
250
300
Pressure
PSIA
400
350
300
250
200
175
100
150
125
70
50
25
0.5
Saturation

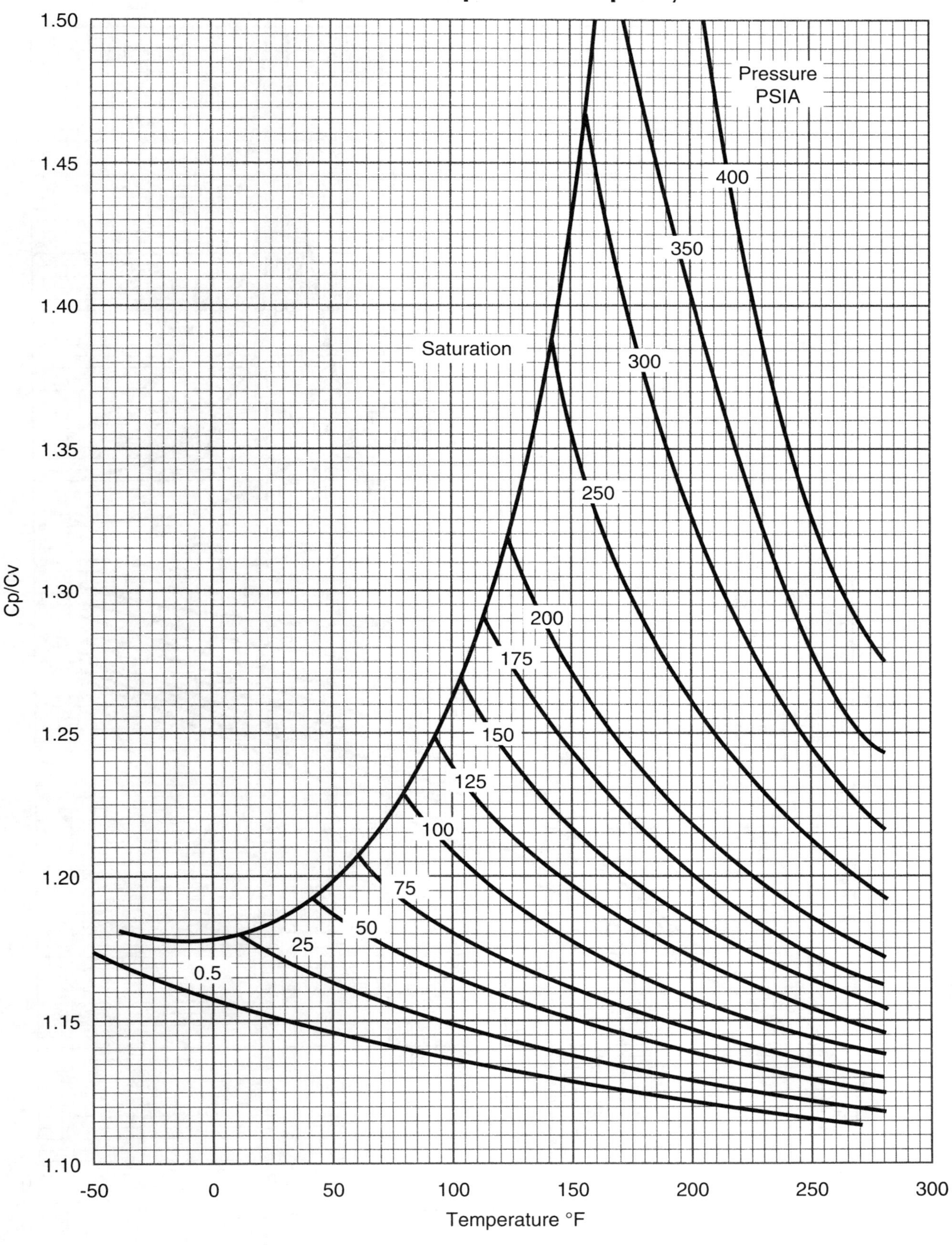
SUVA® MP39 Vapor Heat Capacity Ratio
Pressure PSIA
400
350
300
250
200
175
150
125
100
75
50
25
0.5
Saturation
Cp/Cv
1.50
1.45
1.40
1.35
1.30
1.25
1.20
1.15
1.10
-50
0
50
100
150
200
250
300
Temperature °F

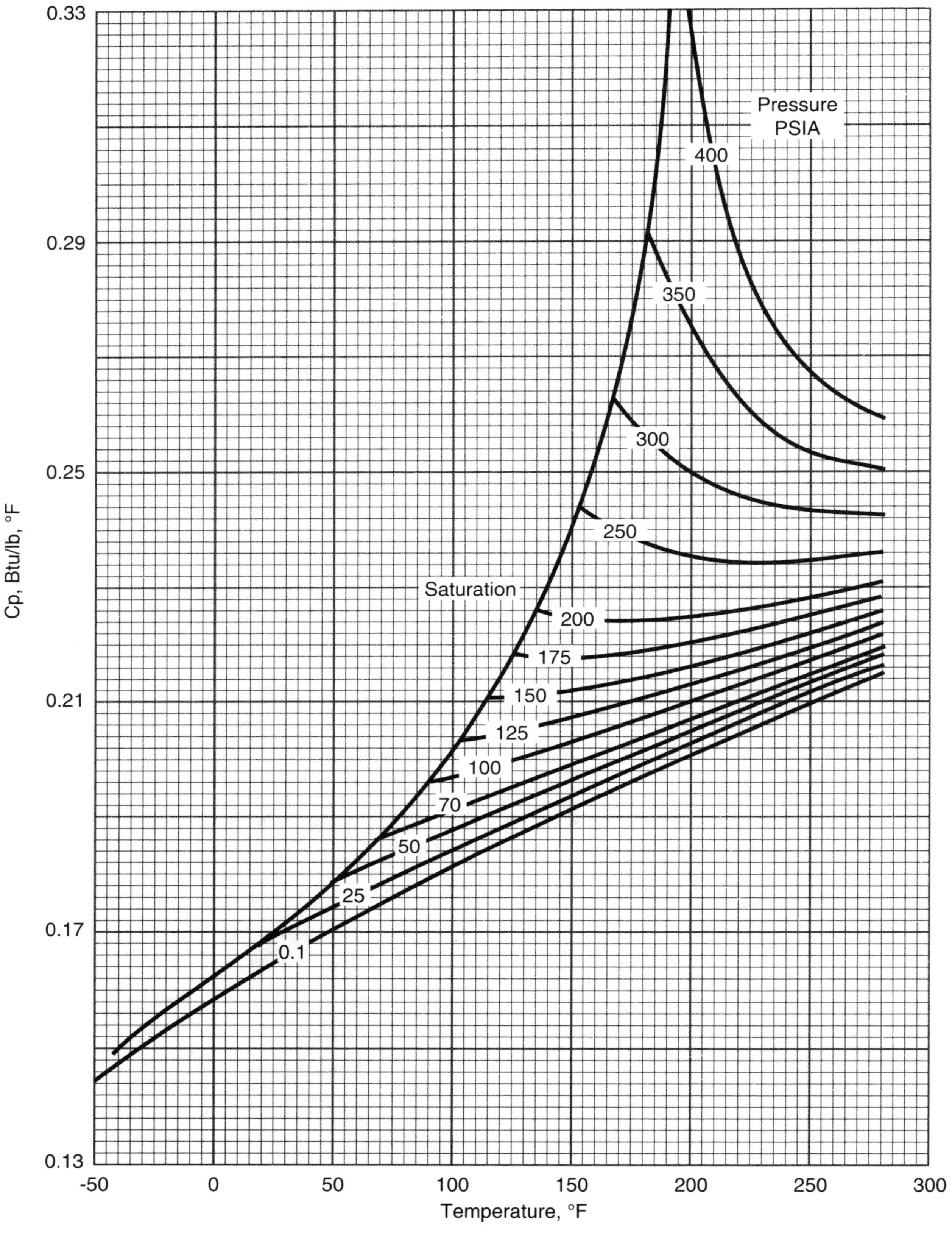
SUVA® MP52 Vapor Heat Capacity
Cp, Btu/lb, °F
0.33
0.29
0.25
0.21
0.17
0.13
-50
0
50
100
150
200
250
300
Temperature, °F
Pressure
PSIA
400
350
300
250
Saturation
200
175
150
125
100
70
50
25
0.1

SUVA® MP52 Vapor Heat Capacity Ratio

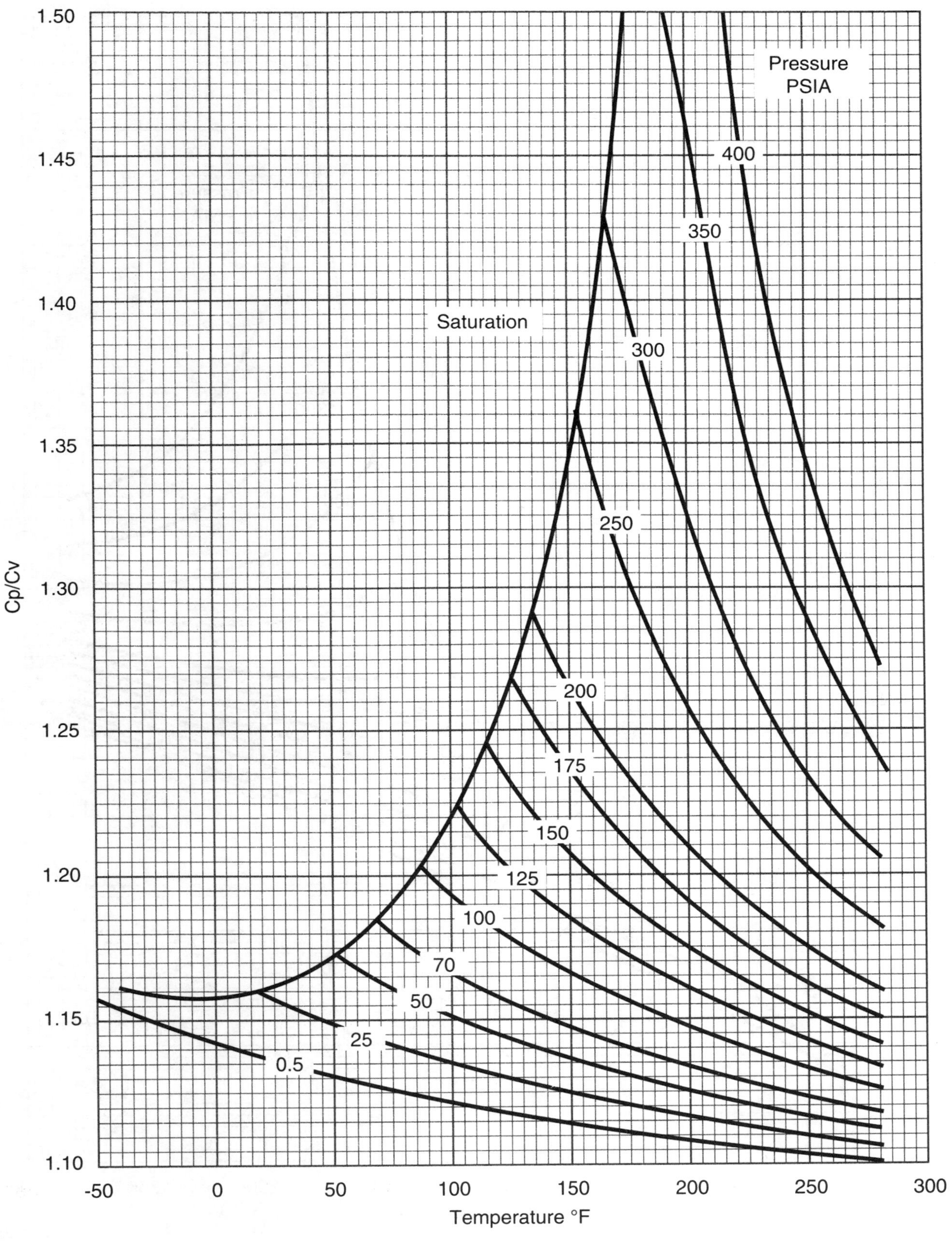

SUVA® MP66 Vapor Heat Capacity

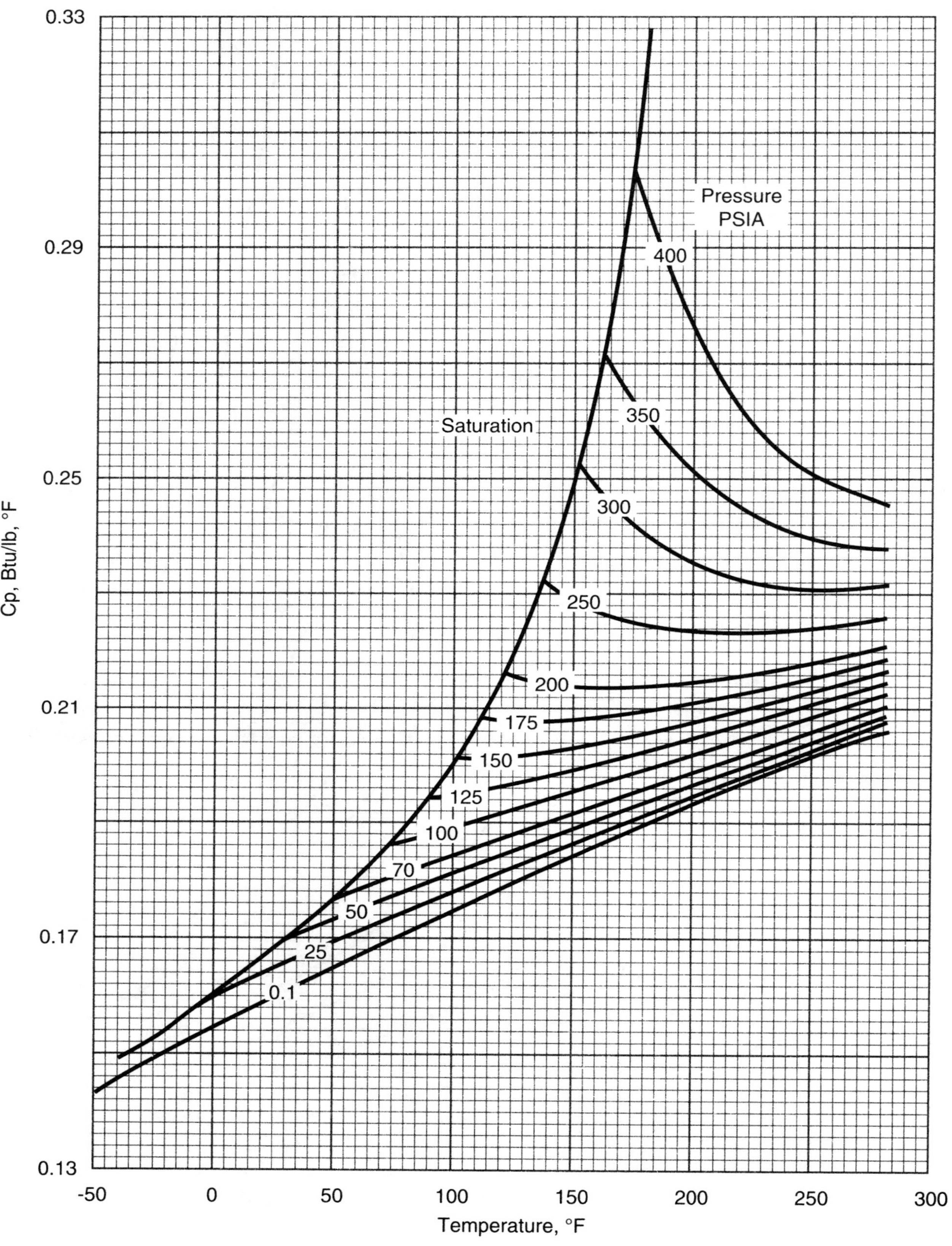

SUVA® MP66 Vapor Heat Capacity Ratio

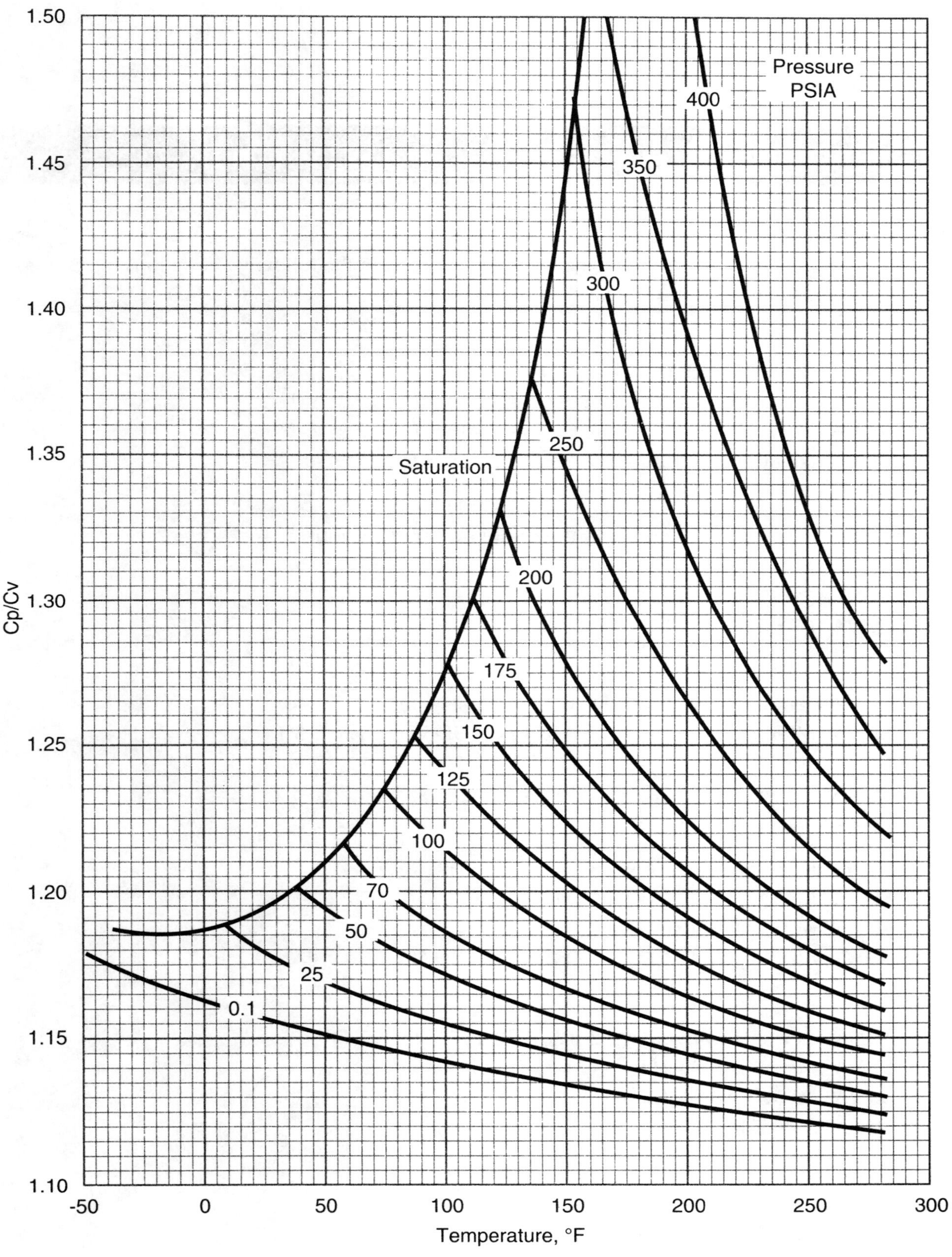

EQUATIONS FOR PROPERTY ESTIMATION

English Units

Curves have been fitted to the measured data to obtain the following equations for estimation of properties within the ranges specified.

Liquid Viscosity in cP (–80°F to 180°F)

SUVA® MP39 $\mu_l = 4.33 - 1.98E\text{-}2\ T + 3.24E\text{-}5\ T^2 - 1.83E\text{-}8\ T^3$

SUVA® MP52 $\mu_l = 4.60 - 2.09E\text{-}2\ T + 3.38E\text{-}5\ T^2 - 1.89E\text{-}8\ T^3$

SUVA® MP66 $\mu_l = 4.21 - 1.93E\text{-}2\ T + 3.16E\text{-}5\ T^2 - 1.79E\text{-}8\ T^3$

Liquid Thermal Conductivity in Btu/hr ft °F (–100°F to 200°F)

SUVA® MP39 $k_l = 0.135 - 1.54E\text{-}4\ T$

SUVA® MP52 $k_l = 0.125 - 1.40E\text{-}4\ T$

SUVA® MP66 $k_l = 0.137 - 1.58E\text{-}4\ T$

Liquid Heat Capacity in Btu/lb °F (–40°F to 200°F)

SUVA® MP39 $C_p = -1.33 + 9.84E\text{-}3\ T - 2.09E\text{-}5\ T^2 + 1.53E\text{-}8\ T^3$

SUVA® MP52 $C_p = -0.948 + 7.47E\text{-}3\ T - 1.60E\text{-}5\ T^2 + 1.20E\text{-}8\ T^3$

SUVA® MP66 $C_p = -1.66 + 1.19E\text{-}2\ T - 2.49E\text{-}5\ T^2 + 1.80E\text{-}8\ T^3$

Vapor Viscosity at One Atmosphere in cP (0°F to 300°F)

SUVA® MP39 $\mu_v = 1.11E\text{-}3 + 2.04E\text{-}5\ T$

SUVA® MP52 $\mu_v = 1.09E\text{-}3 + 2.03E\text{-}5\ T$

SUVA® MP66 $\mu_v = 1.12E\text{-}3 + 2.05E\text{-}5\ T$

Vapor Thermal Conductivity in Btu/lb ft° F (0°F to 300°F)

SUVA® MP39 $k_v = -4.16E\text{-}3 + 2.07E\text{-}5\ T$

SUVA® MP52 $k_v = -4.42E\text{-}3 + 2.13E\text{-}5\ T$

SUVA® MP66 $k_v = -4.02E\text{-}3 + 2.04E\text{-}5\ T$

Where T = Temperature, °R
and °R = °F + 460

Saturated Liquid Viscosity

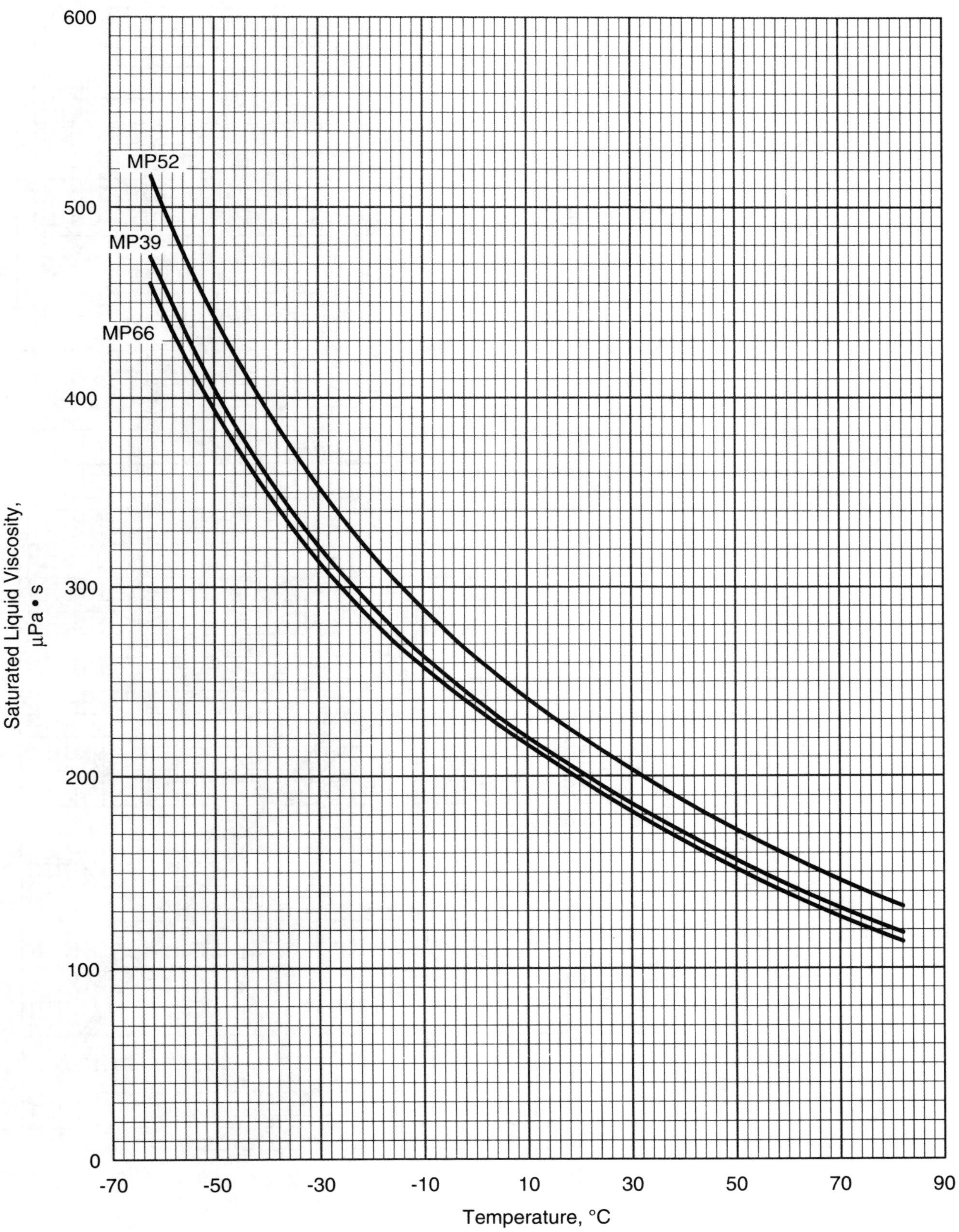

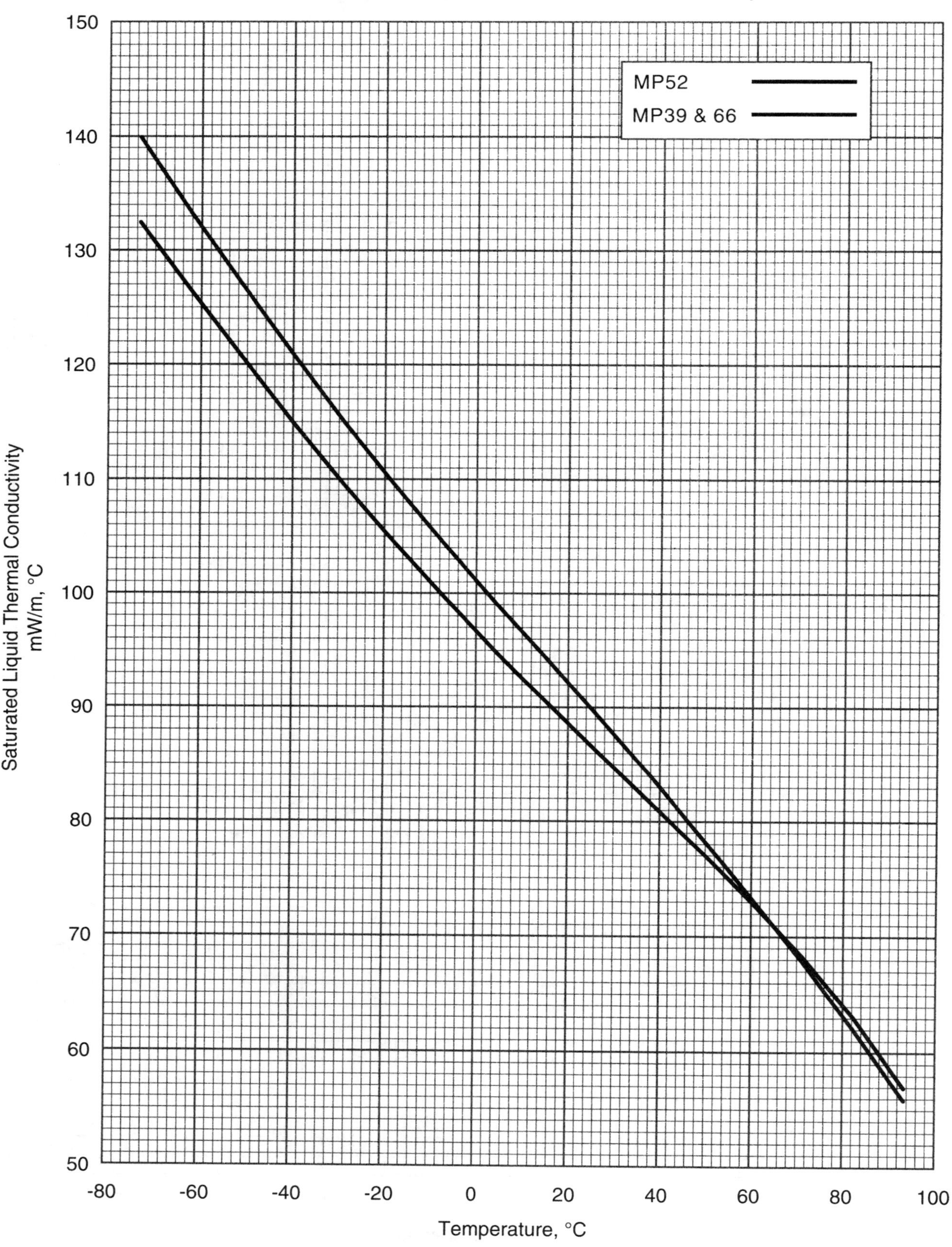

Saturated Liquid Thermal Conductivity
MP52
MP39 & 66
Saturated Liquid Thermal Conductivity
mW/m, °C
150
140
130
120
110
100
90
80
70
60
50
-80
-60
-40
-20
0
20
40
60
80
100
Temperature, °C

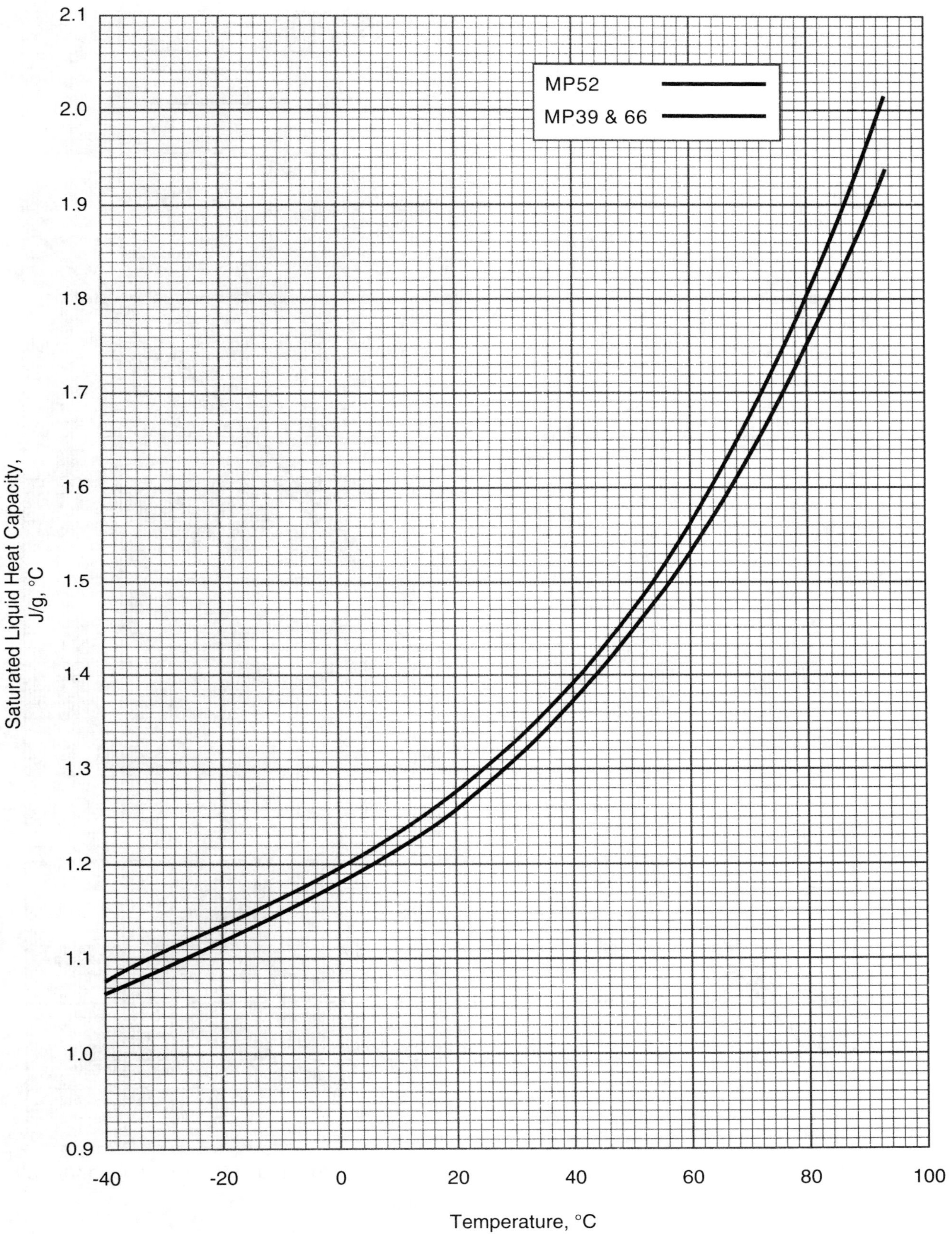
Saturated Liquid Heat Capacity
MP52
MP39 & 66
Saturated Liquid Heat Capacity, J/g, °C
2.1
2.0
1.9
1.8
1.7
1.6
1.5
1.4
1.3
1.2
1.1
1.0
0.9
-40
-20
0
20
40
60
80
100
Temperature, °C

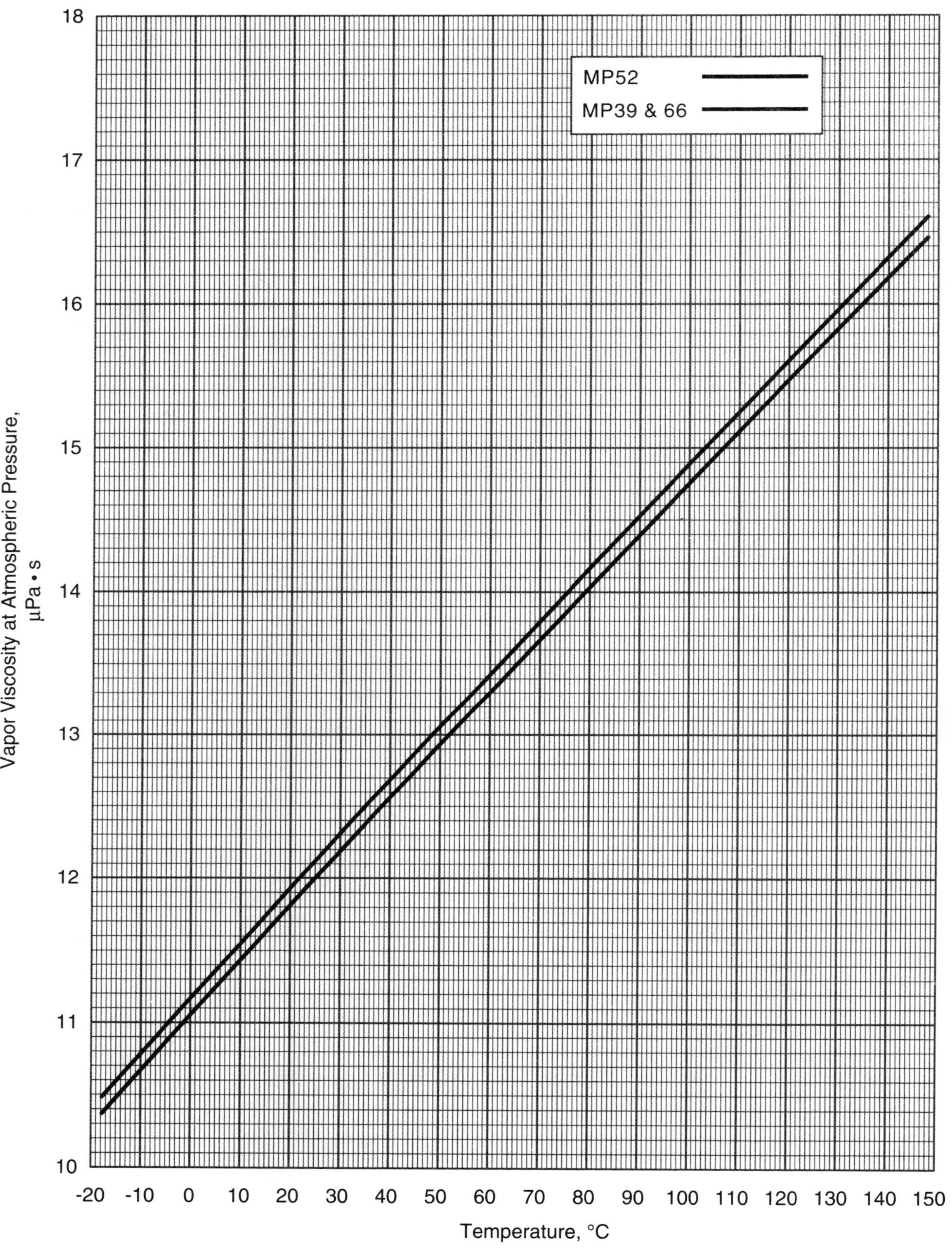
Vapor Viscosity at Atmospheric Pressure
MP52
MP39 & 66
Vapor Viscosity at Atmospheric Pressure, μPa • s
18
17
16
15
14
13
12
11
10
-20 -10 0 10 20 30 40 50 60 70 80 90 100 110 120 130 140 150
Temperature, °C

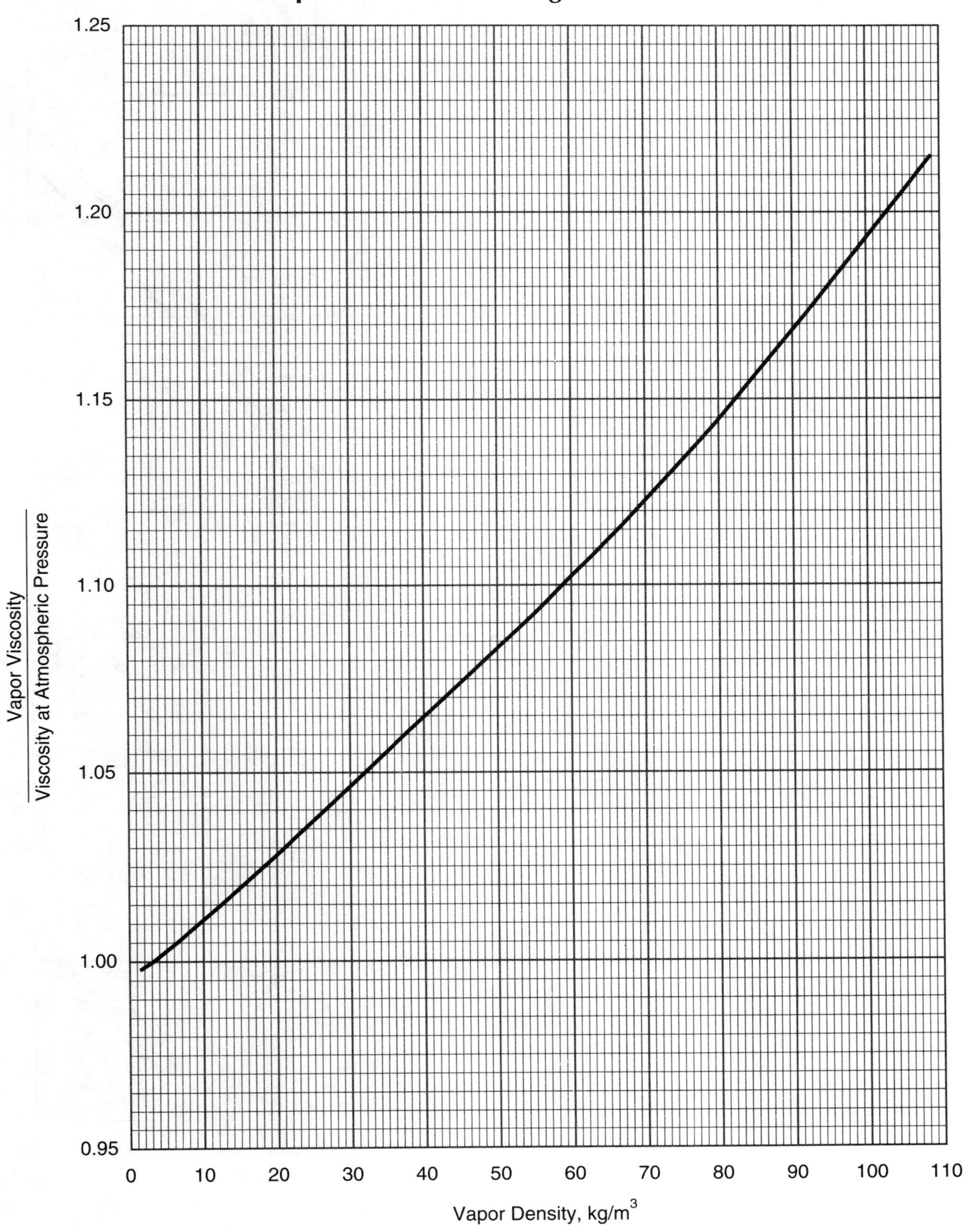
Correction of Vapor Viscosity at
Atmospheric Pressure to Higher Pressures
1.25
1.20
1.15
1.10
1.05
1.00
0.95
Vapor Viscosity
Viscosity at Atmospheric Pressure
0
10
20
30
40
50
60
70
80
90
100
110
Vapor Density, kg/m3

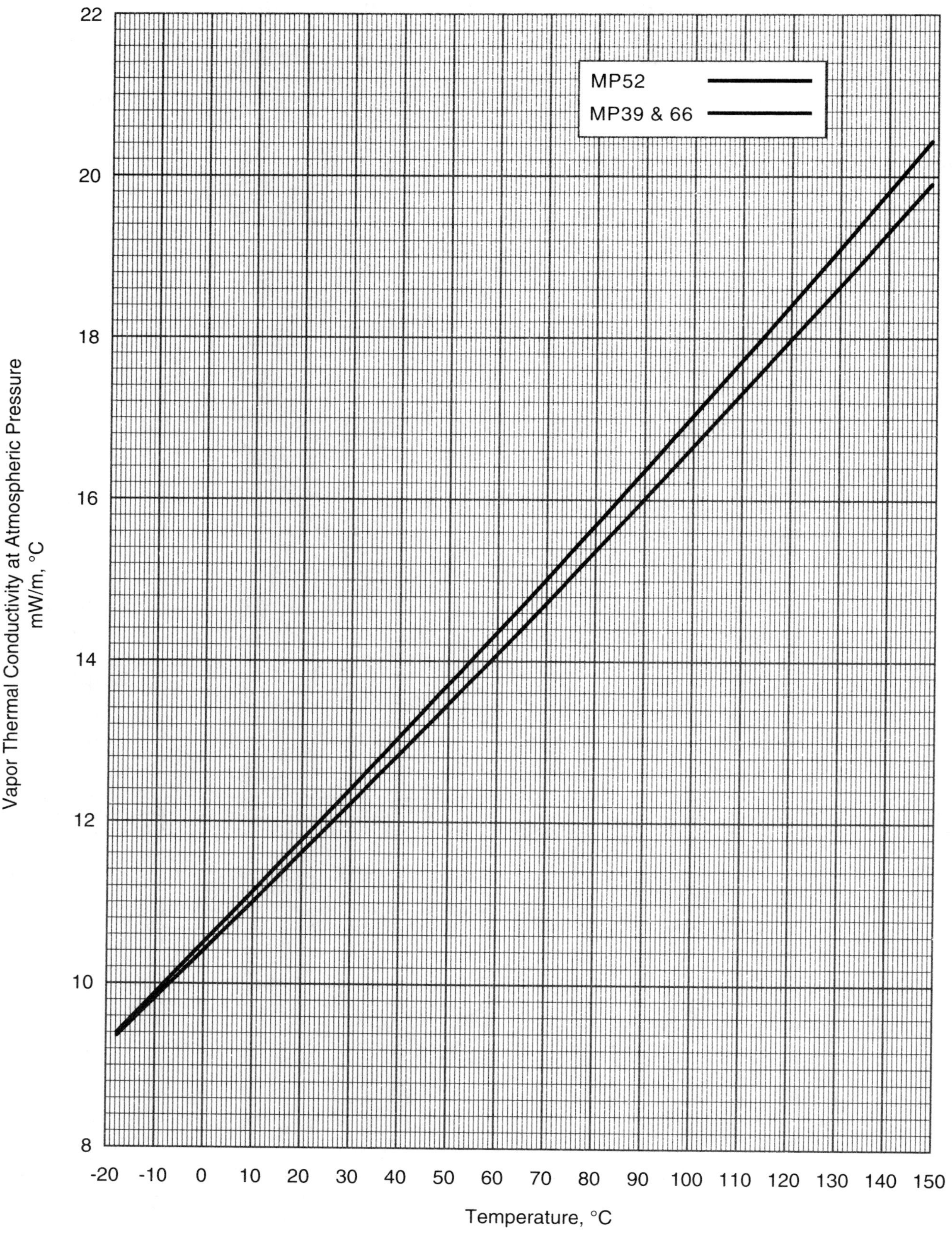
Vapor Thermal Conductivity at Atmospheric Pressure
MP52
MP39 & 66
Vapor Thermal Conductivity at Atmospheric Pressure
mW/m, °C
22
20
18
16
14
12
10
8
-20
-10
0
10
20
30
40
50
60
70
80
90
100
110
120
130
140
150
Temperature, °C

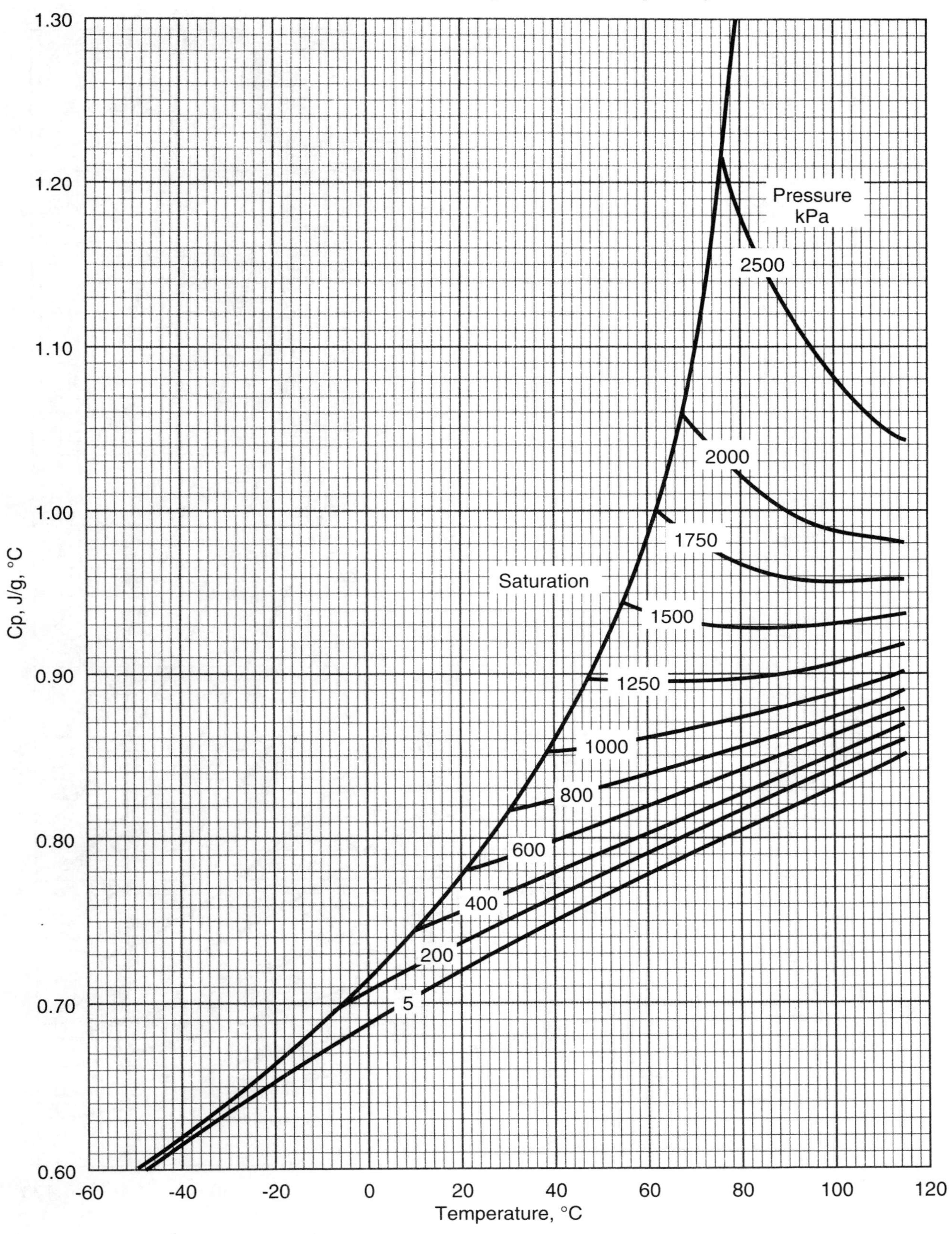
SUVA® MP39 Vapor Heat Capacity
Cp, J/g, °C
Temperature, °C
Pressure kPa
Saturation
2500
2000
1750
1500
1250
1000
800
600
400
200
5
1.30
1.20
1.10
1.00
0.90
0.80
0.70
0.60
-60
-40
-20
0
20
40
60
80
100
120

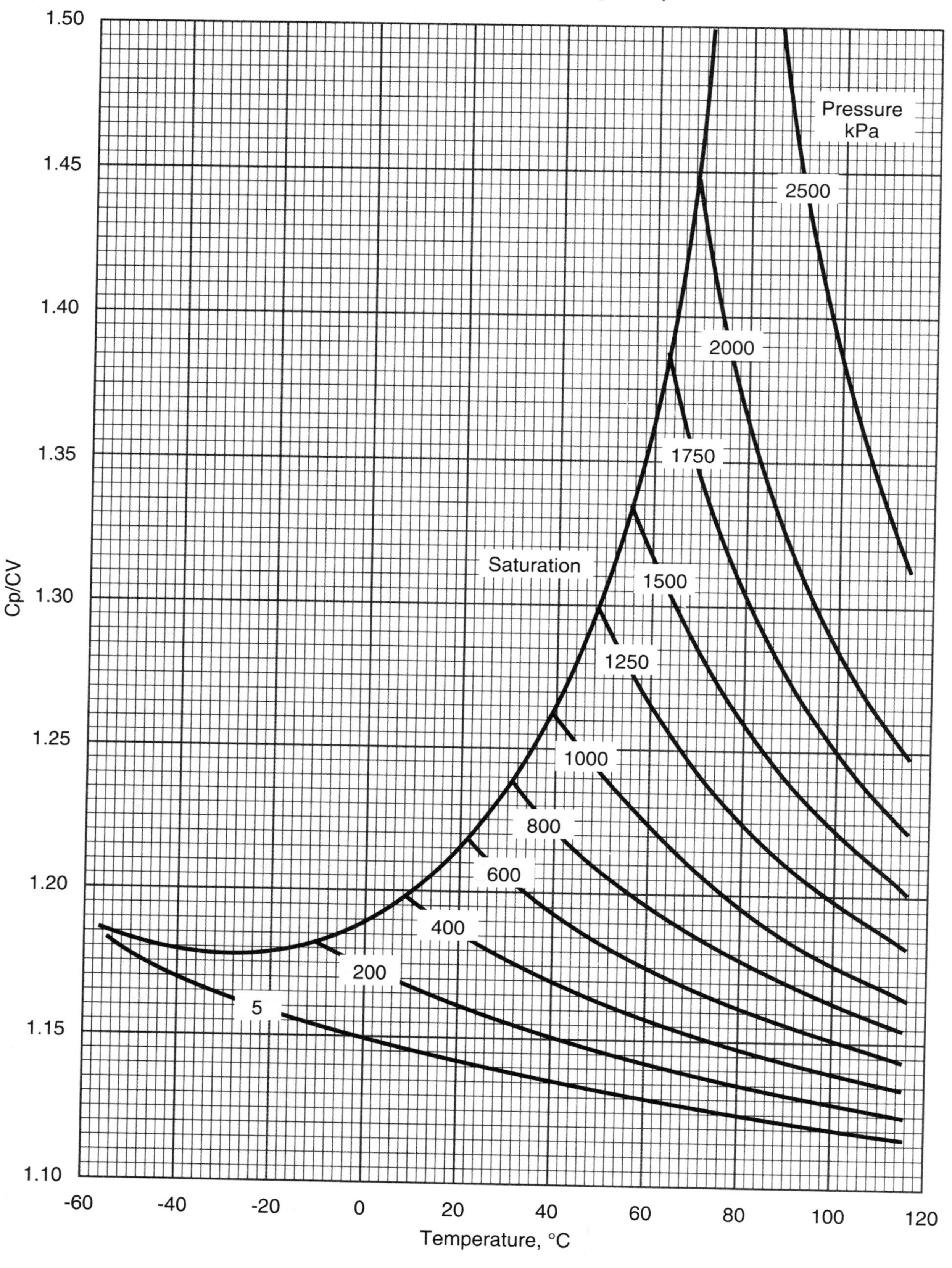
SUVA® MP39 Vapor Heat Capacity Ratio
Cp/CV
1.50
1.45
1.40
1.35
1.30
1.25
1.20
1.15
1.10
-60
-40
-20
0
20
40
60
80
100
120
Temperature, °C
Pressure kPa
2500
2000
1750
1500
1250
1000
800
600
400
200
5
Saturation

SUVA® MP52 Vapor Heat Capacity

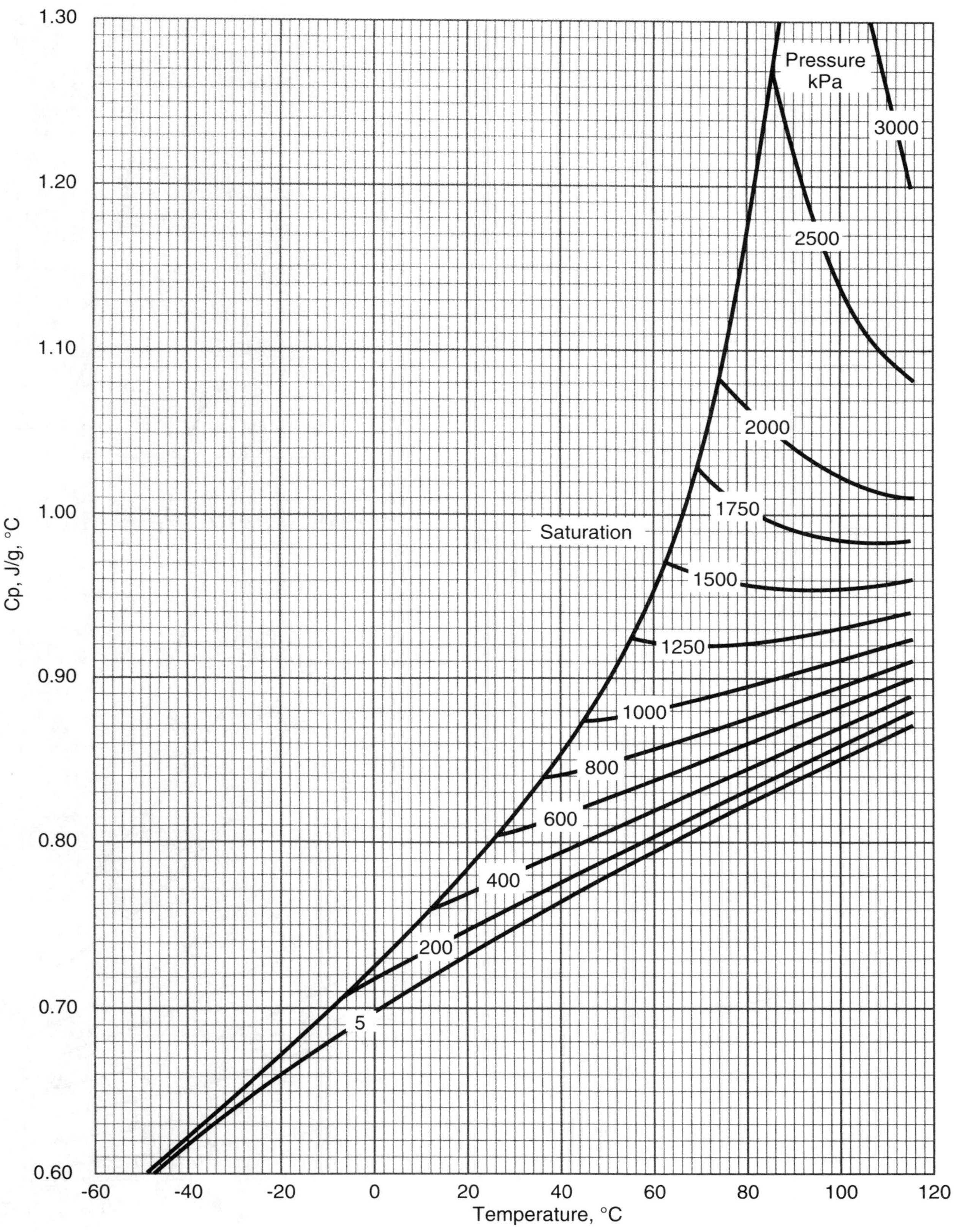

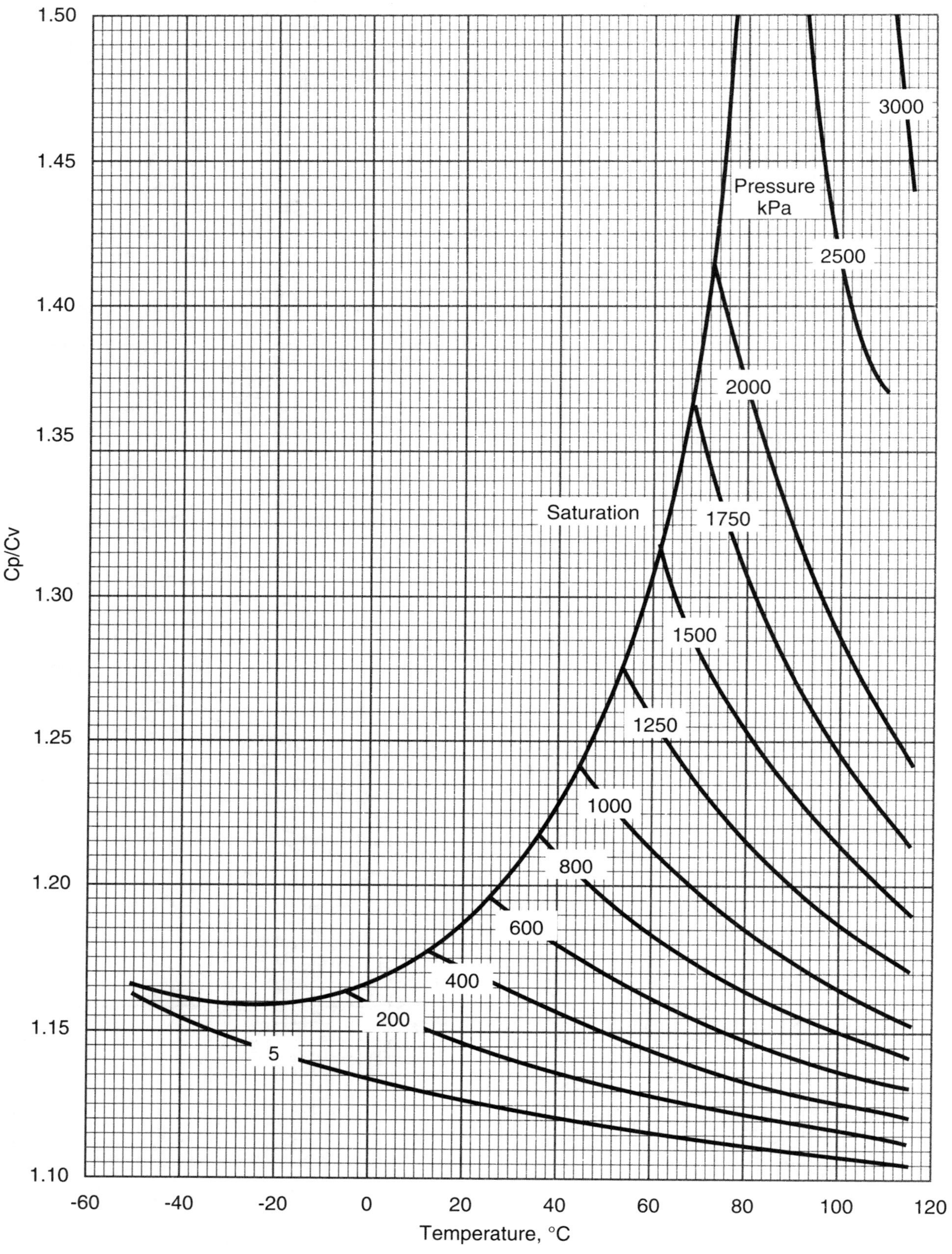
SUVA® MP52 Vapor Heat Capacity Ratio
Cp/Cv
Temperature, °C
Pressure
kPa
Saturation
3000
2500
2000
1750
1500
1250
1000
800
600
400
200
5
1.50
1.45
1.40
1.35
1.30
1.25
1.20
1.15
1.10
-60
-40
-20
0
20
40
60
80
100
120

SUVA® MP66 Vapor Heat Capacity

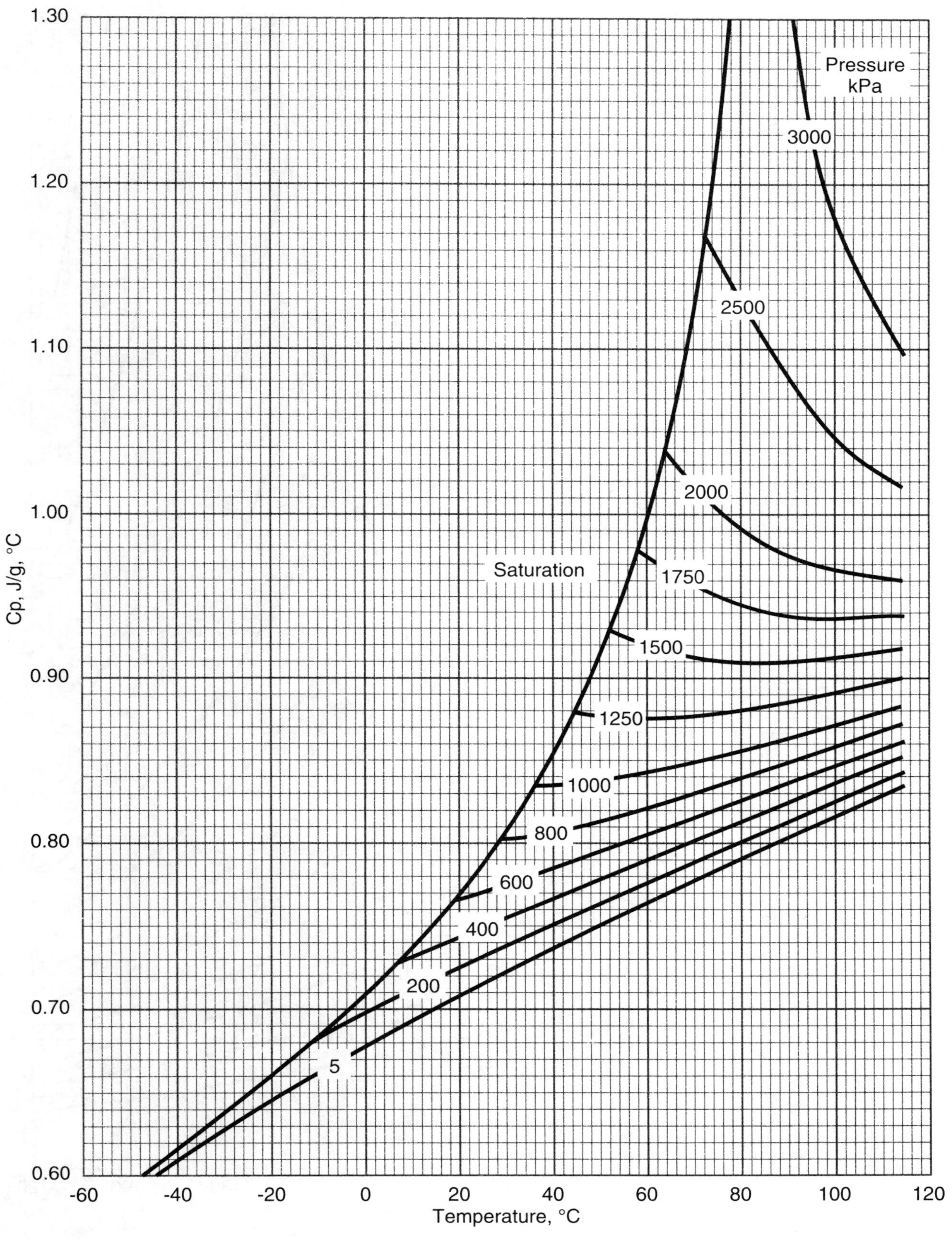

SUVA® MP66 Vapor Heat Capacity Ratio

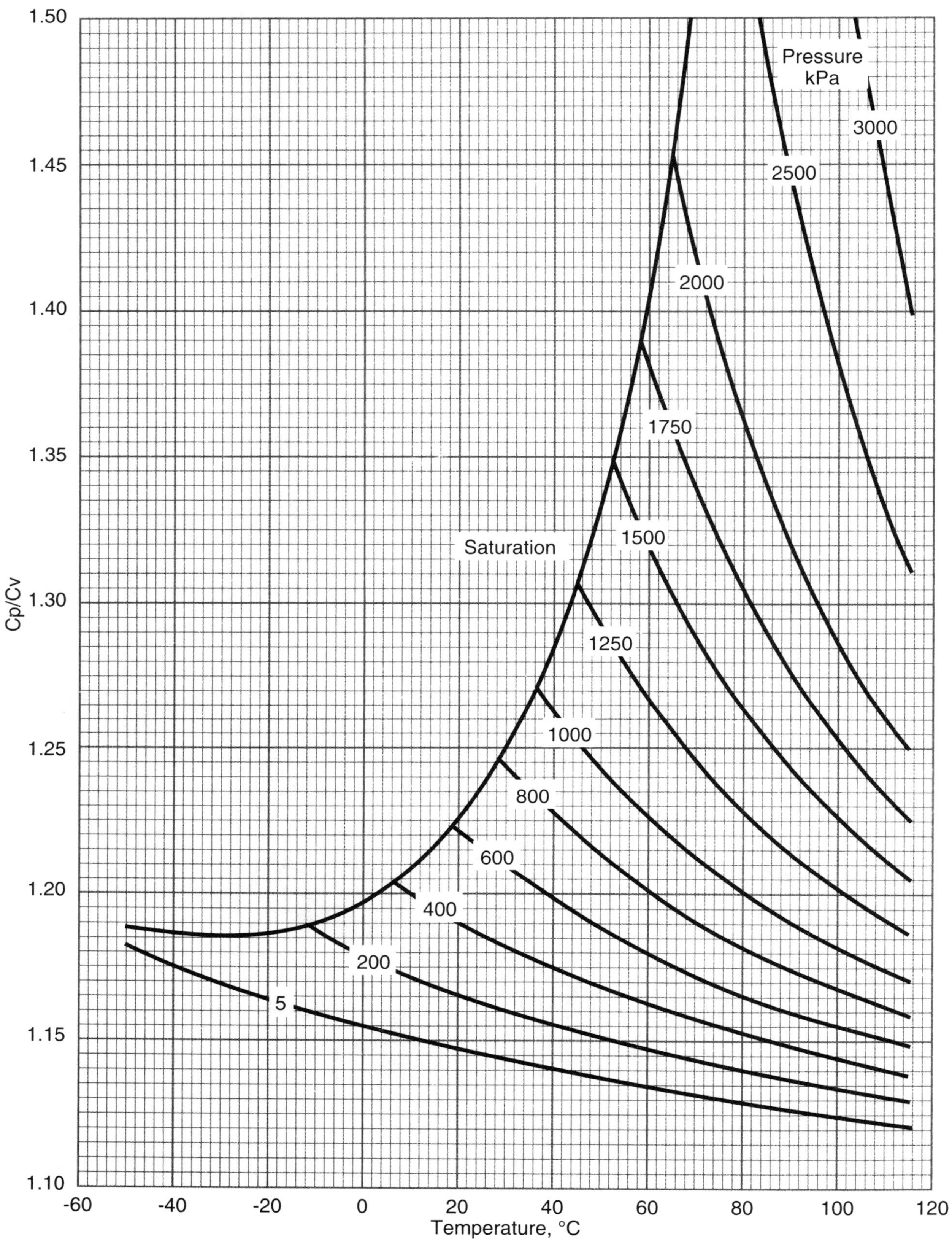

EQUATIONS FOR PROPERTY ESTIMATION

Metric Units

Curves have been fitted to the measured data to obtain the following equations for estimation of properties within the ranges specified.

Liquid Viscosity in μPa·s (–62°C to 82°C)

SUVA® MP39 $= 4334 - 35.73\ T + 0.105\ T^2 - 1.07E\text{-}4\ T^3$

SUVA® MP52 $= 4602 - 37.60\ T + 0.110\ T^2 - 1.11E\text{-}4\ T^3$

SUVA® MP66 $= 4211 - 34.77\ T + 0.103\ T^2 - 1.04E\text{-}4\ T^3$

Liquid Thermal Conductivity in mW/m °C (–75°C to 95°C)

SUVA® MP39 $k_1 = 233 - 0.479\ T$

SUVA® MP52 $k_1 = 217 - 0.434\ T$

SUVA® MP66 $k_1 = 237 - 0.492\ T$

Liquid Heat Capacity in J/g °C (–40°C to 95°C)

SUVA® MP39 $C_p = -5.58 + 7.42E\text{-}2\ T - 2.83E\text{-}4\ T^2 + 3.74E\text{-}7\ T^3$

SUVA® MP52 $C_p = -3.97 + 5.63E\text{-}2\ T - 2.17E\text{-}4\ T^2 + 2.94E\text{-}7\ T^3$

SUVA® MP66 $C_p = -6.95 + 8.93E\text{-}2\ T - 3.38E\text{-}4\ T^2 + 4.39E\text{-}7\ T^3$

Vapor Viscosity at One Atmosphere in μPa·s (–20°C to 150°C)

SUVA® MP39 $\mu_v = 1.11 + 3.67E\text{-}2\ T$

SUVA® MP52 $\mu_v = 1.09 + 3.65E\text{-}2\ T$

SUVA® MP66 $\mu_v = 1.12 + 3.70E\text{-}2\ T$

Vapor Thermal Conductivity in mW/m °C (–20°C to 150°C)

SUVA® MP39 $k_v = -7.19 + 6.45E\text{-}2\ T$

SUVA® MP52 $k_v = -7.63 + 6.63E\text{-}2\ T$

SUVA® MP66 $k_v = -6.95 + 6.34E\text{-}2\ T$

Where T = Temperature, °K
and °K = °C + 273.2

For Sales Information:

Du Pont Chemicals
Customer Service Center, B-15305
Wilmington, DE 19898/U.S.A.
(302) 774-2099
1-800-441-9442

For Technical Information:

Fluorochemicals Laboratory
Wilmington, DE 19898/U.S.A.
(302) 999-3129
1-800-582-5606

Europe
Du Pont de Nemours
International S.A.
2 Chemin du Pavillon
P.O. Box 50
CH-1218 Le Grand-Sacconex
Geneva, Switzerland
41-22-717-5111

Canada
Du Pont Canada, Inc.
P.O. Box 2200, Streetsville
Mississauga, Ontario
L5M 2H3
(416) 821-3300

Mexico
Du Pont, S.A. de C.V.
Homero 206
Col. Chapultepec Morales
C.P. 11570 Mexico, D.F.
52-5-250-8000

South America
Du Pont do Brasil S.A.
Alameda Itapicuru, 506
Alphaville 06400 Barueri
Sao Paulo, Brazil
55-11-421-8509

Du Pont Argentina S.A.
Casilla Correo 1888
Correo Central
1000 Buenos Aires, Argentina
54-1-311-8167

Pacific
Du Pont Australia
P.O. Box 930
North Sydney, NSW 2060
Australia
61-2-923-6165

Japan
Mitsui Du Pont Fluorochemicals
Company, Ltd.
Mitsui Seimei Building
2-3, 1-Chome Ohtemachi
Chiyoda-Ku, Tokyo 100 Japan
81-3-3216-8451

Asia
Du Pont Taiwan
P.O. Box 81-777
Taipei, Taiwan
886-2-514-4400

Du Pont Asia Pacific Limited
P.O. Box TST 98851
Tsim Sha Tsui
Kowloon, Hong Kong
852-734-5345

Du Pont Thailand
P.O. Box 2398
Bangkok 10501, Thailand
66-2-238-4361

Du Pont China Ltd.
Room 1704, Union Bldg.
100 Yanan Rd. East
Shanghai, PR China 200 002
Phone: 86-21-328-3738
Telex: 33448 DCLSH CN
Fax: 86-21-320-2304

Du Pont Far East Inc.
P.O. Box 12396
50776 Kuala Lumpur, Malaysia
Phone: 60-3-232-3522
Telex: (784) 30391 DUFE M
Fax: 60-3-238-7250

Du Pont Korea, Ltd.
C.P.O. Box 5972
Seoul, Korea
82-2-721-5114

Du Pont Singapore Pte. Ltd.
1 Maritime Square #07 01
World Trade Centre
Singapore 0409
65-273-2244

Du Pont Far East, Phillippines
5th Floor, Solid Bank Building
777 Paseo de Roxas
Makati, Metro Manila
Phillippines
63-2-818-9911

Du Pont Far East Inc.
7A Murray's Gate Road
Alwarpet
Madras, 600 018 India
91-44-454-029

Du Pont Far East Inc.-
Pakistan
9 Khayaban-E-Shaheen
Defence Phase 5
Karachi, Pakistan
92-21-533-350

Du Pont Far East Inc.
P.O. Box 2553/Jkt
Jakarta 10001
Indonesia
62-21-517-800

H-45949 1/93

Printed in U.S.A.

233234A

Technical Information

Suva®
alternative refrigerants

ART-5

Retrofit Guidelines for Suva MP39 and Suva MP66

Introduction

Suva MP39 and Suva MP66 are commercially available three-component mixtures of HCFC-22, HFC-152a, and HCFC-124 which have been developed as alternative refrigerants to replace CFC-12 in medium and low temperature refrigeration applications. Suva MP66 is also an excellent alternative refrigerant to replace R-500. Using the retrofit guidelines summarized below, most CFC-12 and R-500 direct expansion systems using positive displacement compressors (i.e., reciprocating, rotary, screw, and scroll) can be easily and economically retrofitted for use with Suva MP39 or Suva MP66. This allows the existing equipment to continue to operate safely and efficiently for the remainder of its useful life, even after CFC-12 and R-500 are no longer available.

Properties and Safety

The Suva MP refrigerant blends offer improved environmental properties versus CFC-12 and R-500, with significantly lower ozone depletion potential (ODP) and global warming potential (GWP) (see *Table 1*). Like CFC-12 and R-500, Suva MP39 and Suva MP66 are nonflammable and have a low degree of toxicity. Refer to DuPont Technical Bulletin P-MP (H-45944-2) for more detailed information on the properties, uses, storage, and handling of Suva MP39 and Suva MP66. Refer to the product Material Safety Data Sheets (MSDS) for more safety information on the use of Suva MP39 and Suva MP66.

Selection of Refrigerant

The Suva MP blends are recommended replacements for CFC-12 and R-500 in direct expansion systems using positive displacement compressors. Suva MP39 and Suva MP66 are near-azeotropes, therefore the vapor composition in the refrigerant cylinder is different from the liquid composition. This small composition difference will not affect performance in direct expansion systems; however, it may impact performance in systems with flooded evaporators. In general, the Suva MP blends are not recommended for use in systems with flooded evaporators.

Suva MP39 is the recommended alternative for most medium temperature CFC-12 systems. With Suva MP39, comparable capacities and efficiencies to CFC-12 are expected in systems operating at evaporator temperatures of –10°F (–23°C) and above, making it suitable for use in such applications as walk-in coolers, food and dairy display cases, beverage dispensers, beverage vending machines, and home refrigerators.

Suva MP66 provides comparable capacity to CFC-12 in systems operating at evaporator temperatures below –10°F (–23°C), making it suitable for use in domestic and commercial freezers and some transport refrigeration equipment.

Suva MP66 is also the recommended alternative for existing R-500 systems. With Suva MP66, capacity, efficiency, discharge temperature, and discharge pressure will all be similar to that of R-500.

Table 1
Suva MP39 and Suva MP66 Physical Properties

Property	Units	R-12	MP39	MP66	R-500
Boiling Pt	°C	–30	–33	–35	–34
(1 atm)	°F	–22	–27	–30	–28
Density, Sat'd	kg/m³	1311	1194	1193	1156
Liquid at 25°C (77°F)	lb/ft³	81.8	74.5	74.5	72.2
Density, Sat'd	kg/m³	37.2	29.0	30.7	36.8
Vapor at 25°C (77°F)	lb/ft³	2.32	1.81	1.92	2.29
Vapor Pressure, Sat'd	kPa (abs)	651	773	819	768
Liquid at 25°C (77°F)	psia	94.5	112.1	118.8	111.5
Ozone Depletion Potential versus R-12	R-12 = 1	1.0	0.03	0.035	0.70
Halocarbon Global Warming Potential versus R-11	R-11 = 1	3.0	0.22	0.24	2.0
Capacity versus R-12*	R-12 = 100	100	108	116	—
MP66 versus R-500**	R-500 = 100	—	—	100	100
Efficiency versus R-12*	R-12 = 100	100	101	101	—
MP66 versus R-500**	R-500 = 100	—	—	100	100

* Conditions: –10°F (–23.3°C) Evaporator/130°F (54.4°C) Condenser/Superheat to 90°F (32.2°C)/Subcool to 90°F (32.2°C)
** Conditions: 35°F (1.7°C) Evaporator/130°F (54.4°C) Condenser/Superheat to 80°F (26.7°C)/Subcool to 125°F (51.6°C)

Lubricant selection is based upon many factors, including compressor wear characteristics, material compatibility, and lubricant/refrigerant miscibility, which can affect oil return to the compressor. In order to maintain the same lubricant/refrigerant miscibility as CFC-12/mineral oil, a lubricant change will be required when retrofitting to Suva MP39 or Suva MP66, as the Suva MP blends are not miscible with mineral oil.

Both Suva MP39 and Suva MP66 are miscible with alkylbenzene lubricants, which are in commercial use today with CFC-12 and R-500 in some refrigeration systems. Alkylbenzene lubricants have been used successfully in thousands of refrigeration systems retrofitted with the Suva MP blends, and are compatible with materials of construction commonly used in CFC systems. In systems already charged with the alkylbenzene lubricant (check with compressor manufacturer for specific lubricant recommendation), no lubricant change is needed when retrofitting with Suva MP39 or Suva MP66.

Before a retrofit is started, it is recommended that the compressor manufacturer be consulted concerning any specific lubricant recommendations for their compressors. Other sources of lubricant information are the DuPont Authorized Distributor, lubricant manufacturers, and system manufacturers.

It is recommended that the filter drier be changed during the retrofit, as is routine practice following system maintenance. There are three types of filter driers commonly used in CFC-12 or R-500 equipment:

- Solid core driers, in which the molecular sieve desiccant is dispersed within a solid core binder.
- Loose filled driers, which contain only the molecular sieve desiccant.
- Compacted bead driers, which also contain only the molecular sieve desiccant, but where the desiccant is compacted in the drier by mechanical pressure, usually a spring.

For solid core driers, consult the drier manufacturer for their recommended drier for use with the Suva MP blends. Some existing models of solid core driers, such as the Sporlan® Catch All® or Alco® ADK, are compatible with the Suva MP blends.

The XH-9 molecular sieve desiccant (manufactured by UOP) or equivalent (such as MS 594 from Grace) is recommended for use in loose filled driers with the Suva MP blends.

Compacted bead driers may use either the XH-9 or XH-6 desiccant or equivalent. Consult the drier manufacturer for their recommendation.

System Modification

The compositions of Suva MP39 and Suva MP66 have been selected to provide comparable performance to CFC-12 or R-500 for specific applications, in terms of both capacity and energy efficiency. As a result, minimal system modifications are anticipated when retrofitting CFC-12 or R-500 systems with Suva MP39 or Suva MP66. Hoses and gasket materials should be reviewed for compatibility with the Suva MP blends. In general, elastomers and plastics recommended for use with HCFC-22 are suitable for use with the Suva MP blends. It is recommended that the equipment manufacturer be consulted for specific hose and gasket recommendations.

Retrofits of CFC-12 or R-500 systems with other alternative refrigerants, such as HCFC-22 or HFC-134a, may require more extensive system modifications (compressor replacement, etc.) to the existing equipment. For some systems, this cost may be prohibitive. Suva MP39 and Suva MP66 provide the service contractor and equipment owner with a cost-effective way to retrofit an existing CFC-12 or R-500 system.

It is important to note that Suva MP39 and Suva MP66 were not designed for use with other refrigerants or additives which have not been clearly specified by DuPont. Mixing CFC-12 or R-500 with a Suva MP refrigerant may have an adverse impact on system performance; therefore, topping off an existing CFC-12 or R-500 charge with Suva MP39 or Suva MP66 is not recommended.

Overview of Retrofit Process

Retrofit of an existing CFC-12 or R-500 system with Suva MP39 or Suva MP66 can be accomplished using service practices and service equipment commonly used by trained mechanics or service contractors in the field. The key steps involved in the retrofit are:

1. Evacuate CFC-12 or R-500 charge from system.
2. Remove mineral oil from compressor and replace with alkylbenzene lubricant.
3. Replace filter drier with new drier compatible with the Suva MP refrigerant blends.
4. Charge system with Suva MP39 or Suva MP66.
5. Start system and adjust charge and/or controls to achieve desired operation.

For the majority of systems, the compressor lubricant change, the filter drier change, and, in systems with expansion valves, a possible adjustment to the superheat setting will be the only system modifications required in a retrofit to Suva MP39 or Suva MP66. For systems which are still under warranty, we do recommend contacting the equipment or compressor manufacturers prior to performing the retrofit concerning warranty terms, as some equipment or compressor warranties may be impacted by a change from the refrigerant originally specified for the system or compressor.

Equipment and Supplies Needed for Retrofit

- Safety equipment (gloves, glasses)
- Manifold gauges
- Thermocouples to read line temperatures
- Vacuum pump
- Leak detection equipment
- Scale
- Recovery unit (RRU30 by Refrigerant Recovery Technologies, Inc. is recommended. See your local Authorized DuPont Distributor.)
- Recovery cylinder
- Container for recovered lubricant
- Replacement lubricant
- Refrigerant cylinder with Suva MP39 or Suva MP66
- Replacement filter drier
- Labels indicating the refrigerant and lubricant charged to the system

Retrofit Procedure

Summarized below is a more detailed discussion of the recommended procedures for retrofitting a CFC-12 or R-500 system with Suva MP39 or Suva MP66. Prior to the retrofit, review the Material Safety Data Sheets for safety information on the use of Suva MP39 or Suva MP66:

1. **Baseline Data with CFC-12 or R-500.** For service contractors performing their initial retrofits with the Suva MP refrigerant blends, it is recommended that system performance data be collected while CFC-12 or R-500 is in the system. This baseline data of temperatures and pressures at various points in the system (evaporator, condenser, compressor suction and discharge, expansion device, etc.) at normal operating conditions can be useful when optimizing operation of the system with the Suva MP39 or Suva MP66. A System Data Sheet is attached for recording this baseline data.
2. **Remove CFC-12 or R-500 Charge.** CFC-12 or R-500 should be removed from the system and collected in a recovery cylinder using a recovery

device capable of pulling 10–15 in. Hg vacuum (50–67 kPa, 0.50–0.67 bar [abs)]). If the recommended CFC-12 or R-500 charge size for the system is not known, weigh the amount of refrigerant removed if possible. The initial quantity of Suva MP39 or Suva MP66 charged in the system can be determined from this amount.

3. **Drain Lubricant from Compressor.** In systems where mineral oil is the existing lubricant, the lubricant will have to be drained from the compressor. This may require removing the compressor from the system, particularly with small hermetic compressors which have no oil drain. In this case, the lubricant can be removed from the compressor by using an oil pump or by draining through the suction line of the compressor. In most small systems, 90–95% of the lubricant can be removed from the compressor in this manner. Larger systems may require drainage from additional points in the system, particularly low spots around the evaporator, to remove the majority of the lubricant. In systems with an oil separator, any lubricant present in the separator should also be drained.

   In all cases, *measure* the amount of lubricant removed from the compressor. Compare to the compressor/system specifications to ensure that 80+% of the lubricant has been removed from the system. Because of the difference in miscibility between CFC-12 or R-500 and the Suva MP blends with mineral oil, 80+% of the mineral oil must be removed to ensure proper oil return and lubrication. If poor system performance is noted on start-up, an additional lubricant change may be required (DuPont experience is that this occurs in <1% of retrofits). Record the amount of lubricant removed on the attached Retrofit Checklist, as this will be needed in the next step.

4. **Charge Compressor with Alkylbenzene Lubricant.** Charge the compressor with the same volume of alkylbenzene lubricant as the volume of mineral oil lubricant removed in step 3. Use a viscosity of alkylbenzene similar to that of the mineral oil used in the system (150 SUS or 32 cSt is typical for medium temperature CFC-12 systems). An alkylbenzene lubricant, such as Zerol® 150 (manufactured by Shrieve Chemical), is recommended. Where possible, check with the compressor manufacturer for specific lubricant recommendations.

   Reinstall Compressor (if removed from system in step 3). Use normal service practices.

5. **Replace Filter Drier.** It is routine practice to replace the filter drier following system maintenance. Replacement driers are available which are compatible with Suva MP39 and Suva MP66.

   For loose filled driers, the XH-9 molecular sieve desiccant (manufactured by UOP) or equivalent (such as MS 594 from Grace) is recommended for use with the Suva MP blends. Compacted bead driers may use either the XH-9 or XH-6 desiccant or equivalent.

   For solid core driers, consult the drier manufacturer for their recommended drier for use with the Suva MP blends. Some existing models of solid core driers, such as the Sporlan® Catch All® or Alco® ADK, are compatible with the Suva MP blends.

6. **Reconnect System and Evacuate.** Use normal service practices. To remove air or other noncondensibles in the system, it is recommended that the system be evacuated to a deep vacuum (29.9 in. Hg vacuum/500 microns/0.14 kPa/ 0.0014 bar [abs]).

   Leak Check System. Use normal service practices. Reevacuate system following leak check.

7. **Charge System with Suva MP39 or Suva MP66.** Suva MP39 and Suva MP66 are near-azeotropic blends, therefore the vapor composition in the refrigerant cylinder is different from the liquid composition. To ensure that the proper blend composition is charged in the system, it is important that *liquid only* be removed from the cylinder. Cylinders of both Suva MP39 and Suva MP66 are equipped with dip tubes, allowing liquid to be removed from the cylinder in the upright position. The proper position is indicated by arrows on the cylinder and cylinder box. Once removed from the cylinder, the Suva MP blends can be charged to the system as vapor as long as all of the liquid removed from the cylinder is transferred to the system.

   Retrofits of CFC-12 Equipment: The refrigeration system will require a *smaller* charge size with Suva MP39 or Suva MP66 than with CFC-12. The optimum charge will vary depending on the operating conditions, size of the evaporator and condenser, size of receiver (if present), and length of pipe or tubing runs in the system. For most systems, the optimum charge will be 75–90% by weight of the original CFC-12 charge. It is recommended that the system be initially charged with 70–75% by weight of the original CFC-12 charge (ex: if original CFC-12 charge was 10 ounces, initially charge 7–7.5 ounces of Suva MP39 or Suva MP66; similarly, if original CFC-12 charge was 300 grams, initially charge 210–220 grams of Suva MP39 or Suva MP66).

Retrofits of R-500 Equipment: The refrigeration system will require a slightly *larger* charge with Suva MP66 than with R-500. For most systems, the optimum charge will be about 105% by weight of the original R-500 charge. It is recommended that the system be initially charged with 95–100% by weight of the original R-500 charge.

Add the initial charge to the high pressure side of the system until the system and cylinder pressure equilibrate. Position the refrigerant filling connections to the low pressure side of the system, start up the compressor, and load the remainder of the refrigerant to the suction line of the system. Since liquid must be removed from the refrigerant cylinder, it is important to charge the refrigerant slowly into the suction line to allow it to flash before it enters the system, in order to avoid damage to the compressor from liquid refrigerant entering the suction side of the compressor. A throttling device may also be used to cause the refrigerant to flash before entering the system.

8. **Adjust Charge.** Let conditions stabilize. If the system is undercharged, add additional Suva MP39 or Suva MP66 in small amounts (still removing liquid from the charging cylinder) until desired operating conditions are achieved.

When the system is lined out, compressor suction pressures for the Suva MP blends should be within about 1 psi (7 kPa, 0.07 bar) of normal system operation with CFC-12 for most medium temperature applications. Compressor discharge pressures will typically be about 10–20 psi (70–140 kPa, 0.7–1.4 bar) higher than normal system operation with CFC-12. For Suva MP66 retrofits of R-500 equipment, compressor discharge pressures will be about 5 psi (34 kPa, 0.34 bar) higher, and compressor suction pressures about 3 psi (18 kPa, 0.18 bar) lower than with R-500.

The Suva MP blends are more sensitive to charge size than CFC-12, therefore system peformance will change more quickly if the system is overcharged (or undercharged) with the Suva MP blends. See the section "How to Determine Suction Pressure, Super Heat, and Subcool" at the end of this guideline for additional information on optimizing system performance.

NOTE: Sight glasses in the liquid line can be used for charging in most systems; however, it is recommended that the initial system charge be determined by measuring operating conditions (discharge and suction pressures, suction line temperature, compressor amps, superheat, etc.). If the sight glass is close to the exit of the condenser or there is very little subcooling prior to the sight glass, bubbles may still be observed in the sight glass when the system is properly charged. Attempting to charge until the sight glass is clear may result in overcharging of refrigerant.

NOTE: Label Components and System. After retrofitting the system with one of the Suva MP blends, label the system components to identify the type of refrigerant (Suva MP39 or Suva MP66) and lubricant (alkylbenzene) in the system, so that the proper referigerant and lubricant will be used to service the equipment in the future. Identification labels are available at your DuPont Authorized Distributor.

Summary

Using the procedures described above, existing CFC-12 and R-500 refrigeration systems can be retrofitted for use with Suva MP39 or Suva MP66, allowing them to continue in service for the remainder of their useful life.

Attached is a Retrofit Checklist, System Data Sheet, and pressure–temperature charts for Suva MP39 and Suva MP66 to assist you in the retrofit process.

Pressure/Temperature Relationship of Suva MP Blends

Temperature Glide

Temperature glide occurs in both the evaporator and the condenser. In the evaporator, assuming constant pressure, the refrigerant blend begins to boil at one temperature and completes boiling at a higher temperature. The difference in these boiling temperatures is called temperature glide. This also occurs in the condenser, except the temperature decreases as the refrigerant vapor condenses. The temperature glide for the Suva MP blends will be in the 8–10°F (4–5°C) range.

How to Read the Tables

Tables 2a and *2b* show the pressure/temperature relationship of Suva MP39 compared with CFC-12; *Tables 3a* and *3b* show the pressure/temperature relationship of Suva MP66 compared with CFC-12 and R-500. As you can see, there are three temperatures shown at a given pressure:

Saturated Liquid Temperature (Bubble Point)—in the condenser, this is the temperature at which the last bit of vapor has condensed. Below this temperature, the refrigerant will be subcooled liquid. This temperature should also be used when determining the pressure/temperature in the refrigerant cylinder.

Saturated Vapor Temperature (Dew Point)—in the evaporator, this is the temperature at which the last drop of liquid has just boiled. Above this temperature, the refrigerant will be superheated vapor.

Average Coil Temperature—the evaporator or condenser will perform like it is operating at this constant temperature. Based on the suction or condenser pressure, use this average temperature to compare coil temperatures (i.e., evaporator or condenser temperatures) with CFC-12 or R-500. For Suva MP39 and Suva MP66, the Average Evaporator Temperature is approximately 4°F (2°C) *lower* than the Saturated Vapor Temperature; the Average Condenser Temperature is approximately 4°F (2°C) *higher* than the Saturated Liquid Temperature.

How to Determine Suction Pressure, Superheat, and Subcool

Suction Pressure

1. Determine the expected evaporator temperature using the CFC-12 or R-500 column (baseline data).
2. Find the same expected evaporator temperature in the "Average Coil Temperature" column for Suva MP39 or Suva MP66, and note the corresponding pressure for this temperature. This is the suction pressure at which the system should operate. (See definition of Average Coil Temperature in previous section for relationship of Saturated Liquid and Saturated Vapor of Suva MP39 and Suva MP66 with Average Coil Temperature.)

Superheat

Using the "Saturated Vapor Temperature" column for Suva MP39 or Suva MP66, the amount of vapor superheat is calculated in the same manner as for CFC-12 and R-500.

Subcool

Using the "Saturated Liquid Temperature" column for Suva MP39 or Suva MP66, the amount of liquid subcool is calculated in the same manner as for CFC-12 and R-500.

Table 2a
Pressure–Temperature Chart
Suva MP39 (psig/°F)

Pressure psig	R-12 Sat. Temp. (°F)	Suva MP39 Sat. Liquid Temp. (°F)	Suva MP39 Sat. Vapor Temp. (°F)	Suva MP39 Avg. Coil Temp. (°F)
20*	–63	–67	–55	–60
15*	–49	–53	–42	–47
10*	–38	–43	–32	–37
5*	–29	–35	–23	–28
0	–22	–27	–16	–21
2	–16	–22	–11	–15
4	–11	–17	–6	–10
6	–7	–13	–2	–6
8	–2	–9	2	–2
10	2	–5	6	2
12	5	–2	9	5
14	9	2	13	9
16	12	5	16	12
18	15	8	19	15
20	18	11	21	17
22	21	14	24	20
24	24	16	27	23
26	27	19	29	25
28	29	21	32	28
30	32	24	34	30
32	34	26	36	32
34	37	28	38	34
36	39	30	40	36
38	41	32	42	38
40	43	34	44	40
42	45	36	46	42
44	47	38	48	44
46	49	40	50	46
48	51	42	52	48
50	53	44	54	50
55	58	48	58	54
60	62	52	62	58
65	66	56	66	62
70	70	59	69	65
75	74	63	73	69
80	77	66	76	71
85	81	69	79	74
90	84	73	82	78
95	87	76	85	81
100	90	78	88	83
105	93	81	90	86
110	96	84	93	89
115	99	87	96	92
120	102	89	98	94
125	104	92	101	97

Pressure psig	R-12 Sat. . Temp. (°F)	Suva MP39 Sat. Liquid Temp. (°F)	Suva MP39 Sat. Vapor Temp. (°F)	Suva MP39 Avg. Coil Temp. (°F)
130	107	94	103	99
135	109	96	105	101
140	112	99	107	103
145	114	101	110	106
150	117	103	112	108
155	119	105	114	110
160	121	108	116	112
165	123	110	118	114
170	125	112	120	116
175	128	114	122	118
180	130	116	124	120
185	132	117	126	122
190	134	119	127	123
195	136	121	129	125
200	138	123	131	128
205	139	125	133	129
210	141	126	134	130
215	143	128	136	132
220	145	130	138	134
225	147	131	139	135
230	148	133	141	137
235	150	135	142	139
240	152	136	144	140
245	154	138	145	142
250	155	139	147	143
255	157	141	148	145
260	158	142	150	146
265	160	144	151	148
270	162	145	153	149
275	163	147	154	151
280	165	148	155	152
285	166	150	157	154
290	168	151	158	155
295	169	152	159	156
300	170	154	161	158
310	173	156	163	160
320	176	159	166	163
330	179	162	168	165
340	182	164	170	167
350	184	167	173	170
360	187	169	175	172
370	189	171	177	174
380	192	174	180	177
390	194	176	182	179
400	196	178	184	181

* Inches Mercury Below One Atmosphere

Table 2b
Pressure–Temperature Chart
Suva MP39 (kPa/°C)

Pressure kPa (abs)	R-12 Sat. Temp. (°C)	Suva MP39 Sat. Liquid Temp. (°C)	Suva MP39 Sat. Vapor Temp. (°C)	Suva MP39 Avg. Coil Temp. (°C)
20	–62.0	–64.0	–57.5	–60.0
40	–49.5	–52.0	–45.5	–48.0
60	–41.5	–44.0	–37.5	–40.0
80	–35.0	–38.0	–32.0	–34.5
100	–30.0	–33.5	–27.0	–29.5
110	–28.0	–31.0	–25.0	–27.5
120	–25.5	–29.0	–23.0	–25.5
130	–24.0	–27.0	–21.0	–23.5
140	–22.0	–25.5	–19.5	–22.0
150	–20.0	–24.0	–17.5	–20.0
160	–18.5	–22.0	–16.0	–18.5
170	–17.0	–20.5	–14.5	–17.0
180	–15.5	–19.5	–13.0	–15.5
190	–14.0	–18.0	–12.0	–14.5
200	–12.5	–16.5	–10.5	–13.0
210	–11.0	–15.5	–9.5	–12.0
220	–10.0	–14.0	–8.0	–10.5
230	–8.5	–13.0	–7.0	–9.5
240	–7.5	–11.5	–6.0	–8.0
250	–6.0	–10.5	–4.5	–7.0
260	–5.0	–9.5	–3.5	–6.0
270	–4.0	–8.5	–2.5	–5.0
280	–3.0	–7.5	–1.5	–4.0
290	–2.0	–6.5	–0.5	–3.0
300	–1.0	–5.5	0.5	–2.0
310	0.0	–4.5	1.5	–1.0
320	1.0	–3.5	2.0	0.0
330	2.0	–2.5	3.0	1.0
340	3.0	–2.0	4.0	1.5
350	4.0	–1.0	4.5	2.5
375	6.0	1.0	7.0	4.5
400	8.0	3.0	8.5	6.5
425	10.0	5.0	10.5	8.5
450	12.0	7.0	12.5	10.5
475	14.0	8.5	14.0	12.0
500	15.5	10.0	15.5	13.5
525	17.5	11.5	17.0	15.0
550	19.0	13.0	18.5	16.5
575	20.5	14.5	20.0	18.0
600	22.0	16.0	21.5	19.5
625	23.5	17.5	23.0	21.0
650	25.0	19.0	24.0	22.0
675	26.5	20.0	25.5	23.5
700	27.5	21.5	26.5	24.5
725	29.0	22.5	28.0	26.0
750	30.5	24.0	29.0	26.5
775	31.5	25.0	30.0	27.5
800	33.0	26.5	31.5	29.0
825	34.0	27.5	32.5	30.0
850	35.0	28.5	33.5	31.0
900	37.5	30.5	35.5	33.0
950	39.5	32.5	37.5	35.0
1000	41.5	34.5	39.5	37.0
1050	43.5	36.5	41.5	39.0
1100	45.5	38.5	43.0	40.5
1150	47.5	40.0	45.0	42.5
1200	49.5	42.0	46.5	44.0
1250	51.0	43.5	48.0	45.5
1300	53.0	45.0	49.5	47.0
1350	54.5	46.5	51.0	48.5
1400	56.0	48.0	52.5	50.0
1450	57.5	49.5	54.0	51.5
1500	59.0	51.0	55.5	53.0
1550	60.5	52.5	57.0	54.5
1600	62.0	54.0	58.0	56.0
1650	63.5	55.0	59.5	57.0
1700	65.0	56.5	60.5	58.5
1750	66.5	58.0	62.0	60.0
1800	68.0	59.0	63.0	61.0
1850	69.0	60.5	64.5	62.5
1900	70.5	61.5	65.5	63.5
1950	71.5	62.5	66.5	64.5
2000	73.0	64.0	68.0	66.0
2050	74.0	65.0	69.0	67.0
2100	75.5	66.0	70.0	68.0
2150	76.5	67.0	71.0	69.0
2200	77.5	68.5	72.0	70.5
2250	79.0	69.5	73.0	71.5
2300	80.0	70.5	74.0	72.5
2350	81.0	71.5	75.0	73.5
2400	82.0	72.5	76.0	74.5
2450	83.0	73.5	77.0	75.5
2500	84.0	74.5	78.0	76.5
2600	86.5	76.5	80.0	78.5
2700	88.5	78.5	81.5	80.0
2800	90.0	80.0	83.5	82.0
2900	92.0	82.0	85.0	83.5
3000	94.0	83.5	86.5	85.0
3100	96.0	85.5	88.0	87.0
3200	97.5	87.0	90.0	88.5

Table 3a
Pressure–Temperature Chart
Suva MP66 (psig/°F)

Pressure psig	R-12 Sat. Temp. (°F)	R-500 Sat. Temp. (°F)	Suva MP66 Sat. Liquid Temp. (°F)	Suva MP66 Sat. Vapor Temp. (°F)	Suva MP66 Avg. Coil Temp. (°F)
20*	–63	–69	–70	–59	–64
15*	–49	–55	–56	–45	–50
10*	–38	–44	–46	–35	–40
5*	–29	–36	–37	–27	–31
0	–22	–28	–30	–20	–24
2	–16	–23	–25	–14	–18
4	–11	–18	–20	–10	–14
6	–7	–14	–16	–6	–10
8	–2	–10	–12	–2	–6
10	2	–6	–8	2	–2
12	5	–2	–5	6	2
14	9	1	–1	9	5
16	12	4	2	12	8
18	15	7	5	15	11
20	18	10	8	18	14
22	21	13	10	20	16
24	24	16	13	23	19
26	27	18	15	25	21
28	29	21	18	28	24
30	32	23	20	30	26
32	34	26	22	32	28
34	37	28	25	34	30
36	39	30	27	37	33
38	41	32	29	39	35
40	43	34	31	41	37
42	45	36	33	42	38
44	47	38	35	44	40
46	49	40	37	46	42
48	51	42	38	48	44
50	53	44	40	50	46
55	58	48	44	54	50
60	62	52	48	58	54
65	66	56	52	61	57
70	70	60	56	65	61
75	74	63	59	68	64
80	77	67	63	72	68
85	81	70	66	75	71
90	84	73	69	78	74
95	87	76	72	81	77
100	90	79	75	83	79
105	93	82	77	86	81
110	96	84	80	89	84
115	99	87	83	91	87
120	102	90	85	94	89
125	104	92	88	96	92

Pressure psig	R-12 Sat. Temp. (°F)	R-500 Sat. Temp. (°F)	Suva MP66 Sat. Liquid Temp. (°F)	Suva MP66 Sat. Vapor Temp. (°F)	Suva MP66 Avg. Coil Temp. (°F)
130	107	95	90	99	94
135	109	97	93	101	97
140	112	99	95	103	99
145	114	102	97	105	101
150	117	104	99	107	103
155	119	106	101	109	105
160	121	108	103	111	107
165	123	110	106	113	110
170	125	112	108	115	112
175	128	114	109	117	113
180	130	116	111	119	115
185	132	118	113	121	117
190	134	120	115	123	119
195	136	122	117	125	121
200	138	124	119	126	123
205	139	126	121	128	125
210	141	128	122	130	126
215	143	129	124	131	128
220	145	131	126	133	130
225	147	133	127	135	131
230	148	134	129	136	133
235	150	136	130	138	134
240	152	138	132	139	136
245	154	139	134	141	138
250	155	141	135	142	139
255	157	142	137	144	141
260	158	144	138	145	142
265	160	145	140	146	143
270	162	147	141	148	145
275	163	148	142	149	146
280	165	150	144	151	148
285	166	151	145	152	149
290	168	153	147	153	150
295	169	154	148	155	152
300	170	155	149	156	153
310	173	158	152	158	155
320	176	161	155	161	158
330	179	163	157	163	160
340	182	166	160	166	163
350	184	168	162	168	165
360	187	171	164	170	167
370	189	173	167	172	170
380	192	176	169	175	172
390	194	178	171	177	174
400	196	180	174	179	177

* Inches Mercury Below One Atmosphere

Table 3b
Pressure–Temperature Chart
Suva MP66 (kPa/°C)

Pressure kPa (abs)	R-12 Sat. Temp. (°C)	R-500 Sat. Temp. (°C)	Suva MP66 Sat. Liquid Temp. (°C)	Suva MP66 Sat. Vapor Temp. (°C)	Suva MP66 Avg. Coil Temp. (°C)
20	–62.0	–65.0	–65.5	–59.0	–62.0
40	–49.5	–53.0	–53.5	–47.0	–50.0
60	–41.5	–45.0	–45.5	–39.5	–42.0
80	–35.0	–39.0	–39.5	–33.5	–36.0
100	–30.0	–33.0	–35.0	–29.0	–31.5
110	–28.0	–31.5	–32.5	–27.0	–29.5
120	–25.5	–29.5	–30.5	–25.0	–27.5
130	–24.0	–27.5	–29.0	–23.0	–25.5
140	–22.0	–26.0	–27.0	–21.5	–24.0
150	–20.0	–24.0	–25.5	–19.5	–22.0
160	–18.5	–22.5	–24.0	–18.0	–20.5
170	–17.0	–21.0	–22.5	–16.5	–19.0
180	–15.5	–19.5	–21.0	–15.0	–17.5
190	–14.0	–18.0	–19.5	–14.0	–16.5
200	–12.5	–17.0	–18.5	–12.5	–15.0
210	–11.0	–15.5	–17.0	–11.5	–14.0
220	–10.0	–14.5	–16.0	–10.0	–12.5
230	–8.5	–13.0	–14.5	–9.0	–11.5
240	–7.5	–12.0	–13.5	–8.0	–10.5
250	–6.0	–11.0	–12.5	–7.0	–9.5
260	–5.0	–9.5	–11.5	–5.5	–8.0
270	–4.0	–8.5	–10.5	–4.5	–7.0
280	–3.0	–7.5	–9.5	–3.5	–6.0
290	–2.0	–6.5	–8.5	–2.5	–5.0
300	–1.0	–5.5	–7.5	–2.0	–4.5
310	0.0	–4.5	–6.5	–1.0	–3.5
320	1.0	–3.5	–5.5	0.0	–2.5
330	2.0	–3.0	–4.5	1.0	–1.5
340	3.0	–2.0	–3.5	1.5	–0.5
350	4.0	–1.0	–3.0	2.5	0.0
375	6.0	1.0	–1.0	4.5	2.0
400	8.0	3.0	1.0	6.5	4.0
425	10.0	5.0	3.0	8.5	6.0
450	12.0	6.5	5.0	10.0	8.0
475	14.0	8.5	6.5	11.5	9.5
500	15.5	10.0	8.0	13.5	11.0
525	17.5	11.5	9.5	15.0	12.5
550	19.0	13.5	11.0	16.5	14.0
575	20.5	15.0	12.5	18.0	15.5
600	22.0	16.0	14.0	19.0	17.0
625	23.5	17.5	15.5	20.5	18.5
650	25.0	19.0	17.0	22.0	20.0
675	26.5	20.5	18.0	23.0	21.0
700	27.5	21.5	19.5	24.5	22.5
725	29.0	23.0	20.5	25.5	23.5

Pressure kPa (abs)	R-12 Sat. Temp. (°C)	R-500 Sat. Temp. (°C)	Suva MP66 Sat. Liquid Temp. (°C)	Suva MP66 Sat. Vapor Temp. (°C)	Suva MP66 Avg. Coil Temp. (°C)
750	30.5	24.0	22.0	26.5	24.5
775	31.5	25.5	23.0	28.0	25.5
800	33.0	26.5	24.0	29.0	26.5
825	34.0	27.5	25.5	30.0	27.5
850	35.0	28.5	26.5	31.0	28.5
900	37.5	31.0	28.5	33.0	30.5
950	39.5	33.0	30.5	35.0	32.5
1000	41.5	35.0	32.5	37.0	34.5
1050	43.5	37.0	34.5	39.0	36.5
1100	45.5	39.0	36.0	40.5	38.0
1150	47.5	40.5	38.0	42.5	40.0
1200	49.5	42.5	39.5	44.0	41.5
1250	51.0	44.0	41.0	45.5	43.0
1300	53.0	45.5	43.0	47.0	45.0
1350	54.5	47.0	44.5	48.5	46.5
1400	56.0	48.5	46.0	50.0	48.0
1450	57.5	50.0	47.5	51.5	49.5
1500	59.0	51.5	49.0	53.0	51.0
1550	60.5	53.0	50.0	54.5	52.0
1600	62.0	54.5	51.5	55.5	53.5
1650	63.5	56.0	53.0	57.0	55.0
1700	65.0	57.0	54.0	58.0	56.0
1750	66.5	58.5	55.5	59.5	57.5
1800	68.0	60.0	56.5	60.5	58.5
1850	69.0	61.0	58.0	62.0	60.0
1900	70.5	62.5	59.0	63.0	61.0
1950	71.5	63.5	60.5	64.0	62.5
2000	73.0	64.5	61.5	65.0	63.5
2050	74.0	66.0	62.5	66.5	64.5
2100	75.5	67.0	63.5	67.5	65.5
2150	76.5	68.0	65.0	68.5	67.0
2200	77.5	69.0	66.0	69.5	68.0
2250	79.0	70.5	67.0	70.5	69.0
2300	80.0	71.5	68.0	71.5	70.0
2350	81.0	72.5	69.0	72.5	71.0
2400	82.0	73.5	70.0	73.5	72.0
2450	83.0	74.5	71.0	74.5	73.0
2500	84.0	75.5	72.0	75.5	74.0
2600	86.5	77.5	74.0	77.0	75.5
2700	88.5	79.5	76.0	79.0	77.5
2800	90.0	81.0	77.5	80.5	79.0
2900	92.0	83.0	79.5	82.5	81.0
3000	94.0	84.5	81.0	84.0	82.5
3100	96.0	86.5	83.0	85.5	84.5
3200	97.5	88.0	84.5	87.0	86.0

Checklist for Suva MP39 or Suva MP66 Retrofit

________ 1. Establish baseline performance with CFC-12 or R-500.
(See data sheet for recommended data.)

________ 2. Remove CFC-12 or R-500 charge from system.
(Need 10–15 in. Hg vacuum [50–67 kPa, 0.50–0.67 bar] to remove charge.)
- Use recovery cylinder/*Do Not Vent to Atmosphere*
- Weigh amount removed (if possible): ____________

________ 3. Drain lubricant charge from compressor (unless alkylbenzene lubricant is already in compressor).
- Measure amount of lubricant removed and record: ______________________

________ 4. Charge alkylbenzene lubricant.
- Recharge with amount equivalent to amount removed in *Step 3*.
- Reinstall compressor (if removed).

________ 5. Replace filter drier with new drier approved for use with Suva MP blends.
- Loose fill driers: use XH-9 desiccant or equivalent
- Compacted bead driers: use XH-9 or XH-6 desiccant or equivalent
- Solid core driers: check with drier manufacturer for recommendation

________ 6. Reconnect system and evacuate with vacuum pump. (Evacuate to full vacuum [29.9 in. Hg vacuum/500 microns/0.14 kPa/0.0014 bar]).
- Leak check system. (Reevacuate system following leak check.)

________ 7. Charge system with Suva MP39 or Suva MP66
- Remove ***Liquid Only*** from cylinder
- Initial charge 70–75% by weight of original CFC-12 charge
- Initial charge 100% by weight of original R-500 charge
- Amount of refrigerant charged: ____________

________ 8. Adjust charge until desired operating conditions are achieved.
- Remove ***Liquid Only*** from cylinder
- If low in charge, add in increments of 3–5% of original CFC-12 or R-500 charge.
- Amount of refrigerant charged: ____________

Total Refrigerant Charged (add 7 and 8) ____________

- Label components and system for type of refrigerant (Suva MP39/Suva MP66) and lubricant (alkylbenzene).

Retrofit is complete!!

System Data Sheet

Type of System/Location: ____________________

Equipment Mfg.: ____________________ Compressor Mfg.: ____________________

Model No.: ____________________ Model No.: ____________________

Serial No.: ____________________ Serial No.: ____________________

CFC-12/R-500 charge size: ____________________ Lubricant type: ____________________

Charge size: ____________________

Drier Mfg.: ____________________ Drier type (check one):

Model No.: ____________________ Loose fill: ____________________

Solid core: ____________________

Condenser cooling medium (air/water): ____________________

Expansion Device (check one): Capillary tube: __________

Expansion valve: __________

If Expansion valve:

Manufacturer: ____________________

Model No.: ____________________

Control/set point: ____________________

Location of sensor: ____________________

Other System Controls (ex.: head press control), Describe: ____________________

____

(circle units used where applicable)

Date/Time				
Refrigerant				
Charge Size (lb, oz/grams)				
Ambient Temp. (°F/°C)				
Relative Humidity				
Compressor:				
Suction T (°F/°C)				
Suction P (psig, psia/kPa, bar)				
Discharge T (°F/°C)				
Discharge P (psig, psia/kPa, bar)				
Box/Fixture T (°F/°C)				
Evaporator:				
Refrigerant Inlet T (°F/°C)				
Refrigerant Outlet T (°F/°C)				
Coil Air/H_2O In T (°F/°C)				
Coil Air/H_2O Out T (°F/°C)				
Refrigerant T at Superht. Ctl. Pt. (°F/°C)				
Condenser:				
Refrigerant Inlet T (°F/°C)				
Refrigerant Outlet T (°F/°C)				
Coil Air/H_2O In T (°F/°C)				
Coil Air/H_2O Out T (°F/°C)				
Exp. Device Inlet T (°F/°C)				
Motor Amps				
Run/Cycle Time				

Comments: ____________________

____

For Sales Information:

DuPont Fluorochemicals
Customer Service Center, B-15305
Wilmington, DE 19898
U.S.A.
(302) 774-2099
800-441-9442

For Technical Information:

Fluorochemicals Laboratory
Wilmington, DE 19898
U.S.A.
(302) 999-3129
800-582-5606

Europe

DuPont de Nemours
International S.A.
2 Chemin du Pavillon
P.O. Box 50
CH-1218 Le Grand-Saconnex
Geneva, Switzerland
41-22-717-5111

Canada

DuPont Canada, Inc.
P.O. Box 2200, Streetsville
Mississauga, Ontario
Canada
L5M 2H3
(905) 821-3300

Mexico

DuPont, S.A. de C.V.
Homero 206
Col. Chapultepec Morales
C.P. 11570 Mexico, D.F.
52-5-250-8000

South America

DuPont do Brasil S.A.
Alameda Itapecuru, 506
Alphaville 06400 Barueri
São Paulo, Brazil
55-11-421-8509

DuPont Argentina S.A.
Casilla Correo 1888
Correo Central
1000 Buenos Aires, Argentina
54-1-311-8167

Pacific

DuPont Australia
P.O. Box 930
North Sydney, NSW 2060
Australia
61-2-923-6165

Japan

Mitsui DuPont Fluorochemicals
Co., Ltd.
Mitsui Seimei Bldg.
2-3, 1-Chome Ohtemachi
Chiyoda-Ku, Tokyo 100 Japan
81-3-3216-8451

Asia

DuPont Taiwan
P.O. Box 81-777
Taipei, Taiwan
886-2-514-4400

DuPont Asia Pacific Limited
P.O. Box TST 98851
Tsim Sha Tsui
Kowloon, Hong Kong
852-734-5345

DuPont Thailand
P.O. Box 2398
Bangkok 10501, Thailand
66-2-238-4361

DuPont China Ltd.
Rm. 1704, Union Bldg.
100 Yenan Rd. East
Shanghai, PR China 200 002
Phone: 86-21-328-3738
Telex: 33448 DCLSH CN
Fax: 86-21-320-2304

DuPont Far East Inc.
P.O. Box 12396
50776 Kuala Lumpur, Malaysia
Phone: 60-3-232-3522
Telex: (784) 30391 DUFE M
Fax: 60-3-238-7250

DuPont Korea Ltd.
C.P.O. Box 5972
Seoul, Korea
82-2-721-5114

DuPont Singapore Pte. Ltd.
1 Maritime Square #07 01
World Trade Centre
Singapore 0409
65-273-2244

DuPont Far East, Philippines
5th Floor, Solid Bank Bldg.
777 Paseo de Roxas
Makati, Metro Manila
Philippines
63-2-818-9911

DuPont Far East Inc.
7A Murray's Gate Road
Alwarpet
Madras, 600 018, India
91-44-454-029

DuPont Far East Inc.—Pakistan
9 Khayaban-E-Shaheen
Defence Phase 5
Karachi, Pakistan
92-21-533-350

DuPont Far East Inc.
P.O. Box 2553/Jkt
Jakarta 10001, Indonesia
62-21-517-800

(12/93) 231598B Printed in U.S.A.
[Replaces: H-42446-1]
Reorder No.: H-42446-2

Suva®

alternative refrigerants

ART-24

Suva Refrigerants for Replacing R12 and R502—Quick Reference

R12 Replacements

Suva	Applications*	Retrofit Notes
MP39	• Commercial retrofits above –10°F (–23°C) evaporator	• One oil change required • Use alkylbenzene lubricant • Better capacity than R12
MP66	• Commercial retrofits below –10°F (–23°C) evaporator • Some truck/trailer retrofits	• One oil change required • Use alkylbenzene lubricant
Cold-MP (HFC-134a)	• All new equipment • Retrofits above 20°F (–7°C) evaporator	• Minimum of three oil changes required • Use polyol ester lubricant • Lower capacity than R12 below 20°F (–7°C) evaporator

R502 Replacements

Suva	Applications*	Retrofit Notes
HP80	• All commercial retrofits	• One oil change required • Use alkylbenzene lubricant • Better capacity than R502
HP81	• Retrofits of ice machines and other self-contained equipment • New ice machines	• One oil change required • Use alkylbenzene lubricant • Better efficiency than R502
HP62	• All new equipment • All commercial retrofits	• Minimum of three oil changes required • Use polyol ester lubricant • Lower discharge temp. than R502

* Consult manufacturer for specific recommendations.

What to Expect After a Typical Retrofit to a Suva Refrigerant (Based on Field Experience)

Suva	Discharge Pressure	Suction Pressure	Discharge Temperature	Refrigeration Capacity	Refrigerant Superheat (without adjusting the TXV)	Energy Efficiency
MP39	+ 20 psi (140 kPa)	Same	+ 20°F (11°C)	+ 10%	– 3°F (2°C)	Small +
MP66	+ 30 psi (210 kPa)	Same	+ 30°F (17°C)	+ 15%	+ 2°F (1°C)	Small +
R134a	+ 30 psi (210 kPa)	– 3 psi (21 kPa)	– 5°F (3°C)	– 10%	– 4°F (2°C)	Small –
HP80	+ 40 psi (275 kPa)	+ 3 psi (21 kPa)	Same	+ 10%	+ 4°F (2°C)	Small –
HP81	+ 30 psi (210 kPa)	Same	+ 15°F (8°C)	+ 5%	+ 1°F (2°C)	Small +
HP62	+ 30 psi (210 kPa)	Same	– 15°F (8°C)	Same	+ 2°F (1°C)	Small –

+ = increase
– = decrease

Notes: MP39, MP66, and R134a are compared to R12
HP80, HP81, and HP62 are compared to R502

Sightglass
Can't always use this to determine charge size. Sometimes system is properly charged, but bubbles still appear. Use suction and discharge pressure, superheat, subcooling, motor amps, receiver level, etc. to determine if system is properly charged.

Compressor Motor Amps
Small increase for all refrigerants. Motor run time will decrease slightly for all refrigerants except R134a.

Charge Size
All refrigerants are typically 80–90% (by weight) of the R12 or R502 charge.

TXV or Capillary Tube
Almost never change; may need to adjust superheat.

Suction Pressure Cut-in/Cut-out Switch
May need to adjust; use PT chart to determine new setting.

Condenser Sizing
Most systems are OK. Some systems in hot climates will have insufficient condenser capacity causing unacceptably high discharge pressure.System modifications will be necessary when this happens.

> ***Note:*** This information is intended to serve as a guide; actual performance may vary.

For Sales Information:
DuPont Fluorochemicals
Customer Service Center, B-15305
Wilmington, DE 19898 U.S.A.
(302) 774-2099 or 800-441-9442

For Technical Information:
Fluorochemicals Laboratory
Wilmington, DE 19898 U.S.A.
(302) 999-3129 or 800-582-5606

Europe
DuPont de Nemours International S.A.
Switzerland
41-22-717-5111

Canada
DuPont Canada, Inc.
(905) 821-3300

Mexico
DuPont, S.A. de C.V.
52-5-250-8000

South America
DuPont do Brasil S.A.
55-11-421-8509

DuPont Argentina S.A.
54-1-311-8167

Pacific
DuPont Australia
61-2-923-6165

Japan
Mitsui DuPont Fluorochemicals Co., Ltd.
81-3-3216-8451

Asia
DuPont Taiwan
886-2-514-4400

DuPont Asia Pacific Limited
852-734-5345

DuPont Thailand
66-2-238-4361

DuPont China Ltd.
86-21-328-3738

DuPont Far East Inc.
60-3-232-3522

DuPont Korea Ltd.
82-2-721-5114

DuPont Singapore Pte. Ltd.
65-273-2244

DuPont Far East, Philippines
63-2-818-9911

DuPont Far East Inc.
India
91-44-454-029

DuPont Far East Inc.—Pakistan
92-21-533-350

DuPont Far East Inc.
Indonesia
62-21-517-800

(11/93) 235727A Printed in U.S.A.
Reorder No.: H-53020

refrigerants

ART-14

Properties and Performance of Suva AC9000 in Air Conditioners and Heat Pumps

Introduction

Chlorodifluoromethane (R-22 or HCFC-22) has been commercially available for use in various refrigeration, industrial cooling, air conditioning, and heat pump applications for over five decades. The low ozone depletion potential of HCFC-22 compared to CFC-11 and CFC-12 and its excellent refrigerant properties have helped facilitate the transition away from CFCs. However, as national and international policy makers continue to strengthen regulations towards the protection of the ozone layer, HCFC-22 and other HCFCs (hydrochlorofluorocarbons) will be phased out. DuPont has announced it will stop production of HCFC-22 for refrigerant sales for new equipment in 2005 and as a service refrigerant in 2020. By identifying potential alternatives for HCFC-22 today, DuPont provides equipment manufacturers and users with time to fully test HCFC-22 alternatives before they are needed.

DuPont has developed Suva AC9000 as the equivalent pressure replacement for HCFC-22 in positive displacement, direct expansion air conditioners and heat pumps.

Lower pressure and higher pressure alternatives to HCFC-22 are also being developed. These products will have either niche applications or be future original equipment alternatives for HCFC-22, as they will require extensive equipment design changes to be used in HCFC-22 air conditioner and heat pump applications. DuPont is also investigating alternatives for HCFC-22 in applications like chiller and industrial cooling systems, and will announce these alternatives in the near future.

Environmental and Safety Properties of Suva AC9000

Suva AC9000 is a ternary mixture of hydrofluorocarbons (HFCs) HFC-32, HFC-125, and HFC-134a in the ratio of 23/25/52 weight percent. Suva AC9000 has zero ozone depletion and the same global warming potential as HCFC-22 (see **Table 1**).

Table 1
Environmental and Safety Properties of Suva AC9000 versus HCFC-22

	Suva AC9000	HCFC-22
Ozone Depletion Potential (CFC-11 = 1.0)	0.00	0.055
Global Warming Potential (CO_2 = 1.0 ([100 year ITH])*	1600	1600
Flammable	No	No

*Integrated Time Horizon

The components of Suva AC9000 have undergone extensive toxicity testing by the Program for Alternative Fluorocarbon Toxicity Testing (PAFT). Results from this testing indicate that the components of Suva AC9000 have very low toxicity. The calculated DuPont Acceptable Exposure Limit (AEL), based upon the AEL for each component, is 1000 ppm, 8- and 12-hour time weighted average (TWA). This AEL is similar to the Threshold Limit Value (TLV) established for HCFC-22.

Suva AC9000 liquid and vapor compositions are nonflammable and will remain nonflammable during shipping, storage, handling, and use in equipment.

Table 2
Performance of Suva AC9000 Relative to HCFC-22 in Multiple Air Conditioners and Heat Pumps

	Suva AC9000		Suva AC9000
Range of Performance: Cooling Mode*		**Range of Performance: Heating Mode****	
Relative Capacity	98% to 103%	Relative Capacity	93% to 106%
Relative Energy Efficiency Ratio (EER)	93% to 97%	Relative Energy Efficiency Ratio (EER)	94% to 97%
Change in Discharge Temperature	−15°F to −8°F (−8.3°C to −4.4°C)	Change in Discharge Temperature	−18°F to 0°F (−10°C to 0°C)
Change in Discharge Pressure	+15 psi to +40 psi (+1.03 bar [+103 kPa] to +2.76 bar [+276 kPa])	Change in Discharge Pressure	+9 psi to +34 psi (+0.62 bar [+62 kPa] to +2.34 bar [+234 kPa])

* Values compared to HCFC-22 in unmodified split system heat pumps and an unmodified window air conditioner using the DOE cooling test conditions A and B.

** Values compared to HCFC-22 in unmodified split system heat pumps and an unmodified window air conditioner using the DOE heating test conditions E and H.

Performance Characteristics in Existing HCFC-22 Designs

At typical air conditioner and heat pump conditions, Suva AC9000 performs comparably to HCFC-22 in existing positive displacement, direct expansion equipment. **Table 2** summarizes the actual performance of Suva AC9000 versus HCFC-22 (cooling and heating modes) in different units designed for HCFC-22. The units were not modified or optimized for performance with Suva AC9000. Department of Energy (DOE) standard test conditions for cooling (test conditions A and B) and heating (test conditions E and H) were used for this comparison.

These results show that Suva AC9000 is an alternative for HCFC-22 that can be used not only in new equipment but also to service existing HCFC-22 equipment. Due to the increase in discharge pressure, it will be necessary to contact the original equipment manufacturer to determine if discharge pressure controls will need to be adjusted to compensate for the higher discharge pressure of Suva AC9000.

Even better performance will be achieved when modifications to heat pump and air conditioning equipment are made to optimize it for use with Suva AC9000.

Influence of Leak/Recharge on Performance

Suva AC9000 has excellent refrigerant behavior even in the event of vapor leaks from a two-phase region of a refrigeration system and subsequent refrigerant recharges.

If there is a Suva AC9000 leak from an operating unit in a two-phase region where mixing occurs (heat exchangers or after expansion device), both vapor and liquid will leak from the unit. The composition of the refrigerant left in the system will remain essentially unchanged from the original composition. After recharging Suva AC9000 to the system to get back to the original charge size, the performance of the unit will be the same as its original performance with Suva AC9000.

However, if the unit is not operating and there is a vapor leak from a static two-phase region, the composition of the refrigerant that remains in the unit will change. The refrigerant remaining in the unit will be more concentrated in the high boiling component (HFC-134a) and less concentrated in the lower boiling components (HFC-32 and HFC-125). The effect of this composition shift on the performance of Suva AC9000 is summarized in **Table 3**. These data summarize the theoretical performance of Suva AC9000 for multiple recharges of the system after 50 weight percent of the refrigerant charge is lost through a vapor leak above a two-phase region.

Table 3
Theoretical Unit Performance After 50 Weight Percent Vapor Leaks and Recharges of Suva AC9000

Recharge No.	Rel. COP*	Rel. Cap.**	Compressor Discharge Temperature	Compressor Discharge Pressure
0	100%	100%	178°F (81.1°C)	261 psig (19.03 bar, 1903 kPa)
1	101%	95%	177°F (80.6°C)	246 psig (18.00 bar, 1800 kPa)
2	101%	93%	177°F (80.6°C)	239 psig (17.51 bar, 1751 kPa)
3	101%	92%	177°F (80.6°C)	236 psig (17.31 bar, 1731 kPa)
4	101%	91%	177°F (80.6°C)	235 psig (17.24 bar, 1724 kPa)
5	101%	91%	177°F (80.6°C)	235 psig (17.24 bar, 1724 kPa)

*Coefficient of Performance (measure of energy efficiency) relative to the Coefficient of Performance of the original charge of Suva AC9000.
**Refrigerant cooling capacity relative to the capacity of the original charge of Suva AC9000.

Three important observations from the data generated in this leak/recharge study are:

- During a vapor leak, the HFC-32 (which is the flammable component in the mixture) remaining in the system decreases in concentration.
- The energy efficiency and discharge temperature and pressure all moved in a favorable direction during the vapor leak/recharge scenario.
- The capacity loss is limited to 9% as the performance of Suva AC9000 levels out after four 50 weight percent leak/recharge scenarios.

Charging a Unit with Suva AC9000

As with any other refrigerant blend, when charging equipment with Suva AC9000, remove liquid refrigerant from the cylinder and then charge this to the unit. Suva AC9000 cylinders are equipped with liquid and vapor valves. The liquid valve is attached to a dip-tube that extends to the bottom of the cylinder so liquid refrigerant can be removed from the cylinder as it is standing upright.

Lubricants

Evaluations of lubricants for use with Suva AC9000 are currently being conducted. Because Suva AC9000 is an HFC refrigerant, for most applications, a lubricant other than mineral oil will be required. Polyol ester lubricants are being studied for use with Suva AC9000 as well as other HFC refrigerants. You may want to discuss specific lubricant recommendations with your compressor manufacturer.

Availability

Suva AC9000 is available now to original equipment manufacturers in test quantities for performance testing. DuPont expects commercial quantities of Suva AC9000 to be available by the mid-1990s.

Summary

Suva AC9000 offers performance and safety characteristics comparable to HCFC-22. Suva AC9000 is nonflammable, has a similar low order of toxicity as HCFC-22, and is formulated to yield comparable energy efficiency and refrigeration capacity under typical air conditioner/heat pump conditions. DuPont believes that it will be the preferred refrigerant for servicing of existing HCFC-22 systems and as an alternative for new equipment being put in the field as refrigerant HCFC-22 is phased out.

For General Information:

DuPont Fluorochemicals
Customer Service Center, B-15305
Wilmington, DE 19898
U.S.A.
In Delaware: (302) 995-2150
800-235-SUVA

For Technical Information:

Fluorochemicals Laboratory
Wilmington, DE 19898
U.S.A.
(302) 999-3129
800-582-5606

Europe

DuPont de Nemours
International S.A.
2 Chemin du Pavillon
P.O. Box 50
CH-1218 Le Grand-Saconnex
Geneva, Switzerland
41-22-717-5111

Canada

DuPont Canada, Inc.
P.O. Box 2200, Streetsville
Mississauga, Ontario
Canada
L5M 2H3
(905) 821-3300

Mexico

DuPont, S.A. de C.V.
Homero 206
Col. Chapultepec Morales
C.P. 11570 Mexico, D.F.
52-5-250-8000

South America

DuPont do Brasil S.A.
Alameda Itapecuru, 506
Alphaville 06400 Barueri
São Paulo, Brazil
55-11-421-8509

DuPont Argentina S.A.
Casilla Correo 1888
Correo Central
1000 Buenos Aires, Argentina
54-1-311-8167

Pacific

DuPont Australia
P.O. Box 930
North Sydney, NSW 2060
Australia
61-2-923-6165

Japan

Mitsui DuPont Fluorochemicals
Co., Ltd.
Mitsui Seimei Bldg.
2-3, 1-Chome Ohtemachi
Chiyoda-Ku, Tokyo 100 Japan
81-3-3216-8451

Asia

DuPont Taiwan
P.O. Box 81-777
Taipei, Taiwan
886-2-514-4400

DuPont Asia Pacific Limited
P.O. Box TST 98851
Tsim Sha Tsui
Kowloon, Hong Kong
852-734-5345

DuPont Thailand
P.O. Box 2398
Bangkok 10501, Thailand
66-2-238-4361

DuPont China Ltd.
Rm. 1704, Union Bldg.
100 Yenan Rd. East
Shanghai, PR China 200 002
Phone: 86-21-328-3738
Telex: 33448 DCLSH CN
Fax: 86-21-320-2304

DuPont Far East Inc.
P.O. Box 12396
50776 Kuala Lumpur, Malaysia
Phone: 60-3-232-3522
Telex: (784) 30391 DUFE M
Fax: 60-3-238-7250

DuPont Korea Ltd.
C.P.O. Box 5972
Seoul, Korea
82-2-721-5114

DuPont Singapore Pte. Ltd.
1 Maritime Square #07 01
World Trade Centre
Singapore 0409
65-273-2244

DuPont Far East, Philippines
5th Floor, Solid Bank Bldg.
777 Paseo de Roxas
Makati, Metro Manila
Philippines
63-2-818-9911

DuPont Far East Inc.
7A Murray's Gate Road
Alwarpet
Madras, 600 018, India
91-44-454-029

DuPont Far East Inc.—Pakistan
9 Khayaban-E-Shaheen
Defence Phase 5
Karachi, Pakistan
92-21-533-350

DuPont Far East Inc.
P.O. Box 2553/Jkt
Jakarta 10001, Indonesia
62-21-517-800

(1/94) 240731A Printed in U.S.A.
Reorder No.: H-47125-1

NEW EQUIPMENT — Medium Temperature

- HFC → **SUVA® Cold MP (134a)**
- HFC → **SUVA® HP62**
- HCFC → **R-22**

NEW EQUIPMENT — Low Temperature

- HFC → **SUVA® HP62 best for all applications**
- HCFC → **R-22**

EXISTING EQUIPMENT — Medium Temperature

HCFC →

From R-12:
- SUVA® MP39 best for most applications*
- SUVA® MP66 for low-temperature and transport applications*
- R-22 (may require compressor change)

From R-502:
- SUVA® HP80 best for most R-502 applications
- R-22 (may require compressor change)

HFC ** **→**

From R-12:
- SUVA® Cold MP best for evaporator temperatures above 20°F (-7°C)

From R-502:
- SUVA® HP62

EXISTING EQUIPMENT — Low Temperature

HCFC →

From R-12:
- SUVA® MP66 (for transport and some other applications)*
- R-22 (may require compressor change)

From R-502:
- SUVA® HP80 best for most R-502 applications*
- SUVA® HP81 for self-contained hermetic equipment*
- R-22 (may require compressor change)

HFC ** **→**

From R-502:
- SUVA® HP62 best for all applications

*** Retrofit to HCFC Service Refrigerant Notes:**
- Cheaper/easier than converting self-contained & some larger units to R-22 or HFC
- Single oil change
- 80-90% of CFC charge
- Alkylbenzene lubricant
- Available now

**** Retrofit to HFC Notes:**
- Often cheaper/easier than converting self-contained & some larger units to R-22
- SUVA® Cold MP & HP62 available now
- Polyol ester lubricant
- Multiple (typically at least 3) oil changes needed

What to Expect After a Typical Retrofit to a SUVA® Refrigerant (Based on Field Experience)

SUVA®	Discharge Pressure	Suction Pressure	Discharge Temperature	Refrigeration Capacity	Refrigerant Superheat (without adjusting the TXV)	Energy Efficiency
MP39	+20 psi (140 kPa)	Same	+20°F (11°C)	+10%	-3°F (2°C)	Small +
MP66	+30 psi (210 kPa)	Same	+30°F (17°C)	+15%	+2°F (1°C)	Small +
R-134a	+30 psi (210 kPa)	-3 psi (21 kPa)	-5°F (3°C)	-10%	-4°F (2°C)	Small -
HP80	+40 psi (275 kPa)	+3 psi (21 kPa)	Same	+10%	+4°F (2°C)	Small -
HP81	+30 psi (210 kPa)	Same	+15°F (8°C)	+5%	+1°F (2°C)	Small +
HP62	+30 psi (210 kPa)	Same	-15°F (8°C)	Same	+2°F (1°C)	Small -

+ = increase - = decrease

Notes: MP39, MP66 and R-134a are compared to R-12. • HP80, HP81 and HP62 are compared to R-502.

Sightglass
Can't always use this to determine charge size. Sometimes system is properly charged, but bubbles still appear. Use suction and discharge pressure, superheat, subcooling, motor amps, receiver level, etc., to determine if system is properly charged.

Compressor Motor Amps
Small increase for all refrigerants. Motor run time will decrease slightly for all refrigerants except R-134a.

Charge Size
All refrigerants are typically 80% to 90% (by weight) of the R-12 or R-502 charge.

TXV or Capillary Tube
Almost never change; may need to adjust superheat.

Suction Pressure Cut-in/ Cut-out Switch
May need to adjust; use PT chart to determine new setting.

Condenser Sizing
Most systems are OK. Some systems in hot climates will have insufficient condenser capacity causing unacceptably high discharge pressure. System modifications will be necessary when this happens.

Note:
This information is intended to serve as a guide; actual performance may vary.

For Sales Information:
DuPont Fluorochemicals
Customer Service Center, B-15305
Wilmington, DE 19898 U.S.A.
(302) 774-2099 or 800-441-9442

For Technical Information:
Fluorochemicals Laboratory
Wilmington, DE 19898 U.S.A.
(302) 999-3129 or 800-582-5606

Europe
DuPont de Nemours
International S.A.
Switzerland
41-22-717-5111

Canada
DuPont Canada, Inc.
(905) 821-3300

Mexico
DuPont, S.A. de C.V.
52-5-250-8000

South America
DuPont do Brasil S.A.
55-11-421-8509

DuPont Argentina S.A.
54-1-311-8167

Pacific
DuPont Australia
61-2-923-6165

Japan
Mitsui DuPont Fluorochemicals Co., Ltd.
81-3-3216-8451

Asia
DuPont Taiwan
886-2-514-4400

DuPont Asia Pacific Limited
852-734-5345

DuPont Thailand
66-2-238-4361

DuPont China Ltd.
86-21-328-3738

DuPont Far East Inc.
60-3-232-3522

DuPont Korea Ltd.
82-2-721-5114

DuPont Singapore Pte. Ltd.
65-273-2244

DuPont Far East, Philippines
63-2-818-9911

DuPont Far East Inc.
India
91-44-454-029

DuPont Far East Inc.–Pakistan
92-21-533-350

DuPont Far East Inc.
Indonesia
62-21-517-800

3/94 Printed in U.S.A.

General Replacement Guide

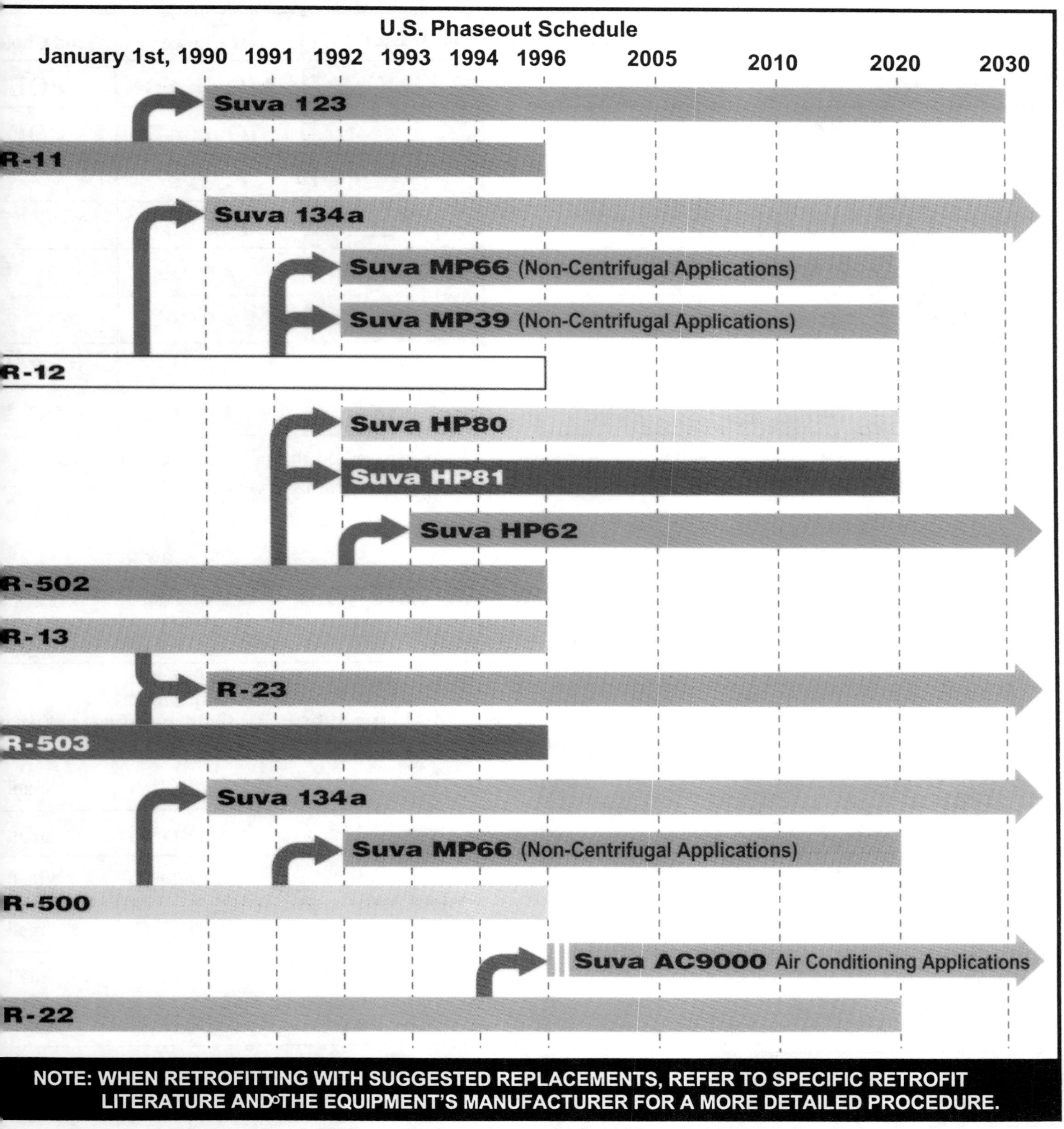

U.S. Phaseout Schedule

January 1st, 1990 1991 1992 1993 1994 1996 2005 2010 2020 2030

Suva 123

R-11

Suva 134a

Suva MP66 (Non-Centrifugal Applications)

Suva MP39 (Non-Centrifugal Applications)

R-12

Suva HP80

Suva HP81

Suva HP62

R-502

R-13

R-23

R-503

Suva 134a

Suva MP66 (Non-Centrifugal Applications)

R-500

Suva AC9000 Air Conditioning Applications

R-22

NOTE: WHEN RETROFITTING WITH SUGGESTED REPLACEMENTS, REFER TO SPECIFIC RETROFIT LITERATURE AND THE EQUIPMENT'S MANUFACTURER FOR A MORE DETAILED PROCEDURE.

Suggested Oil Guide

Refrigerant	1st Choice	2nd Choice
R-11	MO	
R-12	MO or AB	POE
R-13	MO or AB	POE
R-22	MO or AB	POE
R-23	POE (A)	
Suva 123	MO or AB	
Suva 134a	POE (A)	
R-500	MO or AB	POE

Refrigerant	1st Choice	2nd Choic
R-502	MO or AB	POE
R-503	MO or AB	POE
Suva AC9000	POE (A)	
Suva HP62	POE (A)	
Suva HP80	AB (B)	POE
Suva HP81	AB (B)	POE (B)
Suva MP39	AB (B)	POE (B)
Suva MP66	AB (B)	POE (B)

(A) Maximum 5% MO or AB in POE

(B) Maximum 20% MO in AB or POE

NOTE: Where possible use OEM-recommended oil type, charge size, and viscosity.

MO . . . . . . Mineral Oil AB . . . . Alkylbenzene Oil POE . . . . Polyol Ester

What to Expect After a Typical Retrofit to a Suva Refrigeran

(Based on Field Experience)

Suva	Discharge Pressure	Suction Pressure	Discharge Temperature	Refrigeration Capacity	Refrigerant Superheat (without adjusting the TXV)	Energ Efficie
MP39	+20 psi (140 kPa)	Same	+20°F (11°C)	+10%	–3°F (2°C)	Small
MP66	+30 psi (210 kPa)	Same	+30°F (17°C)	+15%	+2°F (1°C)	Small
134a	+30 psi (210 kPa)	–3 psi (21 kPa)	–5°F (3°C)	–10%	–4°F (2°C)	Small
HP80	+40 psi (275 kPa)	+3 psi (21 kPa)	Same	+10%	+4°F (2°C)	Small
HP81	+30 psi (210 kPa)	Same	+15°F (8°C)	+5%	+1°F (2°C)	Small
HP62	+30 psi (210 kPa)	Same	–15°F (8°C)	Same	+2°F (1°C)	Small

\+ = increase
– = decrease

Notes: MP39, MP66, and R134a are compared to R12
HP80, HP81, and HP62 are compared to R502

This information is intended to serve as a guide; actual performance may vary.

H-56604

ICI Klea

The following information is reprinted with permission of ICI Klea, Wilmington, DE.

- *Introduction to Refrigerant Blends: Azeotropes and Zeotropes*
- *KLEA® 407A and KLEA® 407B: Long-Term Replacements for R-502*
- *KLEA® 407C Replacement for HCFC-22*
- *KLEA® 134a Data Sheet*
- *KLEA® 407A Data Sheet*
- *KLEA® 407B Data Sheet*
- *KLEA® 407C Data Sheet*
- *Thermodynamic Properties of KLEA® 134a*
- *Thermodynamic Properties of KLEA® 407A*
- *Thermodynamic Properties of KLEA® 407B*
- *Thermodynamic Properties of KLEA® 407C*
- *KLEA® 134a: Pressure-Enthalpy Diagram*
- *KLEA® 407A: Pressure-Enthalpy Diagram*
- *KLEA® 407B: Pressure-Enthalpy Diagram*
- *KLEA® 407C: Pressure-Enthalpy Diagram*

Introduction to Refrigerant Blends Azeotropes and Zeotropes

ICI Klea

Introduction

ICI, a world leader in the search for CFC and HCFC alternatives, has developed refrigerant blends that offer ease of use, minimal environmental impact, and favorable refrigeration properties. These blends are replacing HCFC-22 and R-502, which are being controlled and phased out by internationally agreed-upon legislation. This note provides an introduction to the differences between azeotropic and zeotropic refrigerant blends and a brief discussion of blend glide, application, and servicing issues.

Why Use Blends At All?

No single fluid matches the physical properties of R-502 or HCFC-22. A refrigerant that is usable for many applications must be practically non-flammable and of low toxicity, in addition to having good thermodynamic properties. The choice of available fluids that meet current requirements is restricted; the best candidate replacement fluids currently available are HFC refrigerants, of which KLEA® 134a and KLEA® 32 are well-known examples.

It is also important to consider the environmental impact associated with the use of a refrigerant. For example, ICI has chosen KLEA 32, as a key component of its low-temperature refrigerants because its direct greenhouse warming potential is low compared to that of other candidate fluids.

The only way to obtain refrigerants that meet current standards yet match the properties of R-502 and HCFC-22 is to use blends of these HFC refrigerants. ICI has chosen to develop its range of KLEA refrigerant blends as retrofittable alternatives to R-502 and HCFC-22 in order to help the industry protect its investment in existing equipment and also to make redesign as simple as possible by providing "lookalike" refrigerants.

What is the ICI Klea Range of Refrigerant Blends?

The ICI Klea range of refrigerant blends currently includes:

KLEA® 407A: Long-term alternative for new and existing low-temperature equipment
KLEA® 407B: Retrofittable alternative for R-502 in applications not covered by KLEA 407A
KLEA® 407C: Alternative for HCFC-22

All of these are blends of KLEA 32, and KLEA® 125 and KLEA 134a; they have zero ozone depletion potential and combine low direct greenhouse warming potential with good energy efficiency to minimize Total Equivalent Warming Impact (TEWI) of systems in which they are used. Other Technical Notes available from ICI describe these refrigerants in more detail.

What are the Differences Between Azeotropes, Zeotropes and NARMS?

All refrigerant blends can be classified as either azeotropes or zeotropes. Some use a third classification; the Near-Azeotropic Refrigerant Mixture, or NARM. Any NARM refrigerant is better defined as a zeotrope, as they must be handled in the same way. The key properties of these blends are summarized below.

Azeotropes have been used for many years. The ASHRAE classification system designates azeotropic refrigerants by assigning a number in the 500 series; the most widely used are R-500 and R-502. An azeotrope is best thought of as a blend that behaves like a single fluid. Its composition is always the same in both liquid and vapor, and it has a unique boiling temperature for a given pressure. In practice this is not true; changes in pressure around a refrigeration system, and differential solubility of the azeotrope components in oil can act to force shifting of the azeotrope components. In practice, this shifting has negligible effect and can normally be ignored.

Zeotropes behave in many respects like pure fluids, however they have two distinguishing characteristics : "boiling range" and "composition shift." These are explained below. ASHRAE awards classification numbers in the 400 series to zeotropic refrigerants.

When a zeotrope is held in a system under pressure so that it forms both vapor and liquid, such as in a cylinder, the compositions of the liquid and the vapor are different. The vapor is enriched in the more volatile components; conversely, the liquid is enriched in the less volatile components. This phenomenon is caused by the different vapor pressures of the components; in fact, nearly all common fluid mixtures are zeotropic rather than azeotropic.

The degree of enrichment depends on the differences in volatility between the components. A practical measure of volatility is the vapor pressure of a refrigerant. For example, a blend of KLEA 32 and KLEA 134a in equal proportions would exhibit a greater degree of enrichment than an equivalent blend of KLEA 32 and KLEA 125, because KLEA 32 and KLEA 125 are of similar vapor pressure whereas KLEA 134a is a lower-pressure fluid.

This enrichment, or "fractionation," causes the second important property of zeotropes; the "boiling range." In other words, a refrigerant will evaporate (or condense) over a range of temperatures at a given pressure. The liquid saturation temperature (or bubble point) is lower than the vapor saturation temperature (or dew point) at constant pressure.

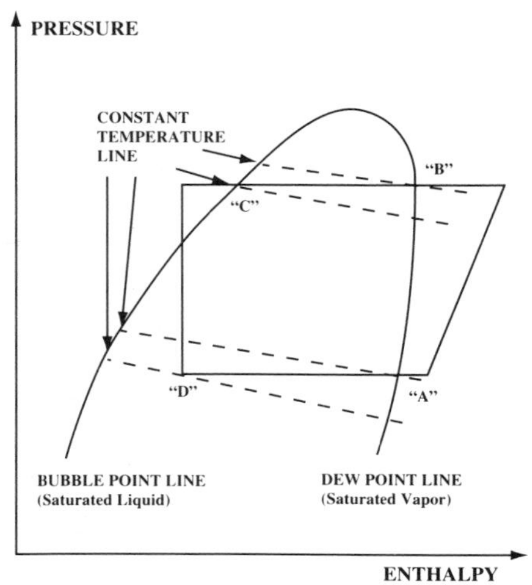

Pressure-Enthalpy Diagram for Non-azeotropic Refrigerant Blends

Any given refrigerant blend has a boiling point for a given pressure, at which vapor starts to form. This is the "bubble point" for that composition and pressure. The bubble point falls between the boiling points of the pure components. Once the liquid mixture reaches the bubble point, it starts to vaporize as heat is added. The vapor formed is enriched in more volatiles, so as the liquid vaporizes, it loses these components at a greater rate than it loses the least volatile component. This means that the composition of the residual liquid shifts towards pure least volatile, and hence the bubble point of the residual liquid rises. Eventually the last drop of liquid is vaporized; at this point the evaporation temperature has risen to a temperature called the "dew point." Another way to think of the dew point is the temperature at which the first drop of liquid condenses from a vapor.

The "boiling range" is the range of temperatures between the bubble and dew points. It is usually much smaller than the difference between the boiling points of each component.

Near-azeotropes are merely zeotropes with a narrow boiling range. However, ICI has not used this definition because it is ambiguous (How near is "near?") and could be misleading. ALL near-azeotropes are ZEOTROPES.

What is the "Glide" of a Refrigerant Blend?

The term "glide" has become widely used in the industry. Nonetheless, there are differing definitions of glide, and this has caused understandable confusion.

ICI terms the difference in temperature between bubble and dew point the "boiling range." In a practical refrigeration system, the boiling range characteristic of a refrigerant blend leads to different temperatures between the inlet and outlet of a direct-expansion evaporator or condenser. This observed difference in the system heat exchangers is termed temperature "glide". In the evaporator, temperature glide will be smaller than the boiling range because the refrigerant will enter the evaporator partially vaporized. Typical boiling ranges and glides for KLEA 407A, 407B and 407C are given in the product Technical Notes. If you find a reference to "glide," be sure to check whether the term is used to mean boiling range or temperature glide.

Is Glide Bad For You?

The phenomenon of glide is in itself neither good nor bad. The glide of all currently available refrigerants including KLEA 407A, 407B, and 407C is relatively small (indeed using some widely accepted definitions based on size of glide, KLEA 407A, 407B and 407C could be called "Near Azeotropes") and in practice has no negative effects on heat exchanger performance. If this were not true, it would be difficult to retrofit these refrigerants, whereas in practice, retrofit is simple and can normally be achieved with no loss in performance.

All major refrigerant suppliers, including ICI, now produce "gliding" refrigerants; consequently there is growing experience of use of zeotropic refrigerants as replacements for CFC-12, HCFC-22 and R-502 at the practical level around the world. Handling and servicing zeotropes can be done using the same techniques commonly used with traditional refrigerants. In fact, many technicians have expressed surprise in their ease of use.

Many designs of heat exchangers in use today for HCFC-22 and R-502 already exhibit a "glide" in temperature as a result of pressure drop, which lowers the evaporating temperature of the refrigerant.

Gliding refrigerants, in fact, offer the potential to improve energy efficiency by matching the change in temperature of the refrigerant in a heat exchanger to the external fluid temperature change; this is currently the subject of research.

Application of Refrigerant Blends

ICI has demonstrated the application of zeotropic refrigerants in partnership with its customers through an ongoing series of field trials and controlled laboratory studies. It has been found that for most existing designs of refrigeration equipment there is no difficulty in using the KLEA range of zeotropic refrigerants. ICI has published a series of Case Studies describing typical experiences covering a wide range of equipment types, from small hermetic systems to large commercial air-conditioning plants.

It is important to remember that in most parts of a refrigeration circuit there is NO DIFFERENCE in the behavior of a zeotrope from that of a pure fluid.The characteristics of a zeotrope only appear in the heat exchangers or in an in-line accumulator or receiver where liquid and vapor are present.

ICI continues to evaluate the use of zeotropic refrigerants in flooded evaporator systems and also supports fundamental research into the heat transfer behavior of zeotropes.

Servicing Issues

The handling and servicing of KLEA zeotropic refrigerants are covered in the following sections. Zeotropes can in many respects be handled the same way as single refrigerants and azeotropes. There are, however, important issues to consider regarding charging and leaking systems with zeotropes.

As with other HFC refrigerants, the use of polyol ester lubricants (POE) are required with all KLEA refrigerants. Filter-driers and other materials compatible with KLEA 134a and other HFC refrigerants are, in general, compatible with KLEA 407A, 407B, and 407C. Check with OEM for specific recommendations.

Charging a System with a KLEA 407-series Refrigerant

All zeotropic refrigerants, including the KLEA 407-series type must be LIQUID-charged at all times to ensure correct composition; this is the major difference in handling between zeotropes and pure fluid or azeotropes. Most cylinders containing blended refrigerants, including KLEA 407-series refrigerants, have dip tubes which allow technicians to liquid charge a system while maintaining an upright cylinder. ALWAYS read the cylinder labels prior to handling a refrigerant. If it is necessary to charge into the low-side of a system, do NOT vapor-charge from the cylinder. Instead, vaporize the liquid refrigerant coming from the cylinder using an expansion device. This will prevent damage to the compressor due to liquid slugging.

Adjustment of Expansion Devices for Retrofitted Equipment

ICI has normally found that adjusting the expansion valve is necessary when retrofitting to these refrigerants in systems designed for R-502 or HCFC-22. The adjustment should normally be to increase the apparent superheat setting by an amount roughly equivalent to the average glide of the refrigerant. The size of increase may also vary according to the system design, operating conditions and evaporator configuration. For this reason the best adjustment method should include some assessment of performance as part of the adjustment. A convenient check may be the air-on/air-off temperature difference over the evaporator, which should be proportional to the load. This will indicate when the best superheat setting has been found. Superheat is calculated by subtracting the suction pressure dew point temperature (i.e. saturated vapor) from the suction line temperature.

Another useful check is to look for evidence of excessive frosting on the suction line, which will indicate insufficient superheat for the refrigerant.

If you have a capillary expansion device, contact your manufacturer for recommendation. ICI has found that for a lot of capillary systems acceptable performance can be achieved without adjusting the capillary. However in some cases extra capillary length will be required: up to 15% has been found necessary in some retrofits. If you find poor capacity and excessive suction frosting then extra capillary length is probably required.

The TXV sensor element should be located on the evaporator outlet pipe so it can sense the vapor temperature. If your existing sensor element in a retrofitted unit is on the inlet side it should be switched to the outlet side.

Frosting of Evaporator Coils

The glide of a zeotropic refrigerant means that the temperature at the evaporator inlet may be several degrees lower than the outlet. Some concern has been expressed that this will lead to excessive rates of frosting at the inlet, hence causing uneven ice formation and a problem on defrost cycles.

Many existing evaporator designs already use variable-space fins with the fins more widely spaced at the inlet; this is because even with a pure refrigerant the highest rates of heat transfer tend to be found in this section of the coil. This helps to counteract the slight increase in heat transfer rate which may be caused by the glide.

In many practical trials no difficulties have been found with the evaporator frosting patterns. If however there is concern then the evaporator inlet temperature may be varied by: adjusting the quality of vapor at evaporator inlet, i.e., adjusting subcool; or the evaporator pressure may be raised to increase the temperatures all through the evaporator.

Leakage of Gliding Refrigerants: Differential Losses

This has been a major concern of refrigeration engineers; it is now possible to describe the findings of thousands of running hours of equipment using a wide variety of gliding refrigerants.

The experience to date can be summaried as follows:

- The R-32/R-125/R-134a fluid system (on which the KLEA 407-series refrigerants are based) has a wide range of compositions that give similar capacity and COP when used in refrigeration and air conditioning equipment. For this reason a differential leak must normally be severe and must take a large proportion of the charge out of the system before a significant degradation of performance is noticed.
- Differential leakage can only occur when the following circumstances arise:
  - The system is at rest
  - Both liquid and vapor are present
  - Leak occurs from the vapor space only and does not entrain liquid

  (Note: It is not possible to selectively leak one component at a time. All refrigerants will leak out at different rates.)
- Running systems almost never leak differentially from the heat exchangers; the only place for differential leakage to occur is from an in-line accumulator or receiver.
- The magnitude of leak required for force a shift away from the "acceptable" composition region will almost certainly lead to other effects of undercharging, e.g. loss of subcooling and reduced evaporator pressure. These will mask the composition effect.
- Even a worst-case leakage of vapor can normally be corrected by topping up with the normal blended composition of refrigerant.

ICI has published detailed information which supply data from leaking systems and show that the effects of differential leakage are slight.

Servicing a Leaking System Containing a KLEA 407-Series Refrigerant

A responsible technician will repair all leaks before additional servicing of the regrigerant system. Follow manufacturers guidelines for servicing equipment with zeotropic refrigerants. Under most circumstances, assuming a minor leak, the system can be topped up by liquid charging the same refrigerant blend with negligible effect on performance. It is recommended that for major leaks, the charge is removed and the system is charged with new refrigerant after the leak has been repaired.

Summary

The difficulties of using zeotropic refrigerants have been exaggerated, partly through lack of experience. The practical experience that the industry has already gained by using KLEA 407A, 407B and 407C demonstrates that service engineers can adapt readily to the new technology that is represented by the alternatives for HCFC-22 and R-502. ICI Klea has undertaken a comprehensive development program in partnership with the industry and now has extensive knowledge of the practicalities of using zeotropic refrigerants over a wide range of system types. For more information on retrofitting or using KLEA 407-series refrigerants call 800-ASK-KLEA.

ICI Klea
Concord Plaza
3411 Silverside Road
P.O. Box 15391
Wilmington, DE 19850

Customer Service: (800) ICI-KLEA or
Technical Assistance: (800) ASK-KLEA
Fax: (302) 887-7706

620250631 01/95

KLEA® 407A and KLEA® 407B: Long-Term Replacements for R-502

ICI Klea

Introduction

ICI Klea now offers KLEA® 407A and KLEA® 407B as commercialized HFC alternatives to R-502 for low-temperature refrigeration applications. ICI has designed these refrigerants using the same principles that were used in bringing KLEA® 134a to market. Considerable effort has been made to produce the best solutions to the challenging problem of developing an R-502 replacement that offers optimum performance coupled with minimal environmental impact.

KLEA 407A and KLEA 407B, which are ternary zeotropic blends of KLEA® 32, KLEA® 125, and KLEA 134a, have been independently tested by Bitzer, Searle, and other manufacturers. Their key properties include:

- Minimum environmental impact
  - Good energy efficiency
  - Low GWP
- Zero ODP
- Non-flammability
- Immediate availability
- Full compatiblity with ICI's EMKARATE™ RL ester oil range
- Performance similar to R-502 in a wide range of applications

Background

ICI is committed to replacing CFCs and HCFCs with HFC solutions that address both technical and environmental concerns. The choice of KLEA 32, KLEA 125 and KLEA 134a as key components in KLEA 407A and KLEA 407B fulfills this commitment.

Formulations

In order to offer the best possible solution, ICI undertook extensive theoretical modeling and practical tests using a series of refrigerant formulations. This work resulted in the development of two HFC refrigerants as alternatives to R-502. These refrigerants have been designed to meet the needs of the widely differing applications previously covered by R-502.

KLEA 407A is the Product of Choice for

- Retrofit of existing systems with moderate condensing temperatures and/or medium to high evaporator temperatures and
- New system design.

ICI has developed KLEA 407B as a refrigerant suitable for retrofitting existing R-502 equipment in situations where KLEA 407A would exhibit a loss of capacity compared to R-502, or for applications where compressor discharge temperature must be maintained at R-502 levels.

System Effects That Influence the Performance of KLEA 407A and KLEA 407B

Volumetric Efficiency of Reciprocating Compressors

The majority of existing R-502 systems use single-stage reciprocating compressors. In such equipment the flow rate of refrigerant through the system is determined by the volumetric efficiency of the compressor, which, in turn, is determined by the ratio of condensing to evaporating pressure. For higher pressure ratios the volumetric efficiency and flow rate will be lower. This ultimately reduces the effective capacity of the refrigeration system.

The ratio of condensing to evaporating pressures for KLEA 407A is similar to that of R-502 for an evaporating temperature greater than approximately –15°F (assuming condensation against ambient air). At these moderate lift conditions, KLEA 407A is the preferred retrofit solution. As the evaporator temperature drops below –15°F, the pressure ratio for KLEA 407A increases above that of R-502, thereby reducing the capacity of the system (relative to R-502). KLEA 407B was formulated for these conditions. KLEA 407B more closely matches the pressure ratio of R-502 under high lift conditions and, therefore, has a higher capacity relative to KLEA 407A for systems operating at high lift conditions. A direct comparison of theoretical refrigeration effects shows that at the same volumetric flow rate, KLEA 407A is relatively equivalent to R-502 in capacity, even at high lift.

Rotary compression technology such as screw and scroll compressors are not as prone to the volumetric efficiency problems of the reciprocating compressors. Use of rotary compression technology in R-502 applications is expected to increase significantly. In new equipment that employs rotary compressor technology, KLEA 407A represents ICI's preferred HFC alternative to R-502 for all temperature conditions.

Heat Transfer Effects

KLEA407A and KLEA 407B are blends of KLEA 32, KLEA 125 and KLEA 134a. As individual components these three ingredients all exhibit heat transfer performance that is significantly better than R-502 or HCFC-22. The exact difference is system specific; however, practical experience has shown that the average effect of the refrigerant on heat transfer is both real and quantifiable. In practical field trials ICI KLEA has found that both KLEA 407A and KLEA 407B require smaller temperature differences than R-502 within the evaporators and condensers to accept and reject heat. This translates to R-502 retrofits with KLEA 407A and KLEA 407B that enjoy higher mean evaporating temperature combined with lower mean condensing temperature. These differences can lead to a significant improvement in real system performance, as compared to the results that might be achieved under similar conditions when using a calorimeter. The improvement is due to the typically equal condensing and evaporating temperatures employed in the calorimeter where the heat transfer effects cannot be taken into account. In essence, the calorimeter gives a conservative prediction relative to real world applications. Research is still underway to characterize local heat transfer behavior during condensation and evaporation of KLEA407A and KLEA 407B.

Choosing Between KLEA 407A and KLEA 407B

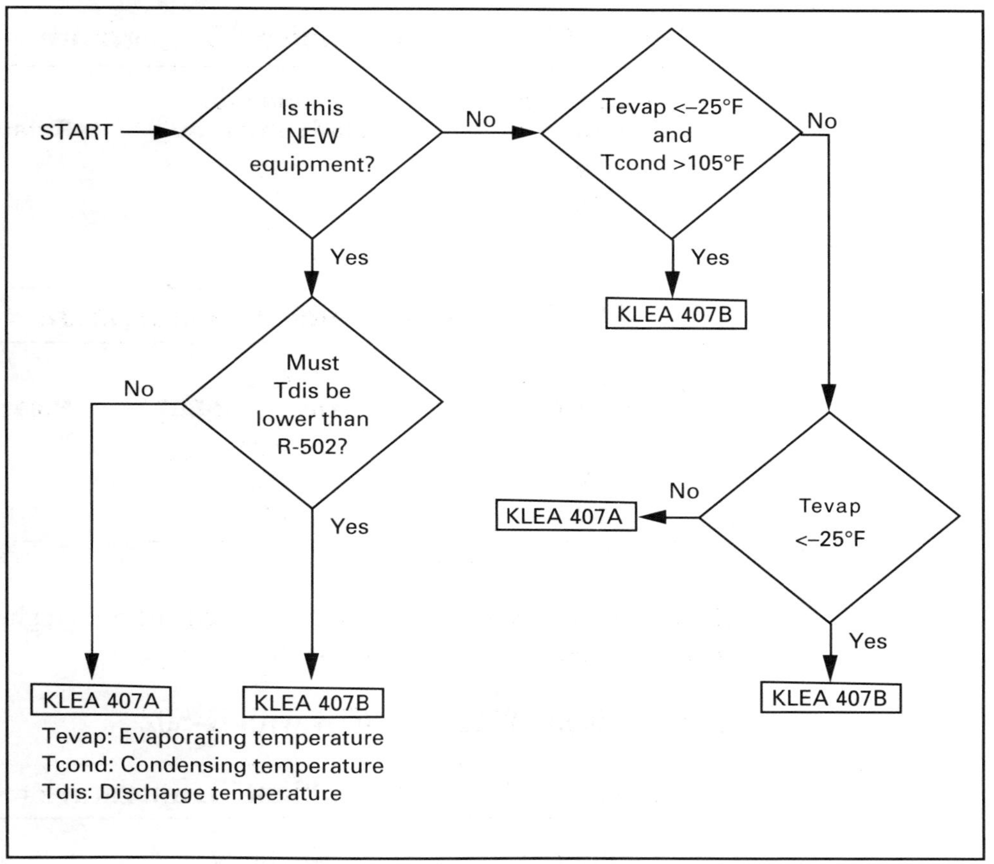

- The above flowchart gives some guidelines for choosing between KLEA 407A and KLEA 407B. Observe the following general principles:
- For retrofit at high lift (–40°F evaporator with 105°F or higher condenser condition), use KLEA 407B
- For retrofit at moderate lift (–20°F evaporator with 120°F condenser condition), use either KLEA 407A or KLEA 407B
- For retrofit at low lift (–15°F evaporator with 105°F condenser condition), use KLEA 407A

Performance Testing

In conjunction with compressor manufacturers and end users, ICI Klea has tested KLEA 407A and KLEA 407B in a range of systems. A set of typical results are shown below for a cold room refrigeration system. The data were generated by the Searle Manufacturing Company.

Comparison of KLEA 407A with R-502

For KLEA 407A—(i) Ambient Temperature = –5°F

Condenser Temperature °F	Capacity Relative to R-502	COP Relative to R-502
99	97%	108%
104	92%	103%
122	91%	105%

For KLEA 407A—(i) Ambient Temperature = –15°F

Condenser Temperature °F	Capacity Relative to R-502	COP Relative to R-502
93	94%	107%
104	91%	101%
122	92%	108%

*Dew point temperature

Discharge temperatures were typically several degrees higher for KLEA407A than for R-502 under the same conditions.

Comparison of KLEA 407B with R-502

For KLEA 407B—(i) Ambient Temperature = –5°F

Condenser Temperature °F	Capacity Relative to R-502	COP Relative to R-502
95	103%	104%
104	97%	99%
122	93%	98%

For KLEA407B—(i) Ambient Temperature = –15°F

Condenser Temperature °F	Capacity Relative to R-502	COP Relative to R-502
93	98%	102%
104	92%	94%
122	89%	94%

*Dew point temperature

Discharge temperatures were typically several degrees lower for KLEA 407B than for R-502 under the same conditions.

Summary

ICI Klea now offers a choice of HFC refrigerants as commercial alternatives to R-502. Independent testing of these refrigerants has demonstrated the technical performance of these products. ICI Klea sees both KLEA 407A and KLEA 407B as effective, long-term replacements for R-502. Our products offer the optimum balance of technical performance and environmental acceptability.

ICI Klea
Concord Plaza
3411 Silverside Road
P.O. Box 15391
Wilmington, DE 19850

Customer Service: (800) ICI-KLEA or
Technical Assistance: (800) ASK-KLEA
Fax: (302) 887-7706

620250640 10/94

KLEA® 407C (KLEA® 66)

Replacement for HCFC-22

KLEA

Introduction

The Montreal Protocol calls for CFC phase out by the end of 1995; EEC Regulations call for phase out by the end of 1994. The need for ozone friendly refrigerants to replace CFCs such as R-11, R-12 and R-502 is thus extremely urgent.

The Protocol also calls for a consumption freeze of HCFCs from the end of 1995 with total phase out by 2030; severe cutbacks will come earlier (90% from 2015, 99.5% from 2020). To comply with these regulations, alternative refrigerants should, wherever possible, contain no chlorine and, therefore, have no ozone depletion potential (ODP). They should also have a minimal global warming potential.

ICI is a world leader in the search for CFC and HCFC alternatives. The first alternative ICI developed, the hydrofluorocarbon (HFC) KLEA® 134a, is now the refrigerant of choice to replace R-12 in a wide range of refrigeration and air conditioning applications. These include air conditioning, domestic refrigeration, automotive air conditioning, high pressure centrifugal chillers, and a variety of commercial refrigeration equipment.

HCFC-22 (R-22) is used extensively in the refrigeration and air conditioning industry in high, medium, and low temperature applications. ICI has carried out a complete survey of all likely replacements for HCFC-22, which combine minimal environmental impact - that is, no ODP and low direct and indirect global warming - with high refrigeration capacity and energy efficiency.

KLEA 407C

ICI has identified a ternary mixture of KLEA® 32, KLEA® 125 and KLEA® 134a as a refrigerant that offers the optimum combination of minimal environmental impact with favorable technical performance. This refrigerant is KLEA® 407C.

The formulation of KLEA 407C has been developed by ICI through testing in its applications laboratories in Europe, the USA and Japan, and through close collaboration with the refrigeration and air conditioning industry. The composition of KLEA 407C is KLEA32/KLEA 125/KLEA 134a (23/25/52 wt%). KLEA 407C is ICI's alternative for HCFC-22 in new equipment. Extensive testing and performance trials have also shown its suitability as a long-term refrigerant that can be used to retrofit many existing applications of HCFC-22, with little or no loss in performance.

Comparison of ODP and HGWP[1]

	Atmospheric Lifetime (Years)	ODP (CFC 11 = 1.0)	HGWP (CFC 11 = 1.0)
HCFC-22	15.30	0.055	0.35
KLEA 32	7.30	0.0	0.14
KLEA 134a	15.50	0.0	0.26
KLEA 125	40.70	0.0	0.90
KLEA 407C	—	0.0	0.39

[1] ODP = Ozone Depletion Potential
HGWP = Halocarbon Global Warming Potential (steady state)

Comparison of Physical Properties of KLEA 407C and HCFC-22

Property	HCFC-22	KLEA 407C
Boiling Point (°F)	-41.47	-34 to -47
Latent Heat of Vaporization (Btu/lb)	100.40	108.20
Density of Saturated Vapor (lb/ft3)	0.294	0.286
Density of Saturated Liquid (lb/ft3)	87.954	86.20
Molecular Weight (lb/lbmole)	86.48	86.20

@ 14.7 psia

Flammability Characteristics

KLEA 407C contains the marginally flammable refrigerant KLEA 32. The flammability characteristics of mixtures of KLEA 32, KLEA 125, and KLEA 134a have been measured by ICI according to ASTM E681-85 and UL 2182 at both room temperature and 100°C; under these conditions, KLEA 407C (designated as R-407C by ASHRAE) is classified as A1/A1. KLEA 407C is recognized by Underwriters Laboratories as "practically nonflammable."

Performance Comparison of KLEA 407C and HCFC-22

The theoretical comparison between KLEA 407C and HCFC-22 in the table below demonstrates the similarity in performance between these refrigerants. ICI technical evaluations, customer trials and field tests demonstrate that KLEA 407C compares very favorably with the performance of HCFC-22 in many applications including heat pumps and air conditioning systems.

Theoretical Comparison of HCFC-22 and KLEA 407C

	COP	Flow Rate (lbs/s)	Discharge Temp. (°F)	Discharge Press. (psia)	Suction Press. (psia)
HCFC-22	4.60	8.86	162	225.90	83.00
KLEA 407C	4.40	8.81	154	242.20	84.20

Theoretical conditions used are evaporating temperature -40°F, condensing temperature 105°F, superheat 10°F, cooling duty 3 tons, compressor efficiency 75% and 0°F sub cooling.

In general, the performance of KLEA 407C is equal to, or better than that of HCFC-22 in tests carried out to date. The graphs of measured performance data found at the end of this document are indicative of typical results.

Thermophysical Properties of KLEA 407C

ICI has produced thermodynamic data tables, pressure-enthalpy diagrams and physical property data sets for KLEA 407C to support customers' system design studies. This information is available from your local ICI representative.

Toxicology

The toxicology of the components KLEA 32, KLEA 125, and KLEA 134a have been subjected to a demanding review both by ICI's own team of product safety specialists and by the Program for Alternative Fluorocarbon Toxicity Testing (PAFT), an industry consortium of which ICI is a founding member.

All three of these refrigerants show very low toxicity. A value of 1000 ppm (8-hour time weighted average value) is therefore recommended as the maximum occupational exposure level (OEL) for each component and their mixtures. This is the highest level assigned to any industrial chemical.

Handling of KLEA 407C

KLEA 407C is a zeotropic mixture; this means that where both liquid and vapor are present (for example, in a storage cylinder) the vapor composition differs from the liquid composition. For this reason KLEA 407C should always be liquid charged into a system. Further details on the handling of KLEA 407C can be found in the document, "Introduction to Refrigerant Blends: Azeotropes and Zeotropes."

The zeotropic nature of KLEA 407C means that differential leakage of a charge from a system is possible. However, theoretical and practical investigations of the effects of leakage from a system have shown that, in general, there will not be a significant degradation of performance relative to the 'as charged' condition.

Lubricants for KLEA 407C

With the introduction of new refrigerants to replace CFCs and HCFCs comes the need to change from the existing mineral or synthetic hydrocarbon oils to lubricants compatible with the new KLEA refrigerants from ICI.

Based on experience in the development of a range of polyol ester lubricants for use with KLEA 134a, ICI has focused on the EMKARATE™RL family of synthetic neopentyl polyol esters. These display a number of features that enable them to be used with KLEA 407C, including excellent thermal stability, excellent chemical stability, good lubricity and good material compatibility.

In addition, ICI has already developed a good understanding of the structure-property relationships of these lubricants through close association with compressor and system manufacturers. This detailed understanding has allowed ICI to rapidly focus on particular polyol ester structures with the right balance of properties for use with KLEA 407C in all application areas.

A particular attraction of these materials from an industry viewpoint is their wide qualification for use in compressors using KLEA 134a. It is, therefore, possible to use the same range of EMKARATE RL lubricants both for KLEA 134a and KLEA 407C. This allows a degree of standardization across applications.

Sealed-tube tests (14 days @ 350°F) have shown that EMKARATE RL ester lubricants from ICI are stable in the presence of the three KLEA 407C components in contact with copper, mild steel, and aluminum. The results obtained with these polyol esters are comparable to those obtained under identical conditions with KLEA 134a and HCFC-22.

An extensive program of work investigating the physical properties of mixtures of KLEA refrigerants with the EMKARATE RL ester lubricants is in progress and much data has been collected on topics including miscibility, mixture viscosity, mixture pressure-temperature-solubility behavior and mixture heat transfer properties.

From the data available so far, the EMKARATE RL ester lubricants perform satisfactorily in each of these areas.

Retrofitting Existing Equipment

ICI Klea has developed a retrofitting procedure suitable for use with KLEA 407C as a natural extension of the procedures for retrofitting R-12 systems with KLEA 134a. This procedure has been carried out with success on a large and growing number of systems designed for HCFC-22. The retrofit procedure has been illustrated by publication of a series of case studies describing the application and performance of KLEA 407C as a direct substitute for HCFC-22. Further details on the retrofit procedure can be found in the ICI document entitled, "Retrofit Guidelines for KLEA® Refrigerants and EMKARATE™ RL Ester Lubricants."

Summary

KLEA 407C represents an excellent combination of minimal environmental impact with similar technical performance as a replacement for HCFC-22 in both retrofit and new equipment design of heat pump and air conditioning applications. ICI remains dedicated to a collaborative effort with equipment manufacturers and end users to ensure that the transition from HCFC-22 to KLEA 407C is as smooth as possible.

Performance of HCFC-22 and KLEA 407C:

COP* vs. Evaporator Temperature

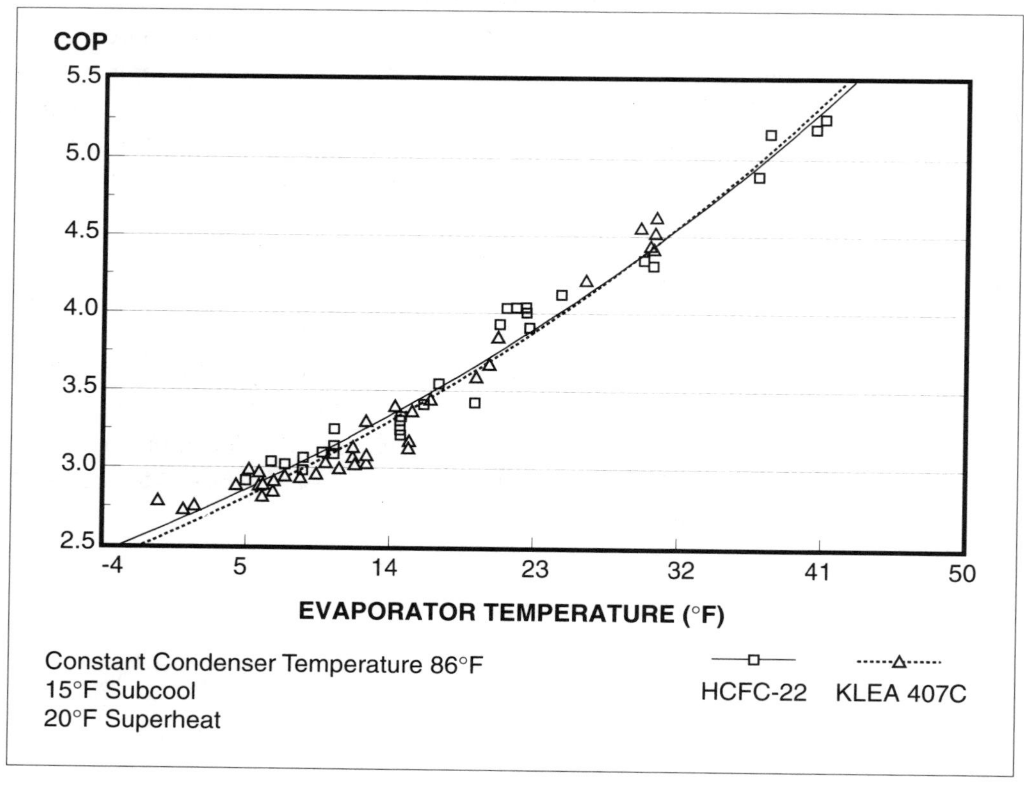

COP* = Coefficient of Performance

Performance of HCFC-22 and KLEA 407C:

Cooling Capacity vs. Evaporator Temperature

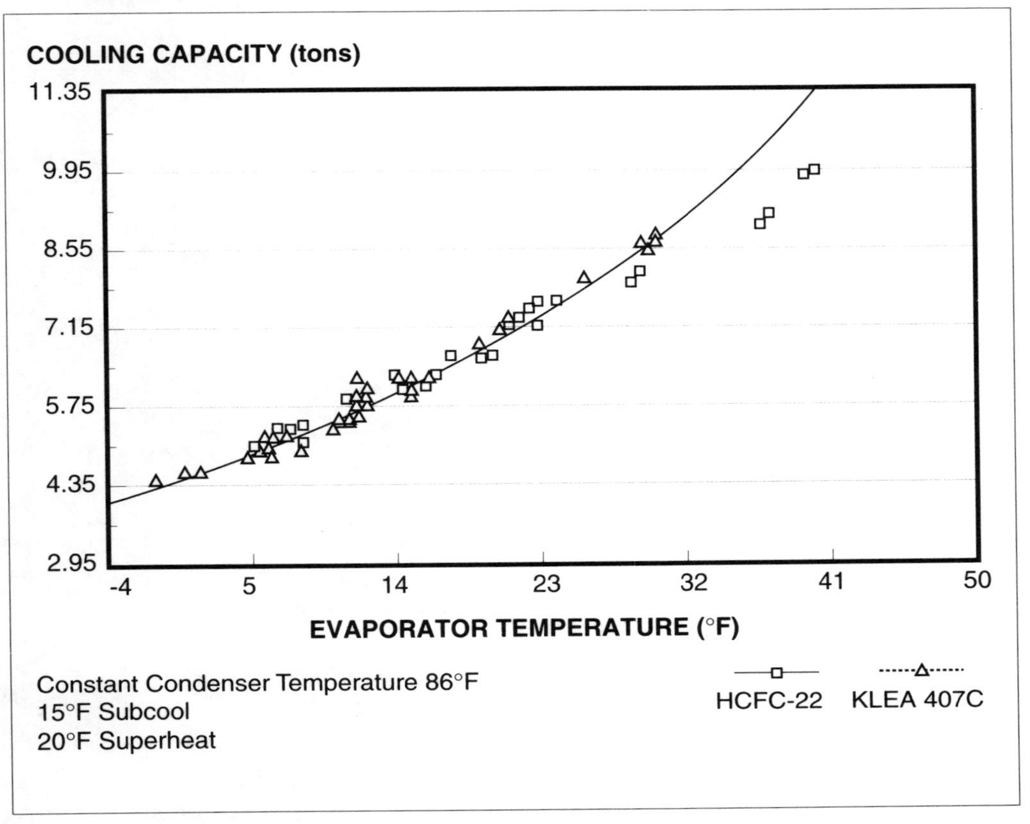

ICI Klea

Concord Plaza
3411 Silverside Rd.
P.O. Box 15391
Wilmington, DE 19850
Customer Service: (800) ICI-KLEA
Technical Assistance: (800) ASK-KLEA
Fax: (302) 887-7706

620250471 1/95

ICI believes all information contained in this document to be accurate at the time of publication but makes no warranty of any kind, either express or implied, regarding the accuracy of any information or the results to be obtained from utilizing such information. Furthermore, the information is intended for use by persons having technical skills and a working knowledge of the system, and is to be used at their own discretion. The user assumes all risks and liability through application or use of the information contained herein and must satisfy himself that the product is entirely suitable for his own purpose and process.

Statements concerning the use of the products or formulations described herein are not to be construed as granting a license under any patent or as recommending the infringement of any patent, and no liability for infringement arising out of any such use is assumed.

KLEA® 134a
Data Sheet

ICI Klea

KLEA® 134a Is 1,1,1,2-Tetrafluoroethane CF_3CH_2F

KLEA® 134a Data Sheet

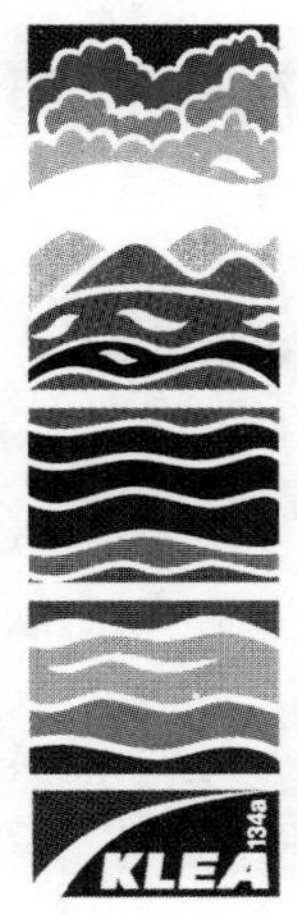

KLEA®134a has been thoroughly tested in a wide range of toxicological studies. The results have shown that KLEA 134a possesses extremely low toxicity and that it will be at least as safe in use as the materials that it replaces. ICI recommends an occupational exposure limit of 1000ppm as an 8 hour time-weighted average. For information on the properties and safe handling of KLEA 134a, please refer to the Material Safety Data Sheet supplied with the product or available upon request. Further details of toxicity tests and their results will also be given, if required.

The data presented here represents a combination of measurements and estimation. ICI Chemicals & Polymers Limited does not guarantee its accuracy and reserves the right to update the information in future in the light of the best available knowledge at the time.

The contents of this note are given in good faith but without any liability attaching to ICI Chemicals & Polymers Limited and it is the user's responsibility to satisfy himself that the product is entirely suitable for his purpose. Freedom from rights must not be assumed.

Physical Property Data For KLEA® 134a*

PROPERTY		UNITS	VALUE
Molecular Weight			102.03
Boiling Point	(14.7 psia)	°F	−15.2
Melting Point		°F	−162.4
Critical Temperature		°F	213.8
Critical Pressure		psia	588.1
Critical Density		lb/cu ft	31.785
Acentric Factor			0.3256
Trouton's Constant		Btu/lb.R	0.2098
Density (liquid)	(70°F)	lb/cu ft	76.255
Density (sat vapor) at normal boiling point		lb/cu ft	0.3287
Coeff. Vol. Therm. Exp. (liquid)	(40°F - 80°F)	1/(°F)	0.001605
Specific Heat (liquid)	(70°F)	Btu/lb.R	0.336
Specific Heat (ideal gas)	(70°F)	Btu/lb.R	0.197
Latent Heat Vaporization	(70°F)	Btu/lb	77.735
Surface Tension		lb_f/in	4.911E-5
Thermal Conductivity (liquid)	(70°F)	Btu/ft.h.R	0.05007
Thermal Conductivity (sat vapor)	(70°F)	Btu/ft.h.R	7.737E-03
Vapor Pressure	(70°F)	psia	85.43
Viscosity (liquid)	(70°F)	lb/ft.h	0.531
Viscosity (vapor)	(70°F)	lb/ft.h	0.0335
Solubility in Water	(68°F, 14.7 psia)	% wt	0.0773

*Properties specified for 99.98 wt % R-134a
Standard States
Enthalpy (−40°F, liquid = 0 Btu/lb.)
Entropy (−40°F, liquid = 0 Btu/lb.R)

KLEA® 134a
Data Sheet

Equation Of State (Martin-Hou)

$$P_r = \frac{RT_r}{V_r - B} + \sum_{i=1,4} \frac{(Ai + BiT_r + Ci \exp(-KT_r))}{(V_r - B)^{(i+1)}}$$

Where: $T_r = T/Tc$, $P_r = P/Pc$, $V_r = V/Vc$
R = 3.82821
B = 0.2124913803
K = 7.250023581
Tc, Pc, Vc = 673.47(R), 588.137(psia), 0.031461(ft^3/lb)

A1,B1,C1 = −10.729649406, 5.0713498381, −467.15522467
A2,B2,C2 = 14.034313767, −8.6811368103, −679.27189635
A3,B3,C3 = −11.321632367, 8.0404407351, 1661.953119
A4,B4,C4 = 3.201606791, −2.3711553933, −620.50640774

Extended Antoine Equation

$$\ln P = A + \frac{B}{C+T} + DT + E\ln(T)$$

P = Vapor Pressure (psia)
T = Temperature (R)
A = 152.7468
B = −10923.7
C = 0
D = 0.019553
E = −22.0068

Latent Heat Of Vaporization

$$dh_{latent} = A + Bx + Cx^2 + Dx^3 + Ex^4$$
where $x = (1-(T/Tc))^{(1/3)}$

A = 0
B = 96.73621
C = 83.64604
D = −61.4725
E = 24.75832
T = Temperature (R)
Tc = Crit. Temp. (R)
dh_{latent} = Btu/lb

Ideal Gas Specific Heat Capacity

$$c_p(ideal) = A + BT + CT^2 + DT^3 + E/T^2$$

A = 0.0343693
B = 3.98764E-4
C = −2.11294E-7
D = 7.29480E-11
E = 0.000000
T = Temperature (R)
c_p (ideal) = Btu/lb.R

KLEA® 134a Data Sheet

Saturated Liquid Enthalpy

$$h_{liquid} = A + Bx + Cx^2 + Dx^3 + Ex^4$$
where $x = (1-(T/Tc))^{(1/3)}$

A = 103.9685
B = −51.9907
C = 25.00528
D = −262.608
E = 71.65015

T = Temperature (R)
Tc = Crit. Temp. (R)
h_{liquid} = Btu/lb

Liquid Density

$$\rho_{liquid} = A + Bx + Cx^2 + Dx^3 + Ex^4$$
where $x = (1-(T/Tc))^{(1/3)}$

A = 31.78511
B = 56.33499
C = 39.7726
D = −31.483

E = 25.95537
T = Temperature (R)
Tc = Crit. Temp. (R)
ρ_{liquid} = lb/ft^3

Liquid Viscosity

$$\ln(\mu)\ (liquid) = A + B/T + C/T^2 + D/T^3$$

A = −5.90347
B = 4193.58
C = −954391
D = 1.12281E+8

T = Temperature (R)
μ (liquid) = lb/ft.h

Liquid Thermal Conductivity

$$K\ (liquid) = A + Bx + Cx^2 + Dx^3$$
where $x = (1-(T/Tc))^{(1/3)}$

A = 2.65879E−2
B = 3.08511E−2
C = −6.96048E−2
D = 1.400742E−1

T = Temperature (R)
Tc = Crit. Temp. (R)
K (liquid) = Btu/ft.h.R

KLEA® 134a
Data Sheet

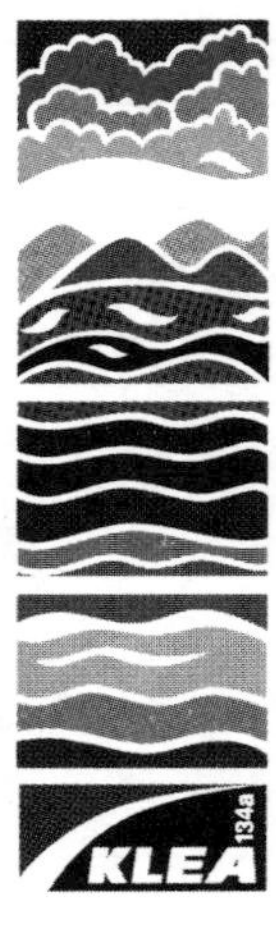

Saturated Vapor Density

$$\rho_{sat\ vapor} = A + Bx + Cx^2 + Dx^3 + Ex^4$$
where $x = (1-(T/Tc))^{(1/3)}$

-60°F TO +120°F

A = 0.595234
B = 162.5833
C = -609.909
D = 759.2125
E = -315.055

T = Temperature (R)
Tc = Crit. Temp. (R)
$\rho_{sat\ vapor}$ = lb/ft^3

+120°F TO +213.8°F

A = 31.78556
B = -59.0152
C = -22.8347
D = 72.57971
E = -16.3007

Saturated Vapor Viscosity

$$\mu\ (sat\ vapor) = A + BT + CT^2 + DT^3$$

A = -0.120667
B = 8.38591E-4
C = -1.653842E-6
D = 1.170777E-9

T = Temperature (R)
μ (sat vapor) = lb/ft.h

Saturated Vapor Thermal Conductivity

$$K(sat\ vapor) = A + BT + CT^2 + DT^3$$

A = -7.28289E-3
B = 3.507797E-5
C = -2.861984E-8
D = 3.007995E-11

T = Temperature (R)
K(sat vapor) = Btu/ft.h.F

KLEA® 134a
Data Sheet

ICI Klea

ICI Klea
Concord Plaza–Tatnall
3411 Silverside Road
P.O. Box 15391
Wilmington, DE 19850
(800) 243-KLEA

620250122
Printed 7/93

KLEA® 407A
(KLEA 60)
Data Sheet

ICI Klea

KLEA® 407A
Data Sheet

KLEA® 407A is a blend of HFCs 32, 125 and 134a designed for low-temperature applications in new refrigeration equipment and also for retrofit in many existing systems. For information on the properties and safe handling of KLEA 407A, please refer to the Material Safety Data Sheet supplied with the product or available upon request.

The data presented here represents a combination of measurements and estimation. ICI Chemicals & Polymers Limited does not guarantee its accuracy and reserves the right to update the information in the future, in the light of the best available knowledge at the time.

The contents of this note are given in good faith but without any liability attaching to ICI Chemicals & Polymers Limited and it is the user's responsibility to satisfy himself that the product is entirely suitable for his purpose. Freedom from rights must not be assumed.

Property		Units	Value
Bubble Point	(1 atm)	°F	–49.9
Dew Point	(1 atm)	°F	–38.0
Bubble Point Pressure	(70°F)	psia	163.2
Estimated Critical Temperature		°F	181.4
Latent Heat Vaporization	(Tm=70°F)	Btu/lb	78.92
Trouton's Constant		Btu/lb R	0.251
Coeff. Vol. Therm. Exp. (liquid, 32–68°F)		$°F^{-1}$	0.00178
Density (sat vapor) at 1 atm		lb/ft^3	0.246

Equation of State (Martin-Hou)

$$Pr = \frac{XTr}{Vr-B} + \sum_{i=1,4} \frac{(Ai + BiTr + Ciexp(-KTr))}{(Vr-B)^{(i+1)}}$$

Where:

Tr = T/Tc, Pr = P/Pc, Vr = V/Vc
X= 3.61723
B= 0.0
K= 5.475
Tc, Pc, Vc = 640.6 R, 658.6 psia, 0.032 cu.ft/lb

A1, B1, C1 = –11.33191275, 6.8075753325, –12.83650902
A2, B2, C2 = 9.1343011237, –5.94976187996, –107.94947217
A3, B3, C3 = –3.925317714, 0.0,0.0
A4, B4, C4 = 0.0, 13.694712938, –1247.8526238

Applicable Range: 0–400 psia, 0–180 R superheat

Saturation Envelope—Bubble Point Temperatures

Bubble Point Temperature (Tb) = $A + BX + CX^2 + DX^3$

Tb = Bubble Point Temperature in °F
X = Ln(P)
P = Pressure in psia

A = –136.5949
B = 31.7022
C = –1.479621
D = 0.62786

KLEA® 407A
Data Sheet

Saturation Envelope—Dew Point Temperatures

Dew Point Temperature (Td) = $A + BX + CX^2 + DX^3$

Td = Dew Point Temperature in °F
X = Ln(P)
P = Pressure in psia

A = –117.658
B = 26.18071
C = 0
D = 0.475794

Saturation Envelope—Mid Point Temperatures

Mid Point Temperature (Tm) = $A + BX + CX^2 + DX^3$

Tm = Average of Dew and Bubble Point Temperatures in °F
X = Ln(P)
P = Pressure in psia

A = –126.9154
B = 28.77087
C = –0.696455
D = 0.548338

Latent Heat Vaporization

$dh_{latent} = A + Bx + Cx^2 + Dx^3 + Ex^4$
Where $x = (1 - (Tm/Tc))^{(1/3)}$

A = –49.2509
B = 343.1947
C = –281.565
D = 140.195
E = 0

Tm = Mid Point Temperature R
Tc = Critical Temperature R
Tc = 640.6 R
dh_{latent} = Btu/lb

Ideal Gas Heat Capacity

$c_p(\text{ideal}) = A + BT + CT^2 + D/T$

A = 0
B = 0.00038745
C = –1.191 E–07
D = 12.058506

T = Temperature R
c_p(ideal) = Btu/lb R

Saturated Liquid Enthalpy

$h_{liquid} = A + Bx + Cx^2 + Dx^3 + Ex^4$
Where $x = (1 - (Tb/Tc))^{(1/3)}$

A = 131.38117
B = –202.8418
C = 201.7119
D = –256.1254
E = 0

Tb = Bubble Point Temperature R
Tc = Critical Temperature R
Tc = 640.6 R
h_{liquid} = Btu/lb

KLEA® 407A
Data Sheet

Liquid Density

$$\rho_{liquid} = A + Bx + Cx^2 + Dx^3 + Ex^4$$
$$\text{Where } x = (1 - (Tb/Tc))^{(1/3)}$$

A =	–22.2403	Tb =	Bubble Point Temperature R
B =	324.5572	Tc =	Critical Temperature R
C =	–416.6396	Tc =	640.6 R
D =	249.6117	ρ_{liquid} =	lb/ft³
E =	0		

Liquid Viscosity

$$\ln(\mu)\ liquid = A + B/Tm + CTm$$

A =	3.148664	μ liquid = cP
B =	–327.43764	Tm = Mid Point Temperature R
C =	–0.0081733	

Liquid Thermal Conductivity

$$K(liquid) = A + Bx + Cx^2 + Dx^3$$
$$\text{Where } x = (1 - (Tm/Tc))^{(1/3)}$$

A =	0.0352464	Tc = 640.6 R
B =	–0.0177842	K(liquid) = Btu/hr.ft.R
C =	0.0391964	Tm = Mid Point Temperature R
D =	0.0722151	Tc = Critical Temperature R

Saturated Vapor Density

$$\rho_{vapor} = A + Bx + Cx^2 + Dx^3 + Ex^4$$
$$\text{Where } x = (1 - (Td/Tc))^{(1/3)}$$

A =	33.90555	Td =	Dew Point Temperature R
B =	–76.47105	Tc =	Critical Temperature R
C =	21.41245	Tc =	640.6 R
D =	27.51538	ρ_{vapor} =	lb/ft³
E =	0		

Vapor Viscosity (Ideal Vapor)

$$\mu_{vapor} = A + BT + CT^2$$

A =	–0.001349	T = Temperature R
B =	0.00002988	μ_{vapor} = cP
C =	–4.676E–09	

Vapor Viscosity (Sat Vapor)

$$\mu_{vapor} = A + BTd + CTd^2 + DTd^3$$

A =	–0.079123	μ_{vapor} = cP
B =	0.00053269	Td = Dew Point Temperature R
C =	–1.09023E–06	
D =	7.84820E–10	

KLEA® 407A
Data Sheet

Vapor Thermal Conductivity (Ideal Vapor)

$$K(vapor) = A + BT + CT^2$$

A = −0.0025242	T	= Temperature R
B = 0.00001397	K(vapor)	= Btu/hr.ft.R
C = 1.12407E −08		

Vapor Thermal Conductivity (Sat Vapor)

$$K(vapor) = A + BTd + CTd^2 + DTd^3$$

A = −0.0559971	K(vapor) = Btu/hr.ft.R
B = 0.00035354	Td = Dew Point Temperature R
C = −7.11567E−07	
D = 5.17638E−10	

Speed of Sound (Sat Vapor)

$$U(vapor) = A + BTd + CTd^2 + D/Td$$

A = −2993.2087	U(vapor) = ft/s
B = 9.38958151	Td = Dew Point Temperature R
C = −0.0079965	
D = 416651.575	

Saturation Envelope

Pressure psia	Temperatures (°F) Bubble Point	Mid Point	Dew Point
10.0	−63.8	−57.7	−51.6
14.7	−49.9	−44.0	−38.0
20.0	−38.0	−32.2	−26.4
30.0	−21.2	−15.5	−9.9
50.0	2.4	7.8	13.2
70.0	19.5	24.8	30.1
100.0	39.3	44.4	49.4
150.0	64.1	68.7	73.4
200.0	83.2	87.5	91.8
250.0	99.0	103.0	107.0
300.0	112.6	116.3	120.0
350.0	124.6	127.9	131.3
400.0	135.3	138.4	141.5

KLEA® 407A
Data Sheet

Liquid Properties

Temp °F	Liquid Density lb/ft³	Liquid Enth Btu/lb	Latent Heat Btu/lb	Liquid Viscosity cP	Liq. Therm Cond Btu/ hr.ft.R
–60.00	88.83	–6.27	104.5	0.39	0.070
–40.00	86.55	0.00	101.3	0.35	0.067
–20.00	84.23	6.34	97.9	0.30	0.064
0.00	81.85	12.79	94.3	0.27	0.061
20.00	79.38	19.36	90.4	0.23	0.058
40.00	76.77	26.09	86.2	0.20	0.055
60.00	73.96	33.05	81.4	0.18	0.052
68.00	72.76	35.91	79.4	0.17	0.050
80.00	70.84	40.31	76.1	0.15	0.048
100.00	67.25	48.03	69.8	0.13	0.045
120.00	62.84	56.46	62.1	0.12	0.042

The temperatures used for liquid density and liquid enthalpy are bubble point temperatures. The rest are mid point temperatures.

Ideal Gas Properties

Temp °F	ID. Gas Heat Cap. Btu/lb R	ID. Gas Viscosity cP	ID. Gas Therm Cond. Btu/hr.ft.R
–60.00	0.166	0.0098	0.0049
–40.00	0.170	0.0104	0.0053
–20.00	0.175	0.0109	0.0058
0.00	0.179	0.0114	0.0063
20.00	0.184	0.0119	0.0068
40.00	0.188	0.0124	0.0073
60.00	0.192	0.0129	0.0078
68.00	0.194	0.0131	0.0080
80.00	0.197	0.0134	0.0083
100.00	0.201	0.0139	0.0088
120.00	0.205	0.0144	0.0094

Saturated Vapor Properties

Temp °F	Sat Vap Density lb/ft³	Sat Vap Viscosity cP	Sat Vap Therm. Cond Btu/hr.ft.R	Speed of Sound ft/s
–60.00	0.212	0.0097	0.0047	524.7
–40.00	0.298	0.0104	0.0053	531.8
–20.00	0.463	0.0110	0.0059	536.9
0.00	0.721	0.0116	0.0064	539.7
20.00	1.091	0.0122	0.0070	539.4
40.00	1.598	0.0128	0.0076	535.8
60.00	2.278	0.0134	0.0082	528.5
68.00	2.610	0.0137	0.0085	524.5
80.00	3.185	0.0142	0.0089	517.2
100.00	4.402	0.0151	0.0097	501.6
120.00	6.077	0.0162	0.0107	481.4

The Temperatures used are dew point temperatures.

Standard States

Enthalpy (–40°F, liquid = 0)

Entropy (–40°F, liquid = 0)

ICI Klea
Concord Plaza
3411 Silverside Road
P.O. Box 15391
Wilmington, DE 19850

Customer Service: (800) ICI-KLEA
Technical Assistance: (800) ASK-KLEA
Fax: (302) 887-7706

620250550 12/94

KLEA® 407B (KLEA 61) Data Sheet

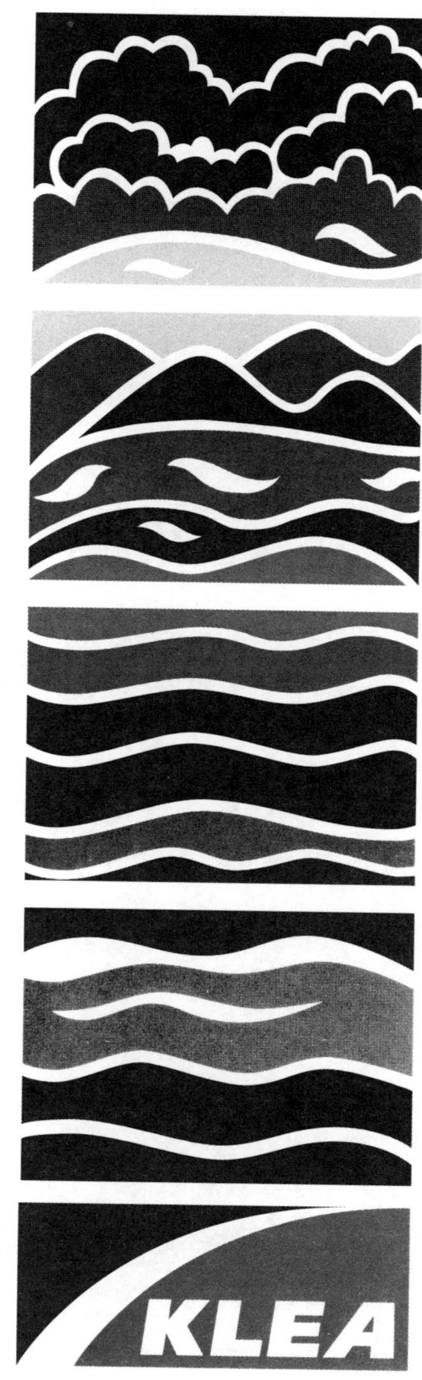

ICI Klea

KLEA® 407B
Data Sheet

KLEA® 407B is a blend of HFCs 32, 125 and 134a designed for use in existing low-temperature refrigeration equipment which is sensitive to discharge temperatures higher than R-502. For information on the properties and safe handling of KLEA 407B, please refer to the Material Safety Data Sheet supplied with the product or available upon request.

The data presented here represents a combination of measurements and estimation. ICI Chemicals & Polymers Limited does not guarantee its accuracy and reserves the right to update the information in the future, in the light of the best available knowledge at the time.

The contents of this note are given in good faith but without any liability attaching to ICI Chemicals & Polymers Limited and it is the user's responsibility to satisfy himself that the product is entirely suitable for his purpose. Freedom from rights must not be assumed.

Property		Units	Value
Bubble Point	(1 atm)	°F	–53.1
Dew Point	(1 atm)	°F	–45.2
Bubble Point Pressure	(70°F)	psia	172.0
Estimated Critical Temperature		°F	168.8
Latent Heat Vaporization	(Tm=70°F)	Btu/lb	63.95
Trouton's Constant		Btu/lb R	0.214
Coeff. Vol. Therm. Exp. (liquid, 32–68°F)		$°F^{-1}$	0.0019
Density (sat vapor) at 1 atm		lb/ft^3	0.348

Equation of State (Martin-Hou)

$$Pr = \frac{XTr}{Vr-B} + \sum_{i=1,4} \frac{(Ai + BiTr + Ciexp(-KTr))}{(Vr-B)^{(i+1)}}$$

Where:

Tr = T/Tc, Pr = P/Pc, Vr = V/Vc
X= 3.59793
B= 0.0
K= 5.475
Tc, Pc, Vc = 628.0 R, 602.8 psia, 0.0302 cu.ft/lb

A1, B1, C1 = –11.060869985, 6.6276740769, –12.981936829
A2, B2, C2 = 8.6098852152, –5.5894832285, –105.81416821
A3, B3, C3 = –2.9039539963, 0.0, 0.0
A4, B4, C4 = 0.0, 9.390662938, –978.64615574

Applicable Range: 0–400 psia, 0–180 R superheat

Saturation Envelope—Bubble Point Temperatures

Bubble Point Temperature (Tb) = $A + BX + CX^2 + DX^3$

Tb = Bubble Point Temperature in °F
X = Ln(P)
P = Pressure in psia

A = –137.976
B = 30.37525
C = –1.159337
D = 0.598706

KLEA® 407B
Data Sheet

Saturation Envelope—Dew Point Temperatures

Dew Point Temperature (Td) = $A + BX + CX^2 + DX^3$

Td = Dew Point Temperature in °F
X = Ln(P)
P = Pressure in psia

A = −123.6996
B = 25.67597
C = 0
D = 0.485421

Saturation Envelope—Mid Point Temperatures

Mid Point Temperature (Tm) = $A + BX + CX^2 + DX^3$

Tm = Average of Dew and Bubble Point Temperatures in °F
X = Ln(P)
P = Pressure in psia

A = −131.1662
B = 28.2911
C = −0.647145
D = 0.547493

Latent Heat Vaporization

$dh_{latent} = A + Bx + Cx^2 + Dx^3 + Ex^4$
Where $x = (1 - (Tm/Tc))^{(1/3)}$

A = −37.930755
B = 264.769088
C = −187.74321
D = 89.4019401
E = 0

Tm = Mid Point Temperature R
Tc = Critical Temperature R
Tc = 628.0 R
DHvap = Btu/lb

Ideal Gas Heat Capacity

$c_p(\text{ideal}) = A + BT + CT^2 + D/T$

A = 0.01049043
B = 0.00038399
C = −1.303E−07
D = 8.0051616

T = Temperature R
c_p(ideal) = Btu/lb R

Saturated Liquid Enthalpy

$h_{liquid} = A + Bx + Cx^2 + Dx^3 + Ex^4$
Where $x = (1 - (Tb/Tc))^{(1/3)}$

A = 108.711344
B = −138.86951
C = 104.542407
D = −188.92302
E = 0

Tb = Bubble Point Temperature R
Tc = Critical Temperature R
Tc = 628.0 R
h_{liquid} = Btu/lb

KLEA® 407B
Data Sheet

Liquid Density

$$\rho_{liquid} = A + Bx + Cx^2 + Dx^3 + Ex^4$$
$$\text{Where } x = (1 - (Tb/Tc))^{(1/3)}$$

A	=	−0.845302	Tb	=	Bubble Point Temperature R
B	=	230.294208	Tc	=	Critical Temperature R
C	=	−258.36608	Tc	=	628.0 R
D	=	165.09403	ρ_{liquid}	=	lb/ft^3
E	=	0			

Liquid Viscosity

$$\ln(\mu)\ liquid = A + B/Tm + CTm$$

A	=	2.414924	μ liquid = cP
B	=	−166.76928	Tm = Mid Point Temperature R
C	=	−0.0074472	

Liquid Thermal Conductivity

$$K(liquid) = A + Bx + Cx^2 + Dx^3$$
$$\text{Where } x = (1 - (Tm/Tc))^{(1/3)}$$

A	=	0.04753921	Tm = Mid Point Temperature R
B	=	−0.0958786	Tc = Critical Temperature R
C	=	0.16260634	Tc= 628.0 R
D	=	0	K(liquid) = Btu/hr.ft.R

Saturated Vapor Density

$$\rho_{vapor} = A + Bx + Cx^2 + Dx^3 + Ex^4$$
$$\text{Where } x = (1 - (Td/Tc))^{(1/3)}$$

A	=	33.3492623	Td	=	Dew Point Temperature R
B	=	−52.142019	Tc	=	Critical Temperature R
C	=	−68.928316	Tc	=	628.0 R
D	=	145.976953	ρ_{vapor}	=	lb/ft^3
E	=	−53.333645			

Vapor Viscosity (Ideal Vapor)

$$\mu_{vapor} = A + BT + CT^2$$

A	=	0	T = Temperature R
B	=	0.00002526	μ_{vapor} = cP
C	=	−5.251E−10	

Vapor Viscosity (Sat Vapor)

$$\mu_{vapor} = A + BTd + CTd^2 + DTd^3$$

A	=	−0.129443	μ_{vapor} = cP
B	=	0.0008556444	Td = Dew Point Temperature R
C	=	−1.77873E−06	
D	=	1.27406E−09	

KLEA® 407B
Data Sheet

Vapor Thermal Conductivity (Ideal Vapor)			
$K(vapor) = A + BT + CT^2$			
A	=	−0.0026324	T = Temperature R
B	=	0.0000155798	K(vapor) = Btu/hr.ft.R
C	=	9.46973E–09	

Vapor Thermal Conductivity (Sat Vapor)			
$K(vapor) = A + BTd + CTd^2 + DTd^3$			
A	=	−0.0868073	K(vapor) = Btu/hr.ft.R
B	=	0.00054822	Td = Dew Point Temperature R
C	=	−1.11668E–06	
D	=	7.97768E–10	

Speed of Sound (Sat Vapor)			
$U(vapor) = A + BTd + CTd^2 + D/Td$			
A	=	−3026.2467	U(vapor) = ft/s
B	=	9.38575386	Td = Dew Point Temperature R
C	=	−0.0080664	
D	=	416232.283	

Saturation Envelope

Pressure psia	Temperatures (°F) Bubble Point	Mid Point	Dew Point
10.0	−66.9	−62.8	−58.7
14.7	−53.1	−49.2	−45.3
20.0	−41.3	−37.5	−33.7
30.0	−24.5	−20.9	−17.3
50.0	−1.0	2.4	5.8
70.0	16.1	19.3	22.6
100.0	35.8	38.9	42.0
150.0	60.4	63.2	66.0
200.0	79.5	82.0	84.5
250.0	95.2	97.5	99.8
300.0	108.7	110.7	112.8
350.0	120.5	122.4	124.3
400.0	131.2	132.9	134.5

KLEA® 407B
Data Sheet

Liquid Properties

Temp °F	Liquid Density lb/ft³	Liquid Enth Btu/lb	Latent Heat Btu/lb	Liquid Viscosity cP	Llq. Therm Cond Btu/ hr.ft.R
–60.00	91.93	–5.84	87.9	0.38	0.062
–40.00	89.53	0.00	85.0	0.33	0.059
–20.00	87.06	5.94	82.0	0.29	0.056
0.00	84.49	11.99	78.7	0.25	0.053
20.00	81.78	18.19	75.1	0.22	0.050
40.00	78.90	24.57	71.2	0.19	0.047
60.00	75.77	31.21	66.7	0.17	0.045
68.00	74.42	33.95	64.7	0.16	0.043
80.00	72.27	38.19	61.6	0.15	0.042
100.00	68.18	45.68	55.4	0.13	0.039
120.00	63.08	54.01	47.6	0.11	0.036

The temperatures used for liquid density and liquid enthalpy are bubble point temperatures. The rest are mid point temperatures.

Ideal Gas Properties

Temp °F	ID. Gas Heat Cap. Btu/lb R	ID. Gas Viscosity cP	ID. Gas Therm Cond. Btu/hr.ft.R
–60.00	0.163	0.0100	0.0051
–40.00	0.168	0.0105	0.0056
–20.00	0.172	0.0110	0.0060
0.00	0.177	0.0115	0.0065
20.00	0.181	0.0120	0.0070
40.00	0.186	0.0125	0.0075
60.00	0.190	0.0130	0.0080
68.00	0.192	0.0132	0.0082
80.00	0.195	0.0135	0.0085
100.00	0.199	0.0140	0.0091
120.00	0.203	0.0145	0.0096

Saturated Vapor Properties

Temp °F	Sat Vap Density lb/ft³	Sat Vap Viscosity cP	Sat Vap Therm. Cond Btu/hr.ft.R	Speed of Sound ft/s
–60.00	0.256	0.0097	0.0049	477.9
–40.00	0.400	0.0105	0.0056	483.8
–20.00	0.637	0.0112	0.0062	487.8
0.00	0.985	0.0118	0.0067	489.2
20.00	1.472	0.0123	0.0073	487.6
40.00	2.134	0.0129	0.0078	482.6
60.00	3.023	0.0137	0.0085	473.8
68.00	3.459	0.0140	0.0088	469.2
80.00	4.220	0.0145	0.0092	460.9
100.00	5.858	0.0156	0.0101	443.7
120.00	8.185	0.0170	0.0111	422.0

The temperatures used are dew point temperatures

Standard States
Enthalpy (–40°F, liquid = 0)
Entropy (–40°F, liquid = 0)

ICI Klea
Concord Plaza
3411 Silverside Road
P.O. Box 15391
Wilmington, DE 19850

Customer Service: (800) ICI-KLEA
Technical Assistance: (800) ASK-KLEA
Fax: (302) 887-7706

620250580 12/94

KLEA® 407C (KLEA 66) Data Sheet

ICI Klea

KLEA® 407C
Data Sheet

KLEA® 407C is a blend of HFCs 32, 125 and 134a designed to replace HCFC-22 in new air conditioning and low-temperature refrigeration equipment and also for retrofit in many existing systems. KLEA 407C offers the optimal combination of minimal environmental impact with favorable technical performance. For information on the properties and safe handling of KLEA 407C, please refer to the Material Safety Data Sheet supplied with the product or available upon request.

The data presented here represents a combination of measurements and estimation. ICI Chemicals & Polymers Limited does not guarantee its accuracy and reserves the right to update the information in the future, in the light of the best available knowledge at the time.

The contents of this note are given in good faith but without any liability attaching to ICI Chemicals & Polymers Limited and it is the user's responsibility to satisfy himself that the product is entirely suitable for his purpose. Freedom from rights must not be assumed.

Property		Units	Value
Bubble Point	(1 atm)	°F	–47.2
Dew Point	(1 atm)	°F	–34.2
Bubble Point Pressure	(70°F)	psia	156
Estimated Critical Temperature		°F	187
Latent Heat Vaporization	(Tm=70°F)	Btu/lb	85.3
Trouton's Constant		Btu/lb R	0.265
Coeff. Vol. Therm. Exp. (liquid, 60°F)		$°R^{-1}$	0.0019
Density (sat vapor) at 1 atm		lb/ft^3	0.285

Equation of State (Martin-Hou)

$$Pr = + \frac{XTr}{Vr-B} + \sum_{i=1,4} \frac{(Ai + BiTr + Ciexp(-KTr))}{(Vr-B)^{(i+1)}}$$

Where:

Tr = T/Tc, Pr = P/Pc, Vr = V/Vc
X = 3.649216
B = 0.0
K = 5.475
Tc, Pc, Vc = 646.6, R 674.7 psia, 0.0327 cu. ft/lb

A1, B1, C1 = –11.576411672, 6.9516394791, –12.992106787
A2, B2, C2 = 9.108927853, –5.8551996466, –101.85219827
A3, B3, C3 = –4.2674117378, 0.0, 0.0
A4, B4, C4 = 17.976354749, 0.0, –1992.5643203

Applicable Range: 0–400 psia, 0–180 R superheat

Saturation Envelope—Bubble Point Temperatures

Bubble Point Temperature (Tb) = $A + BX + CX^2 + DX^3 + EX^4$

Tb = Bubble Point Temperature in °F
X = Ln(P)
P = Pressure in psia

A = –123.1417
B = 19.59164
C = 3.35685
D = –0.181209
E = 0.049304

KLEA® 407C
Data Sheet

Saturation Envelope—Dew Point Temperatures

Dew Point Temperature (Td) = $A + BX + CX^2 + DX^3 + EX^4$

Td = Dew Point Temperature in °F
X = Ln(P)
P = Pressure in psia

A = −119.0841
B = 31.31686
C = −1.91995
D = 0.804863
E = −0.020383

Saturation Envelope—Mid Point Temperatures

Mid Point Temperature (Tm) = $A + BX + CX^2 + DX^3 + EX^4$

Tm = Average of Dew and Bubble Point Temperatures in °F
X = Ln(P)
P = Pressure in psia

A = −121.1129
B = 25.45425
C = 0.718449
D = 0.311827
E = 0.0144605

Latent Heat Vaporization

$dh_{latent} = A + Bx + Cx^2 + Dx^3 + Ex^4$
Where $x = (1 - (Tm/Tc))^{(1/3)}$

A = 94.0883061
B = −723.65623
C = 2719.42721
D = −3539.0967
E = 1670.0172

Tm = Mid Point Temperature R
Tc = Critical Temperature R
Tc = 646.6 R
dh_{latent} = Btu/lb

Ideal Gas Heat Capacity

cp(ideal) = $A + BT + CT^2 + D/T$

A = −2.002556E−2
B = 4.26626E−4
C = −1.430584E−7
D = 15.630503

T = Temperature R
Cp(ideal) = Btu/lb R

Saturated Liquid Enthalpy

$h_{liquid} = A + Bx + Cx^2 + Dx^3 + Ex^4$
Where $x = (1 - (Tb/Tc))^{(1/3)}$

A = 37.5396507
B = 526.55632
C = −1811.0258
D = 2169.01685
E = −1087.0894

Tb = Bubble Point Temperature R
Tc = Critical Temperature R
Tc = 646.6 R
h_{liquid} = Btu/lb

KLEA® 407C Data Sheet

Liquid Density

$$\rho_{liquid} = A + Bx + Cx^2 + Dx^3 + Ex^4$$
$$\text{Where } x = (1 - (Tb/Tc))^{(1/3)}$$

A = −40.606805	Tb =	Bubble Point Temperature R
B = 490.787461	Tc =	Critical Temperature R
C = −955.92001	Tc =	646.6 R
D = 980.476064	ρ_{liquid} =	lb/ft³
E = −357.97408		

Liquid Viscosity

$$\ln(\mu)\ \text{liquid} = A + B/Tm + CTm + DTm^2$$

A = 15.66442	μ_{liquid} = cP
B = −2309.4954	Tm = Mid Point Temperature R
C = −0.0341689	
D = 0.00001796	

Liquid Thermal Conductivity

$$K(\text{liquid}) = A + BTm + CTm^2 + D/Tm$$

A = 0.06874537	Tm = Mid Point Temperature R
B = 0	K(liquid) = Btu/hr.ft.R
C = −1.198298E−7	
D = 9.40172848	

Saturated Vapor Density

$$\rho_{vapor} = A + Bx + Cx^2 + Dx^3 + Ex^4$$
$$\text{Where } x = (1 - (Td/Tc))^{(1/3)}$$

A = 19.6903406	Td =	Dew Point Temperature R
B = 21.4442365	Tc =	Critical Temperature R
C = −242.43767	Tc =	646.6 R
D = 348.817574	ρ_{vapor} =	lb/ft³
E = −146.90014		

Vapor Viscosity (Ideal Vapor)

$$\mu_{vapor} = A + BT + CT^2$$

A = −0.0013724	T = Temperature R
B = 0.00002977	μ_{vapor} = cP
C = −4.726E−09	

Vapor Viscosity (Sat Vapor)

$$\mu_{vapor} = A + BTd + CTd^2 + D/Td$$

A = 0.375554	μ_{vapor} = cP
B = −0.0007599	TD = Dew Point Temperature R
C = 5.489E−07	
D = −60.07482	

KLEA® 407C
Data Sheet

Vapor Thermal Conductivity (Ideal Vapor)

$K(vapor) = A + BT + CT^2$

A = −2.054908E−3	T = Temperature R
B = 1.1506995E−5	K(vapor) = Btu/hr.ft.R
C = 1.3817671E−8	

Vapor Thermal Conductivity (Sat Vapor)

$K(vapor) = A + BTd + CTd^2 + D/Td$

A = 0.24578002	K(vapor) = Btu/hr.ft.R
B = −5.0217916E−4	Td = Dew Point Temperature R
C = 3.7181456E−7	
D = −40.089109	

Speed of Sound (Sat Vapor)

$U(vapor) = A + BTd + CTd^2 + D/Td$

A = −2854.0469	U(vapor) = ft/s
B = 8.98147237	Td = Dew Point Temperature R
C = −7.595246E−3	
D = 406179.685	

Saturation Envelope

Pressure psia	Temperatures (°F) Bubble Point	Mid Point	Dew Point
10.0	−61.1	−54.5	−47.9
20.0	−35.2	−28.9	−22.5
30.0	−18.2	−12.0	−5.8
50.0	5.6	11.5	17.5
70.0	22.9	28.6	34.4
100.0	42.7	48.3	53.9
150.0	67.6	72.8	78.0
200.0	86.8	91.7	96.6
250.0	102.7	107.3	111.8
300.0	116.4	120.6	124.9
350.0	128.4	132.4	136.3
400.0	139.3	142.9	146.5

KLEA® 407C
Data Sheet

Temp °F	Liquid Density lb/ft³	Liquid Enth Btu/lb	Latent Heat Btu/lb	Liquid Viscosity cP	Llq. Therm Cond Btu/ hr.ft.R
Liquid Properties					
–60.00	87.55	–6.58	111.7	0.41	0.073
–40.00	85.45	0.00	108.0	0.36	0.070
–20.00	83.27	6.56	104.4	0.32	0.067
0.00	80.99	13.15	100.7	0.28	0.064
20.00	78.61	19.81	96.74	0.24	0.061
40.00	76.08	26.61	92.51	0.21	0.058
60.00	73.38	33.62	87.84	0.19	0.054
68.00	71.94	37.24	85.28	0.18	0.053
80.00	70.43	40.95	82.52	0.16	0.051
100.00	67.11	48.74	76.26	0.14	0.048
120.00	63.18	57.20	68.66	0.12	0.045

The temperatures used for liquid density and liquid enthalpy are bubble point temperatures. The rest are mid point temperatures.

Temp °F	ID. Gas Heat Cap. Btu/lb R	ID. Gas Viscosity cP	ID. Gas Therm Cond. Btu/hr.ft.R
Ideal Gas Properties			
–60.00	0.167	0.0098	.0048
–40.00	0.171	0.0103	.0052
–20.00	0.175	0.0108	.0057
0.00	0.180	0.0113	.0062
20.00	0.184	0.0118	.0066
40.00	0.189	0.0123	.0071
60.00	0.193	0.0128	.0077
68.00	0.195	0.0130	.0079
80.00	0.198	0.0133	.0082
100.00	0.202	0.0138	.0087
120.00	0.206	0.0143	.0093

Temp °F	Sat Vap Density lb/ft³	Sat Vap Viscosity cP	Sat Vap Therm. Cond Btu/hr.ft.	Speed of Sound ft/s
Saturated Vapor Properties				
–60.00	0.145	0.0092	.0042	539
–40.00	0.246	0.0102	.0050	545
–20.00	0.404	0.0109	.0057	550
0.00	0.633	0.0115	.0063	553
20.00	0.954	0.0121	.0069	553
40.00	1.39	0.0127	.0075	550
60.00	1.98	0.0133	.0081	544
68.00	2.35	0.0135	.0084	539
80.00	2.77	0.0140	.0088	534
100.00	3.83	0.0148	.0096	519
120.00	5.28	0.0158	.0105	501

The Temperatures used are dew point temperatures.

Standard States
Enthalpy (–40°F, liquid = 0)
Entropy (–40°F, liquid = 0)

ICI Klea
Concord Plaza
3411 Silverside Road
P.O. Box 15391
Wilmington, DE 19850

Customer Service: (800) ICI-KLEA
Technical Assistance: (800) ASK-KLEA
Fax: (302) 887-7706

620250610 12/94

Th dynamic Properties of A® 134a

Units

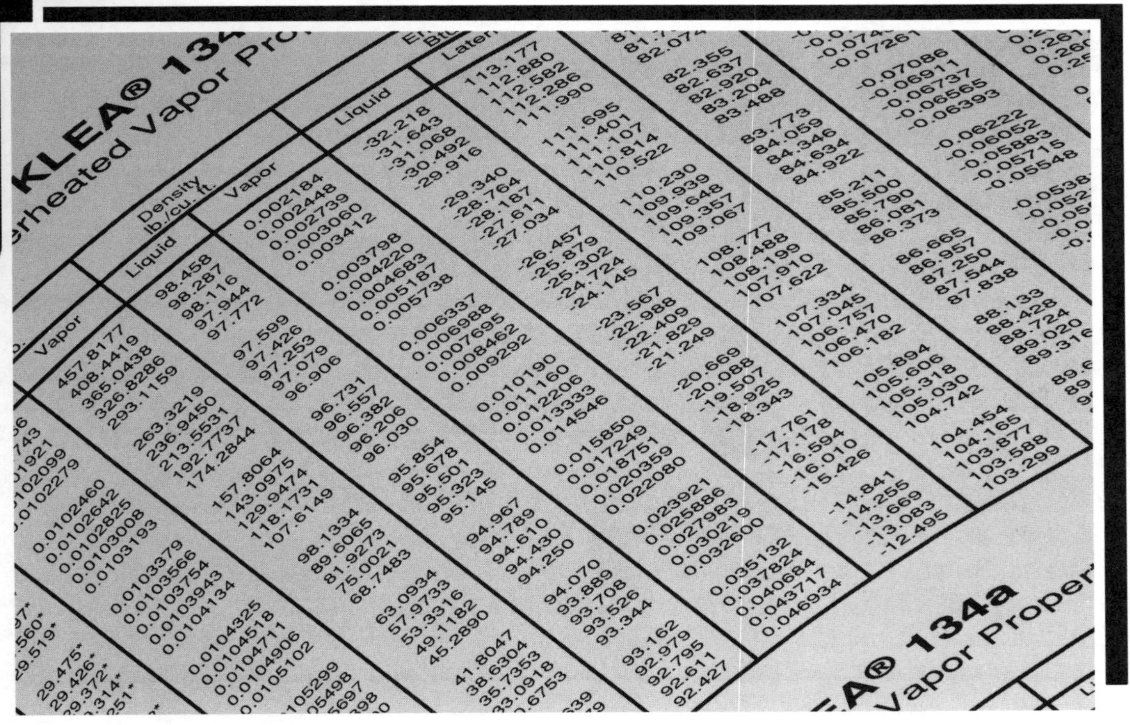

**NOW.
AND FOR
THE FUTURE.**

KLEA® 134a

Saturation Properties

Temp. °F	Pressure lb./sq. in.		Volume cu. ft./lb.		Density lb./cu. ft.		Enthalpy Btu/lb.			Entropy Btu/(lb. °F)		Temp. °R
	Absolute	Gauge	Liquid	Vapor	Liquid	Vapor	Liquid	Latent	Vapor	Liquid	Vapor	
-150	0.07107	29.776*	0.0101566	457.8177	98.458	0.002184	-32.218	113.177	80.959	-0.08888	0.27659	309.67
-148	0.08017	29.758*	0.0101743	408.4419	98.287	0.002448	-31.643	112.880	81.236	-0.08703	0.27514	311.67
-146	0.09027	29.737*	0.0101921	365.0438	98.116	0.002739	-31.068	112.582	81.515	-0.08519	0.27373	313.67
-144	0.10146	29.714*	0.0102099	326.8286	97.944	0.003060	-30.492	112.286	81.794	-0.08336	0.27234	315.67
-142	0.11383	29.689*	0.0102279	293.1159	97.772	0.003412	-29.916	111.990	82.074	-0.08154	0.27099	317.67
-140	0.12749	29.661*	0.0102460	263.3219	97.599	0.003798	-29.340	111.695	82.355	-0.07974	0.26967	319.67
-138	0.14255	29.631*	0.0102642	236.9450	97.426	0.004220	-28.764	111.401	82.637	-0.07794	0.26838	321.67
-136	0.15913	29.597*	0.0102825	213.5531	97.253	0.004683	-28.187	111.107	82.920	-0.07615	0.26712	323.67
-134	0.17735	29.560*	0.0103008	192.7737	97.079	0.005187	-27.611	110.814	83.204	-0.07438	0.26589	325.67
-132	0.19733	29.519*	0.0103193	174.2844	96.906	0.005738	-27.034	110.522	83.488	-0.07261	0.26469	327.67
-130	0.21923	29.475*	0.0103379	157.8064	96.731	0.006337	-26.457	110.230	83.773	-0.07086	0.26351	329.67
-128	0.24319	29.426*	0.0103566	143.0975	96.557	0.006988	-25.879	109.939	84.059	-0.06911	0.26236	331.67
-126	0.26936	29.372*	0.0103754	129.9474	96.382	0.007695	-25.302	109.648	84.346	-0.06737	0.26124	333.67
-124	0.29791	29.314*	0.0103943	118.1731	96.206	0.008462	-24.724	109.357	84.634	-0.06565	0.26014	335.67
-122	0.32902	29.251*	0.0104134	107.6149	96.030	0.009292	-24.145	109.067	84.922	-0.06393	0.25907	337.67
-120	0.36286	29.182*	0.0104325	98.1334	95.854	0.010190	-23.567	108.777	85.211	-0.06222	0.25802	339.67
-118	0.39963	29.107*	0.0104518	89.6065	95.678	0.011160	-22.988	108.488	85.500	-0.06052	0.25700	341.67
-116	0.43953	29.026*	0.0104711	81.9273	95.501	0.012206	-22.409	108.199	85.790	-0.05883	0.25600	343.67
-114	0.48278	28.938*	0.0104906	75.0021	95.323	0.013333	-21.829	107.910	86.081	-0.05715	0.25503	345.67
-112	0.52959	28.843*	0.0105102	68.7483	95.145	0.014546	-21.249	107.622	86.373	-0.05548	0.25407	347.67
-110	0.58021	28.740*	0.0105299	63.0934	94.967	0.015850	-20.669	107.334	86.665	-0.05381	0.25314	349.67
-108	0.63486	28.628*	0.0105498	57.9733	94.789	0.017249	-20.088	107.045	86.957	-0.05216	0.25223	351.67
-106	0.69381	28.508*	0.0105697	53.3316	94.610	0.018751	-19.507	106.757	87.250	-0.05051	0.25135	353.67
-104	0.75732	28.379*	0.0105898	49.1182	94.430	0.020359	-18.925	106.470	87.544	-0.04887	0.25048	355.67
-102	0.82567	28.240*	0.0106100	45.2890	94.250	0.022080	-18.343	106.182	87.838	-0.04724	0.24963	357.67
-100	0.89915	28.090*	0.0106304	41.8047	94.070	0.023921	-17.761	105.894	88.133	-0.04562	0.24880	359.67
-98	0.97805	27.930*	0.0106508	38.6304	93.889	0.025886	-17.178	105.606	88.428	-0.04400	0.24800	361.67
-96	1.06269	27.757*	0.0106714	35.7353	93.708	0.027983	-16.594	105.318	88.724	-0.04239	0.24721	363.67
-94	1.15339	27.573*	0.0106922	33.0918	93.526	0.030219	-16.010	105.030	89.020	-0.04079	0.24644	365.67
-92	1.25048	27.375*	0.0107130	30.6753	93.344	0.032600	-15.426	104.742	89.316	-0.03920	0.24568	367.67
-90	1.35432	27.163*	0.0107340	28.4639	93.162	0.035132	-14.841	104.454	89.613	-0.03761	0.24495	369.67
-88	1.46527	26.938*	0.0107552	26.4379	92.979	0.037824	-14.255	104.165	89.910	-0.03603	0.24423	371.67
-86	1.58369	26.696*	0.0107764	24.5799	92.795	0.040684	-13.669	103.877	90.208	-0.03446	0.24353	373.67
-84	1.70998	26.439*	0.0107978	22.8742	92.611	0.043717	-13.083	103.588	90.505	-0.03289	0.24285	375.67
-82	1.84453	26.165*	0.0108194	21.3067	92.427	0.046934	-12.495	103.299	90.803	-0.03134	0.24218	377.67

* = in. Hg, Vacuum

Temp. °F	Pressure lb./sq. in.		Volume cu. ft./lb.		Density lb./cu. ft.		Enthalpy Btu/lb.			Entropy Btu/(lb. °F)		Temp. °R
	Absolute	Gauge	Liquid	Vapor	Liquid	Vapor	Liquid	Latent	Vapor	Liquid	Vapor	
-80	1.98775	25.874*	0.0108411	19.8646	92.242	0.050341	-11.907	103.009	91.102	-0.02978	0.24153	379.67
-78	2.14006	25.564*	0.0108629	18.5368	92.056	0.053947	-11.319	102.719	91.400	-0.02824	0.24089	381.67
-76	2.30192	25.234*	0.0108849	17.3129	91.870	0.057760	-10.730	102.429	91.699	-0.02670	0.24027	383.67
-74	2.47375	24.884*	0.0109071	16.1838	91.684	0.061790	-10.140	102.138	91.998	-0.02517	0.23966	385.67
-72	2.65604	24.513*	0.0109293	15.1410	91.497	0.066046	-9.549	101.846	92.297	-0.02364	0.23907	387.67
-70	2.84925	24.120*	0.0109518	14.1772	91.309	0.070536	-8.958	101.555	92.596	-0.02212	0.23850	389.67
-68	3.05388	23.703*	0.0109744	13.2856	91.121	0.075270	-8.366	101.262	92.896	-0.02061	0.23793	391.67
-66	3.27042	23.262*	0.0109972	12.4600	90.933	0.080257	-7.774	100.969	93.196	-0.01910	0.23738	393.67
-64	3.49940	22.796*	0.0110201	11.6948	90.743	0.085508	-7.180	100.676	93.495	-0.01760	0.23685	395.67
-62	3.74135	22.303*	0.0110432	10.9850	90.554	0.091033	-6.586	100.381	93.795	-0.01610	0.23632	397.67
-60	3.99680	21.783*	0.0110664	10.3261	90.363	0.096842	-5.992	100.086	94.095	-0.01461	0.23581	399.67
-58	4.26632	21.235*	0.0110898	9.71389	90.173	0.102945	-5.396	99.791	94.395	-0.01313	0.23531	401.67
-56	4.55047	20.656*	0.0111134	9.14461	89.981	0.109354	-4.800	99.494	94.694	-0.01165	0.23483	403.67
-54	4.84984	20.047*	0.0111372	8.61483	89.789	0.116079	-4.203	99.197	94.994	-0.01017	0.23435	405.67
-52	5.16503	19.405*	0.0111611	8.12140	89.597	0.123131	-3.605	98.899	95.294	-0.00870	0.23389	407.67
-50	5.49664	18.730*	0.0111853	7.66149	89.403	0.130523	-3.006	98.600	95.594	-0.00724	0.23344	409.67
-48	5.84529	18.020*	0.0112096	7.23249	89.210	0.138265	-2.407	98.300	95.894	-0.00578	0.23300	411.67
-46	6.21163	17.274*	0.0112340	6.83202	89.015	0.146370	-1.806	97.999	96.193	-0.00433	0.23257	413.67
-44	6.59629	16.491*	0.0112587	6.45791	88.820	0.154849	-1.205	97.698	96.493	-0.00288	0.23216	415.67
-42	6.99995	15.669*	0.0112836	6.10817	88.625	0.163715	-0.603	97.395	96.792	-0.00144	0.23175	417.67
-40	7.42327	14.807*	0.0113086	5.78097	88.428	0.172981	0.000	97.091	97.091	0.00000	0.23135	419.67
-38	7.86694	13.904*	0.0113339	5.47466	88.231	0.182660	0.604	96.786	97.390	0.00143	0.23096	421.67
-36	8.33166	12.958*	0.0113593	5.18770	88.034	0.192764	1.209	96.480	97.689	0.00286	0.23059	423.67
-34	8.81815	11.967*	0.0113849	4.91868	87.835	0.203307	1.814	96.173	97.988	0.00429	0.23022	425.67
-32	9.32712	10.931*	0.0114108	4.66631	87.636	0.214302	2.421	95.865	98.286	0.00571	0.22986	427.67
-30	9.85932	9.8473*	0.0114369	4.42941	87.437	0.225764	3.029	95.556	98.584	0.00712	0.22951	429.67
-28	10.4155	8.7149*	0.0114631	4.20689	87.236	0.237705	3.637	95.245	98.882	0.00853	0.22917	431.67
-26	10.9964	7.5322*	0.0114896	3.99773	87.035	0.250142	4.247	94.933	99.180	0.00994	0.22884	433.67
-24	11.6028	6.2975*	0.0115163	3.80102	86.833	0.263087	4.857	94.620	99.477	0.01134	0.22852	435.67
-22	12.2355	5.0093*	0.0115432	3.61589	86.631	0.276557	5.469	94.305	99.774	0.01273	0.22821	437.67
-20	12.8953	3.6660*	0.0115704	3.44157	86.428	0.290565	6.081	93.990	100.071	0.01413	0.22790	439.67
-18	13.5830	2.2658*	0.0115978	3.27731	86.223	0.305128	6.695	93.672	100.367	0.01552	0.22760	441.67
-16	14.2994	0.8072*	0.0116254	3.12245	86.019	0.320261	7.309	93.353	100.663	0.01690	0.22731	443.67
-14	15.0454	0.3495	0.0116532	2.97637	85.813	0.335979	7.925	93.033	100.958	0.01828	0.22703	445.67
-12	15.8217	1.1258	0.0116813	2.83849	85.607	0.352300	8.542	92.712	101.253	0.01966	0.22676	447.67

* = in. Hg. Vacuum

Temp. °F	Pressure lb./sq. in.		Volume cu. ft./lb.		Density lb./cu. ft.		Enthalpy Btu/lb.			Entropy Btu/(lb. °F)		Temp. °R
	Absolute	Gauge	Liquid	Vapor	Liquid	Vapor	Liquid	Latent	Vapor	Liquid	Vapor	
-10	16.6293	1.9334	0.0117097	2.70827	85.399	0.369239	9.160	92.388	101.548	0.02103	0.22649	449.67
-8	17.4690	2.7731	0.0117383	2.58523	85.191	0.386813	9.779	92.063	101.842	0.02240	0.22623	451.67
-6	18.3417	3.6458	0.0117671	2.46889	84.983	0.405040	10.399	91.737	102.136	0.02377	0.22598	453.67
-4	19.2482	4.5523	0.0117962	2.35885	84.773	0.423936	11.020	91.409	102.429	0.02513	0.22573	455.67
-2	20.1895	5.4936	0.0118256	2.25469	84.562	0.443519	11.642	91.079	102.721	0.02649	0.22549	457.67
0	21.1665	6.4706	0.0118552	2.15607	84.351	0.463808	12.265	90.748	103.013	0.02784	0.22526	459.67
2	22.1800	7.4841	0.0118852	2.06262	84.139	0.484820	12.890	90.414	103.305	0.02919	0.22504	461.67
4	23.2311	8.5352	0.0119154	1.97404	83.925	0.506574	13.516	90.079	103.595	0.03054	0.22482	463.67
6	24.3206	9.6247	0.0119458	1.89004	83.711	0.529090	14.143	89.743	103.885	0.03189	0.22460	465.67
8	25.4495	10.754	0.0119766	1.81033	83.496	0.552386	14.771	89.404	104.175	0.03323	0.22439	467.67
10	26.6188	11.923	0.0120077	1.73466	83.280	0.576483	15.400	89.063	104.464	0.03456	0.22419	469.67
12	27.8293	13.133	0.0120390	1.66279	83.063	0.601400	16.031	88.721	104.752	0.03590	0.22400	471.67
14	29.0822	14.386	0.0120707	1.59449	82.845	0.627158	16.663	88.376	105.039	0.03723	0.22381	473.67
16	30.3784	15.682	0.0121027	1.52957	82.626	0.653778	17.296	88.030	105.326	0.03856	0.22362	475.67
18	31.7188	17.023	0.0121350	1.46782	82.406	0.681281	17.930	87.681	105.611	0.03988	0.22344	477.67
20	33.1045	18.409	0.0121677	1.40907	82.185	0.709690	18.566	87.330	105.896	0.04120	0.22327	479.67
22	34.5364	19.841	0.0122006	1.35313	81.963	0.739026	19.203	86.978	106.181	0.04252	0.22310	481.67
24	36.0157	21.320	0.0122339	1.29986	81.740	0.769312	19.841	86.623	106.464	0.04384	0.22293	483.67
26	37.5433	22.847	0.0122676	1.24911	81.516	0.800571	20.481	86.265	106.746	0.04515	0.22277	485.67
28	39.1203	24.424	0.0123016	1.20073	81.290	0.832828	21.122	85.906	107.028	0.04646	0.22261	487.67
30	40.7478	26.052	0.0123360	1.15459	81.064	0.866106	21.764	85.544	107.308	0.04776	0.22246	489.67
32	42.4267	27.731	0.0123707	1.11058	80.836	0.900429	22.408	85.180	107.588	0.04907	0.22231	491.67
34	44.1581	29.462	0.0124059	1.06858	80.607	0.935825	23.053	84.813	107.866	0.05037	0.22217	493.67
36	45.9432	31.247	0.0124414	1.02847	80.377	0.972317	23.699	84.444	108.144	0.05167	0.22203	495.67
38	47.7830	33.087	0.0124773	0.99016	80.146	1.00993	24.347	84.073	108.420	0.05296	0.22190	497.67
40	49.6786	34.983	0.0125136	0.95356	79.913	1.04870	24.997	83.699	108.695	0.05426	0.22177	499.67
42	51.6311	36.935	0.0125503	0.91857	79.679	1.08865	25.647	83.322	108.969	0.05555	0.22164	501.67
44	53.6416	38.946	0.0125875	0.88511	79.444	1.12980	26.300	82.943	109.242	0.05684	0.22151	503.67
46	55.7112	41.015	0.0126250	0.85310	79.208	1.17220	26.953	82.561	109.514	0.05812	0.22139	505.67
48	57.8411	43.145	0.0126631	0.82247	78.970	1.21585	27.609	82.176	109.784	0.05941	0.22127	507.67
50	60.0323	45.336	0.0127015	0.79314	78.731	1.26081	28.265	81.788	110.054	0.06069	0.22116	509.67
52	62.2861	47.590	0.0127405	0.76505	78.490	1.30710	28.923	81.398	110.321	0.06197	0.22105	511.67
54	64.6036	49.908	0.0127799	0.73815	78.248	1.35475	29.583	81.004	110.588	0.06324	0.22094	513.67
56	66.9860	52.290	0.0128198	0.71236	78.004	1.40379	30.245	80.608	110.853	0.06452	0.22083	515.67
58	69.4343	54.738	0.0128602	0.68763	77.759	1.45427	30.908	80.209	111.116	0.06579	0.22073	517.67

Temp. °F	Pressure lb./sq. in.		Volume cu. ft./lb.		Density lb./cu. ft.		Enthalpy Btu/lb.			Entropy Btu/(lb. °F)		Temp. °R
	Absolute	Gauge	Liquid	Vapor	Liquid	Vapor	Liquid	Latent	Vapor	Liquid	Vapor	
60	71.9499	57.254	0.0129011	0.66392	77.513	1.50621	31.572	79.806	111.378	0.06706	0.22063	519.67
62	74.5338	59.838	0.0129426	0.64117	77.264	1.55965	32.238	79.400	111.639	0.06832	0.22053	521.67
64	77.1873	62.491	0.0129846	0.61934	77.015	1.61463	32.906	78.991	111.897	0.06959	0.22043	523.67
66	79.9116	65.216	0.0130271	0.59837	76.763	1.67119	33.575	78.579	112.155	0.07085	0.22034	525.67
68	82.7080	68.012	0.0130702	0.57824	76.510	1.72937	34.246	78.164	112.410	0.07212	0.22024	527.67
70	85.5776	70.882	0.0131139	0.55890	76.255	1.78921	34.919	77.744	112.664	0.07337	0.22015	529.67
72	88.5216	73.826	0.0131582	0.54032	75.998	1.85076	35.594	77.322	112.916	0.07463	0.22006	531.67
74	91.5414	76.845	0.0132031	0.52245	75.740	1.91405	36.270	76.895	113.166	0.07589	0.21998	533.67
76	94.6381	79.942	0.0132486	0.50527	75.480	1.97913	36.948	76.466	113.414	0.07714	0.21989	535.67
78	97.8131	83.117	0.0132948	0.48875	75.217	2.04605	37.628	76.032	113.660	0.07839	0.21980	537.67
80	101.068	86.372	0.0133417	0.47284	74.953	2.11486	38.310	75.594	113.904	0.07964	0.21972	539.67
82	104.403	89.707	0.0133892	0.45754	74.687	2.18561	38.993	75.153	114.146	0.08089	0.21964	541.67
84	107.821	93.125	0.0134375	0.44280	74.419	2.25835	39.678	74.707	114.385	0.08214	0.21955	543.67
86	111.321	96.626	0.0134865	0.42861	74.148	2.33314	40.366	74.257	114.623	0.08339	0.21947	545.67
88	114.907	100.211	0.0135363	0.41493	73.876	2.41003	41.055	73.803	114.858	0.08463	0.21939	547.67
90	118.579	103.883	0.0135868	0.40175	73.601	2.48908	41.746	73.345	115.091	0.08587	0.21931	549.67
92	122.338	107.642	0.0136381	0.38905	73.324	2.57036	42.439	72.882	115.321	0.08712	0.21923	551.67
94	126.186	111.490	0.0136903	0.37680	73.044	2.65392	43.134	72.414	115.549	0.08836	0.21915	553.67
96	130.125	115.429	0.0137433	0.36499	72.763	2.73983	43.832	71.942	115.774	0.08959	0.21906	555.67
98	134.155	119.459	0.0137973	0.35359	72.478	2.82816	44.531	71.465	115.996	0.09083	0.21898	557.67
100	138.278	123.582	0.0138521	0.34258	72.191	2.91899	45.233	70.983	116.216	0.09207	0.21890	559.67
102	142.495	127.799	0.0139079	0.33196	71.902	3.01238	45.936	70.496	116.433	0.09331	0.21882	561.67
104	146.808	132.112	0.0139646	0.32171	71.609	3.10843	46.643	70.004	116.646	0.09454	0.21873	563.67
106	151.219	136.523	0.0140224	0.31180	71.314	3.20720	47.351	69.506	116.857	0.09577	0.21865	565.67
108	155.728	141.032	0.0140812	0.30223	71.016	3.30879	48.062	69.002	117.064	0.09701	0.21856	567.67
110	160.338	145.642	0.0141412	0.29297	70.716	3.41328	48.775	68.493	117.268	0.09824	0.21847	569.67
112	165.050	150.354	0.0142022	0.28403	70.412	3.52077	49.490	67.978	117.469	0.09947	0.21839	571.67
114	169.865	155.169	0.0142645	0.27538	70.104	3.63137	50.208	67.457	117.666	0.10071	0.21829	573.67
116	174.785	160.089	0.0143279	0.26701	69.794	3.74516	50.929	66.930	117.859	0.10194	0.21820	575.67
118	179.811	165.115	0.0143927	0.25891	69.480	3.86227	51.653	66.396	118.048	0.10317	0.21811	577.67
120	184.946	170.250	0.0144587	0.25108	69.162	3.98282	52.379	65.855	118.234	0.10440	0.21801	579.67
122	190.190	175.494	0.0145261	0.24349	68.841	4.10691	53.108	65.307	118.415	0.10563	0.21791	581.67
124	195.546	180.850	0.0145950	0.23614	68.517	4.23469	53.840	64.752	118.592	0.10686	0.21780	583.67
126	201.015	186.319	0.0146654	0.22903	68.188	4.36628	54.575	64.190	118.765	0.10809	0.21770	585.67
128	206.599	191.903	0.0147373	0.22213	67.855	4.50184	55.313	63.620	118.933	0.10933	0.21758	587.67

Temp. °F	Pressure lb./sq. in.		Volume cu. ft./lb.		Density lb./cu. ft.		Enthalpy Btu/lb.			Entropy Btu/(lb. °F)		Temp. °R
	Absolute	Gauge	Liquid	Vapor	Liquid	Vapor	Liquid	Latent	Vapor	Liquid	Vapor	
130	212.299	197.603	0.0148109	0.21545	67.518	4.64151	56.055	63.041	119.096	0.11056	0.21747	589.67
132	218.118	203.422	0.0148862	0.20897	67.176	4.78547	56.800	62.455	119.254	0.11179	0.21735	591.67
134	224.056	209.360	0.0149633	0.20268	66.830	4.93387	57.548	61.860	119.407	0.11303	0.21723	593.67
136	230.117	215.421	0.0150423	0.19658	66.479	5.08692	58.300	61.255	119.555	0.11427	0.21710	595.67
138	236.302	221.606	0.0151232	0.19067	66.123	5.24479	59.056	60.642	119.697	0.11550	0.21697	597.67
140	242.612	227.916	0.0152063	0.18492	65.762	5.40772	59.815	60.018	119.833	0.11674	0.21683	599.67
142	249.050	234.354	0.0152915	0.17934	65.396	5.57591	60.579	59.384	119.963	0.11798	0.21668	601.67
144	255.617	240.922	0.0153790	0.17392	65.024	5.74961	61.347	58.739	120.086	0.11923	0.21653	603.67
146	262.317	247.621	0.0154690	0.16866	64.645	5.92909	62.120	58.084	120.203	0.12047	0.21637	605.67
148	269.150	254.454	0.0155616	0.16354	64.261	6.11462	62.897	57.416	120.313	0.12172	0.21621	607.67
150	276.119	261.423	0.0156568	0.15857	63.870	6.30651	63.679	56.736	120.415	0.12297	0.21603	609.67
152	283.227	268.531	0.0157550	0.15373	63.472	6.50508	64.467	56.043	120.509	0.12423	0.21585	611.67
154	290.475	275.779	0.0158562	0.14902	63.067	6.71069	65.259	55.336	120.595	0.12549	0.21566	613.67
156	297.865	283.170	0.0159607	0.14443	62.654	6.92372	66.058	54.615	120.673	0.12675	0.21546	615.67
158	305.401	290.705	0.0160687	0.13997	62.233	7.14460	66.863	53.878	120.741	0.12802	0.21525	617.67
160	313.085	298.389	0.0161805	0.13562	61.803	7.37379	67.674	53.125	120.800	0.12930	0.21503	619.67
162	320.919	306.223	0.0162962	0.13138	61.364	7.61179	68.493	52.356	120.848	0.13058	0.21479	621.67
164	328.905	314.209	0.0164163	0.12724	60.915	7.85917	69.318	51.568	120.886	0.13186	0.21455	623.67
166	337.047	322.351	0.0165409	0.12321	60.456	8.11654	70.152	50.760	120.912	0.13316	0.21429	625.67
168	345.347	330.651	0.0166706	0.11927	59.986	8.38459	70.994	49.932	120.926	0.13446	0.21401	627.67
170	353.809	339.113	0.0168057	0.11542	59.504	8.66408	71.844	49.082	120.926	0.13577	0.21372	629.67
172	362.435	347.739	0.0169467	0.11166	59.009	8.95587	72.705	48.207	120.912	0.13709	0.21341	631.67
174	371.228	356.532	0.0170941	0.10798	58.500	9.26092	73.576	47.307	120.884	0.13843	0.21308	633.67
176	380.192	365.496	0.0172486	0.10438	57.976	9.58033	74.459	46.380	120.838	0.13977	0.21274	635.67
178	389.330	374.634	0.0174109	0.10085	57.435	9.91535	75.354	45.422	120.775	0.14113	0.21236	637.67
180	398.645	383.950	0.0175818	0.09740	56.877	10.2674	76.262	44.431	120.693	0.14251	0.21197	639.67
182	408.143	393.447	0.0177622	0.09400	56.299	10.6381	77.185	43.404	120.590	0.14390	0.21154	641.67
184	417.826	403.130	0.0179534	0.09067	55.700	11.0295	78.125	42.338	120.463	0.14531	0.21109	643.67
186	427.698	413.002	0.0181568	0.08738	55.076	11.4438	79.083	41.228	120.311	0.14675	0.21060	645.67
188	437.765	423.069	0.0183739	0.08415	54.425	11.8836	80.062	40.068	120.130	0.14821	0.21007	647.67
190	448.031	433.335	0.0186068	0.08096	53.744	12.3524	81.063	38.854	119.917	0.14970	0.20950	649.67
192	458.501	443.805	0.0188582	0.07780	53.027	12.8540	82.091	37.577	119.668	0.15122	0.20889	651.67
194	469.181	454.485	0.0191311	0.07466	52.271	13.3935	83.149	36.229	119.378	0.15279	0.20821	653.67
196	480.077	465.381	0.0194298	0.07155	51.467	13.9771	84.242	34.797	119.039	0.15440	0.20747	655.67
198	491.196	476.500	0.0197599	0.06843	50.608	14.6133	85.378	33.266	118.644	0.15606	0.20665	657.67

Temp. °F	Pressure lb./sq. in.		Volume cu. ft./lb.		Density lb./cu. ft.		Enthalpy Btu/lb.			Entropy Btu/(lb. °F)		Temp. °R
	Absolute	Gauge	Liquid	Vapor	Liquid	Vapor	Liquid	Latent	Vapor	Liquid	Vapor	
200	502.545	487.849	0.0201290	0.06530	49.680	15.3131	86.564	31.616	118.180	0.15780	0.20573	659.67
202	514.132	499.436	0.0205480	0.06214	48.667	16.0922	87.814	29.818	117.632	0.15963	0.20469	661.67
204	525.968	511.272	0.0210334	0.05891	47.543	16.9738	89.147	27.829	116.976	0.16157	0.20350	663.67
206	538.064	523.368	0.0216121	0.05557	46.270	17.9951	90.592	25.582	116.173	0.16367	0.20210	665.67
208	550.436	535.740	0.0223322	0.05202	44.778	19.2235	92.204	22.952	115.156	0.16601	0.20039	667.67
210	563.103	548.407	0.0232973	0.04805	42.923	20.8105	94.100	19.670	113.769	0.16877	0.19814	669.67
212	576.097	561.401	0.0248172	0.04282	40.295	23.3539	96.663	14.740	111.403	0.17251	0.19445	671.67
213.80	588.137 (CRITICAL)	573.441	0.0314612	0.03146	31.785	31.7852	103.814	0.000	103.814	0.18305	0.18305	673.47

KLEA® 134a

Superheated Vapor Properties

Temp. °F	Absolute Pressure, lb./sq. in.												Temp. °R
	2.0			4.0			6.0			8.0			
	Gauge Pressure = 25.849* Satn. Temp. = -79.83 °F 379.84 °R			Gauge Pressure = 21.777* Satn. Temp. = -59.98 °F 399.69 °R			Gauge Pressure = 17.705* Satn. Temp. = -47.14 °F 412.53 °R			Gauge Pressure = 13.633* Satn. Temp. = -37.42 °F 422.25 °R			
	V	H	S	V	H	S	V	H	S	V	H	S	
SAT N	19.7506	91.126	0.24147	10.3184	94.098	0.23581	7.0576	96.022	0.23282	5.3892	97.477	0.23085	
-78	19.8507	91.425	0.24226										381.67
-76	19.9598	91.752	0.24311										383.67
-74	20.0687	92.080	0.24397										385.67
-72	20.1776	92.408	0.24482										387.67
-70	20.2863	92.738	0.24566										389.67
-68	20.3950	93.068	0.24651										391.67
-66	20.5036	93.400	0.24735										393.67
-64	20.6121	93.732	0.24820										395.67
-62	20.7205	94.065	0.24904										397.67
-60	20.8289	94.400	0.24987										399.67
-58	20.9372	94.735	0.25071	10.3735	94.435	0.23665							401.67
-56	21.0454	95.071	0.25155	10.4292	94.776	0.23749							403.67
-54	21.1535	95.408	0.25238	10.4848	95.119	0.23834							405.67
-52	21.2616	95.746	0.25321	10.5403	95.462	0.23918							407.67
-50	21.3696	96.085	0.25404	10.5958	95.806	0.24003							409.67
-48	21.4775	96.425	0.25487	10.6512	96.151	0.24087							411.67
-46	21.5854	96.765	0.25569	10.7066	96.496	0.24170	7.0793	96.222	0.23330				413.67
-44	21.6932	97.107	0.25652	10.7618	96.843	0.24254	7.1171	96.574	0.23415				415.67
-42	21.8010	97.450	0.25734	10.8171	97.190	0.24337	7.1548	96.926	0.23499				417.67
-40	21.9087	97.793	0.25816	10.8722	97.538	0.24420	7.1925	97.279	0.23584				419.67
-38	22.0163	98.138	0.25898	10.9273	97.887	0.24503	7.2301	97.632	0.23668				421.67
-36	22.1239	98.484	0.25980	10.9823	98.237	0.24586	7.2677	97.987	0.23752	5.4097	97.732	0.23146	423.67
-34	22.2314	98.830	0.26061	11.0373	98.588	0.24669	7.3052	98.342	0.23835	5.4384	98.091	0.23230	425.67
-32	22.3389	99.177	0.26143	11.0923	98.939	0.24751	7.3426	98.697	0.23919	5.4672	98.452	0.23315	427.67
-30	22.4463	99.526	0.26224	11.1471	99.292	0.24833	7.3800	99.054	0.24002	5.4958	98.812	0.23399	429.67
-28	22.5537	99.875	0.26305	11.2020	99.645	0.24915	7.4173	99.411	0.24085	5.5245	99.174	0.23483	431.67
-26	22.6610	100.225	0.26386	11.2568	99.999	0.24997	7.4546	99.769	0.24168	5.5530	99.536	0.23566	433.67
-24	22.7683	100.577	0.26467	11.3115	100.354	0.25079	7.4919	100.128	0.24250	5.5815	99.899	0.23650	435.67
-22	22.8756	100.929	0.26547	11.3662	100.710	0.25160	7.5291	100.488	0.24332	5.6100	100.262	0.23733	437.67
-20	22.9828	101.282	0.26628	11.4208	101.066	0.25242	7.5662	100.848	0.24415	5.6384	100.627	0.23816	439.67
-18	23.0899	101.636	0.26708	11.4754	101.424	0.25323	7.6033	101.209	0.24497	5.6668	100.992	0.23899	441.67
-16	23.1970	101.991	0.26788	11.5300	101.782	0.25404	7.6404	101.571	0.24578	5.6951	101.357	0.23982	443.67
-14	23.3041	102.347	0.26868	11.5845	102.142	0.25484	7.6774	101.934	0.24660	5.7234	101.724	0.24064	445.67
-12	23.4111	102.704	0.26948	11.6389	102.502	0.25565	7.7143	102.298	0.24741	5.7516	102.091	0.24146	447.67

* = in. Hg, Vacuum

Temp. °F	Absolute Pressure, lb./sq. in.												Temp. °R
	2.0			4.0			6.0			8.0			
	Gauge Pressure = 25.849* Satn. Temp. = -79.83 °F 379.84 °R			Gauge Pressure = 21.777* Satn. Temp. = -59.98 °F 399.69 °R			Gauge Pressure = 17.705* Satn. Temp. = -47.14 °F 412.53 °R			Gauge Pressure = 13.633* Satn. Temp. = -37.42 °F 422.25 °R			
	V	H	S	V	H	S	V	H	S	V	H	S	
-10	23.5181	103.061	0.27028	11.6934	102.863	0.25646	7.7513	102.662	0.24822	5.7798	102.458	0.24228	449.67
-8	23.6251	103.420	0.27108	11.7477	103.225	0.25726	7.7881	103.027	0.24903	5.8079	102.827	0.24310	451.67
-6	23.7320	103.780	0.27187	11.8021	103.588	0.25806	7.8250	103.393	0.24984	5.8361	103.196	0.24391	453.67
-4	23.8389	104.140	0.27266	11.8564	103.951	0.25886	7.8618	103.760	0.25065	5.8641	103.566	0.24473	455.67
-2	23.9457	104.502	0.27346	11.9107	104.316	0.25966	7.8986	104.127	0.25145	5.8922	103.937	0.24554	457.67
0	24.0525	104.865	0.27425	11.9649	104.681	0.26045	7.9353	104.496	0.25226	5.9201	104.308	0.24635	459.67
2	24.1593	105.228	0.27504	12.0191	105.047	0.26125	7.9720	104.865	0.25306	5.9481	104.680	0.24716	461.67
4	24.2660	105.592	0.27582	12.0733	105.415	0.26204	8.0087	105.235	0.25386	5.9760	105.053	0.24796	463.67
6	24.3728	105.958	0.27661	12.1275	105.783	0.26284	8.0453	105.606	0.25466	6.0039	105.427	0.24877	465.67
8	24.4794	106.324	0.27739	12.1816	106.152	0.26363	8.0819	105.977	0.25545	6.0318	105.801	0.24957	467.67
10	24.5861	106.691	0.27818	12.2357	106.522	0.26442	8.1185	106.350	0.25625	6.0596	106.176	0.25037	469.67
12	24.6927	107.060	0.27896	12.2897	106.892	0.26520	8.1550	106.723	0.25704	6.0874	106.552	0.25117	471.67
14	24.7993	107.429	0.27974	12.3437	107.264	0.26599	8.1915	107.097	0.25783	6.1152	106.929	0.25197	473.67
16	24.9059	107.799	0.28052	12.3977	107.636	0.26677	8.2280	107.472	0.25862	6.1429	107.307	0.25276	475.67
18	25.0124	108.170	0.28130	12.4517	108.010	0.26756	8.2645	107.848	0.25941	6.1706	107.685	0.25356	477.67
20	25.1189	108.542	0.28208	12.5056	108.384	0.26834	8.3009	108.225	0.26020	6.1983	108.064	0.25435	479.67
22	25.2254	108.915	0.28285	12.5596	108.759	0.26912	8.3373	108.602	0.26098	6.2259	108.444	0.25514	481.67
24	25.3319	109.288	0.28363	12.6134	109.135	0.26990	8.3737	108.981	0.26177	6.2536	108.825	0.25593	483.67
26	25.4383	109.663	0.28440	12.6673	109.512	0.27068	8.4100	109.360	0.26255	6.2812	109.206	0.25671	485.67
28	25.5448	110.039	0.28517	12.7212	109.890	0.27145	8.4463	109.740	0.26333	6.3087	109.588	0.25750	487.67
30	25.6511	110.416	0.28594	12.7750	110.269	0.27223	8.4826	110.121	0.26411	6.3363	109.972	0.25828	489.67
32	25.7575	110.793	0.28671	12.8288	110.648	0.27300	8.5189	110.503	0.26489	6.3638	110.355	0.25907	491.67
34	25.8639	111.172	0.28748	12.8825	111.029	0.27377	8.5552	110.885	0.26567	6.3913	110.740	0.25985	493.67
36	25.9702	111.551	0.28825	12.9363	111.410	0.27455	8.5914	111.269	0.26644	6.4188	111.126	0.26063	495.67
38	26.0765	111.931	0.28901	12.9900	111.793	0.27531	8.6276	111.653	0.26721	6.4462	111.512	0.26140	497.67
40	26.1828	112.313	0.28978	13.0437	112.176	0.27608	8.6638	112.038	0.26799	6.4737	111.899	0.26218	499.67
42	26.2890	112.695	0.29054	13.0974	112.560	0.27685	8.7000	112.424	0.26876	6.5011	112.287	0.26295	501.67
44	26.3953	113.078	0.29130	13.1511	112.945	0.27762	8.7361	112.811	0.26953	6.5285	112.676	0.26373	503.67
46	26.5015	113.462	0.29206	13.2047	113.331	0.27838	8.7722	113.198	0.27029	6.5558	113.065	0.26450	505.67
48	26.6077	113.847	0.29282	13.2583	113.718	0.27914	8.8083	113.587	0.27106	6.5832	113.455	0.26527	507.67
50	26.7139	114.233	0.29358	13.3119	114.105	0.27991	8.8444	113.976	0.27183	6.6105	113.847	0.26604	509.67
52	26.8201	114.620	0.29434	13.3655	114.494	0.28067	8.8805	114.367	0.27259	6.6378	114.239	0.26681	511.67
54	26.9262	115.008	0.29510	13.4191	114.883	0.28143	8.9165	114.758	0.27335	6.6651	114.631	0.26757	513.67
56	27.0324	115.397	0.29585	13.4727	115.274	0.28219	8.9526	115.150	0.27412	6.6924	115.025	0.26834	515.67
58	27.1385	115.786	0.29661	13.5262	115.665	0.28294	8.9886	115.543	0.27488	6.7197	115.420	0.26910	517.67

* = in. Hg. Vacuum

Temp. °F	Absolute Pressure, lb./sq. in. 10.0 — Gauge Pressure = 9.561*; Satn. Temp. = -29.49 °F, 430.18 °R			11.0 — Gauge Pressure = 7.525*; Satn. Temp. = -25.99 °F, 433.68 °R			12.0 — Gauge Pressure = 5.489*; Satn. Temp. = -22.73 °F, 436.94 °R			13.0 — Gauge Pressure = 3.453*; Satn. Temp. = -19.69 °F, 439.98 °R			Temp. °R
	V	H	S	V	H	S	V	H	S	V	H	S	
SAT N	4.3709	98.661	0.22943	3.9965	99.182	0.22884	3.6826	99.665	0.22832	3.4155	100.117	0.22785	
-28	4.3883	98.933	0.23006										431.67
-26	4.4116	99.299	0.23090										433.67
-24	4.4349	99.666	0.23175	4.0178	99.549	0.22968							435.67
-22	4.4581	100.034	0.23259	4.0391	99.918	0.23053	3.6899	99.802	0.22863				437.67
-20	4.4813	100.402	0.23343	4.0604	100.288	0.23138	3.7096	100.174	0.22948				439.67
-18	4.5045	100.771	0.23427	4.0817	100.659	0.23222	3.7293	100.547	0.23033	3.4310	100.434	0.22857	441.67
-16	4.5276	101.140	0.23510	4.1029	101.031	0.23306	3.7489	100.920	0.23117	3.4493	100.809	0.22942	443.67
-14	4.5506	101.510	0.23593	4.1240	101.402	0.23389	3.7685	101.294	0.23201	3.4675	101.185	0.23027	445.67
-12	4.5736	101.881	0.23676	4.1451	101.775	0.23473	3.7880	101.668	0.23285	3.4857	101.561	0.23111	447.67
-10	4.5966	102.252	0.23759	4.1662	102.148	0.23556	3.8075	102.043	0.23369	3.5039	101.937	0.23195	449.67
-8	4.6195	102.624	0.23841	4.1872	102.522	0.23639	3.8269	102.418	0.23452	3.5220	102.315	0.23278	451.67
-6	4.6424	102.997	0.23924	4.2082	102.896	0.23721	3.8463	102.794	0.23535	3.5401	102.692	0.23362	453.67
-4	4.6652	103.370	0.24006	4.2291	103.271	0.23804	3.8657	103.171	0.23618	3.5581	103.071	0.23445	455.67
-2	4.6880	103.744	0.24088	4.2500	103.646	0.23886	3.8850	103.548	0.23700	3.5761	103.450	0.23528	457.67
0	4.7108	104.118	0.24169	4.2709	104.022	0.23968	3.9043	103.926	0.23783	3.5940	103.829	0.23611	459.67
2	4.7335	104.493	0.24251	4.2917	104.399	0.24050	3.9235	104.304	0.23865	3.6119	104.209	0.23693	461.67
4	4.7562	104.869	0.24332	4.3125	104.777	0.24131	3.9427	104.683	0.23947	3.6298	104.589	0.23776	463.67
6	4.7788	105.246	0.24413	4.3333	105.155	0.24213	3.9619	105.063	0.24028	3.6476	104.971	0.23858	465.67
8	4.8015	105.623	0.24494	4.3540	105.533	0.24294	3.9810	105.443	0.24110	3.6654	105.352	0.23939	467.67
10	4.8240	106.001	0.24575	4.3747	105.913	0.24375	4.0001	105.824	0.24191	3.6832	105.735	0.24021	469.67
12	4.8466	106.380	0.24655	4.3953	106.293	0.24456	4.0192	106.205	0.24272	3.7009	106.117	0.24102	471.67
14	4.8691	106.759	0.24735	4.4159	106.674	0.24536	4.0382	106.588	0.24353	3.7186	106.501	0.24183	473.67
16	4.8916	107.139	0.24815	4.4365	107.055	0.24616	4.0572	106.970	0.24434	3.7363	106.885	0.24264	475.67
18	4.9141	107.520	0.24895	4.4571	107.437	0.24697	4.0762	107.354	0.24514	3.7539	107.270	0.24345	477.67
20	4.9365	107.902	0.24975	4.4776	107.820	0.24777	4.0952	107.738	0.24594	3.7715	107.655	0.24426	479.67
22	4.9589	108.284	0.25055	4.4981	108.204	0.24856	4.1141	108.123	0.24674	3.7891	108.041	0.24506	481.67
24	4.9813	108.667	0.25134	4.5186	108.588	0.24936	4.1330	108.508	0.24754	3.8066	108.428	0.24586	483.67
26	5.0037	109.051	0.25213	4.5390	108.973	0.25015	4.1518	108.894	0.24834	3.8242	108.816	0.24666	485.67
28	5.0260	109.436	0.25292	4.5595	109.359	0.25095	4.1707	109.281	0.24913	3.8416	109.204	0.24746	487.67
30	5.0483	109.821	0.25371	4.5799	109.745	0.25174	4.1895	109.669	0.24993	3.8591	109.592	0.24825	489.67
32	5.0706	110.207	0.25450	4.6002	110.132	0.25253	4.2083	110.057	0.25072	3.8766	109.982	0.24905	491.67
34	5.0928	110.594	0.25528	4.6206	110.520	0.25331	4.2270	110.446	0.25151	3.8940	110.372	0.24984	493.67
36	5.1150	110.981	0.25606	4.6409	110.909	0.25410	4.2458	110.836	0.25230	3.9114	110.763	0.25063	495.67
38	5.1372	111.370	0.25685	4.6612	111.298	0.25488	4.2645	111.226	0.25308	3.9287	111.154	0.25142	497.67

* = in. Hg, Vacuum

Temp. °F	Absolute Pressure, lb./sq. in. 10.0			11.0			12.0			13.0			Temp. °R
	Gauge Pressure = 9.561* Satn. Temp. = -29.49 °F 430.18 °R			Gauge Pressure = 7.525* Satn. Temp. = -25.99 °F 433.68 °R			Gauge Pressure = 5.489* Satn. Temp. = -22.73 °F 436.94 °R			Gauge Pressure = 3.453* Satn. Temp. = -19.69 °F 439.98 °R			
	V	H	S	V	H	S	V	H	S	V	H	S	
40	5.1594	111.759	0.25763	4.6815	111.688	0.25567	4.2832	111.617	0.25387	3.9461	111.546	0.25220	499.67
42	5.1816	112.149	0.25841	4.7017	112.079	0.25645	4.3018	112.009	0.25465	3.9634	111.939	0.25299	501.67
44	5.2037	112.539	0.25918	4.7220	112.471	0.25723	4.3205	112.402	0.25543	3.9807	112.333	0.25377	503.67
46	5.2259	112.931	0.25996	4.7422	112.863	0.25800	4.3391	112.795	0.25621	3.9980	112.727	0.25455	505.67
48	5.2480	113.323	0.26073	4.7624	113.256	0.25878	4.3577	113.189	0.25699	4.0153	113.122	0.25533	507.67
50	5.2700	113.716	0.26150	4.7826	113.650	0.25955	4.3763	113.584	0.25776	4.0325	113.518	0.25611	509.67
52	5.2921	114.110	0.26228	4.8027	114.045	0.26033	4.3949	113.980	0.25854	4.0497	113.914	0.25689	511.67
54	5.3141	114.504	0.26305	4.8228	114.440	0.26110	4.4134	114.376	0.25931	4.0669	114.311	0.25766	513.67
56	5.3362	114.899	0.26381	4.8430	114.836	0.26187	4.4319	114.773	0.26008	4.0841	114.709	0.25843	515.67
58	5.3582	115.296	0.26458	4.8631	115.233	0.26264	4.4504	115.171	0.26085	4.1013	115.108	0.25920	517.67
60	5.3802	115.693	0.26535	4.8831	115.631	0.26340	4.4689	115.569	0.26162	4.1184	115.507	0.25997	519.67
62	5.4021	116.090	0.26611	4.9032	116.030	0.26417	4.4874	115.969	0.26239	4.1356	115.908	0.26074	521.67
64	5.4241	116.489	0.26687	4.9233	116.429	0.26493	4.5059	116.369	0.26315	4.1527	116.309	0.26151	523.67
66	5.4460	116.888	0.26763	4.9433	116.829	0.26569	4.5243	116.770	0.26392	4.1698	116.710	0.26228	525.67
68	5.4680	117.288	0.26839	4.9633	117.230	0.26646	4.5427	117.171	0.26468	4.1869	117.113	0.26304	527.67
70	5.4899	117.689	0.26915	4.9833	117.632	0.26722	4.5612	117.574	0.26544	4.2039	117.516	0.26380	529.67
72	5.5118	118.091	0.26991	5.0033	118.034	0.26797	4.5796	117.977	0.26620	4.2210	117.920	0.26456	531.67
74	5.5337	118.493	0.27066	5.0233	118.437	0.26873	4.5979	118.381	0.26696	4.2380	118.324	0.26532	533.67
76	5.5555	118.897	0.27142	5.0432	118.841	0.26949	4.6163	118.786	0.26772	4.2550	118.730	0.26608	535.67
78	5.5774	119.301	0.27217	5.0632	119.246	0.27024	4.6347	119.191	0.26847	4.2720	119.136	0.26684	537.67
80	5.5992	119.706	0.27292	5.0831	119.652	0.27099	4.6530	119.598	0.26923	4.2890	119.543	0.26759	539.67
82	5.6210	120.112	0.27367	5.1030	120.058	0.27175	4.6713	120.005	0.26998	4.3060	119.951	0.26835	541.67
84	5.6429	120.518	0.27442	5.1229	120.466	0.27250	4.6896	120.413	0.27073	4.3230	120.359	0.26910	543.67
86	5.6647	120.926	0.27517	5.1428	120.874	0.27325	4.7079	120.821	0.27148	4.3399	120.769	0.26985	545.67
88	5.6865	121.334	0.27592	5.1627	121.282	0.27399	4.7262	121.231	0.27223	4.3569	121.179	0.27060	547.67
90	5.7082	121.743	0.27666	5.1826	121.692	0.27474	4.7445	121.641	0.27298	4.3738	121.590	0.27135	549.67
92	5.7300	122.153	0.27741	5.2024	122.103	0.27549	4.7628	122.052	0.27373	4.3907	122.001	0.27210	551.67
94	5.7517	122.564	0.27815	5.2223	122.514	0.27623	4.7810	122.464	0.27447	4.4076	122.414	0.27285	553.67
96	5.7735	122.975	0.27889	5.2421	122.926	0.27697	4.7993	122.877	0.27521	4.4245	122.827	0.27359	555.67
98	5.7952	123.388	0.27963	5.2619	123.339	0.27771	4.8175	123.290	0.27596	4.4414	123.241	0.27433	557.67
100	5.8169	123.801	0.28037	5.2817	123.753	0.27846	4.8357	123.704	0.27670	4.4583	123.656	0.27508	559.67
102	5.8387	124.215	0.28111	5.3015	124.167	0.27919	4.8539	124.119	0.27744	4.4751	124.072	0.27582	561.67
104	5.8604	124.629	0.28185	5.3213	124.582	0.27993	4.8721	124.535	0.27818	4.4920	124.488	0.27656	563.67
106	5.8820	125.045	0.28258	5.3411	124.999	0.28067	4.8903	124.952	0.27892	4.5088	124.905	0.27730	565.67
108	5.9037	125.462	0.28332	5.3609	125.416	0.28141	4.9085	125.369	0.27965	4.5257	125.323	0.27804	567.67

* = in. Hg, Vacuum

Temp. °F	Absolute Pressure, lb./sq. in.												Temp. °R
	14.0			15.0			16.0			17.0			
	Gauge Pressure 1.417* Satn. Temp. = -16.83 °F 442.84 °R			Gauge Pressure 0.304 lb./sq. in. Satn. Temp. = -14.12 °F 445.55 °R			Gauge Pressure 1.304 lb./sq. in. Satn. Temp. = -11.55 °F 448.12 °R			Gauge Pressure 2.304 lb./sq. in. Satn. Temp. = -9.11 °F 450.56 °R			
	V	H	S	V	H	S	V	H	S	V	H	S	
SAT N	3.1853	100.541	0.22743	2.9849	100.941	0.22705	2.8087	101.319	0.22670	2.6525	101.679	0.22637	
-16	3.1924	100.697	0.22778										443.67
-14	3.2095	101.074	0.22863	2.9858	100.963	0.22710							445.67
-12	3.2266	101.453	0.22948	3.0019	101.344	0.22795							447.67
-10	3.2436	101.831	0.23032	3.0179	101.724	0.22880	2.8204	101.616	0.22736				449.67
-8	3.2606	102.210	0.23117	3.0339	102.105	0.22964	2.8355	101.999	0.22821	2.6605	101.892	0.22685	451.67
-6	3.2775	102.590	0.23200	3.0499	102.486	0.23049	2.8506	102.382	0.22905	2.6748	102.277	0.22770	453.67
-4	3.2944	102.970	0.23284	3.0657	102.868	0.23133	2.8657	102.766	0.22990	2.6891	102.663	0.22855	455.67
-2	3.3112	103.350	0.23367	3.0816	103.250	0.23216	2.8807	103.150	0.23074	2.7033	103.049	0.22939	457.67
0	3.3280	103.731	0.23450	3.0974	103.633	0.23300	2.8956	103.534	0.23158	2.7175	103.435	0.23023	459.67
2	3.3448	104.113	0.23533	3.1132	104.016	0.23383	2.9105	103.919	0.23241	2.7316	103.821	0.23107	461.67
4	3.3615	104.495	0.23616	3.1289	104.400	0.23466	2.9254	104.305	0.23325	2.7457	104.208	0.23191	463.67
6	3.3782	104.878	0.23698	3.1446	104.784	0.23549	2.9402	104.690	0.23408	2.7598	104.596	0.23274	465.67
8	3.3948	105.261	0.23780	3.1603	105.169	0.23631	2.9550	105.077	0.23490	2.7739	104.984	0.23357	467.67
10	3.4115	105.645	0.23862	3.1759	105.554	0.23713	2.9698	105.463	0.23573	2.7878	105.372	0.23440	469.67
12	3.4280	106.029	0.23944	3.1915	105.940	0.23795	2.9845	105.851	0.23655	2.8018	105.761	0.23523	471.67
14	3.4446	106.414	0.24025	3.2071	106.326	0.23877	2.9992	106.238	0.23737	2.8157	106.150	0.23605	473.67
16	3.4611	106.799	0.24106	3.2226	106.713	0.23958	3.0139	106.627	0.23819	2.8296	106.540	0.23687	475.67
18	3.4776	107.186	0.24187	3.2381	107.101	0.24040	3.0285	107.016	0.23901	2.8435	106.930	0.23769	477.67
20	3.4941	107.572	0.24268	3.2536	107.489	0.24121	3.0431	107.405	0.23982	2.8573	107.321	0.23851	479.67
22	3.5105	107.960	0.24349	3.2690	107.878	0.24202	3.0577	107.795	0.24063	2.8711	107.712	0.23932	481.67
24	3.5269	108.348	0.24429	3.2844	108.267	0.24282	3.0722	108.186	0.24144	2.8849	108.104	0.24013	483.67
26	3.5433	108.736	0.24509	3.2998	108.657	0.24363	3.0867	108.577	0.24225	2.8987	108.496	0.24094	485.67
28	3.5596	109.126	0.24589	3.3151	109.047	0.24443	3.1012	108.968	0.24305	2.9124	108.889	0.24175	487.67
30	3.5759	109.515	0.24669	3.3305	109.438	0.24523	3.1156	109.361	0.24385	2.9261	109.283	0.24255	489.67
32	3.5922	109.906	0.24749	3.3458	109.830	0.24603	3.1301	109.753	0.24466	2.9397	109.677	0.24336	491.67
34	3.6085	110.297	0.24828	3.3610	110.222	0.24682	3.1445	110.147	0.24545	2.9534	110.071	0.24416	493.67
36	3.6247	110.689	0.24907	3.3763	110.615	0.24762	3.1589	110.541	0.24625	2.9670	110.467	0.24496	495.67
38	3.6409	111.082	0.24986	3.3915	111.009	0.24841	3.1732	110.936	0.24705	2.9806	110.862	0.24575	497.67
40	3.6571	111.475	0.25065	3.4067	111.403	0.24920	3.1875	111.331	0.24784	2.9941	111.259	0.24655	499.67
42	3.6733	111.869	0.25144	3.4219	111.798	0.24999	3.2018	111.727	0.24863	3.0077	111.656	0.24734	501.67
44	3.6895	112.263	0.25222	3.4370	112.194	0.25078	3.2161	112.124	0.24942	3.0212	112.053	0.24813	503.67
46	3.7056	112.659	0.25301	3.4522	112.590	0.25156	3.2304	112.521	0.25021	3.0347	112.452	0.24892	505.67
48	3.7217	113.055	0.25379	3.4673	112.987	0.25235	3.2446	112.919	0.25099	3.0482	112.851	0.24971	507.67

* = in. Hg, Vacuum

Temp. °F	Absolute Pressure, lb./sq. in. 14.0			15.0			16.0			17.0			Temp. °R
	Gauge Pressure 1.417* Satn. Temp. = -16.83 °F 442.84 °R			Gauge Pressure 0.304 lb/sq. in. Satn. Temp. = -14.12 °F 445.55 °R			Gauge Pressure 1.304 lb./sq. in. Satn. Temp. = -11.55 °F 448.12 °R			Gauge Pressure 2.304 lb./sq. in. Satn. Temp. = -9.11 °F 450.56 °R			
	V	H	S	V	H	S	V	H	S	V	H	S	
50	3.7378	113.451	0.25457	3.4824	113.384	0.25313	3.2589	113.317	0.25177	3.0616	113.250	0.25050	509.67
52	3.7539	113.849	0.25535	3.4975	113.783	0.25391	3.2731	113.717	0.25256	3.0751	113.650	0.25128	511.67
54	3.7699	114.247	0.25612	3.5125	114.182	0.25469	3.2872	114.117	0.25334	3.0885	114.051	0.25206	513.67
56	3.7860	114.646	0.25690	3.5275	114.581	0.25546	3.3014	114.517	0.25411	3.1019	114.453	0.25284	515.67
58	3.8020	115.045	0.25767	3.5426	114.982	0.25624	3.3156	114.918	0.25489	3.1152	114.855	0.25362	517.67
60	3.8180	115.445	0.25844	3.5576	115.383	0.25701	3.3297	115.320	0.25567	3.1286	115.258	0.25440	519.67
62	3.8340	115.846	0.25921	3.5725	115.785	0.25778	3.3438	115.723	0.25644	3.1419	115.661	0.25517	521.67
64	3.8499	116.248	0.25998	3.5875	116.187	0.25855	3.3579	116.126	0.25721	3.1553	116.065	0.25594	523.67
66	3.8659	116.650	0.26075	3.6025	116.591	0.25932	3.3720	116.530	0.25798	3.1686	116.470	0.25672	525.67
68	3.8818	117.054	0.26152	3.6174	116.995	0.26009	3.3860	116.935	0.25875	3.1819	116.876	0.25749	527.67
70	3.8977	117.458	0.26228	3.6323	117.399	0.26085	3.4001	117.341	0.25952	3.1951	117.282	0.25825	529.67
72	3.9136	117.862	0.26304	3.6472	117.805	0.26162	3.4141	117.747	0.26028	3.2084	117.689	0.25902	531.67
74	3.9295	118.268	0.26380	3.6621	118.211	0.26238	3.4281	118.154	0.26105	3.2216	118.096	0.25979	533.67
76	3.9454	118.674	0.26456	3.6770	118.618	0.26314	3.4421	118.561	0.26181	3.2349	118.505	0.26055	535.67
78	3.9612	119.081	0.26532	3.6918	119.025	0.26390	3.4561	118.970	0.26257	3.2481	118.914	0.26131	537.67
80	3.9771	119.488	0.26608	3.7067	119.434	0.26466	3.4701	119.379	0.26333	3.2613	119.324	0.26207	539.67
82	3.9929	119.897	0.26683	3.7215	119.843	0.26542	3.4840	119.789	0.26409	3.2745	119.734	0.26283	541.67
84	4.0087	120.306	0.26759	3.7363	120.253	0.26617	3.4980	120.199	0.26484	3.2876	120.145	0.26359	543.67
86	4.0245	120.716	0.26834	3.7511	120.663	0.26693	3.5119	120.610	0.26560	3.3008	120.557	0.26435	545.67
88	4.0403	121.127	0.26909	3.7659	121.075	0.26768	3.5258	121.022	0.26635	3.3139	120.970	0.26510	547.67
90	4.0561	121.538	0.26984	3.7807	121.487	0.26843	3.5397	121.435	0.26710	3.3271	121.383	0.26585	549.67
92	4.0718	121.951	0.27059	3.7954	121.900	0.26918	3.5536	121.849	0.26785	3.3402	121.797	0.26661	551.67
94	4.0876	122.364	0.27134	3.8102	122.313	0.26993	3.5675	122.263	0.26860	3.3533	122.212	0.26736	553.67
96	4.1033	122.778	0.27208	3.8249	122.728	0.27067	3.5813	122.678	0.26935	3.3664	122.628	0.26811	555.67
98	4.1191	123.192	0.27283	3.8397	123.143	0.27142	3.5952	123.094	0.27010	3.3795	123.044	0.26885	557.67
100	4.1348	123.608	0.27357	3.8544	123.559	0.27217	3.6090	123.510	0.27085	3.3925	123.461	0.26960	559.67
102	4.1505	124.024	0.27431	3.8691	123.976	0.27291	3.6229	123.927	0.27159	3.4056	123.879	0.27035	561.67
104	4.1662	124.441	0.27505	3.8838	124.393	0.27365	3.6367	124.346	0.27233	3.4187	124.298	0.27109	563.67
106	4.1819	124.858	0.27579	3.8985	124.811	0.27439	3.6505	124.764	0.27307	3.4317	124.717	0.27183	565.67
108	4.1975	125.277	0.27653	3.9132	125.230	0.27513	3.6643	125.184	0.27381	3.4447	125.137	0.27257	567.67
110	4.2132	125.696	0.27727	3.9278	125.650	0.27587	3.6781	125.604	0.27455	3.4577	125.558	0.27331	569.67
112	4.2289	126.116	0.27801	3.9425	126.071	0.27661	3.6919	126.025	0.27529	3.4708	125.980	0.27405	571.67
114	4.2445	126.537	0.27874	3.9571	126.492	0.27734	3.7057	126.447	0.27603	3.4838	126.402	0.27479	573.67
116	4.2602	126.959	0.27948	3.9718	126.914	0.27808	3.7194	126.870	0.27676	3.4968	126.825	0.27553	575.67
118	4.2758	127.381	0.28021	3.9864	127.337	0.27881	3.7332	127.293	0.27750	3.5097	127.249	0.27626	577.67

* = in. Hg, Vacuum

Temp. °F	Absolute Pressure, lb./sq. in.												Temp. °R
	18.0			19.0			20.0			22.0			
	Gauge Pressure 3.304 lb./sq. in.; Satn. Temp. = -6.77 °F, 452.90 °R			Gauge Pressure 4.304 lb./sq. in.; Satn. Temp. = -4.54 °F, 455.13 °R			Gauge Pressure 5.304 lb./sq. in.; Satn. Temp. = -2.40 °F, 457.27 °R			Gauge Pressure 7.304 lb./sq. in.; Satn. Temp. = 1.65 °F, 461.32 °R			
	V	H	S	V	H	S	V	H	S	V	H	S	
SAT N	2.5132	102.022	0.22608	2.3880	102.350	0.22580	2.2749	102.663	0.22554	2.0786	103.254	0.22507	
-6	2.5184	102.172	0.22641										453.67
-4	2.5320	102.559	0.22726	2.3915	102.455	0.22603							455.67
-2	2.5456	102.947	0.22811	2.4044	102.844	0.22688	2.2774	102.741	0.22571				457.67
0	2.5591	103.335	0.22895	2.4174	103.234	0.22773	2.2897	103.132	0.22656				459.67
2	2.5726	103.723	0.22980	2.4302	103.624	0.22858	2.3021	103.524	0.22741	2.0806	103.323	0.22522	461.67
4	2.5860	104.112	0.23064	2.4431	104.014	0.22942	2.3144	103.916	0.22826	2.0920	103.718	0.22608	463.67
6	2.5994	104.501	0.23147	2.4559	104.405	0.23026	2.3266	104.309	0.22911	2.1033	104.114	0.22693	465.67
8	2.6128	104.890	0.23231	2.4686	104.796	0.23110	2.3388	104.701	0.22995	2.1146	104.510	0.22778	467.67
10	2.6261	105.280	0.23314	2.4813	105.187	0.23194	2.3510	105.094	0.23079	2.1258	104.907	0.22863	469.67
12	2.6394	105.670	0.23397	2.4940	105.579	0.23277	2.3632	105.488	0.23162	2.1370	105.303	0.22947	471.67
14	2.6526	106.061	0.23479	2.5067	105.972	0.23360	2.3753	105.882	0.23246	2.1482	105.700	0.23031	473.67
16	2.6659	106.452	0.23562	2.5193	106.364	0.23443	2.3873	106.276	0.23329	2.1594	106.097	0.23114	475.67
18	2.6790	106.844	0.23644	2.5319	106.757	0.23525	2.3994	106.670	0.23411	2.1705	106.495	0.23198	477.67
20	2.6922	107.236	0.23726	2.5444	107.151	0.23607	2.4114	107.065	0.23494	2.1815	106.892	0.23281	479.67
22	2.7053	107.629	0.23808	2.5569	107.545	0.23689	2.4234	107.460	0.23576	2.1926	107.291	0.23364	481.67
24	2.7184	108.022	0.23889	2.5694	107.939	0.23771	2.4353	107.856	0.23658	2.2036	107.689	0.23446	483.67
26	2.7315	108.415	0.23970	2.5819	108.334	0.23852	2.4472	108.253	0.23740	2.2145	108.088	0.23529	485.67
28	2.7445	108.810	0.24051	2.5943	108.730	0.23934	2.4591	108.649	0.23821	2.2255	108.487	0.23611	487.67
30	2.7575	109.204	0.24132	2.6067	109.126	0.24015	2.4710	109.046	0.23903	2.2364	108.887	0.23693	489.67
32	2.7705	109.600	0.24213	2.6191	109.522	0.24096	2.4828	109.444	0.23984	2.2473	109.287	0.23774	491.67
34	2.7835	109.995	0.24293	2.6314	109.919	0.24176	2.4946	109.842	0.24065	2.2582	109.688	0.23855	493.67
36	2.7964	110.392	0.24373	2.6438	110.316	0.24256	2.5064	110.241	0.24145	2.2690	110.089	0.23936	495.67
38	2.8093	110.789	0.24453	2.6561	110.714	0.24337	2.5181	110.640	0.24225	2.2798	110.490	0.24017	497.67
40	2.8222	111.186	0.24533	2.6683	111.113	0.24417	2.5298	111.040	0.24306	2.2906	110.892	0.24098	499.67
42	2.8351	111.584	0.24612	2.6806	111.512	0.24496	2.5416	111.440	0.24386	2.3013	111.295	0.24178	501.67
44	2.8479	111.983	0.24692	2.6928	111.912	0.24576	2.5532	111.841	0.24465	2.3121	111.698	0.24258	503.67
46	2.8607	112.382	0.24771	2.7050	112.312	0.24655	2.5649	112.242	0.24545	2.3228	112.101	0.24338	505.67
48	2.8735	112.782	0.24850	2.7172	112.713	0.24734	2.5765	112.644	0.24624	2.3335	112.505	0.24418	507.67
50	2.8863	113.183	0.24928	2.7294	113.115	0.24813	2.5881	113.047	0.24703	2.3441	112.910	0.24498	509.67
52	2.8990	113.584	0.25007	2.7415	113.517	0.24892	2.5997	113.450	0.24782	2.3548	113.315	0.24577	511.67
54	2.9118	113.985	0.25085	2.7536	113.919	0.24970	2.6113	113.853	0.24861	2.3654	113.720	0.24656	513.67
56	2.9245	114.388	0.25163	2.7657	114.323	0.25049	2.6229	114.258	0.24940	2.3760	114.126	0.24735	515.67
58	2.9372	114.791	0.25241	2.7778	114.727	0.25127	2.6344	114.662	0.25018	2.3866	114.533	0.24814	517.67

Temp. °F	Absolute Pressure, lb./sq. in.												Temp. °R
	18.0			19.0			20.0			22.0			
	Gauge Pressure 3.304 lb./sq. in. Satn. Temp. = -6.77 °F 452.90 °R			Gauge Pressure 4.304 lb./sq. in. Satn. Temp. = -4.54 °F 455.13 °R			Gauge Pressure 5.304 lb./sq. in. Satn. Temp. = -2.40 °F 457.27 °R			Gauge Pressure 7.304 lb./sq. in. Satn. Temp. = 1.65 °F 461.32 °R			
	V	H	S	V	H	S	V	H	S	V	H	S	
60	2.9498	115.195	0.25319	2.7899	115.131	0.25205	2.6459	115.068	0.25096	2.3972	114.940	0.24892	519.67
62	2.9625	115.599	0.25397	2.8019	115.537	0.25283	2.6574	115.474	0.25174	2.4077	115.348	0.24970	521.67
64	2.9751	116.004	0.25474	2.8140	115.942	0.25360	2.6689	115.881	0.25252	2.4183	115.756	0.25049	523.67
66	2.9878	116.410	0.25552	2.8260	116.349	0.25438	2.6803	116.288	0.25329	2.4288	116.165	0.25127	525.67
68	3.0004	116.816	0.25629	2.8380	116.756	0.25515	2.6918	116.696	0.25407	2.4393	116.575	0.25204	527.67
70	3.0130	117.223	0.25706	2.8499	117.164	0.25592	2.7032	117.105	0.25484	2.4498	116.985	0.25282	529.67
72	3.0255	117.631	0.25783	2.8619	117.572	0.25669	2.7146	117.514	0.25561	2.4602	117.396	0.25359	531.67
74	3.0381	118.039	0.25859	2.8739	117.981	0.25746	2.7260	117.924	0.25638	2.4707	117.807	0.25437	533.67
76	3.0506	118.448	0.25936	2.8858	118.391	0.25823	2.7374	118.334	0.25715	2.4811	118.220	0.25514	535.67
78	3.0632	118.858	0.26012	2.8977	118.802	0.25899	2.7488	118.745	0.25792	2.4915	118.632	0.25591	537.67
80	3.0757	119.268	0.26088	2.9096	119.213	0.25976	2.7601	119.157	0.25868	2.5019	119.046	0.25667	539.67
82	3.0882	119.680	0.26165	2.9215	119.625	0.26052	2.7715	119.570	0.25944	2.5123	119.460	0.25744	541.67
84	3.1007	120.091	0.26240	2.9334	120.037	0.26128	2.7828	119.983	0.26021	2.5227	119.874	0.25820	543.67
86	3.1131	120.504	0.26316	2.9452	120.451	0.26204	2.7941	120.397	0.26097	2.5330	120.290	0.25897	545.67
88	3.1256	120.917	0.26392	2.9571	120.865	0.26279	2.8054	120.812	0.26172	2.5434	120.705	0.25973	547.67
90	3.1380	121.331	0.26467	2.9689	121.279	0.26355	2.8167	121.227	0.26248	2.5537	121.122	0.26049	549.67
92	3.1505	121.746	0.26543	2.9807	121.695	0.26430	2.8279	121.643	0.26324	2.5640	121.539	0.26124	551.67
94	3.1629	122.162	0.26618	2.9925	122.111	0.26506	2.8392	122.060	0.26399	2.5743	121.957	0.26200	553.67
96	3.1753	122.578	0.26693	3.0043	122.528	0.26581	2.8505	122.477	0.26474	2.5846	122.376	0.26275	555.67
98	3.1877	122.995	0.26768	3.0161	122.945	0.26656	2.8617	122.895	0.26549	2.5949	122.795	0.26351	557.67
100	3.2001	123.412	0.26842	3.0279	123.363	0.26731	2.8729	123.314	0.26624	2.6052	123.215	0.26426	559.67
102	3.2125	123.831	0.26917	3.0397	123.782	0.26805	2.8841	123.734	0.26699	2.6154	123.636	0.26501	561.67
104	3.2248	124.250	0.26992	3.0514	124.202	0.26880	2.8953	124.154	0.26774	2.6257	124.057	0.26576	563.67
106	3.2372	124.670	0.27066	3.0632	124.622	0.26955	2.9065	124.575	0.26849	2.6359	124.479	0.26651	565.67
108	3.2495	125.090	0.27140	3.0749	125.044	0.27029	2.9177	124.997	0.26923	2.6462	124.902	0.26725	567.67
110	3.2619	125.512	0.27214	3.0866	125.465	0.27103	2.9289	125.419	0.26997	2.6564	125.326	0.26800	569.67
112	3.2742	125.934	0.27288	3.0983	125.888	0.27177	2.9400	125.842	0.27071	2.6666	125.750	0.26874	571.67
114	3.2865	126.357	0.27362	3.1100	126.311	0.27251	2.9512	126.266	0.27145	2.6768	126.175	0.26948	573.67
116	3.2988	126.780	0.27436	3.1217	126.736	0.27325	2.9623	126.691	0.27219	2.6870	126.600	0.27022	575.67
118	3.3111	127.205	0.27509	3.1334	127.160	0.27399	2.9735	127.116	0.27293	2.6972	127.027	0.27096	577.67
120	3.3234	127.630	0.27583	3.1451	127.586	0.27472	2.9846	127.542	0.27367	2.7073	127.454	0.27170	579.67
122	3.3357	128.056	0.27656	3.1567	128.012	0.27545	2.9957	127.969	0.27440	2.7175	127.882	0.27244	581.67
124	3.3480	128.483	0.27729	3.1684	128.440	0.27619	3.0068	128.397	0.27514	2.7276	128.310	0.27317	583.67
126	3.3602	128.910	0.27803	3.1801	128.868	0.27692	3.0179	128.825	0.27587	2.7378	128.739	0.27391	585.67
128	3.3725	129.338	0.27875	3.1917	129.296	0.27765	3.0290	129.254	0.27660	2.7479	129.169	0.27464	587.67

Temp. °F	Absolute Pressure, lb./sq. in. 24.0 — Gauge Pressure 9.304 lb./sq. in.; Satn. Temp. = 5.42 °F, 465.09 °R			26.0 — Gauge Pressure 11.304 lb./sq. in.; Satn. Temp. = 8.95 °F, 468.62 °R			28.0 — Gauge Pressure 13.304 lb./sq. in.; Satn. Temp. = 12.28 °F, 471.95 °R			30.0 — Gauge Pressure 15.304 lb./sq. in.; Satn. Temp. = 15.42 °F, 475.09 °R			Temp. °R
	V	H	S	V	H	S	V	H	S	V	H	S	
SAT N	1.9140	103.801	0.22466	1.7739	104.312	0.22430	1.6531	104.792	0.22397	1.5480	105.243	0.22367	
6	1.9171	103.917	0.22491										465.67
8	1.9276	104.317	0.22577										467.67
10	1.9381	104.716	0.22662	1.7790	104.524	0.22475							469.67
12	1.9485	105.116	0.22747	1.7888	104.927	0.22561							471.67
14	1.9589	105.516	0.22832	1.7986	105.330	0.22646	1.6611	105.142	0.22471				473.67
16	1.9692	105.916	0.22916	1.8083	105.734	0.22731	1.6702	105.549	0.22557	1.5505	105.361	0.22392	475.67
18	1.9796	106.317	0.23000	1.8180	106.137	0.22816	1.6793	105.955	0.22642	1.5591	105.771	0.22478	477.67
20	1.9899	106.718	0.23084	1.8276	106.541	0.22900	1.6884	106.362	0.22727	1.5677	106.182	0.22564	479.67
22	2.0001	107.119	0.23167	1.8372	106.945	0.22984	1.6975	106.769	0.22812	1.5763	106.592	0.22649	481.67
24	2.0104	107.520	0.23250	1.8468	107.349	0.23068	1.7065	107.176	0.22896	1.5848	107.002	0.22734	483.67
26	2.0205	107.922	0.23333	1.8563	107.754	0.23151	1.7155	107.584	0.22980	1.5933	107.412	0.22819	485.67
28	2.0307	108.324	0.23416	1.8658	108.158	0.23234	1.7244	107.991	0.23064	1.6018	107.822	0.22903	487.67
30	2.0409	108.726	0.23498	1.8753	108.563	0.23317	1.7333	108.399	0.23147	1.6102	108.233	0.22987	489.67
32	2.0510	109.129	0.23580	1.8848	108.969	0.23400	1.7422	108.807	0.23230	1.6186	108.644	0.23071	491.67
34	2.0610	109.532	0.23662	1.8942	109.374	0.23482	1.7511	109.215	0.23313	1.6270	109.054	0.23154	493.67
36	2.0711	109.935	0.23744	1.9036	109.780	0.23564	1.7599	109.624	0.23396	1.6353	109.465	0.23237	495.67
38	2.0811	110.339	0.23825	1.9129	110.186	0.23646	1.7687	110.032	0.23478	1.6437	109.877	0.23320	497.67
40	2.0911	110.743	0.23906	1.9223	110.593	0.23727	1.7775	110.441	0.23560	1.6519	110.288	0.23403	499.67
42	2.1011	111.148	0.23987	1.9316	111.000	0.23809	1.7862	110.851	0.23642	1.6602	110.700	0.23485	501.67
44	2.1110	111.553	0.24067	1.9409	111.407	0.23890	1.7950	111.260	0.23723	1.6684	111.112	0.23567	503.67
46	2.1210	111.959	0.24148	1.9501	111.815	0.23971	1.8037	111.670	0.23805	1.6767	111.524	0.23649	505.67
48	2.1309	112.365	0.24228	1.9594	112.223	0.24051	1.8123	112.081	0.23886	1.6848	111.937	0.23730	507.67
50	2.1408	112.771	0.24308	1.9686	112.632	0.24131	1.8210	112.491	0.23966	1.6930	112.350	0.23811	509.67
52	2.1506	113.178	0.24388	1.9778	113.041	0.24212	1.8296	112.903	0.24047	1.7012	112.763	0.23892	511.67
54	2.1605	113.586	0.24467	1.9870	113.451	0.24291	1.8382	113.314	0.24127	1.7093	113.177	0.23973	513.67
56	2.1703	113.994	0.24546	1.9961	113.861	0.24371	1.8468	113.726	0.24207	1.7174	113.591	0.24053	515.67
58	2.1801	114.402	0.24625	2.0053	114.271	0.24451	1.8554	114.138	0.24287	1.7254	114.005	0.24133	517.67
60	2.1899	114.812	0.24704	2.0144	114.682	0.24530	1.8639	114.551	0.24367	1.7335	114.420	0.24213	519.67
62	2.1996	115.221	0.24783	2.0235	115.093	0.24609	1.8725	114.965	0.24446	1.7415	114.835	0.24293	521.67
64	2.2094	115.631	0.24861	2.0326	115.505	0.24688	1.8810	115.378	0.24525	1.7496	115.250	0.24373	523.67
66	2.2191	116.042	0.24940	2.0416	115.918	0.24766	1.8895	115.793	0.24604	1.7576	115.666	0.24452	525.67
68	2.2288	116.453	0.25018	2.0507	116.331	0.24845	1.8979	116.207	0.24683	1.7655	116.083	0.24531	527.67

Temp. °F	Absolute Pressure, lb./sq. in.												Temp. °R
	24.0			26.0			28.0			30.0			
	Gauge Pressure 9.304 lb./sq. in. Satn. Temp. = 5.42 °F 465.09 °R			Gauge Pressure 11.304 lb./sq. in. Satn. Temp. = 8.95 °F 468.62 °R			Gauge Pressure 13.304 lb./sq. in. Satn. Temp. = 12.28 °F 471.95 °R			Gauge Pressure 15.304 lb./sq. in. Satn. Temp. = 15.42 °F 475.09 °R			
	V	H	S	V	H	S	V	H	S	V	H	S	
70	2.2385	116.865	0.25096	2.0597	116.744	0.24923	1.9064	116.622	0.24761	1.7735	116.500	0.24610	529.67
72	2.2482	117.278	0.25173	2.0687	117.158	0.25001	1.9148	117.038	0.24840	1.7814	116.917	0.24689	531.67
74	2.2578	117.691	0.25251	2.0777	117.573	0.25079	1.9232	117.454	0.24918	1.7894	117.335	0.24767	533.67
76	2.2675	118.104	0.25328	2.0867	117.988	0.25156	1.9316	117.871	0.24996	1.7973	117.753	0.24845	535.67
78	2.2771	118.518	0.25406	2.0956	118.404	0.25234	1.9400	118.288	0.25074	1.8052	118.172	0.24923	537.67
80	2.2867	118.933	0.25483	2.1046	118.820	0.25311	1.9484	118.706	0.25151	1.8130	118.592	0.25001	539.67
82	2.2963	119.349	0.25559	2.1135	119.237	0.25388	1.9568	119.125	0.25229	1.8209	119.011	0.25079	541.67
84	2.3059	119.765	0.25636	2.1224	119.654	0.25465	1.9651	119.543	0.25306	1.8288	119.432	0.25156	543.67
86	2.3154	120.181	0.25713	2.1313	120.072	0.25542	1.9734	119.963	0.25383	1.8366	119.853	0.25234	545.67
88	2.3250	120.599	0.25789	2.1402	120.491	0.25619	1.9817	120.383	0.25460	1.8444	120.274	0.25311	547.67
90	2.3345	121.017	0.25865	2.1491	120.910	0.25695	1.9900	120.804	0.25536	1.8522	120.696	0.25388	549.67
92	2.3441	121.435	0.25941	2.1579	121.330	0.25771	1.9983	121.225	0.25613	1.8600	121.119	0.25464	551.67
94	2.3536	121.854	0.26017	2.1668	121.751	0.25847	2.0066	121.647	0.25689	1.8678	121.542	0.25541	553.67
96	2.3631	122.274	0.26093	2.1756	122.172	0.25923	2.0149	122.069	0.25765	1.8755	121.966	0.25617	555.67
98	2.3726	122.695	0.26168	2.1844	122.594	0.25999	2.0231	122.492	0.25841	1.8833	122.390	0.25693	557.67
100	2.3821	123.116	0.26244	2.1932	123.016	0.26075	2.0314	122.916	0.25917	1.8910	122.815	0.25769	559.67
102	2.3915	123.538	0.26319	2.2020	123.439	0.26150	2.0396	123.340	0.25993	1.8988	123.240	0.25845	561.67
104	2.4010	123.960	0.26394	2.2108	123.863	0.26225	2.0478	123.765	0.26068	1.9065	123.666	0.25921	563.67
106	2.4104	124.384	0.26469	2.2196	124.287	0.26300	2.0560	124.190	0.26144	1.9142	124.093	0.25997	565.67
108	2.4199	124.807	0.26544	2.2284	124.712	0.26375	2.0642	124.616	0.26219	1.9219	124.520	0.26072	567.67
110	2.4293	125.232	0.26618	2.2371	125.138	0.26450	2.0724	125.043	0.26294	1.9296	124.948	0.26147	569.67
112	2.4387	125.657	0.26693	2.2459	125.564	0.26525	2.0805	125.471	0.26369	1.9372	125.377	0.26222	571.67
114	2.4481	126.083	0.26767	2.2546	125.991	0.26600	2.0887	125.899	0.26443	1.9449	125.806	0.26297	573.67
116	2.4575	126.510	0.26841	2.2633	126.419	0.26674	2.0968	126.327	0.26518	1.9526	126.235	0.26372	575.67
118	2.4669	126.937	0.26916	2.2720	126.847	0.26748	2.1050	126.757	0.26593	1.9602	126.666	0.26447	577.67
120	2.4763	127.365	0.26989	2.2807	127.276	0.26822	2.1131	127.187	0.26667	1.9678	127.097	0.26521	579.67
122	2.4856	127.794	0.27063	2.2894	127.706	0.26896	2.1212	127.617	0.26741	1.9755	127.529	0.26596	581.67
124	2.4950	128.223	0.27137	2.2981	128.136	0.26970	2.1294	128.049	0.26815	1.9831	127.961	0.26670	583.67
126	2.5043	128.654	0.27211	2.3068	128.567	0.27044	2.1375	128.481	0.26889	1.9907	128.394	0.26744	585.67
128	2.5137	129.085	0.27284	2.3155	128.999	0.27118	2.1456	128.914	0.26963	1.9983	128.828	0.26818	587.67
130	2.5230	129.516	0.27357	2.3241	129.432	0.27191	2.1536	129.347	0.27036	2.0059	129.262	0.26892	589.67
132	2.5323	129.948	0.27431	2.3328	129.865	0.27264	2.1617	129.781	0.27110	2.0134	129.697	0.26965	591.67
134	2.5417	130.382	0.27504	2.3414	130.299	0.27338	2.1698	130.216	0.27183	2.0210	130.133	0.27039	593.67
136	2.5510	130.815	0.27577	2.3501	130.734	0.27411	2.1779	130.651	0.27256	2.0286	130.569	0.27112	595.67
138	2.5603	131.250	0.27649	2.3587	131.169	0.27484	2.1859	131.088	0.27330	2.0361	131.006	0.27185	597.67

Temp. °F	Absolute Pressure, lb./sq. in.												Temp. °R
	32.0			34.0			36.0			38.0			
	Gauge Pressure 17.304 lb./sq. in. Satn. Temp. = 18.41 °F 478.08 °R			Gauge Pressure 19.304 lb./sq. in. Satn. Temp. = 21.26 °F 480.93 °R			Gauge Pressure 21.304 lb./sq. in. Satn. Temp. = 23.98 °F 483.65 °R			Gauge Pressure 23.304 lb./sq. in. Satn. Temp. = 26.59 °F 486.26 °R			
	V	H	S	V	H	S	V	H	S	V	H	S	
SAT N	1.45550	105.670	0.22340	1.37356	106.075	0.22316	1.30041	106.461	0.22293	1.23470	106.829	0.22272	
20	1.46201	105.998	0.22409										479.67
22	1.47016	106.412	0.22495	1.37644	106.230	0.22348							481.67
24	1.47827	106.825	0.22581	1.38419	106.646	0.22434	1.30049	106.465	0.22294				483.67
26	1.48636	107.238	0.22666	1.39191	107.063	0.22520	1.30788	106.885	0.22381				485.67
28	1.49440	107.652	0.22751	1.39959	107.479	0.22606	1.31524	107.304	0.22467	1.23970	107.128	0.22334	487.67
30	1.50242	108.065	0.22835	1.40724	107.895	0.22691	1.32256	107.724	0.22553	1.24674	107.550	0.22420	489.67
32	1.51040	108.478	0.22920	1.41485	108.312	0.22776	1.32985	108.143	0.22638	1.25374	107.972	0.22506	491.67
34	1.51836	108.892	0.23004	1.42244	108.728	0.22860	1.33711	108.562	0.22723	1.26071	108.394	0.22592	493.67
36	1.52628	109.306	0.23087	1.42999	109.144	0.22944	1.34434	108.981	0.22808	1.26764	108.816	0.22677	495.67
38	1.53417	109.720	0.23171	1.43751	109.561	0.23028	1.35153	109.400	0.22892	1.27455	109.238	0.22762	497.67
40	1.54204	110.134	0.23254	1.44501	109.977	0.23112	1.35870	109.820	0.22976	1.28143	109.660	0.22847	499.67
42	1.54988	110.548	0.23336	1.45247	110.394	0.23195	1.36584	110.239	0.23060	1.28827	110.082	0.22931	501.67
44	1.55769	110.962	0.23419	1.45992	110.811	0.23278	1.37295	110.658	0.23144	1.29509	110.504	0.23015	503.67
46	1.56548	111.377	0.23501	1.46733	111.228	0.23361	1.38004	111.078	0.23227	1.30188	110.926	0.23099	505.67
48	1.57324	111.792	0.23583	1.47472	111.645	0.23443	1.38709	111.497	0.23309	1.30865	111.348	0.23182	507.67
50	1.58098	112.207	0.23664	1.48208	112.063	0.23525	1.39413	111.917	0.23392	1.31539	111.770	0.23265	509.67
52	1.58870	112.622	0.23746	1.48942	112.480	0.23607	1.40114	112.337	0.23474	1.32210	112.192	0.23348	511.67
54	1.59639	113.038	0.23827	1.49674	112.898	0.23688	1.40812	112.757	0.23556	1.32879	112.615	0.23430	513.67
56	1.60406	113.454	0.23908	1.50403	113.316	0.23769	1.41508	113.177	0.23638	1.33545	113.037	0.23512	515.67
58	1.61171	113.870	0.23988	1.51131	113.735	0.23850	1.42202	113.598	0.23719	1.34210	113.460	0.23594	517.67
60	1.61933	114.287	0.24069	1.51856	114.153	0.23931	1.42894	114.019	0.23800	1.34872	113.883	0.23675	519.67
62	1.62694	114.704	0.24149	1.52579	114.572	0.24012	1.43584	114.440	0.23881	1.35532	114.306	0.23757	521.67
64	1.63453	115.122	0.24229	1.53300	114.992	0.24092	1.44271	114.861	0.23962	1.36190	114.729	0.23838	523.67
66	1.64210	115.539	0.24308	1.54019	115.411	0.24172	1.44957	115.283	0.24042	1.36845	115.153	0.23918	525.67
68	1.64964	115.958	0.24388	1.54736	115.832	0.24252	1.45640	115.704	0.24122	1.37499	115.576	0.23999	527.67
70	1.65718	116.376	0.24467	1.55451	116.252	0.24331	1.46322	116.127	0.24202	1.38151	116.000	0.24079	529.67
72	1.66469	116.795	0.24546	1.56164	116.673	0.24410	1.47002	116.549	0.24282	1.38801	116.425	0.24159	531.67
74	1.67218	117.215	0.24625	1.56876	117.094	0.24490	1.47680	116.972	0.24361	1.39449	116.850	0.24239	533.67
76	1.67966	117.635	0.24703	1.57586	117.516	0.24568	1.48356	117.396	0.24440	1.40095	117.275	0.24318	535.67
78	1.68713	118.055	0.24781	1.58294	117.938	0.24647	1.49031	117.819	0.24519	1.40740	117.700	0.24397	537.67
80	1.69457	118.476	0.24860	1.59001	118.360	0.24725	1.49704	118.243	0.24598	1.41383	118.126	0.24476	539.67
82	1.70200	118.898	0.24937	1.59706	118.783	0.24804	1.50376	118.668	0.24677	1.42024	118.552	0.24555	541.67
84	1.70942	119.320	0.25015	1.60410	119.207	0.24882	1.51045	119.093	0.24755	1.42664	118.978	0.24634	543.67
86	1.71682	119.742	0.25093	1.61112	119.630	0.24960	1.51714	119.518	0.24833	1.43302	119.405	0.24712	545.67
88	1.72421	120.165	0.25170	1.61812	120.055	0.25037	1.52380	119.944	0.24911	1.43939	119.833	0.24790	547.67

Temp. °F	Absolute Pressure, lb./sq. in. 32.0 — Gauge Pressure 17.304 lb./sq. in.; Satn. Temp. = 18.41 °F, 478.08 °R			34.0 — Gauge Pressure 19.304 lb./sq. in.; Satn. Temp. = 21.26 °F, 480.93 °R			36.0 — Gauge Pressure 21.304 lb./sq. in.; Satn. Temp. = 23.98 °F, 483.65 °R			38.0 — Gauge Pressure 23.304 lb./sq. in.; Satn. Temp. = 26.59 °F, 486.26 °R			Temp. °R
	V	H	S	V	H	S	V	H	S	V	H	S	
90	1.73158	120.588	0.25247	1.62512	120.480	0.25115	1.53046	120.370	0.24989	1.44574	120.260	0.24868	549.67
92	1.73894	121.012	0.25324	1.63209	120.905	0.25192	1.53710	120.797	0.25066	1.45208	120.688	0.24946	551.67
94	1.74628	121.437	0.25401	1.63906	121.331	0.25269	1.54372	121.224	0.25143	1.45841	121.117	0.25024	553.67
96	1.75362	121.862	0.25478	1.64601	121.757	0.25346	1.55034	121.652	0.25220	1.46472	121.546	0.25101	555.67
98	1.76094	122.287	0.25554	1.65295	122.184	0.25422	1.55694	122.080	0.25297	1.47101	121.976	0.25178	557.67
100	1.76824	122.713	0.25630	1.65987	122.611	0.25499	1.56352	122.509	0.25374	1.47730	122.406	0.25255	559.67
102	1.77554	123.140	0.25707	1.66679	123.039	0.25575	1.57010	122.938	0.25451	1.48357	122.836	0.25332	561.67
104	1.78282	123.567	0.25782	1.67369	123.468	0.25651	1.57666	123.368	0.25527	1.48983	123.267	0.25409	563.67
106	1.79009	123.995	0.25858	1.68058	123.897	0.25727	1.58321	123.798	0.25603	1.49608	123.698	0.25485	565.67
108	1.79735	124.423	0.25934	1.68745	124.326	0.25803	1.58975	124.229	0.25679	1.50231	124.130	0.25561	567.67
110	1.80460	124.853	0.26009	1.69432	124.756	0.25879	1.59628	124.660	0.25755	1.50854	124.563	0.25637	569.67
112	1.81184	125.282	0.26085	1.70118	125.187	0.25954	1.60279	125.092	0.25831	1.51475	124.996	0.25713	571.67
114	1.81907	125.712	0.26160	1.70802	125.619	0.26030	1.60930	125.524	0.25906	1.52095	125.430	0.25789	573.67
116	1.82629	126.143	0.26235	1.71486	126.050	0.26105	1.61580	125.957	0.25982	1.52714	125.864	0.25864	575.67
118	1.83350	126.575	0.26309	1.72169	126.483	0.26180	1.62228	126.391	0.26057	1.53333	126.298	0.25940	577.67
120	1.84070	127.007	0.26384	1.72850	126.916	0.26255	1.62876	126.825	0.26132	1.53950	126.733	0.26015	579.67
122	1.84789	127.439	0.26459	1.73531	127.350	0.26329	1.63522	127.260	0.26207	1.54566	127.169	0.26090	581.67
124	1.85507	127.873	0.26533	1.74210	127.784	0.26404	1.64168	127.695	0.26281	1.55181	127.606	0.26165	583.67
126	1.86224	128.307	0.26607	1.74889	128.219	0.26478	1.64813	128.131	0.26356	1.55795	128.043	0.26240	585.67
128	1.86940	128.741	0.26681	1.75567	128.655	0.26553	1.65456	128.567	0.26430	1.56409	128.480	0.26314	587.67
130	1.87655	129.177	0.26755	1.76244	129.091	0.26627	1.66099	129.005	0.26505	1.57021	128.918	0.26389	589.67
132	1.88370	129.612	0.26829	1.76920	129.528	0.26701	1.66741	129.442	0.26579	1.57633	129.357	0.26463	591.67
134	1.89084	130.049	0.26903	1.77595	129.965	0.26774	1.67382	129.881	0.26653	1.58243	129.796	0.26537	593.67
136	1.89796	130.486	0.26976	1.78270	130.403	0.26848	1.68023	130.320	0.26727	1.58853	130.236	0.26611	595.67
138	1.90508	130.924	0.27050	1.78943	130.842	0.26922	1.68662	130.759	0.26800	1.59462	130.677	0.26685	597.67
140	1.91220	131.363	0.27123	1.79616	131.281	0.26995	1.69301	131.200	0.26874	1.60071	131.118	0.26758	599.67
142	1.91930	131.802	0.27196	1.80289	131.721	0.27068	1.69939	131.641	0.26947	1.60678	131.559	0.26832	601.67
144	1.92640	132.242	0.27269	1.80960	132.162	0.27141	1.70576	132.082	0.27020	1.61285	132.002	0.26905	603.67
146	1.93349	132.682	0.27342	1.81631	132.604	0.27214	1.71213	132.524	0.27094	1.61891	132.445	0.26979	605.67
148	1.94058	133.124	0.27415	1.82300	133.046	0.27287	1.71849	132.967	0.27167	1.62496	132.888	0.27052	607.67
150	1.94765	133.566	0.27487	1.82970	133.488	0.27360	1.72484	133.411	0.27239	1.63101	133.333	0.27125	609.67
152	1.95472	134.008	0.27560	1.83638	133.932	0.27433	1.73118	133.855	0.27312	1.63705	133.778	0.27198	611.67
154	1.96179	134.452	0.27632	1.84306	134.376	0.27505	1.73752	134.300	0.27385	1.64308	134.223	0.27270	613.67
156	1.96884	134.896	0.27704	1.84973	134.821	0.27577	1.74385	134.745	0.27457	1.64910	134.670	0.27343	615.67
158	1.97589	135.340	0.27776	1.85640	135.266	0.27650	1.75017	135.191	0.27530	1.65512	135.116	0.27415	617.67

Temp. °F	Absolute Pressure, lb./sq. in. 40.0 Gauge Pressure 25.304 lb./sq. in. Satn. Temp. = 29.09 °F 488.76 °R			42.0 Gauge Pressure 27.304 lb./sq. in. Satn. Temp. = 31.50°F 491.17 °R			44.0 Gauge Pressure 29.304 lb./sq. in. Satn. Temp. = 33.82 °F 493.49 °R			46.0 Gauge Pressure 31.304 lb./sq. in. Satn. Temp. = 36.06 °F 495.73 °R			Temp. °R
	V	H	S	V	H	S	V	H	S	V	H	S	
SAT N	1.17535	107.181	0.22253	1.12145	107.518	0.22235	1.07228	107.841	0.22218	1.02725	108.152	0.22203	
30	1.17843	107.374	0.22293										489.67
32	1.18518	107.800	0.22379	1.12308	107.625	0.22257							491.67
34	1.19189	108.225	0.22466	1.12956	108.053	0.22344	1.07285	107.880	0.22226				493.67
36	1.19857	108.650	0.22552	1.13601	108.481	0.22430	1.07909	108.311	0.22313				495.67
38	1.20521	109.075	0.22637	1.14242	108.909	0.22517	1.08529	108.742	0.22400	1.03307	108.573	0.22287	497.67
40	1.21183	109.499	0.22722	1.14881	109.337	0.22602	1.09146	109.172	0.22486	1.03906	109.006	0.22374	499.67
42	1.21841	109.924	0.22807	1.15516	109.764	0.22688	1.09760	109.602	0.22572	1.04501	109.439	0.22461	501.67
44	1.22497	110.348	0.22892	1.16148	110.191	0.22773	1.10372	110.032	0.22658	1.05093	109.872	0.22547	503.67
46	1.23150	110.773	0.22976	1.16777	110.618	0.22857	1.10980	110.462	0.22743	1.05682	110.304	0.22633	505.67
48	1.23800	111.197	0.23059	1.17404	111.045	0.22942	1.11585	110.892	0.22828	1.06268	110.737	0.22718	507.67
50	1.24448	111.622	0.23143	1.18028	111.472	0.23026	1.12187	111.321	0.22912	1.06851	111.169	0.22803	509.67
52	1.25093	112.046	0.23226	1.18649	111.899	0.23109	1.12787	111.751	0.22996	1.07431	111.601	0.22887	511.67
54	1.25735	112.471	0.23309	1.19268	112.326	0.23192	1.13385	112.180	0.23080	1.08009	112.032	0.22972	513.67
56	1.26375	112.896	0.23391	1.19884	112.753	0.23275	1.13979	112.609	0.23164	1.08584	112.464	0.23056	515.67
58	1.27013	113.321	0.23474	1.20498	113.180	0.23358	1.14572	113.039	0.23247	1.09157	112.896	0.23139	517.67
60	1.27648	113.746	0.23556	1.21109	113.607	0.23440	1.15162	113.468	0.23329	1.09728	113.327	0.23222	519.67
62	1.28282	114.171	0.23637	1.21719	114.035	0.23522	1.15749	113.897	0.23412	1.10296	113.759	0.23305	521.67
64	1.28913	114.596	0.23719	1.22326	114.462	0.23604	1.16335	114.327	0.23494	1.10861	114.191	0.23388	523.67
66	1.29542	115.022	0.23800	1.22931	114.890	0.23686	1.16918	114.756	0.23576	1.11425	114.622	0.23470	525.67
68	1.30169	115.447	0.23880	1.23534	115.317	0.23767	1.17499	115.136	0.23658	1.11986	115.054	0.23552	527.67
70	1.30794	115.873	0.23961	1.24135	115.745	0.23848	1.18078	115.616	0.23739	1.12545	115.486	0.23634	529.67
72	1.31417	116.300	0.24041	1.24734	116.173	0.23929	1.18655	116.046	0.23820	1.13103	115.918	0.23715	531.67
74	1.32038	116.726	0.24121	1.25331	116.602	0.24009	1.19230	116.476	0.23901	1.13658	116.350	0.23796	533.67
76	1.32658	117.153	0.24201	1.25926	117.030	0.24089	1.19804	116.907	0.23981	1.14211	116.782	0.23877	535.67
78	1.33276	117.580	0.24281	1.26520	117.459	0.24169	1.20375	117.337	0.24061	1.14763	117.214	0.23958	537.67
80	1.33892	118.007	0.24360	1.27111	117.888	0.24249	1.20945	117.768	0.24141	1.15313	117.647	0.24038	539.67
82	1.34506	118.435	0.24439	1.27701	118.317	0.24328	1.21513	118.199	0.24221	1.15861	118.080	0.24118	541.67
84	1.35119	118.863	0.24518	1.28290	118.747	0.24407	1.22079	118.630	0.24301	1.16407	118.513	0.24198	543.67
86	1.35730	119.292	0.24597	1.28877	119.177	0.24486	1.22644	119.062	0.24380	1.16952	118.946	0.24277	545.67
88	1.36340	119.720	0.24675	1.29462	119.608	0.24565	1.23207	119.494	0.24459	1.17495	119.380	0.24357	547.67
90	1.36948	120.150	0.24754	1.30046	120.038	0.24643	1.23769	119.926	0.24538	1.18036	119.813	0.24436	549.67
92	1.37555	120.579	0.24832	1.30628	120.469	0.24722	1.24329	120.359	0.24616	1.18576	120.247	0.24515	551.67
94	1.38160	121.009	0.24909	1.31209	120.901	0.24800	1.24888	120.792	0.24695	1.19115	120.682	0.24593	553.67
96	1.38764	121.440	0.24987	1.31788	121.333	0.24878	1.25445	121.225	0.24773	1.19652	121.117	0.24672	555.67
98	1.39366	121.871	0.25064	1.32366	121.765	0.24955	1.26001	121.659	0.24851	1.20187	121.552	0.24750	557.67

Temp. °F	Absolute Pressure, lb./sq. in.												Temp. °R
	40.0			42.0			44.0			46.0			
	Gauge Pressure = 25.304 lb./sq. in. Satn. Temp. = 29.09 °F 488.76 °R			Gauge Pressure = 27.304 lb./sq. in. Satn. Temp. = 31.50°F 491.17 °R			Gauge Pressure = 29.304 lb./sq. in. Satn. Temp. = 33.82 °F 493.49 °R			Gauge Pressure = 31.304 lb./sq. in. Satn. Temp. = 36.06 °F 495.73 °R			
	V	H	S	V	H	S	V	H	S	V	H	S	
100	1.39968	122.302	0.25142	1.32943	122.198	0.25033	1.26555	122.093	0.24928	1.20721	121.987	0.24828	559.67
102	1.40568	122.734	0.25219	1.33518	122.631	0.25110	1.27108	122.527	0.25006	1.21254	122.423	0.24905	561.67
104	1.41166	123.166	0.25295	1.34093	123.064	0.25187	1.27660	122.962	0.25083	1.21786	122.859	0.24983	563.67
106	1.41764	123.599	0.25372	1.34666	123.498	0.25264	1.28211	123.397	0.25160	1.22316	123.296	0.25060	565.67
108	1.42360	124.032	0.25448	1.35237	123.933	0.25341	1.28761	123.833	0.25237	1.22845	123.732	0.25137	567.67
110	1.42955	124.465	0.25525	1.35808	124.367	0.25417	1.29309	124.269	0.25314	1.23373	124.170	0.25214	569.67
112	1.43549	124.900	0.25601	1.36377	124.803	0.25493	1.29856	124.705	0.25390	1.23900	124.608	0.25291	571.67
114	1.44142	125.334	0.25677	1.36946	125.239	0.25569	1.30402	125.142	0.25466	1.24426	125.046	0.25367	573.67
116	1.44734	125.770	0.25752	1.37513	125.675	0.25645	1.30947	125.580	0.25543	1.24950	125.485	0.25444	575.67
118	1.45325	126.205	0.25828	1.38079	126.112	0.25721	1.31491	126.018	0.25619	1.25474	125.924	0.25520	577.67
120	1.45915	126.642	0.25903	1.38644	126.549	0.25797	1.32033	126.456	0.25694	1.25996	126.363	0.25596	579.67
122	1.46504	127.078	0.25979	1.39208	126.987	0.25872	1.32575	126.895	0.25770	1.26517	126.803	0.25672	581.67
124	1.47092	127.516	0.26054	1.39772	127.426	0.25947	1.33116	127.335	0.25845	1.27038	127.244	0.25747	583.67
126	1.47679	127.954	0.26129	1.40334	127.864	0.26022	1.33656	127.775	0.25921	1.27557	127.685	0.25823	585.67
128	1.48265	128.392	0.26203	1.40895	128.304	0.26097	1.34194	128.215	0.25996	1.28075	128.126	0.25898	587.67
130	1.48850	128.831	0.26278	1.41455	128.744	0.26172	1.34732	128.656	0.26071	1.28593	128.568	0.25973	589.67
132	1.49434	129.271	0.26352	1.42015	129.185	0.26247	1.35269	129.098	0.26145	1.29109	129.011	0.26048	591.67
134	1.50017	129.711	0.26427	1.42574	129.626	0.26321	1.35805	129.540	0.26220	1.29625	129.454	0.26123	593.67
136	1.50600	130.152	0.26501	1.43131	130.068	0.26395	1.36341	129.983	0.26294	1.30140	129.898	0.26197	595.67
138	1.51181	130.593	0.26575	1.43688	130.510	0.26470	1.36875	130.426	0.26369	1.30654	130.342	0.26272	597.67
140	1.51762	131.035	0.26649	1.44244	130.953	0.26543	1.37409	130.870	0.26443	1.31167	130.786	0.26346	599.67
142	1.52342	131.478	0.26722	1.44800	131.396	0.26617	1.37942	131.314	0.26517	1.31679	131.232	0.26420	601.67
144	1.52922	131.921	0.26796	1.45354	131.840	0.26691	1.38474	131.759	0.26591	1.32191	131.678	0.26494	603.67
146	1.53500	132.365	0.26869	1.45908	132.285	0.26765	1.39005	132.205	0.26664	1.32701	132.124	0.26568	605.67
148	1.54078	132.810	0.26942	1.46461	132.730	0.26838	1.39535	132.651	0.26738	1.33211	132.571	0.26642	607.67
150	1.54655	133.255	0.27016	1.47013	133.176	0.26911	1.40065	133.097	0.26811	1.33720	133.018	0.26715	609.67
152	1.55232	133.700	0.27089	1.47565	133.623	0.26984	1.40594	133.545	0.26884	1.34229	133.467	0.26789	611.67
154	1.55807	134.147	0.27161	1.48116	134.070	0.27057	1.41122	133.993	0.26958	1.34737	133.915	0.26862	613.67
156	1.56382	134.594	0.27234	1.48666	134.518	0.27130	1.41650	134.441	0.27031	1.35244	134.365	0.26935	615.67
158	1.56957	135.041	0.27307	1.49215	134.966	0.27203	1.42177	134.890	0.27103	1.35750	134.814	0.27008	617.67
160	1.57531	135.490	0.27379	1.49764	135.415	0.27275	1.42703	135.340	0.27176	1.36256	135.265	0.27081	619.67
162	1.58104	135.939	0.27452	1.50313	135.865	0.27348	1.43229	135.791	0.27249	1.36761	135.716	0.27153	621.67
164	1.58676	136.388	0.27524	1.50860	136.315	0.27420	1.43754	136.242	0.27321	1.37265	136.168	0.27226	623.67
166	1.59248	136.838	0.27596	1.51407	136.766	0.27492	1.44279	136.693	0.27393	1.37769	136.620	0.27298	625.67
168	1.59819	137.289	0.27668	1.51954	137.218	0.27564	1.44802	137.145	0.27466	1.38272	137.073	0.27371	627.67

Temp. °F	Absolute Pressure, lb./sq. in.												Temp. °R
	48.0			50.0			52.0			54.0			
	Gauge Pressure = 33.304 lb./sq. in. Satn. Temp. = 38.23 °F 497.90 °R			Gauge Pressure = 35.304 lb./sq. in. Satn. Temp. = 40.33 °F 500.00 °R			Gauge Pressure = 37.304 lb./sq. in. Satn. Temp. = 42.37 °F 502.04 °R			Gauge Pressure = 39.304 lb./sq. in. Satn. Temp. = 44.35 °F 504.02 °R			
	V	H	S	V	H	S	V	H	S	V	H	S	
SAT N	0.98583	108.452	0.22188	0.94762	108.741	0.22174	0.91225	109.020	0.22161	0.87940	109.290	0.22149	
40	0.99097	108.838	0.22266										499.67
42	0.99675	109.274	0.22353	0.95230	109.107	0.22247							501.67
44	1.00250	109.710	0.22439	0.95789	109.546	0.22335	0.91668	109.380	0.22233				503.67
46	1.00821	110.145	0.22526	0.96345	109.984	0.22422	0.92209	109.821	0.22320	0.88375	109.656	0.22222	505.67
48	1.01390	110.580	0.22611	0.96898	110.422	0.22508	0.92747	110.262	0.22407	0.88900	110.100	0.22309	507.67
50	1.01955	111.015	0.22697	0.97447	110.859	0.22594	0.93282	110.702	0.22494	0.89422	110.543	0.22396	509.67
52	1.02518	111.449	0.22782	0.97994	111.296	0.22680	0.93814	111.142	0.22580	0.89941	110.986	0.22483	511.67
54	1.03078	111.884	0.22867	0.98538	111.733	0.22765	0.94344	111.581	0.22666	0.90456	111.428	0.22569	513.67
56	1.03636	112.318	0.22951	0.99079	112.170	0.22850	0.94870	112.020	0.22751	0.90969	111.870	0.22655	515.67
58	1.04191	112.752	0.23035	0.99618	112.606	0.22934	0.95394	112.459	0.22836	0.91480	112.311	0.22741	517.67
60	1.04743	113.186	0.23119	1.00154	113.043	0.23018	0.95915	112.898	0.22921	0.91987	112.752	0.22826	519.67
62	1.05293	113.619	0.23202	1.00688	113.479	0.23102	0.96434	113.337	0.23005	0.92492	113.193	0.22910	521.67
64	1.05841	114.053	0.23285	1.01219	113.915	0.23185	0.96950	113.775	0.23089	0.92995	113.634	0.22995	523.67
66	1.06386	114.487	0.23368	1.01748	114.351	0.23269	0.97464	114.213	0.23172	0.93495	114.074	0.23079	525.67
68	1.06930	114.921	0.23450	1.02275	114.787	0.23351	0.97976	114.651	0.23255	0.93993	114.515	0.23162	527.67
70	1.07471	115.355	0.23532	1.02800	115.222	0.23434	0.98486	115.089	0.23338	0.94488	114.955	0.23246	529.67
72	1.08010	115.789	0.23614	1.03323	115.658	0.23516	0.98993	115.527	0.23421	0.94982	115.395	0.23328	531.67
74	1.08547	116.223	0.23695	1.03843	116.094	0.23598	0.99498	115.965	0.23503	0.95473	115.835	0.23411	533.67
76	1.09083	116.657	0.23777	1.04362	116.530	0.23679	1.00002	116.403	0.23585	0.95962	116.275	0.23493	535.67
78	1.09616	117.091	0.23857	1.04878	116.966	0.23761	1.00503	116.841	0.23667	0.96449	116.715	0.23575	537.67
80	1.10147	117.525	0.23938	1.05393	117.403	0.23842	1.01002	117.279	0.23748	0.96935	117.155	0.23657	539.67
82	1.10677	117.960	0.24018	1.05906	117.839	0.23922	1.01500	117.717	0.23829	0.97418	117.594	0.23738	541.67
84	1.11205	118.394	0.24099	1.06417	118.275	0.24003	1.01996	118.155	0.23910	0.97900	118.034	0.23819	543.67
86	1.11731	118.829	0.24178	1.06927	118.712	0.24083	1.02490	118.594	0.23990	0.98380	118.474	0.23900	545.67
88	1.12256	119.265	0.24258	1.07435	119.149	0.24163	1.02982	119.032	0.24070	0.98858	118.915	0.23981	547.67
90	1.12779	119.700	0.24337	1.07941	119.586	0.24242	1.03473	119.471	0.24150	0.99334	119.355	0.24061	549.67
92	1.13301	120.136	0.24417	1.08445	120.023	0.24322	1.03962	119.909	0.24230	0.99809	119.795	0.24141	551.67
94	1.13821	120.571	0.24495	1.08949	120.460	0.24401	1.04449	120.348	0.24309	1.00282	120.236	0.24221	553.67
96	1.14339	121.008	0.24574	1.09450	120.898	0.24480	1.04936	120.788	0.24389	1.00754	120.677	0.24300	555.67
98	1.14856	121.444	0.24652	1.09950	121.336	0.24558	1.05420	121.227	0.24468	1.01224	121.118	0.24379	557.67
100	1.15372	121.881	0.24731	1.10449	121.774	0.24637	1.05903	121.667	0.24546	1.01693	121.559	0.24458	559.67
102	1.15886	122.318	0.24809	1.10946	122.213	0.24715	1.06385	122.107	0.24625	1.02160	122.000	0.24537	561.67
104	1.16400	122.756	0.24886	1.11443	122.652	0.24793	1.06865	122.547	0.24703	1.02626	122.442	0.24615	563.67
106	1.16911	123.193	0.24964	1.11937	123.091	0.24871	1.07345	122.988	0.24781	1.03091	122.884	0.24694	565.67
108	1.17422	123.632	0.25041	1.12431	123.530	0.24948	1.07822	123.428	0.24859	1.03554	123.326	0.24772	567.67

Temp. °F	Absolute Pressure, lb./sq. in.												Temp. °R
	48.0			50.0			52.0			54.0			
	Gauge Pressure = 33.304 lb./sq. in. Satn. Temp. = 38.23 °F 497.90 °R			Gauge Pressure = 35.304 lb/sq. in. Satn. Temp. = 40.33 °F 500.00 °R			Gauge Pressure = 37.304 lb./sq. in. Satn. Temp. = 42.37 °F 502.04 °R			Gauge Pressure = 39.304 lb./sq. in. Satn. Temp. = 44.35 °F 504.02 °R			
	V	H	S	V	H	S	V	H	S	V	H	S	
110	1.17931	124.070	0.25118	1.12923	123.970	0.25026	1.08299	123.870	0.24936	1.04016	123.768	0.24850	569.67
112	1.18439	124.509	0.25195	1.13414	124.410	0.25103	1.08774	124.311	0.25014	1.04477	124.211	0.24927	571.67
114	1.18946	124.949	0.25272	1.13904	124.851	0.25180	1.09248	124.753	0.25091	1.04936	124.654	0.25005	573.67
116	1.19452	125.389	0.25349	1.14393	125.292	0.25257	1.09721	125.195	0.25168	1.05395	125.098	0.25082	575.67
118	1.19957	125.829	0.25425	1.14880	125.734	0.25333	1.10193	125.638	0.25245	1.05852	125.542	0.25159	577.67
120	1.20461	126.270	0.25501	1.15367	126.175	0.25410	1.10664	126.081	0.25321	1.06308	125.986	0.25235	579.67
122	1.20963	126.711	0.25577	1.15852	126.618	0.25486	1.11134	126.524	0.25397	1.06763	126.430	0.25312	581.67
124	1.21465	127.152	0.25653	1.16337	127.060	0.25562	1.11602	126.968	0.25474	1.07217	126.875	0.25388	583.67
126	1.21966	127.594	0.25728	1.16820	127.504	0.25637	1.12070	127.412	0.25550	1.07671	127.321	0.25465	585.67
128	1.22465	128.037	0.25804	1.17303	127.947	0.25713	1.12537	127.857	0.25625	1.08123	127.766	0.25541	587.67
130	1.22964	128.480	0.25879	1.17784	128.391	0.25789	1.13002	128.302	0.25701	1.08574	128.212	0.25616	589.67
132	1.23462	128.924	0.25954	1.18265	128.836	0.25864	1.13467	128.748	0.25776	1.09024	128.659	0.25692	591.67
134	1.23959	129.368	0.26029	1.18745	129.281	0.25939	1.13931	129.194	0.25852	1.09473	129.106	0.25767	593.67
136	1.24455	129.812	0.26104	1.19223	129.726	0.26014	1.14394	129.640	0.25927	1.09921	129.554	0.25843	595.67
138	1.24950	130.257	0.26179	1.19701	130.172	0.26089	1.14856	130.087	0.26002	1.10368	130.002	0.25918	597.67
140	1.25444	130.703	0.26253	1.20178	130.619	0.26163	1.15317	130.535	0.26076	1.10815	130.450	0.25993	599.67
142	1.25938	131.149	0.26327	1.20655	131.066	0.26238	1.15777	130.983	0.26151	1.11260	130.899	0.26067	601.67
144	1.26430	131.596	0.26401	1.21130	131.514	0.26312	1.16237	131.431	0.26225	1.11705	131.348	0.26142	603.67
146	1.26922	132.043	0.26475	1.21605	131.962	0.26386	1.16695	131.880	0.26300	1.12149	131.798	0.26216	605.67
148	1.27413	132.491	0.26549	1.22078	132.410	0.26460	1.17153	132.330	0.26374	1.12592	132.248	0.26291	607.67
150	1.27904	132.939	0.26623	1.22552	132.859	0.26534	1.17610	132.780	0.26448	1.13035	132.699	0.26365	609.67
152	1.28393	133.388	0.26696	1.23024	133.309	0.26607	1.18067	133.230	0.26522	1.13476	133.151	0.26439	611.67
154	1.28882	133.838	0.26770	1.23496	133.760	0.26681	1.18523	133.681	0.26595	1.13917	133.603	0.26512	613.67
156	1.29370	134.288	0.26843	1.23966	134.210	0.26754	1.18977	134.133	0.26669	1.14357	134.055	0.26586	615.67
158	1.29858	134.738	0.26916	1.24437	134.662	0.26827	1.19432	134.585	0.26742	1.14797	134.508	0.26659	617.67
160	1.30345	135.190	0.26989	1.24906	135.114	0.26900	1.19885	135.038	0.26815	1.15236	134.962	0.26733	619.67
162	1.30831	135.641	0.27062	1.25375	135.567	0.26973	1.20338	135.491	0.26888	1.15674	135.416	0.26806	621.67
164	1.31317	136.094	0.27134	1.25843	136.020	0.27046	1.20791	135.945	0.26961	1.16111	135.871	0.26879	623.67
166	1.31802	136.547	0.27207	1.26311	136.474	0.27119	1.21242	136.400	0.27034	1.16548	136.326	0.26952	625.67
168	1.32286	137.001	0.27279	1.26778	136.928	0.27191	1.21693	136.855	0.27106	1.16984	136.782	0.27024	627.67
170	1.32770	137.455	0.27352	1.27244	137.383	0.27264	1.22144	137.311	0.27179	1.17420	137.238	0.27097	629.67
172	1.33253	137.910	0.27424	1.27710	137.839	0.27336	1.22593	137.767	0.27251	1.17855	137.695	0.27170	631.67
174	1.33736	138.365	0.27496	1.28176	138.295	0.27408	1.23043	138.224	0.27324	1.18289	138.153	0.27242	633.67
176	1.34218	138.822	0.27568	1.28640	138.752	0.27480	1.23491	138.681	0.27396	1.18723	138.611	0.27314	635.67
178	1.34699	139.278	0.27639	1.29104	139.209	0.27552	1.23939	139.139	0.27468	1.19157	139.070	0.27386	637.67

Temp. °F	56.0 V	56.0 H	56.0 S	58.0 V	58.0 H	58.0 S	60.0 V	60.0 H	60.0 S	62.0 V	62.0 H	62.0 S	Temp. °R
	Absolute Pressure, lb./sq. in.												
	56.0			58.0			60.0			62.0			
	Gauge Pressure 41.304 lb./sq. in. Satn. Temp. = 46.27 °F 505.94 °R			Gauge Pressure 43.304 lb./sq. in. Satn. Temp. = 48.15 °F 507.82 °R			Gauge Pressure 45.304 lb./sq. in. Satn. Temp. = 49.97 °F 509.64 °R			Gauge Pressure 47.304 lb./sq. in. Satn. Temp. = 51.75 °F 511.42 °R			
	V	H	S	V	H	S	V	H	S	V	H	S	
SAT N	0.84882	109.551	0.22138	0.82027	109.804	0.22127	0.79356	110.050	0.22116	0.76851	110.288	0.22106	
48	0.85324	109.936	0.22214										507.67
50	0.85833	110.383	0.22301	0.82489	110.220	0.22208	0.79363	110.056	0.22117				509.67
52	0.86340	110.828	0.22389	0.82984	110.669	0.22296	0.79848	110.508	0.22206	0.76911	110.345	0.22117	511.67
54	0.86843	111.273	0.22475	0.83476	111.116	0.22384	0.80329	110.958	0.22294	0.77383	110.798	0.22206	513.67
56	0.87344	111.717	0.22562	0.83965	111.564	0.22470	0.80808	111.408	0.22381	0.77852	111.251	0.22294	515.67
58	0.87841	112.162	0.22648	0.84451	112.010	0.22557	0.81284	111.858	0.22468	0.78317	111.704	0.22381	517.67
60	0.88336	112.605	0.22733	0.84935	112.457	0.22643	0.81756	112.307	0.22555	0.78780	112.155	0.22468	519.67
62	0.88829	113.049	0.22818	0.85415	112.903	0.22729	0.82226	112.755	0.22641	0.79240	112.606	0.22555	521.67
64	0.89319	113.492	0.22903	0.85893	113.348	0.22814	0.82694	113.203	0.22727	0.79698	113.057	0.22641	523.67
66	0.89806	113.934	0.22988	0.86369	113.793	0.22899	0.83159	113.651	0.22812	0.80153	113.507	0.22727	525.67
68	0.90291	114.377	0.23072	0.86842	114.238	0.22983	0.83621	114.098	0.22897	0.80605	113.956	0.22812	527.67
70	0.90774	114.819	0.23155	0.87313	114.683	0.23067	0.84081	114.545	0.22981	0.81054	114.406	0.22897	529.67
72	0.91254	115.261	0.23239	0.87782	115.127	0.23151	0.84538	114.991	0.23065	0.81502	114.855	0.22982	531.67
74	0.91733	115.703	0.23322	0.88248	115.571	0.23234	0.84994	115.438	0.23149	0.81947	115.303	0.23066	533.67
76	0.92209	116.145	0.23404	0.88713	116.015	0.23317	0.85447	115.884	0.23233	0.82390	115.751	0.23150	535.67
78	0.92683	116.587	0.23487	0.89175	116.459	0.23400	0.85898	116.330	0.23316	0.82831	116.199	0.23233	537.67
80	0.93155	117.029	0.23569	0.89635	116.903	0.23482	0.86347	116.775	0.23399	0.83269	116.647	0.23317	539.67
82	0.93626	117.471	0.23650	0.90093	117.346	0.23565	0.86794	117.221	0.23481	0.83706	117.095	0.23399	541.67
84	0.94094	117.913	0.23732	0.90549	117.790	0.23646	0.87239	117.667	0.23563	0.84140	117.542	0.23482	543.67
86	0.94561	118.355	0.23813	0.91004	118.234	0.23728	0.87682	118.112	0.23645	0.84573	117.990	0.23564	545.67
88	0.95026	118.796	0.23894	0.91457	118.677	0.23809	0.88124	118.558	0.23726	0.85004	118.437	0.23646	547.67
90	0.95489	119.238	0.23974	0.91908	119.121	0.23890	0.88563	119.003	0.23808	0.85433	118.884	0.23727	549.67
92	0.95951	119.680	0.24054	0.92357	119.565	0.23970	0.89001	119.448	0.23888	0.85860	119.331	0.23809	551.67
94	0.96411	120.123	0.24134	0.92805	120.009	0.24051	0.89438	119.894	0.23969	0.86286	119.778	0.23889	553.67
96	0.96869	120.565	0.24214	0.93251	120.453	0.24131	0.89872	120.339	0.24049	0.86710	120.225	0.23970	555.67
98	0.97326	121.007	0.24294	0.93695	120.897	0.24210	0.90305	120.785	0.24129	0.87133	120.673	0.24050	557.67
100	0.97781	121.450	0.24373	0.94138	121.341	0.24290	0.90737	121.231	0.24209	0.87554	121.120	0.24130	559.67
102	0.98235	121.893	0.24452	0.94580	121.785	0.24369	0.91167	121.676	0.24289	0.87973	121.567	0.24210	561.67
104	0.98688	122.336	0.24531	0.95020	122.230	0.24448	0.91596	122.122	0.24368	0.88391	122.015	0.24290	563.67
106	0.99139	122.779	0.24609	0.95459	122.674	0.24527	0.92023	122.569	0.24447	0.88807	122.462	0.24369	565.67
108	0.99589	123.223	0.24687	0.95897	123.119	0.24605	0.92449	123.015	0.24526	0.89222	122.910	0.24448	567.67

Temp. °F	Absolute Pressure, lb./sq. in.												Temp. °R
	56.0			58.0			60.0			62.0			
	Gauge Pressure = 41.304 lb./sq. in.; Satn. Temp. = 46.27 °F, 505.94 °R			Gauge Pressure = 43.304 lb./sq. in.; Satn. Temp. = 48.15 °F, 507.82 °R			Gauge Pressure = 45.304 lb./sq. in.; Satn. Temp. = 49.97 °F, 509.64 °R			Gauge Pressure = 47.304 lb./sq. in.; Satn. Temp. = 51.75 °F, 511.42 °R			
	V	H	S	V	H	S	V	H	S	V	H	S	
110	1.00038	123.667	0.24765	0.96333	123.564	0.24684	0.92873	123.461	0.24604	0.89636	123.358	0.24527	569.67
112	1.00485	124.111	0.24843	0.96768	124.010	0.24762	0.93297	123.908	0.24683	0.90049	123.806	0.24605	571.67
114	1.00931	124.555	0.24921	0.97201	124.455	0.24840	0.93719	124.355	0.24761	0.90460	124.254	0.24684	573.67
116	1.01376	125.000	0.24998	0.97634	124.901	0.24917	0.94140	124.802	0.24838	0.90870	124.703	0.24762	575.67
118	1.01820	125.445	0.25075	0.98065	125.348	0.24995	0.94559	125.250	0.24916	0.91279	125.152	0.24839	577.67
120	1.02263	125.890	0.25152	0.98495	125.794	0.25072	0.94978	125.698	0.24993	0.91686	125.601	0.24917	579.67
122	1.02704	126.336	0.25229	0.98924	126.241	0.25149	0.95395	126.146	0.25071	0.92093	126.050	0.24994	581.67
124	1.03145	126.782	0.25306	0.99352	126.688	0.25225	0.95811	126.594	0.25147	0.92498	126.499	0.25072	583.67
126	1.03584	127.228	0.25382	0.99779	127.136	0.25302	0.96226	127.043	0.25224	0.92902	126.949	0.25149	585.67
128	1.04023	127.675	0.25458	1.00205	127.584	0.25378	0.96641	127.492	0.25301	0.93305	127.399	0.25225	587.67
130	1.04460	128.122	0.25534	1.00630	128.032	0.25455	0.97054	127.941	0.25377	0.93708	127.850	0.25302	589.67
132	1.04897	128.570	0.25610	1.01054	128.481	0.25530	0.97466	128.391	0.25453	0.94109	128.301	0.25378	591.67
134	1.05332	129.018	0.25686	1.01476	128.930	0.25606	0.97877	128.841	0.25529	0.94509	128.752	0.25454	593.67
136	1.05767	129.467	0.25761	1.01898	129.379	0.25682	0.98287	129.292	0.25605	0.94908	129.204	0.25530	595.67
138	1.06201	129.916	0.25836	1.02319	129.829	0.25757	0.98696	129.743	0.25681	0.95306	129.655	0.25606	597.67
140	1.06633	130.365	0.25911	1.02740	130.280	0.25832	0.99105	130.194	0.25756	0.95704	130.108	0.25681	599.67
142	1.07065	130.815	0.25986	1.03159	130.730	0.25908	0.99512	130.646	0.25831	0.96100	130.560	0.25757	601.67
144	1.07496	131.265	0.26061	1.03577	131.182	0.25982	0.99919	131.098	0.25906	0.96496	131.014	0.25832	603.67
146	1.07927	131.716	0.26135	1.03995	131.633	0.26057	1.00325	131.550	0.25981	0.96891	131.467	0.25907	605.67
148	1.08356	132.167	0.26210	1.04412	132.085	0.26132	1.00730	132.003	0.26056	0.97284	131.921	0.25982	607.67
150	1.08785	132.619	0.26284	1.04828	132.538	0.26206	1.01134	132.457	0.26130	0.97678	132.375	0.26057	609.67
152	1.09213	133.071	0.26358	1.05243	132.991	0.26280	1.01537	132.911	0.26205	0.98070	132.830	0.26131	611.67
154	1.09640	133.524	0.26432	1.05658	133.445	0.26354	1.01940	133.365	0.26279	0.98462	133.286	0.26205	613.67
156	1.10067	133.977	0.26506	1.06071	133.899	0.26428	1.02342	133.820	0.26353	0.98852	133.741	0.26279	615.67
158	1.10493	134.431	0.26579	1.06485	134.354	0.26502	1.02743	134.276	0.26427	0.99243	134.198	0.26353	617.67
160	1.10918	134.885	0.26653	1.06897	134.809	0.26575	1.03144	134.732	0.26500	0.99632	134.654	0.26427	619.67
162	1.11342	135.340	0.26726	1.07309	135.264	0.26649	1.03543	135.188	0.26574	1.00021	135.112	0.26501	621.67
164	1.11766	135.796	0.26799	1.07720	135.721	0.26722	1.03943	135.645	0.26647	1.00409	135.569	0.26574	623.67
166	1.12189	136.252	0.26872	1.08130	136.177	0.26795	1.04341	136.103	0.26720	1.00796	136.028	0.26648	625.67
168	1.12612	136.708	0.26945	1.08540	136.635	0.26868	1.04739	136.561	0.26794	1.01183	136.486	0.26721	627.67
170	1.13033	137.165	0.27018	1.08949	137.092	0.26941	1.05136	137.019	0.26866	1.01569	136.946	0.26794	629.67
172	1.13455	137.623	0.27090	1.09357	137.551	0.27014	1.05533	137.478	0.26939	1.01954	137.406	0.26867	631.67
174	1.13875	138.081	0.27163	1.09765	138.010	0.27086	1.05929	137.938	0.27012	1.02339	137.866	0.26940	633.67
176	1.14295	138.540	0.27235	1.10172	138.469	0.27159	1.06324	138.398	0.27084	1.02723	138.327	0.27012	635.67
178	1.14715	139.000	0.27307	1.10579	138.929	0.27231	1.06719	138.859	0.27157	1.03107	138.788	0.27085	637.67

Temp. °F	Absolute Pressure, lb./sq. in.												Temp. °R
	64.0			66.0			68.0			70.0			
	Gauge Pressure 49.304 lb./sq. in. Satn. Temp. = 53.48 °F 513.15 °R			Gauge Pressure 51.304 lb./sq. in. Satn. Temp. = 55.18 °F 514.85 °R			Gauge Pressure 53.304 lb./sq. in. Satn. Temp. = 56.83 °F 516.50 °R			Gauge Pressure 55.304 lb./sq. in. Satn. Temp. = 58.45 °F 518.12 °R			
	V	H	S	V	H	S	V	H	S	V	H	S	
SAT N	0.74498	110.519	0.22097	0.72281	110.744	0.22088	0.70191	110.963	0.22079	0.68216	111.176	0.22071	
54	0.74617	110.637	0.22120										513.67
56	0.75077	111.093	0.22208	0.72466	110.932	0.22124							515.67
58	0.75533	111.548	0.22296	0.72915	111.390	0.22213	0.70447	111.231	0.22131				517.67
60	0.75987	112.002	0.22384	0.73360	111.848	0.22301	0.70885	111.692	0.22220	0.68548	111.534	0.22140	519.67
62	0.76438	112.456	0.22471	0.73803	112.304	0.22389	0.71320	112.151	0.22308	0.68976	111.996	0.22228	521.67
64	0.76886	112.909	0.22558	0.74242	112.760	0.22476	0.71751	112.609	0.22396	0.69400	112.457	0.22317	523.67
66	0.77332	113.362	0.22644	0.74679	113.215	0.22563	0.72180	113.067	0.22483	0.69821	112.918	0.22404	525.67
68	0.77775	113.814	0.22730	0.75113	113.670	0.22649	0.72606	113.524	0.22570	0.70240	113.378	0.22492	527.67
70	0.78215	114.265	0.22815	0.75545	114.124	0.22735	0.73030	113.981	0.22656	0.70656	113.837	0.22579	529.67
72	0.78653	114.717	0.22900	0.75974	114.577	0.22820	0.73451	114.437	0.22742	0.71069	114.295	0.22665	531.67
74	0.79088	115.167	0.22985	0.76401	115.030	0.22905	0.73869	114.892	0.22827	0.71480	114.753	0.22751	533.67
76	0.79522	115.618	0.23069	0.76825	115.483	0.22990	0.74285	115.347	0.22912	0.71888	115.210	0.22836	535.67
78	0.79953	116.068	0.23153	0.77247	115.935	0.23074	0.74699	115.802	0.22997	0.72294	115.667	0.22922	537.67
80	0.80382	116.518	0.23237	0.77667	116.387	0.23158	0.75111	116.256	0.23081	0.72698	116.123	0.23006	539.67
82	0.80809	116.967	0.23320	0.78085	116.839	0.23242	0.75520	116.710	0.23165	0.73100	116.579	0.23091	541.67
84	0.81234	117.417	0.23403	0.78501	117.290	0.23325	0.75927	117.163	0.23249	0.73499	117.035	0.23175	543.67
86	0.81657	117.866	0.23485	0.78915	117.742	0.23408	0.76333	117.616	0.23332	0.73897	117.490	0.23258	545.67
88	0.82078	118.315	0.23567	0.79327	118.193	0.23490	0.76736	118.069	0.23415	0.74292	117.945	0.23341	547.67
90	0.82497	118.764	0.23649	0.79737	118.644	0.23572	0.77138	118.522	0.23498	0.74686	118.400	0.23424	549.67
92	0.82914	119.213	0.23731	0.80145	119.094	0.23654	0.77537	118.975	0.23580	0.75077	118.854	0.23507	551.67
94	0.83330	119.662	0.23812	0.80552	119.545	0.23736	0.77935	119.427	0.23662	0.75467	119.308	0.23589	553.67
96	0.83744	120.111	0.23893	0.80957	119.995	0.23817	0.78332	119.879	0.23743	0.75855	119.762	0.23671	555.67
98	0.84157	120.560	0.23973	0.81360	120.446	0.23898	0.78726	120.331	0.23824	0.76241	120.216	0.23752	557.67
100	0.84568	121.009	0.24054	0.81761	120.896	0.23979	0.79119	120.783	0.23905	0.76626	120.670	0.23833	559.67
102	0.84977	121.457	0.24134	0.82161	121.347	0.24059	0.79510	121.236	0.23986	0.77009	121.124	0.23914	561.67
104	0.85385	121.906	0.24213	0.82560	121.797	0.24139	0.79900	121.688	0.24066	0.77391	121.577	0.23995	563.67
106	0.85791	122.355	0.24293	0.82957	122.248	0.24219	0.80288	122.140	0.24146	0.77771	122.031	0.24075	565.67
108	0.86196	122.805	0.24372	0.83353	122.699	0.24298	0.80675	122.592	0.24226	0.78149	122.485	0.24155	567.67
110	0.86600	123.254	0.24451	0.83747	123.149	0.24378	0.81060	123.044	0.24306	0.78526	122.938	0.24235	569.67
112	0.87003	123.703	0.24530	0.84140	123.600	0.24457	0.81445	123.496	0.24385	0.78902	123.392	0.24315	571.67
114	0.87404	124.153	0.24609	0.84531	124.051	0.24535	0.81827	123.949	0.24464	0.79277	123.846	0.24394	573.67
116	0.87803	124.603	0.24687	0.84922	124.502	0.24614	0.82209	124.401	0.24543	0.79650	124.299	0.24473	575.67
118	0.88202	125.053	0.24765	0.85311	124.954	0.24692	0.82589	124.854	0.24621	0.80021	124.753	0.24552	577.67

Temp. °F	Absolute Pressure, lb./sq. in.												Temp. °R
	64.0			66.0			68.0			70.0			
	Gauge Pressure 49.304 lb./sq. in. Satn. Temp. = 53.48 °F 513.15 °R			Gauge Pressure 51.304 lb./sq. in. Satn. Temp. = 55.18 °F 514.85 °R			Gauge Pressure 53.304 lb./sq. in. Satn. Temp. = 56.83 °F 516.50 °R			Gauge Pressure 55.304 lb./sq. in. Satn. Temp. = 58.45 °F 518.12 °R			
	V	H	S	V	H	S	V	H	S	V	H	S	
120	0.88599	125.503	0.24843	0.85699	125.405	0.24770	0.82968	125.307	0.24699	0.80392	125.208	0.24630	579.67
122	0.88996	125.954	0.24920	0.86085	125.857	0.24848	0.83346	125.760	0.24777	0.80761	125.662	0.24708	581.67
124	0.89391	126.404	0.24998	0.86471	126.309	0.24926	0.83722	126.213	0.24855	0.81130	126.116	0.24786	583.67
126	0.89785	126.855	0.25075	0.86856	126.761	0.25003	0.84098	126.666	0.24933	0.81497	126.571	0.24864	585.67
128	0.90178	127.307	0.25152	0.87239	127.213	0.25080	0.84472	127.120	0.25010	0.81863	127.026	0.24942	587.67
130	0.90570	127.758	0.25228	0.87621	127.666	0.25157	0.84845	127.574	0.25087	0.82227	127.481	0.25019	589.67
132	0.90961	128.210	0.25305	0.88002	128.119	0.25234	0.85218	128.028	0.25164	0.82591	127.936	0.25096	591.67
134	0.91350	128.662	0.25381	0.88383	128.573	0.25310	0.85589	128.482	0.25241	0.82954	128.391	0.25173	593.67
136	0.91739	129.115	0.25457	0.88762	129.026	0.25386	0.85959	128.937	0.25317	0.83316	128.847	0.25249	595.67
138	0.92127	129.568	0.25533	0.89140	129.480	0.25462	0.86328	129.392	0.25393	0.83676	129.303	0.25326	597.67
140	0.92514	130.021	0.25609	0.89518	129.935	0.25538	0.86697	129.847	0.25469	0.84036	129.760	0.25402	599.67
142	0.92901	130.475	0.25685	0.89894	130.389	0.25614	0.87064	130.303	0.25545	0.84395	130.216	0.25478	601.67
144	0.93286	130.929	0.25760	0.90270	130.844	0.25690	0.87431	130.759	0.25621	0.84753	130.673	0.25554	603.67
146	0.93670	131.384	0.25835	0.90645	131.300	0.25765	0.87796	131.215	0.25696	0.85110	131.131	0.25630	605.67
148	0.94054	131.838	0.25910	0.91019	131.755	0.25840	0.88161	131.672	0.25772	0.85467	131.589	0.25705	607.67
150	0.94437	132.294	0.25985	0.91392	132.212	0.25915	0.88525	132.129	0.25847	0.85822	132.047	0.25780	609.67
152	0.94819	132.749	0.26059	0.91764	132.668	0.25990	0.88888	132.587	0.25922	0.86177	132.505	0.25855	611.67
154	0.95200	133.206	0.26134	0.92136	133.125	0.26064	0.89251	133.045	0.25996	0.86530	132.964	0.25930	613.67
156	0.95580	133.662	0.26208	0.92506	133.583	0.26139	0.89612	133.503	0.26071	0.86883	133.423	0.26005	615.67
158	0.95960	134.119	0.26282	0.92876	134.041	0.26213	0.89973	133.962	0.26145	0.87236	133.883	0.26080	617.67
160	0.96339	134.577	0.26356	0.93246	134.499	0.26287	0.90333	134.421	0.26220	0.87587	134.343	0.26154	619.67
162	0.96718	135.035	0.26430	0.93614	134.958	0.26361	0.90693	134.881	0.26294	0.87938	134.803	0.26228	621.67
164	0.97095	135.493	0.26504	0.93982	135.417	0.26435	0.91051	135.341	0.26368	0.88288	135.264	0.26302	623.67
166	0.97472	135.952	0.26577	0.94349	135.877	0.26508	0.91410	135.801	0.26441	0.88637	135.725	0.26376	625.67
168	0.97848	136.412	0.26650	0.94716	136.337	0.26582	0.91767	136.262	0.26515	0.88986	136.187	0.26450	627.67
170	0.98224	136.872	0.26724	0.95082	136.798	0.26655	0.92124	136.724	0.26588	0.89334	136.650	0.26523	629.67
172	0.98599	137.333	0.26797	0.95447	137.259	0.26728	0.92480	137.186	0.26662	0.89682	137.112	0.26597	631.67
174	0.98973	137.794	0.26870	0.95811	137.721	0.26801	0.92835	137.648	0.26735	0.90028	137.575	0.26670	633.67
176	0.99347	138.255	0.26942	0.96175	138.183	0.26874	0.93190	138.111	0.26808	0.90374	138.039	0.26743	635.67
178	0.99720	138.717	0.27015	0.96539	138.646	0.26947	0.93544	138.575	0.26880	0.90720	138.503	0.26816	637.67
180	1.00093	139.180	0.27087	0.96902	139.110	0.27019	0.93898	139.039	0.26953	0.91065	138.968	0.26889	639.67
182	1.00465	139.643	0.27160	0.97264	139.573	0.27092	0.94251	139.504	0.27026	0.91409	139.433	0.26961	641.67
184	1.00837	140.107	0.27232	0.97626	140.038	0.27164	0.94603	139.969	0.27098	0.91753	139.899	0.27034	643.67
186	1.01208	140.571	0.27304	0.97987	140.503	0.27236	0.94955	140.434	0.27170	0.92096	140.365	0.27106	645.67
188	1.01578	141.036	0.27376	0.98347	140.968	0.27308	0.95307	140.900	0.27242	0.92439	140.832	0.27178	647.67

Temp. °F	Absolute Pressure, lb./sq. in.												Temp. °R
	72.0			74.0			76.0			78.0			
	Gauge Pressure 57.304 lb./sq. in. Satn. Temp. = 60.04 °F 519.71 °R			Gauge Pressure 59.304 lb./sq. in. Satn. Temp. = 61.59 °F 521.26 °R			Gauge Pressure 61.304 lb./sq. in. Satn. Temp. = 63.11 °F 522.78 °R			Gauge Pressure 63.304 lb./sq. in. Satn. Temp. = 64.60 °F 524.27 °R			
	V	H	S	V	H	S	V	H	S	V	H	S	
SAT N	0.66347	111.383	0.22063	0.64575	111.585	0.22055	0.62893	111.783	0.22047	0.61294	111.975	0.22040	
62	0.66759	111.839	0.22150	0.64659	111.681	0.22073							521.67
64	0.67176	112.304	0.22239	0.65070	112.148	0.22163	0.63072	111.991	0.22087				523.67
66	0.67591	112.767	0.22327	0.65478	112.615	0.22251	0.63474	112.460	0.22177	0.61571	112.305	0.22103	525.67
68	0.68002	113.229	0.22415	0.65884	113.080	0.22340	0.63874	112.929	0.22266	0.61964	112.776	0.22193	527.67
70	0.68411	113.691	0.22502	0.66286	113.544	0.22428	0.64270	113.396	0.22354	0.62355	113.246	0.22282	529.67
72	0.68818	114.152	0.22589	0.66686	114.008	0.22515	0.64663	113.862	0.22442	0.62743	113.715	0.22370	531.67
74	0.69221	114.612	0.22676	0.67083	114.471	0.22602	0.65054	114.327	0.22529	0.63128	114.183	0.22458	533.67
76	0.69622	115.072	0.22762	0.67477	114.933	0.22688	0.65442	114.792	0.22616	0.63510	114.650	0.22545	535.67
78	0.70021	115.531	0.22847	0.67869	115.394	0.22774	0.65828	115.256	0.22703	0.63890	115.116	0.22632	537.67
80	0.70418	115.990	0.22932	0.68259	115.855	0.22860	0.66211	115.719	0.22789	0.64267	115.582	0.22718	539.67
82	0.70812	116.448	0.23017	0.68646	116.315	0.22945	0.66592	116.182	0.22874	0.64642	116.047	0.22804	541.67
84	0.71204	116.906	0.23101	0.69031	116.775	0.23030	0.66971	116.644	0.22959	0.65015	116.511	0.22890	543.67
86	0.71594	117.363	0.23185	0.69414	117.234	0.23114	0.67347	117.105	0.23044	0.65385	116.975	0.22975	545.67
88	0.71982	117.820	0.23269	0.69795	117.693	0.23198	0.67722	117.566	0.23128	0.65753	117.438	0.23060	547.67
90	0.72368	118.276	0.23352	0.70174	118.152	0.23282	0.68094	118.027	0.23212	0.66119	117.901	0.23144	549.67
92	0.72752	118.733	0.23435	0.70551	118.610	0.23365	0.68464	118.487	0.23296	0.66483	118.363	0.23228	551.67
94	0.73134	119.189	0.23518	0.70926	119.068	0.23448	0.68833	118.947	0.23379	0.66845	118.825	0.23312	553.67
96	0.73515	119.644	0.23600	0.71299	119.526	0.23530	0.69199	119.406	0.23462	0.67206	119.286	0.23395	555.67
98	0.73893	120.100	0.23682	0.71671	119.983	0.23612	0.69564	119.865	0.23544	0.67564	119.747	0.23478	557.67
100	0.74270	120.556	0.23763	0.72041	120.440	0.23694	0.69927	120.324	0.23627	0.67921	120.208	0.23560	559.67
102	0.74646	121.011	0.23844	0.72409	120.897	0.23776	0.70289	120.783	0.23708	0.68276	120.668	0.23642	561.67
104	0.75020	121.466	0.23925	0.72776	121.354	0.23857	0.70648	121.242	0.23790	0.68629	121.128	0.23724	563.67
106	0.75392	121.921	0.24006	0.73141	121.811	0.23938	0.71007	121.700	0.23871	0.68981	121.589	0.23806	565.67
108	0.75763	122.377	0.24086	0.73504	122.268	0.24018	0.71363	122.158	0.23952	0.69331	122.048	0.23887	567.67
110	0.76132	122.832	0.24166	0.73866	122.724	0.24099	0.71718	122.617	0.24033	0.69679	122.508	0.23968	569.67
112	0.76500	123.287	0.24246	0.74227	123.181	0.24179	0.72072	123.075	0.24113	0.70027	122.968	0.24048	571.67
114	0.76867	123.742	0.24325	0.74586	123.638	0.24258	0.72424	123.533	0.24193	0.70372	123.427	0.24128	573.67
116	0.77232	124.197	0.24405	0.74944	124.094	0.24338	0.72775	123.991	0.24273	0.70717	123.887	0.24208	575.67
118	0.77596	124.653	0.24484	0.75300	124.551	0.24417	0.73124	124.449	0.24352	0.71059	124.346	0.24288	577.67
120	0.77958	125.108	0.24562	0.75655	125.008	0.24496	0.73473	124.907	0.24431	0.71401	124.806	0.24367	579.67
122	0.78320	125.564	0.24641	0.76009	125.465	0.24575	0.73820	125.365	0.24510	0.71741	125.265	0.24447	581.67
124	0.78680	126.019	0.24719	0.76362	125.922	0.24653	0.74165	125.824	0.24589	0.72081	125.725	0.24525	583.67
126	0.79039	126.475	0.24797	0.76714	126.379	0.24731	0.74510	126.282	0.24667	0.72418	126.185	0.24604	585.67
128	0.79397	126.931	0.24875	0.77064	126.836	0.24809	0.74853	126.740	0.24745	0.72755	126.644	0.24682	587.67

Temp. °F	Absolute Pressure, lb./sq. in.												Temp. °R
	72.0			74.0			76.0			78.0			
	Gauge Pressure = 57.304 lb./sq. in.; Satn. Temp. = 60.04 °F, 519.71 °R			Gauge Pressure = 59.304 lb./sq. in.; Satn. Temp. = 61.59 °F, 521.26 °R			Gauge Pressure = 61.304 lb./sq. in.; Satn. Temp. = 63.11 °F, 522.78 °R			Gauge Pressure = 63.304 lb./sq. in.; Satn. Temp. = 64.60 °F, 524.27 °R			
	V	H	S	V	H	S	V	H	S	V	H	S	
130	0.79754	127.387	0.24952	0.77414	127.293	0.24887	0.75196	127.199	0.24823	0.73091	127.104	0.24760	589.67
132	0.80110	127.844	0.25029	0.77762	127.751	0.24964	0.75537	127.658	0.24901	0.73425	127.564	0.24838	591.67
134	0.80465	128.300	0.25107	0.78109	128.209	0.25042	0.75877	128.117	0.24978	0.73759	128.024	0.24916	593.67
136	0.80818	128.757	0.25183	0.78455	128.667	0.25119	0.76216	128.576	0.25055	0.74091	128.485	0.24993	595.67
138	0.81171	129.214	0.25260	0.78801	129.125	0.25196	0.76554	129.035	0.25132	0.74422	128.945	0.25071	597.67
140	0.81523	129.672	0.25336	0.79145	129.583	0.25272	0.76891	129.495	0.25209	0.74753	129.406	0.25148	599.67
142	0.81874	130.130	0.25413	0.79488	130.042	0.25348	0.77227	129.955	0.25286	0.75082	129.866	0.25224	601.67
144	0.82224	130.588	0.25489	0.79830	130.501	0.25425	0.77562	130.415	0.25362	0.75410	130.328	0.25301	603.67
146	0.82573	131.046	0.25564	0.80172	130.961	0.25501	0.77897	130.875	0.25438	0.75738	130.789	0.25377	605.67
148	0.82921	131.505	0.25640	0.80512	131.420	0.25576	0.78230	131.336	0.25514	0.76064	131.250	0.25453	607.67
150	0.83268	131.964	0.25715	0.80852	131.880	0.25652	0.78563	131.796	0.25590	0.76390	131.712	0.25529	609.67
152	0.83615	132.423	0.25791	0.81191	132.340	0.25727	0.78894	132.258	0.25665	0.76715	132.175	0.25605	611.67
154	0.83961	132.883	0.25866	0.81529	132.801	0.25802	0.79225	132.719	0.25741	0.77039	132.637	0.25680	613.67
156	0.84305	133.343	0.25941	0.81866	133.262	0.25877	0.79555	133.181	0.25816	0.77362	133.100	0.25755	615.67
158	0.84650	133.803	0.26015	0.82203	133.723	0.25952	0.79884	133.643	0.25891	0.77684	133.563	0.25831	617.67
160	0.84993	134.264	0.26090	0.82539	134.185	0.26027	0.80213	134.106	0.25966	0.78006	134.026	0.25905	619.67
162	0.85336	134.725	0.26164	0.82874	134.647	0.26101	0.80541	134.569	0.26040	0.78327	134.490	0.25980	621.67
164	0.85678	135.187	0.26238	0.83208	135.110	0.26176	0.80868	135.032	0.26115	0.78647	134.954	0.26055	623.67
166	0.86019	135.649	0.26312	0.83541	135.573	0.26250	0.81194	135.496	0.26189	0.78966	135.419	0.26129	625.67
168	0.86359	136.112	0.26386	0.83874	136.036	0.26324	0.81519	135.960	0.26263	0.79285	135.884	0.26203	627.67
170	0.86699	136.575	0.26460	0.84206	136.500	0.26398	0.81844	136.425	0.26337	0.79603	136.349	0.26277	629.67
172	0.87038	137.038	0.26533	0.84538	136.964	0.26471	0.82169	136.890	0.26411	0.79920	136.815	0.26351	631.67
174	0.87377	137.502	0.26606	0.84869	137.429	0.26545	0.82492	137.355	0.26484	0.80237	137.281	0.26425	633.67
176	0.87715	137.967	0.26680	0.85199	137.894	0.26618	0.82815	137.821	0.26557	0.80553	137.748	0.26498	635.67
178	0.88052	138.432	0.26753	0.85529	138.360	0.26691	0.83137	138.288	0.26631	0.80868	138.215	0.26572	637.67
180	0.88389	138.897	0.26826	0.85858	138.826	0.26764	0.83459	138.754	0.26704	0.81183	138.683	0.26645	639.67
182	0.88725	139.363	0.26898	0.86186	139.292	0.26837	0.83780	139.222	0.26777	0.81497	139.151	0.26718	641.67
184	0.89061	139.829	0.26971	0.86514	139.759	0.26909	0.84101	139.689	0.26850	0.81811	139.619	0.26791	643.67
186	0.89396	140.296	0.27043	0.86841	140.227	0.26982	0.84421	140.158	0.26922	0.82124	140.088	0.26864	645.67
188	0.89731	140.764	0.27116	0.87168	140.695	0.27054	0.84740	140.626	0.26995	0.82437	140.557	0.26936	647.67
190	0.90065	141.232	0.27188	0.87494	141.164	0.27127	0.85059	141.096	0.27067	0.82749	141.027	0.27009	649.67
192	0.90398	141.700	0.27260	0.87820	141.633	0.27199	0.85378	141.565	0.27139	0.83060	141.498	0.27081	651.67
194	0.90731	142.169	0.27332	0.88145	142.103	0.27271	0.85695	142.036	0.27211	0.83371	141.969	0.27153	653.67
196	0.91063	142.639	0.27403	0.88470	142.573	0.27343	0.86013	142.506	0.27283	0.83681	142.440	0.27225	655.67
198	0.91395	143.109	0.27475	0.88794	143.043	0.27414	0.86330	142.978	0.27355	0.83991	142.912	0.27297	657.67

Temp. °F	80.0: V	80.0: H	80.0: S	82.0: V	82.0: H	82.0: S	84.0: V	84.0: H	84.0: S	86.0: V	86.0: H	86.0: S	Temp. °R
	Absolute Pressure, lb./sq. in.												
	80.0			82.0			84.0			86.0			
	Gauge Pressure 65.304 lb./sq. in.; Satn. Temp. = 66.06 °F, 525.73 °R			Gauge Pressure 67.304 lb./sq. in.; Satn. Temp. = 67.50 °F, 527.17 °R			Gauge Pressure 69.304 lb./sq. in.; Satn. Temp. = 68.91 °F, 528.58 °R			Gauge Pressure 71.304 lb./sq. in.; Satn. Temp. = 70.29 °F, 529.96 °R			
	V	H	S	V	H	S	V	H	S	V	H	S	
SAT N	0.59772	112.163	0.22033	0.58322	112.346	0.22027	0.56938	112.525	0.22020	0.55616	112.700	0.22014	
68	0.60148	112.622	0.22121	0.58418	112.466	0.22049							527.67
70	0.60533	113.094	0.22210	0.58798	112.941	0.22139	0.57143	112.787	0.22070				529.67
72	0.60916	113.566	0.22299	0.59176	113.416	0.22229	0.57516	113.264	0.22160	0.55931	113.111	0.22091	531.67
74	0.61295	114.037	0.22387	0.59550	113.890	0.22318	0.57886	113.741	0.22249	0.56297	113.590	0.22181	533.67
76	0.61672	114.507	0.22475	0.59922	114.362	0.22406	0.58253	114.216	0.22338	0.56659	114.068	0.22271	535.67
78	0.62046	114.976	0.22563	0.60291	114.833	0.22494	0.58617	114.690	0.22426	0.57019	114.545	0.22360	537.67
80	0.62418	115.444	0.22649	0.60657	115.304	0.22581	0.58979	115.163	0.22514	0.57376	115.021	0.22448	539.67
82	0.62787	115.911	0.22736	0.61021	115.774	0.22668	0.59338	115.635	0.22602	0.57730	115.496	0.22536	541.67
84	0.63154	116.377	0.22822	0.61383	116.243	0.22755	0.59694	116.107	0.22688	0.58082	115.969	0.22623	543.67
86	0.63519	116.843	0.22907	0.61742	116.711	0.22841	0.60048	116.577	0.22775	0.58432	116.442	0.22710	545.67
88	0.63881	117.309	0.22992	0.62099	117.178	0.22926	0.60400	117.047	0.22861	0.58779	116.914	0.22796	547.67
90	0.64242	117.773	0.23077	0.62454	117.645	0.23011	0.60750	117.516	0.22946	0.59124	117.386	0.22882	549.67
92	0.64600	118.238	0.23161	0.62807	118.112	0.23096	0.61097	117.984	0.23031	0.59466	117.856	0.22968	551.67
94	0.64956	118.701	0.23245	0.63157	118.577	0.23180	0.61443	118.452	0.23116	0.59807	118.326	0.23053	553.67
96	0.65310	119.165	0.23329	0.63506	119.043	0.23264	0.61786	118.920	0.23200	0.60145	118.796	0.23137	555.67
98	0.65663	119.628	0.23412	0.63853	119.507	0.23348	0.62128	119.386	0.23284	0.60482	119.264	0.23221	557.67
100	0.66014	120.090	0.23495	0.64198	119.972	0.23431	0.62468	119.853	0.23367	0.60816	119.733	0.23305	559.67
102	0.66362	120.552	0.23577	0.64541	120.436	0.23513	0.62805	120.319	0.23451	0.61149	120.200	0.23389	561.67
104	0.66710	121.014	0.23659	0.64883	120.900	0.23596	0.63141	120.784	0.23533	0.61480	120.668	0.23472	563.67
106	0.67055	121.476	0.23741	0.65222	121.363	0.23678	0.63476	121.249	0.23616	0.61809	121.135	0.23554	565.67
108	0.67399	121.938	0.23823	0.65561	121.826	0.23760	0.63809	121.714	0.23698	0.62137	121.601	0.23637	567.67
110	0.67742	122.399	0.23904	0.65897	122.289	0.23841	0.64140	122.179	0.23779	0.62463	122.068	0.23719	569.67
112	0.68083	122.860	0.23985	0.66232	122.752	0.23922	0.64469	122.643	0.23861	0.62787	122.534	0.23800	571.67
114	0.68422	123.321	0.24065	0.66566	123.215	0.24003	0.64797	123.107	0.23942	0.63110	122.999	0.23882	573.67
116	0.68760	123.782	0.24145	0.66898	123.677	0.24083	0.65124	123.571	0.24023	0.63431	123.465	0.23963	575.67
118	0.69097	124.243	0.24225	0.67229	124.140	0.24164	0.65449	124.035	0.24103	0.63751	123.930	0.24043	577.67
120	0.69432	124.704	0.24305	0.67558	124.602	0.24244	0.65773	124.499	0.24183	0.64070	124.395	0.24124	579.67
122	0.69766	125.165	0.24384	0.67887	125.064	0.24323	0.66096	124.963	0.24263	0.64387	124.860	0.24204	581.67
124	0.70099	125.626	0.24463	0.68213	125.526	0.24402	0.66417	125.426	0.24343	0.64703	125.325	0.24284	583.67
126	0.70431	126.087	0.24542	0.68539	125.989	0.24482	0.66737	125.890	0.24422	0.65018	125.790	0.24363	585.67
128	0.70761	126.548	0.24621	0.68863	126.451	0.24560	0.67056	126.353	0.24501	0.65331	126.255	0.24443	587.67

Temp. °F	Absolute Pressure, lb./sq. in.												Temp. °R
	80.0			82.0			84.0			86.0			
	Gauge Pressure 65.304 lb./sq. in. Satn. Temp. = 66.06 °F 525.73 °R			Gauge Pressure 67.304 lb./sq. in. Satn. Temp. = 67.50 °F 527.17 °R			Gauge Pressure 69.304 lb./sq. in. Satn. Temp. = 68.91 °F 528.58 °R			Gauge Pressure 71.304 lb./sq. in. Satn. Temp. = 70.29 °F 529.96 °R			
	V	H	S	V	H	S	V	H	S	V	H	S	
130	0.71090	127.009	0.24699	0.69187	126.913	0.24639	0.67373	126.817	0.24580	0.65643	126.720	0.24522	589.67
132	0.71418	127.470	0.24777	0.69509	127.376	0.24717	0.67689	127.280	0.24658	0.65954	127.185	0.24600	591.67
134	0.71745	127.931	0.24855	0.69830	127.838	0.24795	0.68005	127.744	0.24736	0.66264	127.650	0.24679	593.67
136	0.72071	128.393	0.24933	0.70150	128.301	0.24873	0.68319	128.208	0.24814	0.66573	128.115	0.24757	595.67
138	0.72396	128.854	0.25010	0.70469	128.763	0.24950	0.68632	128.672	0.24892	0.66880	128.580	0.24835	597.67
140	0.72720	129.316	0.25087	0.70786	129.226	0.25028	0.68944	129.136	0.24970	0.67187	129.045	0.24912	599.67
142	0.73043	129.778	0.25164	0.71103	129.689	0.25105	0.69255	129.600	0.25047	0.67492	129.510	0.24990	601.67
144	0.73365	130.240	0.25241	0.71419	130.152	0.25182	0.69565	130.064	0.25124	0.67797	129.976	0.25067	603.67
146	0.73686	130.702	0.25317	0.71734	130.616	0.25258	0.69874	130.529	0.25201	0.68101	130.441	0.25144	605.67
148	0.74006	131.165	0.25393	0.72048	131.079	0.25335	0.70182	130.993	0.25277	0.68403	130.907	0.25221	607.67
150	0.74325	131.628	0.25469	0.72361	131.543	0.25411	0.70490	131.458	0.25354	0.68705	131.373	0.25297	609.67
152	0.74644	132.091	0.25545	0.72673	132.007	0.25487	0.70796	131.923	0.25430	0.69006	131.839	0.25374	611.67
154	0.74961	132.555	0.25621	0.72985	132.472	0.25563	0.71102	132.389	0.25506	0.69306	132.305	0.25450	613.67
156	0.75278	133.018	0.25696	0.73295	132.936	0.25638	0.71406	132.854	0.25582	0.69605	132.772	0.25526	615.67
158	0.75594	133.482	0.25772	0.73605	133.401	0.25714	0.71710	133.320	0.25657	0.69903	133.238	0.25601	617.67
160	0.75909	133.947	0.25847	0.73914	133.867	0.25789	0.72013	133.786	0.25732	0.70201	133.705	0.25677	619.67
162	0.76223	134.411	0.25922	0.74222	134.332	0.25864	0.72316	134.253	0.25808	0.70497	134.173	0.25752	621.67
164	0.76537	134.876	0.25996	0.74529	134.798	0.25939	0.72617	134.719	0.25883	0.70793	134.640	0.25827	623.67
166	0.76850	135.342	0.26071	0.74836	135.264	0.26013	0.72918	135.186	0.25957	0.71088	135.108	0.25902	625.67
168	0.77162	135.808	0.26145	0.75142	135.731	0.26088	0.73218	135.654	0.26032	0.71383	135.577	0.25977	627.67
170	0.77473	136.274	0.26219	0.75447	136.198	0.26162	0.73517	136.122	0.26106	0.71677	136.045	0.26052	629.67
172	0.77784	136.740	0.26293	0.75752	136.665	0.26236	0.73816	136.590	0.26181	0.71970	136.514	0.26126	631.67
174	0.78094	137.207	0.26367	0.76056	137.133	0.26310	0.74114	137.058	0.26255	0.72262	136.983	0.26200	633.67
176	0.78404	137.675	0.26441	0.76359	137.601	0.26384	0.74411	137.527	0.26328	0.72554	137.453	0.26274	635.67
178	0.78713	138.142	0.26514	0.76662	138.070	0.26458	0.74708	137.996	0.26402	0.72845	137.923	0.26348	637.67
180	0.79021	138.611	0.26587	0.76964	138.539	0.26531	0.75004	138.466	0.26476	0.73135	138.394	0.26422	639.67
182	0.79328	139.079	0.26661	0.77265	139.008	0.26604	0.75299	138.936	0.26549	0.73425	138.864	0.26495	641.67
184	0.79636	139.549	0.26734	0.77566	139.478	0.26677	0.75594	139.407	0.26622	0.73714	139.336	0.26568	643.67
186	0.79942	140.018	0.26806	0.77866	139.948	0.26750	0.75888	139.878	0.26695	0.74003	139.807	0.26642	645.67
188	0.80248	140.488	0.26879	0.78166	140.419	0.26823	0.76182	140.349	0.26768	0.74291	140.279	0.26715	647.67
190	0.80553	140.959	0.26952	0.78465	140.890	0.26896	0.76475	140.821	0.26841	0.74578	140.752	0.26787	649.67
192	0.80858	141.430	0.27024	0.78763	141.362	0.26968	0.76768	141.293	0.26914	0.74865	141.225	0.26860	651.67
194	0.81162	141.901	0.27096	0.79061	141.834	0.27041	0.77060	141.766	0.26986	0.75151	141.698	0.26933	653.67
196	0.81466	142.373	0.27168	0.79359	142.307	0.27113	0.77351	142.240	0.27058	0.75437	142.172	0.27005	655.67
198	0.81769	142.846	0.27240	0.79656	142.780	0.27185	0.77642	142.713	0.27131	0.75723	142.647	0.27077	657.67

Temp. °F	88.0 Gauge Pressure 73.304 lb./sq. in. Satn. Temp. = 71.65 °F 531.32 °R			90.0 Gauge Pressure 75.304 lb./sq. in. Satn. Temp. = 72.99 °F 532.66 °R			92.0 Gauge Pressure 77.304 lb./sq. in. Satn. Temp. = 74.30 °F 533.97 °R			94.0 Gauge Pressure 79.304 lb./sq. in. Satn. Temp. = 75.59 °F 535.26 °R			Temp. °R
	V	H	S	V	H	S	V	H	S	V	H	S	
SAT N	0.54353	112.871	0.22008	0.53143	113.039	0.22002	0.51984	113.203	0.21996	0.50873	113.363	0.21991	
72	0.54416	112.956	0.22024										531.67
74	0.54778	113.438	0.22114	0.53324	113.285	0.22048							533.67
76	0.55136	113.919	0.22204	0.53679	113.769	0.22139	0.52282	113.617	0.22074	0.50943	113.463	0.22009	535.67
78	0.55492	114.399	0.22294	0.54030	114.251	0.22229	0.52630	114.102	0.22164	0.51288	113.951	0.22100	537.67
80	0.55844	114.877	0.22383	0.54379	114.733	0.22318	0.52975	114.586	0.22254	0.51629	114.438	0.22191	539.67
82	0.56194	115.355	0.22471	0.54725	115.213	0.22407	0.53317	115.069	0.22343	0.51968	114.924	0.22281	541.67
84	0.56542	115.831	0.22559	0.55068	115.691	0.22495	0.53657	115.550	0.22432	0.52304	115.408	0.22370	543.67
86	0.56887	116.306	0.22646	0.55409	116.169	0.22583	0.53994	116.031	0.22520	0.52637	115.891	0.22458	545.67
88	0.57229	116.781	0.22733	0.55747	116.646	0.22670	0.54328	116.510	0.22608	0.52968	116.373	0.22547	547.67
90	0.57570	117.254	0.22819	0.56083	117.122	0.22757	0.54660	116.988	0.22695	0.53296	116.854	0.22634	549.67
92	0.57908	117.727	0.22905	0.56417	117.597	0.22843	0.54990	117.466	0.22782	0.53622	117.333	0.22721	551.67
94	0.58244	118.199	0.22990	0.56749	118.071	0.22929	0.55317	117.942	0.22868	0.53945	117.812	0.22808	553.67
96	0.58577	118.671	0.23075	0.57078	118.545	0.23014	0.55642	118.418	0.22954	0.54266	118.290	0.22894	555.67
98	0.58909	119.141	0.23160	0.57405	119.018	0.23099	0.55965	118.893	0.23039	0.54586	118.767	0.22980	557.67
100	0.59239	119.612	0.23244	0.57731	119.490	0.23184	0.56287	119.367	0.23124	0.54903	119.243	0.23065	559.67
102	0.59567	120.081	0.23328	0.58054	119.961	0.23268	0.56606	119.841	0.23208	0.55218	119.719	0.23150	561.67
104	0.59893	120.551	0.23411	0.58376	120.433	0.23351	0.56923	120.314	0.23292	0.55531	120.194	0.23234	563.67
106	0.60218	121.019	0.23494	0.58695	120.903	0.23435	0.57238	120.786	0.23376	0.55842	120.668	0.23318	565.67
108	0.60540	121.488	0.23577	0.59013	121.373	0.23518	0.57552	121.258	0.23459	0.56152	121.142	0.23402	567.67
110	0.60861	121.956	0.23659	0.59330	121.843	0.23600	0.57864	121.729	0.23542	0.56459	121.615	0.23485	569.67
112	0.61181	122.423	0.23741	0.59645	122.312	0.23683	0.58174	122.201	0.23625	0.56766	122.088	0.23568	571.67
114	0.61499	122.891	0.23823	0.59958	122.781	0.23764	0.58483	122.671	0.23707	0.57070	122.560	0.23650	573.67
116	0.61815	123.358	0.23904	0.60269	123.250	0.23846	0.58790	123.141	0.23789	0.57373	123.032	0.23733	575.67
118	0.62130	123.825	0.23985	0.60580	123.718	0.23927	0.59096	123.611	0.23870	0.57674	123.504	0.23814	577.67
120	0.62443	124.291	0.24066	0.60888	124.187	0.24008	0.59400	124.081	0.23952	0.57974	123.975	0.23896	579.67
122	0.62755	124.758	0.24146	0.61196	124.655	0.24089	0.59703	124.551	0.24032	0.58272	124.446	0.23977	581.67
124	0.63066	125.224	0.24226	0.61501	125.122	0.24169	0.60004	125.020	0.24113	0.58569	124.917	0.24058	583.67
126	0.63376	125.690	0.24306	0.61806	125.590	0.24249	0.60304	125.489	0.24193	0.58865	125.387	0.24138	585.67
128	0.63684	126.157	0.24385	0.62109	126.058	0.24329	0.60603	125.958	0.24273	0.59159	125.858	0.24218	587.67
130	0.63991	126.623	0.24464	0.62412	126.525	0.24408	0.60900	126.427	0.24353	0.59453	126.328	0.24298	589.67
132	0.64297	127.089	0.24543	0.62713	126.993	0.24487	0.61197	126.896	0.24432	0.59744	126.798	0.24378	591.67
134	0.64601	127.555	0.24622	0.63012	127.460	0.24566	0.61492	127.364	0.24511	0.60035	127.268	0.24457	593.67
136	0.64905	128.021	0.24700	0.63311	127.927	0.24645	0.61786	127.833	0.24590	0.60324	127.738	0.24536	595.67
138	0.65207	128.488	0.24778	0.63608	128.395	0.24723	0.62078	128.301	0.24669	0.60613	128.208	0.24615	597.67

Absolute Pressure, lb./sq. in.

Temp. °F	Absolute Pressure, lb./sq. in.												Temp. °R
	88.0			90.0			92.0			94.0			
	Gauge Pressure 73.304 lb./sq. in. Satn. Temp. = 71.65 °F 531.32 °R			Gauge Pressure 75.304 lb./sq. in. Satn. Temp. = 72.99 °F 532.66 °R			Gauge Pressure 77.304 lb./sq. in. Satn. Temp. = 74.30 °F 533.97 °R			Gauge Pressure 79.304 lb./sq. in. Satn. Temp. = 75.59 °F 535.26 °R			
	V	H	S	V	H	S	V	H	S	V	H	S	
140	0.65509	128.954	0.24856	0.63905	128.862	0.24801	0.62370	128.770	0.24747	0.60900	128.678	0.24693	599.67
142	0.65809	129.420	0.24934	0.64200	129.330	0.24879	0.62661	129.239	0.24825	0.61186	129.147	0.24772	601.67
144	0.66109	129.887	0.25011	0.64495	129.797	0.24957	0.62950	129.707	0.24903	0.61471	129.617	0.24850	603.67
146	0.66407	130.353	0.25089	0.64788	130.265	0.25034	0.63239	130.176	0.24980	0.61755	130.087	0.24927	605.67
148	0.66704	130.820	0.25165	0.65080	130.733	0.25111	0.63527	130.645	0.25057	0.62038	130.557	0.25005	607.67
150	0.67001	131.287	0.25242	0.65372	131.201	0.25188	0.63813	131.114	0.25134	0.62321	131.027	0.25082	609.67
152	0.67296	131.754	0.25319	0.65662	131.669	0.25265	0.64099	131.583	0.25211	0.62602	131.497	0.25159	611.67
154	0.67591	132.221	0.25395	0.65952	132.137	0.25341	0.64384	132.053	0.25288	0.62882	131.968	0.25236	613.67
156	0.67885	132.689	0.25471	0.66241	132.606	0.25417	0.64668	132.522	0.25364	0.63161	132.438	0.25312	615.67
158	0.68178	133.156	0.25547	0.66529	133.074	0.25493	0.64951	132.992	0.25440	0.63440	132.909	0.25389	617.67
160	0.68470	133.624	0.25622	0.66816	133.543	0.25569	0.65233	133.461	0.25516	0.63718	133.379	0.25465	619.67
162	0.68761	134.093	0.25698	0.67102	134.012	0.25645	0.65515	133.932	0.25592	0.63994	133.850	0.25541	621.67
164	0.69052	134.561	0.25773	0.67388	134.482	0.25720	0.65795	134.402	0.25668	0.64270	134.322	0.25616	623.67
166	0.69342	135.030	0.25848	0.67672	134.951	0.25795	0.66075	134.872	0.25743	0.64546	134.793	0.25692	625.67
168	0.69631	135.499	0.25923	0.67957	135.421	0.25870	0.66354	135.343	0.25818	0.64820	135.265	0.25767	627.67
170	0.69919	135.968	0.25998	0.68240	135.892	0.25945	0.66633	135.814	0.25893	0.65094	135.737	0.25842	629.67
172	0.70207	136.438	0.26072	0.68522	136.362	0.26020	0.66911	136.286	0.25968	0.65367	136.209	0.25917	631.67
174	0.70494	136.908	0.26147	0.68804	136.833	0.26094	0.67188	136.757	0.26042	0.65639	136.682	0.25992	633.67
176	0.70780	137.379	0.26221	0.69085	137.304	0.26168	0.67464	137.229	0.26117	0.65911	137.154	0.26066	635.67
178	0.71066	137.850	0.26295	0.69366	137.776	0.26242	0.67740	137.702	0.26191	0.66182	137.627	0.26140	637.67
180	0.71351	138.321	0.26368	0.69646	138.248	0.26316	0.68015	138.174	0.26265	0.66452	138.101	0.26214	639.67
182	0.71635	138.792	0.26442	0.69925	138.720	0.26390	0.68289	138.647	0.26339	0.66722	138.575	0.26288	641.67
184	0.71919	139.264	0.26515	0.70204	139.193	0.26463	0.68563	139.121	0.26412	0.66991	139.049	0.26362	643.67
186	0.72202	139.737	0.26589	0.70482	139.666	0.26537	0.68836	139.595	0.26486	0.67259	139.523	0.26436	645.67
188	0.72485	140.209	0.26662	0.70759	140.139	0.26610	0.69108	140.069	0.26559	0.67527	139.998	0.26509	647.67
190	0.72767	140.683	0.26735	0.71036	140.613	0.26683	0.69380	140.543	0.26632	0.67795	140.474	0.26583	649.67
192	0.73049	141.156	0.26808	0.71312	141.087	0.26756	0.69652	141.018	0.26705	0.68061	140.949	0.26656	651.67
194	0.73329	141.630	0.26880	0.71588	141.562	0.26829	0.69922	141.494	0.26778	0.68327	141.425	0.26729	653.67
196	0.73610	142.105	0.26953	0.71863	142.037	0.26901	0.70193	141.970	0.26851	0.68593	141.902	0.26801	655.67
198	0.73890	142.580	0.27025	0.72138	142.513	0.26974	0.70462	142.446	0.26923	0.68858	142.379	0.26874	657.67
200	0.74169	143.055	0.27097	0.72412	142.989	0.27046	0.70732	142.923	0.26996	0.69122	142.856	0.26946	659.67
202	0.74448	143.531	0.27169	0.72686	143.466	0.27118	0.71000	143.400	0.27068	0.69386	143.334	0.27019	661.67
204	0.74726	144.008	0.27241	0.72959	143.943	0.27190	0.71269	143.877	0.27140	0.69650	143.812	0.27091	663.67
206	0.75004	144.485	0.27313	0.73232	144.420	0.27262	0.71536	144.356	0.27212	0.69913	144.291	0.27163	665.67
208	0.75282	144.962	0.27384	0.73504	144.898	0.27334	0.71804	144.834	0.27284	0.70175	144.770	0.27235	667.67

Temp. °F	Absolute Pressure, lb./sq. in.												Temp. °R
	96.0			98.0			100.0			105.0			
	Gauge Pressure 81.304 lb./sq. in. Satn. Temp. = 76.86 °F 536.53 °R			Gauge Pressure 83.304 lb./sq. in. Satn. Temp. = 78.12 °F 537.79 °R			Gauge Pressure 85.304 lb./sq. in. Satn. Temp. = 79.35 °F 539.02 °R			Gauge Pressure 90.304 lb./sq. in. Satn. Temp. = 82.35 °F 542.02 °R			
	V	H	S	V	H	S	V	H	S	V	H	S	
SAT N	0.49806	113.520	0.21985	0.48781	113.674	0.21980	0.47795	113.825	0.21975	0.45490	114.188	0.21962	
78	0.49999	113.799	0.22037										537.67
80	0.50338	114.289	0.22128	0.49096	114.138	0.22066	0.47903	113.986	0.22005				539.67
82	0.50673	114.777	0.22218	0.49429	114.630	0.22157	0.48233	114.480	0.22096				541.67
84	0.51005	115.264	0.22308	0.49758	115.119	0.22247	0.48559	114.973	0.22187	0.45753	114.600	0.22038	543.67
86	0.51335	115.750	0.22397	0.50085	115.608	0.22337	0.48883	115.464	0.22277	0.46070	115.099	0.22130	545.67
88	0.51662	116.235	0.22486	0.50409	116.095	0.22426	0.49203	115.954	0.22367	0.46384	115.595	0.22220	547.67
90	0.51987	116.718	0.22574	0.50730	116.581	0.22515	0.49522	116.442	0.22456	0.46695	116.091	0.22311	549.67
92	0.52309	117.200	0.22662	0.51049	117.065	0.22603	0.49837	116.929	0.22544	0.47004	116.584	0.22400	551.67
94	0.52629	117.681	0.22749	0.51365	117.549	0.22690	0.50150	117.415	0.22632	0.47310	117.077	0.22489	553.67
96	0.52946	118.161	0.22835	0.51679	118.031	0.22777	0.50461	117.900	0.22719	0.47613	117.567	0.22578	555.67
98	0.53262	118.640	0.22921	0.51991	118.513	0.22863	0.50770	118.384	0.22806	0.47914	118.057	0.22666	557.67
100	0.53575	119.119	0.23007	0.52301	118.993	0.22949	0.51076	118.867	0.22893	0.48213	118.546	0.22753	559.67
102	0.53886	119.596	0.23092	0.52608	119.473	0.23035	0.51380	119.348	0.22979	0.48509	119.033	0.22840	561.67
104	0.54196	120.073	0.23177	0.52914	119.952	0.23120	0.51682	119.830	0.23064	0.48803	119.519	0.22927	563.67
106	0.54503	120.550	0.23261	0.53218	120.430	0.23205	0.51982	120.310	0.23149	0.49096	120.005	0.23013	565.67
108	0.54809	121.025	0.23345	0.53519	120.908	0.23289	0.52281	120.789	0.23234	0.49386	120.489	0.23098	567.67
110	0.55112	121.500	0.23429	0.53819	121.385	0.23373	0.52577	121.268	0.23318	0.49674	120.973	0.23183	569.67
112	0.55415	121.975	0.23512	0.54118	121.861	0.23456	0.52872	121.746	0.23402	0.49961	121.456	0.23268	571.67
114	0.55715	122.449	0.23595	0.54414	122.337	0.23540	0.53165	122.224	0.23485	0.50245	121.938	0.23352	573.67
116	0.56014	122.923	0.23677	0.54709	122.812	0.23622	0.53456	122.701	0.23568	0.50528	122.419	0.23436	575.67
118	0.56311	123.396	0.23759	0.55003	123.287	0.23705	0.53746	123.177	0.23651	0.50809	122.900	0.23519	577.67
120	0.56607	123.869	0.23841	0.55294	123.761	0.23787	0.54034	123.653	0.23733	0.51089	123.381	0.23602	579.67
122	0.56901	124.341	0.23922	0.55585	124.235	0.23868	0.54321	124.129	0.23815	0.51367	123.860	0.23685	581.67
124	0.57194	124.813	0.24003	0.55874	124.709	0.23950	0.54606	124.604	0.23897	0.51644	124.340	0.23767	583.67
126	0.57485	125.285	0.24084	0.56161	125.183	0.24031	0.54889	125.079	0.23978	0.51919	124.818	0.23849	585.67
128	0.57776	125.757	0.24164	0.56447	125.656	0.24111	0.55172	125.554	0.24059	0.52192	125.297	0.23930	587.67
130	0.58064	126.229	0.24244	0.56732	126.129	0.24192	0.55453	126.028	0.24139	0.52464	125.775	0.24012	589.67
132	0.58352	126.700	0.24324	0.57016	126.602	0.24272	0.55733	126.502	0.24220	0.52735	126.253	0.24093	591.67
134	0.58638	127.171	0.24404	0.57298	127.074	0.24351	0.56011	126.976	0.24300	0.53005	126.730	0.24173	593.67
136	0.58924	127.642	0.24483	0.57579	127.547	0.24431	0.56288	127.450	0.24379	0.53273	127.207	0.24253	595.67
138	0.59208	128.114	0.24562	0.57859	128.019	0.24510	0.56564	127.924	0.24459	0.53540	127.684	0.24333	597.67

Temp. °F	Absolute Pressure, lb./sq. in.												Temp. °R
	96.0			98.0			100.0			105.0			
	Gauge Pressure = 81.304 lb./sq. in. Satn. Temp. = 76.86 °F 536.53 °R			Gauge Pressure = 83.304 lb./sq. in. Satn. Temp. = 78.12 °F 537.79 °R			Gauge Pressure = 85.304 lb./sq. in. Satn. Temp. = 79.35 °F 539.02 °R			Gauge Pressure = 90.304 lb./sq. in. Satn. Temp. = 82.35 °F 542.02 °R			
	V	H	S	V	H	S	V	H	S	V	H	S	
140	0.59491	128.585	0.24641	0.58138	128.491	0.24589	0.56839	128.397	0.24538	0.53806	128.161	0.24413	599.67
142	0.59772	129.056	0.24719	0.58416	128.963	0.24667	0.57113	128.871	0.24617	0.54071	128.637	0.24492	601.67
144	0.60053	129.527	0.24797	0.58693	129.436	0.24746	0.57386	129.344	0.24695	0.54334	129.114	0.24571	603.67
146	0.60333	129.998	0.24875	0.58968	129.908	0.24824	0.57657	129.817	0.24773	0.54597	129.590	0.24650	605.67
148	0.60612	130.469	0.24953	0.59243	130.380	0.24902	0.57928	130.291	0.24851	0.54858	130.066	0.24729	607.67
150	0.60889	130.940	0.25030	0.59516	130.852	0.24979	0.58198	130.764	0.24929	0.55119	130.542	0.24807	609.67
152	0.61166	131.411	0.25107	0.59789	131.324	0.25057	0.58466	131.237	0.25007	0.55378	131.018	0.24885	611.67
154	0.61442	131.882	0.25184	0.60061	131.797	0.25134	0.58734	131.711	0.25084	0.55637	131.494	0.24962	613.67
156	0.61717	132.354	0.25261	0.60332	132.269	0.25211	0.59001	132.184	0.25161	0.55894	131.971	0.25040	615.67
158	0.61991	132.825	0.25337	0.60602	132.742	0.25287	0.59267	132.658	0.25238	0.56151	132.447	0.25117	617.67
160	0.62265	133.297	0.25414	0.60871	133.215	0.25364	0.59532	133.132	0.25314	0.56407	132.923	0.25194	619.67
162	0.62537	133.769	0.25490	0.61139	133.687	0.25440	0.59796	133.606	0.25391	0.56661	133.399	0.25271	621.67
164	0.62809	134.241	0.25566	0.61406	134.161	0.25516	0.60059	134.080	0.25467	0.56915	133.876	0.25347	623.67
166	0.63080	134.714	0.25641	0.61673	134.634	0.25592	0.60322	134.554	0.25543	0.57169	134.352	0.25424	625.67
168	0.63350	135.186	0.25717	0.61939	135.107	0.25667	0.60584	135.028	0.25618	0.57421	134.829	0.25500	627.67
170	0.63619	135.659	0.25792	0.62204	135.581	0.25742	0.60845	135.503	0.25694	0.57672	135.305	0.25575	629.67
172	0.63888	136.132	0.25867	0.62468	136.055	0.25818	0.61105	135.977	0.25769	0.57923	135.782	0.25651	631.67
174	0.64155	136.605	0.25942	0.62732	136.529	0.25893	0.61365	136.452	0.25844	0.58173	136.260	0.25727	633.67
176	0.64423	137.079	0.26016	0.62995	137.003	0.25967	0.61623	136.928	0.25919	0.58423	136.737	0.25802	635.67
178	0.64689	137.553	0.26091	0.63257	137.478	0.26042	0.61881	137.403	0.25994	0.58671	137.214	0.25877	637.67
180	0.64955	138.027	0.26165	0.63518	137.953	0.26116	0.62139	137.879	0.26068	0.58919	137.692	0.25952	639.67
182	0.65220	138.502	0.26239	0.63779	138.428	0.26190	0.62396	138.355	0.26143	0.59166	138.170	0.26026	641.67
184	0.65485	138.977	0.26313	0.64039	138.904	0.26264	0.62652	138.831	0.26217	0.59413	138.649	0.26101	643.67
186	0.65749	139.452	0.26387	0.64299	139.380	0.26338	0.62907	139.308	0.26291	0.59659	139.127	0.26175	645.67
188	0.66012	139.927	0.26460	0.64558	139.856	0.26412	0.63162	139.785	0.26364	0.59904	139.606	0.26249	647.67
190	0.66275	140.403	0.26534	0.64817	140.333	0.26485	0.63416	140.263	0.26438	0.60149	140.085	0.26323	649.67
192	0.66537	140.880	0.26607	0.65074	140.810	0.26559	0.63670	140.740	0.26511	0.60393	140.565	0.26396	651.67
194	0.66798	141.356	0.26680	0.65332	141.288	0.26632	0.63923	141.218	0.26585	0.60636	141.045	0.26470	653.67
196	0.67059	141.834	0.26753	0.65588	141.765	0.26705	0.64176	141.697	0.26658	0.60879	141.525	0.26543	655.67
198	0.67320	142.311	0.26825	0.65844	142.244	0.26778	0.64428	142.176	0.26731	0.61122	142.005	0.26617	657.67
200	0.67580	142.789	0.26898	0.66100	142.722	0.26850	0.64679	142.655	0.26803	0.61363	142.486	0.26690	659.67
202	0.67839	143.268	0.26970	0.66355	143.201	0.26923	0.64930	143.135	0.26876	0.61605	142.967	0.26762	661.67
204	0.68098	143.746	0.27043	0.66610	143.681	0.26995	0.65181	143.615	0.26949	0.61845	143.449	0.26835	663.67
206	0.68357	144.226	0.27115	0.66864	144.161	0.27067	0.65431	144.095	0.27021	0.62086	143.931	0.26908	665.67
208	0.68615	144.705	0.27187	0.67118	144.641	0.27139	0.65680	144.576	0.27093	0.62325	144.414	0.26980	667.67

Temp. °F	110.0 — Gauge Pressure 95.304 lb./sq. in.; Satn. Temp. = 85.25 °F, 544.92 °R			115.0 — Gauge Pressure 100.304 lb./sq. in.; Satn. Temp. = 88.05 °F, 547.72 °R			120.0 — Gauge Pressure 105.304 lb./sq. in.; Satn. Temp. = 90.76 °F, 550.43 °R			125.0 — Gauge Pressure 110.304 lb./sq. in.; Satn. Temp. = 93.39 °F, 553.06 °R			Temp. °R
	Absolute Pressure, lb./sq. in.												
	V	H	S	V	H	S	V	H	S	V	H	S	
SAT N	0.43386	114.534	0.21950	0.41459	114.864	0.21939	0.39686	115.179	0.21928	0.38050	115.479	0.21917	
86	0.43503	114.724	0.21985										545.67
88	0.43811	115.228	0.22077										547.67
90	0.44116	115.730	0.22169	0.41752	115.361	0.22029							549.67
92	0.44419	116.231	0.22260	0.42049	115.869	0.22122	0.39868	115.498	0.21986				551.67
94	0.44719	116.730	0.22350	0.42344	116.375	0.22213	0.40158	116.012	0.22079	0.38138	115.639	0.21946	553.67
96	0.45016	117.227	0.22440	0.42636	116.880	0.22304	0.40445	116.523	0.22171	0.38421	116.158	0.22039	555.67
98	0.45310	117.723	0.22529	0.42925	117.382	0.22394	0.40730	117.033	0.22262	0.38702	116.675	0.22132	557.67
100	0.45602	118.218	0.22617	0.43211	117.883	0.22484	0.41011	117.541	0.22353	0.38980	117.190	0.22225	559.67
102	0.45892	118.711	0.22705	0.43495	118.382	0.22573	0.41290	118.047	0.22443	0.39255	117.703	0.22316	561.67
104	0.46179	119.203	0.22793	0.43777	118.880	0.22662	0.41567	118.551	0.22533	0.39527	118.214	0.22407	563.67
106	0.46465	119.694	0.22880	0.44056	119.377	0.22750	0.41841	119.053	0.22622	0.39796	118.723	0.22497	565.67
108	0.46748	120.184	0.22966	0.44333	119.872	0.22837	0.42113	119.555	0.22711	0.40064	119.230	0.22586	567.67
110	0.47029	120.673	0.23052	0.44608	120.366	0.22924	0.42382	120.054	0.22798	0.40328	119.736	0.22675	569.67
112	0.47308	121.160	0.23137	0.44881	120.859	0.23010	0.42650	120.553	0.22886	0.40591	120.240	0.22764	571.67
114	0.47586	121.647	0.23222	0.45152	121.351	0.23096	0.42915	121.050	0.22973	0.40851	120.743	0.22852	573.67
116	0.47861	122.133	0.23307	0.45421	121.842	0.23182	0.43178	121.546	0.23059	0.41110	121.244	0.22939	575.67
118	0.48135	122.619	0.23391	0.45688	122.332	0.23267	0.43439	122.041	0.23145	0.41366	121.744	0.23026	577.67
120	0.48407	123.103	0.23475	0.45953	122.822	0.23351	0.43699	122.535	0.23230	0.41620	122.243	0.23112	579.67
122	0.48677	123.587	0.23558	0.46217	123.310	0.23435	0.43957	123.028	0.23315	0.41872	122.741	0.23197	581.67
124	0.48946	124.071	0.23641	0.46479	123.798	0.23519	0.44213	123.520	0.23400	0.42123	123.238	0.23283	583.67
126	0.49213	124.554	0.23724	0.46739	124.285	0.23602	0.44467	124.012	0.23484	0.42372	123.734	0.23368	585.67
128	0.49479	125.036	0.23806	0.46998	124.771	0.23685	0.44719	124.502	0.23567	0.42619	124.229	0.23452	587.67
130	0.49744	125.518	0.23888	0.47255	125.257	0.23768	0.44971	124.992	0.23650	0.42865	124.723	0.23536	589.67
132	0.50007	125.999	0.23969	0.47511	125.742	0.23850	0.45220	125.481	0.23733	0.43108	125.216	0.23619	591.67
134	0.50268	126.480	0.24051	0.47766	126.227	0.23932	0.45468	125.970	0.23816	0.43351	125.709	0.23702	593.67
136	0.50529	126.961	0.24131	0.48019	126.711	0.24013	0.45715	126.458	0.23898	0.43592	126.201	0.23785	595.67
138	0.50788	127.441	0.24212	0.48271	127.195	0.24094	0.45960	126.945	0.23979	0.43831	126.692	0.23868	597.67
140	0.51045	127.921	0.24292	0.48521	127.678	0.24175	0.46204	127.432	0.24061	0.44070	127.183	0.23949	599.67
142	0.51302	128.401	0.24372	0.48771	128.161	0.24255	0.46447	127.919	0.24142	0.44306	127.673	0.24031	601.67
144	0.51557	128.880	0.24452	0.49019	128.644	0.24335	0.46689	128.405	0.24222	0.44542	128.162	0.24112	603.67
146	0.51812	129.360	0.24531	0.49266	129.126	0.24415	0.46929	128.890	0.24303	0.44776	128.651	0.24193	605.67
148	0.52065	129.839	0.24610	0.49512	129.609	0.24495	0.47168	129.376	0.24383	0.45009	129.140	0.24274	607.67

Temp. °F	Absolute Pressure, lb./sq. in.												Temp. °R
	110.0			115.0			120.0			125.0			
	Gauge Pressure = 95.304 lb./sq. in. Satn. Temp. = 85.25 °F 544.92 °R			Gauge Pressure = 100.304 lb./sq. in. Satn. Temp. = 88.05 °F 547.72 °R			Gauge Pressure = 105.304 lb./sq. in. Satn. Temp. = 90.76 °F 550.43 °R			Gauge Pressure = 110.304 lb./sq. in. Satn. Temp. = 93.39 °F 553.06 °R			
	V	H	S	V	H	S	V	H	S	V	H	S	
150	0.52317	130.318	0.24688	0.49756	130.091	0.24574	0.47406	129.861	0.24462	0.45241	129.629	0.24354	609.67
152	0.52568	130.797	0.24767	0.50000	130.573	0.24653	0.47643	130.346	0.24542	0.45472	130.117	0.24434	611.67
154	0.52818	131.276	0.24845	0.50243	131.054	0.24731	0.47879	130.831	0.24621	0.45702	130.604	0.24514	613.67
156	0.53068	131.754	0.24923	0.50484	131.536	0.24810	0.48114	131.315	0.24700	0.45930	131.092	0.24593	615.67
158	0.53316	132.233	0.25001	0.50725	132.017	0.24888	0.48348	131.799	0.24778	0.46158	131.579	0.24672	617.67
160	0.53563	132.712	0.25078	0.50965	132.499	0.24966	0.48580	132.283	0.24857	0.46385	132.066	0.24751	619.67
162	0.53810	133.191	0.25155	0.51203	132.980	0.25043	0.48812	132.767	0.24935	0.46610	132.553	0.24829	621.67
164	0.54055	133.670	0.25232	0.51441	133.462	0.25120	0.49043	133.251	0.25012	0.46835	133.039	0.24907	623.67
166	0.54300	134.148	0.25309	0.51678	133.943	0.25197	0.49273	133.735	0.25090	0.47058	133.526	0.24985	625.67
168	0.54544	134.627	0.25385	0.51914	134.424	0.25274	0.49502	134.219	0.25167	0.47281	134.012	0.25063	627.67
170	0.54787	135.107	0.25461	0.52150	134.906	0.25351	0.49731	134.703	0.25244	0.47503	134.498	0.25140	629.67
172	0.55029	135.586	0.25537	0.52384	135.387	0.25427	0.49958	135.187	0.25321	0.47724	134.985	0.25217	631.67
174	0.55270	136.065	0.25613	0.52618	135.869	0.25503	0.50185	135.671	0.25397	0.47944	135.471	0.25294	633.67
176	0.55511	136.545	0.25689	0.52851	136.350	0.25579	0.50411	136.155	0.25473	0.48164	135.957	0.25371	635.67
178	0.55751	137.024	0.25764	0.53083	136.832	0.25655	0.50636	136.639	0.25549	0.48383	136.443	0.25447	637.67
180	0.55990	137.504	0.25839	0.53314	137.314	0.25730	0.50860	137.123	0.25625	0.48600	136.930	0.25523	639.67
182	0.56229	137.984	0.25914	0.53545	137.796	0.25806	0.51084	137.607	0.25701	0.48818	137.416	0.25599	641.67
184	0.56467	138.464	0.25989	0.53775	138.279	0.25881	0.51307	138.091	0.25776	0.49034	137.902	0.25675	643.67
186	0.56704	138.945	0.26063	0.54005	138.761	0.25956	0.51529	138.576	0.25851	0.49250	138.389	0.25750	645.67
188	0.56941	139.426	0.26138	0.54233	139.244	0.26030	0.51750	139.060	0.25926	0.49465	138.876	0.25825	647.67
190	0.57177	139.907	0.26212	0.54462	139.727	0.26105	0.51971	139.545	0.26001	0.49679	139.363	0.25900	649.67
192	0.57412	140.388	0.26286	0.54689	140.210	0.26179	0.52192	140.030	0.26075	0.49893	139.849	0.25975	651.67
194	0.57647	140.870	0.26360	0.54916	140.693	0.26253	0.52411	140.516	0.26150	0.50106	140.337	0.26050	653.67
196	0.57881	141.351	0.26433	0.55142	141.177	0.26327	0.52630	141.001	0.26224	0.50318	140.824	0.26124	655.67
198	0.58115	141.834	0.26507	0.55368	141.661	0.26401	0.52849	141.487	0.26298	0.50530	141.312	0.26199	657.67
200	0.58348	142.316	0.26580	0.55593	142.145	0.26474	0.53066	141.973	0.26372	0.50741	141.799	0.26273	659.67
202	0.58580	142.799	0.26653	0.55817	142.630	0.26547	0.53284	142.459	0.26445	0.50952	142.287	0.26347	661.67
204	0.58812	143.282	0.26726	0.56041	143.115	0.26621	0.53500	142.946	0.26519	0.51162	142.776	0.26420	663.67
206	0.59044	143.766	0.26799	0.56265	143.600	0.26694	0.53717	143.432	0.26592	0.51371	143.264	0.26494	665.67
208	0.59274	144.250	0.26871	0.56488	144.085	0.26766	0.53932	143.920	0.26665	0.51580	143.753	0.26567	667.67
210	0.59505	144.734	0.26944	0.56710	144.571	0.26839	0.54147	144.407	0.26738	0.51789	144.242	0.26640	669.67
212	0.59735	145.219	0.27016	0.56932	145.058	0.26912	0.54362	144.895	0.26811	0.51997	144.731	0.26713	671.67
214	0.59964	145.704	0.27088	0.57154	145.544	0.26984	0.54576	145.383	0.26883	0.52204	145.221	0.26786	673.67
216	0.60193	146.190	0.27160	0.57375	146.031	0.27056	0.54790	145.872	0.26956	0.52411	145.711	0.26859	675.67
218	0.60422	146.676	0.27232	0.57595	146.519	0.27128	0.55003	146.360	0.27028	0.52617	146.201	0.26931	677.67

Temp. °F	Absolute Pressure, lb./sq. in. 130.0 — Gauge Pressure = 115.304 lb./sq. in., Satn. Temp. = 95.94 °F, 555.61 °R			135.0 — Gauge Pressure = 120.304 lb./sq. in., Satn. Temp. = 98.41 °F, 558.08 °R			140.0 — Gauge Pressure = 125.304 lb./sq. in., Satn. Temp. = 100.82 °F, 560.49 °R			145.0 — Gauge Pressure = 130.304 lb./sq. in., Satn. Temp. = 103.17 °F, 562.84 °R			Temp. °R
	V	H	S	V	H	S	V	H	S	V	H	S	
SAT N	0.36535	115.767	0.21907	0.35128	116.042	0.21897	0.33817	116.305	0.21887	0.32594	116.558	0.21877	
96	0.36544	115.783	0.21910										555.67
98	0.36822	116.309	0.22004										557.67
100	0.37096	116.831	0.22098	0.35343	116.463	0.21972							559.67
102	0.37368	117.351	0.22190	0.35612	116.991	0.22066	0.33974	116.621	0.21943				561.67
104	0.37636	117.869	0.22282	0.35878	117.516	0.22159	0.34238	117.154	0.22038	0.32702	116.783	0.21917	563.67
106	0.37902	118.385	0.22374	0.36141	118.039	0.22252	0.34498	117.685	0.22132	0.32961	117.322	0.22012	565.67
108	0.38165	118.899	0.22464	0.36401	118.560	0.22344	0.34756	118.213	0.22225	0.33217	117.858	0.22107	567.67
110	0.38426	119.411	0.22554	0.36659	119.079	0.22435	0.35010	118.739	0.22317	0.33469	118.391	0.22201	569.67
112	0.38685	119.921	0.22644	0.36913	119.595	0.22526	0.35262	119.262	0.22409	0.33719	118.922	0.22294	571.67
114	0.38941	120.430	0.22733	0.37166	120.110	0.22616	0.35512	119.784	0.22500	0.33966	119.450	0.22386	573.67
116	0.39195	120.937	0.22821	0.37416	120.623	0.22705	0.35759	120.303	0.22590	0.34210	119.976	0.22477	575.67
118	0.39446	121.442	0.22909	0.37664	121.134	0.22793	0.36003	120.820	0.22680	0.34452	120.500	0.22568	577.67
120	0.39696	121.947	0.22996	0.37910	121.644	0.22882	0.36246	121.336	0.22769	0.34691	121.021	0.22658	579.67
122	0.39944	122.449	0.23082	0.38153	122.152	0.22969	0.36486	121.850	0.22858	0.34928	121.541	0.22748	581.67
124	0.40190	122.951	0.23168	0.38395	122.659	0.23056	0.36724	122.362	0.22946	0.35163	122.059	0.22837	583.67
126	0.40434	123.452	0.23254	0.38635	123.165	0.23143	0.36960	122.873	0.23033	0.35396	122.575	0.22925	585.67
128	0.40676	123.951	0.23339	0.38873	123.669	0.23229	0.37194	123.382	0.23120	0.35626	123.090	0.23013	587.67
130	0.40916	124.450	0.23424	0.39109	124.172	0.23314	0.37426	123.890	0.23206	0.35855	123.603	0.23100	589.67
132	0.41155	124.947	0.23508	0.39343	124.674	0.23399	0.37656	124.397	0.23292	0.36082	124.115	0.23187	591.67
134	0.41393	125.444	0.23592	0.39576	125.175	0.23484	0.37885	124.902	0.23377	0.36307	124.625	0.23273	593.67
136	0.41628	125.940	0.23675	0.39807	125.676	0.23568	0.38112	125.407	0.23462	0.36530	125.134	0.23358	595.67
138	0.41863	126.435	0.23758	0.40037	126.175	0.23651	0.38337	125.910	0.23546	0.36752	125.642	0.23443	597.67
140	0.42096	126.930	0.23841	0.40265	126.673	0.23735	0.38561	126.413	0.23630	0.36972	126.149	0.23528	599.67
142	0.42327	127.424	0.23923	0.40491	127.171	0.23817	0.38784	126.915	0.23714	0.37191	126.655	0.23612	601.67
144	0.42557	127.917	0.24005	0.40717	127.668	0.23900	0.39005	127.415	0.23797	0.37408	127.159	0.23696	603.67
146	0.42786	128.409	0.24086	0.40941	128.164	0.23982	0.39224	127.915	0.23880	0.37623	127.663	0.23779	605.67
148	0.43014	128.902	0.24168	0.41163	128.660	0.24064	0.39442	128.415	0.23962	0.37837	128.166	0.23862	607.67
150	0.43240	129.393	0.24248	0.41385	129.155	0.24145	0.39659	128.913	0.24044	0.38050	128.669	0.23945	609.67
152	0.43466	129.884	0.24329	0.41605	129.649	0.24226	0.39875	129.411	0.24125	0.38262	129.170	0.24027	611.67
154	0.43690	130.375	0.24409	0.41824	130.143	0.24307	0.40089	129.909	0.24207	0.38472	129.671	0.24109	613.67
156	0.43913	130.866	0.24489	0.42042	130.637	0.24387	0.40303	130.406	0.24287	0.38681	130.171	0.24190	615.67
158	0.44135	131.356	0.24568	0.42259	131.130	0.24467	0.40515	130.902	0.24368	0.38889	130.671	0.24271	617.67

Temp. °F	Absolute Pressure, lb./sq. in. 130.0 — Gauge Pressure 115.304 lb./sq. in.; Satn. Temp. = 95.94 °F, 555.61 °R			135.0 — Gauge Pressure 120.304 lb./sq. in.; Satn. Temp. = 98.41 °F, 558.08 °R			140.0 — Gauge Pressure 125.304 lb./sq. in.; Satn. Temp. = 100.82 °F, 560.49 °R			145.0 — Gauge Pressure 130.304 lb./sq. in.; Satn. Temp. = 103.17 °F, 562.84 °R			Temp. °R
	V	H	S	V	H	S	V	H	S	V	H	S	
160	0.44355	131.846	0.24647	0.42474	131.623	0.24547	0.40726	131.398	0.24448	0.39095	131.170	0.24352	619.67
162	0.44575	132.335	0.24726	0.42689	132.116	0.24626	0.40936	131.893	0.24528	0.39301	131.669	0.24432	621.67
164	0.44794	132.825	0.24805	0.42903	132.608	0.24705	0.41144	132.389	0.24607	0.39505	132.167	0.24512	623.67
166	0.45012	133.314	0.24883	0.43115	133.100	0.24784	0.41352	132.883	0.24687	0.39709	132.665	0.24592	625.67
168	0.45229	133.803	0.24961	0.43327	133.591	0.24862	0.41559	133.378	0.24766	0.39911	133.162	0.24671	627.67
170	0.45445	134.292	0.25039	0.43538	134.083	0.24940	0.41765	133.872	0.24844	0.40113	133.659	0.24750	629.67
172	0.45660	134.780	0.25116	0.43748	134.574	0.25018	0.41970	134.366	0.24923	0.40313	134.156	0.24829	631.67
174	0.45875	135.269	0.25194	0.43957	135.065	0.25096	0.42174	134.860	0.25001	0.40513	134.652	0.24907	633.67
176	0.46088	135.758	0.25271	0.44165	135.556	0.25173	0.42377	135.353	0.25078	0.40711	135.148	0.24986	635.67
178	0.46301	136.246	0.25347	0.44372	136.047	0.25250	0.42580	135.847	0.25156	0.40909	135.644	0.25063	637.67
180	0.46513	136.735	0.25424	0.44579	136.538	0.25327	0.42781	136.340	0.25233	0.41106	136.140	0.25141	639.67
182	0.46724	137.223	0.25500	0.44784	137.029	0.25404	0.42982	136.833	0.25310	0.41302	136.635	0.25218	641.67
184	0.46935	137.712	0.25576	0.44989	137.520	0.25480	0.43182	137.326	0.25387	0.41497	137.131	0.25296	643.67
186	0.47144	138.201	0.25652	0.45194	138.011	0.25556	0.43381	137.819	0.25463	0.41692	137.626	0.25372	645.67
188	0.47353	138.689	0.25727	0.45397	138.502	0.25632	0.43579	138.312	0.25539	0.41885	138.121	0.25449	647.67
190	0.47562	139.178	0.25803	0.45600	138.993	0.25708	0.43777	138.805	0.25615	0.42078	138.616	0.25525	649.67
192	0.47769	139.667	0.25878	0.45802	139.483	0.25783	0.43974	139.298	0.25691	0.42271	139.112	0.25601	651.67
194	0.47976	140.156	0.25953	0.46003	139.975	0.25859	0.44170	139.791	0.25767	0.42462	139.607	0.25677	653.67
196	0.48183	140.646	0.26028	0.46204	140.466	0.25934	0.44366	140.284	0.25842	0.42653	140.102	0.25753	655.67
198	0.48388	141.135	0.26102	0.46404	140.957	0.26008	0.44561	140.778	0.25917	0.42843	140.597	0.25828	657.67
200	0.48593	141.624	0.26177	0.46604	141.448	0.26083	0.44755	141.271	0.25992	0.43033	141.092	0.25903	659.67
202	0.48798	142.114	0.26251	0.46803	141.940	0.26157	0.44949	141.764	0.26067	0.43222	141.588	0.25978	661.67
204	0.49002	142.604	0.26325	0.47001	142.432	0.26232	0.45142	142.258	0.26141	0.43410	142.083	0.26053	663.67
206	0.49205	143.094	0.26398	0.47199	142.924	0.26306	0.45335	142.752	0.26216	0.43598	142.579	0.26128	665.67
208	0.49408	143.585	0.26472	0.47396	143.416	0.26380	0.45526	143.246	0.26290	0.43785	143.074	0.26202	667.67
210	0.49610	144.076	0.26545	0.47593	143.908	0.26453	0.45718	143.740	0.26364	0.43972	143.570	0.26276	669.67
212	0.49812	144.567	0.26618	0.47789	144.401	0.26527	0.45909	144.234	0.26437	0.44158	144.066	0.26350	671.67
214	0.50013	145.058	0.26692	0.47984	144.894	0.26600	0.46099	144.729	0.26511	0.44343	144.562	0.26424	673.67
216	0.50214	145.549	0.26764	0.48179	145.387	0.26673	0.46289	145.223	0.26584	0.44528	145.059	0.26498	675.67
218	0.50414	146.041	0.26837	0.48374	145.880	0.26746	0.46478	145.718	0.26657	0.44712	145.555	0.26571	677.67
220	0.50614	146.533	0.26910	0.48568	146.374	0.26819	0.46667	146.213	0.26730	0.44896	146.052	0.26644	679.67
222	0.50813	147.026	0.26982	0.48761	146.868	0.26891	0.46855	146.709	0.26803	0.45080	146.549	0.26717	681.67
224	0.51012	147.519	0.27054	0.48954	147.362	0.26964	0.47043	147.205	0.26876	0.45262	147.046	0.26790	683.67
226	0.51211	148.012	0.27126	0.49147	147.857	0.27036	0.47230	147.701	0.26948	0.45445	147.544	0.26863	685.67
228	0.51409	148.506	0.27198	0.49339	148.352	0.27108	0.47417	148.197	0.27020	0.45627	148.042	0.26935	687.67

Temp. °F	Absolute Pressure, lb./sq. in.												Temp. °R
	150.0			160.0			170.0			180.0			
	Gauge Pressure 135.304 lb./sq. in. Satn. Temp. = 105.45 °F 565.12 °R			Gauge Pressure 145.304 lb./sq. in. Satn. Temp. = 109.85 °F 569.52 °R			Gauge Pressure 155.304 lb./sq. in. Satn. Temp. = 114.06 °F 573.73 °R			Gauge Pressure 165.304 lb./sq. in. Satn. Temp. = 118.07 °F 577.74 °R			
	V	H	S	V	H	S	V	H	S	V	H	S	
SAT N	0.31448	116.799	0.21867	0.29364	117.253	0.21848	0.27514	117.671	0.21829	0.25862	118.055	0.21810	
106	0.31518	116.949	0.21894										565.67
108	0.31773	117.494	0.21990										567.67
110	0.32023	118.035	0.22085	0.29382	117.294	0.21855							569.67
112	0.32271	118.573	0.22179	0.29627	117.849	0.21953							571.67
114	0.32516	119.109	0.22273	0.29870	118.401	0.22049							573.67
116	0.32758	119.642	0.22366	0.30109	118.949	0.22144	0.27746	118.221	0.21925				575.67
118	0.32998	120.172	0.22457	0.30346	119.494	0.22239	0.27981	118.783	0.22022				577.67
120	0.33235	120.700	0.22549	0.30579	120.037	0.22333	0.28213	119.342	0.22119	0.26085	118.611	0.21906	579.67
122	0.33469	121.226	0.22639	0.30810	120.576	0.22425	0.28441	119.896	0.22214	0.26313	119.183	0.22005	581.67
124	0.33701	121.750	0.22729	0.31038	121.113	0.22518	0.28667	120.448	0.22309	0.26538	119.751	0.22102	583.67
126	0.33931	122.272	0.22819	0.31263	121.647	0.22609	0.28890	120.996	0.22403	0.26760	120.315	0.22199	585.67
128	0.34159	122.792	0.22907	0.31486	122.180	0.22700	0.29110	121.542	0.22496	0.26979	120.876	0.22294	587.67
130	0.34385	123.311	0.22995	0.31707	122.709	0.22790	0.29328	122.085	0.22588	0.27194	121.433	0.22389	589.67
132	0.34609	123.827	0.23083	0.31926	123.237	0.22879	0.29543	122.625	0.22679	0.27407	121.987	0.22483	591.67
134	0.34830	124.343	0.23170	0.32143	123.763	0.22968	0.29756	123.162	0.22770	0.27618	122.537	0.22576	593.67
136	0.35051	124.857	0.23256	0.32357	124.288	0.23056	0.29967	123.698	0.22860	0.27826	123.086	0.22668	595.67
138	0.35269	125.369	0.23342	0.32570	124.810	0.23144	0.30175	124.231	0.22950	0.28031	123.631	0.22759	597.67
140	0.35485	125.881	0.23427	0.32781	125.331	0.23231	0.30382	124.763	0.23038	0.28235	124.174	0.22850	599.67
142	0.35700	126.391	0.23512	0.32990	125.850	0.23317	0.30586	125.292	0.23127	0.28436	124.714	0.22940	601.67
144	0.35914	126.900	0.23597	0.33198	126.368	0.23403	0.30789	125.820	0.23214	0.28635	125.253	0.23029	603.67
146	0.36126	127.408	0.23681	0.33403	126.885	0.23488	0.30990	126.346	0.23301	0.28832	125.789	0.23118	605.67
148	0.36336	127.915	0.23764	0.33608	127.400	0.23573	0.31189	126.870	0.23388	0.29028	126.323	0.23206	607.67
150	0.36545	128.421	0.23848	0.33810	127.915	0.23658	0.31387	127.393	0.23473	0.29221	126.856	0.23293	609.67
152	0.36753	128.926	0.23930	0.34012	128.428	0.23742	0.31583	127.915	0.23559	0.29413	127.387	0.23380	611.67
154	0.36960	129.431	0.24013	0.34211	128.940	0.23825	0.31777	128.435	0.23644	0.29603	127.916	0.23467	613.67
156	0.37165	129.934	0.24095	0.34410	129.451	0.23909	0.31970	128.954	0.23728	0.29792	128.443	0.23553	615.67
158	0.37369	130.437	0.24176	0.34607	129.961	0.23991	0.32162	129.472	0.23812	0.29979	128.969	0.23638	617.67
160	0.37571	130.940	0.24257	0.34803	130.470	0.24074	0.32352	129.989	0.23896	0.30164	129.494	0.23723	619.67
162	0.37773	131.441	0.24338	0.34998	130.979	0.24156	0.32541	130.504	0.23979	0.30348	130.018	0.23807	621.67
164	0.37973	131.943	0.24419	0.35191	131.486	0.24237	0.32728	131.019	0.24061	0.30531	130.540	0.23891	623.67
166	0.38173	132.443	0.24499	0.35383	131.994	0.24318	0.32914	131.533	0.24144	0.30712	131.061	0.23974	625.67
168	0.38371	132.944	0.24579	0.35574	132.500	0.24399	0.33100	132.046	0.24226	0.30893	131.581	0.24057	627.67

Temp. °F	Absolute Pressure, lb./sq. in.												Temp. °R
	150.0			160.0			170.0			180.0			
	Gauge Pressure 135.304 lb./sq. in. Satn. Temp. = 105.45 °F 565.12 °R			Gauge Pressure 145.304 lb./sq. in. Satn. Temp. = 109.85 °F 569.52 °R			Gauge Pressure 155.304 lb./sq. in. Satn. Temp. = 114.06 °F 573.73 °R			Gauge Pressure 165.304 lb./sq. in. Satn. Temp. = 118.07 °F 577.74 °R			
	V	H	S	V	H	S	V	H	S	V	H	S	
170	0.38568	133.444	0.24658	0.35765	133.006	0.24480	0.33284	132.558	0.24307	0.31071	132.100	0.24140	629.67
172	0.38765	133.943	0.24737	0.35954	133.511	0.24560	0.33467	133.070	0.24388	0.31249	132.618	0.24222	631.67
174	0.38960	134.442	0.24816	0.36142	134.016	0.24639	0.33648	133.580	0.24469	0.31426	133.135	0.24304	633.67
176	0.39155	134.941	0.24895	0.36329	134.520	0.24719	0.33829	134.091	0.24549	0.31601	133.652	0.24385	635.67
178	0.39348	135.439	0.24973	0.36515	135.024	0.24798	0.34009	134.600	0.24629	0.31775	134.167	0.24466	637.67
180	0.39541	135.938	0.25051	0.36700	135.527	0.24877	0.34188	135.109	0.24709	0.31949	134.682	0.24547	639.67
182	0.39733	136.436	0.25129	0.36884	136.031	0.24955	0.34365	135.618	0.24788	0.32121	135.196	0.24627	641.67
184	0.39924	136.933	0.25206	0.37068	136.533	0.25034	0.34542	136.126	0.24867	0.32292	135.710	0.24707	643.67
186	0.40114	137.431	0.25284	0.37250	137.036	0.25112	0.34718	136.633	0.24946	0.32463	136.223	0.24786	645.67
188	0.40303	137.929	0.25361	0.37432	137.538	0.25189	0.34893	137.141	0.25025	0.32632	136.736	0.24866	647.67
190	0.40492	138.426	0.25437	0.37613	138.040	0.25267	0.35068	137.648	0.25103	0.32801	137.248	0.24945	649.67
192	0.40680	138.923	0.25514	0.37793	138.542	0.25344	0.35241	138.154	0.25181	0.32968	137.759	0.25023	651.67
194	0.40867	139.421	0.25590	0.37972	139.044	0.25421	0.35414	138.660	0.25258	0.33135	138.270	0.25102	653.67
196	0.41054	139.918	0.25666	0.38151	139.545	0.25497	0.35586	139.166	0.25336	0.33301	138.781	0.25180	655.67
198	0.41239	140.415	0.25741	0.38329	140.047	0.25574	0.35757	139.672	0.25413	0.33467	139.292	0.25257	657.67
200	0.41425	140.912	0.25817	0.38506	140.548	0.25650	0.35927	140.178	0.25489	0.33631	139.802	0.25335	659.67
202	0.41609	141.410	0.25892	0.38683	141.049	0.25726	0.36097	140.683	0.25566	0.33795	140.312	0.25412	661.67
204	0.41793	141.907	0.25967	0.38859	141.550	0.25801	0.36266	141.189	0.25642	0.33958	140.821	0.25489	663.67
206	0.41976	142.404	0.26042	0.39034	142.052	0.25877	0.36434	141.694	0.25718	0.34120	141.331	0.25565	665.67
208	0.42159	142.902	0.26117	0.39209	142.553	0.25952	0.36602	142.199	0.25794	0.34282	141.840	0.25642	667.67
210	0.42341	143.399	0.26191	0.39383	143.054	0.26027	0.36769	142.704	0.25869	0.34443	142.349	0.25718	669.67
212	0.42522	143.897	0.26265	0.39556	143.555	0.26102	0.36935	143.209	0.25945	0.34603	142.858	0.25794	671.67
214	0.42703	144.395	0.26339	0.39729	144.057	0.26176	0.37101	143.714	0.26020	0.34763	143.367	0.25870	673.67
216	0.42884	144.893	0.26413	0.39901	144.558	0.26250	0.37266	144.219	0.26095	0.34922	143.875	0.25945	675.67
218	0.43064	145.391	0.26487	0.40073	145.060	0.26325	0.37431	144.724	0.26169	0.35080	144.384	0.26020	677.67
220	0.43243	145.889	0.26560	0.40244	145.561	0.26398	0.37595	145.229	0.26244	0.35238	144.893	0.26095	679.67
222	0.43422	146.388	0.26634	0.40415	146.063	0.26472	0.37759	145.734	0.26318	0.35395	145.401	0.26170	681.67
224	0.43600	146.887	0.26707	0.40585	146.565	0.26546	0.37922	146.240	0.26392	0.35552	145.910	0.26244	683.67
226	0.43778	147.386	0.26779	0.40754	147.067	0.26619	0.38084	146.745	0.26466	0.35708	146.419	0.26319	685.67
228	0.43955	147.885	0.26852	0.40924	147.570	0.26692	0.38246	147.250	0.26539	0.35864	146.927	0.26393	687.67
230	0.44132	148.385	0.26925	0.41092	148.072	0.26765	0.38408	147.756	0.26613	0.36019	147.436	0.26467	689.67
232	0.44309	148.885	0.26997	0.41260	148.575	0.26838	0.38569	148.262	0.26686	0.36174	147.945	0.26540	691.67
234	0.44485	149.385	0.27069	0.41428	149.078	0.26911	0.38729	148.768	0.26759	0.36328	148.454	0.26614	693.67
236	0.44660	149.885	0.27141	0.41595	149.581	0.26983	0.38889	149.274	0.26832	0.36481	148.963	0.26687	695.67
238	0.44835	150.386	0.27213	0.41762	150.085	0.27055	0.39049	149.780	0.26905	0.36635	149.473	0.26760	697.67

Temp. °F	Absolute Pressure, lb./sq. in.												Temp. °R
	190.0			200.0			220.0			240.0			
	Gauge Pressure 175.304 lb./sq. in. Satn. Temp. = 121.93 °F 581.60 °R			Gauge Pressure 185.304 lb./sq. in. Satn. Temp. = 125.63 °F 585.30 °R			Gauge Pressure 205.304 lb./sq. in. Satn. Temp. = 132.64 °F 592.31 °R			Gauge Pressure 225.304 lb./sq. in. Satn. Temp. = 139.18 °F 598.85 °R			
	V	H	S	V	H	S	V	H	S	V	H	S	
SAT N	0.24376	118.409	0.21791	0.23032	118.733	0.21772	0.20694	119.304	0.21731	0.18726	119.778	0.21688	
122	0.24384	118.430	0.21795										581.67
124	0.24610	119.017	0.21895										583.67
126	0.24832	119.599	0.21995	0.23073	118.844	0.21790							585.67
128	0.25051	120.177	0.22093	0.23293	119.442	0.21892							587.67
130	0.25266	120.750	0.22191	0.23510	120.034	0.21993							589.67
132	0.25478	121.320	0.22287	0.23723	120.621	0.22092							591.67
134	0.25688	121.885	0.22383	0.23932	121.203	0.22190	0.20839	119.728	0.21803				593.67
136	0.25894	122.448	0.22477	0.24139	121.781	0.22288	0.21050	120.345	0.21906				595.67
138	0.26098	123.006	0.22571	0.24342	122.355	0.22384	0.21256	120.956	0.22009				597.67
140	0.26300	123.562	0.22664	0.24542	122.925	0.22479	0.21458	121.561	0.22110	0.18812	120.045	0.21733	599.67
142	0.26499	124.115	0.22756	0.24740	123.492	0.22573	0.21657	122.160	0.22210	0.19018	120.688	0.21840	601.67
144	0.26695	124.665	0.22847	0.24936	124.055	0.22667	0.21853	122.755	0.22308	0.19219	121.324	0.21946	603.67
146	0.26890	125.213	0.22938	0.25128	124.615	0.22760	0.22046	123.345	0.22406	0.19416	121.952	0.22049	605.67
148	0.27082	125.758	0.23027	0.25319	125.172	0.22851	0.22235	123.930	0.22502	0.19609	122.573	0.22152	607.67
150	0.27273	126.301	0.23117	0.25507	125.726	0.22942	0.22422	124.511	0.22598	0.19798	123.189	0.22253	609.67
152	0.27461	126.842	0.23205	0.25694	126.278	0.23033	0.22607	125.088	0.22692	0.19984	123.798	0.22353	611.67
154	0.27648	127.380	0.23293	0.25878	126.827	0.23122	0.22789	125.662	0.22786	0.20167	124.402	0.22451	613.67
156	0.27833	127.917	0.23381	0.26061	127.374	0.23211	0.22968	126.233	0.22879	0.20347	125.002	0.22549	615.67
158	0.28017	128.452	0.23467	0.26241	127.919	0.23300	0.23145	126.800	0.22971	0.20524	125.596	0.22645	617.67
160	0.28198	128.986	0.23553	0.26420	128.462	0.23387	0.23321	127.364	0.23062	0.20699	126.187	0.22741	619.67
162	0.28379	129.517	0.23639	0.26597	129.003	0.23475	0.23494	127.925	0.23152	0.20871	126.773	0.22835	621.67
164	0.28557	130.048	0.23724	0.26773	129.542	0.23561	0.23665	128.484	0.23242	0.21041	127.356	0.22929	623.67
166	0.28735	130.577	0.23809	0.26947	130.079	0.23647	0.23835	129.041	0.23331	0.21209	127.935	0.23022	625.67
168	0.28910	131.104	0.23893	0.27119	130.615	0.23733	0.24003	129.595	0.23420	0.21374	128.510	0.23113	627.67
170	0.29085	131.631	0.23977	0.27290	131.149	0.23818	0.24169	130.146	0.23507	0.21538	129.083	0.23204	629.67
172	0.29258	132.156	0.24060	0.27460	131.682	0.23902	0.24333	130.696	0.23595	0.21700	129.653	0.23295	631.67
174	0.29431	132.680	0.24143	0.27628	132.213	0.23986	0.24496	131.244	0.23681	0.21859	130.220	0.23384	633.67
176	0.29601	133.203	0.24225	0.27796	132.743	0.24070	0.24658	131.790	0.23767	0.22017	130.784	0.23473	635.67
178	0.29771	133.725	0.24307	0.27961	133.272	0.24153	0.24818	132.334	0.23853	0.22174	131.346	0.23562	637.67
180	0.29940	134.246	0.24389	0.28126	133.800	0.24235	0.24976	132.877	0.23938	0.22329	131.905	0.23649	639.67
182	0.30107	134.766	0.24470	0.28290	134.327	0.24318	0.25134	133.418	0.24022	0.22482	132.463	0.23736	641.67
184	0.30274	135.286	0.24551	0.28452	134.853	0.24399	0.25290	133.957	0.24106	0.22634	133.018	0.23823	643.67
186	0.30439	135.805	0.24632	0.28614	135.378	0.24481	0.25445	134.495	0.24190	0.22784	133.572	0.23908	645.67
188	0.30604	136.323	0.24712	0.28774	135.902	0.24562	0.25599	135.032	0.24273	0.22933	134.123	0.23994	647.67

Temp. °F	Absolute Pressure, lb./sq. in. 190.0 Gauge Pressure 175.304 lb./sq. in. Satn. Temp. = 121.93 °F 581.60 °R			200.0 Gauge Pressure 185.304 lb./sq. in. Satn. Temp. = 125.63 °F 585.30 °R			220.0 Gauge Pressure 205.304 lb./sq. in. Satn. Temp. = 132.64 °F 592.31 °R			240.0 Gauge Pressure 225.304 lb./sq. in. Satn. Temp. = 139.18 °F 598.85 °R			Temp. °R
	V	H	S	V	H	S	V	H	S	V	H	S	
190	0.30768	136.840	0.24791	0.28933	136.425	0.24643	0.25751	135.568	0.24355	0.23081	134.673	0.24079	649.67
192	0.30930	137.357	0.24871	0.29092	136.947	0.24723	0.25903	136.102	0.24437	0.23228	135.221	0.24163	651.67
194	0.31092	137.873	0.24950	0.29249	137.469	0.24803	0.26053	136.636	0.24519	0.23373	135.768	0.24247	653.67
196	0.31253	138.389	0.25029	0.29406	137.990	0.24882	0.26203	137.168	0.24600	0.23518	136.314	0.24330	655.67
198	0.31413	138.904	0.25107	0.29561	138.510	0.24962	0.26351	137.700	0.24681	0.23661	136.858	0.24413	657.67
200	0.31573	139.419	0.25185	0.29716	139.030	0.25040	0.26499	138.231	0.24762	0.23803	137.400	0.24495	659.67
202	0.31731	139.934	0.25263	0.29870	139.549	0.25119	0.26645	138.760	0.24842	0.23944	137.942	0.24577	661.67
204	0.31889	140.448	0.25341	0.30023	140.068	0.25197	0.26791	139.289	0.24922	0.24084	138.482	0.24659	663.67
206	0.32046	140.962	0.25418	0.30176	140.587	0.25275	0.26936	139.818	0.25001	0.24223	139.021	0.24740	665.67
208	0.32202	141.475	0.25495	0.30328	141.105	0.25353	0.27080	140.345	0.25081	0.24361	139.560	0.24821	667.67
210	0.32358	141.988	0.25572	0.30478	141.622	0.25430	0.27223	140.872	0.25159	0.24498	140.097	0.24901	669.67
212	0.32513	142.501	0.25648	0.30629	142.139	0.25508	0.27366	141.399	0.25238	0.24635	140.634	0.24981	671.67
214	0.32667	143.014	0.25725	0.30778	142.656	0.25584	0.27507	141.925	0.25316	0.24770	141.169	0.25061	673.67
216	0.32821	143.527	0.25801	0.30927	143.173	0.25661	0.27648	142.450	0.25394	0.24905	141.704	0.25140	675.67
218	0.32974	144.039	0.25876	0.31075	143.690	0.25737	0.27788	142.975	0.25471	0.25039	142.238	0.25219	677.67
220	0.33126	144.552	0.25952	0.31223	144.206	0.25813	0.27928	143.499	0.25549	0.25172	142.772	0.25297	679.67
222	0.33278	145.064	0.26027	0.31370	144.722	0.25889	0.28067	144.023	0.25626	0.25305	143.305	0.25376	681.67
224	0.33429	145.576	0.26102	0.31516	145.238	0.25965	0.28205	144.547	0.25702	0.25436	143.837	0.25454	683.67
226	0.33580	146.088	0.26177	0.31662	145.753	0.26040	0.28342	145.071	0.25779	0.25567	144.369	0.25531	685.67
228	0.33730	146.600	0.26252	0.31807	146.269	0.26115	0.28479	145.594	0.25855	0.25698	144.900	0.25609	687.67
230	0.33879	147.112	0.26326	0.31952	146.785	0.26190	0.28616	146.117	0.25931	0.25827	145.431	0.25686	689.67
232	0.34028	147.625	0.26400	0.32096	147.300	0.26265	0.28751	146.639	0.26007	0.25956	145.961	0.25763	691.67
234	0.34177	148.137	0.26474	0.32239	147.816	0.26339	0.28886	147.162	0.26082	0.26085	146.491	0.25839	693.67
236	0.34325	148.649	0.26548	0.32382	148.331	0.26413	0.29021	147.684	0.26157	0.26213	147.021	0.25915	695.67
238	0.34473	149.161	0.26621	0.32525	148.847	0.26487	0.29155	148.206	0.26232	0.26340	147.550	0.25991	697.67
240	0.34620	149.674	0.26695	0.32667	149.362	0.26561	0.29289	148.728	0.26307	0.26466	148.079	0.26067	699.67
242	0.34766	150.186	0.26768	0.32808	149.878	0.26635	0.29422	149.250	0.26381	0.26593	148.608	0.26142	701.67
244	0.34912	150.699	0.26841	0.32949	150.393	0.26708	0.29554	149.772	0.26456	0.26718	149.137	0.26218	703.67
246	0.35058	151.212	0.26913	0.33090	150.909	0.26781	0.29686	150.294	0.26530	0.26843	149.665	0.26293	705.67
248	0.35203	151.725	0.26986	0.33230	151.425	0.26854	0.29818	150.815	0.26604	0.26968	150.193	0.26367	707.67
250	0.35348	152.238	0.27058	0.33370	151.941	0.26927	0.29949	151.337	0.26677	0.27092	150.721	0.26442	709.67
252	0.35493	152.751	0.27131	0.33509	152.457	0.27000	0.30079	151.859	0.26751	0.27215	151.249	0.26516	711.67
254	0.35637	153.265	0.27203	0.33648	152.973	0.27072	0.30209	152.381	0.26824	0.27338	151.777	0.26590	713.67
256	0.35780	153.778	0.27275	0.33787	153.489	0.27144	0.30339	152.903	0.26897	0.27461	152.305	0.26664	715.67
258	0.35924	154.292	0.27346	0.33925	154.006	0.27216	0.30468	153.425	0.26970	0.27583	152.832	0.26738	717.67

Temp. °F	Absolute Pressure, lb./sq. in.												Temp. °R
	260.0			280.0			300.0			350.0			
	Gauge Pressure = 245.304 lb./sq. in. Satn. Temp. = 145.31 °F 604.98 °R			Gauge Pressure = 265.304 lb./sq. in. Satn. Temp. = 151.10 °F 610.77 °R			Gauge Pressure = 285.304 lb./sq. in. Satn. Temp. = 156.57 °F 616.24 °R			Gauge Pressure = 335.304 lb./sq. in. Satn. Temp. = 169.10 °F 628.77 °R			
	V	H	S	V	H	S	V	H	S	V	H	S	
SAT N	0.17045	120.164	0.21643	0.15590	120.468	0.21594	0.14315	120.693	0.21540	0.11713	120.927	0.21385	
146	0.17116	120.396	0.21681										605.67
148	0.17317	121.067	0.21792										607.67
150	0.17514	121.727	0.21900										609.67
152	0.17706	122.379	0.22007	0.15681	120.787	0.21646							611.67
154	0.17894	123.023	0.22112	0.15880	121.485	0.21760							613.67
156	0.18079	123.659	0.22216	0.16073	122.171	0.21871							615.67
158	0.18259	124.289	0.22318	0.16261	122.846	0.21981	0.14459	121.221	0.21626				617.67
160	0.18437	124.912	0.22418	0.16445	123.512	0.22088	0.14655	121.947	0.21743				619.67
162	0.18611	125.529	0.22518	0.16625	124.170	0.22194	0.14845	122.658	0.21858				621.67
164	0.18782	126.141	0.22616	0.16800	124.819	0.22299	0.15029	123.357	0.21970				623.67
166	0.18950	126.748	0.22713	0.16973	125.461	0.22401	0.15209	124.045	0.22080				625.67
168	0.19116	127.350	0.22809	0.17141	126.096	0.22503	0.15384	124.723	0.22188				627.67
170	0.19279	127.948	0.22904	0.17307	126.724	0.22603	0.15556	125.392	0.22295	0.11806	121.306	0.21446	629.67
172	0.19440	128.541	0.22998	0.17470	127.347	0.22701	0.15723	126.052	0.22399	0.12007	122.132	0.21576	631.67
174	0.19599	129.131	0.23092	0.17630	127.965	0.22799	0.15887	126.704	0.22502	0.12200	122.934	0.21703	633.67
176	0.19756	129.717	0.23184	0.17788	128.577	0.22896	0.16048	127.349	0.22604	0.12385	123.714	0.21826	635.67
178	0.19911	130.300	0.23276	0.17943	129.185	0.22991	0.16206	127.987	0.22704	0.12563	124.477	0.21946	637.67
180	0.20064	130.879	0.23366	0.18096	129.788	0.23085	0.16361	128.620	0.22803	0.12736	125.223	0.22063	639.67
182	0.20215	131.456	0.23456	0.18247	130.387	0.23179	0.16513	129.246	0.22901	0.12904	125.955	0.22177	641.67
184	0.20364	132.029	0.23546	0.18395	130.983	0.23272	0.16663	129.868	0.22998	0.13067	126.673	0.22289	643.67
186	0.20512	132.600	0.23634	0.18542	131.574	0.23363	0.16810	130.484	0.23093	0.13225	127.380	0.22399	645.67
188	0.20658	133.169	0.23722	0.18687	132.163	0.23454	0.16956	131.096	0.23188	0.13380	128.077	0.22506	647.67
190	0.20803	133.735	0.23809	0.18830	132.748	0.23545	0.17099	131.703	0.23282	0.13531	128.763	0.22612	649.67
192	0.20946	134.299	0.23896	0.18972	133.330	0.23634	0.17240	132.307	0.23374	0.13678	129.441	0.22716	651.67
194	0.21088	134.861	0.23982	0.19112	133.909	0.23723	0.17379	132.906	0.23466	0.13823	130.111	0.22819	653.67
196	0.21229	135.421	0.24068	0.19250	134.486	0.23811	0.17517	133.502	0.23557	0.13964	130.773	0.22920	655.67
198	0.21368	135.979	0.24153	0.19387	135.060	0.23898	0.17653	134.095	0.23647	0.14103	131.428	0.23020	657.67
200	0.21507	136.535	0.24237	0.19523	135.632	0.23985	0.17787	134.684	0.23737	0.14240	132.077	0.23118	659.67
202	0.21644	137.090	0.24321	0.19657	136.201	0.24071	0.17920	135.271	0.23826	0.14374	132.720	0.23216	661.67
204	0.21779	137.643	0.24405	0.19790	136.769	0.24157	0.18051	135.855	0.23914	0.14506	133.357	0.23312	663.67
206	0.21914	138.195	0.24487	0.19922	137.334	0.24242	0.18181	136.436	0.24001	0.14636	133.989	0.23407	665.67
208	0.22048	138.745	0.24570	0.20052	137.898	0.24327	0.18310	137.015	0.24088	0.14764	134.616	0.23501	667.67

Temp. °F	Absolute Pressure, lb./sq. in.												Temp. °R
	260.0			280.0			300.0			350.0			
	Gauge Pressure = 245.304 lb./sq. in.; Satn. Temp. = 145.31 °F, 604.98 °R			Gauge Pressure = 265.304 lb./sq. in.; Satn. Temp. = 151.10 °F, 610.77 °R			Gauge Pressure = 285.304 lb./sq. in.; Satn. Temp. = 156.57 °F, 616.24 °R			Gauge Pressure = 335.304 lb./sq. in.; Satn. Temp. = 169.10 °F, 628.77 °R			
	V	H	S	V	H	S	V	H	S	V	H	S	
210	0.22181	139.294	0.24652	0.20182	138.460	0.24411	0.18437	137.591	0.24174	0.14890	135.239	0.23594	669.67
212	0.22312	139.842	0.24734	0.20310	139.020	0.24494	0.18563	138.165	0.24260	0.15015	135.858	0.23686	671.67
214	0.22443	140.388	0.24815	0.20438	139.579	0.24577	0.18688	138.738	0.24345	0.15137	136.472	0.23778	673.67
216	0.22573	140.934	0.24896	0.20564	140.136	0.24660	0.18811	139.308	0.24430	0.15258	137.083	0.23868	675.67
218	0.22702	141.478	0.24976	0.20689	140.691	0.24742	0.18934	139.876	0.24514	0.15378	137.690	0.23958	677.67
220	0.22831	142.021	0.25056	0.20814	141.246	0.24824	0.19056	140.443	0.24597	0.15496	138.294	0.24047	679.67
222	0.22958	142.564	0.25136	0.20937	141.799	0.24905	0.19176	141.008	0.24680	0.15613	138.895	0.24135	681.67
224	0.23085	143.106	0.25215	0.21060	142.351	0.24986	0.19296	141.571	0.24763	0.15729	139.493	0.24223	683.67
226	0.23211	143.646	0.25294	0.21182	142.902	0.25066	0.19415	142.133	0.24845	0.15843	140.089	0.24310	685.67
228	0.23336	144.187	0.25373	0.21303	143.452	0.25146	0.19532	142.694	0.24926	0.15956	140.681	0.24396	687.67
230	0.23460	144.726	0.25451	0.21423	144.001	0.25226	0.19649	143.253	0.25007	0.16068	141.272	0.24482	689.67
232	0.23584	145.265	0.25529	0.21542	144.549	0.25305	0.19765	143.811	0.25088	0.16179	141.860	0.24567	691.67
234	0.23707	145.803	0.25607	0.21661	145.096	0.25384	0.19881	144.368	0.25169	0.16289	142.445	0.24651	693.67
236	0.23829	146.341	0.25685	0.21779	145.642	0.25463	0.19995	144.923	0.25249	0.16398	143.029	0.24735	695.67
238	0.23951	146.878	0.25762	0.21896	146.188	0.25541	0.20109	145.478	0.25328	0.16506	143.611	0.24819	697.67
240	0.24072	147.414	0.25838	0.22013	146.732	0.25619	0.20222	146.032	0.25408	0.16613	144.191	0.24902	699.67
242	0.24192	147.951	0.25915	0.22129	147.277	0.25697	0.20334	146.585	0.25486	0.16719	144.769	0.24985	701.67
244	0.24312	148.486	0.25991	0.22244	147.820	0.25774	0.20446	147.137	0.25565	0.16824	145.346	0.25067	703.67
246	0.24432	149.022	0.26067	0.22359	148.363	0.25851	0.20557	147.688	0.25643	0.16929	145.921	0.25148	705.67
248	0.24551	149.557	0.26143	0.22473	148.906	0.25928	0.20667	148.239	0.25721	0.17032	146.494	0.25229	707.67
250	0.24669	150.092	0.26218	0.22587	149.448	0.26005	0.20777	148.788	0.25799	0.17135	147.066	0.25310	709.67
252	0.24787	150.626	0.26294	0.22700	149.989	0.26081	0.20886	149.337	0.25876	0.17237	147.637	0.25390	711.67
254	0.24904	151.160	0.26369	0.22812	150.530	0.26157	0.20994	149.886	0.25953	0.17339	148.207	0.25470	713.67
256	0.25021	151.694	0.26443	0.22924	151.071	0.26232	0.21102	150.434	0.26030	0.17440	148.775	0.25550	715.67
258	0.25137	152.228	0.26518	0.23035	151.611	0.26308	0.21210	150.981	0.26106	0.17540	149.343	0.25629	717.67
260	0.25253	152.762	0.26592	0.23146	152.151	0.26383	0.21316	151.528	0.26182	0.17639	149.909	0.25708	719.67
262	0.25368	153.295	0.26666	0.23257	152.691	0.26458	0.21423	152.075	0.26258	0.17738	150.475	0.25786	721.67
264	0.25483	153.829	0.26740	0.23367	153.231	0.26532	0.21528	152.621	0.26333	0.17836	151.039	0.25864	723.67
266	0.25597	154.362	0.26813	0.23476	153.770	0.26607	0.21634	153.166	0.26409	0.17933	151.603	0.25942	725.67
268	0.25711	154.895	0.26887	0.23585	154.309	0.26681	0.21738	153.712	0.26484	0.18030	152.166	0.26020	727.67
270	0.25825	155.428	0.26960	0.23694	154.848	0.26755	0.21843	154.257	0.26559	0.18127	152.728	0.26097	729.67
272	0.25938	155.962	0.27033	0.23802	155.387	0.26829	0.21947	154.802	0.26633	0.18223	153.289	0.26174	731.67
274	0.26051	156.495	0.27106	0.23909	155.926	0.26902	0.22050	155.346	0.26707	0.18318	153.850	0.26250	733.67
276	0.26163	157.028	0.27178	0.24017	156.464	0.26976	0.22153	155.890	0.26782	0.18413	154.410	0.26326	735.67
278	0.26275	157.561	0.27251	0.24123	157.003	0.27049	0.22255	156.434	0.26855	0.18507	154.969	0.26402	737.67

Temp. °F	Absolute Pressure, lb./sq. in.												Temp. °R
	400.0			450.0			500.0			550.0			
	Gauge Pressure = 385.304 lb./sq. in. Satn. Temp. = 180.29 °F 639.96 °R			Gauge Pressure = 435.304 lb./sq. in. Satn. Temp. = 190.38 °F 650.05 °R			Gauge Pressure = 485.304 lb./sq. in. Satn. Temp. = 199.56 °F 659.23 °R			Gauge Pressure = 535.304 lb./sq. in. Satn. Temp. = 207.93 °F 667.60 °R			
	V	H	S	V	H	S	V	H	S	V	H	S	
SAT N	0.096904	120.680	0.21191	0.080355	119.873	0.20939	0.066001	118.290	0.20594	0.052149	115.196	0.20046	
182	0.098801	121.525	0.21323										641.67
184	0.100885	122.468	0.21470										643.67
186	0.102850	123.371	0.21610										645.67
188	0.104717	124.241	0.21744										647.67
190	0.106499	125.083	0.21874										649.67
192	0.108208	125.901	0.22000	0.082418	120.869	0.21092							651.67
194	0.109854	126.697	0.22122	0.084735	122.006	0.21266							653.67
196	0.111442	127.475	0.22241	0.086861	123.067	0.21428							655.67
198	0.112980	128.237	0.22356	0.088837	124.069	0.21581							657.67
200	0.114472	128.984	0.22470	0.090693	125.024	0.21726	0.066766	118.688	0.20655				659.67
202	0.115923	129.718	0.22581	0.092450	125.940	0.21865	0.069795	120.283	0.20896				661.67
204	0.117336	130.440	0.22690	0.094122	126.824	0.21998	0.072373	121.664	0.21105				663.67
206	0.118715	131.151	0.22797	0.095721	127.680	0.22127	0.074658	122.910	0.21292				665.67
208	0.120062	131.852	0.22902	0.097257	128.511	0.22252	0.076732	124.058	0.21464	0.052374	115.326	0.20065	667.67
210	0.121379	132.545	0.23006	0.098737	129.322	0.22373	0.078646	125.133	0.21625	0.057157	118.097	0.20480	669.67
212	0.122670	133.228	0.23108	0.100168	130.114	0.22491	0.080434	126.151	0.21777	0.060496	120.052	0.20771	671.67
214	0.123935	133.905	0.23208	0.101554	130.890	0.22606	0.082117	127.122	0.21921	0.063211	121.661	0.21010	673.67
216	0.125176	134.574	0.23307	0.102901	131.651	0.22719	0.083714	128.055	0.22059	0.065557	123.070	0.21219	675.67
218	0.126396	135.236	0.23405	0.104210	132.399	0.22830	0.085236	128.955	0.22192	0.067651	124.345	0.21408	677.67
220	0.127595	135.893	0.23502	0.105487	133.135	0.22938	0.086695	129.828	0.22321	0.069561	125.523	0.21581	679.67
222	0.128774	136.543	0.23598	0.106733	133.859	0.23044	0.088097	130.676	0.22446	0.071330	126.627	0.21744	681.67
224	0.129935	137.189	0.23692	0.107951	134.574	0.23149	0.089449	131.503	0.22567	0.072984	127.673	0.21897	683.67
226	0.131079	137.829	0.23786	0.109142	135.279	0.23252	0.090758	132.311	0.22685	0.074544	128.671	0.22042	685.67
228	0.132206	138.465	0.23878	0.110310	135.976	0.23354	0.092026	133.102	0.22800	0.076025	129.629	0.22182	687.67
230	0.133318	139.096	0.23970	0.111455	136.666	0.23454	0.093259	133.879	0.22913	0.077439	130.553	0.22316	689.67
232	0.134416	139.724	0.24061	0.112579	137.348	0.23552	0.094458	134.641	0.23023	0.078793	131.449	0.22446	691.67
234	0.135499	140.347	0.24151	0.113683	138.023	0.23650	0.095628	135.392	0.23131	0.080096	132.319	0.22571	693.67
236	0.136569	140.967	0.24240	0.114768	138.692	0.23746	0.096770	136.131	0.23238	0.081354	133.166	0.22693	695.67
238	0.137626	141.584	0.24329	0.115837	139.355	0.23841	0.097886	136.860	0.23342	0.082570	133.995	0.22812	697.67
240	0.138671	142.198	0.24416	0.116889	140.013	0.23936	0.098979	137.579	0.23445	0.083749	134.805	0.22928	699.67
242	0.139705	142.808	0.24503	0.117925	140.666	0.24029	0.100050	138.290	0.23547	0.084896	135.600	0.23042	701.67
244	0.140728	143.416	0.24590	0.118947	141.313	0.24121	0.101100	138.992	0.23647	0.086011	136.381	0.23153	703.67
246	0.141740	144.020	0.24676	0.119954	141.957	0.24212	0.102131	139.687	0.23745	0.087099	137.149	0.23262	705.67
248	0.142742	144.623	0.24761	0.120949	142.596	0.24303	0.103144	140.376	0.23843	0.088161	137.905	0.23369	707.67

Temp. °F	Absolute Pressure, lb./sq. in.												Temp. °R
	400.0			450.0			500.0			550.0			
	Gauge Pressure = 385.304 lb./sq. in. Satn. Temp. = 180.29 °F 639.96 °R			Gauge Pressure = 435.304 lb./sq. in. Satn. Temp. = 190.38 °F 650.05 °R			Gauge Pressure = 485.304 lb./sq. in. Satn. Temp. = 199.56 °F 659.23 °R			Gauge Pressure = 535.304 lb./sq. in. Satn. Temp. = 207.93 °F 667.60 °R			
	V	H	S	V	H	S	V	H	S	V	H	S	
250	0.143734	145.223	0.24846	0.121931	143.232	0.24392	0.104141	141.058	0.23939	0.089199	138.650	0.23474	709.67
252	0.144717	145.821	0.24930	0.122901	143.863	0.24481	0.105121	141.733	0.24034	0.090215	139.385	0.23578	711.67
254	0.145691	146.416	0.25013	0.123859	144.492	0.24569	0.106086	142.404	0.24128	0.091211	140.111	0.23679	713.67
256	0.146657	147.010	0.25096	0.124807	145.117	0.24657	0.107038	143.069	0.24221	0.092188	140.829	0.23780	715.67
258	0.147614	147.602	0.25179	0.125744	145.739	0.24744	0.107976	143.729	0.24313	0.093147	141.539	0.23879	717.67
260	0.148563	148.192	0.25261	0.126672	146.358	0.24830	0.108901	144.384	0.24405	0.094089	142.242	0.23977	719.67
262	0.149504	148.780	0.25343	0.127590	146.974	0.24915	0.109814	145.035	0.24495	0.095015	142.938	0.24073	721.67
264	0.150438	149.366	0.25424	0.128498	147.587	0.25000	0.110716	145.683	0.24584	0.095927	143.627	0.24169	723.67
266	0.151365	149.952	0.25505	0.129398	148.199	0.25085	0.111606	146.326	0.24673	0.096824	144.311	0.24263	725.67
268	0.152285	150.535	0.25585	0.130290	148.807	0.25168	0.112486	146.966	0.24761	0.097709	144.989	0.24356	727.67
270	0.153199	151.118	0.25665	0.131173	149.414	0.25252	0.113356	147.602	0.24849	0.098581	145.663	0.24449	729.67
272	0.154106	151.699	0.25744	0.132049	150.019	0.25334	0.114217	148.235	0.24935	0.099441	146.331	0.24540	731.67
274	0.155006	152.278	0.25824	0.132917	150.621	0.25417	0.115069	148.865	0.25021	0.100289	146.995	0.24631	733.67
276	0.155901	152.857	0.25902	0.133778	151.222	0.25498	0.115911	149.492	0.25107	0.101127	147.654	0.24721	735.67
278	0.156790	153.435	0.25981	0.134632	151.821	0.25580	0.116746	150.117	0.25191	0.101955	148.310	0.24810	737.67
280	0.157673	154.011	0.26059	0.135479	152.418	0.25661	0.117572	150.739	0.25276	0.102773	148.961	0.24898	739.67
282	0.158550	154.587	0.26136	0.136320	153.014	0.25741	0.118391	151.359	0.25359	0.103581	149.609	0.24985	741.67
284	0.159423	155.162	0.26214	0.137154	153.608	0.25821	0.119202	151.976	0.25442	0.104381	150.254	0.25072	743.67
286	0.160290	155.736	0.26291	0.137982	154.201	0.25901	0.120006	152.591	0.25525	0.105172	150.896	0.25158	745.67
288	0.161152	156.309	0.26368	0.138805	154.793	0.25980	0.120803	153.204	0.25607	0.105955	151.534	0.25244	747.67
290	0.162009	156.881	0.26444	0.139622	155.383	0.26059	0.121593	153.815	0.25689	0.106730	152.170	0.25329	749.67
292	0.162862	157.453	0.26520	0.140433	155.972	0.26137	0.122377	154.424	0.25770	0.107497	152.803	0.25413	751.67
294	0.163710	158.024	0.26596	0.141239	156.560	0.26215	0.123155	155.032	0.25851	0.108257	153.433	0.25497	753.67
296	0.164553	158.594	0.26672	0.142040	157.147	0.26293	0.123927	155.638	0.25931	0.109011	154.061	0.25580	755.67
298	0.165392	159.164	0.26747	0.142836	157.733	0.26370	0.124693	156.242	0.26011	0.109757	154.687	0.25663	757.67
300	0.166227	159.733	0.26822	0.143627	158.317	0.26448	0.125454	156.845	0.26090	0.110497	155.311	0.25745	759.67
302	0.167058	160.302	0.26897	0.144414	158.901	0.26524	0.126209	157.447	0.26169	0.111231	155.932	0.25827	761.67
304	0.167885	160.870	0.26971	0.145196	159.485	0.26601	0.126959	158.047	0.26248	0.111959	156.552	0.25908	763.67
306	0.168708	161.438	0.27046	0.145973	160.067	0.26677	0.127704	158.646	0.26326	0.112681	157.169	0.25989	765.67
308	0.169527	162.005	0.27120	0.146746	160.649	0.26753	0.128444	159.243	0.26404	0.113398	157.785	0.26069	767.67
310	0.170342	162.572	0.27193	0.147515	161.230	0.26828	0.129179	159.840	0.26482	0.114109	158.400	0.26149	769.67
312	0.171154	163.139	0.27267	0.148280	161.810	0.26904	0.129909	160.435	0.26559	0.114814	159.012	0.26228	771.67
314	0.171962	163.706	0.27340	0.149041	162.390	0.26979	0.130636	161.030	0.26636	0.115515	159.624	0.26307	773.67
316	0.172767	164.272	0.27413	0.149798	162.969	0.27053	0.131357	161.623	0.26713	0.116211	160.234	0.26386	775.67
318	0.173568	164.838	0.27486	0.150551	163.547	0.27128	0.132075	162.216	0.26789	0.116902	160.842	0.26465	777.67

ICI Klea
Concord Plaza
3411 Silverside Road
P.O. Box 15391
Wilmington, DE 19850

Customer Service: (800) ICI-KLEA or
Technical Assistance: (800) ASK-KLEA
Fax: (302) 887-7706

ICI believes all information contained in this document to be accurate at the time of publication but makes no warranty of any kind, either express or implied, regarding the accuracy of any information or the results to be obtained from utilizing such information. Furthermore, the information is intended for use by persons having technical skills and a working knowledge of the system, and is to be used at their own discretion. The user assumes all risks and liability through application or use of the information contained herein and must satisfy himself that the product is entirely suitable for his own purpose and process.

Statements concerning the use of the products or formulations described herein are not to be construed as granting a license under any patent, or as recommending the infringement of any patent, and no liability for infringement arising out of any such use is assumed.

620250011 3/95

730

Thermodynamic Properties of KLEA® 407A (KLEA® 60)

Units

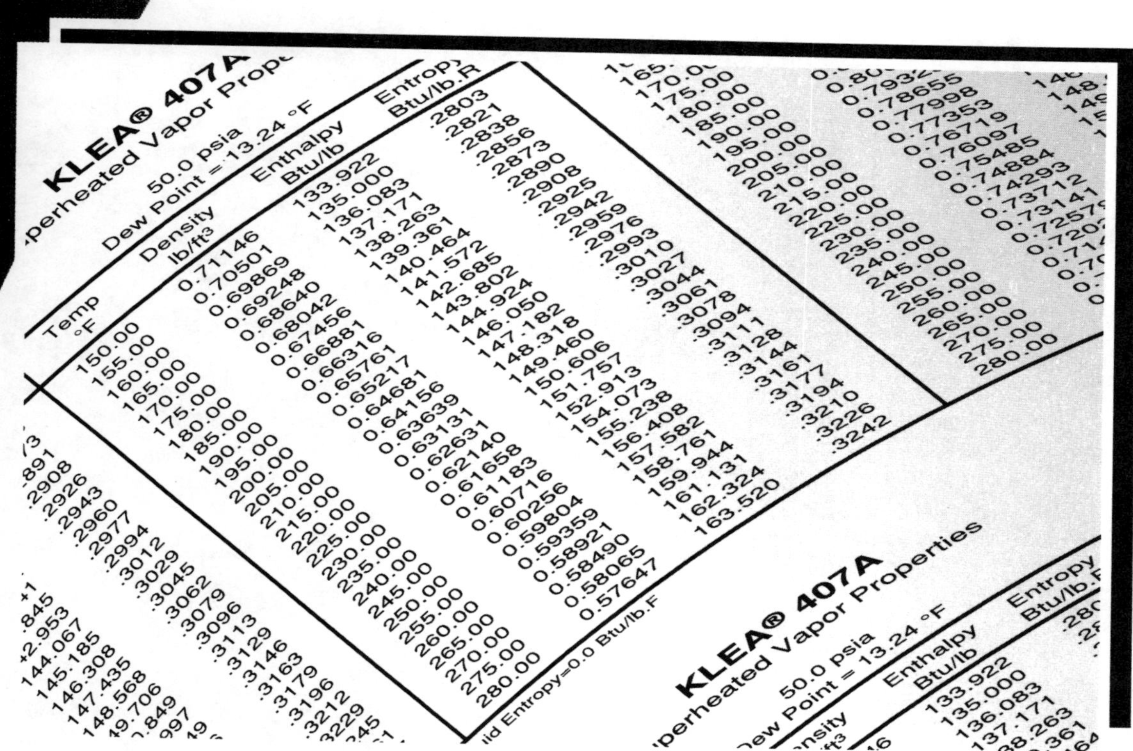

NOW.
AND FOR
THE FUTURE.

Thermodynamic Property Data for

KLEA® 407A

British Units

Saturated Liquid and Saturated Vapor Properties
Superheated Vapor Properties
Evaporator Inlet Temperatures

RHS14YR/JDM91-363P

SYSTEM PERFORMANCE WITH NON-AZEOTROPIC REFRIGERANT BLENDS

- With a non-azeotropic refrigerant blend the composition of the vapour changes in the evaporator and the condenser.
- Evaporator inlet and outlet temperatures are different.
- Condenser inlet and outlet temperatures are different.
- At all other points in the system the fluid behaves as normal.
- System design path.
  - Select evaporator outlet (Dew point 'A') against the desired cold space temperature.
  - Condenser inlet and outlet temperatures 'B' & 'C' should be sufficient to reject heat.
  - Liquid enthalpy at expansion device and table 3 can be used to get evaporator inlet temperature 'D'.
  - Refrigeration effect is enthalpy change 'D' to 'A' as normal.

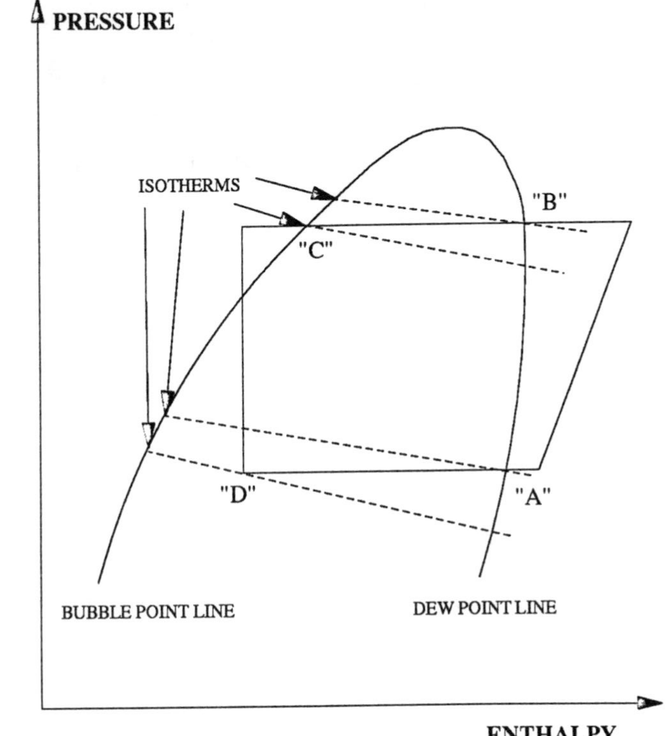

Pressure-Enthalpy Diagram for Non-azeotropic Refrigerant Blends

KLEA® 407A

Saturated Liquid and Saturated Vapor Properties

Table 1 Sheet 1

Pressure psia	Dew Point °F	Bubble Point °F	Liquid Density lb/ft³	Vapor Density lb/ft³	Liquid Enthalpy Btu/lb	Vapor Enthalpy Btu/lb	Vapor Entropy Btu/lb.F
10.00	-51.56	-63.75	89.12989	0.21028	-7.618	96.761	.24138
11.00	-48.33	-60.44	88.77540	0.22988	-6.552	97.252	.24053
12.00	-45.31	-57.36	88.44392	0.24937	-5.562	97.709	.23976
13.00	-42.49	-54.48	88.13212	0.26876	-4.637	98.136	.23907
14.00	-39.84	-51.77	87.83736	0.28807	-3.767	98.537	.23844
15.00	-37.33	-49.20	87.55751	0.30730	-2.945	98.916	.23786
16.00	-34.94	-46.77	87.29083	0.32646	-2.166	99.274	.23733
17.00	-32.68	-44.45	87.03588	0.34555	-1.425	99.615	.23684
18.00	-30.51	-42.24	86.79146	0.36458	-.718	99.940	.23638
19.00	-28.44	-40.12	86.55654	0.38356	-.041	100.250	.23595
20.00	-26.44	-38.09	86.33024	0.40249	.608	100.548	.23555
21.00	-24.53	-36.14	86.11180	0.42137	1.233	100.833	.23517
22.00	-22.69	-34.26	85.90057	0.44021	1.834	101.107	.23481
23.00	-20.91	-32.44	85.69597	0.45901	2.415	101.371	.23448
24.00	-19.19	-30.68	85.49750	0.47778	2.976	101.626	.23416
25.00	-17.52	-28.98	85.30470	0.49651	3.520	101.872	.23385
26.00	-15.90	-27.33	85.11718	0.51521	4.046	102.110	.23357
27.00	-14.34	-25.73	84.93458	0.53388	4.558	102.341	.23329
28.00	-12.81	-24.18	84.75658	0.55252	5.055	102.565	.23303
29.00	-11.33	-22.66	84.58289	0.57113	5.538	102.781	.23278
30.00	-9.89	-21.19	84.41325	0.58973	6.010	102.992	.23254
31.00	-8.48	-19.76	84.24741	0.60830	6.469	103.197	.23230
32.00	-7.11	-18.36	84.08517	0.62685	6.917	103.396	.23208
33.00	-5.77	-16.99	83.92633	0.64539	7.354	103.590	.23187
34.00	-4.47	-15.66	83.77069	0.66390	7.782	103.780	.23166
35.00	-3.19	-14.35	83.61811	0.68240	8.200	103.964	.23146
36.00	-1.94	-13.08	83.46841	0.70089	8.610	104.144	.23127
37.00	-0.71	-11.83	83.32147	0.71936	9.010	104.320	.23109
38.00	0.47	-10.60	83.17715	0.73782	9.403	104.492	.23091
39.00	1.65	-9.40	83.03532	0.75627	9.788	104.659	.23074
40.00	2.80	-8.23	82.89588	0.77471	10.166	104.823	.23057

Standard state : At -40°F, Liquid Enthalpy=0.0 Btu/lb, Liquid Entropy=0.0 Btu/lb.F

Version 2a 1st September 1993

KLEA® 407A

Saturated Liquid and Saturated Vapor Properties

Table 1 Sheet 2

Pressure psia	Dew Point °F	Bubble Point °F	Liquid Density lb/ft³	Vapor Density lb/ft³	Liquid Enthalpy Btu/lb	Vapor Enthalpy Btu/lb	Vapor Entropy Btu/lb.F
40.00	2.80	-8.23	82.89588	0.77471	10.166	104.823	.23057
45.00	8.24	-2.67	82.23097	0.86678	11.957	105.594	.22980
50.00	13.24	2.42	81.61242	0.95871	13.607	106.292	.22913
55.00	17.87	7.15	81.03220	1.05059	15.141	106.930	.22853
60.00	22.18	11.56	80.48426	1.14248	16.577	107.517	.22799
65.00	26.23	15.70	79.96390	1.23444	17.931	108.060	.22750
70.00	30.05	19.60	79.46738	1.32651	19.213	108.565	.22706
75.00	33.66	23.30	78.99168	1.41874	20.433	109.036	.22664
80.00	37.09	26.81	78.53435	1.51117	21.598	109.477	.22626
85.00	40.36	30.16	78.09331	1.60382	22.714	109.891	.22590
90.00	43.49	33.36	77.66683	1.69673	23.787	110.282	.22556
95.00	46.48	36.44	77.25344	1.78992	24.820	110.650	.22524
100.00	49.36	39.39	76.85188	1.88343	25.818	110.998	.22493
105.00	52.13	42.23	76.46104	1.97726	26.784	111.327	.22464
110.00	54.80	44.97	76.07996	2.07145	27.721	111.640	.22435
115.00	57.38	47.62	75.70781	2.16601	28.630	111.936	.22408
120.00	59.88	50.19	75.34384	2.26096	29.515	112.218	.22382
125.00	62.30	52.67	74.98738	2.35632	30.377	112.487	.22356
130.00	64.64	55.08	74.63785	2.45211	31.218	112.742	.22332
135.00	66.92	57.42	74.29470	2.54835	32.039	112.985	.22308
140.00	69.13	59.70	73.95744	2.64505	32.842	113.217	.22284
145.00	71.28	61.92	73.62566	2.74224	33.628	113.438	.22261
150.00	73.38	64.08	73.29893	2.83991	34.398	113.649	.22238
155.00	75.42	66.19	72.97689	2.93810	35.153	113.850	.22216
160.00	77.41	68.24	72.65922	3.03681	35.894	114.042	.22194

Standard state : At -40°F, Liquid Enthalpy=0.0 Btu/lb, Liquid Entropy=0.0 Btu/lb.F

Version 2a 1st September 1993

KLEA® 407A

Saturated Liquid and Saturated Vapor Properties

Table 1 Sheet 3

Pressure psia	Dew Point °F	Bubble Point °F	Liquid Density lb/ft³	Vapor Density lb/ft³	Liquid Enthalpy Btu/lb	Vapor Enthalpy Btu/lb	Vapor Entropy Btu/lb.F
160.00	77.41	68.24	72.65922	3.03681	35.894	114.042	.22194
170.00	81.26	72.22	72.03570	3.23587	37.338	114.401	.22151
180.00	84.94	76.02	71.42614	3.43721	38.734	114.727	.22109
190.00	88.46	79.66	70.82859	3.64096	40.089	115.023	.22067
200.00	91.84	83.17	70.24132	3.84724	41.407	115.292	.22026
210.00	95.10	86.55	69.66279	4.05617	42.692	115.535	.21986
220.00	98.23	89.81	69.09157	4.26788	43.946	115.754	.21945
230.00	101.26	92.95	68.52638	4.48250	45.173	115.950	.21904
240.00	104.19	96.00	67.96600	4.70017	46.375	116.125	.21864
250.00	107.02	98.96	67.40927	4.92102	47.555	116.279	.21823
260.00	109.77	101.83	66.85508	5.14520	48.715	116.414	.21782
270.00	112.44	104.62	66.30231	5.37286	49.857	116.529	.21741
280.00	115.03	107.33	65.74989	5.60418	50.982	116.626	.21699
290.00	117.55	109.97	65.19670	5.83932	52.092	116.706	.21656
300.00	120.00	112.54	64.64158	6.07847	53.189	116.768	.21613
310.00	122.39	115.05	64.08332	6.32181	54.274	116.813	.21570
320.00	124.71	117.51	63.52064	6.56956	55.348	116.841	.21525
330.00	126.98	119.90	62.95209	6.82194	56.413	116.854	.21480
340.00	129.20	122.25	62.37612	7.07919	57.469	116.849	.21434
350.00	131.37	124.54	61.79093	7.34157	58.518	116.829	.21387
360.00	133.48	126.78	61.19445	7.60936	59.562	116.793	.21339
370.00	135.55	128.98	60.58422	7.88285	60.600	116.740	.21290
380.00	137.58	131.14	59.95728	8.16238	61.635	116.672	.21240
390.00	139.56	133.26	59.30995	8.44832	62.667	116.586	.21189
400.00	141.50	135.33	58.63753	8.74104	63.698	116.485	.21136
410.00	143.41	137.37	57.93383	9.04100	64.728	116.366	.21081
420.00	145.27	139.38	57.19036	9.34866	65.758	116.230	.21026
430.00	147.10	141.35	56.39485	9.66457	66.790	116.076	.20968

Standard state : At -40°F, Liquid Enthalpy=0.0 Btu/lb, Liquid Entropy=0.0 Btu/lb.F

Version 2a 1st September 1993

KLEA® 407A

Superheated Vapor Properties

Table 2 Sheet 1

10.0 psia, Dew Point = -51.56 °F				20.0 psia, Dew Point = -26.44 °F				30.0 psia, Dew Point = -9.89 °F			
Temp °F	Density lb/ft³	Enthalpy btu/lb	Entropy btu/lb.R	Temp °F	Density lb/ft³	Enthalpy btu/lb	Entropy btu/lb.R	Temp °F	Density lb/ft³	Enthalpy btu/lb	Entropy btu/lb.R
-50.00	0.20942	97.025	.2420								
-45.00	0.20675	97.871	.2441								
-40.00	0.20414	98.722	.2461								
-35.00	0.20160	99.578	.2481								
-30.00	0.19912	100.440	.2502								
-25.00	0.19671	101.308	.2522	-25.00	0.40100	100.802	.2361				
-20.00	0.19436	102.181	.2542	-20.00	0.39594	101.685	.2382				
-15.00	0.19206	103.059	.2562	-15.00	0.39102	102.573	.2402				
-10.00	0.18982	103.944	.2581	-10.00	0.38623	103.466	.2422				
-5.00	0.18764	104.833	.2601	-5.00	0.38156	104.365	.2441	-5.00	0.58239	103.881	.2345
0.00	0.18550	105.728	.2621	0.00	0.37701	105.268	.2461	0.00	0.57510	104.794	.2365
5.00	0.18342	106.629	.2640	5.00	0.37258	106.177	.2481	5.00	0.56800	105.712	.2385
10.00	0.18138	107.535	.2659	10.00	0.36825	107.091	.2500	10.00	0.56110	106.634	.2405
15.00	0.17939	108.447	.2679	15.00	0.36403	108.010	.2520	15.00	0.55437	107.562	.2424
20.00	0.17744	109.364	.2698	20.00	0.35991	108.935	.2539	20.00	0.54782	108.495	.2444
25.00	0.17554	110.286	.2717	25.00	0.35589	109.865	.2559	25.00	0.54144	109.433	.2463
30.00	0.17368	111.215	.2736	30.00	0.35197	110.800	.2578	30.00	0.53522	110.375	.2483
35.00	0.17186	112.148	.2755	35.00	0.34813	111.741	.2597	35.00	0.52915	111.323	.2502
40.00	0.17007	113.087	.2774	40.00	0.34438	112.686	.2616	40.00	0.52323	112.276	.2521
45.00	0.16833	114.032	.2793	45.00	0.34072	113.637	.2635	45.00	0.51744	113.234	.2540
50.00	0.16662	114.982	.2812	50.00	0.33713	114.594	.2654	50.00	0.51180	114.197	.2559
55.00	0.16494	115.937	.2830	55.00	0.33363	115.555	.2672	55.00	0.50629	115.165	.2578
60.00	0.16331	116.898	.2849	60.00	0.33020	116.522	.2691	60.00	0.50090	116.138	.2597
65.00	0.16170	117.864	.2867	65.00	0.32684	117.494	.2710	65.00	0.49564	117.116	.2616
70.00	0.16012	118.836	.2886	70.00	0.32356	118.471	.2728	70.00	0.49049	118.100	.2634
75.00	0.15858	119.813	.2904	75.00	0.32034	119.454	.2747	75.00	0.48545	119.088	.2653
80.00	0.15707	120.796	.2922	80.00	0.31719	120.442	.2765	80.00	0.48053	120.081	.2671
85.00	0.15558	121.784	.2941	85.00	0.31410	121.435	.2783	85.00	0.47571	121.080	.2690
90.00	0.15413	122.777	.2959	90.00	0.31108	122.433	.2802	90.00	0.47099	122.084	.2708
95.00	0.15270	123.776	.2977	95.00	0.30811	123.437	.2820	95.00	0.46637	123.092	.2726

Standard state : At -40°F, Liquid Enthalpy=0.0 Btu/lb, Liquid Entropy=0.0 Btu/lb.F

Version 2a 1st September 1993

KLEA® 407A

Superheated Vapor Properties

Table 2 Sheet 2

10.0 psia Dew Point = -51.56 °F				20.0 psia Dew Point = -26.44°F				30.0 psia Dew Point = -9.89 °F			
Temp °F	Density lb/ft³	Enthalpy btu/lb	Entropy btu/lb.R	Temp °F	Density lb/ft³	Enthalpy btu/lb	Entropy btu/lb.R	Temp °F	Density lb/ft³	Enthalpy btu/lb	Entropy btu/lb.R
100.00	0.15130	124.779	.2995	100.00	0.30521	124.445	.2838	100.00	0.46184	124.106	.2744
105.00	0.14992	125.789	.3013	105.00	0.30236	125.459	.2856	105.00	0.45741	125.125	.2763
110.00	0.14857	126.803	.3031	110.00	0.29956	126.478	.2874	110.00	0.45307	126.149	.2781
115.00	0.14725	127.823	.3049	115.00	0.29682	127.503	.2892	115.00	0.44881	127.178	.2799
120.00	0.14594	128.848	.3066	120.00	0.29413	128.532	.2910	120.00	0.44464	128.212	.2817
125.00	0.14467	129.879	.3084	125.00	0.29149	129.567	.2928	125.00	0.44055	129.251	.2834
130.00	0.14341	130.914	.3102	130.00	0.28890	130.607	.2945	130.00	0.43653	130.295	.2852
135.00	0.14218	131.955	.3119	135.00	0.28635	131.651	.2963	135.00	0.43260	131.344	.2870
140.00	0.14096	133.001	.3137	140.00	0.28385	132.701	.2980	140.00	0.42873	132.398	.2888
145.00	0.13977	134.052	.3154	145.00	0.28140	133.757	.2998	145.00	0.42494	133.458	.2905
150.00	0.13860	135.108	.3172	150.00	0.27899	134.817	.3015	150.00	0.42122	134.522	.2923
155.00	0.13745	136.170	.3189	155.00	0.27662	135.882	.3033	155.00	0.41756	135.591	.2940
160.00	0.13632	137.237	.3206	160.00	0.27429	136.953	.3050	160.00	0.41398	136.666	.2958
165.00	0.13520	138.309	.3223	165.00	0.27200	138.029	.3067	165.00	0.41045	137.746	.2975
170.00	0.13411	139.386	.3241	170.00	0.26976	139.109	.3085	170.00	0.40699	138.830	.2992
175.00	0.13303	140.468	.3258	175.00	0.26755	140.195	.3102	175.00	0.40359	139.920	.3009
180.00	0.13197	141.556	.3275	180.00	0.26537	141.287	.3119	180.00	0.40025	141.015	.3027
185.00	0.13093	142.648	.3292	185.00	0.26324	142.383	.3136	185.00	0.39696	142.115	.3044
190.00	0.12990	143.746	.3309	190.00	0.26114	143.484	.3153	190.00	0.39373	143.220	.3061
195.00	0.12889	144.848	.3326	195.00	0.25907	144.590	.3170	195.00	0.39056	144.329	.3078
200.00	0.12790	145.956	.3343	200.00	0.25703	145.701	.3187	200.00	0.38744	145.444	.3095
205.00	0.12692	147.068	.3359	205.00	0.25503	146.817	.3204	205.00	0.38437	146.563	.3112
210.00	0.12596	148.186	.3376	210.00	0.25306	147.937	.3221	210.00	0.38135	147.687	.3129
215.00	0.12501	149.308	.3393	215.00	0.25112	149.063	.3237	215.00	0.37838	148.816	.3145
220.00	0.12407	150.436	.3409	220.00	0.24922	150.194	.3254	220.00	0.37546	149.951	.3162
225.00	0.12315	151.568	.3426	225.00	0.24734	151.330	.3271	225.00	0.37258	151.090	.3179
230.00	0.12224	152.705	.3443	230.00	0.24549	152.471	.3287	230.00	0.36975	152.234	.3195

Standard state : At -40°F, Liquid Enthalpy=0.0 Btu/lb, Liquid Entropy=0.0 Btu/lb.F

Version 2a 1st September 1993

KLEA® 407A

Superheated Vapor Properties

Table 2 Sheet 3

40.0 psia, Dew Point = 2.80 °F				50.0 psia, Dew Point = 13.24 °F				60.0 psia, Dew Point = 22.18 °F			
Temp °F	Density lb/ft³	Enthalpy btu/lb	Entropy btu/lb.R	Temp °F	Density lb/ft³	Enthalpy btu/lb	Entropy btu/lb.R	Temp °F	Density lb/ft³	Enthalpy btu/lb	Entropy btu/lb.R
0.00	0.78043	105.231	.2314								
5.00	0.77030	106.164	.2334								
10.00	0.76047	107.100	.2354								
15.00	0.75092	108.042	.2374	15.00	0.95428	106.624	.2298				
20.00	0.74164	108.988	.2394	20.00	0.94191	107.576	.2318				
25.00	0.73261	109.939	.2413	25.00	0.92991	108.531	.2338	25.00	1.13389	108.060	.2291
30.00	0.72383	110.895	.2433	30.00	0.91825	109.491	.2358	30.00	1.11900	109.030	.2311
35.00	0.71527	111.856	.2452	35.00	0.90692	110.456	.2377	35.00	1.10457	110.004	.2331
40.00	0.70694	112.821	.2471	40.00	0.89591	111.425	.2397	40.00	1.09056	110.982	.2351
45.00	0.69882	113.791	.2490	45.00	0.88520	112.398	.2416	45.00	1.07696	111.964	.2370
50.00	0.69091	114.766	.2509	50.00	0.87477	113.376	.2435	50.00	1.06375	112.951	.2390
55.00	0.68319	115.746	.2528	55.00	0.86462	114.359	.2455	55.00	1.05091	113.941	.2409
60.00	0.67565	116.731	.2547	60.00	0.85473	115.346	.2474	60.00	1.03843	114.936	.2428
65.00	0.66830	117.721	.2566	65.00	0.84509	116.338	.2493	65.00	1.02628	115.936	.2447
70.00	0.66112	118.715	.2585	70.00	0.83569	117.334	.2512	70.00	1.01445	116.939	.2466
75.00	0.65411	119.715	.2603	75.00	0.82653	118.335	.2530	75.00	1.00293	117.947	.2485
80.00	0.64726	120.719	.2622	80.00	0.81758	119.341	.2549	80.00	0.99171	118.960	.2504
85.00	0.64056	121.728	.2640	85.00	0.80885	120.352	.2568	85.00	0.98076	119.977	.2523
90.00	0.63402	122.743	.2658	90.00	0.80032	121.367	.2586	90.00	0.97009	120.999	.2542
95.00	0.62761	123.762	.2677	95.00	0.79199	122.387	.2605	95.00	0.95968	122.025	.2560
100.00	0.62135	124.786	.2695	100.00	0.78385	123.412	.2623	100.00	0.94951	123.056	.2579
105.00	0.61521	125.815	.2713	105.00	0.77589	124.441	.2642	105.00	0.93958	124.091	.2597
110.00	0.60921	126.849	.2731	110.00	0.76810	125.475	.2660	110.00	0.92988	125.131	.2615
115.00	0.60333	127.887	.2749	115.00	0.76049	126.514	.2678	115.00	0.92041	126.175	.2634
120.00	0.59757	128.931	.2767	120.00	0.75304	127.558	.2696	120.00	0.91114	127.224	.2652
125.00	0.59193	129.980	.2785	125.00	0.74575	128.607	.2714	125.00	0.90208	128.278	.2670
130.00	0.58641	131.033	.2803	130.00	0.73860	129.660	.2732	130.00	0.89322	129.337	.2688
135.00	0.58099	132.092	.2821	135.00	0.73161	130.719	.2750	135.00	0.88455	130.400	.2706
140.00	0.57568	133.155	.2838	140.00	0.72476	131.782	.2768	140.00	0.87606	131.467	.2724
145.00	0.57047			145.00	0.71804	132.849	.2785	145.00	0.86775	132.540	.2742

Standard state : At -40°F, Liquid Enthalpy=0.0 Btu/lb, Liquid Entropy=0.0 Btu/lb.F

Version 2a 1st September 1993

KLEA® 407A

Superheated Vapor Properties

Table 2 Sheet 4

40.0 psia, Dew Point = 2.80 °F				50.0 psia, Dew Point = 13.24 °F				60.0 psia, Dew Point = 22.18 °F			
Temp °F	Density lb/ft³	Enthalpy btu/lb	Entropy btu/lb.R	Temp °F	Density lb/ft³	Enthalpy btu/lb	Entropy btu/lb.R	Temp °F	Density lb/ft³	Enthalpy btu/lb	Entropy btu/lb.R
150.00	0.56536	134.224	.2856	150.00	0.71146	133.922	.2803	150.00	0.85961	133.617	.2759
155.00	0.56034	135.297	.2873	155.00	0.70501	135.000	.2821	155.00	0.85164	134.699	.2777
160.00	0.55542	136.376	.2891	160.00	0.69869	136.083	.2838	160.00	0.84383	135.787	.2795
165.00	0.55059	137.460	.2908	165.00	0.69248	137.171	.2856	165.00	0.83617	136.879	.2812
170.00	0.54585	138.548	.2926	170.00	0.68640	138.263	.2873	170.00	0.82867	137.976	.2830
175.00	0.54120	139.642	.2943	175.00	0.68042	139.361	.2890	175.00	0.82131	139.078	.2847
180.00	0.53663	140.741	.2960	180.00	0.67456	140.464	.2908	180.00	0.81409	140.185	.2864
185.00	0.53214	141.845	.2977	185.00	0.66881	141.572	.2925	185.00	0.80701	141.297	.2882
190.00	0.52773	142.953	.2994	190.00	0.66316	142.685	.2942	190.00	0.80006	142.414	.2899
195.00	0.52340	144.067	.3012	195.00	0.65761	143.802	.2959	195.00	0.79325	143.535	.2916
200.00	0.51914	145.185	.3029	200.00	0.65217	144.924	.2976	200.00	0.78655	144.661	.2933
205.00	0.51495	146.308	.3045	205.00	0.64681	146.050	.2993	205.00	0.77998	145.791	.2950
210.00	0.51084	147.435	.3062	210.00	0.64156	147.182	.3010	210.00	0.77353	146.926	.2967
215.00	0.50679	148.568	.3079	215.00	0.63639	148.318	.3027	215.00	0.76719	148.066	.2984
220.00	0.50281	149.706	.3096	220.00	0.63131	149.460	.3044	220.00	0.76097	149.212	.3001
225.00	0.49890	150.849	.3113	225.00	0.62631	150.606	.3061	225.00	0.75485	150.362	.3018
230.00	0.49505	151.997	.3129	230.00	0.62140	151.757	.3078	230.00	0.74884	151.517	.3035
235.00	0.49126	153.149	.3146	235.00	0.61658	152.913	.3094	235.00	0.74293	152.676	.3052
240.00	0.48754	154.306	.3163	240.00	0.61183	154.073	.3111	240.00	0.73712	153.840	.3068
245.00	0.48387	155.467	.3179	245.00	0.60716	155.238	.3128	245.00	0.73141	155.008	.3085
250.00	0.48026	156.634	.3196	250.00	0.60256	156.408	.3144	250.00	0.72579	156.181	.3102
255.00	0.47671	157.804	.3212	255.00	0.59804	157.582	.3161	255.00	0.72027	157.358	.3118
260.00	0.47321	158.980	.3229	260.00	0.59359	158.761	.3177	260.00	0.71483	158.540	.3135
265.00	0.46976	160.160	.3245	265.00	0.58921	159.944	.3194	265.00	0.70949	159.726	.3151
270.00	0.46637	161.344	.3261	270.00	0.58490	161.131	.3210	270.00	0.70422	160.917	.3167
275.00	0.46303	162.534	.3277	275.00	0.58065	162.324	.3226	275.00	0.69905	162.113	.3184
280.00	0.45974	163.727	.3294	280.00	0.57647	163.520	.3242	280.00	0.69395	163.312	.3200

Standard state : At -40°F, Liquid Enthalpy=0.0 Btu/lb, Liquid Entropy=0.0 Btu/lb.F

Version 2a 1st September 1993

KLEA® 407A

Superheated Vapor Properties

Table 2 Sheet 5

70.0 psia, Dew Point = 30.05 °F				80.0 psia, Dew Point = 37.09 °F				90.0 psia, Dew Point = 43.49 °F			
Temp °F	Density lb/ft³	Enthalpy btu/lb	Entropy btu/lb.R	Temp °F	Density lb/ft³	Enthalpy btu/lb	Entropy btu/lb.R	Temp °F	Density lb/ft³	Enthalpy btu/lb	Entropy btu/lb.R
40.00	1.29139	109.539	.2290	40.00	1.49896	110.058	.2274				
45.00	1.27457	110.527	.2310	45.00	1.47852	111.060	.2294	45.00	1.68943	110.588	.2262
50.00	1.25826	111.519	.2330	50.00	1.45876	112.066	.2314	50.00	1.66578	111.604	.2282
55.00	1.24244	112.514	.2350	55.00	1.43963	113.074	.2334	55.00	1.64294	112.623	.2302
60.00	1.22709	113.514	.2369	60.00	1.42109	114.087	.2353	60.00	1.62087	113.646	.2321
65.00	1.21218	114.517	.2389	65.00	1.40312	115.103	.2373	65.00	1.59951	114.671	.2341
70.00	1.19768	115.524	.2408	70.00	1.38569	116.123	.2392	70.00	1.57884	115.700	.2361
75.00	1.18359	116.536	.2427	75.00	1.36877	117.147	.2411	75.00	1.55881	116.733	.2380
80.00	1.16987	117.551	.2446	80.00	1.35233	118.174	.2430	80.00	1.53938	117.769	.2399
85.00	1.15652	118.571	.2465	85.00	1.33636	119.206	.2450	85.00	1.52054	118.808	.2418
90.00	1.14352	119.595	.2484	90.00	1.32082	120.242	.2468	90.00	1.50224	119.852	.2437
95.00	1.13085	120.624	.2503	95.00	1.30570	121.281	.2487	95.00	1.48446	120.899	.2456
100.00	1.11849	121.656	.2521	100.00	1.29098	122.325	.2506	100.00	1.46717	121.949	.2475
105.00	1.10644	122.693	.2540	105.00	1.27664	123.373	.2525	105.00	1.45036	123.004	.2494
110.00	1.09469	123.735	.2559	110.00	1.26267	124.425	.2543	110.00	1.43399	124.063	.2513
115.00	1.08321	124.781	.2577	115.00	1.24904	125.481	.2562	115.00	1.41805	125.126	.2531
120.00	1.07200	125.831	.2595	120.00	1.23575	126.542	.2580	120.00	1.40253	126.192	.2550
125.00	1.06106	126.886	.2614	125.00	1.22279	127.607	.2598	125.00	1.38739	127.263	.2568
130.00	1.05036	127.945	.2632	130.00	1.21013	128.676	.2617	130.00	1.37264	128.338	.2586
135.00	1.03990	129.008	.2650	135.00	1.19776	129.749	.2635	135.00	1.35824	129.417	.2605
140.00	1.02967	130.077	.2668	140.00	1.18568	130.827	.2653	140.00	1.34419	130.500	.2623
145.00	1.01967	131.149	.2686	145.00	1.17388	131.909	.2671	145.00	1.33046	131.588	.2641
150.00	1.00988	132.226	.2704	150.00	1.16233	132.996	.2689	150.00	1.31706	132.680	.2659
155.00	1.00029	133.308	.2722	155.00	1.15104	134.088	.2706	155.00	1.30396	133.777	.2677
160.00	0.99091	134.395	.2739	160.00	1.14000	135.185	.2724	160.00	1.29116	134.879	.2695
165.00	0.98172	135.488	.2757	165.00	1.12919	136.286	.2742	165.00	1.27865	135.985	.2712
170.00	0.97272	136.584	.2775	170.00	1.11862	137.392	.2760	170.00	1.26641	137.095	.2730
175.00	0.96390	137.685	.2792	175.00	1.10826	138.503	.2777	175.00	1.25443	138.211	.2748
180.00	0.95526	138.792	.2810	180.00	1.09811	139.619	.2795	180.00	1.24271	139.332	.2765
185.00	0.94678	139.904	.2827	185.00	1.08818	140.740	.2812	185.00	1.23123	140.457	.2783

Standard state : At -40°F, Liquid Enthalpy=0.0 Btu/lb, Liquid Entropy=0.0 Btu/lb.F

Version 2a 1st September 1993

KLEA® 407A

Superheated Vapor Properties

Table 2 Sheet 6

70.0 psia, Dew Point = 30.05 °F				80.0 psia, Dew Point = 37.09 °F				90.0 psia, Dew Point = 43.49 °F			
Temp °F	Density lb/ft³	Enthalpy btu/lb	Entropy btu/lb.R	Temp °F	Density lb/ft³	Enthalpy btu/lb	Entropy btu/lb.R	Temp °F	Density lb/ft³	Enthalpy btu/lb	Entropy btu/lb.R
190.00	0.93848	142.140	.2862	190.00	1.07844	141.865	.2829	190.00	1.22000	141.587	.2800
195.00	0.93033	143.266	.2879	195.00	1.06890	142.994	.2847	195.00	1.20899	142.720	.2818
200.00	0.92233	144.395	.2896	200.00	1.05954	144.128	.2864	200.00	1.19821	143.858	.2835
205.00	0.91449	145.530	.2914	205.00	1.05036	145.266	.2881	205.00	1.18764	145.001	.2852
210.00	0.90679	146.669	.2931	210.00	1.04136	146.409	.2898	210.00	1.17728	146.148	.2869
215.00	0.89923	147.812	.2948	215.00	1.03253	147.557	.2915	215.00	1.16712	147.299	.2887
220.00	0.89181	148.962	.2965	220.00	1.02386	148.710	.2932	220.00	1.15716	148.457	.2904
225.00	0.88452	150.116	.2982	225.00	1.01536	149.868	.2949	225.00	1.14739	149.619	.2921
230.00	0.87736	151.274	.2998	230.00	1.00701	151.030	.2966	230.00	1.13780	150.785	.2938
235.00	0.87033	152.437	.3015	235.00	0.99881	152.197	.2983	235.00	1.12839	151.955	.2955
240.00	0.86342	153.605	.3032	240.00	0.99076	153.368	.3000	240.00	1.11915	153.130	.2971
245.00	0.85663	154.777	.3049	245.00	0.98285	154.544	.3017	245.00	1.11008	154.309	.2988
250.00	0.84996	155.953	.3065	250.00	0.97508	155.723	.3033	250.00	1.10117	155.493	.3005
255.00	0.84340	157.134	.3082	255.00	0.96745	156.908	.3050	255.00	1.09243	156.680	.3022
260.00	0.83694	158.319	.3098	260.00	0.95994	158.096	.3067	260.00	1.08383	157.872	.3038
265.00	0.83060	159.508	.3115	265.00	0.95256	159.289	.3083	265.00	1.07539	159.068	.3055
270.00	0.82436	160.702	.3131	270.00	0.94531	160.486	.3100	270.00	1.06708	160.269	.3071
275.00	0.81821	161.901	.3148	275.00	0.93817	161.688	.3116	275.00	1.05892	161.474	.3088
280.00	0.81217	163.103	.3164	280.00	0.93115	162.893	.3132	280.00	1.05090	162.683	.3104
285.00	0.80622	164.310	.3180	285.00	0.92425	164.104	.3149	285.00	1.04301	163.896	.3121
290.00	0.80037	165.522	.3196	290.00	0.91746	165.318	.3165	290.00	1.03525	165.113	.3137
295.00	0.79461	166.738	.3213	295.00	0.91077	166.537	.3181	295.00	1.02762	166.335	.3153
300.00	0.78893	167.958	.3229	300.00	0.90419	167.760	.3197	300.00	1.02010	167.561	.3169
305.00	0.78335	169.182	.3245	305.00	0.89771	168.987	.3213	305.00	1.01271	168.791	.3185
310.00	0.77784	170.411	.3261	310.00	0.89134	170.219	.3229	310.00	1.00544	170.026	.3202

Standard state : At -40°F, Liquid Enthalpy=0.0 Btu/lb, Liquid Entropy=0.0 Btu/lb.F

Version 2a   1st September 1993

KLEA® 407A

Superheated Vapor Properties

Table 2 Sheet 7

100.0psia Dew Point = 49.36 °F				130.0 psia Dew Point = 64.64 °F				160.0 psia Dew Point = 77.41 °F			
Temp °F	Density lb/ft³	Enthalpy btu/lb	Entropy btu/lb.R	Temp °F	Density lb/ft³	Enthalpy btu/lb	Entropy btu/lb.R	Temp °F	Density lb/ft³	Enthalpy btu/lb	Entropy btu/lb.R
50.00	1.87994	111.128	.2252								
55.00	1.85294	112.159	.2272								
60.00	1.82691	113.192	.2292								
65.00	1.80179	114.228	.2312	65.00	2.44937	112.818	.2235				
70.00	1.77752	115.267	.2331	70.00	2.41162	113.892	.2255				
75.00	1.75406	116.309	.2351	75.00	2.37539	114.968	.2275				
80.00	1.73135	117.354	.2371	80.00	2.34058	116.045	.2295	80.00	3.01042	114.620	.2230
85.00	1.70935	118.402	.2390	85.00	2.30708	117.123	.2315	85.00	2.96110	115.738	.2251
90.00	1.68803	119.453	.2409	90.00	2.27482	118.203	.2335	90.00	2.91399	116.855	.2271
95.00	1.66735	120.508	.2428	95.00	2.24370	119.286	.2354	95.00	2.86891	117.972	.2291
100.00	1.64728	121.567	.2447	100.00	2.21367	120.370	.2374	100.00	2.82570	119.090	.2311
105.00	1.62778	122.629	.2466	105.00	2.18464	121.457	.2393	105.00	2.78422	120.208	.2331
110.00	1.60884	123.695	.2485	110.00	2.15657	122.547	.2413	110.00	2.74435	121.327	.2351
115.00	1.59041	124.764	.2504	115.00	2.12939	123.640	.2432	115.00	2.70598	122.448	.2371
120.00	1.57248	125.837	.2522	120.00	2.10306	124.735	.2451	120.00	2.66900	123.569	.2390
125.00	1.55502	126.914	.2541	125.00	2.07753	125.833	.2469	125.00	2.63332	124.693	.2409
130.00	1.53802	127.995	.2559	130.00	2.05277	126.935	.2488	130.00	2.59887	125.819	.2429
135.00	1.52145	129.080	.2577	135.00	2.02872	128.039	.2507	135.00	2.56557	126.946	.2448
140.00	1.50529	130.169	.2596	140.00	2.00535	129.147	.2525	140.00	2.53336	128.076	.2467
145.00	1.48953	131.262	.2614	145.00	1.98264	130.258	.2544	145.00	2.50216	129.209	.2485
150.00	1.47415	132.359	.2632	150.00	1.96054	131.373	.2562	150.00	2.47193	130.344	.2504
155.00	1.45914	133.462	.2650	155.00	1.93904	132.493	.2581	155.00	2.44261	131.484	.2523
160.00	1.44447	134.569	.2668	160.00	1.91810	133.617	.2599	160.00	2.41416	132.628	.2541
165.00	1.43015	135.680	.2686	165.00	1.89770	134.745	.2617	165.00	2.38653	133.774	.2560
170.00	1.41615	136.796	.2703	170.00	1.87782	135.876	.2635	170.00	2.35969	134.923	.2578
175.00	1.40247	137.916	.2721	175.00	1.85843	137.012	.2653	175.00	2.33359	136.077	.2596
180.00	1.38909	139.042	.2739	180.00	1.83952	138.154	.2671	180.00	2.30820	137.236	.2614
185.00	1.37600	140.172	.2756	185.00	1.82107	139.299	.2689	185.00	2.28350	138.398	.2632
190.00	1.36319	141.306	.2774	190.00	1.80306	140.447	.2706	190.00	2.25944	139.563	.2650
195.00	1.35065	142.444	.2791	195.00	1.78546	141.600	.2724	195.00	2.23600	140.732	.2668

Standard state : At -40°F, Liquid Enthalpy=0.0 Btu/lb, Liquid Entropy=0.0 Btu/lb.F

KLEA® 407A

Superheated Vapor Properties

Table 2 Sheet 8

100.0psia Dew Point = 49.36 °F				130.0 psia Dew Point = 64.64 °F				160.0 psia Dew Point = 77.41 °F			
Temp °F	Density lb/ft³	Enthalpy btu/lb	Entropy btu/lb.R	Temp °F	Density lb/ft³	Enthalpy btu/lb	Entropy btu/lb.R	Temp °F	Density lb/ft³	Enthalpy btu/lb	Entropy btu/lb.R
200.00	1.33838	143.587	.2809	200.00	1.76827	142.756	.2742	200.00	2.21316	141.903	.2686
205.00	1.32635	144.733	.2826	205.00	1.75147	143.917	.2759	205.00	2.19088	143.078	.2704
210.00	1.31457	145.884	.2843	210.00	1.73504	145.080	.2777	210.00	2.16914	144.257	.2722
215.00	1.30303	147.040	.2861	215.00	1.71897	146.249	.2794	215.00	2.14792	145.440	.2739
220.00	1.29171	148.201	.2878	220.00	1.70325	147.424	.2811	220.00	2.12720	146.629	.2757
225.00	1.28062	149.368	.2895	225.00	1.68786	148.603	.2829	225.00	2.10697	147.822	.2774
230.00	1.26975	150.538	.2912	230.00	1.67280	149.786	.2846	230.00	2.08720	149.019	.2792
235.00	1.25908	151.712	.2929	235.00	1.65805	150.973	.2863	235.00	2.06787	150.219	.2809
240.00	1.24861	152.891	.2946	240.00	1.64361	152.164	.2880	240.00	2.04897	151.422	.2826
245.00	1.23834	154.074	.2963	245.00	1.62945	153.358	.2897	245.00	2.03049	152.629	.2843
250.00	1.22825	155.261	.2979	250.00	1.61558	154.557	.2914	250.00	2.01240	153.840	.2861
255.00	1.21835	156.452	.2996	255.00	1.60198	155.759	.2931	255.00	1.99469	155.054	.2878
260.00	1.20863	157.647	.3013	260.00	1.58864	156.965	.2948	260.00	1.97735	156.272	.2895
265.00	1.19908	158.847	.3029	265.00	1.57556	158.176	.2964	265.00	1.96037	157.494	.2912
270.00	1.18970	160.051	.3046	270.00	1.56272	159.390	.2981	270.00	1.94373	158.719	.2928
275.00	1.18049	161.259	.3062	275.00	1.55012	160.608	.2998	275.00	1.92742	159.948	.2945
280.00	1.17143	162.471	.3079	280.00	1.53776	161.830	.3014	280.00	1.91144	161.181	.2962
285.00	1.16252	163.687	.3095	285.00	1.52561	163.056	.3031	285.00	1.89576	162.417	.2979
290.00	1.15376	164.908	.3112	290.00	1.51369	164.286	.3047	290.00	1.88038	163.657	.2995
295.00	1.14515	166.133	.3128	295.00	1.50198	165.520	.3064	295.00	1.86529	164.901	.3012
300.00	1.13668	167.362	.3144	300.00	1.49047	166.759	.3080	300.00	1.85048	166.149	.3028
305.00	1.12835	168.595	.3160	305.00	1.47916	168.001	.3096	305.00	1.83595	167.400	.3045
310.00	1.12015	169.832	.3176	310.00	1.46805	169.247	.3113	310.00	1.82168	168.655	.3061
315.00	1.11209	171.073	.3192	315.00	1.45712	170.497	.3129	315.00	1.80766	169.914	.3077
320.00	1.10415	172.319	.3208	320.00	1.44637	171.751	.3145	320.00	1.79389	171.177	.3094
325.00	1.09633	173.569	.3224	325.00	1.43581	173.009	.3161	325.00	1.78036	172.444	.3110

Standard state : At -40°F, Liquid Enthalpy=0.0 Btu/lb, Liquid Entropy=0.0 Btu/lb.F

Version 2a 1st September 1993

KLEA® 407A

Superheated Vapor Properties

Table 2 Sheet 9

190.0psia Dew Point = 88.46 °F				220.0 psia Dew Point = 98.23 °F				250.0 psia Dew Point = 107.02 °F			
Temp °F	Density lb/ft³	Enthalpy btu/lb	Entropy btu/lb.R	Temp °F	Density lb/ft³	Enthalpy btu/lb	Entropy btu/lb.R	Temp °F	Density lb/ft³	Enthalpy btu/lb	Entropy btu/lb.R
90.00	3.62046	115.380	.2213								
95.00	3.55598	116.544	.2234								
100.00	3.49478	117.704	.2255	100.00	4.23789	116.182	.2202				
105.00	3.43654	118.862	.2276	105.00	4.15618	117.393	.2224				
110.00	3.38102	120.018	.2296	110.00	4.07913	118.599	.2245	110.00	4.85771	117.034	.2196
115.00	3.32797	121.174	.2316	115.00	4.00627	119.799	.2266	115.00	4.75688	118.295	.2218
120.00	3.27720	122.329	.2336	120.00	3.93717	120.996	.2287	120.00	4.66247	119.547	.2239
125.00	3.22854	123.483	.2356	125.00	3.87147	122.190	.2307	125.00	4.57372	120.792	.2261
130.00	3.18182	124.638	.2376	130.00	3.80888	123.381	.2327	130.00	4.49001	122.029	.2282
135.00	3.13691	125.794	.2395	135.00	3.74913	124.571	.2348	135.00	4.41082	123.262	.2303
140.00	3.09369	126.950	.2415	140.00	3.69198	125.759	.2367	140.00	4.33569	124.490	.2323
145.00	3.05203	128.108	.2434	145.00	3.63723	126.947	.2387	145.00	4.26425	125.715	.2343
150.00	3.01183	129.267	.2453	150.00	3.58469	128.134	.2407	150.00	4.19616	126.937	.2364
155.00	2.97302	130.430	.2472	155.00	3.53421	129.325	.2426	155.00	4.13115	128.160	.2384
160.00	2.93551	131.596	.2491	160.00	3.48566	130.517	.2446	160.00	4.06897	129.384	.2403
165.00	2.89922	132.764	.2510	165.00	3.43890	131.710	.2465	165.00	4.00941	130.606	.2423
170.00	2.86409	133.934	.2528	170.00	3.39381	132.904	.2484	170.00	3.95226	131.828	.2443
175.00	2.83004	135.108	.2547	175.00	3.35029	134.101	.2503	175.00	3.89736	133.051	.2462
180.00	2.79703	136.287	.2565	180.00	3.30825	135.302	.2522	180.00	3.84454	134.278	.2481
185.00	2.76500	137.468	.2584	185.00	3.26760	136.504	.2540	185.00	3.79368	135.504	.2500
190.00	2.73391	138.651	.2602	190.00	3.22827	137.708	.2559	190.00	3.74465	136.731	.2519
195.00	2.70369	139.837	.2620	195.00	3.19017	138.914	.2577	195.00	3.69732	137.959	.2538
200.00	2.67432	141.026	.2638	200.00	3.15324	140.121	.2596	200.00	3.65159	139.188	.2557
205.00	2.64575	142.217	.2656	205.00	3.11741	141.331	.2614	205.00	3.60737	140.417	.2575
210.00	2.61793	143.411	.2674	210.00	3.08262	142.542	.2632	210.00	3.56457	141.648	.2594
215.00	2.59085	144.610	.2692	215.00	3.04883	143.758	.2650	215.00	3.52310	142.882	.2612
220.00	2.56446	145.815	.2710	220.00	3.01599	144.980	.2668	220.00	3.48291	144.123	.2630
225.00	2.53874	147.023	.2728	225.00	2.98406	146.205	.2686	225.00	3.44392	145.366	.2649
230.00	2.51366	148.234	.2745	230.00	2.95299	147.432	.2704	230.00	3.40608	146.610	.2667
235.00	2.48919	149.448	.2763	235.00	2.92274	148.661	.2722	235.00	3.36933	147.857	.2685

Standard state : At -40°F, Liquid Enthalpy=0.0 Btu/lb, Liquid Entropy=0.0 Btu/lb.F

KLEA® 407A

Superheated Vapor Properties

Table 2 Sheet 10

190.0psia Dew Point = 88.46 °F				220.0 psia Dew Point = 98.23 °F				250.0 psia Dew Point = 107.02 °F			
Temp °F	Density lb/ft³	Enthalpy btu/lb	Entropy btu/lb.R	Temp °F	Density lb/ft³	Enthalpy btu/lb	Entropy btu/lb.R	Temp °F	Density lb/ft³	Enthalpy btu/lb	Entropy btu/lb.R
240.00	2.46531	150.666	.2780	240.00	2.89328	149.894	.2739	240.00	3.33360	149.105	.2703
245.00	2.44199	151.886	.2798	245.00	2.86457	151.129	.2757	245.00	3.29886	150.356	.2720
250.00	2.41921	153.110	.2815	250.00	2.83657	152.366	.2775	250.00	3.26504	151.608	.2738
255.00	2.39695	154.337	.2832	255.00	2.80925	153.607	.2792	255.00	3.23212	152.863	.2756
260.00	2.37519	155.567	.2849	260.00	2.78259	154.850	.2809	260.00	3.20004	154.121	.2773
265.00	2.35390	156.801	.2866	265.00	2.75656	156.097	.2827	265.00	3.16877	155.381	.2791
270.00	2.33308	158.038	.2883	270.00	2.73114	157.346	.2844	270.00	3.13828	156.643	.2808
275.00	2.31270	159.278	.2900	275.00	2.70629	158.598	.2861	275.00	3.10853	157.908	.2825
280.00	2.29275	160.522	.2917	280.00	2.68199	159.854	.2878	280.00	3.07949	159.176	.2843
285.00	2.27321	161.769	.2934	285.00	2.65824	161.112	.2895	285.00	3.05112	160.447	.2860
290.00	2.25406	163.020	.2951	290.00	2.63499	162.374	.2912	290.00	3.02341	161.720	.2877
295.00	2.23531	164.274	.2967	295.00	2.61224	163.639	.2929	295.00	2.99633	162.997	.2894
300.00	2.21692	165.532	.2984	300.00	2.58997	164.908	.2945	300.00	2.96985	164.276	.2911
305.00	2.19889	166.793	.3001	305.00	2.56816	166.179	.2962	305.00	2.94394	165.558	.2928
310.00	2.18120	168.058	.3017	310.00	2.54679	167.454	.2979	310.00	2.91859	166.844	.2944
315.00	2.16386	169.326	.3033	315.00	2.52585	168.732	.2995	315.00	2.89378	168.132	.2961
320.00	2.14683	170.598	.3050	320.00	2.50532	170.014	.3012	320.00	2.86949	169.423	.2978
325.00	2.13012	171.874	.3066	325.00	2.48519	171.298	.3028	325.00	2.84569	170.718	.2994
330.00	2.11372	173.153	.3082	330.00	2.46545	172.587	.3044	330.00	2.82238	172.016	.3011
335.00	2.09761	174.436	.3099	335.00	2.44608	173.878	.3061	335.00	2.79953	173.317	.3027
340.00	2.08178	175.722	.3115	340.00	2.42708	175.173	.3077	340.00	2.77712	174.621	.3043
345.00	2.06623	177.012	.3131	345.00	2.40842	176.472	.3093	345.00	2.75515	175.928	.3060
350.00	2.05096	178.306	.3147	350.00	2.39010	177.774	.3109	350.00	2.73360	177.239	.3076
355.00	2.03594	179.603	.3163	355.00	2.37212	179.080	.3125	355.00	2.71245	178.552	.3092
360.00	2.02118	180.904	.3179	360.00	2.35445	180.388	.3141	360.00	2.69170	179.870	.3108
365.00	2.00666	182.209	.3195	365.00	2.33709	181.701	.3157	365.00	2.67133	181.190	.3124

Standard state : At -40°F, Liquid Enthalpy=0.0 Btu/lb, Liquid Entropy=0.0 Btu/lb.F

Version 2a 1st September 1993

KLEA® 407A

Superheated Vapor Properties

Table 2 Sheet 11

280.0psia
Dew Point = 115.03 °F

Temp °F	Density lb/ft³	Enthalpy btu/lb	Entropy btu/lb.R
120.00	5.47381	117.947	.2193
125.00	5.35241	119.259	.2215
130.00	5.23951	120.559	.2237
135.00	5.13401	121.847	.2259
140.00	5.03501	123.126	.2281
145.00	4.94178	124.397	.2302
150.00	4.85370	125.662	.2323
155.00	4.77025	126.926	.2343
160.00	4.69101	128.187	.2364
165.00	4.61559	129.444	.2384
170.00	4.54365	130.698	.2404
175.00	4.47491	131.953	.2424
180.00	4.40913	133.209	.2443
185.00	4.34608	134.463	.2463
190.00	4.28555	135.717	.2482
195.00	4.22736	136.970	.2501
200.00	4.17136	138.222	.2521
205.00	4.11739	139.474	.2539
210.00	4.06531	140.727	.2558
215.00	4.01503	141.982	.2577
220.00	3.96643	143.243	.2596
225.00	3.91942	144.506	.2614
230.00	3.87391	145.769	.2632
235.00	3.82981	147.033	.2651
240.00	3.78706	148.299	.2669
245.00	3.74556	149.566	.2687
250.00	3.70527	150.835	.2705
255.00	3.66611	152.106	.2723
260.00	3.62804	153.378	.2740
265.00	3.59099	154.652	.2758

310.0 psia
Dew Point = 122.39 °F

Temp °F	Density lb/ft³	Enthalpy btu/lb	Entropy btu/lb.R
125.00	6.23475	117.546	.2170
130.00	6.07921	118.932	.2193
135.00	5.93645	120.296	.2216
140.00	5.80453	121.643	.2239
145.00	5.68193	122.974	.2261
150.00	5.56742	124.293	.2283
155.00	5.46004	125.607	.2304
160.00	5.35900	126.915	.2325
165.00	5.26360	128.214	.2346
170.00	5.17327	129.507	.2367
175.00	5.08753	130.799	.2387
180.00	5.00597	132.089	.2407
185.00	4.92822	133.377	.2427
190.00	4.85396	134.660	.2447
195.00	4.78291	135.942	.2467
200.00	4.71482	137.221	.2486
205.00	4.64946	138.499	.2506
210.00	4.58664	139.775	.2525
215.00	4.52617	141.053	.2544
220.00	4.46793	142.338	.2563
225.00	4.41177	143.622	.2582
230.00	4.35756	144.906	.2600
235.00	4.30517	146.190	.2619
240.00	4.25450	147.474	.2637
245.00	4.20545	148.760	.2656
250.00	4.15792	150.046	.2674
255.00	4.11184	151.333	.2692
260.00	4.06712	152.622	.2710
265.00	4.02369	153.911	.2728

340.0 psia
Dew Point = 129.20 °F

Temp °F	Density lb/ft³	Enthalpy btu/lb	Entropy btu/lb.R
130.00	7.04549	117.087	.2147
135.00	6.84627	118.562	.2172
140.00	6.66641	120.003	.2196
145.00	6.50241	121.416	.2220
150.00	6.35170	122.807	.2243
155.00	6.21230	124.186	.2265
160.00	6.08268	125.552	.2288
165.00	5.96158	126.904	.2309
170.00	5.84796	128.245	.2331
175.00	5.74098	129.580	.2352
180.00	5.63997	130.912	.2373
185.00	5.54431	132.237	.2393
190.00	5.45350	133.557	.2414
195.00	5.36708	134.871	.2434
200.00	5.28467	136.181	.2454
205.00	5.20594	137.487	.2474
210.00	5.13058	138.791	.2493
215.00	5.05833	140.095	.2512
220.00	4.98899	141.405	.2532
225.00	4.92235	142.712	.2551
230.00	4.85823	144.019	.2570
235.00	4.79646	145.325	.2589
240.00	4.73688	146.630	.2608
245.00	4.67934	147.935	.2626
250.00	4.62374	149.240	.2645
255.00	4.56995	150.545	.2663
260.00	4.51786	151.851	.2681
265.00	4.46739	153.157	.2699

Standard state : At -40°F, Liquid Enthalpy=0.0 Btu/lb, Liquid Entropy=0.0 Btu/lb.F

Version 2a 1st September 1993

KLEA® 407A

Superheated Vapor Properties

Table 2 Sheet 12

280.0psia Dew Point = 115.03 °F				310.0 psia Dew Point = 122.39 °F				340.0 psia Dew Point = 129.20 °F			
Temp °F	Density lb/ft³	Enthalpy btu/lb	Entropy btu/lb.R	Temp °F	Density lb/ft³	Enthalpy btu/lb	Entropy btu/lb.R	Temp °F	Density lb/ft³	Enthalpy btu/lb	Entropy btu/lb.R
270.00	3.55492	155.929	.2776	270.00	3.98149	155.203	.2745	270.00	4.41843	154.465	.2717
275.00	3.51979	157.208	.2793	275.00	3.94045	156.496	.2763	275.00	4.37092	155.773	.2735
280.00	3.48555	158.489	.2810	280.00	3.90053	157.791	.2781	280.00	4.32477	157.083	.2753
285.00	3.45216	159.772	.2828	285.00	3.86165	159.088	.2798	285.00	4.27992	158.394	.2770
290.00	3.41959	161.058	.2845	290.00	3.82379	160.386	.2816	290.00	4.23630	159.706	.2788
295.00	3.38780	162.346	.2862	295.00	3.78689	161.687	.2833	295.00	4.19385	161.020	.2806
300.00	3.35675	163.637	.2879	300.00	3.75090	162.990	.2850	300.00	4.15252	162.336	.2823
305.00	3.32642	164.931	.2896	305.00	3.71580	164.296	.2867	305.00	4.11225	163.654	.2840
310.00	3.29679	166.227	.2913	310.00	3.68153	165.603	.2884	310.00	4.07300	164.973	.2857
315.00	3.26781	167.526	.2930	315.00	3.64807	166.914	.2901	315.00	4.03472	166.295	.2875
320.00	3.23947	168.828	.2947	320.00	3.61539	168.226	.2918	320.00	3.99738	167.619	.2892
325.00	3.21174	170.132	.2963	325.00	3.58344	169.541	.2935	325.00	3.96092	168.945	.2909
330.00	3.18460	171.440	.2980	330.00	3.55221	170.859	.2952	330.00	3.92531	170.273	.2925
335.00	3.15802	172.750	.2996	335.00	3.52166	172.179	.2968	335.00	3.89053	171.604	.2942
340.00	3.13200	174.064	.3013	340.00	3.49177	173.502	.2985	340.00	3.85653	172.937	.2959
345.00	3.10650	175.380	.3029	345.00	3.46252	174.828	.3001	345.00	3.82328	174.273	.2976
350.00	3.08151	176.700	.3046	350.00	3.43387	176.157	.3018	350.00	3.79076	175.611	.2992
355.00	3.05701	178.022	.3062	355.00	3.40582	177.488	.3034	355.00	3.75894	176.952	.3009
360.00	3.03298	179.348	.3078	360.00	3.37833	178.823	.3051	360.00	3.72778	178.295	.3025
365.00	3.00942	180.676	.3094	365.00	3.35139	180.160	.3067	365.00	3.69728	179.641	.3041
370.00	2.98630	182.008	.3110	370.00	3.32498	181.500	.3083	370.00	3.66740	180.990	.3058
375.00	2.96360	183.343	.3126	375.00	3.29908	182.843	.3099	375.00	3.63812	182.341	.3074
380.00	2.94133	184.682	.3142	380.00	3.27368	184.190	.3115	380.00	3.60942	183.695	.3090
385.00	2.91946	186.023	.3158	385.00	3.24875	185.539	.3131	385.00	3.58129	185.052	.3106
390.00	2.89797	187.368	.3174	390.00	3.22429	186.891	.3147	390.00	3.55369	186.412	.3122
395.00	2.87687	188.716	.3190	395.00	3.20027	188.246	.3163	395.00	3.52662	187.775	.3138

Standard state : At -40°F, Liquid Enthalpy=0.0 Btu/lb, Liquid Entropy=0.0 Btu/lb.F

Version 2a 1st September 1993

KLEA® 407A

Superheated Vapor Properties

Table 2 Sheet 13

370.0psia Dew Point = 135.55 °F				400.0 psia Dew Point = 141.5 °F				430.0 psia Dew Point = 147.1 °F			
Temp °F	Density lb/ft³	Enthalpy btu/lb	Entropy btu/lb.R	Temp °F	Density lb/ft³	Enthalpy btu/lb	Entropy btu/lb.R	Temp °F	Density lb/ft³	Enthalpy btu/lb	Entropy btu/lb.R
140.00	7.65730	118.145	.2153								
145.00	7.43105	119.677	.2178	145.00	8.51611	117.678	.2133				
150.00	7.22809	121.169	.2203	150.00	8.23158	119.321	.2160	150.00	9.42631	117.158	.2115
155.00	7.04403	122.635	.2226	155.00	7.98137	120.911	.2186	155.00	9.06838	118.943	.2144
160.00	6.87567	124.076	.2250	160.00	7.75797	122.456	.2211	160.00	8.76117	120.642	.2171
165.00	6.72055	125.495	.2273	165.00	7.55613	123.965	.2236	165.00	8.49169	122.275	.2198
170.00	6.57674	126.896	.2295	170.00	7.37202	125.443	.2259	170.00	8.25151	123.857	.2223
175.00	6.44274	128.286	.2317	175.00	7.20278	126.900	.2282	175.00	8.03482	125.403	.2247
180.00	6.31736	129.668	.2339	180.00	7.04626	128.344	.2305	180.00	7.83747	126.924	.2271
185.00	6.19959	131.038	.2360	185.00	6.90072	129.769	.2327	185.00	7.65633	128.417	.2294
190.00	6.08859	132.399	.2381	190.00	6.76474	131.179	.2349	190.00	7.48896	129.888	.2317
195.00	5.98364	133.751	.2402	195.00	6.63718	132.577	.2370	195.00	7.33344	131.340	.2339
200.00	5.88414	135.097	.2422	200.00	6.51709	133.964	.2391	200.00	7.18823	132.775	.2361
205.00	5.78958	136.437	.2442	205.00	6.40366	135.342	.2412	205.00	7.05209	134.197	.2383
210.00	5.69951	137.771	.2462	210.00	6.29622	136.711	.2433	210.00	6.92398	135.608	.2404
215.00	5.61355	139.104	.2482	215.00	6.19420	138.077	.2453	215.00	6.80304	137.011	.2425
220.00	5.53138	140.442	.2502	220.00	6.09713	139.447	.2473	220.00	6.68859	138.416	.2445
225.00	5.45272	141.776	.2522	225.00	6.00461	140.810	.2493	225.00	6.58001	139.813	.2466
230.00	5.37729	143.108	.2541	230.00	5.91624	142.170	.2513	230.00	6.47676	141.203	.2486
235.00	5.30486	144.437	.2560	235.00	5.83168	143.525	.2533	235.00	6.37837	142.587	.2506
240.00	5.23521	145.765	.2579	240.00	5.75064	144.877	.2552	240.00	6.28442	143.966	.2526
245.00	5.16816	147.091	.2598	245.00	5.67287	146.227	.2571	245.00	6.19455	145.341	.2545
250.00	5.10352	148.416	.2617	250.00	5.59811	147.574	.2590	250.00	6.10844	146.712	.2565
255.00	5.04114	149.741	.2635	255.00	5.52616	148.920	.2609	255.00	6.02581	148.081	.2584
260.00	4.98088	151.065	.2654	260.00	5.45683	150.264	.2628	260.00	5.94641	149.446	.2603
265.00	4.92262	152.389	.2672	265.00	5.38996	151.607	.2647	265.00	5.87000	150.810	.2622
270.00	4.86623	153.714	.2691	270.00	5.32537	152.949	.2665	270.00	5.79640	152.171	.2641
275.00	4.81160	155.038	.2709	275.00	5.26295	154.291	.2683	275.00	5.72541	153.532	.2659
280.00	4.75865	156.363	.2727	280.00	5.20255	155.633	.2702	280.00	5.65686	154.891	.2678
285.00	4.70727	157.689	.2744	285.00	5.14406	156.975	.2720	285.00	5.59061	156.250	.2696

Standard state : At -40°F, Liquid Enthalpy=0.0 Btu/lb, Liquid Entropy=0.0 Btu/lb.F

KLEA® 407A

Superheated Vapor Properties

Table 2 Sheet 14

370.0psia Dew Point = 135.55 °F				400.0 psia Dew Point = 141.5 °F				430.0 psia Dew Point = 147.1 °F			
Temp °F	Density lb/ft³	Enthalpy btu/lb	Entropy btu/lb.R	Temp °F	Density lb/ft³	Enthalpy btu/lb	Entropy btu/lb.R	Temp °F	Density lb/ft³	Enthalpy btu/lb	Entropy btu/lb.R
290.00	4.65739	159.016	.2762	290.00	5.08737	158.317	.2738	290.00	5.52653	157.608	.2714
295.00	4.60893	160.344	.2780	295.00	5.03239	159.660	.2756	295.00	5.46447	158.967	.2732
300.00	4.56181	161.674	.2797	300.00	4.97901	161.003	.2773	300.00	5.40434	160.325	.2750
305.00	4.51598	163.004	.2815	305.00	4.92717	162.348	.2791	305.00	5.34602	161.683	.2768
310.00	4.47136	164.337	.2832	310.00	4.87678	163.693	.2808	310.00	5.28942	163.042	.2786
315.00	4.42791	165.670	.2850	315.00	4.82777	165.039	.2826	315.00	5.23445	164.402	.2803
320.00	4.38556	167.006	.2867	320.00	4.78007	166.387	.2843	320.00	5.18102	165.763	.2821
325.00	4.34428	168.343	.2884	325.00	4.73362	167.737	.2860	325.00	5.12906	167.124	.2838
330.00	4.30400	169.683	.2901	330.00	4.68837	169.087	.2878	330.00	5.07850	168.487	.2856
335.00	4.26470	171.024	.2918	335.00	4.64425	170.440	.2895	335.00	5.02927	169.851	.2873
340.00	4.22632	172.368	.2935	340.00	4.60123	171.794	.2912	340.00	4.98130	171.216	.2890
345.00	4.18884	173.713	.2951	345.00	4.55925	173.150	.2929	345.00	4.93455	172.583	.2907
350.00	4.15221	175.061	.2968	350.00	4.51826	174.508	.2945	350.00	4.88896	173.952	.2924
355.00	4.11639	176.411	.2985	355.00	4.47823	175.868	.2962	355.00	4.84447	175.322	.2941
360.00	4.08137	177.764	.3001	360.00	4.43912	177.230	.2979	360.00	4.80104	176.694	.2958
365.00	4.04710	179.119	.3018	365.00	4.40088	178.594	.2995	365.00	4.75863	178.067	.2974
370.00	4.01357	180.476	.3034	370.00	4.36350	179.961	.3012	370.00	4.71719	179.443	.2991
375.00	3.98073	181.836	.3050	375.00	4.32692	181.330	.3028	375.00	4.67669	180.821	.3008
380.00	3.94857	183.199	.3067	380.00	4.29113	182.701	.3045	380.00	4.63709	182.201	.3024
385.00	3.91707	184.564	.3083	385.00	4.25609	184.074	.3061	385.00	4.59835	183.583	.3040
390.00	3.88619	185.932	.3099	390.00	4.22178	185.451	.3077	390.00	4.56044	184.967	.3057
395.00	3.85592	187.303	.3115	395.00	4.18816	186.829	.3093	395.00	4.52333	186.354	.3073
400.00	3.82624	188.676	.3131	400.00	4.15522	188.210	.3110	400.00	4.48699	187.743	.3089
405.00	3.79713	190.052	.3147	405.00	4.12294	189.594	.3126	405.00	4.45139	189.134	.3105
410.00	3.76856	191.431	.3163	410.00	4.09128	190.980	.3142	410.00	4.41651	190.528	.3121
415.00	3.74053	192.813	.3179	415.00	4.06023	192.369	.3158	415.00	4.38232	191.924	.3137

Standard state : At -40°F, Liquid Enthalpy=0.0 Btu/lb, Liquid Entropy=0.0 Btu/lb.F

Version 2a 1st September 1993

TABLE 3

TABLE OF EVAPORATOR INLET TEMPERATURES

(1) Read the enthalpy value at the expansion valve along top of the table.

(2) Read down the table for the evaporator operating pressure.

(3) The value in the table is the evaporator inlet temperature in °F.

(4) The evaporator outlet temperature is the dew point temperature at the evaporator operating pressure.

KLEA® 407A

Evaporator Inlet Temperatures

Table 3 Sheet 1

Pressure psia	Enthalpy in btu/lb -5.00	0.00	5.00	10.00	15.00	20.00	25.00	30.00	35.00
	°F	°F	°F	°F	°F	°F	°F	°F	°F
10.00	-63.55	-63.15	-62.73	-62.28	-61.81	-61.31	-60.79	-60.24	-59.67
15.00		-48.97	-48.56	-48.12	-47.66	-47.18	-46.67	-46.14	-45.59
20.00			-37.74	-37.31	-36.86	-36.38	-35.89	-35.37	-34.83
25.00			-28.86	-28.44	-28.00	-27.53	-27.04	-26.53	-26.00
30.00			-24.36	-20.86	-20.42	-19.96	-19.48	-18.98	-18.45
35.00				-14.20	-13.77	-13.31	-12.84	-12.34	-11.82
40.00				-8.75	-7.82	-7.36	-6.89	-6.40	-5.88
45.00					-2.41	-1.96	-1.49	-1.00	-.49
50.00					2.55	3.00	3.46	3.95	4.46
55.00						7.59	8.05	8.54	9.04
60.00						11.87	12.33	12.81	13.31
65.00						15.89	16.35	16.83	17.32
70.00						19.68	20.13	20.61	21.10
75.00							23.72	24.19	24.68
80.00							27.13	27.60	28.09
85.00							30.38	30.85	31.33
90.00							33.48	33.95	34.44
95.00							36.46	36.93	37.41
100.00								39.78	40.27

KLEA® 407A

Superheated Vapor Properties

Table 3 Sheet 2

Pressure psia	Enthalpy in btu/lb 40.00	45.00	50.00	55.00	60.00	65.00	70.00	75.00	80.00
	°F	°F	°F	°F	°F	°F	°F	°F	°F
10.00	-59.07	-58.46	-57.82	-57.17	-56.50	-55.82	-55.14	-54.46	-53.78
15.00	-45.01	-44.42	-43.80	-43.16	-42.51	-41.85	-41.18	-40.51	-39.83
20.00	-34.27	-33.68	-33.08	-32.46	-31.82	-31.17	-30.51	-29.84	-29.17
25.00	-25.45	-24.87	-24.28	-23.67	-23.04	-22.40	-21.74	-21.08	-20.42
30.00	-17.91	-17.34	-16.75	-16.15	-15.53	-14.89	-14.25	-13.59	-12.93
35.00	-11.28	-10.72	-10.14	-9.55	-8.93	-8.30	-7.66	-7.01	-6.35
40.00	-5.35	-4.80	-4.22	-3.63	-3.02	-2.40	-1.76	-1.12	-.46
45.00	.04	.59	1.15	1.74	2.34	2.96	3.59	4.23	4.88
50.00	4.98	5.53	6.09	6.67	7.27	7.88	8.51	9.15	9.80
55.00	9.56	10.10	10.66	11.24	11.83	12.44	13.07	13.70	14.35
60.00	13.83	14.37	14.92	15.50	16.09	16.70	17.32	17.95	18.59
65.00	17.84	18.37	18.93	19.50	20.08	20.69	21.30	21.93	22.57
70.00	21.62	22.15	22.70	23.27	23.85	24.45	25.06	25.69	26.33
75.00	25.20	25.72	26.27	26.84	27.42	28.01	28.63	29.25	29.88
80.00	28.60	29.12	29.67	30.23	30.81	31.40	32.01	32.63	33.26
85.00	31.84	32.36	32.91	33.47	34.04	34.63	35.24	35.86	36.49
90.00	34.94	35.46	36.00	36.56	37.13	37.72	38.33	38.94	39.57
95.00	37.91	38.43	38.97	39.53	40.10	40.68	41.29	41.90	42.52
100.00	40.77	41.29	41.82	42.38	42.95	43.53	44.13	44.74	45.36

Notes

ICI Klea
Concord Plaza
3411 Silverside Road
P.O. Box 15391
Wilmington, DE 19850

Customer Service: (800) ICI-KLEA or
Technical Assistance: (800) ASK-KLEA
Fax: (302) 887-7706

620250371 3/95

407B

Thermodynamic Property Data for KLEA® 407B (KLEA® 61)

British Units

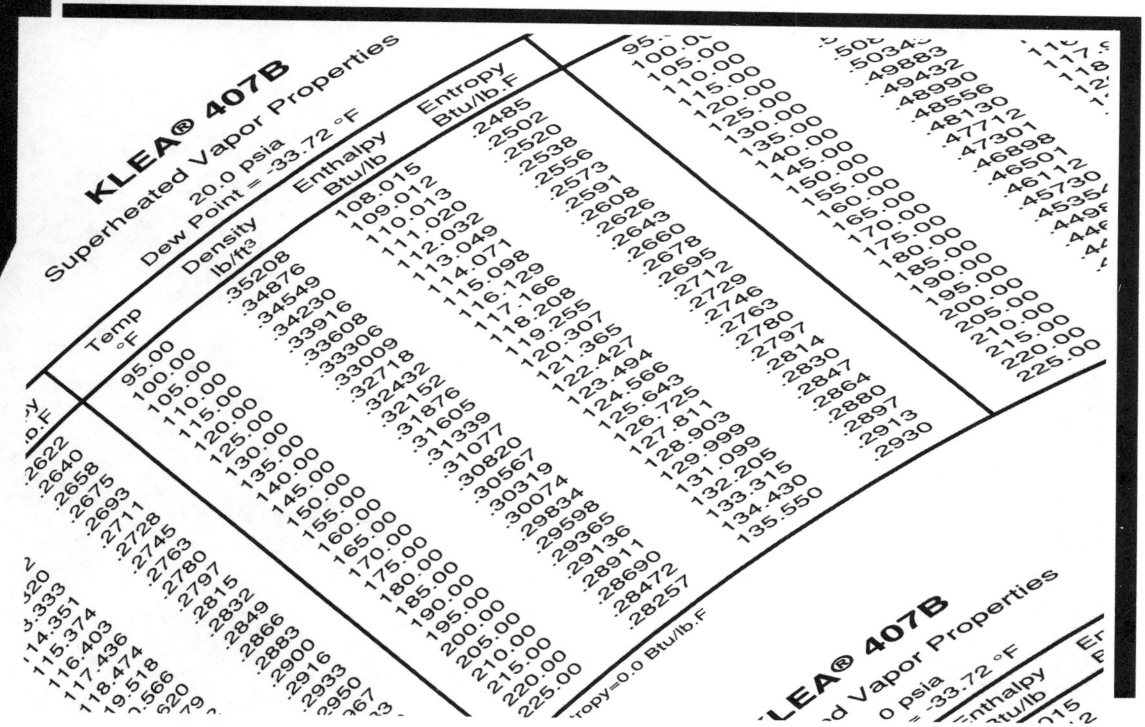

**NOW.
AND FOR
THE FUTURE.**

Thermodynamic Property Data for

KLEA® 407B

British Units

Saturated Liquid and Saturated Vapor Properties
Superheated Vapor Properties
Evaporator Inlet Temperatures

RHS14YR/JDM91-353P

SYSTEM PERFORMANCE WITH NON-AZEOTROPIC REFRIGERANT BLENDS

- With a non-azeotropic refrigerant blend the composition of the vapour changes in the evaporator and the condenser.
- Evaporator inlet and outlet temperatures are different.
- Condenser inlet and outlet temperatures are different.
- At all other points in the system the fluid behaves as normal.
- System design path.
  - Select evaporator outlet (Dew point 'A') against the desired cold space temperature.
  - Condenser inlet and outlet temperatures 'B' & 'C' should be sufficient to reject heat.
  - Liquid enthalpy at expansion device and table 3 can be used to get evaporator inlet temperature 'D'.
  - Refrigeration effect is enthalpy change 'D' to 'A' as normal.

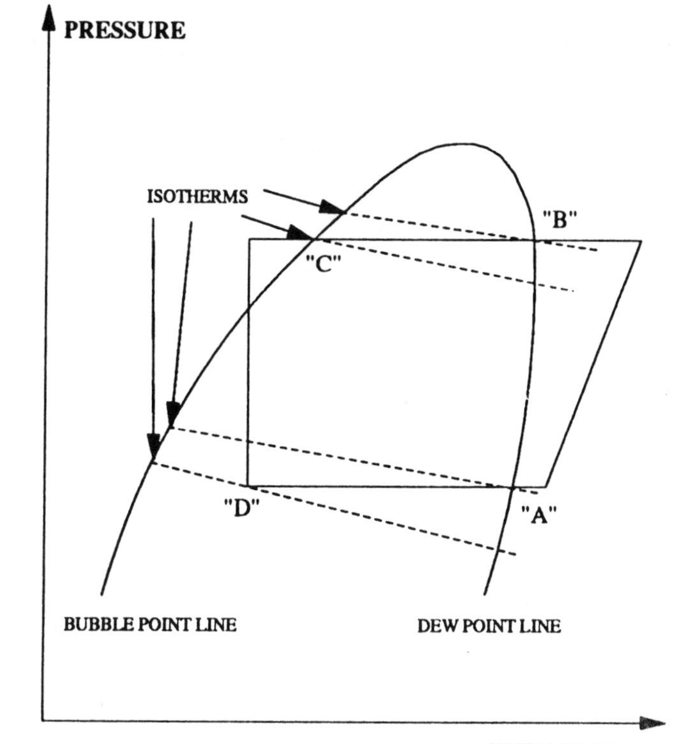

Pressure-Enthalpy Diagram for Non-azeotropic Refrigerant Blends

KLEA® 407B

Saturated Liquid and Saturated Vapor Properties

Table 1 Sheet 1

Pressure psia	Dew Point °F	Bubble Point °F	Liquid Density lb/ft³	Vapor Density lb/ft³	Liquid Enthalpy Btu/lb	Vapor Enthalpy Btu/lb	Vapor Entropy Btu/lb.F
10.00	-58.67	-66.85	92.630	.24489	-7.995	80.474	.20372
11.00	-55.46	-63.56	92.255	.26773	-7.014	80.951	.20312
12.00	-52.47	-60.50	91.904	.29044	-6.102	81.396	.20257
13.00	-49.67	-57.64	91.574	.31305	-5.248	81.811	.20209
14.00	-47.03	-54.94	91.262	.33556	-4.445	82.202	.20165
15.00	-44.54	-52.39	90.965	.35798	-3.687	82.571	.20125
16.00	-42.17	-49.97	90.682	.38032	-2.967	82.921	.20089
17.00	-39.92	-47.67	90.412	.40259	-2.282	83.254	.20056
18.00	-37.76	-45.47	90.152	.42479	-1.627	83.571	.20025
19.00	-35.70	-43.36	89.903	.44693	-1.001	83.874	.19996
20.00	-33.72	-41.34	89.662	.46901	-.399	84.165	.19969
21.00	-31.82	-39.40	89.430	.49105	.179	84.444	.19944
22.00	-29.99	-37.53	89.205	.51304	.737	84.713	.19921
23.00	-28.22	-35.72	88.988	.53498	1.275	84.972	.19899
24.00	-26.50	-33.97	88.777	.55688	1.796	85.221	.19878
25.00	-24.85	-32.28	88.571	.57875	2.300	85.463	.19859
26.00	-23.24	-30.64	88.372	.60058	2.789	85.697	.19841
27.00	-21.68	-29.04	88.177	.62239	3.264	85.923	.19823
28.00	-20.16	-27.50	87.987	.64416	3.726	86.142	.19807
29.00	-18.69	-25.99	87.802	.66591	4.176	86.356	.19791
30.00	-17.25	-24.53	87.621	.68763	4.614	86.563	.19776
31.00	-15.85	-23.10	87.445	.70933	5.041	86.764	.19762
32.00	-14.48	-21.70	87.271	.73102	5.458	86.960	.19748
33.00	-13.15	-20.34	87.102	.75268	5.865	87.152	.19735
34.00	-11.85	-19.02	86.936	.77432	6.263	87.338	.19722
35.00	-10.57	-17.72	86.773	.79595	6.653	87.520	.19710
36.00	-9.33	-16.45	86.613	.81757	7.034	87.697	.19699
37.00	-8.11	-15.20	86.456	.83917	7.407	87.870	.19688
38.00	-6.91	-13.98	86.302	.86076	7.774	88.040	.19677
39.00	-5.74	-12.79	86.150	.88234	8.133	88.205	.19667
40.00	-4.60	-11.62	86.001	.90392	8.485	88.367	.19657

Standard state : At -40°F, Liquid Enthalpy=0.0 Btu/lb, Liquid Entropy=0.0 Btu/lb.F

Version 2a 1st September 1993

KLEA® 407B

Saturated Liquid and Saturated Vapor Properties

Table 1 Sheet 2

Pressure psia	Dew Point °F	Bubble Point °F	Liquid Density lb/ft³	Vapor Density lb/ft³	Liquid Enthalpy Btu/lb	Vapor Enthalpy Btu/lb	Vapor Entropy Btu/lb.F
40.00	-4.60	-11.62	86.001	.90392	8.485	88.367	.19657
45.00	.83	-6.08	85.290	1.01168	10.156	89.129	.19612
50.00	5.82	-1.00	84.627	1.11935	11.697	89.821	.19573
55.00	10.44	3.71	84.005	1.22704	13.131	90.454	.19540
60.00	14.75	8.10	83.417	1.33481	14.476	91.037	.19510
65.00	18.79	12.23	82.858	1.44275	15.743	91.578	.19484
70.00	22.60	16.11	82.324	1.55089	16.945	92.081	.19460
75.00	26.21	19.80	81.812	1.65930	18.089	92.552	.19438
80.00	29.64	23.30	81.319	1.76802	19.182	92.993	.19418
85.00	32.91	26.63	80.844	1.87709	20.230	93.409	.19399
90.00	36.04	29.83	80.384	1.98654	21.238	93.800	.19381
95.00	39.04	32.89	79.937	2.09641	22.210	94.171	.19365
100.00	41.92	35.83	79.503	2.20672	23.148	94.521	.19349
105.00	44.69	38.66	79.080	2.31752	24.057	94.854	.19334
110.00	47.37	41.39	78.668	2.42881	24.939	95.169	.19319
115.00	49.95	44.03	78.265	2.54064	25.796	95.469	.19305
120.00	52.45	46.58	77.870	2.65302	26.630	95.755	.19291
125.00	54.87	49.06	77.484	2.76598	27.442	96.028	.19277
130.00	57.22	51.46	77.104	2.87954	28.235	96.287	.19264
135.00	59.50	53.79	76.731	2.99373	29.010	96.535	.19251
140.00	61.72	56.06	76.365	3.10856	29.768	96.772	.19238
145.00	63.88	58.27	76.004	3.22406	30.510	96.998	.19226
150.00	65.98	60.42	75.648	3.34025	31.237	97.214	.19213
155.00	68.03	62.52	75.298	3.45715	31.950	97.420	.19201
160.00	70.03	64.57	74.951	3.57478	32.651	97.618	.19188

Standard state : At -40°F, Liquid Enthalpy=0.0 Btu/lb, Liquid Entropy=0.0 Btu/lb.F

Version 2a 1st September 1993

KLEA® 407B

Saturated Liquid and Saturated Vapor Properties

Table 1 Sheet 3

Pressure psia	Dew Point °F	Bubble Point °F	Liquid Density lb/ft³	Vapor Density lb/ft³	Liquid Enthalpy Btu/lb	Vapor Enthalpy Btu/lb	Vapor Entropy Btu/lb.F
160.00	70.03	64.57	74.951	3.57478	32.651	97.618	.19188
170.00	73.89	68.52	74.271	3.81234	34.016	97.987	.19163
180.00	77.58	72.30	73.605	4.05307	35.338	98.324	.19138
190.00	81.12	75.93	72.951	4.29717	36.622	98.632	.19113
200.00	84.52	79.42	72.308	4.54480	37.872	98.912	.19088
210.00	87.79	82.78	71.674	4.79616	39.090	99.167	.19062
220.00	90.94	86.02	71.046	5.05143	40.281	99.397	.19035
230.00	93.99	89.15	70.425	5.31080	41.448	99.605	.19008
240.00	96.93	92.18	69.808	5.57449	42.592	99.791	.18980
250.00	99.78	95.12	69.194	5.84272	43.716	99.956	.18952
260.00	102.55	97.97	68.583	6.11573	44.821	100.101	.18923
270.00	105.23	100.74	67.972	6.39375	45.911	100.227	.18892
280.00	107.84	103.44	67.361	6.67707	46.986	100.334	.18861
290.00	110.38	106.06	66.748	6.96595	48.049	100.423	.18829
300.00	112.85	108.62	66.133	7.26072	49.100	100.493	.18796
310.00	115.25	111.11	65.514	7.56170	50.141	100.546	.18762
320.00	117.60	113.54	64.889	7.86925	51.173	100.582	.18726
330.00	119.89	115.92	64.258	8.18377	52.198	100.599	.18689
340.00	122.12	118.24	63.618	8.50569	53.217	100.600	.18651
350.00	124.31	120.52	62.968	8.83548	54.232	100.583	.18612
360.00	126.44	122.74	62.306	9.17367	55.242	100.548	.18571
370.00	128.53	124.92	61.629	9.52082	56.251	100.495	.18528
380.00	130.58	127.06	60.935	9.87759	57.259	100.424	.18484
390.00	132.58	129.16	60.221	10.24468	58.267	100.334	.18437
400.00	134.54	131.21	59.482	10.62292	59.277	100.225	.18389
410.00	136.47	133.23	58.714	11.01322	60.290	100.096	.18339
420.00	138.35	135.22	57.911	11.41663	61.308	99.946	.18286
430.00	140.20	137.17	57.064	11.83434	62.333	99.774	.18230

Standard state : At -40°F, Liquid Enthalpy=0.0 Btu/lb, Liquid Entropy=0.0 Btu/lb.F

KLEA® 407B

Superheated Vapor Properties

Table 2 Sheet 1

10.0 psia, Dew Point = -58.67 °F				20.0 psia, Dew Point = -33.72 °F				30.0 psia, Dew Point = -17.25 °F			
Temp °F	Density lb/ft³	Enthalpy Btu/lb	Entropy Btu/lb.F	Temp °F	Density lb/ft³	Enthalpy Btu/lb	Entropy Btu/lb.F	Temp °F	Density lb/ft³	Enthalpy Btu/lb	Entropy Btu/lb.F
-55.00	.24252	81.077	.2052								
-50.00	.23937	81.905	.2073								
-45.00	.23630	82.738	.2093								
-40.00	.23332	83.576	.2113								
-35.00	.23041	84.421	.2133								
-30.00	.22757	85.270	.2153	-30.00	.46446	84.806	.2012				
-25.00	.22481	86.126	.2173	-25.00	.45850	85.670	.2032				
-20.00	.22212	86.987	.2192	-20.00	.45270	86.540	.2052				
-15.00	.21949	87.854	.2212	-15.00	.44705	87.416	.2072	-15.00	.68356	86.961	.1987
-10.00	.21693	88.726	.2231	-10.00	.44156	88.296	.2091	-10.00	.67469	87.851	.2006
-5.00	.21443	89.604	.2251	-5.00	.43621	89.182	.2111	-5.00	.66607	88.746	.2026
.00	.21199	90.488	.2270	.00	.43099	90.073	.2130	.00	.65770	89.646	.2046
5.00	.20960	91.377	.2289	5.00	.42591	90.970	.2150	5.00	.64955	90.550	.2066
10.00	.20727	92.272	.2308	10.00	.42095	91.872	.2169	10.00	.64162	91.460	.2085
15.00	.20499	93.173	.2328	15.00	.41612	92.779	.2188	15.00	.63390	92.375	.2104
20.00	.20277	94.078	.2347	20.00	.41140	93.692	.2207	20.00	.62639	93.295	.2124
25.00	.20059	94.990	.2365	25.00	.40679	94.610	.2226	25.00	.61906	94.220	.2143
30.00	.19846	95.907	.2384	30.00	.40229	95.533	.2245	30.00	.61193	95.150	.2162
35.00	.19637	96.829	.2403	35.00	.39790	96.462	.2264	35.00	.60496	96.086	.2181
40.00	.19434	97.757	.2422	40.00	.39361	97.396	.2283	40.00	.59817	97.026	.2200
45.00	.19234	98.690	.2440	45.00	.38941	98.335	.2302	45.00	.59154	97.972	.2219
50.00	.19038	99.629	.2459	50.00	.38531	99.280	.2320	50.00	.58507	98.922	.2237
55.00	.18847	100.574	.2477	55.00	.38129	100.229	.2339	55.00	.57875	99.878	.2256
60.00	.18659	101.523	.2496	60.00	.37737	101.184	.2357	60.00	.57257	100.838	.2275
65.00	.18476	102.478	.2514	65.00	.37352	102.144	.2376	65.00	.56654	101.804	.2293
70.00	.18296	103.439	.2532	70.00	.36976	103.110	.2394	70.00	.56064	102.775	.2312
75.00	.18119	104.404	.2550	75.00	.36608	104.081	.2412	75.00	.55487	103.751	.2330
80.00	.17946	105.375	.2568	80.00	.36247	105.056	.2431	80.00	.54922	104.732	.2348
85.00	.17776	106.352	.2586	85.00	.35894	106.038	.2449	85.00	.54370	105.718	.2366
90.00	.17610	107.333	.2604	90.00	.35548	107.024	.2467	90.00	.53829	106.709	.2384

Standard state : At -40°F, Liquid Enthalpy=0.0 Btu/lb, Liquid Entropy=0.0 Btu/lb.F

Version 2a 1st September 1993

Superheated Vapor Properties

Table 2 Sheet 2

10.0 psia, Dew Point = -58.67 °F				20.0 psia, Dew Point = -33.72 °F				30.0 psia, Dew Point = -17.25 °F			
Temp °F	Density lb/ft³	Enthalpy Btu/lb	Entropy Btu/lb.F	Temp °F	Density lb/ft³	Enthalpy Btu/lb	Entropy Btu/lb.F	Temp °F	Density lb/ft³	Enthalpy Btu/lb	Entropy Btu/lb.F
95.00	.17447	108.320	.2622	95.00	.35208	108.015	.2485	95.00	.53300	107.705	.2402
100.00	.17286	109.312	.2640	100.00	.34876	109.012	.2502	100.00	.52782	108.706	.2420
105.00	.17129	110.310	.2658	105.00	.34549	110.013	.2520	105.00	.52274	109.712	.2438
110.00	.16975	111.312	.2675	110.00	.34230	111.020	.2538	110.00	.51777	110.723	.2456
115.00	.16823	112.320	.2693	115.00	.33916	112.032	.2556	115.00	.51289	111.739	.2474
120.00	.16674	113.333	.2711	120.00	.33608	113.049	.2573	120.00	.50811	112.760	.2492
125.00	.16528	114.351	.2728	125.00	.33306	114.071	.2591	125.00	.50343	113.786	.2509
130.00	.16385	115.374	.2745	130.00	.33009	115.098	.2608	130.00	.49883	114.817	.2527
135.00	.16244	116.403	.2763	135.00	.32718	116.129	.2626	135.00	.49432	115.853	.2544
140.00	.16105	117.436	.2780	140.00	.32432	117.166	.2643	140.00	.48990	116.894	.2562
145.00	.15969	118.474	.2797	145.00	.32152	118.208	.2660	145.00	.48556	117.939	.2579
150.00	.15835	119.518	.2815	150.00	.31876	119.255	.2678	150.00	.48130	118.990	.2596
155.00	.15703	120.566	.2832	155.00	.31605	120.307	.2695	155.00	.47712	120.046	.2614
160.00	.15574	121.620	.2849	160.00	.31339	121.365	.2712	160.00	.47301	121.107	.2631
165.00	.15446	122.679	.2866	165.00	.31077	122.427	.2729	165.00	.46898	122.173	.2648
170.00	.15321	123.742	.2883	170.00	.30820	123.494	.2746	170.00	.46501	123.244	.2665
175.00	.15198	124.811	.2900	175.00	.30567	124.566	.2763	175.00	.46112	124.319	.2682
180.00	.15077	125.884	.2916	180.00	.30319	125.643	.2780	180.00	.45730	125.400	.2699
185.00	.14958	126.963	.2933	185.00	.30074	126.725	.2797	185.00	.45354	126.485	.2716
190.00	.14840	128.046	.2950	190.00	.29834	127.811	.2814	190.00	.44985	127.575	.2733
195.00	.14725	129.134	.2967	195.00	.29598	128.903	.2830	195.00	.44622	128.670	.2750
200.00	.14611	130.227	.2983	200.00	.29365	129.999	.2847	200.00	.44265	129.769	.2766
205.00	.14500	131.324	.3000	205.00	.29136	131.099	.2864	205.00	.43914	130.873	.2783
210.00	.14389	132.427	.3016	210.00	.28911	132.205	.2880	210.00	.43568	131.981	.2800
215.00	.14281	133.534	.3033	215.00	.28690	133.315	.2897	215.00	.43229	133.095	.2816
220.00	.14174	134.646	.3049	220.00	.28472	134.430	.2913	220.00	.42894	134.213	.2833
225.00	.14069	135.762	.3066	225.00	.28257	135.550	.2930	225.00	.42566	135.336	.2849

Standard state : At -40°F, Liquid Enthalpy=0.0 Btu/lb, Liquid Entropy=0.0 Btu/lb.F

KLEA® 407B

Superheated Vapor Properties

Table 2 Sheet 3

40.0 psia, Dew Point = -4.60 °F				50.0 psia, Dew Point = 5.82 °F				60.0 psia, Dew Point = 14.75 °F			
Temp °F	Density lb/ft³	Enthalpy Btu/lb	Entropy Btu/lb.F	Temp °F	Density lb/ft³	Enthalpy Btu/lb	Entropy Btu/lb.F	Temp °F	Density lb/ft³	Enthalpy Btu/lb	Entropy Btu/lb.F
.00	.89290	89.203	.1984								
5.00	.88125	90.117	.2004								
10.00	.86995	91.036	.2023	10.00	1.10670	90.597	.1974				
15.00	.85897	91.959	.2043	15.00	1.09201	91.529	.1994	15.00	1.33387	91.085	.1952
20.00	.84829	92.887	.2062	20.00	1.07776	92.466	.2013	20.00	1.31555	92.031	.1972
25.00	.83792	93.820	.2082	25.00	1.06394	93.407	.2033	25.00	1.29782	92.982	.1992
30.00	.82782	94.757	.2101	30.00	1.05052	94.353	.2052	30.00	1.28064	93.937	.2011
35.00	.81799	95.700	.2120	35.00	1.03749	95.304	.2072	35.00	1.26400	94.896	.2031
40.00	.80842	96.647	.2139	40.00	1.02482	96.259	.2091	40.00	1.24786	95.859	.2050
45.00	.79910	97.599	.2158	45.00	1.01250	97.218	.2110	45.00	1.23220	96.827	.2069
50.00	.79001	98.556	.2177	50.00	1.00051	98.182	.2129	50.00	1.21699	97.798	.2088
55.00	.78115	99.518	.2196	55.00	.98884	99.151	.2148	55.00	1.20221	98.775	.2108
60.00	.77250	100.485	.2214	60.00	.97747	100.124	.2167	60.00	1.18784	99.755	.2127
65.00	.76406	101.457	.2233	65.00	.96640	101.102	.2185	65.00	1.17386	100.740	.2145
70.00	.75583	102.434	.2252	70.00	.95560	102.085	.2204	70.00	1.16026	101.729	.2164
75.00	.74778	103.415	.2270	75.00	.94507	103.073	.2223	75.00	1.14701	102.723	.2183
80.00	.73992	104.401	.2288	80.00	.93480	104.065	.2241	80.00	1.13411	103.721	.2201
85.00	.73224	105.393	.2307	85.00	.92477	105.062	.2259	85.00	1.12153	104.724	.2220
90.00	.72473	106.389	.2325	90.00	.91498	106.063	.2278	90.00	1.10926	105.732	.2238
95.00	.71739	107.390	.2343	95.00	.90542	107.070	.2296	95.00	1.09729	106.743	.2257
100.00	.71020	108.396	.2361	100.00	.89607	108.081	.2314	100.00	1.08561	107.760	.2275
105.00	.70317	109.407	.2379	105.00	.88694	109.096	.2332	105.00	1.07421	108.781	.2293
110.00	.69629	110.422	.2397	110.00	.87801	110.117	.2350	110.00	1.06307	109.806	.2311
115.00	.68955	111.443	.2415	115.00	.86927	111.142	.2368	115.00	1.05219	110.836	.2329
120.00	.68295	112.468	.2433	120.00	.86073	112.172	.2386	120.00	1.04156	111.871	.2347
125.00	.67649	113.498	.2450	125.00	.85236	113.206	.2404	125.00	1.03116	112.910	.2365
130.00	.67016	114.533	.2468	130.00	.84417	114.246	.2421	130.00	1.02099	113.954	.2383
135.00	.66395	115.573	.2485	135.00	.83615	115.290	.2439	135.00	1.01104	115.003	.2400
140.00	.65786	116.618	.2503	140.00	.82830	116.338	.2457	140.00	1.00130	116.056	.2418
145.00	.65189	117.667	.2520	145.00	.82060	117.392	.2474	145.00	.99177	117.113	.2436

Standard state : At -40°F, Liquid Enthalpy=0.0 Btu/lb, Liquid Entropy=0.0 Btu/lb.F

KLEA® 407B

Superheated Vapor Properties

Table 2 Sheet 4

40.0 psia, Dew Point = -4.60 °F				50.0 psia, Dew Point = 5.82 °F				60.0 psia, Dew Point = 14.75 °F			
Temp °F	Density lb/ft³	Enthalpy Btu/lb	Entropy Btu/lb.F	Temp °F	Density lb/ft³	Enthalpy Btu/lb	Entropy Btu/lb.F	Temp °F	Density lb/ft³	Enthalpy Btu/lb	Entropy Btu/lb.F
150.00	.64604	118.721	.2538	150.00	.81306	118.450	.2491	150.00	.98243	118.175	.2453
155.00	.64030	119.781	.2555	155.00	.80566	119.514	.2509	155.00	.97329	119.243	.2471
160.00	.63466	120.846	.2572	160.00	.79842	120.583	.2526	160.00	.96433	120.317	.2488
165.00	.62913	121.916	.2590	165.00	.79131	121.657	.2543	165.00	.95556	121.395	.2505
170.00	.62371	122.991	.2607	170.00	.78433	122.735	.2561	170.00	.94695	122.477	.2522
175.00	.61838	124.070	.2624	175.00	.77749	123.818	.2578	175.00	.93852	123.564	.2540
180.00	.61315	125.154	.2641	180.00	.77078	124.906	.2595	180.00	.93025	124.656	.2557
185.00	.60801	126.243	.2658	185.00	.76419	125.999	.2612	185.00	.92214	125.753	.2574
190.00	.60296	127.336	.2675	190.00	.75773	127.096	.2629	190.00	.91418	126.854	.2591
195.00	.59800	128.435	.2691	195.00	.75138	128.198	.2646	195.00	.90637	127.959	.2608
200.00	.59313	129.537	.2708	200.00	.74514	129.304	.2663	200.00	.89871	129.069	.2625
205.00	.58834	130.645	.2725	205.00	.73901	130.415	.2679	205.00	.89118	130.183	.2642
210.00	.58363	131.756	.2742	210.00	.73299	131.530	.2696	210.00	.88380	131.301	.2658
215.00	.57900	132.873	.2758	215.00	.72708	132.650	.2713	215.00	.87654	132.425	.2675
220.00	.57445	133.994	.2775	220.00	.72127	133.774	.2729	220.00	.86941	133.553	.2692
225.00	.56998	135.120	.2791	225.00	.71555	134.903	.2746	225.00	.86241	134.685	.2708
230.00	.56557	136.251	.2808	230.00	.70994	136.037	.2762	230.00	.85553	135.822	.2725
235.00	.56124	137.385	.2824	235.00	.70441	137.175	.2779	235.00	.84877	136.963	.2741
240.00	.55698	138.525	.2840	240.00	.69898	138.318	.2795	240.00	.84212	138.109	.2758
245.00	.55279	139.669	.2857	245.00	.69364	139.464	.2812	245.00	.83559	139.259	.2774
250.00	.54866	140.817	.2873	250.00	.68838	140.615	.2828	250.00	.82916	140.413	.2790
255.00	.54459	141.969	.2889	255.00	.68321	141.771	.2844	255.00	.82284	141.571	.2807
260.00	.54059	143.126	.2905	260.00	.67812	142.931	.2860	260.00	.81662	142.734	.2823
265.00	.53665	144.287	.2921	265.00	.67311	144.095	.2876	265.00	.81051	143.901	.2839
270.00	.53277	145.453	.2937	270.00	.66818	145.263	.2892	270.00	.80449	145.072	.2855
275.00	.52895	146.623	.2953	275.00	.66332	146.435	.2908	275.00	.79856	146.247	.2871
280.00	.52519	147.797	.2969	280.00	.65854	147.612	.2924	280.00	.79273	147.427	.2887

Standard state : At -40°F, Liquid Enthalpy=0.0 Btu/lb, Liquid Entropy=0.0 Btu/lb.F

Version 2a 1st September 1993

KLEA® 407B

Superheated Vapor Properties

Table 2 Sheet 5

70.0 psia, Dew Point = 22.60 °F				80.0 psia, Dew Point = 29.64 °F				90.0 psia, Dew Point = 36.04 °F			
Temp °F	Density lb/ft³	Enthalpy Btu/lb	Entropy Btu/lb.F	Temp °F	Density lb/ft³	Enthalpy Btu/lb	Entropy Btu/lb.F	Temp °F	Density lb/ft³	Enthalpy Btu/lb	Entropy Btu/lb.F
25.00	1.54035	92.543	.1956								
30.00	1.51891	93.508	.1975	30.00	1.76617	93.063	.1943				
35.00	1.49820	94.476	.1995	35.00	1.74083	94.042	.1963				
40.00	1.47815	95.448	.2015	40.00	1.71637	95.025	.1983	40.00	1.96330	94.587	.1954
45.00	1.45875	96.424	.2034	45.00	1.69275	96.010	.2003	45.00	1.93491	95.583	.1974
50.00	1.43994	97.404	.2053	50.00	1.66991	96.999	.2022	50.00	1.90754	96.582	.1993
55.00	1.42171	98.389	.2073	55.00	1.64782	97.992	.2041	55.00	1.88113	97.585	.2013
60.00	1.40401	99.377	.2092	60.00	1.62643	98.989	.2061	60.00	1.85561	98.590	.2033
65.00	1.38683	100.369	.2111	65.00	1.60570	99.989	.2080	65.00	1.83094	99.599	.2052
70.00	1.37013	101.365	.2130	70.00	1.58560	100.993	.2099	70.00	1.80706	100.612	.2071
75.00	1.35391	102.366	.2148	75.00	1.56609	102.001	.2118	75.00	1.78394	101.628	.2090
80.00	1.33812	103.371	.2167	80.00	1.54714	103.013	.2137	80.00	1.76153	102.647	.2109
85.00	1.32276	104.380	.2186	85.00	1.52874	104.029	.2155	85.00	1.73979	103.670	.2128
90.00	1.30779	105.394	.2204	90.00	1.51084	105.049	.2174	90.00	1.71868	104.697	.2147
95.00	1.29322	106.411	.2223	95.00	1.49343	106.073	.2193	95.00	1.69819	105.728	.2165
100.00	1.27901	107.434	.2241	100.00	1.47649	107.101	.2211	100.00	1.67827	106.763	.2184
105.00	1.26516	108.460	.2259	105.00	1.45999	108.134	.2229	105.00	1.65890	107.802	.2202
110.00	1.25165	109.491	.2277	110.00	1.44391	109.170	.2248	110.00	1.64006	108.844	.2221
115.00	1.23846	110.526	.2296	115.00	1.42824	110.211	.2266	115.00	1.62171	109.891	.2239
120.00	1.22559	111.566	.2314	120.00	1.41296	111.256	.2284	120.00	1.60384	110.942	.2257
125.00	1.21301	112.610	.2331	125.00	1.39805	112.306	.2302	125.00	1.58643	111.996	.2275
130.00	1.20072	113.659	.2349	130.00	1.38350	113.359	.2320	130.00	1.56945	113.055	.2293
135.00	1.18871	114.712	.2367	135.00	1.36929	114.417	.2338	135.00	1.55290	114.118	.2311
140.00	1.17697	115.769	.2385	140.00	1.35541	115.479	.2356	140.00	1.53674	115.185	.2329
145.00	1.16549	116.831	.2402	145.00	1.34185	116.546	.2373	145.00	1.52096	116.256	.2347
150.00	1.15425	117.897	.2420	150.00	1.32859	117.616	.2391	150.00	1.50556	117.332	.2365
155.00	1.14325	118.970	.2438	155.00	1.31563	118.694	.2409	155.00	1.49051	118.414	.2382
160.00	1.13249	120.048	.2455	160.00	1.30295	119.776	.2426	160.00	1.47581	119.501	.2400
165.00	1.12195	121.130	.2472	165.00	1.29055	120.862	.2444	165.00	1.46144	120.592	.2418
170.00	1.11162	122.216	.2490	170.00	1.27841	121.953	.2461	170.00	1.44738	121.687	.2435

Standard state : At -40°F, Liquid Enthalpy=0.0 Btu/lb, Liquid Entropy=0.0 Btu/lb.F

KLEA® 407B

Superheated Vapor Properties

Table 2 Sheet 6

70.0 psia, Dew Point = 22.60 °F				80.0 psia, Dew Point = 29.64 °F				90.0 psia, Dew Point = 36.04 °F			
Temp °F	Density lb/ft³	Enthalpy Btu/lb	Entropy Btu/lb.F	Temp °F	Density lb/ft³	Enthalpy Btu/lb	Entropy Btu/lb.F	Temp °F	Density lb/ft³	Enthalpy Btu/lb	Entropy Btu/lb.F
175.00	1.10151	123.308	.2507	175.00	1.26653	123.049	.2478	175.00	1.43364	122.787	.2452
180.00	1.09160	124.404	.2524	180.00	1.25490	124.149	.2496	180.00	1.42019	123.892	.2470
185.00	1.08189	125.504	.2541	185.00	1.24350	125.253	.2513	185.00	1.40702	125.000	.2487
190.00	1.07237	126.609	.2558	190.00	1.23234	126.362	.2530	190.00	1.39414	126.113	.2504
195.00	1.06303	127.718	.2575	195.00	1.22140	127.475	.2547	195.00	1.38152	127.230	.2521
200.00	1.05388	128.831	.2592	200.00	1.21068	128.592	.2564	200.00	1.36916	128.351	.2538
205.00	1.04489	129.949	.2609	205.00	1.20016	129.714	.2581	205.00	1.35704	129.477	.2555
210.00	1.03607	131.071	.2626	210.00	1.18985	130.840	.2598	210.00	1.34517	130.606	.2572
215.00	1.02742	132.198	.2643	215.00	1.17974	131.970	.2615	215.00	1.33353	131.740	.2589
220.00	1.01892	133.330	.2660	220.00	1.16981	133.105	.2631	220.00	1.32212	132.879	.2606
225.00	1.01058	134.466	.2676	225.00	1.16007	134.245	.2648	225.00	1.31092	134.022	.2623
230.00	1.00238	135.606	.2693	230.00	1.15051	135.388	.2665	230.00	1.29994	135.169	.2640
235.00	.99433	136.751	.2709	235.00	1.14112	136.536	.2681	235.00	1.28916	136.321	.2656
240.00	.98642	137.899	.2726	240.00	1.13191	137.688	.2698	240.00	1.27859	137.476	.2673
245.00	.97865	139.052	.2742	245.00	1.12285	138.845	.2714	245.00	1.26820	138.636	.2689
250.00	.97101	140.210	.2759	250.00	1.11395	140.005	.2731	250.00	1.25800	139.799	.2706
255.00	.96350	141.371	.2775	255.00	1.10521	141.169	.2747	255.00	1.24799	140.967	.2722
260.00	.95612	142.537	.2791	260.00	1.09662	142.338	.2763	260.00	1.23815	142.139	.2738
265.00	.94886	143.706	.2807	265.00	1.08818	143.511	.2780	265.00	1.22848	143.314	.2755
270.00	.94172	144.880	.2823	270.00	1.07988	144.688	.2796	270.00	1.21898	144.494	.2771
275.00	.93469	146.058	.2840	275.00	1.07171	145.869	.2812	275.00	1.20964	145.678	.2787
280.00	.92778	147.241	.2856	280.00	1.06368	147.054	.2828	280.00	1.20045	146.866	.2803
285.00	.92097	148.427	.2872	285.00	1.05578	148.243	.2844	285.00	1.19142	148.058	.2819
290.00	.91428	149.618	.2888	290.00	1.04801	149.436	.2860	290.00	1.18254	149.254	.2835
295.00	.90768	150.812	.2903	295.00	1.04036	150.633	.2876	295.00	1.17381	150.454	.2851
300.00	.90119	152.011	.2919	300.00	1.03283	151.834	.2892	300.00	1.16521	151.658	.2867

Standard state : At -40°F, Liquid Enthalpy=0.0 Btu/lb, Liquid Entropy=0.0 Btu/lb.F

Version 2a 1st September 1993

KLEA® 407B

Superheated Vapor Properties

Table 2 Sheet 7

100.0psia Dew Point = 41.92 °F				130.0 psia Dew Point = 57.22 °F				160.0 psia Dew Point = 70.03 °F			
Temp °F	Density lb/ft³	Enthalpy Btu/lb	Entropy Btu/lb.F	Temp °F	Density lb/ft³	Enthalpy Btu/lb	Entropy Btu/lb.F	Temp °F	Density lb/ft³	Enthalpy Btu/lb	Entropy Btu/lb.F
45.00	2.18606	95.142	.1947								
50.00	2.15356	96.152	.1967								
55.00	2.12228	97.165	.1987								
60.00	2.09214	98.181	.2007	60.00	2.85318	96.872	.1938				
65.00	2.06307	99.199	.2026	65.00	2.80734	97.925	.1958				
70.00	2.03501	100.220	.2045	70.00	2.76346	98.979	.1978				
75.00	2.00788	101.245	.2065	75.00	2.72139	100.034	.1998	75.00	3.51173	98.707	.1939
80.00	1.98164	102.273	.2084	80.00	2.68099	101.091	.2017	80.00	3.45142	99.803	.1960
85.00	1.95624	103.304	.2103	85.00	2.64216	102.150	.2037	85.00	3.39397	100.898	.1980
90.00	1.93163	104.338	.2122	90.00	2.60477	103.211	.2056	90.00	3.33916	101.993	.2000
95.00	1.90777	105.376	.2141	95.00	2.56874	104.274	.2076	95.00	3.28675	103.088	.2020
100.00	1.88462	106.418	.2159	100.00	2.53398	105.339	.2095	100.00	3.23656	104.184	.2039
105.00	1.86213	107.463	.2178	105.00	2.50041	106.407	.2114	105.00	3.18842	105.280	.2059
110.00	1.84029	108.512	.2196	110.00	2.46795	107.478	.2133	110.00	3.14218	106.378	.2078
115.00	1.81906	109.565	.2215	115.00	2.43655	108.552	.2151	115.00	3.09771	107.478	.2097
120.00	1.79841	110.622	.2233	120.00	2.40614	109.629	.2170	120.00	3.05489	108.579	.2117
125.00	1.77830	111.682	.2251	125.00	2.37667	110.708	.2189	125.00	3.01360	109.682	.2135
130.00	1.75873	112.747	.2269	130.00	2.34809	111.791	.2207	130.00	2.97375	110.786	.2154
135.00	1.73966	113.815	.2287	135.00	2.32035	112.877	.2225	135.00	2.93525	111.894	.2173
140.00	1.72107	114.887	.2305	140.00	2.29341	113.967	.2244	140.00	2.89802	113.003	.2192
145.00	1.70294	115.963	.2323	145.00	2.26723	115.060	.2262	145.00	2.86199	114.115	.2210
150.00	1.68525	117.043	.2341	150.00	2.24177	116.156	.2280	150.00	2.82709	115.230	.2228
155.00	1.66799	118.130	.2359	155.00	2.21700	117.259	.2298	155.00	2.79326	116.352	.2247
160.00	1.65114	119.222	.2376	160.00	2.19289	118.367	.2316	160.00	2.76045	117.478	.2265
165.00	1.63468	120.318	.2394	165.00	2.16942	119.478	.2334	165.00	2.72862	118.607	.2283
170.00	1.61861	121.418	.2412	170.00	2.14655	120.593	.2351	170.00	2.69770	119.739	.2301
175.00	1.60289	122.523	.2429	175.00	2.12426	121.713	.2369	175.00	2.66765	120.875	.2319
180.00	1.58753	123.632	.2447	180.00	2.10253	122.836	.2387	180.00	2.63844	122.015	.2337
185.00	1.57251	124.745	.2464	185.00	2.08133	123.963	.2404	185.00	2.61003	123.158	.2355
190.00	1.55781	125.862	.2481	190.00	2.06064	125.094	.2422	190.00	2.58237	124.303	.2373

Standard state : At -40°F, Liquid Enthalpy=0.0 Btu/lb, Liquid Entropy=0.0 Btu/lb.F

KLEA® 407B

Superheated Vapor Properties

Table 2 Sheet 8

100.0psia Dew Point = 41.92 °F				130.0 psia Dew Point = 57.22 °F				160.0 psia Dew Point = 70.03 °F			
Temp °F	Density lb/ft³	Enthalpy Btu/lb	Entropy Btu/lb.F	Temp °F	Density lb/ft³	Enthalpy Btu/lb	Entropy Btu/lb.F	Temp °F	Density lb/ft³	Enthalpy Btu/lb	Entropy Btu/lb.F
195.00	1.54343	126.983	.2498	195.00	2.04043	126.228	.2439	195.00	2.55543	125.452	.2390
200.00	1.52936	128.108	.2515	200.00	2.02070	127.367	.2456	200.00	2.52918	126.605	.2408
205.00	1.51557	129.238	.2532	205.00	2.00142	128.508	.2474	205.00	2.50359	127.760	.2425
210.00	1.50207	130.371	.2549	210.00	1.98257	129.654	.2491	210.00	2.47863	128.919	.2443
215.00	1.48884	131.509	.2566	215.00	1.96413	130.803	.2508	215.00	2.45427	130.082	.2460
220.00	1.47587	132.651	.2583	220.00	1.94610	131.958	.2525	220.00	2.43049	131.249	.2477
225.00	1.46316	133.798	.2600	225.00	1.92846	133.117	.2542	225.00	2.40728	132.420	.2494
230.00	1.45070	134.949	.2617	230.00	1.91119	134.279	.2559	230.00	2.38460	133.595	.2511
235.00	1.43848	136.104	.2634	235.00	1.89429	135.445	.2576	235.00	2.36243	134.773	.2528
240.00	1.42649	137.263	.2650	240.00	1.87773	136.614	.2593	240.00	2.34076	135.954	.2545
245.00	1.41472	138.426	.2667	245.00	1.86151	137.788	.2609	245.00	2.31956	137.139	.2562
250.00	1.40317	139.592	.2683	250.00	1.84561	138.965	.2626	250.00	2.29882	138.327	.2579
255.00	1.39184	140.763	.2700	255.00	1.83002	140.146	.2642	255.00	2.27853	139.518	.2596
260.00	1.38070	141.938	.2716	260.00	1.81474	141.331	.2659	260.00	2.25866	140.713	.2612
265.00	1.36977	143.117	.2732	265.00	1.79976	142.519	.2675	265.00	2.23920	141.912	.2629
270.00	1.35903	144.300	.2749	270.00	1.78505	143.711	.2692	270.00	2.22013	143.114	.2645
275.00	1.34848	145.487	.2765	275.00	1.77063	144.907	.2708	275.00	2.20145	144.320	.2662
280.00	1.33811	146.677	.2781	280.00	1.75647	146.107	.2724	280.00	2.18313	145.529	.2678
285.00	1.32792	147.872	.2797	285.00	1.74256	147.310	.2741	285.00	2.16518	146.742	.2695
290.00	1.31789	149.071	.2813	290.00	1.72891	148.518	.2757	290.00	2.14756	147.958	.2711
295.00	1.30804	150.273	.2829	295.00	1.71550	149.729	.2773	295.00	2.13029	149.178	.2727
300.00	1.29835	151.480	.2845	300.00	1.70233	150.943	.2789	300.00	2.11333	150.401	.2743
305.00	1.28881	152.690	.2861	305.00	1.68939	152.162	.2805	305.00	2.09669	151.628	.2759
310.00	1.27943	153.905	.2877	310.00	1.67666	153.384	.2821	310.00	2.08035	152.859	.2775
315.00	1.27021	155.123	.2893	315.00	1.66416	154.610	.2837	315.00	2.06431	154.093	.2791
320.00	1.26112	156.345	.2908	320.00	1.65186	155.840	.2853	320.00	2.04855	155.330	.2807

Standard state : At -40°F, Liquid Enthalpy=0.0 Btu/lb, Liquid Entropy=0.0 Btu/lb.F

Version 2a 1st September 1993

KLEA® 407B

Superheated Vapor Properties

Table 2 Sheet 9

190.0psia Dew Point = 81.12 °F				220.0 psia Dew Point = 90.94 °F				250.0 psia Dew Point = 99.78 °F			
Temp °F	Density lb/ft³	Enthalpy Btu/lb	Entropy Btu/lb.F	Temp °F	Density lb/ft³	Enthalpy Btu/lb	Entropy Btu/lb.F	Temp °F	Density lb/ft³	Enthalpy Btu/lb	Entropy Btu/lb.F
85.00	4.23207	99.519	.1928								
90.00	4.15242	100.660	.1949								
95.00	4.07712	101.797	.1969	95.00	4.96348	100.368	.1921				
100.00	4.00574	102.933	.1989	100.00	4.86156	101.557	.1942	100.00	5.83651	100.011	.1896
105.00	3.93791	104.066	.2010	105.00	4.76598	102.739	.1963	105.00	5.69937	101.264	.1918
110.00	3.87330	105.198	.2030	110.00	4.67599	103.917	.1984	110.00	5.57250	102.503	.1940
115.00	3.81163	106.329	.2049	115.00	4.59100	105.089	.2005	115.00	5.45447	103.733	.1962
120.00	3.75267	107.460	.2069	120.00	4.51051	106.259	.2025	120.00	5.34415	104.953	.1983
125.00	3.69620	108.592	.2088	125.00	4.43407	107.426	.2045	125.00	5.24060	106.167	.2004
130.00	3.64203	109.724	.2108	130.00	4.36132	108.591	.2065	130.00	5.14307	107.374	.2024
135.00	3.59000	110.856	.2127	135.00	4.29193	109.755	.2085	135.00	5.05090	108.577	.2045
140.00	3.53994	111.990	.2146	140.00	4.22562	110.918	.2104	140.00	4.96357	109.776	.2065
145.00	3.49173	113.125	.2165	145.00	4.16215	112.080	.2123	145.00	4.88061	110.973	.2085
150.00	3.44525	114.261	.2183	150.00	4.10128	113.243	.2142	150.00	4.80161	112.167	.2104
155.00	3.40039	115.405	.2202	155.00	4.04285	114.412	.2162	155.00	4.72626	113.367	.2124
160.00	3.35707	116.552	.2221	160.00	3.98670	115.584	.2181	160.00	4.65427	114.568	.2143
165.00	3.31519	117.702	.2239	165.00	3.93267	116.757	.2199	165.00	4.58537	115.768	.2163
170.00	3.27467	118.853	.2257	170.00	3.88061	117.930	.2218	170.00	4.51934	116.967	.2182
175.00	3.23543	120.007	.2276	175.00	3.83041	119.106	.2237	175.00	4.45594	118.167	.2201
180.00	3.19741	121.165	.2294	180.00	3.78194	120.285	.2255	180.00	4.39501	119.369	.2220
185.00	3.16053	122.326	.2312	185.00	3.73510	121.465	.2274	185.00	4.33637	120.571	.2238
190.00	3.12475	123.488	.2330	190.00	3.68980	122.646	.2292	190.00	4.27988	121.774	.2257
195.00	3.08999	124.653	.2348	195.00	3.64595	123.829	.2310	195.00	4.22538	122.978	.2275
200.00	3.05622	125.821	.2366	200.00	3.60346	125.015	.2328	200.00	4.17275	124.182	.2294
205.00	3.02338	126.992	.2383	205.00	3.56226	126.202	.2346	205.00	4.12188	125.388	.2312
210.00	2.99142	128.165	.2401	210.00	3.52228	127.391	.2364	210.00	4.07267	126.595	.2330
215.00	2.96031	129.342	.2418	215.00	3.48345	128.584	.2382	215.00	4.02501	127.805	.2348
220.00	2.93001	130.524	.2436	220.00	3.44573	129.781	.2399	220.00	3.97884	129.019	.2366
225.00	2.90049	131.709	.2453	225.00	3.40906	130.980	.2417	225.00	3.93406	130.234	.2384
230.00	2.87171	132.896	.2470	230.00	3.37339	132.182	.2434	230.00	3.89061	131.452	.2401

Standard state : At -40°F, Liquid Enthalpy=0.0 Btu/lb, Liquid Entropy=0.0 Btu/lb.F

Version 2a 1st September 1993

KLEA® 407B

Superheated Vapor Properties

Table 2 Sheet 10

190.0psia Dew Point = 81.12 °F				220.0 psia Dew Point = 90.94 °F				250.0 psia Dew Point = 99.78 °F			
Temp °F	Density lb/ft³	Enthalpy Btu/lb	Entropy Btu/lb.F	Temp °F	Density lb/ft³	Enthalpy Btu/lb	Entropy Btu/lb.F	Temp °F	Density lb/ft³	Enthalpy Btu/lb	Entropy Btu/lb.F
235.00	2.84363	134.087	.2488	235.00	3.33868	133.387	.2452	235.00	3.84842	132.671	.2419
240.00	2.81623	135.281	.2505	240.00	3.30486	134.594	.2469	240.00	3.80741	133.893	.2437
245.00	2.78949	136.477	.2522	245.00	3.27192	135.803	.2486	245.00	3.76755	135.116	.2454
250.00	2.76336	137.677	.2539	250.00	3.23980	137.016	.2503	250.00	3.72876	136.342	.2471
255.00	2.73784	138.880	.2556	255.00	3.20848	138.231	.2520	255.00	3.69099	137.570	.2489
260.00	2.71289	140.086	.2573	260.00	3.17791	139.449	.2537	260.00	3.65421	138.801	.2506
265.00	2.68849	141.296	.2589	265.00	3.14806	140.670	.2554	265.00	3.61836	140.034	.2523
270.00	2.66462	142.508	.2606	270.00	3.11892	141.894	.2571	270.00	3.58341	141.270	.2540
275.00	2.64127	143.724	.2623	275.00	3.09044	143.120	.2588	275.00	3.54931	142.508	.2557
280.00	2.61841	144.943	.2639	280.00	3.06260	144.350	.2605	280.00	3.51603	143.748	.2574
285.00	2.59602	146.166	.2656	285.00	3.03538	145.583	.2621	285.00	3.48353	144.992	.2590
290.00	2.57409	147.392	.2672	290.00	3.00875	146.818	.2638	290.00	3.45179	146.238	.2607
295.00	2.55261	148.621	.2688	295.00	2.98269	148.057	.2654	295.00	3.42076	147.487	.2624
300.00	2.53155	149.853	.2705	300.00	2.95718	149.299	.2671	300.00	3.39043	148.739	.2640
305.00	2.51090	151.089	.2721	305.00	2.93221	150.544	.2687	305.00	3.36077	149.993	.2657
310.00	2.49066	152.328	.2737	310.00	2.90774	151.792	.2703	310.00	3.33175	151.251	.2673
315.00	2.47080	153.570	.2753	315.00	2.88376	153.043	.2719	315.00	3.30335	152.511	.2689
320.00	2.45131	154.816	.2769	320.00	2.86027	154.297	.2736	320.00	3.27554	153.774	.2706
325.00	2.43218	156.065	.2785	325.00	2.83723	155.555	.2752	325.00	3.24830	155.040	.2722
330.00	2.41341	157.318	.2801	330.00	2.81463	156.815	.2768	330.00	3.22162	156.309	.2738
335.00	2.39497	158.573	.2817	335.00	2.79247	158.079	.2784	335.00	3.19547	157.581	.2754
340.00	2.37686	159.833	.2833	340.00	2.77072	159.346	.2799	340.00	3.16984	158.857	.2770
345.00	2.35908	161.095	.2848	345.00	2.74938	160.617	.2815	345.00	3.14471	160.135	.2786
350.00	2.34160	162.361	.2864	350.00	2.72842	161.890	.2831	350.00	3.12005	161.416	.2802
355.00	2.32442	163.631	.2880	355.00	2.70784	163.167	.2847	355.00	3.09587	162.700	.2818
360.00	2.30753	164.904	.2895	360.00	2.68763	164.447	.2862	360.00	3.07213	163.987	.2833

Standard state : At -40°F, Liquid Enthalpy=0.0 Btu/lb, Liquid Entropy=0.0 Btu/lb.F

Version 2a 1st September 1993

KLEA® 407B

Superheated Vapor Properties

Table 2 Sheet 11

280.0psia Dew Point = 107.84 °F				310.0 psia Dew Point = 115.25 °F				340.0 psia Dew Point = 122.12 °F			
Temp °F	Density lb/ft³	Enthalpy Btu/lb	Entropy Btu/lb.F	Temp °F	Density lb/ft³	Enthalpy Btu/lb	Entropy Btu/lb.F	Temp °F	Density lb/ft³	Enthalpy Btu/lb	Entropy Btu/lb.F
110.00	6.59943	100.907	.1896								
115.00	6.43146	102.218	.1919								
120.00	6.27755	103.510	.1942	120.00	7.35042	101.875	.1899				
125.00	6.13551	104.787	.1963	125.00	7.14998	103.244	.1923	125.00	8.33884	101.466	.1880
130.00	6.00366	106.051	.1985	130.00	6.96798	104.588	.1946	130.00	8.07717	102.931	.1905
135.00	5.88064	107.305	.2006	135.00	6.80127	105.911	.1968	135.00	7.84441	104.355	.1929
140.00	5.76537	108.551	.2027	140.00	6.64749	107.219	.1990	140.00	7.63469	105.748	.1952
145.00	5.65695	109.789	.2048	145.00	6.50478	108.512	.2011	145.00	7.44380	107.116	.1975
150.00	5.55463	111.022	.2068	150.00	6.37167	109.795	.2032	150.00	7.26863	108.464	.1997
155.00	5.45780	112.259	.2088	155.00	6.24701	111.078	.2053	155.00	7.10683	109.807	.2019
160.00	5.36598	113.495	.2108	160.00	6.12986	112.356	.2074	160.00	6.95662	111.138	.2041
165.00	5.27868	114.727	.2128	165.00	6.01942	113.628	.2095	165.00	6.81646	112.458	.2062
170.00	5.19551	115.957	.2148	170.00	5.91496	114.894	.2115	170.00	6.68514	113.768	.2083
175.00	5.11611	117.186	.2167	175.00	5.81592	116.156	.2135	175.00	6.56164	115.071	.2103
180.00	5.04019	118.415	.2186	180.00	5.72178	117.417	.2154	180.00	6.44512	116.369	.2124
185.00	4.96747	119.643	.2205	185.00	5.63212	118.674	.2174	185.00	6.33488	117.661	.2144
190.00	4.89771	120.870	.2224	190.00	5.54655	119.929	.2193	190.00	6.23029	118.948	.2164
195.00	4.83069	122.096	.2243	195.00	5.46473	121.182	.2213	195.00	6.13083	120.230	.2183
200.00	4.76623	123.323	.2262	200.00	5.38637	122.432	.2232	200.00	6.03605	121.509	.2203
205.00	4.70414	124.549	.2280	205.00	5.31119	123.682	.2251	205.00	5.94554	122.785	.2222
210.00	4.64427	125.776	.2299	210.00	5.23898	124.931	.2269	210.00	5.85896	124.058	.2241
215.00	4.58647	127.004	.2317	215.00	5.16951	126.180	.2288	215.00	5.77600	125.331	.2260
220.00	4.53064	128.237	.2335	220.00	5.10262	127.433	.2306	220.00	5.69641	126.606	.2279
225.00	4.47665	129.470	.2353	225.00	5.03813	128.685	.2325	225.00	5.61994	127.880	.2298
230.00	4.42440	130.704	.2371	230.00	4.97590	129.938	.2343	230.00	5.54638	129.153	.2316
235.00	4.37378	131.940	.2389	235.00	4.91578	131.192	.2361	235.00	5.47553	130.425	.2335
240.00	4.32471	133.177	.2407	240.00	4.85765	132.445	.2379	240.00	5.40720	131.698	.2353
245.00	4.27710	134.416	.2424	245.00	4.80139	133.700	.2397	245.00	5.34125	132.970	.2371
250.00	4.23088	135.656	.2442	250.00	4.74689	134.956	.2415	250.00	5.27752	134.242	.2389
255.00	4.18598	136.898	.2459	255.00	4.69405	136.213	.2432	255.00	5.21587	135.515	.2407

Standard state : At -40°F, Liquid Enthalpy=0.0 Btu/lb, Liquid Entropy=0.0 Btu/lb.F

Version 2a 1st September 1993

KLEA® 407B

Superheated Vapor Properties

Table 2 Sheet 12

280.0psia Dew Point = 107.84 °F				310.0 psia Dew Point = 115.25 °F				340.0 psia Dew Point = 122.12 °F			
Temp °F	Density lb/ft³	Enthalpy Btu/lb	Entropy Btu/lb.F	Temp °F	Density lb/ft³	Enthalpy Btu/lb	Entropy Btu/lb.F	Temp °F	Density lb/ft³	Enthalpy Btu/lb	Entropy Btu/lb.F
260.00	4.14232	138.142	.2477	260.00	4.64279	137.471	.2450	260.00	5.15619	136.789	.2425
265.00	4.09985	139.388	.2494	265.00	4.59302	138.731	.2467	265.00	5.09837	138.064	.2442
270.00	4.05851	140.636	.2511	270.00	4.54466	139.993	.2485	270.00	5.04230	139.339	.2460
275.00	4.01825	141.886	.2528	275.00	4.49765	141.256	.2502	275.00	4.98790	140.616	.2477
280.00	3.97902	143.139	.2545	280.00	4.45191	142.521	.2519	280.00	4.93506	141.894	.2495
285.00	3.94077	144.394	.2562	285.00	4.40740	143.787	.2536	285.00	4.88371	143.173	.2512
290.00	3.90346	145.651	.2579	290.00	4.36404	145.056	.2553	290.00	4.83379	144.454	.2529
295.00	3.86705	146.910	.2596	295.00	4.32179	146.327	.2570	295.00	4.78521	145.737	.2546
300.00	3.83150	148.172	.2612	300.00	4.28060	147.600	.2587	300.00	4.73791	147.021	.2563
305.00	3.79678	149.437	.2629	305.00	4.24042	148.875	.2604	305.00	4.69184	148.307	.2580
310.00	3.76285	150.704	.2646	310.00	4.20120	150.152	.2620	310.00	4.64694	149.595	.2597
315.00	3.72969	151.974	.2662	315.00	4.16292	151.432	.2637	315.00	4.60316	150.885	.2613
320.00	3.69725	153.246	.2678	320.00	4.12552	152.714	.2653	320.00	4.56045	152.177	.2630
325.00	3.66552	154.522	.2695	325.00	4.08897	153.999	.2670	325.00	4.51876	153.472	.2647
330.00	3.63447	155.799	.2711	330.00	4.05325	155.286	.2686	330.00	4.47805	154.768	.2663
335.00	3.60406	157.080	.2727	335.00	4.01831	156.575	.2702	335.00	4.43827	156.067	.2679
340.00	3.57429	158.363	.2743	340.00	3.98413	157.867	.2719	340.00	4.39940	157.368	.2696
345.00	3.54512	159.650	.2759	345.00	3.95067	159.162	.2735	345.00	4.36140	158.671	.2712
350.00	3.51654	160.939	.2775	350.00	3.91792	160.459	.2751	350.00	4.32423	159.977	.2728
355.00	3.48853	162.231	.2791	355.00	3.88585	161.759	.2767	355.00	4.28786	161.285	.2744
360.00	3.46105	163.525	.2807	360.00	3.85443	163.062	.2783	360.00	4.25226	162.595	.2760
365.00	3.43411	164.823	.2823	365.00	3.82363	164.367	.2799	365.00	4.21741	163.908	.2776
370.00	3.40768	166.124	.2838	370.00	3.79345	165.675	.2814	370.00	4.18327	165.224	.2792
375.00	3.38174	167.427	.2854	375.00	3.76385	166.985	.2830	375.00	4.14982	166.542	.2808
380.00	3.35627	168.734	.2870	380.00	3.73482	168.299	.2846	380.00	4.11703	167.863	.2824
385.00	3.33127	170.043	.2885	385.00	3.70633	169.615	.2861	385.00	4.08489	169.186	.2840

Standard state : At -40°F, Liquid Enthalpy=0.0 Btu/lb, Liquid Entropy=0.0 Btu/lb.F

Version 2a 1st September 1993

KLEA® 407B

Superheated Vapor Properties

Table 2 Sheet 13

370.0psia Dew Point = 128.53 °F				400.0 psia Dew Point = 134.54 °F				430.0 psia Dew Point = 140.20 °F			
Temp °F	Density lb/ft³	Enthalpy Btu/lb	Entropy Btu/lb.F	Temp °F	Density lb/ft³	Enthalpy Btu/lb	Entropy Btu/lb.F	Temp °F	Density lb/ft³	Enthalpy Btu/lb	Entropy Btu/lb.F
130.00	9.40885	100.977	.1861								
135.00	9.06507	102.565	.1888	135.00	10.57627	100.392	.1842				
140.00	8.76736	104.088	.1913	140.00	10.11994	102.141	.1871				
145.00	8.50450	105.563	.1938	145.00	9.73860	103.787	.1898	145.00	11.24773	101.658	.1854
150.00	8.26902	107.001	.1961	150.00	9.41023	105.359	.1924	150.00	10.75831	103.454	.1884
155.00	8.05575	108.422	.1985	155.00	9.12160	106.891	.1949	155.00	10.34980	105.156	.1912
160.00	7.86096	109.824	.2007	160.00	8.86414	108.386	.1973	160.00	9.99868	106.785	.1938
165.00	7.68172	111.204	.2030	165.00	8.63171	109.846	.1997	165.00	9.69049	108.355	.1963
170.00	7.51576	112.568	.2051	170.00	8.41988	111.280	.2020	170.00	9.41573	109.880	.1988
175.00	7.36128	113.920	.2073	175.00	8.22530	112.693	.2042	175.00	9.16782	111.372	.2011
180.00	7.21685	115.263	.2094	180.00	8.04546	114.091	.2064	180.00	8.94204	112.838	.2034
185.00	7.08129	116.596	.2115	185.00	7.87832	115.473	.2086	185.00	8.73481	114.280	.2057
190.00	6.95360	117.921	.2135	190.00	7.72224	116.841	.2107	190.00	8.54334	115.702	.2079
195.00	6.83295	119.237	.2155	195.00	7.57589	118.199	.2128	195.00	8.36545	117.107	.2100
200.00	6.71864	120.548	.2175	200.00	7.43817	119.546	.2148	200.00	8.19940	118.498	.2121
205.00	6.61006	121.854	.2195	205.00	7.30814	120.886	.2168	205.00	8.04374	119.877	.2142
210.00	6.50670	123.155	.2214	210.00	7.18504	122.218	.2188	210.00	7.89730	121.246	.2163
215.00	6.40809	124.454	.2234	215.00	7.06819	123.547	.2208	215.00	7.75908	122.607	.2183
220.00	6.31386	125.754	.2253	220.00	6.95704	124.875	.2228	220.00	7.62829	123.967	.2203
225.00	6.22368	127.051	.2272	225.00	6.85111	126.198	.2247	225.00	7.50421	125.319	.2223
230.00	6.13722	128.346	.2291	230.00	6.74994	127.518	.2266	230.00	7.38622	126.666	.2243
235.00	6.05421	129.640	.2309	235.00	6.65316	128.835	.2285	235.00	7.27379	128.008	.2262
240.00	5.97442	130.932	.2328	240.00	6.56042	130.149	.2304	240.00	7.16643	129.346	.2281
245.00	5.89760	132.223	.2346	245.00	6.47142	131.460	.2323	245.00	7.06374	130.680	.2300
250.00	5.82357	133.514	.2365	250.00	6.38588	132.770	.2341	250.00	6.96536	132.011	.2319
255.00	5.75214	134.804	.2383	255.00	6.30357	134.079	.2360	255.00	6.87096	133.340	.2338
260.00	5.68315	136.094	.2401	260.00	6.22428	135.387	.2378	260.00	6.78025	134.666	.2356
265.00	5.61645	137.385	.2419	265.00	6.14779	136.694	.2396	265.00	6.69297	135.991	.2374
270.00	5.55190	138.675	.2436	270.00	6.07394	138.000	.2414	270.00	6.60889	137.315	.2393
275.00	5.48939	139.966	.2454	275.00	6.00256	139.307	.2432	275.00	6.52780	138.638	.2411

Standard state : At -40°F, Liquid Enthalpy=0.0 Btu/lb, Liquid Entropy=0.0 Btu/lb.F

KLEA® 407B

Superheated Vapor Properties

Table 2 Sheet 14

370.0psia Dew Point = 128.53 °F				400.0 psia Dew Point = 134.54 °F				430.0 psia Dew Point = 140.20 °F			
Temp °F	Density lb/ft³	Enthalpy Btu/lb	Entropy Btu/lb.F	Temp °F	Density lb/ft³	Enthalpy Btu/lb	Entropy Btu/lb.F	Temp °F	Density lb/ft³	Enthalpy Btu/lb	Entropy Btu/lb.F
280.00	5.42880	141.258	.2472	280.00	5.93350	140.614	.2450	280.00	6.44952	139.960	.2429
285.00	5.37003	142.551	.2489	285.00	5.86664	141.920	.2467	285.00	6.37387	141.282	.2446
290.00	5.31297	143.845	.2506	290.00	5.80184	143.228	.2485	290.00	6.30068	142.603	.2464
295.00	5.25754	145.140	.2523	295.00	5.73900	144.536	.2502	295.00	6.22983	143.925	.2482
300.00	5.20365	146.436	.2541	300.00	5.67801	145.844	.2519	300.00	6.16117	145.247	.2499
305.00	5.15124	147.734	.2558	305.00	5.61877	147.154	.2537	305.00	6.09459	146.569	.2516
310.00	5.10023	149.033	.2575	310.00	5.56119	148.465	.2554	310.00	6.02997	147.892	.2534
315.00	5.05055	150.334	.2591	315.00	5.50520	149.777	.2571	315.00	5.96722	149.216	.2551
320.00	5.00215	151.636	.2608	320.00	5.45071	151.090	.2588	320.00	5.90623	150.540	.2568
325.00	4.95496	152.941	.2625	325.00	5.39766	152.405	.2604	325.00	5.84693	151.866	.2585
330.00	4.90893	154.247	.2641	330.00	5.34597	153.722	.2621	330.00	5.78922	153.193	.2602
335.00	4.86402	155.555	.2658	335.00	5.29559	155.040	.2638	335.00	5.73303	154.521	.2618
340.00	4.82017	156.865	.2674	340.00	5.24646	156.359	.2654	340.00	5.67830	155.851	.2635
345.00	4.77734	158.177	.2691	345.00	5.19851	157.681	.2671	345.00	5.62495	157.182	.2652
350.00	4.73549	159.492	.2707	350.00	5.15172	159.004	.2687	350.00	5.57293	158.514	.2668
355.00	4.69458	160.808	.2723	355.00	5.10601	160.329	.2703	355.00	5.52217	159.848	.2685
360.00	4.65457	162.127	.2739	360.00	5.06136	161.657	.2720	360.00	5.47262	161.184	.2701
365.00	4.61544	163.448	.2755	365.00	5.01772	162.986	.2736	365.00	5.42424	162.522	.2717
370.00	4.57714	164.771	.2771	370.00	4.97504	164.317	.2752	370.00	5.37697	163.862	.2734
375.00	4.53964	166.097	.2787	375.00	4.93330	165.651	.2768	375.00	5.33077	165.203	.2750
380.00	4.50292	167.425	.2803	380.00	4.89245	166.987	.2784	380.00	5.28559	166.547	.2766
385.00	4.46694	168.756	.2819	385.00	4.85246	168.325	.2800	385.00	5.24141	167.892	.2782
390.00	4.43169	170.089	.2835	390.00	4.81330	169.665	.2816	390.00	5.19817	169.240	.2798
395.00	4.39714	171.424	.2850	395.00	4.77494	171.007	.2831	395.00	5.15585	170.589	.2813
400.00	4.36325	172.762	.2866	400.00	4.73736	172.352	.2847	400.00	5.11441	171.941	.2829
405.00	4.33002	174.103	.2882	405.00	4.70052	173.699	.2863	405.00	5.07381	173.295	.2845

Standard state : At -40°F, Liquid Enthalpy=0.0 Btu/lb, Liquid Entropy=0.0 Btu/lb.F

Version 2a 1st September 1993

TABLE 3

TABLE OF EVAPORATOR INLET TEMPERATURES

(1) Read the enthalpy value at the expansion valve along top of the table.

(2) Read down the table for the evaporator operating pressure.

(3) The value in the table is the evaporator inlet temperature in °F.

(4) The evaporator outlet temperature is the dew point temperature at the evaporator operating pressure.

KLEA® 407B

Evaporator Inlet Temperatures

Table 3 Sheet 1

Pressure psia	Enthalpy in Btu/lb -5.00	0.00	5.00	10.00	15.00	20.00	25.00	30.00	35.00
	°F	°F	°F	°F	°F	°F	°F	°F	°F
10.00	-66.70	-66.45	-66.18	-65.89	-65.57	-65.24	-64.88	-64.50	-64.08
15.00	-56.81	-52.20	-51.94	-51.66	-51.35	-51.03	-50.69	-50.32	-49.92
20.00		-41.32	-41.06	-40.78	-40.48	-40.17	-39.84	-39.48	-39.10
25.00			-32.13	-31.86	-31.57	-31.26	-30.93	-30.58	-30.21
30.00			-24.51	-24.23	-23.94	-23.64	-23.31	-22.97	-22.61
35.00			-23.24	-17.53	-17.25	-16.94	-16.63	-16.29	-15.93
40.00				-11.54	-11.25	-10.95	-10.64	-10.30	-9.95
45.00				-11.47	-5.81	-5.51	-5.20	-4.87	-4.52
50.00				-6.61	-.81	-.51	-.20	.12	.47
55.00					3.82	4.11	4.42	4.75	5.09
60.00					8.13	8.43	8.73	9.06	9.40
65.00					9.81	12.48	12.78	13.10	13.44
70.00						16.29	16.60	16.92	17.25
75.00						19.91	20.21	20.53	20.86
80.00						23.34	23.65	23.96	24.30
85.00						25.90	26.92	27.24	27.57
90.00							30.05	30.37	30.70
95.00							33.05	33.37	33.70
100.00							35.94	36.25	36.58

KLEA® 407B

Evaporator Inlet Temperatures

Table 3 Sheet 2

Pressure psia	Enthalpy in Btu/lb 40.00	45.00	50.00	55.00	60.00	65.00	70.00	75.00	80.00
	°F	°F	°F	°F	°F	°F	°F	°F	°F
10.00	-63.63	-63.15	-62.63	-62.08	-61.48	-60.85	-60.18	-59.47	-58.74
15.00	-49.50	-49.05	-48.56	-48.04	-47.48	-46.89	-46.26	-45.60	-45.47
20.00	-38.69	-38.25	-37.79	-37.29	-36.76	-36.19	-35.59	-34.96	-34.30
25.00	-29.81	-29.39	-28.94	-28.46	-27.95	-27.40	-26.83	-26.22	-25.58
30.00	-22.22	-21.81	-21.37	-20.90	-20.40	-19.88	-19.32	-18.73	-18.11
35.00	-15.55	-15.14	-14.71	-14.26	-13.77	-13.26	-12.72	-12.14	-11.54
40.00	-9.57	-9.18	-8.75	-8.31	-7.83	-7.33	-6.80	-6.24	-5.65
45.00	-4.15	-3.75	-3.34	-2.90	-2.44	-1.94	-1.42	-.87	-.29
50.00	.84	1.22	1.63	2.06	2.52	3.01	3.52	4.06	4.63
55.00	5.45	5.83	6.24	6.66	7.12	7.59	8.10	8.63	9.18
60.00	9.76	10.14	10.53	10.96	11.40	11.87	12.37	12.89	13.44
65.00	13.80	14.17	14.57	14.98	15.42	15.89	16.38	16.89	17.43
70.00	17.61	17.98	18.37	18.78	19.22	19.68	20.16	20.67	21.20
75.00	21.21	21.58	21.97	22.38	22.81	23.27	23.74	24.25	24.77
80.00	24.64	25.01	25.40	25.80	26.23	26.68	27.15	27.65	28.17
85.00	27.91	28.28	28.66	29.06	29.49	29.93	30.40	30.89	31.41
90.00	31.04	31.40	31.78	32.18	32.60	33.04	33.51	33.99	34.50
95.00	34.04	34.40	34.78	35.17	35.59	36.03	36.49	36.97	37.47
100.00	36.92	37.28	37.65	38.05	38.46	38.89	39.35	39.83	40.33

Notes

ICI Klea
Concord Plaza
3411 Silverside Road
P.O. Box 15391
Wilmington, DE 19850

Customer Service: (800) ICI-KLEA or
Technical Assistance: (800) ASK-KLEA
Fax: (302) 887-7706

620250391 3/95

Thermodynamic Properties of KLEA® 407C (KLEA® 66)

British Units

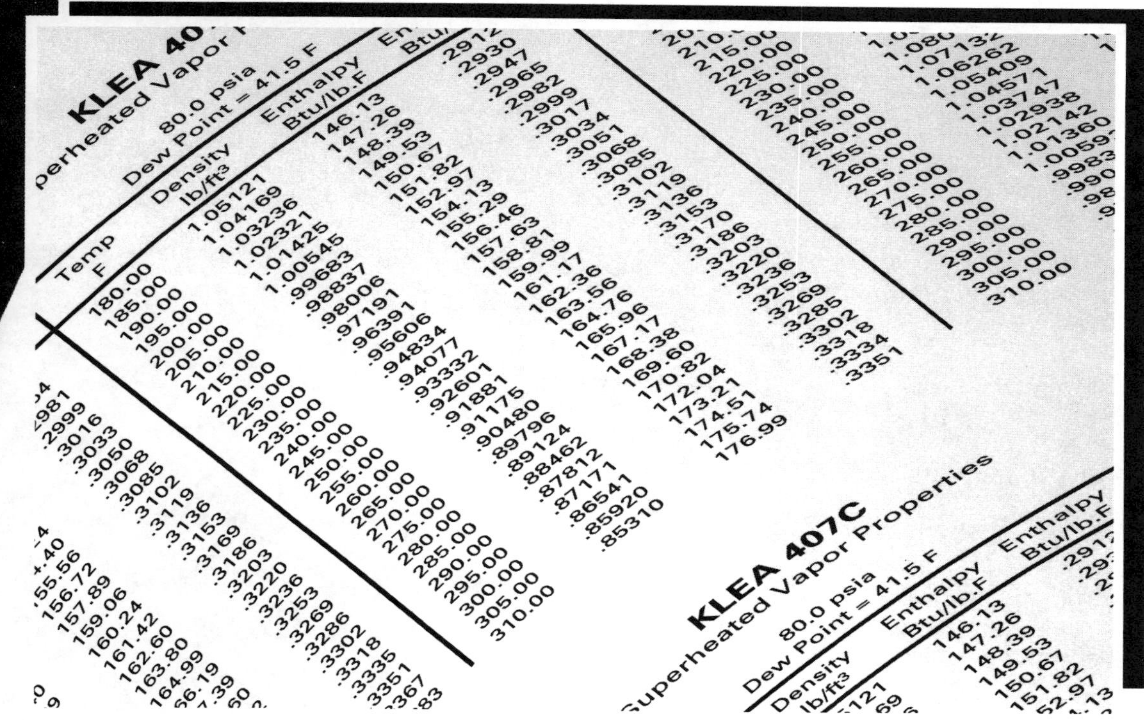

**NOW.
AND FOR
THE FUTURE.**

Thermodynamic Property Data for

KLEA® 407C

British Units

Saturated Liquid and Saturated Vapor Properties
Superheated Vapor Properties
Evaporator Inlet Temperatures

SYSTEM PERFORMANCE WITH NON-AZEOTROPIC REFRIGERANT BLENDS

- With a non-azeotropic refrigerant blend the composition of the vapour changes in the evaporator and the condenser.

- Evaporator inlet and outlet temperatures are different.

- Condenser inlet and outlet temperatures are different.

- At all other points in the system the fluid behaves as normal.

- System design path.

  - Select evaporator outlet (Dew point 'A') against the desired cold space temperature.

  - Condenser inlet and outlet temperatures 'B' & 'C' should be sufficient to reject heat.

  - Liquid enthalpy at expansion device and table 3 can be used to get evaporator inlet temperature 'D'.

  - Refrigeration effect is enthalpy change 'D' to 'A' as normal.

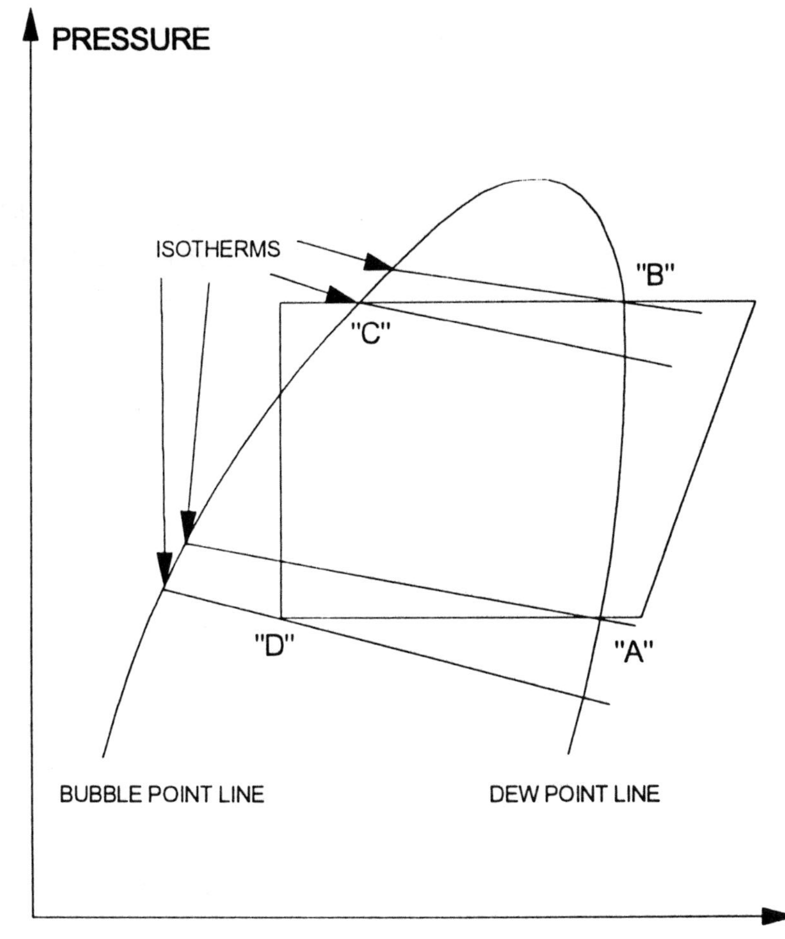

Pressure - Enthalpy Diagram for Non-azeotropic Refrigerant Blends

KLEA® 407C

Saturated Liquid and Saturated Vapor Properties

Table1 Sheet 1

Pressure psia	Dew Point °F	Bubble Point °F	Liquid Density lb/ft³	Vapor Density lb/ft³	Liquid Enthalpy Btu/lb	Vapor Enthalpy Btu/lb	Vapor Entropy Btu/lb.F
10.00	-47.90	-61.06	87.659	.19929	-6.946	103.715	.25630
11.00	-44.64	-57.72	87.313	.21786	-5.841	104.216	.25536
12.00	-41.59	-54.62	86.990	.23632	-4.815	104.682	.25453
13.00	-38.75	-51.72	86.686	.25469	-3.857	105.117	.25377
14.00	-36.07	-48.99	86.398	.27298	-2.956	105.526	.25307
15.00	-33.53	-46.40	86.125	.29119	-2.106	105.912	.25244
16.00	-31.13	-43.95	85.865	.30933	-1.300	106.277	.25185
17.00	-28.84	-41.62	85.617	.32741	-.533	106.625	.25130
18.00	-26.65	-39.40	85.379	.34543	.199	106.956	.25080
19.00	-24.56	-37.26	85.150	.36340	.899	107.272	.25032
20.00	-22.55	-35.22	84.929	.38133	1.570	107.575	.24988
21.00	-20.62	-33.25	84.716	.39920	2.215	107.865	.24946
22.00	-18.76	-31.35	84.511	.41704	2.837	108.144	.24906
23.00	-16.96	-29.53	84.311	.43484	3.437	108.413	.24869
24.00	-15.23	-27.76	84.118	.45260	4.017	108.673	.24833
25.00	-13.55	-26.05	83.930	.47033	4.578	108.923	.24799
26.00	-11.92	-24.39	83.748	.48802	5.122	109.166	.24767
27.00	-10.34	-22.78	83.570	.50569	5.650	109.400	.24736
28.00	-8.80	-21.21	83.397	.52334	6.163	109.628	.24707
29.00	-7.31	-19.69	83.228	.54096	6.663	109.848	.24679
30.00	-5.85	-18.21	83.063	.55855	7.149	110.063	.24652
31.00	-4.44	-16.76	82.901	.57613	7.623	110.271	.24626
32.00	-3.05	-15.35	82.743	.59368	8.085	110.474	.24601
33.00	-1.70	-13.98	82.589	.61122	8.537	110.671	.24577
34.00	-.38	-12.64	82.438	.62874	8.978	110.863	.24554
35.00	.90	-11.32	82.289	.64624	9.409	111.051	.24531
36.00	2.16	-10.04	82.144	.66373	9.831	111.234	.24510
37.00	3.40	-8.78	82.001	.68120	10.245	111.413	.24489
38.00	4.61	-7.55	81.860	.69867	10.650	111.587	.24469
39.00	5.79	-6.34	81.722	.71612	11.047	111.758	.24449
40.00	6.95	-5.16	81.587	.73356	11.437	111.924	.24430

Standard state: At -40°F, Liquid Enthalpy = 0.0 Btu/lb, Liquid Entropy = 0.0 Btu/lb.F

KLEA® 407C

Saturated Liquid and Saturated Vapor Properties

Table1 Sheet 2

Pressure psia	Dew Point °F	Bubble Point °F	Liquid Density lb/ft^3	Vapor Density lb/ft^3	Liquid Enthalpy Btu/lb	Vapor Enthalpy Btu/lb	Vapor Entropy Btu/lb.F
40.00	6.95	-5.16	81.587	.73356	11.437	111.924	.24430
45.00	12.44	.43	80.940	.82063	13.282	112.707	.24343
50.00	17.47	5.57	80.339	.90755	14.982	113.416	.24266
55.00	22.14	10.32	79.776	.99440	16.562	114.064	.24198
60.00	26.48	14.76	79.244	1.08125	18.040	114.659	.24137
65.00	30.56	18.92	78.739	1.16813	19.434	115.210	.24081
70.00	34.40	22.85	78.257	1.25511	20.753	115.721	.24030
75.00	38.04	26.57	77.796	1.34222	22.007	116.199	.23983
80.00	41.50	30.10	77.352	1.42949	23.205	116.646	.23938
85.00	44.79	33.47	76.925	1.51695	24.353	117.065	.23897
90.00	47.94	36.69	76.512	1.60464	25.456	117.460	.23858
95.00	50.96	39.78	76.111	1.69257	26.518	117.832	.23821
100.00	53.85	42.75	75.722	1.78077	27.543	118.184	.23785
105.00	56.64	45.61	75.344	1.86927	28.536	118.517	.23752
110.00	59.33	48.37	74.975	1.95807	29.498	118.833	.23719
115.00	61.93	51.04	74.615	2.04721	30.432	119.133	.23688
120.00	64.44	53.62	74.263	2.13669	31.341	119.417	.23658
125.00	66.87	56.12	73.918	2.22654	32.226	119.688	.23628
130.00	69.23	58.54	73.580	2.31677	33.089	119.946	.23600
135.00	71.52	60.90	73.249	2.40740	33.932	120.191	.23572
140.00	73.74	63.19	72.923	2.49844	34.756	120.425	.23546
145.00	75.91	65.42	72.602	2.58991	35.562	120.648	.23519
150.00	78.02	67.59	72.287	2.68182	36.352	120.860	.23493
155.00	80.07	69.71	71.976	2.77419	37.126	121.063	.23468
160.00	82.08	71.78	71.670	2.86702	37.886	121.256	.23443

Standard state: At -40°F, Liquid Enthalpy = 0.0 Btu/lb, Liquid Entropy = 0.0 Btu/lb.F

KLEA® 407C

Saturated Liquid and Saturated Vapor Properties

Table1 Sheet 3

Pressure psia	Dew Point °F	Bubble Point °F	Liquid Density lb/ft³	Vapor Density lb/ft³	Liquid Enthalpy Btu/lb	Vapor Enthalpy Btu/lb	Vapor Entropy Btu/lb.F
160.00	82.08	71.78	71.670	2.86702	37.886	121.256	.23443
170.00	85.95	75.78	71.068	3.05416	39.367	121.616	.23394
180.00	89.64	79.60	70.481	3.24333	40.798	121.944	.23347
190.00	93.19	83.27	69.905	3.43465	42.187	122.241	.23300
200.00	96.59	86.80	69.339	3.62823	43.538	122.511	.23254
210.00	99.86	90.20	68.783	3.82418	44.853	122.755	.23209
220.00	103.01	93.48	68.233	4.02261	46.138	122.974	.23164
230.00	106.05	96.65	67.690	4.22362	47.394	123.170	.23119
240.00	109.00	99.71	67.152	4.42735	48.625	123.345	.23074
250.00	111.84	102.69	66.617	4.63391	49.832	123.499	.23030
260.00	114.60	105.58	66.086	4.84343	51.019	123.633	.22985
270.00	117.28	108.38	65.556	5.05603	52.186	123.747	.22940
280.00	119.88	111.11	65.026	5.27187	53.336	123.844	.22895
290.00	122.41	113.77	64.496	5.49109	54.471	123.923	.22849
300.00	124.88	116.36	63.964	5.71383	55.591	123.984	.22803
310.00	127.27	118.89	63.430	5.94028	56.699	124.029	.22756
320.00	129.61	121.36	62.891	6.17059	57.795	124.056	.22709
330.00	131.89	123.77	62.347	6.40496	58.881	124.068	.22661
340.00	134.12	126.13	61.795	6.64359	59.959	124.064	.22613
350.00	136.29	128.44	61.234	6.88669	61.028	124.043	.22563
360.00	138.41	130.70	60.661	7.13448	62.091	124.007	.22513
370.00	140.49	132.92	60.074	7.38723	63.148	123.955	.22462
380.00	142.52	135.09	59.469	7.64518	64.200	123.887	.22409
390.00	144.51	137.22	58.841	7.90865	65.249	123.803	.22356
400.00	146.46	139.31	58.184	8.17794	66.296	123.702	.22301
410.00	148.37	141.37	57.488	8.45339	67.340	123.586	.22245
420.00	150.24	143.38	56.738	8.73540	68.385	123.453	.22188
430.00	152.08	145.37	55.909	9.02438	69.430	123.303	.22130

Standard state: At -40°F, Liquid Enthalpy = 0.0 Btu/lb, Liquid Entropy = 0.0 Btu/lb.F

KLEA® 407C

Superheated Vapor Properties

Table 2 Sheet 1

10 psia Dew Point -47.90 °F				20.0 psia Dew Point -22.55 °F				30.0 psia Dew Point -5.85 °F			
Temp °F	Density lb/ft3	Enthalpy Btu/lb	Entropy Btu/lb.F	Temp °F	Density lb/ft3	Enthalpy Btu/lb	Entropy Btu/lb.F	Temp °F	Density lb/ft3	Enthalpy Btu/lb	Entropy Btu/lb.F
-45.00	.19781	104.21	.2575								
-40.00	.19532	105.07	.2596								
-35.00	.19289	105.93	.2616								
-30.00	.19052	106.80	.2636								
-25.00	.18821	107.67	.2656								
-20.00	.18596	108.55	.2677	-20.00	.37887	108.03	.2509				
-15.00	.18376	109.43	.2697	-15.00	.37416	108.92	.2529				
-10.00	.18162	110.32	.2716	-10.00	.36957	109.82	.2549				
-5.00	.17953	111.22	.2736	-5.00	.36511	110.73	.2569	-5.00	.55734	110.22	.2469
.00	.17748	112.12	.2756	.00	.36075	111.64	.2589	.00	.55036	111.14	.2489
5.00	.17549	113.02	.2776	5.00	.35651	112.55	.2609	5.00	.54357	112.06	.2509
10.00	.17354	113.94	2795	10.00	.35237	113.47	.2629	10.00	.53696	112.99	.2529
15.00	.17163	114.85	.2814	15.00	.34833	114.40	.2648	15.00	.53052	113.93	.2548
20.00	.16977	115.78	.2834	20.00	.34439	115.33	.2668	20.00	.52425	114.86	.2568
25.00	.16795	116.70	.2853	25.00	.34054	116.26	.2687	25.00	.51814	115.81	.2588
30.00	.16617	117.64	.2872	30.00	.33678	117.20	.2707	30.00	.51218	116.76	.2607
35.00	.16443	118.58	.2891	35.00	.33311	118.15	.2726	35.00	.50637	117.71	.2627
40.00	.16272	119.52	.2910	40.00	.32952	119.10	.2745	40.00	.50070	118.67	.2646
45.00	.16105	120.47	.2929	45.00	.32602	120.06	.2764	45.00	.49517	119.63	.2665
50.00	.15941	121.43	.2948	50.00	.32259	121.02	.2783	50.00	.48977	120.60	.2684
55.00	.15781	122.39	.2967	55.00	.31923	121.99	.2802	55.00	.48449	121.58	.2703
60.00	.15624	123.35	.2986	60.00	.31595	122.96	.2821	60.00	.47933	122.56	.2722
65.00	.15471	124.33	.3004	65.00	.31274	123.94	.2839	65.00	.47429	123.54	.2741
70.00	.15320	125.30	.3023	70.00	.30959	124.92	.2858	70.00	.46937	124.53	.2760
75.00	.15172	126.29	.3041	75.00	.30652	125.91	.2877	75.00	.46455	125.53	.2778
80.00	.15028	127.28	.3060	80.00	.30350	126.90	.2895	80.00	.45983	126.53	.2797
85.00	.14886	128.27	.3078	85.00	.30055	127.90	.2914	85.00	.45522	127.53	.2816
90.00	.14746	129.27	.3096	90.00	.29765	128.91	.2932	90.00	.45070	128.54	.2834
95.00	.14610	130.27	.3114	95.00	.29481	129.92	.2950	95.00	.44628	129.56	.2852

Standard state: At -40°F, Liquid Enthalpy = 0.0 Btu/lb, Liquid Entropy = 0.0 Btu/lb.F

KLEA® 407C

Superheated Vapor Properties

Table 2 Sheet 2

10 psia, Dew Point -47.90 ˚F				20.0 psia, Dew Point -22.55 ˚F				30.0 psia, Dew Point -5.85 ˚F			
Temp ˚F	Density lb/ft3	Enthalpy Btu/lb	Entropy Btu/lb.F	Temp ˚F	Density lb/ft3	Enthalpy Btu/lb	Entropy Btu/lb.F	Temp ˚F	Density lb/ft3	Enthalpy Btu/lb	Entropy Btu/lb.F
100.00	.14476	131.28	.3132	100.00	.29203	130.93	.2968	100.00	.44195	130.58	.2871
105.00	.14344	132.30	.3151	105.00	.28930	131.95	.2987	105.00	.43771	131.60	.2889
110.00	.14215	133.32	.3169	110.00	.28663	132.98	.3005	110.00	.43355	132.63	.2907
115.00	.14088	134.34	.3186	115.00	.28401	134.01	.3023	115.00	.42947	133.67	.2925
120.00	.13963	135.38	.3204	120.00	.28143	135.05	.3041	120.00	.42548	134.71	.2943
125.00	.13841	136.41	.3222	125.00	.27890	136.09	.3059	125.00	.42156	135.76	.2961
130.00	.13721	137.46	.3240	130.00	.27642	137.13	.3076	130.00	.41772	136.81	.2979
135.00	.13603	138.50	.3258	135.00	.27399	138.18	.3094	135.00	.41395	137.86	.2997
140.00	.13487	139.56	.3275	140.00	.27160	139.24	.3112	140.00	.41026	138.92	.3015
145.00	.13373	140.61	.3293	145.00	.26925	140.30	.3129	145.00	.40663	139.99	.3032
150.00	.13261	141.68	.3310	150.00	.26694	141.37	.3147	150.00	.40306	141.06	.3050
155.00	.13150	142.74	.3328	155.00	.26468	142.44	.3165	155.00	.39957	142.14	.3068
160.00	.13042	143.82	.3345	160.00	.26245	143.52	.3182	160.00	.39613	143.22	.3085
165.00	.12936	144.90	.3362	165.00	.26026	144.60	.3199	165.00	.39276	144.31	.3103
170.00	.12831	145.98	.3380	170.00	.25811	145.69	.3217	170.00	.38945	145.40	.3120
175.00	.12728	147.07	.3397	175.00	.25599	146.78	.3234	175.00	.38619	146.50	.3137
180.00	.12626	148.17	.3414	180.00	.25391	147.88	.3251	180.00	.38299	147.60	.3155
185.00	.12527	149.27	.3431	185.00	.25187	148.99	.3268	185.00	.37985	148.71	.3172
190.00	.12428	150.37	.3448	190.00	.24986	150.10	.3286	190.00	.37676	149.82	.3189
195.00	.12332	151.48	.3465	195.00	.24788	151.21	.3303	195.00	.37372	150.93	.3206
200.00	.12237	152.60	.3482	200.00	.24593	152.33	.3320	200.00	.37073	152.06	.3223
205.00	.12143	153.72	.3499	205.00	.24402	153.45	.3337	205.00	.36779	153.18	.3240
210.00	.12051	154.84	.3516	210.00	.24213	154.58	.3354	210.00	.36490	154.32	.3257
215.00	.11960	155.97	.3533	215.00	.24028	155.71	.3370	215.00	.36206	155.45	.3274
220.00	.11870	157.11	.3550	220.00	.23845	156.85	.3387	220.00	.35926	156.60	.3291
225.00	.11782	158.25	.3566	225.00	.23665	158.00	.3404	225.00	.35651	157.75	.3308
230.00	.11696	159.39	.3583	230.00	.23488	159.15	.3421	230.00	.35380	158.90	.3325
235.00	.11610	160.54	.3600	235.00	.23314	160.30	.3437	235.00	.35114	160.06	.3341

Standard state: At -40˚F, Liquid Enthalpy = 0.0 Btu/lb, Liquid Entropy = 0.0 Btu/lb.F

KLEA® 407C

Superheated Vapor Properties

Table 2 Sheet 3

40.0 psia Dew Point = 6.95 °F				50.0 psia Dew Point = 17.47 °F				60.0 psia Dew Point = 26.48 °F			
Temp °F	Density lb/ft³	Enthalpy Btu/lb	Entropy Btu/lb.F	Temp °F	Density lb/ft³	Enthalpy Btu/lb	Entropy Btu/lb.F	Temp °F	Density lb/ft³	Enthalpy Btu/lb	Entropy Btu/lb.F
10.00	.72785	112.50	.2455								
15.00	.71870	113.44	.2475								
20.00	.70981	114.39	.2495	20.00	.90161	113.90	.2437				
25.00	.70117	115.34	.2515	25.00	.89011	114.86	.2457				
30.00	.69276	116.30	.2535	30.00	.87894	115.83	.2477	30.00	1.07126	115.35	.2428
35.00	.68456	117.26	.2554	35.00	.86809	116.80	.2496	35.00	1.05742	116.33	.2448
40.00	.67659	118.23	.2574	40.00	.85755	117.78	.2516	40.00	1.04400	117.31	.2468
45.00	.66881	119.20	.2593	45.00	.84729	118.76	.2535	45.00	1.03097	118.30	.2487
50.00	.66123	120.18	.2612	50.00	.83730	119.74	.2555	50.00	1.01832	119.30	.2507
55.00	.65384	121.16	.2631	55.00	.82758	120.73	.2574	55.00	1.00602	120.30	.2526
60.00	.64663	122.15	.2650	60.00	.81811	121.73	.2593	60.00	.99406	121.30	.2546
65.00	.63959	123.14	.2669	65.00	.80888	122.73	.2613	65.00	.98242	122.30	.2565
70.00	.63272	124.13	.2688	70.00	.79988	123.73	.2632	70.00	.97109	123.32	.2584
75.00	.62600	125.14	.2707	75.00	.79110	124.74	.2651	75.00	.96005	124.33	.2603
80.00	.61944	126.14	.2726	80.00	.78253	125.75	.2669	80.00	.94930	125.35	.2622
85.00	.61303	127.15	.2744	85.00	.77417	126.77	.2688	85.00	.93881	126.37	.2641
90.00	.60676	128.17	.2763	90.00	.76600	127.79	.2707	90.00	.92859	127.40	.2660
95.00	.60063	129.19	.2782	95.00	.75802	128.82	.2725	95.00	.91861	128.44	.2679
100.00	.59463	130.22	.2800	100.00	.75023	129.85	.2744	100.00	.90888	129.48	.2697
105.00	.58876	131.25	.2818	105.00	.74260	130.89	.2762	105.00	.89937	130.52	.2716
110.00	.58302	132.28	.2837	110.00	.73515	131.93	.2781	110.00	.89008	131.57	.2734
115.00	.57739	133.32	.2855	115.00	.72786	132.97	.2799	115.00	.88100	132.62	.2753
120.00	.57188	134.37	.2873	120.00	.72072	134.02	.2817	120.00	.87213	133.67	.2771
125.00	.56648	135.42	.2891	125.00	.71374	135.08	.2835	125.00	.86345	134.74	.2789
130.00	.56119	136.48	.2909	130.00	.70690	136.14	.2853	130.00	.85497	135.80	.2807
135.00	.55600	137.54	.2927	135.00	.70021	137.21	.2871	135.00	.84666	136.87	.2825
140.00	.55091	138.60	.2945	140.00	.69365	138.28	.2889	140.00	.83853	137.95	.2843
145.00	.54593	139.67	.2962	145.00	.68722	139.35	.2907	145.00	.83057	139.03	.2861
150.00	.54103	140.75	.2980	150.00	.68092	140.43	.2925	150.00	.82278	140.11	.2879

Standard state: At -40 °F, Liquid Enthalpy = 0.0 Btu/lb, Liquid Entropy = 0.0 Btu/lb.F

KLEA® 407C

Superheated Vapor Properties

Table 2 Sheet 4

40.0 psia Dew Point = 6.95 ˚F				50.0 psia Dew Point = 17.47 ˚F				60.0 psia Dew Point = 26.48 ˚F			
Temp ˚F	Density lb/ft^3	Enthalpy Btu/lb	Entropy Btu/lb.F	Temp ˚F	Density lb/ft^3	Enthalpy Btu/lb	Entropy Btu/lb.F	Temp ˚F	Density lb/ft^3	Enthalpy Btu/lb	Entropy Btu/lb.F
155.00	.53623	141.83	.2998	155.00	.67474	141.52	.2943	155.00	.81514	141.20	.2897
160.00	.53153	142.92	.3015	160.00	.66868	142.61	.2960	160.00	.80766	142.30	.2915
165.00	.52690	144.01	.3033	165.00	.66274	143.70	.2978	165.00	.80033	143.40	.2933
170.00	.52237	145.10	.3050	170.00	.65691	144.80	.2996	170.00	.79314	144.50	.2950
175.00	.51791	146.20	.3068	175.00	.65120	145.91	.3013	175.00	.78609	145.61	.2968
180.00	.51353	147.31	.3085	180.00	.64558	147.02	.3030	180.00	.77918	146.73	.2985
185.00	.50924	148.42	.3102	185.00	.64007	148.13	.3048	185.00	.77240	147.85	.3003
190.00	.50501	149.54	.3120	190.00	.63467	149.26	.3065	190.00	.76575	148.97	.3020
195.00	.50087	150.66	.3137	195.00	.62935	150.38	.3082	195.00	.75922	150.10	.3037
200.00	.49679	151.78	.3154	200.00	.62414	151.51	.3100	200.00	.75281	151.23	.3055
205.00	.49278	152.92	.3171	205.00	.61901	152.65	.3117	205.00	.74651	152.37	.3072
210.00	.48884	154.05	.3188	210.00	.61398	153.78	.3134	210.00	.74033	153.52	.3089
215.00	.48497	155.19	.3205	215.00	.60903	154.93	.3151	215.00	.73426	154.66	.3106
220.00	.48116	156.34	.3222	220.00	.60416	156.08	.3168	220.00	.72830	155.82	.3123
225.00	.47741	157.49	.3239	225.00	.59938	157.24	.3185	225.00	.72244	156.98	.3140
230.00	.47373	158.65	.3256	230.00	.59468	158.40	.3202	230.00	.71668	158.14	.3157
235.00	.47010	159.81	.3273	235.00	.59006	159.56	.3219	235.00	.71102	159.31	.3174
240.00	.46653	160.98	.3289	240.00	.58551	160.73	.3235	240.00	.70546	160.48	.3191
245.00	.46302	162.15	.3306	245.00	.58104	161.90	.3252	245.00	.69999	161.66	.3207
250.00	.45957	163.32	.3323	250.00	.57664	163.08	.3269	250.00	.69461	162.84	.3224
255.00	.45617	164.50	.3339	255.00	.57231	164.27	.3285	255.00	.68932	164.03	.3241
260.00	.45282	165.69	.3356	260.00	.56805	165.46	.3302	260.00	.68412	165.22	.3257
265.00	.44952	166.88	.3372	265.00	.56385	166.65	.3318	265.00	.67900	166.42	.3274
270.00	.44627	168.07	.3389	270.00	.55973	167.85	.3335	270.00	.67396	167.62	.3291
275.00	.44307	169.27	.3405	275.00	.55566	169.05	.3351	275.00	.66900	168.83	.3307
280.00	.43992	170.47	.3421	280.00	.55166	170.26	.3368	280.00	.66412	170.04	.3323
285.00	.43682	171.68	.3438	285.00	.54772	171.47	.3384	285.00	.65931	171.25	.3340

Standard state: At -40˚F, Liquid Enthalpy = 0.0 Btu/lb, Liquid Entropy = 0.0 Btu/lb.F

KLEA® 407C

Superheated Vapor Properties

Table 2 Sheet 5

70.0 psia Dew Point = 34.4 ˚F				80.0 psia Dew Point = 41.5 ˚F				90.0 psia Dew Point = 47.94 ˚F			
Temp ˚F	Density lb/ft³	Enthalpy Btu/lb	Entropy Btu/lb.F	Temp ˚F	Density lb/ft³	Enthalpy Btu/lb	Entropy Btu/lb.F	Temp ˚F	Density lb/ft³	Enthalpy Btu/lb	Entropy Btu/lb.F
35.00	1.25309	115.84	.2405								
40.00	1.23644	116.84	.2425								
45.00	1.22032	117.84	.2445	45.00	1.41582	117.35	.2408				
50.00	1.20469	118.84	.2465	50.00	1.39687	118.37	.2428	50.00	1.59538	117.88	.2394
55.00	1.18953	119.85	.2485	55.00	1.37852	119.39	.2448	55.00	1.57347	118.91	.2414
60.00	1.17481	120.86	.2504	60.00	1.36075	120.41	.2468	60.00	1.55229	119.94	.2434
65.00	1.16052	121.87	.2524	65.00	1.34352	121.43	.2487	65.00	1.53181	120.98	.2454
70.00	1.14663	122.89	.2543	70.00	1.32681	122.46	.2507	70.00	1.51198	122.01	.2474
75.00	1.13312	123.92	.2562	75.00	1.31059	123.49	.2526	75.00	1.49277	123.06	.2493
80.00	1.11998	124.94	.2581	80.00	1.29483	124.53	.2545	80.00	1.47414	124.10	.2513
85.00	1.10719	125.97	.2601	85.00	1.27952	125.57	.2564	85.00	1.45607	125.15	.2532
90.00	1.09473	127.01	.2619	90.00	1.26462	126.61	.2584	90.00	1.43852	126.20	.2551
95.00	1.08258	128.05	.2638	95.00	1.25013	127.66	.2603	95.00	1.42147	127.25	.2570
100.00	1.07075	129.10	.2657	100.00	1.23602	128.71	.2621	100.00	1.40489	128.31	.2589
105.00	1.05921	130.14	.2676	105.00	1.22228	129.76	.2640	105.00	1.38877	129.38	.2608
110.00	1.04794	131.20	.2694	110.00	1.20889	130.82	.2659	110.00	1.37308	130.44	.2627
115.00	1.03695	132.26	.2713	115.00	1.19583	131.89	.2677	115.00	1.35781	131.52	.2646
120.00	1.02621	133.32	.2731	120.00	1.18310	132.96	.2696	120.00	1.34292	132.59	.2664
125.00	1.01572	134.39	.2749	125.00	1.17067	134.03	.2714	125.00	1.32842	133.67	.2683
130.00	1.00547	135.46	.2768	130.00	1.15854	135.11	.2733	130.00	1.31427	134.75	.2701
135.00	.99546	136.53	.2786	135.00	1.14669	136.19	.2751	135.00	1.30047	135.84	.2720
140.00	.98566	137.61	.2804	140.00	1.13512	137.27	.2769	140.00	1.28700	136.93	.2738
145.00	.97607	138.70	.2822	145.00	1.12380	138.37	.2787	145.00	1.27385	138.03	.2756
150.00	.96670	139.79	.2840	150.00	1.11274	139.46	.2805	150.00	1.26100	139.13	.2774
155.00	.95752	140.88	.2858	155.00	1.10193	140.56	.2823	155.00	1.24845	140.23	.2792
160.00	.94853	141.98	.2876	160.00	1.09135	141.66	.2841	160.00	1.23618	141.34	.2810
165.00	.93973	143.09	.2893	165.00	1.08099	142.77	.2859	165.00	1.22419	142.46	.2828
170.00	.93110	144.20	.2911	170.00	1.07086	143.89	.2877	170.00	1.21245	143.58	.2846
175.00	.92266	145.31	.2929	175.00	1.06093	145.01	.2894	175.00	1.20097	144.70	.2864

Standard state: At -40˚F, Liquid Enthalpy = 0.0 Btu/lb, Liquid Entropy = 0.0 Btu/lb.F

Superheated Vapor Properties

Table 2 Sheet 6

Temp °F	70.0 psia, Dew Point = 34.4 °F: Density lb/ft³	Enthalpy Btu/lb	Entropy Btu/lb.F	Temp °F	80.0 psia, Dew Point = 41.5 °F: Density lb/ft³	Enthalpy Btu/lb	Entropy Btu/lb.F	Temp °F	90.0 psia, Dew Point = 47.94 °F: Density lb/ft³	Enthalpy Btu/lb	Entropy Btu/lb.F
180.00	.91437	146.43	.2946	180.00	1.05121	146.13	.2912	180.00	1.18974	145.83	.2882
185.00	.90626	147.55	.2964	185.00	1.04169	147.26	.2930	185.00	1.17874	146.96	.2899
190.00	.89830	148.68	.2981	190.00	1.03236	148.39	.2947	190.00	1.16797	148.10	.2917
195.00	.89049	149.82	.2999	195.00	1.02321	149.53	.2965	195.00	1.15742	149.24	.2934
200.00	.88283	150.95	.3016	200.00	1.01425	150.67	.2982	200.00	1.14709	150.39	.2952
205.00	.87532	152.10	.3033	205.00	1.00545	151.82	.2999	205.00	1.13696	151.54	.2969
210.00	.86794	153.24	.3050	210.00	.99683	152.97	.3017	210.00	1.12703	152.70	.2986
215.00	.86070	154.40	.3068	215.00	.98837	154.13	.3034	215.00	1.11729	153.86	.3004
220.00	.85359	155.56	.3085	220.00	.98006	155.29	.3051	220.00	1.10774	155.02	.3021
225.00	.84661	156.72	.3102	225.00	.97191	156.46	.3068	225.00	1.09838	156.20	.3038
230.00	.83975	157.89	.3119	230.00	.96391	157.63	.3085	230.00	1.08919	157.37	.3055
235.00	.83302	159.06	.3136	235.00	.95606	158.81	.3102	235.00	1.08017	158.55	.3072
240.00	.82640	160.24	.3153	240.00	.94834	159.99	.3119	240.00	1.07132	159.74	.3089
245.00	.81989	161.42	.3169	245.00	.94077	161.17	.3136	245.00	1.06262	160.93	.3106
250.00	.81350	162.60	.3186	250.00	.93332	162.36	.3153	250.00	1.05409	162.12	.3123
255.00	.80722	163.80	.3203	255.00	.92601	163.56	.3170	255.00	1.04571	163.32	.3140
260.00	.80103	164.99	.3220	260.00	.91881	164.76	.3186	260.00	1.03747	164.52	.3157
265.00	.79496	166.19	.3236	265.00	.91175	165.96	.3203	265.00	1.02938	165.73	.3173
270.00	.78898	167.39	.3253	270.00	.90480	167.17	.3220	270.00	1.02142	166.94	.3190
275.00	.78310	168.60	.3269	275.00	.89796	168.38	.3236	275.00	1.01360	168.15	.3207
280.00	.77731	169.82	.3286	280.00	.89124	169.60	.3253	280.00	1.00592	169.37	.3223
285.00	.77161	171.03	.3302	285.00	.88462	170.82	.3269	285.00	.99836	170.60	.3240
290.00	.76600	172.26	.3318	290.00	.87812	172.04	.3285	290.00	.99092	171.83	.3256
295.00	.76049	173.48	.3335	295.00	.87171	173.27	.3302	295.00	.98361	173.06	.3273
300.00	.75505	174.71	.3351	300.00	.86541	174.51	.3318	300.00	.97641	174.30	.3289
305.00	.74970	175.95	.3367	305.00	.85920	175.74	.3334	305.00	.96933	175.54	.3305
310.00	.74443	177.19	.3383	310.00	.85310	176.99	.3351	310.00	.96236	176.78	.3321

Standard state: At -40˚F, Liquid Enthalpy = 0.0 Btu/lb, Liquid Entropy = 0.0 Btu/lb.F

KLEA® 407C

Superheated Vapor Properties

Table 2 Sheet 7

100.0 psia Dew Point = 53.85 °F				130.0 psia Dew Point = 69.23 °F				160.0 psia Dew Point = 82.08 °F			
Temp °F	Density lb/ft³	Enthalpy Btu/lb	Entropy Btu/lb.F	Temp °F	Density lb/ft³	Enthalpy Btu/lb	Entropy Btu/lb.F	Temp °F	Density lb/ft³	Enthalpy Btu/lb	Entropy Btu/lb.F
55.00	1.77492	118.42	.2383								
60.00	1.74993	119.47	.2403								
65.00	1.72582	120.51	.2423								
70.00	1.70253	121.56	.2443	70.00	2.31128	120.11	.2363				
75.00	1.68001	122.61	.2463	75.00	2.27644	121.2	.2384				
80.00	1.65822	123.66	.2483	80.00	2.24298	122.29	.2404				
85.00	1.63712	124.72	.2502	85.00	2.21078	123.38	.2424	85.00	2.83953	121.92	.2356
90.00	1.61667	125.78	.2521	90.00	2.17977	124.47	.2444	90.00	2.79414	123.05	.2377
95.00	1.59683	126.84	.2541	95.00	2.14988	125.56	.2464	95.00	2.75072	124.18	.2398
100.00	1.57758	127.91	.2560	100.00	2.12102	126.65	.2483	100.00	2.70911	125.31	.2418
105.00	1.55888	128.98	.2579	105.00	2.09314	127.75	.2503	105.00	2.66918	126.44	.2438
110.00	1.54070	130.06	.2598	110.00	2.06617	128.85	.2522	110.00	2.63081	127.57	.2458
115.00	1.52303	131.14	.2617	115.00	2.04008	129.95	.2541	115.00	2.59389	128.70	.2478
120.00	1.50584	132.22	.2635	120.00	2.01479	131.06	.2561	120.00	2.55831	129.83	.2497
125.00	1.48910	133.30	.2654	125.00	1.99028	132.17	.2580	125.00	2.52400	130.97	.2517
130.00	1.47279	134.39	.2673	130.00	1.96651	133.28	.2599	130.00	2.49088	132.10	.2536
135.00	1.45690	135.49	.2691	135.00	1.94342	134.39	.2617	135.00	2.45886	133.24	.2555
140.00	1.44141	136.58	.2710	140.00	1.92099	135.51	.2636	140.00	2.42789	134.38	.2574
145.00	1.42630	137.69	.2728	145.00	1.89919	136.63	.2655	145.00	2.39790	135.53	.2593
150.00	1.41156	138.79	.2746	150.00	1.87798	137.75	.2673	150.00	2.36885	136.67	.2612
155.00	1.39717	139.90	.2764	155.00	1.85735	138.88	.2692	155.00	2.34067	137.82	.2631
160.00	1.38311	141.02	.2782	160.00	1.83725	140.02	.2710	160.00	2.31334	138.97	.2650
165.00	1.36938	142.14	.2800	165.00	1.81768	141.15	.2728	165.00	2.28679	140.13	.2668
170.00	1.35596	143.26	.2818	170.00	1.79860	142.29	.2746	170.00	2.26100	141.29	.2687
175.00	1.34284	144.39	.2836	175.00	1.77999	143.44	.2765	175.00	2.23592	142.45	.2705
180.00	1.33001	145.52	.2854	180.00	1.76185	144.59	.2783	180.00	2.21153	143.62	.2724
185.00	1.31746	146.66	.2872	185.00	1.74414	145.74	.2801	185.00	2.18780	144.79	.2742
190.00	1.30518	147.80	.2889	190.00	1.72685	146.9	.2818	190.00	2.16468	145.97	.2760
195.00	1.29316	148.95	.2907	195.00	1.70997	148.06	.2836	195.00	2.14217	147.15	.2778

Standard state: At -40°F, Liquid Enthalpy = 0.0 Btu/lb, Liquid Entropy = 0.0 Btu/lb.F

Superheated Vapor Properties

Table 2 Sheet 8

100.0 psia, Dew Point = 53.85 ˚F				130.0 psia, Dew Point = 69.23 ˚F				160.0 psia, Dew Point = 82.08 ˚F			
Temp ˚F	Density lb/ft³	Enthalpy Btu/lb	Entropy Btu/lb.F	Temp ˚F	Density lb/ft³	Enthalpy Btu/lb	Entropy Btu/lb.F	Temp ˚F	Density lb/ft³	Enthalpy Btu/lb	Entropy Btu/lb.F
200.00	1.28139	150.10	.2924	200.00	1.69347	149.23	.2854	200.00	2.12022	148.33	.2796
205.00	1.26986	151.26	.2942	205.00	1.67735	150.40	.2872	205.00	2.09882	149.51	.2814
210.00	1.25857	152.42	.2959	210.00	1.66158	151.57	.2889	210.00	2.07794	150.70	.2832
215.00	1.24750	153.58	.2976	215.00	1.64616	152.75	.2907	215.00	2.05756	151.90	.2850
220.00	1.23665	154.75	.2994	220.00	1.63108	153.94	.2924	220.00	2.03766	153.10	.2867
225.00	1.22602	155.93	.3011	225.00	1.61631	155.12	.2942	225.00	2.01822	154.30	.2885
230.00	1.21559	157.11	.3028	230.00	1.60186	156.32	.2959	230.00	1.99924	155.51	.2902
235.00	1.20537	158.30	.3045	235.00	1.58772	157.52	.2976	235.00	1.98068	156.72	.2920
240.00	1.19533	159.48	.3062	240.00	1.57386	158.72	.2994	240.00	1.96254	157.93	.2937
245.00	1.18549	160.68	.3079	245.00	1.56028	159.92	.3011	245.00	1.94479	159.15	.2955
250.00	1.17582	161.87	.3096	250.00	1.54697	161.13	.3028	250.00	1.92742	160.38	.2972
255.00	1.16633	163.08	.3113	255.00	1.53392	162.35	.3045	255.00	1.91043	161.60	.2989
260.00	1.15702	164.28	.3130	260.00	1.52113	163.56	.3062	260.00	1.89378	162.83	.3006
265.00	1.14786	165.49	.3147	265.00	1.50858	164.78	.3079	265.00	1.87748	164.07	.3024
270.00	1.13887	166.71	.3163	270.00	1.49627	166.01	.3096	270.00	1.86151	165.30	.3041
275.00	1.13004	167.93	.3180	275.00	1.48419	167.24	.3113	275.00	1.84586	166.54	.3057
280.00	1.12136	169.15	.3197	280.00	1.47233	168.47	.3129	280.00	1.83052	167.79	.3074
285.00	1.11282	170.38	.3213	285.00	1.46069	169.71	.3146	285.00	1.81547	169.04	.3091
290.00	1.10443	171.61	.3230	290.00	1.44926	170.95	.3163	290.00	1.80072	170.29	.3108
295.00	1.09618	172.85	.3246	295.00	1.43802	172.20	.3179	295.00	1.78624	171.55	.3125
300.00	1.08806	174.09	.3263	300.00	1.42699	173.45	.3196	300.00	1.77203	172.81	.3141
305.00	1.08008	175.33	.3279	305.00	1.41615	174.70	.3212	305.00	1.75809	174.07	.3158
310.00	1.07222	176.58	.3295	310.00	1.40549	175.96	.3229	310.00	1.74440	175.34	.3174
315.00	1.06449	177.83	.3311	315.00	1.39501	177.22	.3245	315.00	1.73095	176.61	.3191
320.00	1.05688	179.09	.3328	320.00	1.38471	178.49	.3261	320.00	1.71774	177.89	.3207
325.00	1.04940	180.35	.3344	325.00	1.37458	179.76	.3277	325.00	1.70477	179.17	.3224
330.00	1.04202	181.62	.3360	330.00	1.36462	181.04	.3294	330.00	1.69201	180.45	.3240

Standard state: At -40˚F, Liquid Enthalpy = 0.0 Btu/lb, Liquid Entropy = 0.0 Btu/lb.F

KLEA® 407C

Superheated Vapor Properties

Table 2 Sheet 9

190.0 psia Dew Point = 93.19 °F				220.0 psia Dew Point = 103.01 °F				250.0 psia Dew Point = 111.84 °F			
Temp °F	Density lb/ft³	Enthalpy Btu/lb	Entropy Btu/lb.F	Temp °F	Density lb/ft³	Enthalpy Btu/lb	Entropy Btu/lb.F	Temp °F	Density lb/ft³	Enthalpy Btu/lb	Entropy Btu/lb.F
95.00	3.41244	122.67	.2338								
100.00	3.35331	123.84	.2359								
105.00	3.29708	125.02	.2380	105.00	3.99166	123.46	.2325				
110.00	3.24349	126.19	.2400	110.00	3.91699	124.69	.2347				
115.00	3.19232	127.36	.2421	115.00	3.84643	125.90	.2368	115.00	4.57272	124.31	.2317
120.00	3.14336	128.52	.2441	120.00	3.77956	127.12	.2389	120.00	4.48089	125.58	.2339
125.00	3.09645	129.69	.2461	125.00	3.71602	128.33	.2410	125.00	4.39466	126.84	.2361
130.00	3.05142	130.86	.2481	130.00	3.65552	129.53	.2430	130.00	4.31340	128.10	.2382
135.00	3.00816	132.03	.2501	135.00	3.59779	130.74	.2451	135.00	4.23659	129.35	.2403
140.00	2.96652	133.20	.2520	140.00	3.54260	131.94	.2471	140.00	4.16378	130.60	.2424
145.00	2.92640	134.37	.2540	145.00	3.48975	133.14	.2491	145.00	4.09459	131.84	.2445
150.00	2.88771	135.54	.2559	150.00	3.43905	134.34	.2510	150.00	4.02869	133.08	.2465
155.00	2.85035	136.71	.2578	155.00	3.39036	135.55	.2530	155.00	3.96580	134.31	.2485
160.00	2.81424	137.89	.2597	160.00	3.34353	136.75	.2550	160.00	3.90568	135.55	.2505
165.00	2.77932	139.07	.2616	165.00	3.29844	137.95	.2569	165.00	3.84810	136.79	.2525
170.00	2.74551	140.25	.2635	170.00	3.25497	139.16	.2588	170.00	3.79287	138.02	.2545
175.00	2.71275	141.43	.2654	175.00	3.21302	140.37	.2607	175.00	3.73983	139.26	.2565
180.00	2.68099	142.62	.2672	180.00	3.17250	141.58	.2626	180.00	3.68882	140.50	.2584
185.00	2.65018	143.81	.2691	185.00	3.13333	142.79	.2645	185.00	3.63971	141.74	.2603
190.00	2.62026	145.01	.2709	190.00	3.09543	144.01	.2664	190.00	3.59237	142.98	.2623
195.00	2.59120	146.20	.2728	195.00	3.05873	145.23	.2683	195.00	3.54669	144.22	.2642
200.00	2.56295	147.40	.2746	200.00	3.02315	146.45	.2701	200.00	3.50257	145.46	.2660
205.00	2.53547	148.60	.2764	205.00	2.98864	147.67	.2720	205.00	3.45991	146.70	.2679
210.00	2.50872	149.81	.2782	210.00	2.95515	148.89	.2738	210.00	3.41862	147.94	.2698
215.00	2.48267	151.02	.2800	215.00	2.92261	150.12	.2756	215.00	3.37863	149.19	.2716
220.00	2.45730	152.24	.2818	220.00	2.89099	151.35	.2775	220.00	3.33988	150.45	.2735
225.00	2.43257	153.46	.2836	225.00	2.86026	152.59	.2793	225.00	3.30230	151.70	.2753
230.00	2.40846	154.68	.2854	230.00	2.83035	153.83	.2811	230.00	3.26583	152.96	.2772
235.00	2.38494	155.91	.2872	235.00	2.80125	155.07	.2829	235.00	3.23041	154.22	.2790

Standard state: At -40°F, Liquid Enthalpy = 0.0 Btu/lb, Liquid Entropy = 0.0 Btu/lb.F

Version 2a 1st January 1994

KLEA® 407C

Superheated Vapor Properties

Table 2 Sheet 10

190.0 psia, Dew Point = 93.19 °F				220.0 psia, Dew Point = 103.01 °F				250.0 psia, Dew Point = 111.84 °F			
Temp °F	Density lb/ft³	Enthalpy Btu/lb	Entropy Btu/lb.F	Temp °F	Density lb/ft³	Enthalpy Btu/lb	Entropy Btu/lb.F	Temp °F	Density lb/ft³	Enthalpy Btu/lb	Entropy Btu/lb.F
240.00	2.36199	157.14	.2889	240.00	2.77290	156.32	.2847	240.00	3.19600	155.49	.2808
245.00	2.33958	158.37	.2907	245.00	2.74527	157.57	.2864	245.00	3.16253	156.75	.2826
250.00	2.31769	159.61	.2924	250.00	2.71834	158.82	.2882	250.00	3.12997	158.02	.2844
255.00	2.29631	160.84	.2942	255.00	2.69207	160.07	.2900	255.00	3.09827	159.29	.2862
260.00	2.27540	162.09	.2959	260.00	2.66643	161.33	.2917	260.00	3.06739	160.56	.2879
265.00	2.25495	163.33	.2976	265.00	2.64140	162.59	.2935	265.00	3.03729	161.83	.2897
270.00	2.23495	164.58	.2993	270.00	2.61696	163.85	.2952	270.00	3.00794	163.11	.2915
275.00	2.21537	165.84	.3011	275.00	2.59307	165.12	.2969	275.00	2.97931	164.39	.2932
280.00	2.19621	167.09	.3028	280.00	2.56972	166.39	.2986	280.00	2.95137	165.67	.2950
285.00	2.17744	168.35	.3045	285.00	2.54688	167.66	.3004	285.00	2.92408	166.95	.2967
290.00	2.15906	169.62	.3061	290.00	2.52454	168.93	.3021	290.00	2.89743	168.24	.2984
295.00	2.14105	170.88	.3078	295.00	2.50268	170.21	.3038	295.00	2.87138	169.53	.3001
300.00	2.12339	172.15	.3095	300.00	2.48128	171.49	.3055	300.00	2.84591	170.83	.3018
305.00	2.10608	173.43	.3112	305.00	2.46032	172.78	.3071	305.00	2.82100	172.12	.3035
310.00	2.08911	174.71	.3128	310.00	2.43979	174.07	.3088	310.00	2.79663	173.42	.3052
315.00	2.07245	175.99	.3145	315.00	2.41967	175.36	.3105	315.00	2.77277	174.73	.3069
320.00	2.05611	177.27	.3162	320.00	2.39996	176.66	.3122	320.00	2.74942	176.03	.3086
325.00	2.04007	178.56	.3178	325.00	2.38062	177.95	.3138	325.00	2.72655	177.34	.3103
330.00	2.02432	179.86	.3195	330.00	2.36166	179.26	.3155	330.00	2.70414	178.65	.3119
335.00	2.00886	181.15	.3211	335.00	2.34306	180.56	.3171	335.00	2.68217	179.97	.3136
340.00	1.99368	182.45	.3227	340.00	2.32481	181.87	.3188	340.00	2.66065	181.29	.3152
345.00	1.97876	183.76	.3243	345.00	2.30689	183.19	.3204	345.00	2.63953	182.61	.3169
350.00	1.96410	185.06	.3260	350.00	2.28931	184.50	.3220	350.00	2.61883	183.94	.3185
355.00	1.94969	186.38	.3276	355.00	2.27203	185.82	.3237	355.00	2.59851	185.27	.3202
360.00	1.93552	187.69	.3292	360.00	2.25507	187.15	.3253	360.00	2.57857	186.60	.3218
365.00	1.92160	189.01	.3308	365.00	2.23840	188.47	.3269	365.00	2.55900	187.93	.3234
370.00	1.90790	190.33	.3324	370.00	2.22203	189.81	.3285	370.00	2.53978	189.27	.3251

Standard state: At -40°F, Liquid Enthalpy = 0.0 Btu/lb, Liquid Entropy = 0.0 Btu/lb.F

KLEA® 407C

Superheated Vapor Properties

Table 2 Sheet 11

280.0 psia Dew Point = 119.88 °F				310.0 psia Dew Point = 127.27 °F				340.0 psia Dew Point = 134.12 °F			
Temp °F	Density lb/ft^3	Enthalpy Btu/lb	Entropy Btu/lb.F	Temp °F	Density lb/ft^3	Enthalpy Btu/lb	Entropy Btu/lb.F	Temp °F	Density lb/ft^3	Enthalpy Btu/lb	Entropy Btu/lb.F
120.00	5.26901	123.88	.2290								
125.00	5.15022	125.21	.2313								
130.00	5.03994	126.54	.2336	130.00	5.85837	124.80	.2289				
135.00	4.93706	127.85	.2358	135.00	5.71799	126.19	.2312	135.00	6.61003	124.33	.2266
140.00	4.84064	129.15	.2379	140.00	5.58858	127.57	.2335	140.00	6.43158	125.81	.2291
145.00	4.74994	130.44	.2401	145.00	5.46855	128.93	.2358	145.00	6.26950	127.26	.2315
150.00	4.66434	131.73	.2422	150.00	5.35665	130.27	.2380	150.00	6.12100	128.68	.2338
155.00	4.58331	133.01	.2443	155.00	5.25185	131.60	.2402	155.00	5.98399	130.09	.2361
160.00	4.50642	134.28	.2464	160.00	5.15336	132.93	.2423	160.00	5.85685	131.48	.2383
165.00	4.43328	135.56	.2484	165.00	5.06046	134.25	.2444	165.00	5.73826	132.85	.2406
170.00	4.36356	136.82	.2504	170.00	4.97258	135.56	.2465	170.00	5.62716	134.22	.2427
175.00	4.29697	138.09	.2524	175.00	4.88922	136.87	.2486	175.00	5.52268	135.57	.2449
180.00	4.23327	139.37	.2544	180.00	4.80998	138.18	.2507	180.00	5.42414	136.92	.2470
185.00	4.17223	140.63	.2564	185.00	4.73449	139.48	.2527	185.00	5.33093	138.27	.2491
190.00	4.11367	141.90	.2584	190.00	4.66244	140.78	.2547	190.00	5.24250	139.61	.2512
195.00	4.05739	143.17	.2603	195.00	4.59354	142.08	.2567	195.00	5.15843	140.94	.2532
200.00	4.00324	144.44	.2622	200.00	4.52753	143.37	.2587	200.00	5.07831	142.27	.2552
205.00	3.95107	145.70	.2642	205.00	4.46421	144.67	.2606	205.00	5.00181	143.59	.2572
210.00	3.90075	146.97	.2661	210.00	4.40337	145.96	.2625	210.00	4.92864	144.91	.2592
215.00	3.85216	148.24	.2679	215.00	4.34483	147.25	.2645	215.00	4.85852	146.23	.2612
220.00	3.80522	149.51	.2698	220.00	4.28847	148.55	.2664	220.00	4.79126	147.56	.2631
225.00	3.75983	150.79	.2717	225.00	4.23414	149.86	.2683	225.00	4.72667	148.89	.2651
230.00	3.71591	152.07	.2736	230.00	4.18172	151.16	.2702	230.00	4.66454	150.21	.2670
235.00	3.67335	153.35	.2754	235.00	4.13108	152.46	.2721	235.00	4.60471	151.54	.2689
240.00	3.63210	154.63	.2772	240.00	4.08212	153.76	.2739	240.00	4.54704	152.86	.2708
245.00	3.59208	155.91	.2791	245.00	4.03474	155.06	.2758	245.00	4.49137	154.18	.2727
250.00	3.55323	157.20	.2809	250.00	3.98884	156.36	.2776	250.00	4.43758	155.51	.2746
255.00	3.51548	158.48	.2827	255.00	3.94435	157.67	.2795	255.00	4.38557	156.83	.2764
260.00	3.47878	159.77	.2845	260.00	3.90119	158.97	.2813	260.00	4.33523	158.15	.2783

Standard state: At -40°F, Liquid Enthalpy = 0.0 Btu/lb, Liquid Entropy = 0.0 Btu/lb.F

KLEA® 407C

Superheated Vapor Properties

Table 2 Sheet 12

280.0 psia, Dew Point = 119.88 ˚F				310.0 psia, Dew Point = 127.27 ˚F				340.0 psia, Dew Point =134.12˚F			
Temp ˚F	Density lb/ft³	Enthalpy Btu/lb	Entropy Btu/lb.F	Temp ˚F	Density lb/ft³	Enthalpy Btu/lb	Entropy Btu/lb.F	Temp ˚F	Density lb/ft³	Enthalpy Btu/lb	Entropy Btu/lb.F
265.00	3.44308	161.06	.2863	265.00	3.85929	160.28	.2831	265.00	4.28645	159.48	.2801
270.00	3.40833	162.35	.2881	270.00	3.81858	161.58	.2849	270.00	4.23916	160.80	.2819
275.00	3.37449	163.65	.2898	275.00	3.77900	162.89	.2867	275.00	4.19328	162.13	.2837
280.00	3.34151	164.94	.2916	280.00	3.74050	164.20	.2885	280.00	4.14872	163.45	.2855
285.00	3.30935	166.24	.2933	285.00	3.70303	165.52	.2902	285.00	4.10543	164.78	.2873
290.00	3.27799	167.54	.2951	290.00	3.66653	166.83	.2920	290.00	4.06334	166.11	.2891
295.00	3.24738	168.84	.2968	295.00	3.63097	168.15	.2937	295.00	4.02239	167.44	.2909
300.00	3.21750	170.15	.2985	300.00	3.59629	169.46	.2955	300.00	3.98252	168.77	.2926
305.00	3.18831	171.46	.3002	305.00	3.56247	170.79	.2972	305.00	3.94369	170.11	.2944
310.00	3.15979	172.77	.3020	310.00	3.52947	172.11	.2989	310.00	3.90585	171.44	.2961
315.00	3.13191	174.08	.3037	315.00	3.49725	173.44	.3007	315.00	3.86895	172.78	.2979
320.00	3.10464	175.40	.3053	320.00	3.46577	174.76	.3024	320.00	3.83295	174.12	.2996
325.00	3.07797	176.72	.3070	325.00	3.43502	176.09	.3041	325.00	3.79782	175.46	.3013
330.00	3.05186	178.04	.3087	330.00	3.40495	177.43	.3058	330.00	3.76351	176.81	.3030
335.00	3.02630	179.37	.3104	335.00	3.37555	178.76	.3074	335.00	3.73000	178.15	.3047
340.00	3.00127	180.70	.3121	340.00	3.34678	180.10	.3091	340.00	3.69725	179.50	.3064
345.00	2.97675	182.03	.3137	345.00	3.31863	181.45	.3108	345.00	3.66523	180.86	.3081
350.00	2.95273	183.37	.3154	350.00	3.29107	182.79	.3125	350.00	3.63391	182.21	.3098
355.00	2.92917	184.70	.3170	355.00	3.26408	184.14	.3141	355.00	3.60327	183.57	.3114
360.00	2.90608	186.05	.3187	360.00	3.23763	185.49	.3158	360.00	3.57329	184.93	.3131
365.00	2.88343	187.39	.3203	365.00	3.21172	186.84	.3174	365.00	3.54392	186.29	.3148
370.00	2.86120	188.74	.3219	370.00	3.18632	188.20	.3191	370.00	3.51516	187.66	.3164
375.00	2.83939	190.09	.3235	375.00	3.16141	189.56	.3207	375.00	3.48699	189.03	.3181
380.00	2.81799	191.44	.3252	380.00	3.13698	190.92	.3223	380.00	3.45938	190.40	.3197
385.00	2.79697	192.80	.3268	385.00	3.11301	192.29	.3239	385.00	3.43230	191.77	.3213
390.00	2.77633	194.16	.3284	390.00	3.08949	193.66	.3256	390.00	3.40576	193.15	.3230
395.00	2.75605	195.53	.3300	395.00	3.06641	195.03	.3272	395.00	3.37972	194.53	.3246

Standard state: At -40˚F, Liquid Enthalpy = 0.0 Btu/lb, Liquid Entropy = 0.0 Btu/lb.F

KLEA® 407C

Superheated Vapor Properties

Table 2 Sheet 13

370.0 psia Dew Point = 140.49 °F				400.0 psia Dew Point = 146.46 °F				430.0 psia Dew Point = 152.08 °F			
Temp °F	Density lb/ft³	Enthalpy Btu/lb	Entropy Btu/lb.F	Temp °F	Density lb/ft³	Enthalpy Btu/lb	Entropy Btu/lb.F	Temp °F	Density lb/ft³	Enthalpy Btu/lb	Entropy Btu/lb.F
145.00	7.18365	125.38	.2270								
150.00	6.98113	126.92	.2295	150.00	7.97715	124.91	.2250				
155.00	6.79832	128.42	.2320	155.00	7.72442	126.55	.2277	155.00	8.81480	124.39	.2231
160.00	6.63170	129.90	.2344	160.00	7.50033	128.15	.2303	160.00	8.49963	126.16	.2259
165.00	6.47862	131.34	.2367	165.00	7.29891	129.70	.2328	165.00	8.22602	127.86	.2287
170.00	6.33706	132.77	.2390	170.00	7.11595	131.21	.2352	170.00	7.98402	129.49	.2313
175.00	6.20542	134.19	.2412	175.00	6.94834	132.70	.2375	175.00	7.76695	131.08	.2338
180.00	6.08245	135.60	.2434	180.00	6.79376	134.18	.2398	180.00	7.57018	132.65	.2362
185.00	5.96713	136.99	.2456	185.00	6.65037	135.63	.2421	185.00	7.39025	134.18	.2386
190.00	5.85858	138.37	.2477	190.00	6.51667	137.07	.2443	190.00	7.22450	135.68	.2409
195.00	5.75608	139.75	.2498	195.00	6.39146	138.49	.2465	195.00	7.07090	137.16	.2432
200.00	5.65899	141.11	.2519	200.00	6.27376	139.90	.2487	200.00	6.92780	138.63	.2455
205.00	5.56681	142.47	.2540	205.00	6.16274	141.30	.2508	205.00	6.79389	140.08	.2476
210.00	5.47909	143.83	.2560	210.00	6.05771	142.70	.2529	210.00	6.66809	141.51	.2498
215.00	5.39542	145.18	.2580	215.00	5.95808	144.08	.2549	215.00	6.54951	142.94	.2519
220.00	5.31551	146.54	.2600	220.00	5.86338	145.48	.2570	220.00	6.43744	144.38	.2540
225.00	5.23906	147.89	.2620	225.00	5.77321	146.86	.2590	225.00	6.33126	145.80	.2561
230.00	5.16581	149.25	.2640	230.00	5.68715	148.25	.2610	230.00	6.23041	147.21	.2582
235.00	5.09551	150.59	.2659	235.00	5.60488	149.62	.2630	235.00	6.13439	148.62	.2602
240.00	5.02795	151.94	.2678	240.00	5.52609	151.00	.2650	240.00	6.04280	150.03	.2622
245.00	4.96294	153.29	.2698	245.00	5.45051	152.37	.2669	245.00	5.95526	151.42	.2642
250.00	4.90030	154.63	.2717	250.00	5.37792	153.74	.2689	250.00	5.87146	152.82	.2662
255.00	4.83988	155.98	.2735	255.00	5.30810	155.10	.2708	255.00	5.79109	154.21	.2681
260.00	4.78154	157.32	.2754	260.00	5.24085	156.47	.2727	260.00	5.71391	155.60	.2701
265.00	4.72516	158.66	.2773	265.00	5.17602	157.83	.2746	265.00	5.63970	156.98	.2720
270.00	4.67060	160.00	.2791	270.00	5.11344	159.19	.2765	270.00	5.56824	158.36	.2739
275.00	4.61778	161.35	.2810	275.00	5.05297	160.55	.2783	275.00	5.49936	159.74	.2758
280.00	4.56658	162.69	.2828	280.00	4.99449	161.91	.2802	280.00	5.43288	161.12	.2777
285.00	4.51693	164.03	.2846	285.00	4.93788	163.27	.2820	285.00	5.36867	162.50	.2795

Standard state: At -40°F, Liquid Enthalpy = 0.0 Btu/lb, Liquid Entropy = 0.0 Btu/lb.F

KLEA® 407C

Superheated Vapor Properties

Table 2 Sheet 14

370.0 psia Dew Point = 140.49 ˚F				400.0 psia Dew Point = 146.46 ˚F				430.0 psia Dew Point =152.08˚F			
Temp ˚F	Density lb/ft³	Enthalpy Btu/lb	Entropy Btu/lb.F	Temp ˚F	Density lb/ft³	Enthalpy Btu/lb	Entropy Btu/lb.F	Temp ˚F	Density lb/ft³	Enthalpy Btu/lb	Entropy Btu/lb.F
290.00	4.46873	165.38	.2864	290.00	4.88303	164.63	.2838	290.00	5.30657	163.88	.2814
295.00	4.42192	166.72	.2882	295.00	4.82985	165.99	.2856	295.00	5.24647	165.26	.2832
300.00	4.37642	168.07	.2900	300.00	4.77825	167.36	.2874	300.00	5.18825	166.64	.2850
305.00	4.33217	169.42	.2917	305.00	4.72814	168.72	.2892	305.00	5.13180	168.01	.2868
310.00	4.28911	170.77	.2935	310.00	4.67944	170.08	.2910	310.00	5.07704	169.39	.2886
315.00	4.24717	172.12	.2952	315.00	4.63209	171.45	.2928	315.00	5.02387	170.77	.2904
320.00	4.20632	173.47	.2970	320.00	4.58603	172.81	.2945	320.00	4.97221	172.15	.2922
325.00	4.16650	174.82	.2987	325.00	4.54118	174.18	.2963	325.00	4.92199	173.53	.2939
330.00	4.12766	176.18	.3004	330.00	4.49749	175.55	.2980	330.00	4.87312	174.91	.2957
335.00	4.08976	177.54	.3021	335.00	4.45492	176.92	.2997	335.00	4.82556	176.29	.2974
340.00	4.05276	178.90	.3039	340.00	4.41340	178.29	.3015	340.00	4.77923	177.68	.2992
345.00	4.01663	180.26	.3056	345.00	4.37289	179.67	.3032	345.00	4.73408	179.06	.3009
350.00	3.98133	181.63	.3072	350.00	4.33336	181.04	.3049	350.00	4.69007	180.45	.3026
355.00	3.94682	183.00	.3089	355.00	4.29476	182.42	.3066	355.00	4.64712	181.84	.3043
360.00	3.91308	184.37	.3106	360.00	4.25704	183.80	.3083	360.00	4.60522	183.23	.3060
365.00	3.88007	185.74	.3123	365.00	4.22018	185.18	.3099	365.00	4.56430	184.62	.3077
370.00	3.84777	187.11	.3139	370.00	4.18415	186.57	.3116	370.00	4.52432	186.02	.3094
375.00	3.81614	188.49	.3156	375.00	4.14890	187.95	.3133	375.00	4.48526	187.41	.3111
380.00	3.78518	189.87	.3172	380.00	4.11441	189.34	.3149	380.00	4.44707	188.81	.3128
385.00	3.75485	191.26	.3189	385.00	4.08065	190.74	.3166	385.00	4.40971	190.21	.3144
390.00	3.72512	192.64	.3205	390.00	4.04759	192.13	.3182	390.00	4.37317	191.62	.3161
395.00	3.69599	194.03	.3221	395.00	4.01522	193.53	.3199	395.00	4.33740	193.02	.3177
400.00	3.66742	195.42	.3238	400.00	3.98349	194.93	.3215	400.00	4.30238	194.43	.3194
405.00	3.63940	196.82	.3254	405.00	3.95240	196.33	.3231	405.00	4.26808	195.84	.3210
410.00	3.61192	198.21	.3270	410.00	3.92192	197.73	.3248	410.00	4.23447	197.25	.3226
415.00	3.58494	199.61	.3286	415.00	3.89203	199.14	.3264	415.00	4.20153	198.67	.3243
420.00	3.55847	201.02	.3302	420.00	3.86270	200.55	.3280	420.00	4.16924	200.09	.3259

Standard state: At -40˚F, Liquid Enthalpy = 0.0 Btu/lb, Liquid Entropy = 0.0 Btu/lb.F

TABLE 3

TABLE OF EVAPORATOR INLET TEMPERATURES

(1) Read the enthalpy value at the expansion valve along the top of the table.

(2) Read down the table for the evaporator operating pressure.

(3) The value in the table is the evaporator inlet temperature in ˚F.

(4) The evaporator outlet temperature is the dew point temperature at the evaporator operating pressure.

KLEA® 407C

Evaporator Inlet Temperatures

Table 3 Sheet 1

Pressure psia	Enthalpy in Btu/lb								
	-5.0	0.0	5.0	10.0	15.0	20.0	25.0	30.0	35.0
	°F	°F	°F	°F	°F	°F	°F	°F	°F
10.00	-60.87	-60.39	-59.89	-59.36	-58.81	-58.24	-57.66	-57.05	-56.43
15.00		-46.20	-45.71	-45.19	-44.66	-44.10	-43.53	-42.94	-42.33
20.00		-40.01	-34.88	-34.38	-33.85	-33.30	-32.74	-32.15	-31.56
25.00			-26.00	-25.50	-24.98	-24.44	-23.89	-23.31	-22.72
30.00			-24.77	-17.92	-17.41	-16.87	-16.32	-15.75	-15.16
35.00				-11.26	-10.75	-10.22	-9.67	-9.11	-8.53
40.00				-9.54	-4.80	-4.27	-3.73	-3.16	-2.59
45.00					.61	1.13	1.67	2.23	2.81
50.00					5.57	6.09	6.63	7.19	7.76
55.00						10.68	11.22	11.77	12.34
60.00						14.97	15.50	16.05	16.62
65.00						18.98	19.51	20.06	20.63
70.00						20.61	23.30	23.85	24.41
75.00							26.89	27.43	27.99
80.00							30.29	30.84	31.39
85.00							33.54	34.08	34.64
90.00							34.47	37.19	37.74
95.00							35.36	40.16	40.72
100.00								43.02	43.57

KLEA® 407C

Evaporator Inlet Temperatures

Table 3 Sheet 2

Pressure psia	Enthalpy in Btu/lb 40.0	45.0	50.0	55.0	60.0	65.0	70.0	75.0	80.0
	˚F	˚F	˚F	˚F	˚F	˚F	˚F	˚F	˚F
10.00	-55.79	-55.15	-54.50	-53.84	-53.19	-52.54	-51.89	-51.26	-50.64
15.00	-41.71	-41.07	-40.43	-39.79	-39.14	-38.49	-37.84	-37.20	-36.57
20.00	-30.94	-30.32	-29.68	-29.04	-28.39	-27.75	-27.10	-26.46	-25.83
25.00	-22.11	-21.49	-20.86	-20.22	-19.58	-18.94	-18.29	-17.65	-17.01
30.00	-14.56	-13.95	-13.32	-12.69	-12.05	-11.40	-10.76	-10.12	-9.48
35.00	-7.93	-7.32	-6.70	-6.07	-5.43	-4.79	-4.15	-3.50	-2.86
40.00	-1.99	-1.39	-.77	-.14	.49	1.13	1.78	2.42	3.06
45.00	3.40	4.00	4.61	5.24	5.87	6.51	7.15	7.80	8.44
50.00	8.34	8.94	9.56	10.18	10.81	11.45	12.09	12.73	13.37
55.00	12.93	13.52	14.13	14.75	15.38	16.02	16.66	17.30	17.94
60.00	17.20	17.79	18.40	19.02	19.65	20.28	20.92	21.56	22.20
65.00	21.21	21.80	22.41	23.02	23.65	24.28	24.92	25.56	26.20
70.00	24.99	25.58	26.18	26.80	27.42	28.05	28.69	29.33	29.97
75.00	28.57	29.16	29.76	30.37	31.00	31.63	32.26	32.90	33.54
80.00	31.97	32.56	33.16	33.77	34.39	35.02	35.66	36.30	36.94
85.00	35.21	35.80	36.40	37.01	37.63	38.26	38.89	39.53	40.17
90.00	38.31	38.90	39.50	40.11	40.72	41.35	41.99	42.62	43.26
95.00	41.29	41.87	42.47	43.07	43.69	44.32	44.95	45.59	46.23
100.00	44.14	44.72	45.32	45.93	46.54	47.17	47.80	48.44	49.08

Notes

ICI Klea
Concord Plaza
3411 Silverside Road
P.O. Box 15391
Wilmington, DE 19850

Customer Service: (800) ICI-KLEA or
Technical Assistance: (800) ASK-KLEA
Fax: (302) 887-7706

620250411 3/95

KLEA 134a

Pressure – Enthalpy Diagram

BRITISH UNITS

DATE APR 92

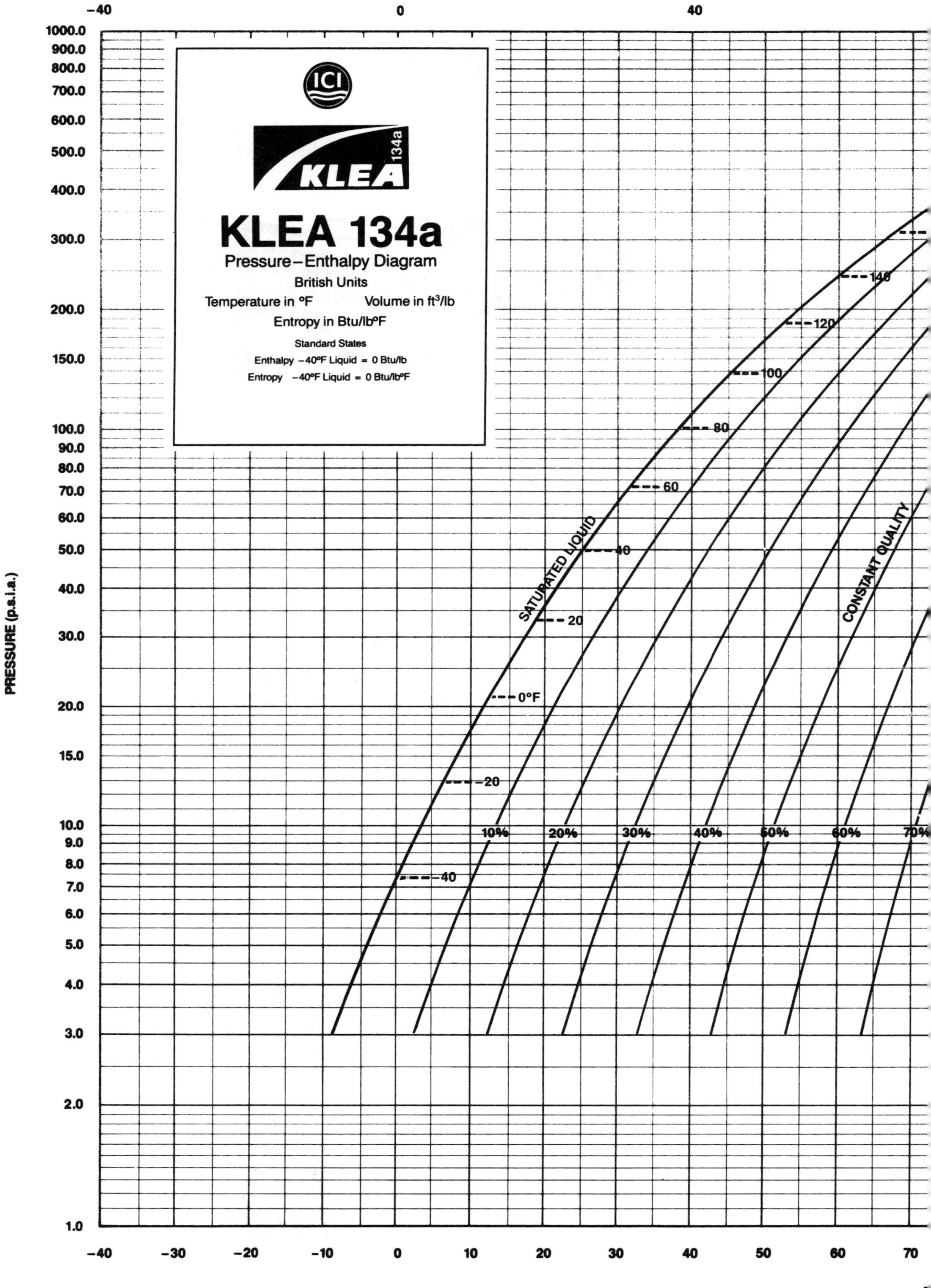

KLEA 134a
Pressure–Enthalpy Diagram
British Units
Temperature in °F
Volume in ft³/lb
Entropy in Btu/lb°F
Standard States
Enthalpy −40°F Liquid = 0 Btu/lb
Entropy −40°F Liquid = 0 Btu/lb°F
PRESSURE (p.s.i.a.)
SATURATED LIQUID
CONSTANT QUALITY
10%
20%
30%
40%
50%
60%
70%
−40
−20
0°F
20
40
60
80
100
120
140
1000.0
900.0
800.0
700.0
600.0
500.0
400.0
300.0
200.0
150.0
100.0
90.0
80.0
70.0
60.0
50.0
40.0
30.0
20.0
15.0
10.0
9.0
8.0
7.0
6.0
5.0
4.0
3.0
2.0
1.0
−40
−30
−20
−10
0
10
20
30
40
50
60
70

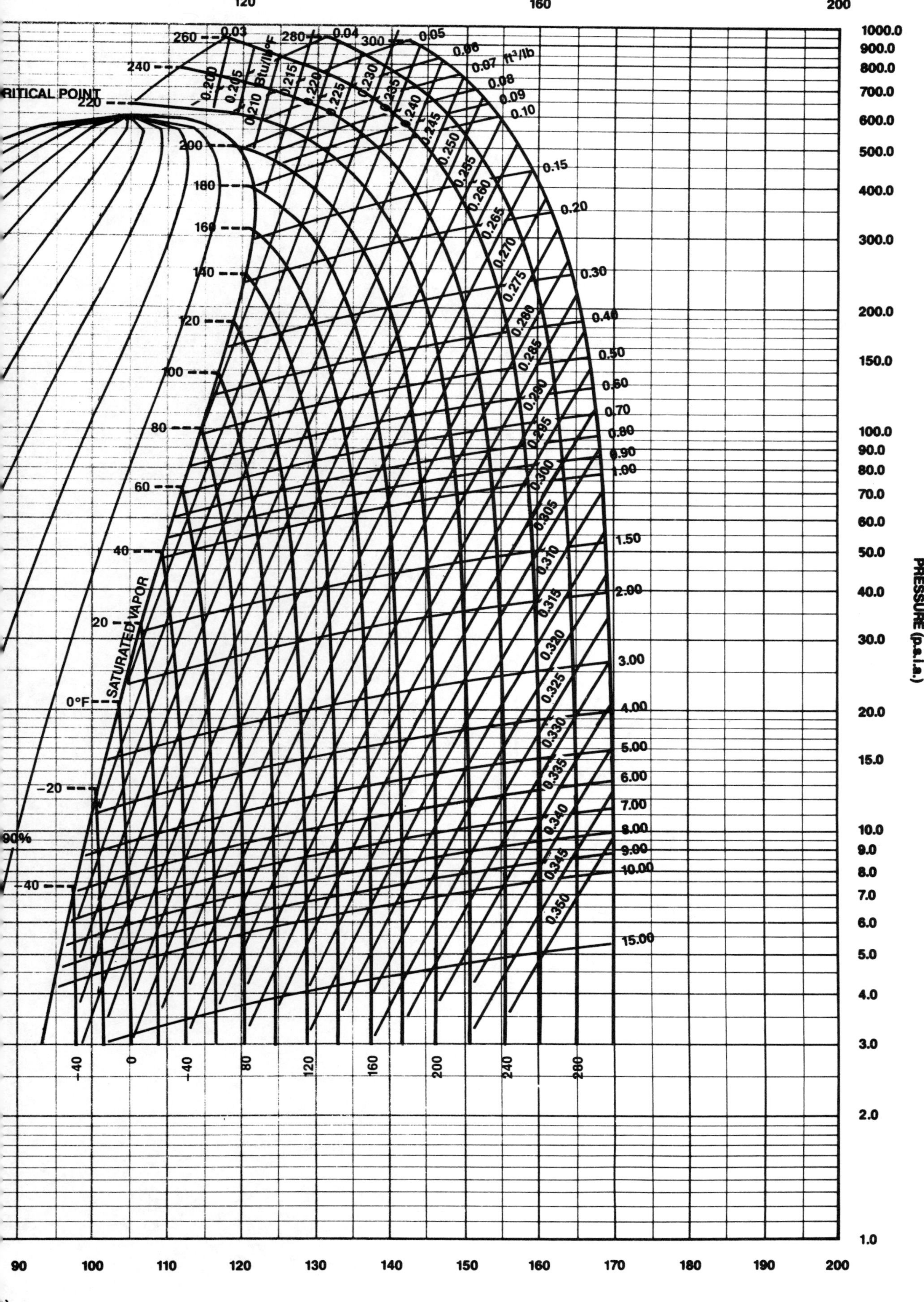

CRITICAL POINT
SATURATED VAPOR
Btu/lb°F
ft³/lb
PRESSURE (p.s.i.a.)
90%

407A

ICI Klea Pressure-Enthalpy Diagram KLEA® 407A (KLEA® 60)

Units

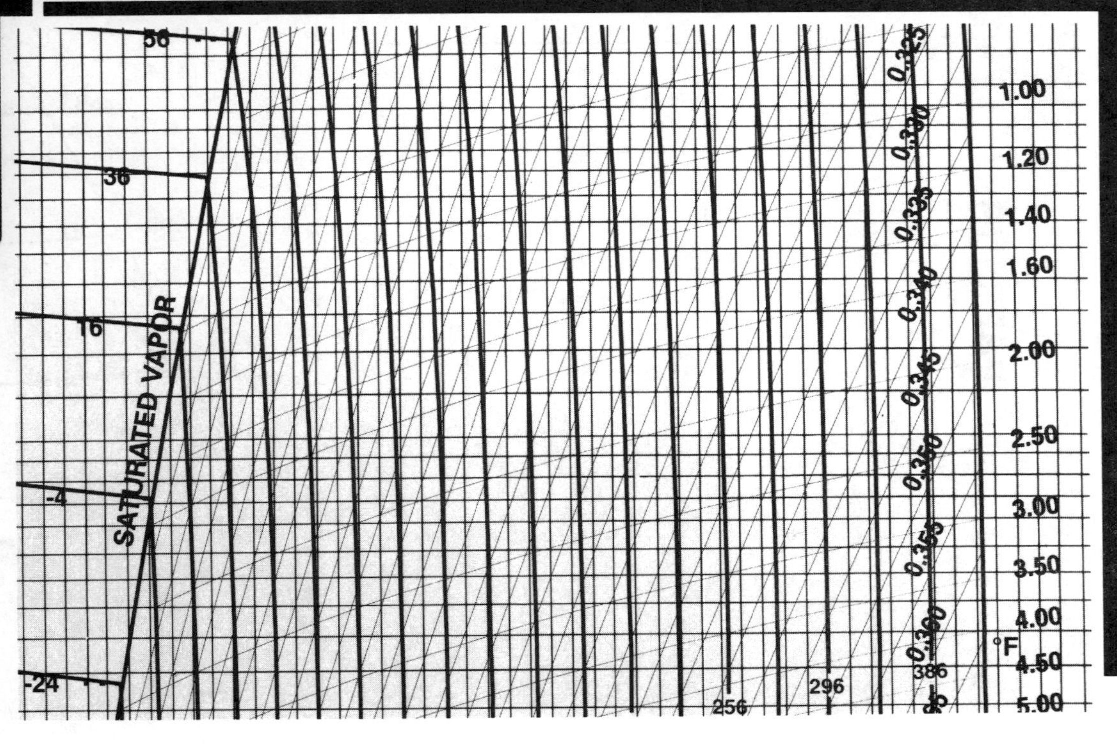

**NOW.
AND FOR
THE FUTURE.**

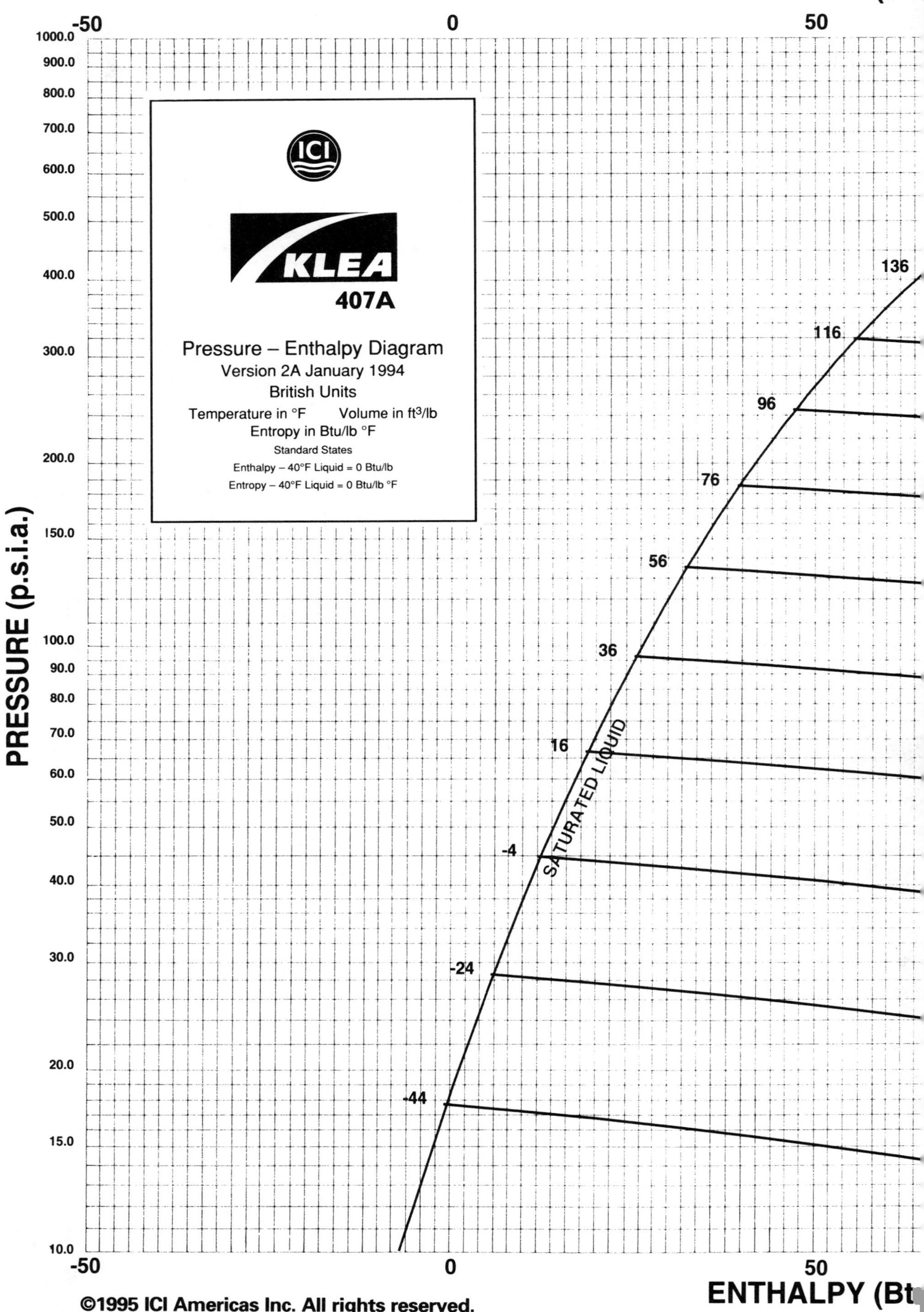
ENTHALPY (Bt
-50
0
50
1000.0
900.0
800.0
700.0
600.0
500.0
400.0
300.0
200.0
150.0
100.0
90.0
80.0
70.0
60.0
50.0
40.0
30.0
20.0
15.0
10.0
PRESSURE (p.s.i.a.)
ICI
KLEA
407A
Pressure – Enthalpy Diagram
Version 2A January 1994
British Units
Temperature in °F Volume in ft3/lb
Entropy in Btu/lb °F
Standard States
Enthalpy – 40°F Liquid = 0 Btu/lb
Entropy – 40°F Liquid = 0 Btu/lb °F
136
116
96
76
56
36
16
-4
-24
-44
SATURATED LIQUID
-50
0
50
ENTHALPY (Bt

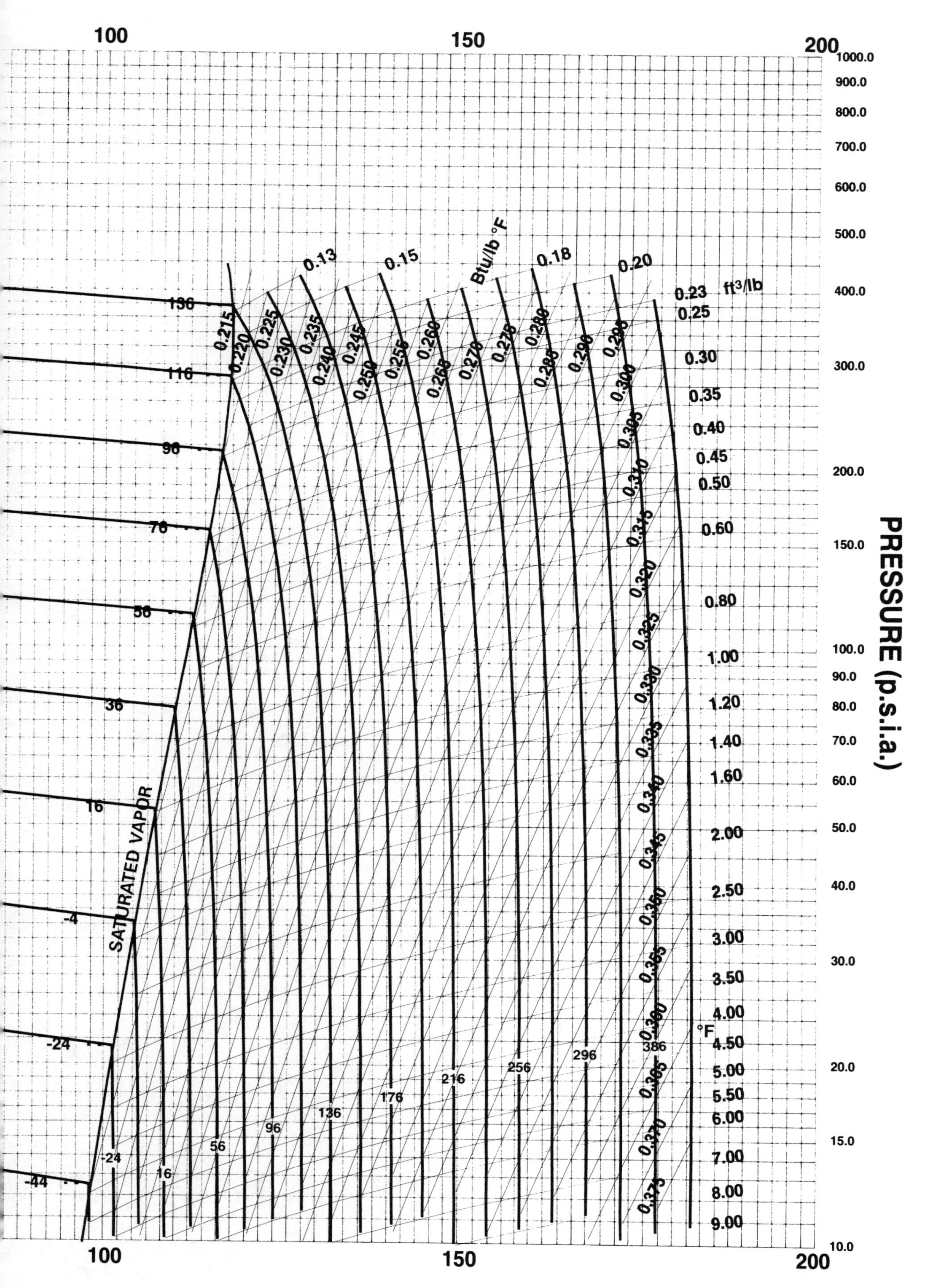

100
150
200
PRESSURE (p.s.i.a.)
1000.0
900.0
800.0
700.0
600.0
500.0
400.0
300.0
200.0
150.0
100.0
90.0
80.0
70.0
60.0
50.0
40.0
30.0
20.0
15.0
10.0
Btu/lb °F
0.13
0.15
0.18
0.20
0.23
ft³/lb
0.25
0.30
0.35
0.40
0.45
0.50
0.60
0.80
1.00
1.20
1.40
1.60
2.00
2.50
3.00
3.50
4.00
4.50
5.00
5.50
6.00
7.00
8.00
9.00
0.215
0.220
0.225
0.230
0.235
0.240
0.245
0.250
0.255
0.260
0.265
0.270
0.275
0.280
0.285
0.290
0.295
0.300
0.305
0.310
0.315
0.320
0.325
0.330
0.335
0.340
0.345
0.350
0.355
0.360
0.365
0.370
0.375
136
116
96
76
56
36
16
-4
-24
-44
SATURATED VAPOR
°F
386
296
256
216
176
136
96
56
16
-24

ICI Klea
Concord Plaza
3411 Silverside Road
P.O. Box 15391
Wilmington, DE 19850

Customer Service: (800) ICI-KLEA or
Technical Assistance: (800) ASK-KLEA
Fax: (302) 887-7706

620250560 4/95

407B

ICI Klea Pressure-Enthalpy Diagram KLEA® 407B (KLEA® 61)

British Units

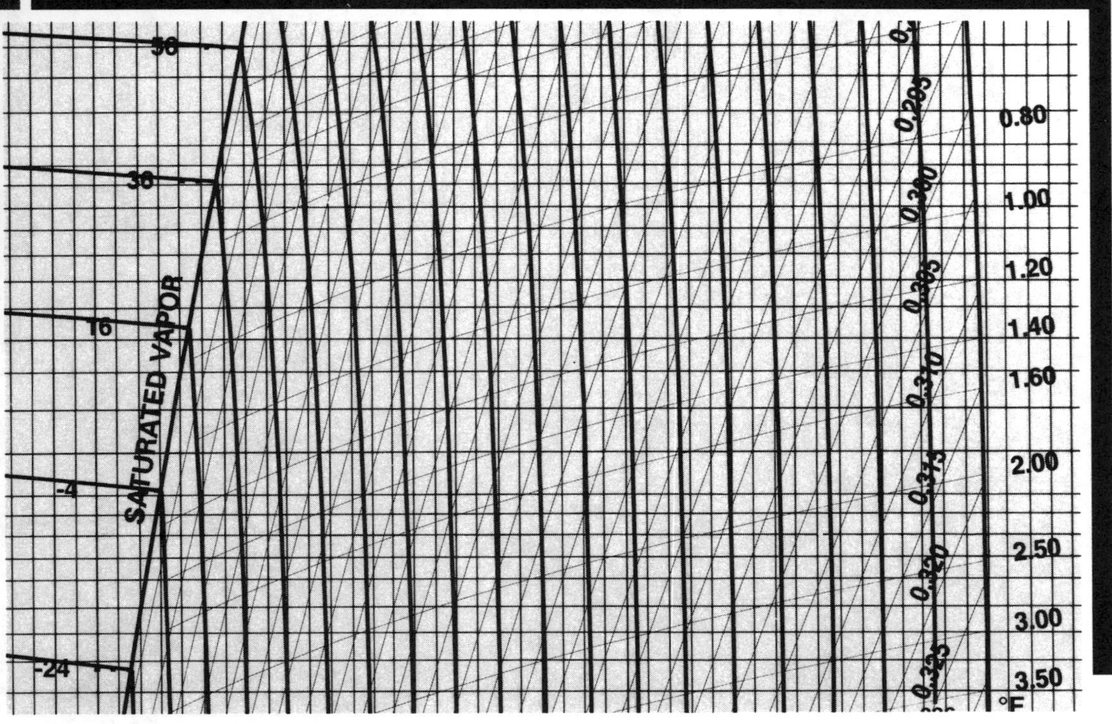

NOW. AND FOR THE FUTURE.

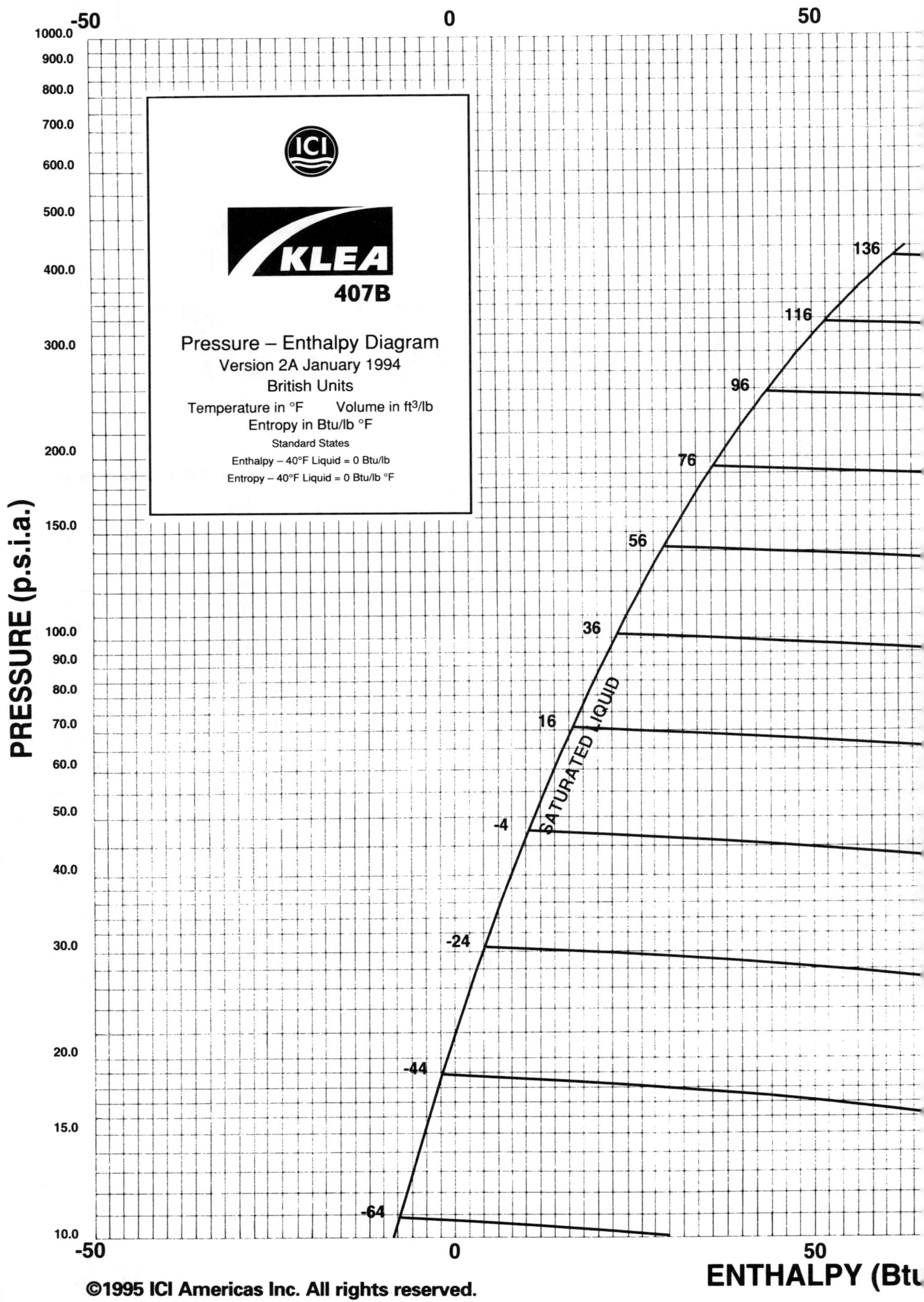

ENTHALPY (Btu
-50
0
50
1000.0
900.0
800.0
700.0
600.0
500.0
400.0
300.0
200.0
150.0
100.0
90.0
80.0
70.0
60.0
50.0
40.0
30.0
20.0
15.0
10.0
PRESSURE (p.s.i.a.)
ICI
KLEA
407B
Pressure – Enthalpy Diagram
Version 2A January 1994
British Units
Temperature in °F Volume in ft3/lb
Entropy in Btu/lb °F
Standard States
Enthalpy – 40°F Liquid = 0 Btu/lb
Entropy – 40°F Liquid = 0 Btu/lb °F
136
116
96
76
56
36
16
-4
-24
-44
-64
SATURATED LIQUID
-50
0
50
ENTHALPY (Btu

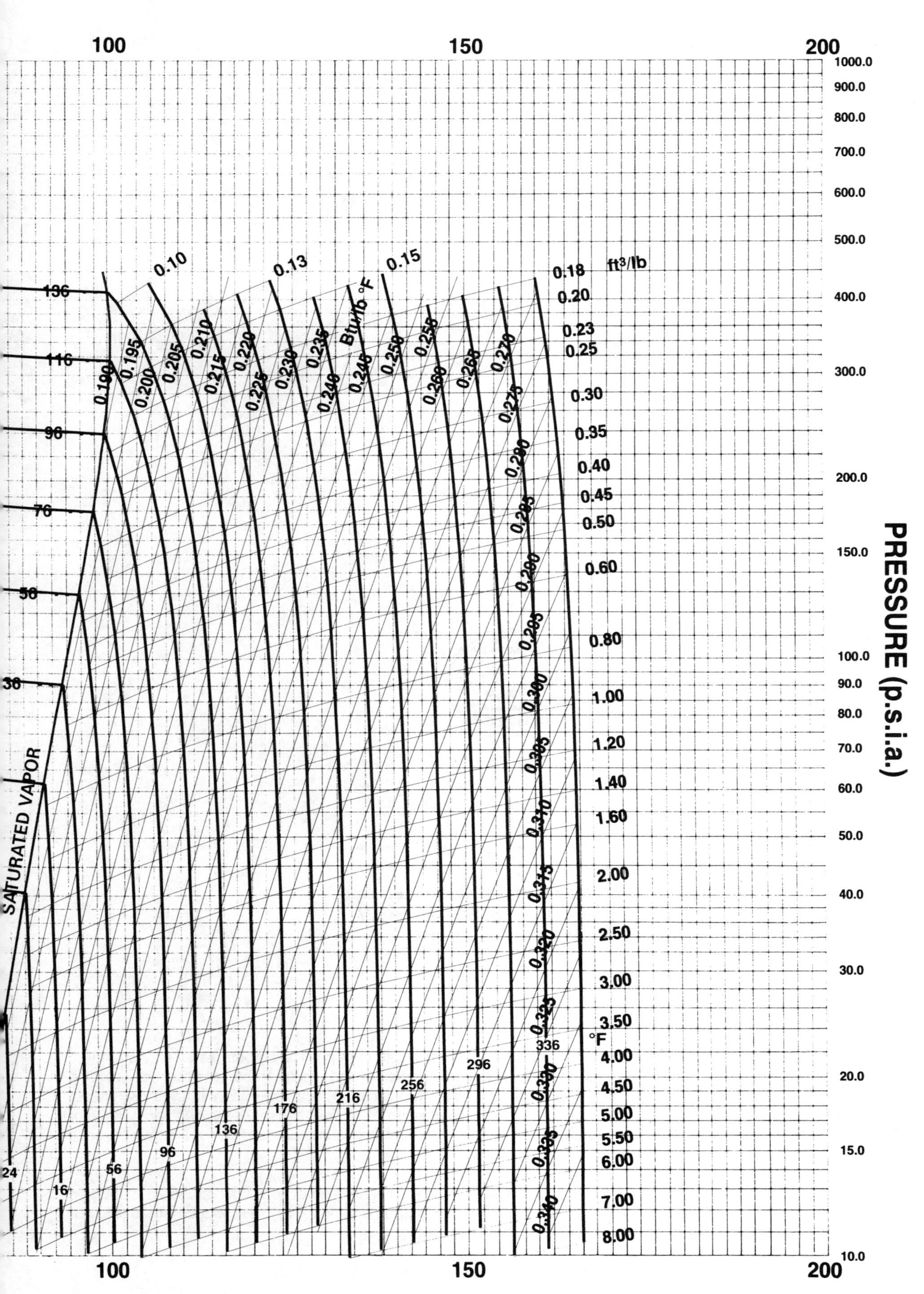

100
150
200
PRESSURE (p.s.i.a.)
1000.0
900.0
800.0
700.0
600.0
500.0
400.0
300.0
200.0
150.0
100.0
90.0
80.0
70.0
60.0
50.0
40.0
30.0
20.0
15.0
10.0
SATURATED VAPOR
0.10
0.13
0.15
0.18
ft³/lb
Btu/lb °F
0.20
0.23
0.25
0.30
0.35
0.40
0.45
0.50
0.60
0.80
1.00
1.20
1.40
1.60
2.00
2.50
3.00
3.50
4.00
4.50
5.00
5.50
6.00
7.00
8.00
°F
336
296
256
216
176
136
96
56
16
24

ICI Klea
Concord Plaza
3411 Silverside Road
P.O. Box 15391
Wilmington, DE 19850

Customer Service: (800) ICI-KLEA or
Technical Assistance: (800) ASK-KLEA
Fax: (302) 887-7706

ICI believes all information contained in this document to be accurate at the time of publication but makes no warranty of any kind, either express or implied, regarding the accuracy of any information or the results to be obtained from utilizing such information. Furthermore, the information is intended for use by persons having technical skills and a working knowledge of the system, and is to be used at their own discretion. The user assumes all risks and liability through application or use of the information contained herein and must satisfy himself that the product is entirely suitable for his own purpose and process.

Statements concerning the use of the products or formulations described herein are not to be construed as granting a license under any patent, or as recommending the infringement of any patent, and no liability for infringement arising out of any such use is assumed.

620250590 4/95

407C

ICI Klea Pressure-Enthalpy Diagram 407C (KLEA® 66)

Units

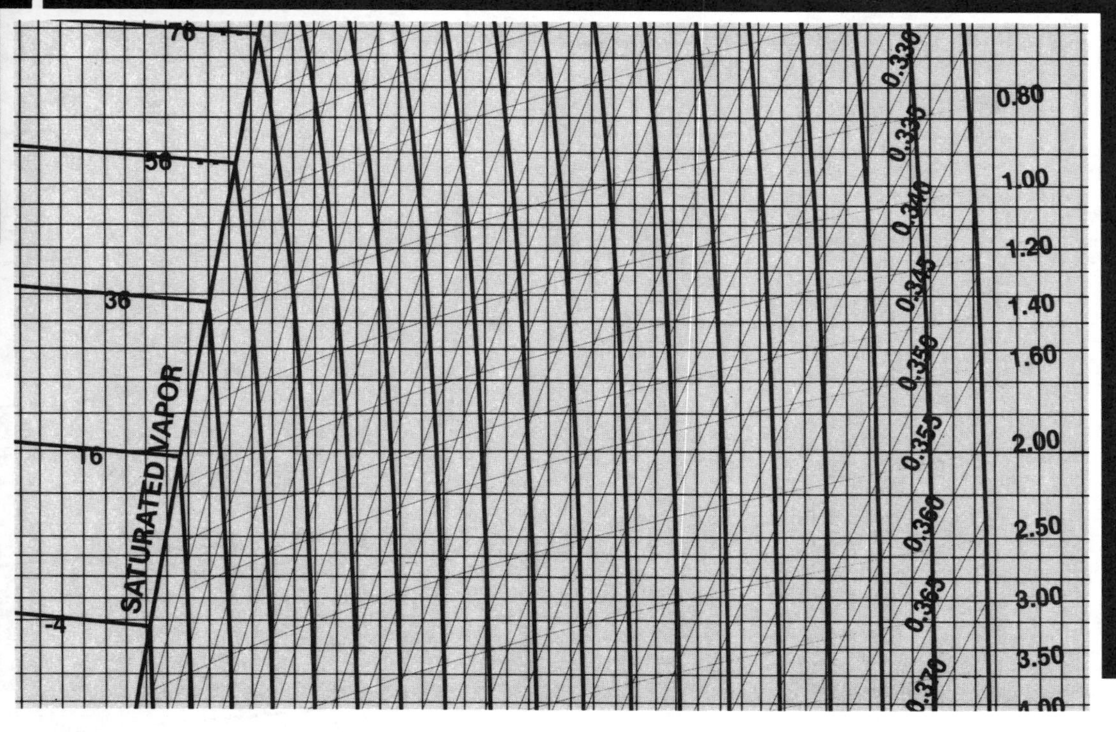

**NOW.
AND FOR
THE FUTURE.**

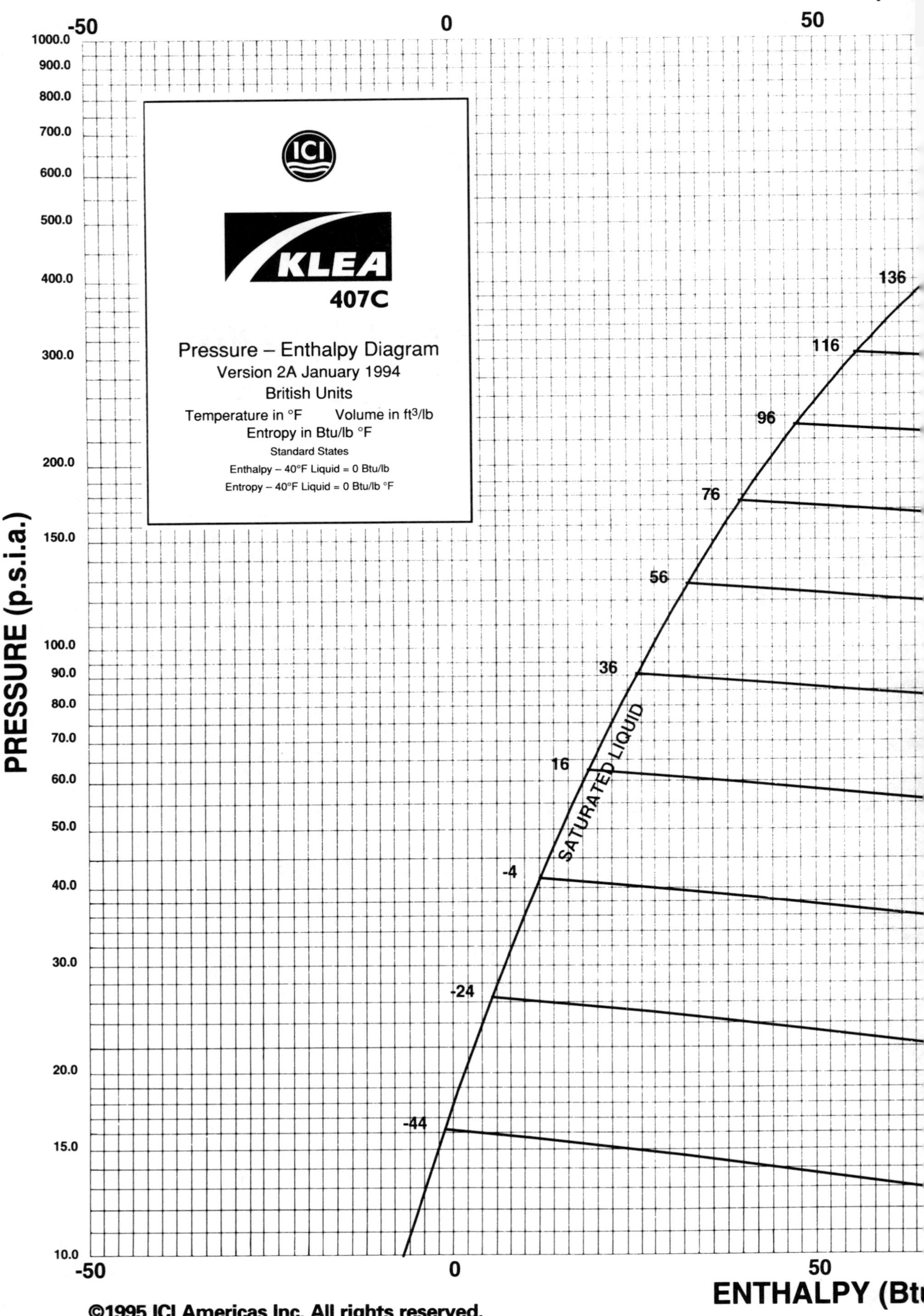

ENTHALPY (Bt
-50
0
50
1000.0
900.0
800.0
700.0
600.0
500.0
400.0
300.0
200.0
150.0
100.0
90.0
80.0
70.0
60.0
50.0
40.0
30.0
20.0
15.0
10.0
PRESSURE (p.s.i.a.)
ICI
KLEA
407C
Pressure – Enthalpy Diagram
Version 2A January 1994
British Units
Temperature in °F Volume in ft3/lb
Entropy in Btu/lb °F
Standard States
Enthalpy – 40°F Liquid = 0 Btu/lb
Entropy – 40°F Liquid = 0 Btu/lb °F
136
116
96
76
56
36
16
-4
-24
-44
SATURATED LIQUID
-50
0
50
ENTHALPY (Bt

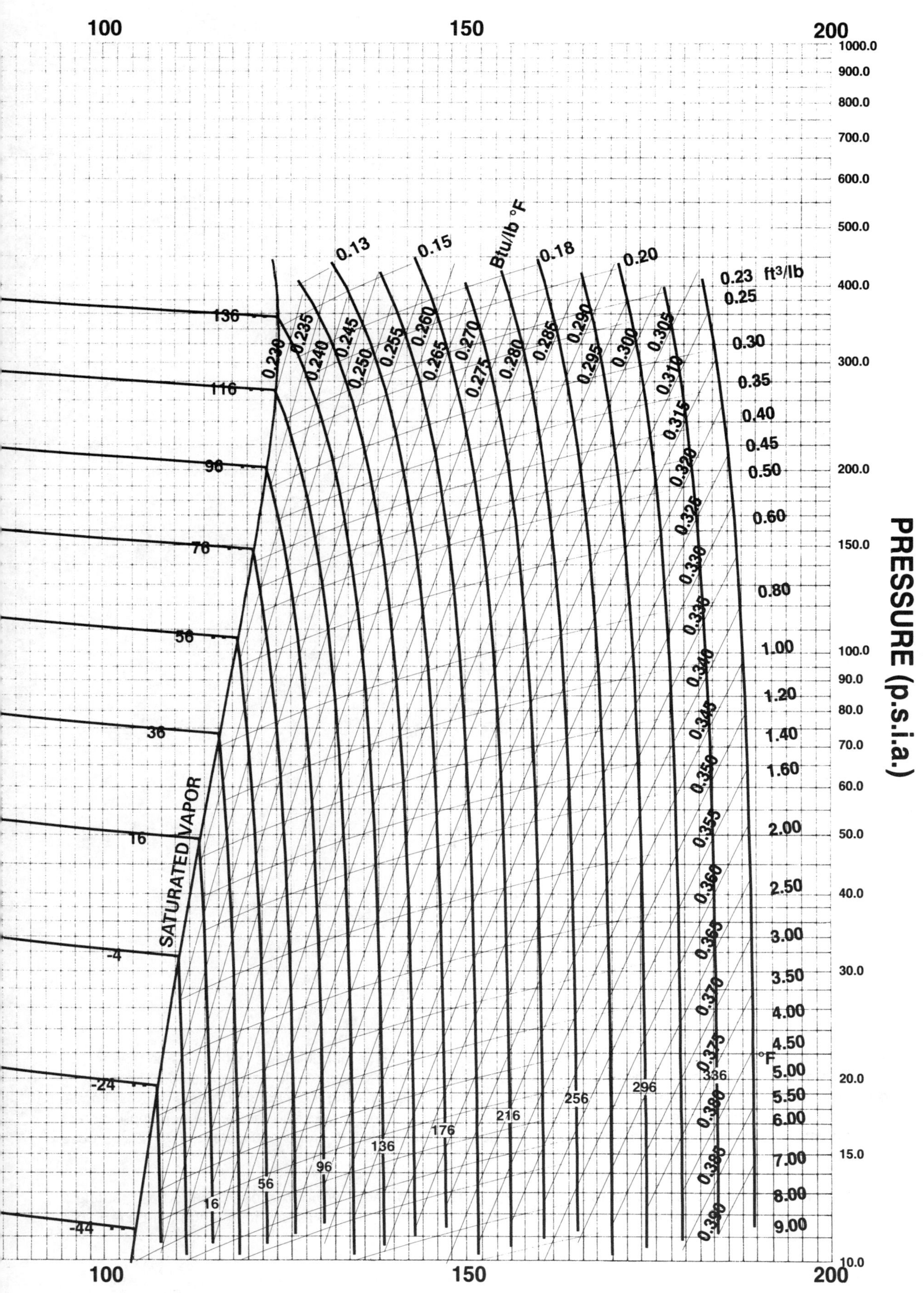

100
150
200
PRESSURE (p.s.i.a.)
SATURATED VAPOR
Btu/lb °F
ft³/lb
°F

ICI Klea
Concord Plaza
3411 Silverside Road
P.O. Box 15391
Wilmington, DE 19850

Customer Service: (800) ICI-KLEA or
Technical Assistance: (800) ASK-KLEA
Fax: (302) 887-7706

620250620 4/95

Elf Atochem North America

The following information is reprinted with permission of Elf Atochem North America, Inc.:

- *Forane® Retrofit Training Guide*
- *TECH Digest:*
  - *Forane® FX-56*
  - *Forane® 123*
  - *Forane® 134a*
  - *Forane® 404A*
  - *Forane® 408A*
- *Product Information for Forane® FX 10 (R-408A) Saturated Properties*
- *Product Information for Forane® FX 56 (R-409A) Saturated Properties*
- *Retrofitting Automotive Air Conditioners from R-12 to Forane® 134a*
- *Retrofitting Centrifugal Chillers from R-12 to Forane® 134a*
- *New England Supermarket Retrofits Complete Refrigeration System from R-12 to Forane® 134a*
- *Elf Lubricant's Procedure for Flushing Lubricants From Refrigeration Systems*
- *Alternative Refrigerant Blends*

Forane®

RETROFIT

Training Guide

RETROFIT TRAINING GUIDE

ELF ATOCHEM NORTH AMERICA, INC.

INDEX

RETROFIT TRAINING MANUAL

ELF ATOCHEM NORTH AMERICA, INC.

INDEX (Continued)

Page

IX. Appendix

I. INTRODUCTION

As a result of the CFC phaseout, occurring from the Montreal Protocol and Clean Air Act, the HVAC&R industry has been placed in a state of uncertainty. Traditional practices and applications involving CFC refrigerants will no longer exist after production of CFC's end on December 31,1995. Elf Atochem, along with other refrigerant manufacturers have developed and are continuing to develop CFC-free refrigerants for use in new and existing air-conditioning, chiller and refrigeration systems.

Manufacturers of HVAC&R equipment are developing equipment to operate with the new line of refrigerants being produced. This equipment will offer excellent performance and reliability, similar to traditional CFC systems. New equipment applications are well defined and will use a refrigerant specified by the manufacturer. In the case of equipment already in service the refrigerant choices are less clear. HVAC&R systems that are in good condition and have the potential to run for many years need to be addressed. If these systems are to be utilized in the most economically and environmentally acceptable manner, a plan that insures a readily available supply of CFC free refrigerant must be developed.

The choices that an equipment operator or owner has for maintaining an economical and environmentally responsible store or facility are difficult unless a clear understanding of all the available options are obtained. When exploring the options available for effective refrigerant management, keep in mind that the ultimate solution is dependent upon many different factors for each piece of equipment. Considerations such as age, location, duty, future expansion, capital expenditure, and regulatory issues will weigh heavily on the development of a refrigerant management plan.

Elf Atochem believes that the key to any successful refrigerant management program is education and the ability to remain current on all issues involved. This manual will be used as a tool to keep you updated on all key issues and procedures affecting the HVAC&R industry. It is designed to be used in conjunction with all industry regulations, guidelines and procedures in place at the time of use.

Elf Atochem North America, Inc. believes that the information and recommendations contained herein (including data and statements) are accurate as of the date hereof. **NO WARRANTY OF FITNESS FOR ANY PARTICULAR PURPOSE, WARRANTY OF MERCHANTABILITY, OR ANY OTHER WARRANTY, EXPRESSED OR IMPLIED, IS MADE CONCERNING THE INFORMATION PROVIDED HEREIN.** Further, since the methods of use of the information contained herein is beyond the control of Elf Atochem, Elf Atochem expressly disclaims any and all liability as to any results obtained or arising from any use of such information.

II. REGULATIONS UPDATE

A. 1990 CLEAN AIR ACT

In accordance with the revisions in 1990 of the Clean Air Act, Elf Atochem N.A. will be phasing out the old CFC's and bringing in the new technology of HCFC's and HFC's and the appropriate blends to replace them. The amendments to the CAA are more stringent then the targeted phaseout by the United Nation's Montreal Protocol. The CAA requires 10-20% less CFC production per year then the Montreal Protocol on Substances that Deplete the Ozone (see CFC Production Under each Act). A ban on CFC production will go into effect on January 1, 1996. An important difference between the Montreal Protocol and the CAA is that the EPA is required, by the CAA, to develop a complex regulatory program that not only mandates a phase out of U.S. CFC and HCFC production, but also requires evaluations of CFC alternatives and establishes stringent controls on commercial and industrial use of ozone-depleting substances.

CFC PRODUCTION UNDER EACH ACT OF GOVERNMENT

YEAR	MONTREAL PROTOCOL	COPENHAGEN AMENDMENTS	1990 CLEAN AIR ACT
1991	100%	100%	85%
1992	100%	75%	80%
1993	80%	50%	75%
1994	80%	25%	65%
1995	50%	25%	50%
1996	50%	0%	40%
1997	15%	0%	15%
1998	15%	0%	15%
1999	15%	0%	15%
2000	0%	0%	0%

WILL ENFORCE MOST STRINGENT LAWS IN CASE OF CONFLICT

**** THE EPA HAS ISSUED THE POLICY THAT IN CASE OF CONFLICT BETWEEN THE CAA AND THE MONTREAL PROTOCOL (including amendments) THE MOST STRINGENT POLICY WILL BE ENFORCED. ELF ATOCHEM N.A. AND THE U.S. EPA WILL FOLLOW THE COPENHAGEN AMENDMENTS.

CLEAN AIR ACT DEADLINES:

1992

July 1 — Venting ban of class I and II substances during maintenance, service, repair, or disposal of appliances or industrial process refrigeration equipment.

Nov. 15 — No nonessential class I substances designated by the EPA may be sold or distributed in interstate commerce.

1993

May 15 — Containers of class I or class II substances and products containing class I substances must have warning labels.

— Warning labels may be required for products manufactured with class I substances or that contain class II substances.

— All requirements of CAA Title VI must be met by U.S. government procurement regulations.

Nov. 11 — As of this date, EPA will enforce warning label requirements.

1994

Nov. 15 — Products releasing class II substances that are designated nonessential by the CAA or EPA cannot be sold or distributed in interstate commerce.

1995

Nov. 15 — Ban on venting of substitutes for class I and II substances during maintenance, service, repair or disposal of appliances or industrial process refrigeration equipment, except for substitutes the EPA deems as not harmful to the environment.

2015

Jan. 1 — All products containing class II substances sold or distributed in interstate commerce must have warning labels attached.

May 15 — All products manufactured with class I or class II substances that are sold or distributed in interstate commerce must have warning labels.

CAA Section 611 requires warning labels to be placed on containers with class I or class II substances in them at certain dates. All warning labels must state the following:

WARNING: CONTAINS {NAME OF SUBSTANCE}, A SUBSTANCE WHICH HARMS PUBLIC HEALTH AND ENVIRONMENT BY DESTROYING OZONE IN THE UPPER ATMOSPHERE.

B. MONTREAL PROTOCOL

The Montreal Protocol on Substances that Deplete the Ozone Layer was preceded by the Vienna Convention for the Protection of the Ozone Layer, and together these were the starting points for global cooperation for the protection of the ozone layer in the stratosphere. The Parties, those who are Protocol countries, had the Executive Director of UNEP to prepare a Montreal Protocol 'Handbook', and to update the 'Handbook' as necessary after each meeting of the Parties. The most recent amendments took place at Copenhagen, Denmark in November of 1992. More than 90 nations have ratified the Montreal Protocol, and 33 of those have ratified the 1990 London amendments. In case of conflict with the Clean Air Act, the most stringent ruling shall take precedence.

The Copenhagen amendments were the following:

- Phase-out of CFCs, carbon tetrachloride and methyl chloroform required by January 1, 1996; {instead of Jan. 2000}
- An interim 75-percent reduction in CFC production and consumption is required by Jan. 1, 1994.
- Halon phase-out was accelerated to Jan. 1, 1994.
- HCFCs must be phased out by 2030 with a 1996 production freeze based on production levels of 1986.
- 1995 production must be frozen at 1991 levels for methyl bromide production and consumption.

**** The EPA has issued its policy of enforcing the most stringent law pertaining to each issue in case of conflict between the CAA and Montreal Protocol.

C. REFRIGERANT HANDLING REGULATIONS

The Environmental Protection Agency has issued regulations which apply and regulate the handling, recovery, and recycling of CFCs and HCFCs.

Section 82.118

- Wholesalers, retailers and distributors must pass through to the purchaser all labeling information that accompanies the products. Wholesalers, retailers and distributer may rely on the accuracy of the labelling information for the product, and has no duty to investigate if a) the supplier has a contractual obligation to the wholesaler, retailer or distributer to label products accurately and in accordance with labeling regulations for CFCs and HCFCs, or b) the wholesaler, retailer or distributor has a reasonable belief that the supplier is complying with the applicable regulations.

Section 82.154

- Effective June 14, 1993, no person maintaining, servicing, repairing or disposing of appliances may knowingly vent or otherwise release into the atmosphere any class I or II substance used as a refrigerant in such equipment. De minimis releases arising from good faith attempts to recycle or recover refrigerants are not prohibited so long as the requirements of Sections 82.156 and 82.158 are met and the regulations regarding servicing motor vehicle air conditioners are satisfied.

- Effective July 13, 1993, no person may open an appliance, except Motor Vehicle Air Conditioners, for maintenance, service or repair, and no person may dispose of appliances except for small appliances, MVACs and MVAC — like appliances[without observing the required practices set forth in Sect. 82.156 and the equipment specified in Sect. 82.158.

- Effective June 14, 1993, no person shall alter recovery or recycling equipment in any manner that will cause the equipment not to meet the standards of Sect. 82.158 without submitting for retesting and recertification.

- Effective August 12, 1993, certification must be submitted to the EPA pursuant to Sect. 82.162 that the person servicing, repairing, disposing, or performing maintenance on appliances, with certain exceptions, has acquired certified recovery or recycling equipment and is complying with applicable regulations regarding this rule and that the equipment meets standards set forth in Sect. 82.158.

- Effective August 12, 1993, until Nov. 13, 1995, no person may sell or offer for sale for use as a refrigerant any class I or class II substance consisting wholly or in part of used refrigerant unless the refrigerant has been reclaimed by a certified reclaimer pursuant to Section 82.164 and 82.152.

- Effective August 12, 1993, no person reclaiming refrigerant may release more than 1.5% of the refrigerant received by them.

- Effective November 15, 1993, no person may sell or distribute any appliance unless the equipment is equipped with a servicing aperture or process stub, as appropriate, to facilitate the removal of refrigerant at servicing and disposal.

- Effective November 14, 1994, no person may open an appliance for servicing unless certified as a technician for that type of appliance pursuant to Sect. 82.161 and a certificate may only be issued through a training program that complies with all standards of Sect. 82.161 and Appendix D and has been granted approval.

- Effective November 14, 1994, no person may sell or distribute, or offer for sale or distribution, any class I or class II substance unless: 1) buyer is a certified technician pursuant to Section 82.161 and 40 CFR Part 82 Subpart B; 2) refrigerant is sold only for eventual resale to certified parties; 3) refrigerant is contained in an appliance; 4) refrigerant is charged into appliance by a certified technician during maintenance, service, or repair.

Section 82.156 Required Practices

•• Effective July 13, 1993, when opening appliances for service, except for MVACs, for maintenance, repair, service, or disposal, the technician must evacuate the refrigerant into a recovery or recycling machine that meets the standards of Sect. 82.158. When evacuating, vacuum levels must reach specified conditions (Miscellaneous Section, Table 12) for each type of system. In case of a leak where the desired vacuum level cannot be obtained, the leak must be isolated wherever possible and the system must be evacuated to the lowest level possible.

- Effective July 13, 1993, persons who take the final step in the disposal process of a small appliance, room air-conditioning, MVACs, or MVAC-like appliances must either recover remaining refrigerant from the equipment in compliance with Section 82.156 (g) and (h) or verify the charge has been evacuated from the appliance prior to disposal. Such verification must include a signed statement; containing name, address of the person recovering refrigerant, and date the refrigerant was recovered. A contract that the refrigerant will be removed prior to delivery will also be accepted; from the person from whom the appliance or shipment of appliances is obtained that all refrigerant that had not leaked previously had been recovered in obtained that all refrigerant that had not leaked previously had been recovered in accordance with Section 82.156 (g) and (h).

- Effective July 13, 1993, all persons opening appliances, except for small alliances and MVACs, for service must have at least one piece of certified recovery or recycling equipment at their place of business.

Section 82.161 Technician Certification

- Effective November 14, 1994, persons who maintain, service, dispose or repair appliances, with certain exceptions, must be certified by an approved technician certification program. Small appliance technicians must achieve Type I certification; high or very-high pressure appliance technicians must achieve Type II certification; low pressure appliance technicians must achieve Type III certification; persons who service all of the above must achieve the Universal technician certification.

Section 82.162 Certification by Owners of Recovery and Recycling Equipment

- No later than August 12, 1993, or within 20 days of commencing business for persons not in business at the time of promulgation, businesses must certify to the EPA that such owner's recovery or recycling equipment is certified and complies with all applicable requirements.

Section 82.166 Reporting and Record Keeping Requirements

Effective as of May 14, 1993:

Certain records, discussed as follows, must be maintained for three years after they are generated:

- Invoices reflecting the name of the purchaser, date of sale and type and quantity of refrigerant sold.

- Technician certification affirmation must be supplied by the purchaser to the wholesaler who will keep this information on file.

- For each transaction, reclaimers must maintain records of the name and address of persons sending them material for reclamation and the quantity of the material sent.

- Reclaimers must maintain records of quantity of material sent for reclamation, mass of refrigerant reclaimed, and mass of waste products. Reclaimers must report such information to the EPA within 30 days of the end of each calendar year.

- Persons disposing of small appliances, MVACs and MVAC-like appliances must maintain copies of statements pursuant to Section 82.156.

- Service preformed on appliances containing 50 or more pounds must be accompanied by an invoice to the owner of the refrigerant identifying the amount of refrigerant added to the appliance.

- Appliances that contain 50 or more pounds of refrigerant must have proper service records accompanying them.

- Technician certification must be displayed at the place of business.

D. UL GUIDELINE 2154

The main objective of Underwriter Laboratory's guideline 2154 is to insure the procedural safety of retrofitting equipment used in HVAC&R equipment, both commercial and residential units. The regulations include sections on construction and operations for file conversion/retrofits, material and refrigerant compatibility requirements for field conversions/retrofits, and field conversion and safety requirements both procedures and guidelines.

E. ASHRAE STANDARD 15

The American Society of Heating, Refrigeration and Air Conditioning Engineers issued these standards to improve the safety of the technicians working on cooling systems. The standards regulate areas both on and near the properties where the facilities are located and assist in aiding the technicians decision making responsibilities when it comes to working in an enclosed area or an area the technician may feel is dangerous. This standard tells the technician what a dangerous application and area is specifically.

F. SAE J STANDARDS

The Society of Automotive Engineers has issued numerous standards concerning the refrigeration industry. These are listed in the appendix as well as the newest standard 2154a-c on retrofitting used equipment. These standards give guidelines for safety, equipment, and procedures associated with the use of all refrigerants for automotive applications.

III. PRODUCT INFORMATION

Elf Atochem has supplied, and continues to supply a wide range of Chlorofluorocarbons (CFC) and Hydrochlorofluorocarbons (HCFC), both as single component refrigerants or in the form of blended refrigerants as in the case of R-500 and R-502. Also, in response to environmental concerns about the thinning of the ozone layer, Elf Atochem has become the worldwide leader in the production and supply of alternative Hydrofluorocarbons (HFC) with zero ozone depletion potential (ODP).

The following is a summary of the wide range of refrigerants currently offered along with some of their most important properties. Properties for CFC refrigerants are provided only as a reference to aid in the search of a suitable alternative. Therefore, please keep in mind that their supply will become limited as the regulations limiting or prohibiting their use take effect.

In the event that you require information beyond the scope of what is covered in this manual, please contact our retrofit customer service phone number at 1-(800)-RETRO94. This number will put you in contact with personnel who can provide more detailed information from our extensive databases, or in case of new information, our research and development (R&D) laboratories in the U.S and France can provide the information as applicable.

A. CHLOROFLUOROCARBONS (CFC)

FORANE® 11

FORANE® 12

FORANE® 500

FORANE® 502

B. HYDROCHLOROFLUOROCARBONS (HCFC)

FORANE® FX-10

FORANE® 22

FORANE® FX-56

FORANE® 123

C. HYDROFLUOROCARBONS (HFC)

FORANE® 134a

FORANE® 404 A (FX-70)

IV. REFRIGERANT MANAGEMENT OPTIONS

One of the first steps for addressing the CFC issue is to develop a refrigerant management program for your equipment. You may choose to do this within your organization or hire a consultant to develop a program. Either way the decision to start must be initiated by you.

When deciding a course of action for a system or series of systems four options become the basis for handling the impending CFC production phase out. A brief explanation of each follows and will serve as a starting point for the evaluation of most projects.

Option 1. Ignore - This response can lead to only one result, loss of business and increased expenses. The loss may result from equipment downtime, lack of refrigerant supplies, loss of customer base due to inability to address important issues and the list goes on. Increased expenses may be in the form of increased refrigerant costs, labor costs, downtime or regulatory violations. Needless to say, this option should be avoided at all costs.

Option 2. Containment - A good choice for equipment and systems targeted for replacement or phaseout in the next 3 years or less. Tightening of the systems current CFC refrigerant supply, along with CFC's reclaimed from retrofitted systems should be sufficient to assure continued operation of this type of equipment at reasonable costs. For systems that are projected to remain in service longer than 3 years careful consideration must be given to the availability of economical refrigerant resources.

Option 3. Retrofitting - The subject of this manual and popular choice for millions of systems in good operating condition. Extends the useful life of equipment for indefinite periods of time at economically feasible rates by using an alternative refrigerant that is environmentally more attractive than traditional CFC's. CFC's recovered may be used in systems that have been designated for containment. Elf Atochem offers a refrigerant cleaning service to return the old refrigerant to ARI-700 standards. (See Rollover Program)

Option 4. Replacement - This is the most expensive of the options and preferred choice for equipment that is at the end of its useful life or is not worthy of retrofitting or containment. New equipment is designed to use the same refrigerants that are being used in retrofit applications thereby reducing the number and types of refrigerants needed at each location.

By utilizing one or a combination of the refrigerant management options, transformation to a CFC free equipment environment can be accomplished with the most efficient means.

V. PROMOTING A RETROFIT

As the CFC production phaseout approaches, the HVAC&R community is gearing up to offer alternative refrigerants, programs and services to escort their customers into the new CFC-free environment.

One of the most valuable services that can be offered to customers is a good education. An educated, well informed customer will be able to make the best decision on how to deal with the CFC phaseout for their system. A great number of customer's have existing systems that are in service and require attention to remain in service beyond the impending CFC phase out. These customers have four basic options:

1. Ignore
2. Contain and tighten existing systems
3. Convert/Retrofit existing systems
4. Replace old systems with new CFC-free equipment

Options 1, 2 and 4 were discussed earlier in this manual. Option 3 - Convert/Retrofit, is fast becoming the most popular choice to extend the life of the large number of systems currently using CFC's.

Retrofitting is best described as a process or procedure that uses existing equipment in conjunction with the new line of refrigerants and lubricants without major component replacement in order to extend the "life" of the equipment and reduce the environmental concerns associated with non-retrofitted equipment.

When looking at a system and deciding if retrofitting is a viable solution, the customer should be aware of several positive benefits with this option:

1. **Environmentally Aware:** Retrofitting with HFC's and HCFC's is an environmentally aware solution. The new refrigerants offer low to zero ozone depletion levels. This means a lot to an environmentally conscious customer and consumer.

2. **Adequate Supply and Availability:** The simple issue of supply and demand will cause availability of refrigerant to dwindle and prices to escalate. By retrofitting, refrigerant supplies are assured and costs offer greater stability compared to the CFC's. OEMs can only produce a limited amount of chillers and other units per year, and with the rush to buy new equipment that will take place if no one acts now, equipment and parts will be limited. It pays to be one step ahead.

3. **Reduced Costs:** Retrofitting offers reduced costs when compared to completely replacing the system. In most cases, retrofits require only refrigerant, lubricant and labor costs.

4. **Long Term Solution:** Retrofitting is a long term solution - it provides a continued operation of the equipment at the lowest possible operating costs - now and in the future. Future tax increases on CFC's will mean continual operating costs for non-retrofitted systems. A retrofitted system will not encounter these costs in the foreseeable future.

5. **Opportunity to Upgrade and Repair Current System:** Retrofitting offers the opportunity to upgrade and repair systems that have been operating at less than optimal levels leading to improved performance and efficiencies for such systems. In many cases, the retrofit cost can be offset with maintenance previously needed.

6. **Attractive payback periods:** Payback periods for retrofit costs are attractive when considering cost savings on refrigerant, maintenance practices, potential fines and in some cases loss of customer base due to customer awareness of the CFC issue. Additionally, selling the CFC refrigerant back to your distributor can help offset the cost of the retrofit procedure.

DELAYING OR IGNORING THE CFC PHASEOUT WILL ONLY LEAD TO FUTURE COST INCREASES FROM LABOR, LOSS OF PRODUCTION DUE TO DOWNTIME, ESCALATING REFRIGERANT COSTS AND POTENTIAL FINES FROM IMPROPER SERVICING.

A. FACTORS INFLUENCING

JUSTIFICATION OF A RETROFIT

The justification for retrofitting a particular system or series of systems can be a complicated process at times. Many factors can figure in the final decision of whether or not to retrofit: age, size, location, application, life of process and the actual cost of the retrofit. Of these, cost can be the ultimate factor in selling or performing the retrofit.

When determining costs associated with a particular project several items should be addressed including the following items:

1. Refrigerant costs present and future
2. Refrigerant supply and availability
3. Replacement cost of new equipment
4. Difficulty in performing the retrofit
5. Age and location of equipment
6. Type of new refrigerant and lubrication
7. Possible loss of income due to consumer environmental concern
8. Efficiency of the system

Refrigerant costs are obviously of great concern as the CFC taxes increase and the availability of CFC's begin to diminish. When considering a retrofit it must be kept in mind that as the alternative non-chlorine containing refrigerants become more readily available the costs associated with the usage and purchase will decrease in comparison with traditional CFC's. As the impending 1995 phaseout of CFC production approaches, refrigerant manufacturers including Elf Atochem are currently building or have built new manufacturing facilities to produce the new alternative refrigerants.

HVAC&R equipment has historically had the reputation for longevity when it has been well maintained. It has also had the reputation for being a substantial monetary investment initially. It is with these two factors in mind that Elf Atochem has taken the initiative to develop long-term replacements for the traditional CFC refrigerants as opposed to interim HCFC replacements. When retrofitting an existing system , Elf Atochem believes in choosing the ultimate long-term replacement where possible. One retrofit for the life of the equipment as opposed to stop-gap measures. Retrofitting offers new-life and longevity to the existing CFC equipment and will continue to do so at an increasing economically feasible rate. Certain applications where mineral oil cannot be removed efficiently may warrant the use of an HCFC blend that tolerates higher levels of residual mineral oil, thous reducing the overall cost of the retrofit.

When choosing the type of replacement refrigerant for retrofit applications, remember to think of the best long-term approach (HFC's) even though it may cost a few dollars more initially. In most commercial semi-hermetic refrigeration and chilled water cases the difference in costs amount to merely a few gallons of lubricant for a flushing procedure. These few extra dollars initially can turn in to considerable savings in just a few years as you are assured that by choosing the chlorine free alternative, retrofitting will be done only once with a readily available and environmentally accepted product.

B. ELF ATOCHEM'S POSITION ON RETROFITTING

Elf Atochem is committed to making the retrofit process as easy and painless as possible for its customers. To achieve this we will provide technical data and information as necessary, as well as supplying the customer's choice of refrigerant(s). However, the choice of the refrigerant to be used in a retrofit will certainly impact not only the amount of labor and cost involved in the short term, but also the long term in the form of higher costs for maintenance, or possibly the need for a second retrofit should interim HCFC refrigerants be phased out sooner.

Customers are currently faced with two basic choices when selecting a refrigerant to retrofit a system that is currently running with CFC's: 1) HCFC's and 2) HFC's. It is Elf Atochem's position that whenever possible, and economically feasible, all retrofits should be performed with HFC's for several reasons.

- ***PERMANENT SOLUTION***

  HFC's have been identified as long term refrigerants by virtually all OEM's. Most new equipment is either being redesigned or adapted to be used with HFC's. HCFC blends are viewed only as a temporary solution to CFC's. No new equipment is being designed or modified to use HCFC blends. HCFC's are on the EPA's "hit list" as controlled substances and are slated for elimination as soon as the year 2010. It is very possible that this date will accelerate forward in a fashion similar to the CFC's. Use of the HCFC blends should be used only when lubricant flushing causes the retrofit of a system to become too labor intensive as compared to the total cost of the retrofit (small hermetic compressors).
- ***ENVIRONMENTALLY AWARE***

  HFC's have an ozone depletion potential (O.D.P.) equal to zero. All HCFC's, since they are chlorinated compounds, have ODP values greater than zero[1]. Consumer awareness of the Ozone Depletion Potential value of refrigerants is increasing rapidly. The environmental awareness of consumers can effect business should certain facilities choose to keep CFC's or HCFC's. Many consumers will only "do business" with those firms viewed as environmentally aware or "Green".
- ***FUTURE AVAILABILITY***

  HCFC's are currently regulated and their production may be eliminated as soon as the year 2010. This means that in the future HCFC's will become scarce as we get closer to the elimination deadline. It is also possible, as with the case of CFC's that the deadline could get moved up, making availability an even greater problem in the near future. HFC's are not regulated and are not scheduled for phaseout therefore, only unlimited supplies are forecast for HFC's.

It is with these factors in mind that Elf Atochem prefers the movement towards the HFC's versus HCFC's. In some cases, such as small hermetic systems, removal of the mineral lubricant may become to labor intensive to justify the use of an HFC. These cases should then be considered for HCFC's because of their ability to tolerate higher levels of residual mineral oil, thus reducing the number of oil flushes. Additionally, small hermetic systems in general do not offer "life" periods as long as other systems.

Elf Atochem will strive to provide a wide variety of refrigerants that the HVAC&R community has accepted and which we view as potential long term replacements.

C. APPLICATION OF ELF ATOCHEM'S ALTERNATIVE RETROFIT REFRIGERANTS

Forane 134a: A single component HFC replacement for R-12/R-500 applications in the medium and high temperature ranges. Zero ODP.

Applicable areas:

Commercial medium and high temperature refrigeration and central chilled water systems. Automotive air-conditioning.

Lubricant:

Automotive applications: polyalyklglycol

All others: Polyolester lubricant

Forane FX-56: An HCFC blend (22/142b/124) for the replacement of R-12 . Primarily intended for the small hermetic compressors where removal of mineral oil is complicated.

Lubricant:

Mineral oil, Polyolester, Alkylbenzene

Forane 404A (FX-70): An HFC blend (143a/125/134a) for replacement of R-502. Zero ODP providing an excellent long-term new equipment/ retrofit for R-502.

Lubricant:

Polyolester

Forane HCFC-123: An HCFC single component refrigerant for the replacement of R-11.

Lubricant:

Mineral oil

VI. LUBRICANTS

Lubricants are used to protect against wear between any two mechanical surfaces that may come in contact. They do this by forming a thin hydrodynamic oil film that keeps the surfaces separated and thus protected. This simple principle minimizes wear between pistons and cylinder walls, between the rolling elements in a bearing, between the tips of the rotors and the compressor chambers in a rotary compressor, etc.

A secondary purpose of oil in compressors and motors is sealing. By filling the gap between the piston and the walls in a motor or compressor, or between the vanes and the compression chamber, oil prevents blow bye, thereby making the compression cycle more efficient.

In summary, lubricant oils increase the durability of a system by preventing wear and enhancing system performance by improving sealing. An optimum oil will do both jobs efficiently while also maintaining its stability and being compatible with the system components.

Choosing the right oil requires a great amount of chemical testing to determine the stability and compatibility of the different base fluids and its additives such as antiwear (AW) compounds, stabilizers, etc., as well as a considerable amount of mechanical testing to determine how well a lubricant oil does its job. Also, the chemical interaction amongst the refrigerant, metal surfaces and the oil itself need to considered, as in the case of CFC-12 and mineral oil, where the Chlorine from the refrigerant acts on the metals to improve the lubrication capacity of the oil.

There are some other properties that also must be considered when choosing an oil, for example its hygroscopicity, or affinity to absorb water. Under normal conditions, mineral oils absorb only a very small amount of water. Excess free water will not mix with the oil and will be mechanically carried by it around the system where it may end up in the filter dryer or, depending on the amount, it could freeze, cause corrosion, or have some other detrimental effect. This fact is illustrated by common wisdom in "oil (mineral oil) and water do not mix". Synthetic oils used in refrigeration are capable of holding far larger amounts of water than mineral oils. In fact some, as the oil used in automotive HFC-134a systems are "water soluble" and therefore could absorb any amount of water. This will not result in free water in most cases, but it will contribute to system corrosion, base stock oil decomposition, etc. Handling of synthetic based refrigeration oils should be performed carefully to avoid exposure to air and its moisture. Standard lubricant oil handling precautions should include; keeping containers capped at all times when not in use, usage of smaller containers over larger ones, complete evacuation of the system before charging with oil, and any other measures that insure the integrity of the oil.

Typically, chemical testing is done using "sealed tube stability tests". These are sealed containers where metal coupons of steel, copper and aluminum are submerged in the oil and baked at high temperature for 14 days. By examining the condition of the coupons oil companies can determine oil compatibility with the different metals. By testing the oil itself, one can determine its stability. Mechanical tests are done in special machines that rotate a round pin on a 'V' shaped block (V-block tests) and/or by rotating a fixture ending on 4 identical balls on a flat surface (4-ball tests). All these tests are standardized and follow a consistent set of rules for their evaluation and comparison of their results.

Finally, once a lubricant oil has been developed and optimized by an oil company, it must be subjected to rigorous testing by the compressor manufacturers. O.E.M.'s subject the oil to a manufacturer specific set of tests on the actual equipment they intend to use the oil in, until they are satisfied that it performs according to all their specifications. It is because of this that compressor manufacturer's recommendations are important in determining the correct lubrication for any system being evaluated.

The following tables illustrate the preferred choices of lubricant oils for the different refrigerants, and some of the typical oil applications currently in the market, where PAG's (Poly Alkaline Glycols) and POE's (Polyolesters) are used. Note that oils are mentioned only as base stocks. For specific oil viscosities and anti-wear additives necessary refer to manufacturer's recommendations.

TABLE 1. LUBRICANT COMPATIBILITY

REFRIGERANT	M.O.	P.A.G.	A.B.	P.O.E.
R-12	YES	NO	YES	YES
R-22	YES	NO	YES	YES
R-500	YES	NO	YES	YES
R-502	YES	NO	YES	YES
R-134a	NO	YES	NO	YES
R-404A(FX-70)	NO	NO	NO	YES
FX-56	YES	NO	YES	YES

*M.O. (Mineral Oil)
PAG (Poly Alkaline Glycol)
A.B.(Alkylbenzene)
POE (Polyolester)

VI. LUBRICANT

A. FLUSHING PROCEDURES

A lot of confusion is associated with this particular issue. It is a well known fact that the new line of refrigerants require a new type of lubricant, primarily synthetic based ones such as the polyolesters. Because mineral oil is not miscible with the new refrigerants it must be removed or "flushed" from the system before charging with the new refrigerant. The procedures for the actual removal of the mineral oil are not clearly defined and depend a great deal on the type of system being retrofitted. Since there is no clear cut way of removing the mineral oil from a system the following procedures serve only as suggestions for facilitating the removal of the oil. Experimentation may lead to quicker and easier procedures. Table 2 indicates experimental mineral oil levels remaining in a typical semi-hermetic system after a varying number of lubricant flushes.

Procedure A:

Step 1. Remove the current charge of mineral oil from the system at all accessible oil removal locations.

Step 2. Replace with an equivalent charge of the new lubricant. (Although the mineral oil and new refrigerants are not miscible, the new lubricant and old refrigerants are.)

Step 3. Operate the system for approximately 24-48 hours to circulate the refrigerant and new lubricant through out the system. This procedure returns the mineral oil with the new lubricant and the mineral oil can therefore be drained with the lubricant charge to remove the remaining traces of mineral oil from the system.

Step 4. Repeat step 3 until the desired level of residual mineral oil is reached. The residual levels are of great debate and will vary from manufacturer to manufacturer. It is recommended that you follow the manufacturers guideline to avoid any possible warranty issues. Experience has shown that levels at 5% or less cause no noticeable operating problems, and can be reached after 3 flushes. Test kits or refractometers are available to test the residual levels at the job sight.

Step 5. Recover old refrigerant and begin the retrofit.

Remember that the above procedures are only suggestions that the experience of Elf Atochem indicates have worked well in the past. It should be understood that as long as the residual levels are reduced to the appropriate levels, any effective oil removal process can be used.

TABLE 2:

Number of Flushes versus Mineral oil Residual Levels for a typical System. Please note that different systems may experience different residual oil levels. These numbers are for reference only.

Flush #	50%*	40%*	30%*	20%*	10%*
1	25%	16%	9%	4%	1%
2	12.5%	6.4%	2.7%	.8%	.1%
3	6.25%	2.56%	.8%	.16%	.01%
4	3.1%	1.0%	.25%	.03%	0%

* Indicates the starting level of mineral oil remaining in system after initial draining of the original mineral oil charge.

VII. SYSTEM COMPONENT INFORMATION

A. TERMINOLOGY COMMONLY USED

IN REFRIGERATION AND AIR CONDITIONING WHEN DEALING WITH ALTERNATE REFRIGERANTS

Early refrigeration and air-conditioning applications primarily used CFC-12 as the refrigerant of choice. Then, as refrigeration and air conditioning applications became more specific and complex, more specialized refrigerants were developed. Now, when non-ozone depleting alternative refrigerants are being developed, the HVAC&R market is becoming "flooded" with different refrigerants described as "CFC", "HCFC", "HFC", "single component", "blended refrigerant" (or simply "blend"), "azeotrope", "near azeotrope", having "glide", etc. But exactly, what does it all mean?. In this section we will try to provide you with a simple understanding of the terminology used when dealing with refrigerants in today's market place and specifically, how it affects you.

First, lets begin with CFC (chlorofluorocarbons), HCFC hydrochlorofluorocarbons) and HFC (hydrofluorocarbons). All refrigerants are just chemical compounds made up of a combination of chlorine (the first 'C'), fluorine (the 'F'), hydrogen (the 'H') and carbon (the last 'C') molecules. These names, or acronyms, simply tell you what basic elements make up a particular refrigerant molecule, with different compositions being identified by means of the numbers associated with them. For example, even though R-11 (CCl_3F) and R-12 (CCl_2F_2) are both CFC's, the number of chlorine, fluorine and carbon atoms are different in each of them. R-11 and R-12 contain 3 and 2, 1 and 2 and 1 and 1 chlorine, fluorine and carbon atoms respectively. Incidentally, refrigerant names like CFC-12, R-12 or F-12 are just synonyms commonly used where the R means refrigerant and the F means Forane®.

When a refrigerant is entirely composed of the same molecule, ie. it is made up of only one molecule type, then it is referred to as a "single component" refrigerant. CFC-12 and HFC-134a are examples of single component refrigerants. When two or more single component refrigerants are mixed, the result is a blended refrigerant, almost universally known as "blend". FX-56 and FX-70 are examples of blends. Blends are classified as CFC, HCFC and HFC depending on their most ozone harming component, that is, if a blend contains a CFC, then it is a CFC regardless of the other components, if it contains a HCFC but not a CFC it is a HCFC, and if it is made entirely of HFC, it is a HFC. Blends are also classified based on the number of single refrigerant components they contain as binary (2), ternary (3),and so on, indicating the number of single components that make-up the blend composition.

Blends can also be described as being azeotropes or near azeotropes. By definition, an azeotrope blend is one that can not be separated into its components by distillation, and thus behaves as a single component refrigerant with a single boiling point at a particular pressure, temperature and composition for system purposes. An example of an azeotrope blend is R-502, which is a combination of HCFC-22 (48.8%) and CFC-115 (51.2%). A near-azeotrope blend on the other hand is one that 'almost' behaves like an azeotrope but could separate (or fractionate) a small amount and does not have a single boiling point. In other words, a near azeotrope blend behaves somewhat like a single refrigerant with a few exceptions. Most alternate refrigerant blends in the market today are near azeotropes. In most system applications near-azeotropes "act" very similar to single component refrigerants.

When dealing with near azeotrope blends in a refrigeration or air conditioning system, there is a characteristic that has to be taken into account, that characteristic is the "glide" of the blend. Since a near azeotrope blend does not have a single boiling point and its components can fractionate, then, as it passes through the evaporator, the component with the lowest boiling point will begin evaporating first, then the next lowest boiling point component and so forth until all the liquid is completely evaporated. It can be seen that because of this phenomena, the evaporator will not be at a constant temperature, but there will be a variation in temperature from inlet to outlet. This variation in temperature from inlet to outlet is known as the "glide" of the blend. Depending on the magnitude of the glide, it will affect the system in several ways. First, since the evaporator is no longer at a constant temperature, the set temperature will have to be the average temperature. This in turn will affect the system controls, as for example the thermal expansion valve, that senses temperature at the outlet and could be fooled to think that the temperature there is higher than it should be. Also, since the evaporator has a temperature gradient, in some units it is possible to experience frosting at the outlet, a typical indication of low charge in a system with no glide, but a perfectly normal characteristic for refrigerants with glide. In general, for most applications, if glide is taken into account and compensated for, no problems should be experienced and the system should work adequately after a properly performed retrofit procedure.

When dealing with near azeotrope blends, there are some other precautions that must be taken. Since the blends can fractionate, only charge systems in the liquid phase, never in the gas phase to avoid changing the composition. Charging from the liquid phase can result in a higher amount of the low boiling component being introduced in the system. Topping off system leaks may also have to be treated differently. A leak from the liquid side of the system will release proportional amounts of each of the refrigerant components. A leak from the gas side will again tend to fractionate and leak a disproportionate amount of the lower boiling components. Ideally, in the presence of a leak, the charge should be recovered and the system recharged. In practice, as a rule of thumb for most blends, a leak of less than 50% of the total charge can be "topped off" with liquid without any major effects on system performance.

These, and other specific steps necessary to retrofit to a blend will be covered in detail in the text of this manual. Please note also that the above explanations only cover a particular group of refrigerants. Some other refrigerants like ammonia (NH_3) and hydrocarbons (HC) have not been covered here because they are beyond the scope of this text, even though some retrofit blends may contain a very small amount of HC.

B. CONTROL COMPATIBILITY

When retrofitting to the new line of refrigerants it should be noted that certain characteristics will be altered in the system. Controls such as high pressure cut-out, low pressure cut-out, oil pressure regulating, and capacity loading controls may require slight adjustments to account for the variations in pressures between the old and new refrigerants. Additionally, care should be taken to clean traces of mineral oil from the controls directly connected to the refrigerant circuit of the system to reduce the contamination of oil and assure proper operation of the control. Unloading and loading devices operating on motor current may require adjustment to account for slight operating changes from the old refrigerant. Some unloaders may require new seals/seats (contact the manufacturer for details).

Solenoid valves are generally compatible with the new line of refrigerants and usually require no modification. In general compatibility is not an issue with HFC-134a, FX-56, FX-70. R-123 should be checked against the equipment manufacturers guidelines.

C. EXPANSION DEVICE COMPATIBILITY

When retrofitting to the new line of refrigerants it should be noted slight variations in the operating pressures of the new refrigerants will occur. These variations will affect the operation of the expansion device. The function of the expansion device is to reduce the pressure and temperature within the liquid phase of a refrigerant by means of a restricting action. This in turn reduces the evaporating point of the refrigerant to temperatures within the desired cooling range and allows the refrigerant to absorb heat from the "load" area. Properties of the new refrigerants will be slightly different than the refrigerants they are replacing causing different flow rates through the expansion device. These differences will account for fluctuating superheats, pressure drops, and capacity differences through the device.

Devices such as a ***Thermostatic Expansion Valve*** (TEV), used on direct expansion evaporators (DX systems), may require merely an adjustment of the valve throttle to avoid flooding of the evaporator and correct superheat settings. Superheat settings should remain at the manufacturers guidelines before and after the retrofit. Since the operation of the TEV is based upon pressure differentials operation on "fixed" expansion valves should be acceptable as well.

More complicated procedures may become necessary for applications that use ***orifice plates/tubes*** such as a centrifugal chillers. These type of devices may require assistance from the chiller manufacturer for resizing the orifices to provide proper flow through the device and similar capacity ratings. Generally, most medium temperature chillers require no modification for use with HFC-134a. R-123 may require adjustment, consult the manufacturer for details.

Finally, ***capillary expansion*** devices require little adaptation other than complete removal of the original mineral oil charge or the use of HCFC blends tolerating higher residual mineral oil content.

D. DESICCANT COMPATIBILITY

The function of the desiccant in a system is to remove any moisture that might have entered with a) the refrigerant or lubricant during charging, b) with air depending on the level and length of time of the vacuum achieved, and c) through elastomer hoses or seals, especially in the case of automotive air conditioners. By removing moisture from the system, it is protected from rust or freezing. Desiccants are also capable of scavenging for acids formed during system operation, thus protecting it from corrosion. In addition, in the case of in-line dryers, filtering for larger pieces of debris is also accomplished.

Most desiccants used in systems today are molecular sieve type. A molecular sieve acts by attracting water molecules into molecular 'holes' (voids between molecules) and electrically holding them there. By controlling the size of these 'holes', molecular sieves can be made to adsorb water molecules more or less rapidly, the larger the 'holes' the quicker the moisture pick up. However, by opening the size of the molecular 'holes' in the sieves other products may also be trapped there, for example, refrigerant or oil molecules. This attraction of other compounds is clearly undesirable since the total water capacity of the molecular sieve is reduced.

Different refrigerants and oils have different molecular sizes, therefore, a desiccant that worked well with a particular refrigerant or oil may not work well with its substitutes. Besides the obvious problems with the reduction of the desiccant water capacity, when refrigerant or lubricant are trapped in the desiccant they may react chemically with some of its components and result in undesirable products. This is why it is necessary to pay special attention to desiccants and refrigerants.

Desiccant compatibility with the different refrigerants is not so clear cut and it has been the object of exhaustive studies by different molecular sieve manufacturing companies. This problem is especially difficult when blends of refrigerants are involved. As a rule of thumb, if a particular refrigerant is not compatible with a type of molecular sieve, any blends containing that refrigerant should not be used with that desiccant either, however, there are some exceptions to this rule. Table 2 shows refrigerant to desiccant compatibility that is based on data obtained by UOP (manufacturer of Molsiv® molecular sieves) at their labs. It is complete and accurate at the time of printing, but new data is continuously being added. For specific information not contained here, please consult the desiccant manufacturer.

Desiccant physical shape may also be important. It is recommended that all retrofits, especially when switching to HFC-134a, use solid core or compacted bead type sieves in order to minimize attrition of the desiccant into the system. In some cases, light material incompatibilities may be overcome if the reduction in physical properties (increased attrition, etc.) is taken care of by using the right type of sieve packaging.

Table 3: REFRIGERANT TO DESICCANT MATERIAL COMPATIBILITY

	4A-XH-5	XH-7	4A-XH-6	XH-9
CFC-11	YES	YES	YES	YES
CFC-12	YES	YES	YES	YES
CFC-113	YES	YES	YES	YES
HCFC-123	N/A	N/A	N/A	N/A
HCFC-124	YES	YES	YES	YES
HFC-125	YES	YES	YES	YES
HFC-134a	NO(1)	YES	YES	YES
HFC-404A	NO	YES	YES	YES
HFC-143a	N/A	N/A	YES	YES
HCFC-22	NO	NO	YES	YES
HFC-152a	NO	NO	YES(2)	YES
HFC-32	N/A	N/A	N/A	N/A

NOTES:

(1) For automotive retrofits, if the 4A-XH-5 desiccant in use contains more than 3 wt. % of moisture, it could be used with HFC-134a with minimum risk.

(2) This combination should be carefully evaluated for a particular application, since some chemical reactions, not affecting desiccant water capacity, were found in the laboratory. However, this combination is currently used in some installations using R-500 (26% HFC-152a) today without problems.

VIII. RETROFIT PROCEDURES

The following procedures for retrofitting from a given CFC to one of the alternative refrigerants are intended to serve as a general basis for the overall procedure involved. Use of the guidelines along with any pertinent manufacturers recommendations should assure a successful retrofit. Due to the great number and complexity of systems used within the HVAC&R community it is impossible to cover every application. Should a particular system not be covered contact the equipment manufacturer or Elf Atochems technical support number at 1-800-RETRO94 for assistance. Certain manufacturers require specific lubricating requirements to maintain warranties, consult them for assistance when necessary. Elf Atochem believes that the following procedures are correct and in accordance with most manufacturers guidelines. Elf Atochem reserves the right to update these procedures as deemed necessary, and makes no implied warranty for retrofitted equipment. Should ELF Atochem's guidelines conflict with original equipment manufacturers' guidelines, it is recommended that the OEM's guidelines be used.

A. HERMETIC RECIPROCATING\SCROLL

RETROFIT PROCEDURE

R-12 to Forane FX-56

Step 1.

Gather baseline data from R-12 system to be used to optimize the system with FX-56. Note the current R-12 charge,lubricant charge,existing operating temperatures and pressures,and overall system performance. (Refer to Retrofit Checklist included in Appendix A).

Step 2.

Recover the existing R-12 charge using standard industry recovery equipment and guidelines. Elf Atochem has a refrigerant reclamation service available to handle the recovered R-12 (refer to Forane Rollover Program).

Step 3.

Removal of existing mineral oil from the system is not necessary because FX-56 is compatible with mineral oil, polyolesters,and alkylbenzenes.

Step 4.

Replace filter driers and examine sight glass for compatibility to new moisture level indication levels necessary (150 ppm). Due to the ability of the new line of refrigerants to retain moisture it is highly advised that this step is not omitted.

Step 5.

Evacuate the system using a deep vacuum (at least 500 microns) to insure that remaining traces of moisture have been removed.

Step 6.

Charge system with Forane FX-56 refrigerant in the liquid phase only. The approximate FX-56 charge for most applications will be 90% of the original R-12 charge. Refer to the pressure temperature charts for final adjustment of charge. It is not recommended to charge by visual indication through the sight glass because of the nature of the refrigerant and lubricant to appear "cloudy" in the liquid portion of the system, even at the proper charge.

Step 7.

Place proper markings and identification on the system to indicate that the system has been retrofitted to FX-56 and appropriate lubricant. Indicate the new charge of FX-56 in a visible location.

Step 8.

Start the system and make final expansion valve adjustments to achieve proper superheat settings. Normal operating pressures of FX-56 vary from 15-25% higher on the low-side and 20% higher on the high-side of most typical refrigeration applications.

B. HERMETIC RECIPROCATING/SCROLL

RETROFIT PROCEDURE

R-502 to Forane 404A (FX-70)

Step 1.

Gather baseline data from R-502 system to be used to optimize the system with FX-70 and polyolester lubricant. Note the current R-502 charge,lubricant charge,existing operating temperatures and pressures, and overall system performance.(Refer to Retrofit Checklist included in Appendix A)

Step 2.

Recover the existing R-502 charge using standard industry recovery equipment and guidelines. Elf Atochem has a refrigerant reclamation service available to handle the recovered R-502 (refer to Forane Rollover Program).

Step 3.

Removal of existing mineral oil from the system. It is important that the existing mineral oil used in the current system be removed and that the remaining residual mineral oil content left in the system be reduced to a level of 5 % or less. This can best be accomplished by using the flushing attachment of a typical recovery/reclaim machine and circulating R-502 through the system for approximately 30 minutes. Experience has shown that for most systems the desired levels are reached within 30 minutes of circulation.

Step 4.

Replace filter driers and examine sight glass for compatibility to new moisture level indication levels necessary (150 ppm). Due to the ability of the new line of refrigerants to retain moisture it is highly advised that this step is not omitted.

Step 5.

Evacuate the system using a deep vacuum (at least 500 microns) to insure that remaining traces of moisture have been removed.

Step 6.

Charge compressor with proper polyolester lubricant charge and Forane FX-70 refrigerant. Charge in the liquid phase only to avoid altering the original composition of FX-70. The approximate FX-70 charge for most applications will be 85-90% of the original charge. Refer to the pressure temperature charts for final adjustment of charge. It is not recommended to charge by visual indication through the sight glass because of the nature of the refrigerant and lubricant to appear “cloudy” in the liquid portion of the system, even at the proper charge.

Step 7.

Place proper markings and identification on the system to indicate that the system has been retrofitted to FX-70 and polyolester lubricants. Indicate the new charge of FX-70 in a visible location.

Step 8.

Start the system and make final expansion valve adjustments to achieve proper superheat settings. Normal operating pressures of FX-70 vary from 4-6% higher on the low-side and 8-10% higher on the high-side of most typical refrigeration applications.

NOTE: Due to the higher operating pressures associated with the use of FX-70, as opposed to R-502 , consult OEM product specific retrofit requirements for any and all pressure relief modifications and/or requirements.

B. SEMI-HERMETIC RECIPROCATING

RETROFIT PROCEDURE

R-12 to Forane 134a

Step 1.

Gather baseline data from R-12 system to be used to optimize the system with R-134a and polyolester lubricant. Note the current R-12 charge,lubricant charge, existing operating temperatures and pressures, and overall system performance. (Refer to Retrofit Checklist included in Appendix A)

Step 2.

Removal of existing mineral oil from the system. It is important that the existing mineral oil used in the current system be removed and the remaining residual mineral oil content left in the system be reduced to a level of 5 % or less. This can best be accomplished by draining the mineral oil from all accessible points in the system (compressor, oil separator, low spots in the evaporator) and replacing with an equivalent charge of polyolester lubricant. Once this has been done operate the system with the R-12 for a period of time to insure proper miscibility of the two lubricants. Test for mineral oil residual content and repeat step 2 if necessary until the desired 5% level is obtained. Experience has shown that for most systems the desired levels are reached within three cycles operating at 24 hour intervals.

Step 3.

Recover the existing R-12 charge and lubricant charge using standard industry recovery equipment and guidelines. Elf Atochem has a refrigerant reclamation service available to handle the recovered R-12 (refer to Forane Rollover Program).

Step 4.

Replace filter driers with new cores or compacted bead desiccant and examine sight glass for compatibility to new moisture level indication levels necessary (150 ppm). Due to the ability of the new line of refrigerants to retain moisture it is highly advised that this step is not omitted.

Step 5.

Evacuate the system using a deep vacuum (at least 500 microns) to insure that remaining traces of moisture have been removed.

Step 6.

Charge compressor with proper polyolester lubricant charge and Forane 134a refrigerant. The approximate R-134a charge for most medium and high temperature applications will be 90% of the original charge. Refer to the pressure temperature charts for final adjustment of charge. It is not recommended to charge by visual indication through the sight glass due to the nature of the refrigerant and lubricant to appear “cloudy” in the liquid portion of the system, even at the proper charge.

Step 7.

Place proper markings and identification on the system to indicate that the system has been retrofitted to R-134a and polyolester lubricants. Indicate the new charge of R-134a in a visible location.

Step 8.

Start the system and make final expansion valve adjustments to achieve proper superheat settings. Normal operating pressures of R-134a vary from 2-5% lower on the low-side and 2-5% higher on the high-side of most typical refrigeration applications.

B. SEMI-HERMETIC RECIPROCATING

RETROFIT PROCEDURE

R-502 to Forane 404A (FX-70)

Step 1.

Gather baseline data from R-502 system to be used to optimize the system with FX-70 and polyolester lubricant. Note the current R-502 charge,lubricant charge,existing operating temperatures and pressures, and overall system performance. (Refer to Retrofit Checklist included in Appendix A).

Step 2.

Removal of existing mineral oil from the system. It is important that the existing mineral oil used in the current system be removed and that the remaining residual mineral oil content left in the system be reduced to a level of 5 % or less. This can best be accomplished by draining the mineral oil from all accessible points in the system (compressor, oil separator, low spots in the evaporator) and replacing with an equivalent charge of polyolester lubricant. Once this has been done operate the system with the R-502 for a period of time to insure proper miscibility of the two lubricants. Test for mineral oil residual content and repeat step 2 if necessary until the desired 5% level is obtained. Experience has shown that for most systems the desired levels are reached within three cycles operating at 24 hour intervals.

Step 3.

Recover the existing R-502 charge and lubricant charge using standard industry recovery equipment and guidelines. Elf Atochem has a refrigerant reclamation service available to handle the recovered R-502 (refer to Forane Rollover Program).

Step 4.

Replace filter driers with new cores or compacted bead desiccant and examine sight glass for compatibility to new moisture level indication levels necessary (150 ppm). Due to the ability of the new line of refrigerants to retain moisture it is highly advised that this step is not omitted.

Step 5.

Evacuate the system using a deep vacuum (at least 500 microns) to insure that remaining traces of moisture have been removed.

Step 6.

Charge compressor with proper polyolester lubricant charge and Forane FX-70 refrigerant. Charge in the liquid phase only in order to assure that the composition integrity remains intact. The approximate FX-70 charge for most applications will be 85-90% of the original R-502 charge. Refer to the pressure temperature charts for final adjustment of charge. It is not recommended to charge by visual indication through the sight glass due to the nature of the refrigerant and lubricant to appear "cloudy" in the liquid portion of the system, even at the proper charge.

Step 7.

Place proper markings and identification on the system to indicate that the system has been retrofitted to FX-70 and polyolester lubricants. Indicate the new charge of FX-70 in a visible location.

Step 8.

Start the system and make final expansion valve adjustments to achieve proper superheat settings. FX-70's normal operating pressures vary from 4-6% higher on the low-side and 8-10% higher on the high-side of most refrigeration applications.

NOTE: Due to the higher operating pressures associated with the use of FX-70, as opposed to R-502 , consult OEM product specific retrofit requirements for any and all pressure relief modifications and/or requirements.

C. SCREW

COMPRESSOR RETROFIT PROCEDURE

R-12 to Forane 134a

Step 1.

Gather baseline data from R-12 system to be used to optimize the system with R-134a and polyolester lubricant. Note the current R-12 charge, lubricant charge, existing operating temperatures and pressures, and overall system performance. (Refer to Retrofit Checklist included in Appendix A).

Step 2.

Removal of existing mineral oil from the system. It is important that the existing mineral oil used in the current system be removed and that the remaining residual mineral oil content left in the system be reduced to a level of 5 % or less. This can best be accomplished by draining the mineral oil from all accessible points in the system (compressor, oil separator, low spots in the evaporator) and replacing with an equivalent charge of polyolester lubricant. Once this has been done operate the system with the R-12 for a period of time to insure proper miscibility of the two lubricants. Test for mineral oil residual content and repeat step 2 if necessary until the desired 5% level is obtained. Experience has shown that for most systems the desired levels are reached within three cycles operating at 24 hour intervals.

Step 3.

Recover the existing R-12 charge and lubricant charge using standard industry recovery equipment and guidelines. Elf Atochem has a refrigerant reclamation service available to handle the recovered R-12 (refer to Forane Rollover Program).

Step 4.

Replace filter driers with new cores or compacted bead desiccant and examine sight glass for compatibility to new moisture level indication levels necessary (150 ppm). Due to the ability of the new line of refrigerants to retain moisture it is highly advised that this step is not omitted.

Step 5.

Evacuate the system using a deep vacuum (at least 500 microns) to insure that remaining traces of moisture have been removed.

Step 6.

Charge compressor with proper polyolester lubricant charge and Forane 134a refrigerant. The approximate R-134a charge for most medium and high temperature applications will be 90% of the original charge. Refer to the pressure temperature charts for final adjustment of charge. It is not recommended to charge by visual indication through the sight glass because of the nature of the refrigerant and lubricant to appear "cloudy" in the liquid portion of the system, even at the proper charge.

Step 7.

Place proper markings and identification on the system to indicate that the system has been retrofitted to R-134a and polyolester lubricants. Indicate the new charge of R-134a in a visible location.

Step 8.

Start the system and make final expansion valve adjustments to achieve proper superheat settings. R-134a's normal operating pressures vary from 2-5% lower on the low-side and 2-5% higher on the high-side of most refrigeration applications.

C. SCREW

COMPRESSOR RETROFIT PROCEDURE

R-502 to Forane 404A (FX-70)

Step 1.

Gather baseline data from R-502 system to be used to optimize the system with FX-70 and polyolester lubricant. Note the current R-502 charge,lubricant charge, existing operating temperatures and pressures,and overall system performance.(Refer to Retrofit Checklist included in Appendix A).

Step 2.

Removal of existing mineral oil from the system. It is important that the existing mineral oil used in the current system be removed and that the remaining residual mineral oil content left in the system be reduced to a level of 5 % or less. This can best be accomplished by draining the mineral oil from all accessible points in the system (compressor, oil separator, low spots in the evaporator) and replacing with an equivalent charge of polyolester lubricant. Once this has been done operate the system with the R-502 for a period of time to insure proper miscibility of the two lubricants. Test for mineral oil residual content and repeat step 2 if necessary until the desired 5% level is obtained. Experience has shown that for most systems the desired levels are reached within three cycles operating at 24 hour intervals.

Step 3.

Recover the existing R-502 charge and lubricant charge using standard industry recovery equipment and guidelines. Elf Atochem has a refrigerant reclamation service available to handle the recovered R-502 (refer to Forane Rollover Program).

Step 4.

Replace filter driers with new cores or compacted bead desiccant and examine sight glass for compatibility to new moisture level indication levels necessary (150 ppm). Due to the ability of the new line of refrigerants to retain moisture it is highly advised that this step is not omitted.

Step 5.

Evacuate the system using a deep vacuum (at least 500 microns) to insure that remaining traces of moisture have been removed.

Step 6.

Charge compressor with proper polyolester lubricant charge and Forane FX-70 refrigerant. Charge in the liquid phase only to insure composition integrity. The approximate FX-70 charge for most applications will be 85-90% of the original charge. Refer to the pressure temperature charts for final adjustment of charge. It is not recommended to charge by visual indication through the sight glass because of the nature of the refrigerant and lubricant to appear "cloudy" in the liquid portion of the system, even at the proper charge.

Step 7.

Place proper markings and identification on the system to indicate that the system has been retrofitted to FX-70 and polyolester lubricants. Indicate the new charge of FX-70 in a visible location.

Step 8.

Start the system and make final expansion valve adjustments to achieve proper superheat settings. FX-70's normal operating pressures vary from 4-6% higher on the low-side and 8-10% higher on the high-side of most applications.

NOTE: Due to the higher operating pressures associated with the use of FX-70, as opposed to R-502, consult OEM product specific retrofit requirements for any and all pressure relief modifications and/or requirements.

D. HERMETIC AND OPEN DRIVE CENTRIFUGAL

RETROFIT PROCEDURE

R-12/R-500 to Forane 134a

Most medium temperature single and multi- stage centrifugal R-12/R-500 chillers can be retrofitted to HFC-134a with minimal changes. Normally only the lubricant and minor control modifications are necessary for use of HFC-134a. Due to the complexity and size requirements for most multi-stage low temperature centrifugal chillers, it is recommended that the retrofit engineering study of these types of systems be handled by qualified manufacturers representatives or consultants. By following manufacturers recommendations most systems can be expected to perform at previous R-12/R-500 specifications. In most cases optimization results in reliable long term service for the life of the chiller without diminishing the capacity of the system.

Most manufacturers offer a complete engineering analysis of the existing equipment and can predict capacity ratings in systems being considered for retrofit. HFC-134a offers excellent performance in optimized centrifugal systems.

Pre-retrofit procedures can be performed to facilitate the retrofit process. Changing the mineral oil to the new polyolester lubricant can be done during routine maintenance to initiate the flushing procedure for reducing the mineral oil content of the system to the required 3% level. Generally, material compatibility is not a concern with HFC-134a or polyolester lubricants. The following steps serve as a generic guideline for many centrifugal systems:

Step 1.

Gather baseline data of running R-12 system. Leak test system. Calculate actual full load condition and determine if a gearset change is necessary to maintain capacity.(Multi-stage units)

Step 2.

Use one of the oil flushing procedure to remove the mineral oil.

Step 3.

Run system with R-12 and polyolester lubricant to “flush out” the mineral oil to the desired 3% level.(For Flushing Procedure #1 Only)

Step 4.

Recover R-12 charge per recovery equipment manufacturers guidelines.

Step 5.

Evacuate system to manufacturers recommendations.

Step 6.

Replace lubricant with new charge of polyolester lubricant.

Step 7.

Charge with HFC-134a. (approximately 90-95% of R-12)

Step 8.

Start System and adjust final charge with pressure/temperature charts.

Step 9.

Leak test system

Step 10.

Re-label system with HFC-134a and polyolester lubricant markings.

E. HERMETIC AND OPEN DRIVE CENTRIFUGAL

RETROFIT PROCEDURE

R-11 to Forane 123

Due to the compatibility issues associated with the use of R-123 in centrifugal chillers it is recommended that the retrofit of these types of systems be evaluated on an individual basis by qualified manufacturers representatives or certified service personnel. Modifications for use with R-123 may include impeller changes, gear synchronization,seal and gasket replacement and possible motor modification. By following manufacturers recommendations most systems can be expected to perform comparable to the previous R-11 specifications. Optimization results in reliable long term service for the life of the chiller without diminishing the capacity of the system.

At this time no HFC refrigerant exists for the direct retrofit of an R-11 machine. Therefore, should it become advantageous to retrofit to HCFC 123 all manufacturers guidelines and handling procedures should be followed in order to achieve optimal results.

F. AUTOMOTIVE

RETROFIT PROCEDURE
CFC-12 to HFC-134a

Automotive air conditioners, also known as mobile air conditioners (MACs), even though small in size do not lack in complexity. MACs pose a special problem for retrofitting due to the presence of elastomer hoses (several materials); variable system operation (compressor RPM is a multiple of engine RPM); multitude of compressor types (rotary vane, piston, scroll, etc); expansion device type (fixed orifice tube or thermal expansion valve (TXV)), etc. All of the above, plus a variety of vehicle specific problems, such as age, geographic location, etc. make retrofitting a MAC a challenging project.

All refrigerant and system handling regulations that apply to stationary air conditioners and refrigeration units, also apply to MACs. In addition, a set of Society of Automotive Engineers (SAE) J-standards specific to mobile applications also apply. A summary of all these standards is included in chapter II of this manual for your information. One of the most important regulations deals with the retrofitting of the service ports. Typically, MACs have 2 service ports, one on each side of the system. The high side is a 3/16" flare fitting and the low side a standard 1/4" refrigeration flare fitting, both with external threads. After a system retrofit is completed, these fittings must be changed to FORANE-134a approved fittings per SAE J-639 (internal, metric threads) in such a way that the CFC-12 original fittings are permanently disabled.

Regarding the refrigerant choice for a retrofit, overwhelmingly, the mobile air conditioning industry has chosen HFC-134a as the leading candidate and Elf Atochem fully supports this position. However, while HFC-134a is the only pure refrigerant available, there are several other candidates in the market in the form of blends, and servicemen should be aware of them to avoid possible cross contamination of refrigerants in their equipment. The Mobile Air Conditioning Society (M.A.C.S.) has petitioned the U.S. EPA to ban the use of any refrigerant other than HFC-134a for MAC retrofits.

For lubricant oils, there is currently a choice of 2 synthetic materials: Poly Alkaline Glycols (PAGs) or Polyolesters (POEs). Although it varies with the car manufacturer, most have chosen PAGs as their OEM fluid, as well as their retrofit fluid. However, in some instances a manufacturer may recommend the use of a PAG for OEM and a POE for retrofits. Be sure to check with the vehicle manufacturer for any oil specifications if available. If no oil is specified for retrofits, then use the recommended OEM oil.

The retrofit procedure that follows is a recommendation developed and tested by Elf Atochem in al fleet of vehicles, and is based on SAE, M.A.C.S. and industry recommendations. In general, if a vehicle manufacturer has developed a specific retrofit procedure, that procedure and not the one listed here should be followed.

Step 1.

Thoroughly leak check and evaluate the system for signs of previous leaks, defective components, etc. Replace or repair as necessary after charge and recovery. Empty systems should be charged with a small amount of CFC-12 to leak check.

Step 2.

Recover CFC-12 charge into a suitable container by means of approved recovery equipment.

At this point it should be decided whether the system will be power flushed with CFC-12 to remove the original mineral oil or not. Power flushing means pumping liquid CFC-12 refrigerant in a closed loop that includes the system. This procedure is performed with a special unit, sometimes contained in the refrigerant recovery equipment, that pumps the refrigerant into the system, recovers it, separates any dissolved oil and reintroduces the oil-free refrigerant to the loop. By running this process for a relatively short period of time (about 30 min.) most of the mineral oil is removed from a system. The decision to power flush a system should be made based on car or compressor manufacturer recommendations, age of the system, labor cost and proper equipment availability. The following steps assume that a system will be power flushed, with special instructions for non-flushed systems.

Step 3.

Pull a system vacuum to 29 in of Hg for 5 min. (if not flushing evacuate at the same level for 45 min. and go to step 7).

Step 4.

Connect the power flushing equipment and flush for 30 min. or longer. Systems with a TXV will need external heat to 'open' the valve.

Step 5.

Recover liquid CFC-12 refrigerant used to flush and evacuate to 29 in of Hg for 30 min.

Step 6.

Add the recommended amount of HFC-134a compatible lubricant per system/compressor manufacturer's specifications. Usually 6 to 8 fl. oz.

Step 7.

Install SAE approved HFC-134a fitting disabling all other CFC-12 fittings in the system.

Step 8.

Recharge with FORANE-134a using 90% by weight of the original CFC-12 charge.

Step 9.

Leak check system again, paying special attention to any connections that may have been worked on.

Step 10.

Clearly label the system indicating it has been retrofitted to HFC-134a and a synthetic oil.

IX. APPENDIX

A. Forane Rollover Program

B. Glossary of Terms

C. Retrofit Checklist

D. U.L. Guideline 2154

E. A.S.H.R.A.E. Standard 15

F. S.A.E. J-Standards

G. Pressure Temperature Charts

H. Miscellaneous Lubricant Information

FORANE® ROLLOVER REFRIGERANT RECLAMATION PROGRAM

FORANE® ROLLOVER PROGRAM:

°The following used refrigerants will be accepted for reclaim: R11, R12, R22, R113, R114, R500 and R502.

°100 lb. and 1000 lb. recovery cylinders and 200 lb. drums will be supplied by Elf Atochem.

°Wholesaler owned 50 lb. recovery cylinders will be accepted. Elf Atochem will provide a shipping crate to facilitate the return of the 50 lb. recovery cylinders.

°Credits will be issued to the wholesaler for returned used refrigerant based on the quality and type of refrigerant.

°Used refrigerant can be reclaimed, repackaged and returned to the wholesaler for a cleaning fee. This option is available for those wholesalers who do not wish to give up ownership of their refrigerant.

°Non-reclaimable refrigerant from air conditioning or refrigeration systems will be indemnified and disposed at no charge.

°A used refrigerant analytical service is also offered. This service allows customers to have material tested to determine its suitability for reclamation at a reasonable fee. Sample cylinder kits with labels, filling instructions, and shipping instructions will be shipped upon request of an analysis.

°Used refrigerant will be reprocessed/reclaimed to meet ARI Standard 700.

For further information on this topic please call 1-800-648-7480 for your free copy of the Forane Rollover Refrigerant Reclamation Program.

GLOSSARY

Azeotrope - blends comprising components of different volatilities that do not change volumetric composition or saturation temperature as they vaporate or condense.

CFC - a chlorofluorocarbon molecule consisting of chlorine, fluorine, and carbon atoms.

Expansion Valve - a device used to cause same phase pressure drops in fluids within the circuit of the refrigeration system.

Glide - difference between the starting and ending temperatures of a phase-change process by a refrigerant within a component of a refrigerating system, excluding any subcooling or superheating. Usually used to describe condensation or evaporation of a zeotrope.

HCFC - a hydrochlorofluorocarbon molecule composed of hydrogen, chlorine, fluorine, and carbon atoms. Much less potential to deplete the ozone because of the present hydrogen atom that provides stability to the molecule.

HFC - a hydrofluorocarbon molecule composed of hydrogen, fluorine, and carbon atoms. A non-ozone depleting molecule.

Orifice - a plate or tube used to create a pressure drop without phase change within the refrigerant circuit of a system.

Polyolester/Polyalkyl/Glycol - synthetic oils that provide the same lubrication but add a resistance to chemical breakdown because they are not derived from a natural resource such as crude oil.

Superheat - a superheated vapor is a vapor of which the temperature is higher than the saturation temperature. When liquid is still present in the gas, this is a vapor, when the gas no longer contains liquid because it has evaporated, this vapor is said to be superheated.

Zeotrope - blends comprising of components of different volatilities that change volumetric composition and saturation temperatures as they evaporate or condense at constant pressure.

RETROFIT CHECKLIST

1. Necessary Equipment:

___ Recovery Unit
___ Multi-refrigerant leak detector
___ Vacuum Pump with fresh lubricant
___ Thermometer
___ Service Manifold Gauges
___ Safety Equipment (glasses,gloves, etc.)
___ Waste oil container
___ Pressure/Temperature Charts
___ Baseline data from original system
___ Replacement filter driers
___ New lubricant
___ New refrigerant
___ Residual mineral oil test kit
___ New refrigerant and lubricant labels

2. Preparatory Work

___ Material compatibility check
___ Change mineral oil to new lubricant
___ Cycle new lubricant with CFC for at least 24 hrs.
___ Test mineral oil residual in new lubricant with available test kits
___ Residual mineral content below recommended levels indicate system is ready to retrofit

3. Post-retrofit activities:

___ Re- identify system for new refrigerant & lubricant
___ Leak test of system
___ Performance check of system

UL GUIDELINES

As a result of national and international environmental protocol restrictions on the use of ozone depleting chemicals, Underwriters Laboratories has proposed new requirements under the UL guidelines 2154.

UL2154A: CONSTRUCTION AND OPERATION FOR FIELD CONVERSION/ RETROFIT OF PRODUCTS TO CHANGE TO AN ALTERNATIVE REFRIGERANT

-Refrigerating System

- Converting equipment to use alternative refrigerants may involve replacing and/or adding refrigerant containing parts, such as filter-driers, filters, moisture indicators, and strainers.

-Design Pressure

- Some equipment may be marked "test pressure" and for this purpose that may be taken as design pressure. Minimum design pressure shall not be less than the saturation pressure of refrigerant at the following temperatures:

- 80 °F for low sides; 105 °F for water-cooled sides; 125 °F for air-cooled sides. (corresponding pressures are in following table)

-Parts Subject to Pressure

- For components containing refrigerant, the ultimate strength will be determined by examining the existing unit nameplate and multiplying the design pressure by three for low side parts and five for high side parts, or by obtaining information from UL or the manufacturer. Pressure vessels bearing the ASME Code "U" symbol complying with standard regulations are to be considered accurate and quotable, the "UM" symbol must be tested however.

-Remote Condensers and Evaporators

- The ultimate strength of a remote condenser shall be no less than five times the original design pressure or five-and-a-half times the maximum setting for the pressure limiting device employed in the refrigeration system, whichever is higher.

- A remote evaporator shall have an ultimate strength of not less than three times the saturation pressure at 80 °F of the refrigerant being used; for a hot gas defrost system this should be at 125 °F.

-Pressure Limiting Device

- Maximum cutout pressure that device maybe set shall not exceed 90% of one fifth of the ultimate strength of high side parts; design pressure of high side vessels; the setting of the pressure relief device. On an air-cooled system with no more than 22 lb_m of refrigerant may have a maximum cutout not exceeding one third the ultimate strength or ninety percent of the setting of the pressure relief device. There shall be no shutoff valves between the compressor and the PLD.

-Pressure Relief Valve

- No shutoff valve shall be placed between the PRV and the section being protected.

-Unitary and Self-Contained Equipment

- Compliance with the performance requirements pertaining to input current or pressures for all unitary and self-contained equipment employing the alternative refrigerant shall be determined by: comparing the characteristics of the alternative refrigerant to the previously used refrigerant; calorimeter tests on the compressor comparing the alternative refrigerant with the previously used refrigerant; testing the unit with the alternative refrigerant under the conditions outlined in the applicable UL Standard for Safety for the equipment involved.

- Other than Unitary and Self-Contained Equipment

- On the equipment that employs a compressor where testing is not conducted in the applicable Standard for the equipment involved, the MCC value is used to determine the RLA of the compressor in order to determine the acceptability of the controls and wiring.

- Identification

- Equipment that has been retrofitted shall be permanently marked adjacent to the existing equipment nameplate in accordance with appropriate end-product requirements with the following:

FIELD RETROFITTED TO USE {kind of refrigerant and lubricant}; DO NOT ADD MINERAL OIL; the electric rating if changed; the high and low side design pressures if changed; alternative refrigerant amount in pounds; minimum circuit ampacity; maximum overcurrent protection if changed; required type of equipment;month and year of retrofit.

UL2154B INSULATING MATERIAL AND REFRIGERANT COMPATIBILITY REQUIREMENTS FOR FIELD CONVERSIONS/RETROFIT OF PRODUCTS TO CHANGE TO AN ALTERNATIVE REFRIGERANT

-Compatibility of Materials

- Alternative refrigerant compatibility with existing material shall be determined by motor insulation materials subjected to compatibility tests specified in the Standard for Hermetic Refrigerant Motor-Compressors, UL984 or other accepted safety test measures of its equivalence.

-Compatibility Exposures

- A control exposure shall be 1000 hours exposed to the current refrigerant and lubricant.

- Motor insulating materials and motorettes shall also be exposed to current refrigerant and lubricant for 500 hours followed by 500 hours to the alternative refrigerant and lubricant at a ratio of 50:50. This is to be carried out in a stainless steel enclosure at 127 °C and 200-300 psig pressure. For R-11 and 123 the temperature shall be 100 °C.

- Samples of the motor insulating materials shall be tested after the first 500 hours, after 168 hours of the second exposure, after 336 hours of the second exposure, and after the second 500 hours of exposure. Additional evaluation will be conducted in conjunction with required tests after a 24 hour bakeout at 150 °C.

UL2154C REFRIGERANT FIELD CONVERSION/RETROFIT SAFETY REQUIREMENTS - PROCEDURES AND GUIDELINES

-Conversion Guidelines

- Trained service personnel following sound engineering practices and all regulations and codes shall convert the equipment to use and alternative refrigerant in a safe and orderly manner.

- A final copy of the instructions/procedures shall be provided to the retrofitters and they shall check the equipment to verify that it is grounded before any work begins.

-Refrigerant Recovery

- All venting regulations for Section 608 of the EPA's Clean Air Act shall apply.

- Containers shall comply with DOT specifications, 49CFR, and shall be identified by size and type and marked as to type of refrigerant.

- All leaks shall be repaired before charging the equipment with the alternative refrigerant.

- The Material Safety Data Sheet (MSDS) shall be available to the retrofitters to take necessary precautions.

-Compressor Lubricant

- The lubricant removed from the compressor/system shall be disposed of in accordance with all federal, state, and local regulations.

A.S.H.R.A.E. STANDARD 15

The American Society of Heating, Refrigerating and Air-Conditioning Engineers issued there standards 15 regulations in 1992. These standards are targeted at the safety of the persons and property on or near the premises where refrigeration facilities are located. The guidelines pinpoint area of accidental injury or property damage:

Personal injury from inadequate precautions might occur from:

- rupture of a part or an explosion with the risk from flying pieces of metal or from structural collapse.
- release of refrigerant from a fracture, from a leaking seal, or from incorrect operation.
- fire resulting from or intensified by burning or deflagration of escaping lubricant or refrigerant.

Damage from accidental release of refrigerants might occur from:

- suffocation from heavier than air refrigerants in unventilated spaces.
- narcotic and cardiac sensitation effects
- toxic effects of vapor or the decomposition products due to vapor contact with flames or hot surfaces
- corrosive attack on the eyes, skin, and other tissues
- freezing of tissue by contact with refrigerant

Refrigerants are classified by ASHRAE Standard 34 into safety groups as illustrated in the flammability/safety matrix. As evident by the chemical listing, Elf Atochem sells mostly A1 category refrigerants and all of our refrigerants abide by ASHRAE guidelines.

Regulations in Standard 15 include:

- Requirements for Refrigerant Use — where you can operate refrigeration equipment.
- Design and Construction of Equipment Systems — 1) materials must be suitable for the punishment and production they will endure or require; 2) pressure vessels shall comply with the rules of the ASME Boiler and Pressure Vessel Code; 3) refrigerant piping, valves, fittings and related parts must meet regulations for strength and discharging locations.
- Pressure Limiting Devices — settings and connections of these devices.

- Pressure Relief Protection — each system must have some sort of a pressure relief valve or device, and regulations and suggestions for sizing and locations in conjunction with Design and Construction of Equipment Systems.
- Installation Requirements — location of piping, foundations, water connections, etc. and machinery room general requirements.
- Field Pressure Test — each system must be tested on sight to ensure tight fittings.
- General Requirements — signs, storage, maintenance and responsibility of operation and emergency shutdown.
- Reference section

***> To purchase the latest copy of this manual, write to ASHRAE Publication Sales Department, 1791 Tullie Circle, NE, Atlanta, GA 30329.

SAE J STANDARDS

These service procedure standards (SAE J series) provide guidelines for repairing vehicles and operating equipment.

SAE J639 - Standards for the safety and containment of refrigerant for mechanical vapor compression systems used for mobile air conditioning systems.

SAE J1989 - Standards on: refrigerant recovery procedures; service with manifold gage set; recycled refrigerant checking procedure for stored portable auxiliary containers; containers for storage of recycled refrigerant; transfer of recycled refrigerant; and disposal of empty/near empty containers.

SAE J1990 - Standard for: recycling equipment; specification and general description; refrigeration recycle equipment requirements; safety requirements; operating instructions; and testing.

SAE J1991 - Standard for: recycled refrigerant for motor vehicles; purity specification; refrigeration recycle equipment used in direct mobile air-conditioning service operations requirement; purity specification of recycled R-12 refrigerant supplied in containers from other recycle sources; and operation of recycle equipment.

SAE J2099 - Standard of purity for recycled R-134a for use in mobile air conditioning systems. Hermetically sealed, refrigerant cargo systems are not covered by this standard.

SAE J2196 - Standard for service hoses used for automotive air-conditioning systems, including; reinforced rubber, reinforced thermoplastic etc. hose assemblies used for conducting liquid and gaseous refrigerant for service connections.

SAE J2197 - Standard to ensure that specific and unique fittings for service equipment are used in maintaining R-134a systems to avoid cross mixing of refrigerant and lubricants from CFC based systems.

SAE J2209 - Standards for extraction equipment in use with R-12 for mobile air-conditioning systems.

SAE J2210 - Standards on recycling equipment for use with R-134a for mobile air-conditioning systems.

SAE J2211 - Standards for containment of R-134a when servicing mobile air-conditioner systems.

SAE J2219 - Refrigerant information sheet on issues that concern the mobile air-conditioning industry such as standards on; refrigerant recycling; refrigerant handling/identification to prevent cross-contamination; consequences of cross-contamination; flushing systems; and leak detection.

*For copies of any of these standards please write to:

SAE
Customer Service
400 Commonwealth Dr.
Warrendale, PA 15096-0001

or call:

(412) 776-4970

TABLE 1
REFRIGERANT/LUBRICATION APPLICATION INFORMATION

CFC	REPLACEMENT	LUBRICANT	APPLICATION TEMPERATURES
R-11	HCFC 123	MINERAL OIL	MED TEMP.
R-12	HFC-134a	POLYOLESTER	MED/HIGH TEMP
R-12	HCFC FX-56	MINERAL OIL	LOW/MED TEMP
R-500	HFC-134a	POLYOLESTER	MED/HIGH TEMP
R-502	HFC-404A	POLYOLESTER	LOW/MED TEMP

TABLE 2
CAPACITY INFORMATION EVAPORATOR TEMPERATURE

	-30•F	-20•F	-10•F	0•F	10•F	20•F	30•F_
FX-56	+2	+2	+2	+2	+2	+2	+2
R-123	NA	NA	NA	NA	NA	NA	0
R-134a	-14	-13	-10	-8	-4	0	0
R-404A	+3	+3	+4	+4	+4	+4	+4

*NOTE: CAPACITY INFORMATION IS BASED ON STANDARD CONDENSING TEMPERATURES WITH 0• SUBCOOLING FOR EACH APPLICATION. THESE CAPACITIES SERVE ONLY AS AN INDICATION OF EXPECTED RESULTS. IT SHOULD BE NOTED THAT CAPACITIES CAN VARY SIGNIFICANTLY DEPENDING ON ACTUAL SYSTEM CONFIGURATION.

1 Actual ODP values for the different HCFC's varies with the particular refrigerant. HCFC-22, as an example has been assigned a value of 0.050.

Notes

elf atochem
ATO

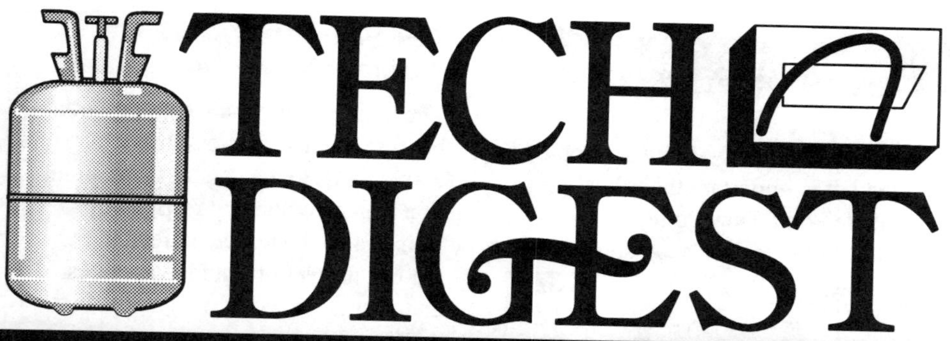

Published by Elf Atochem North America, Inc., Fluorochemicals, 2000 Market Street, Philadelphia, PA 19103

Forane® FX-56

Forane® FX-56 is a low ozone depleting blend of HCFC refrigerants R-22, R-124 and R-142b. Forane FX-56 is formulated to closely resemble the properties of R-12.

Retrofit

FX-56 is a refrigerant alternative for retrofit of R-12 in low to medium temperature systems where removal of mineral oil is difficult. These systems typically consist of hermetically sealed systems for transport refrigeration, food storage, and vending/beverage systems applications.

FX-56 provides a slightly higher capacity than R-12 and R-134a in lower temperature applications.

Lubrication

For intended applications, FX-56 is sufficient for use with mineral, alkylbenzene or polyolester oils. Miscibility is important for proper oil return to the compressor. Changing the existing lubricant is not required in most cases. (*See Retrofit Section*)

Charging

Forane FX-56 must be introduced into equipment or systems only as a liquid. Charging as a vapor will change the composition of the blend slightly, and affect the performance of the system.

Follow charging instructions on the cylinder. The approximate FX-56 charge for most applications will be 85-90% of the original (R-12) charge.

If a leak were to occur in a cylinder or in the vapor space of a system at rest, fractionation of the blend may cause a permanent change in composition of the refrigerant charge.

Performance

Evaporator pressures using FX-56 are similar to operating pressures for R-12. For higher temperatures at the condenser, FX-56 exhibits slightly higher (10-20 psig) pressures.

Equal or better heat transfer characteristics are obtained when using FX-56. Temperature glide can be compensated when using FX-56 in most direct expansion evaporators.

This brochure provides a broad description of properties and technical information to determine if Forane FX-56 meets your system needs.

Forane® FX-56: Basic Property Data

Chemical Formula:	R-22	($CHClF_2$)- 60 wt.%
	R-124	(CF_3CHClF)- 25 wt.%
	R-142b	(CH_3CClF_2)- 15 wt.%
Average Molecular Weight:		97.45
Bubble Point @ 1 atm:		- 29.6°F
Density of Saturated Liquid @ 80°F:		76.1 lb./cu. ft.
Density of Saturated Vapor @ b.p.:		0.306 lb./cu. ft.
Critical Temperature:		224.6°F
Critical Pressure:		652.5 psig
Saturated Liquid Pressure at 80°F:		106.2 psig
Latent Heat of Vaporization:		97.3 BTU/lb.
Specific Heat of Liquid @ 80°F:		0.535 BTU/lb. °F
Specific Heat of Vapor @ 1 atm:		0.336 BTU/lb. °F
Maximum Temperature Glide:		15.2°F
Flammability Limit:		non-flammable
Ozone Depletion Potential (ODP):		0.05
Halocarbon Greenhouse Warming Potential (HGWP):		0.3

Definition of Terms

Since Forane® FX-56 is a zeotropic blend, it is important the terms Bubble Point, Dew Point, Fractionation, and Glide are understood.

FX-56 (°F)		R-22	R-124	R-142b
Dew	Bubble	(°F)	(°F)	(°F)
6.3	-8.2	-20.0	33.9	39.8

TABLE 1: FX-56 and component saturation temperatures at 10 psig.

Bubble Point
(Saturated Liquid Temperature)

The temperature at which FX-56 (at constant pressure) begins to evaporate. In other words, the Bubble Point is the temperature where the first bubble of vapor appears in liquid FX-56. The bubble point is equivalent to the boiling point for single component refrigerants. From Table 1, at 10 psig, the Bubble Point for FX-56 is -8.2 °F. The graph in Figure 1 plots the Bubble temperatures for various pressures. The Bubble Point temperature is indicated in Figure 1 as point 1. At operating conditions to the left of the Bubble Point line, the refrigerant is a subcooled liquid.

Dew Point
(Saturated Vapor Temperature)

The temperature where condensation begins (at constant pressure), which corresponds to the condensation point of a single component refrigerant. This is also the temperature at which the last droplet of liquid evaporates and saturated gas exists. Table 1 lists the Dew Point temperature of 6.3°F at 10 psig. This point is shown as Point 2 in Figure 1. At operating conditions to the right of this line, the refrigerant is at a superheated vapor state.

Bubble Point and Dew Point are used to describe the behavior of zeotropic blends in an evaporator and condenser. "Boiling Point" is not appropriate since the temperature of the blend changes as it evaporates or condenses.

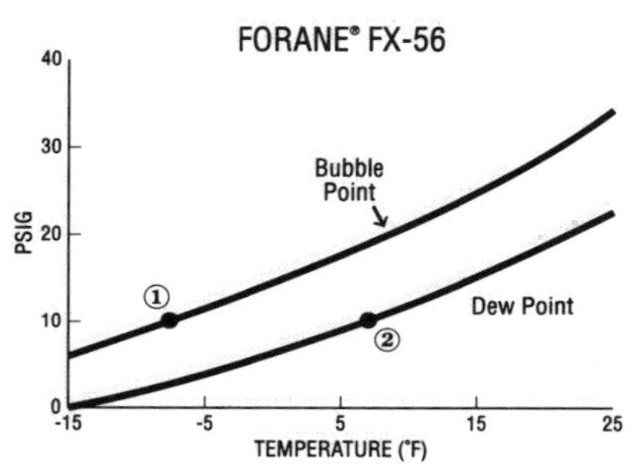

FIGURE 1:
FX-56 pressure-temperature graph

Fractionation

The change in composition of a refrigerant blend when it changes phase from liquid to vapor (evaporation) or from vapor to liquid (condensation). For FX-56, fractionation occurs between its Bubble and Dew Points (points 1 and 2). Since the components of FX-56 evaporate (or condense) at different rates in the evaporator (or condenser), the composition of FX-56 constantly changes between the Bubble and Dew Points. Once the temperature passes the Dew Point (or to the right of the Dew Point line), the refrigerant is in a superheated vapor state.

Glide

The difference in temperature between the evaporator outlet and inlet due to fractionation of the blend. Theoretically, this can be calculated by finding the difference between the Dew and Bubble temperatures at constant pressure. Actual measurements may differ slightly depending on the state of the liquid refrigerant at either end of the evaporator (or condenser). Pressure losses through the evaporator may also affect glide. At most common system pressures, FX-56 has a temperature glide of 10-12°F.

Typical Behavior of FX-56 in the Evaporator

This example describes typical conditions for achieving an average evaporator temperature of 0°F. (See Figure 2)

① Before the expansion valve, FX-56 is at a saturated liquid state. For example, if the pressure of FX-56 is at 15.3 psig, the temperature of FX-56 is 2°F. This point is on the Bubble point line of the curve (sat. liquid state).

② As the temperature increases, FX-56 begins to evaporate. The resulting vapor that forms first contains more of the higher pressure component (R-22). As the vapor separates from the liquid, the remaining liquid shifts in composition towards the less volatile components (more R-124 and R-142b than R-22). As the composition of the liquid (or vapor) changes, the Bubble Point temperature (or Dew Point temperature) of the remaining refrigerant changes as well, causing a temperature glide.

③ Fractionation continues as the lesser volatile components (R-124, R-142b) boil more rapidly along with the remaining R-22. For FX-56 at 15.3 psig, the temperature is 15°F.

④ FX-56 has completely evaporated and has returned to its original composition.

Retrofitting with FX-56

Retrofitting R-12 systems to FX-56 is recommended where R-134a is not practical. Systems where mineral oil removal is difficult are good candidates for FX-56. These include vending/beverage machines, transport, restaurant, and home refrigeration systems. Retrofit projects should be included as part of an overall refrigerant management program.

RETROFIT PROCEDURES

1. Gather baseline data from system using R-12.
2. Recover existing R-12 charge.
3. Mineral oil removal is not necessary in most cases. If oil miscibility becomes a concern at lower temperatures (less than 0°F), oil return can be improved by using at least 30% alkylbenzene lubricant mixed with mineral oil. FX-56 is fully miscible with pure alkylbenzene or polyolester lubricants.
4. Replace filter driers.
5. Evacuate system using a deep vacuum.
6. Charge FX-56 refrigerant in the liquid phase only. (Approximately 85-90% of original charge).
7. Properly mark and identify FX-56 refrigerant charge on the system.
8. Start system and adjust expansion valve for proper superheat settings if applicable.

Setting System Temperature Using FX-56

It is important to gather baseline data prior to retrofitting systems with new refrigerants such as FX-56.

Setting System Temperatures:

- From baseline data using R-12, take the desired evaporator temperature using R-12 and add 5°F. This gives the Dew Point (vapor) temperature for FX-56 (outlet of evaporator). The 5°F compensates for the glide across the evaporator when using FX-56.

EXAMPLE: Evaporator operating temperature using R-12: 10°F

10°F + 5°F (½ of FX-56 glide) = 15°F Dew Point (vapor) temperature at evaporator outlet (if 0°F superheat).

- Using the pressure-temperature chart for FX-56 (the pressure temperature chart in this brochure can be used), the Dew Point pressure at 15°F is 15.3 psig. This pressure is equal to your suction pressure of the compressor.

- Notice that the vapor temperature of FX-56 at the outlet is higher than the operating temperature of R-12. In contrast, at the evaporator inlet, the temperature of FX-56 (liquid) is colder than the R-12 operating condition. The average temperature across the evaporator is 10°F.

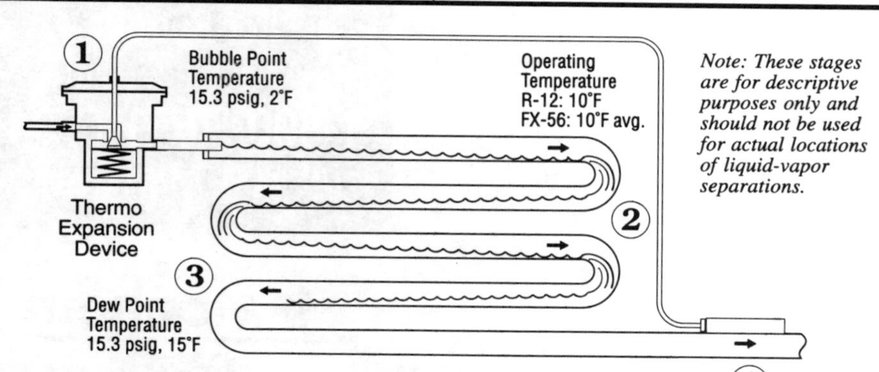

FIGURE 2: FX-56 fractionation in the evaporator. Bubble and Dew Point temperatures for FX-56 at 15.3 psig.

Forane® FX-56: Pressure Temperature Chart

Temp (°F)	Bubble (Liquid) Pressure (psig)	Dew (Vapor) Pressure (psig)	R-12 (psig)
-30	**0.4**	**9.9**	**5.5**
-25	1.9	**6.8**	**2.3**
-20	4.1	**3.7**	0.6
-15	6.5	0.2	2.4
-10	8.8	2.1	4.5
-5	11.7	4.3	6.7
0	14.5	6.5	9.2
5	17.9	9.3	11.8
10	21.3	12.0	14.6
15	25.3	15.3	17.7
20	29.4	18.5	21.0
25	34.1	22.3	24.6
30	38.8	26.1	28.4
35	44.1	30.6	32.6
40	49.5	35.0	37.0
45	55.5	40.2	41.7
50	61.6	45.4	46.7
55	68.6	50.6	52.0
60	75.6	55.7	57.7
65	83.5	63.4	63.8
70	91.4	71.1	70.2
75	100.1	78.9	77.0
80	108.8	86.7	84.2
85	118.9	95.6	91.8
90	128.9	104.3	99.8
95	139.9	114.3	108.3
100	151.0	124.1	117.2
105	163.0	135.2	126.6
110	175.0	146.3	136.4
115	188.4	158.7	146.8
120	201.8	171.1	157.7
125	216.7	185.0	169.1
130	231.6	198.9	181.0
135	247.7	214.0	193.5
140	263.9	229.1	206.6

Bold Numerals - Inches Hg. Below 1 ATM

Elf Atochem Cylinder Identification

TYPE	COLOR CODE	SIZES NET LBS.
FX-56	Tan	30 (B)

Other Forane® Alternative Refrigerants

TYPE	COLOR CODE	SIZES NET LBS.
R-22 ($CHClF_2$)	Green	30 (B), 50 (C), 125 (D)
R-123 ($CHCl_2CF_3$)	Lt. Blue Grey	100 (E), 200 (E)
R-404A	Orange	24 (B), 100 (D)
R-134a (CF_3CH_2F)	Light Blue	30 (B), 125 (D)
FX-10	Medium Purple	24 (B), 100 (D)

Container Style

24/30 lb. (B)

50 lb. (C)

100/125 lb. (D)

100/200 lb. Drum (E)

For Additional Forane® FX-56 Literature, Training Guides and Case Histories, call

1-800-343-7940

For Retrofit Assistance, call

1-800-RETRO 94

(1-800-738-7694)

elf atochem

ATO

elf atochem
ATO

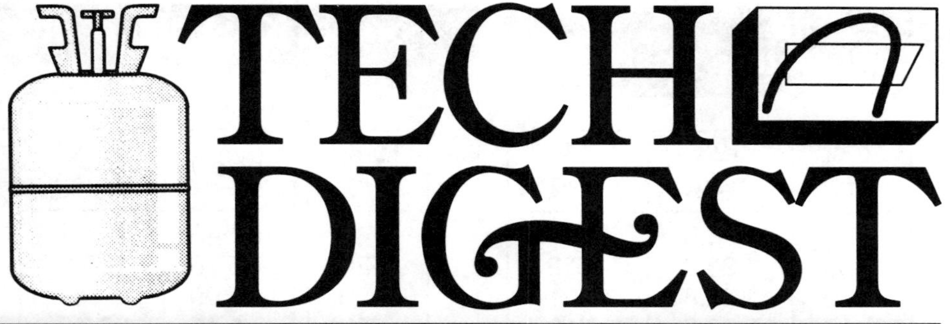

Published by Elf Atochem North America, Inc., Fluorochemicals, 2000 Market Street, Philadelphia, PA 19103

Forane® 123

(1, 1-Dichloro-2, 2, 2 Trifluoroethane)

Forane® 123 is a very low ozone-depletion-potential (ODP), single component refrigerant with properties similar to R-11. Most new Low Pressure centrifugal chillers are designed for use with R-123. R-123 may also be used to retrofit existing R-11 chillers.

Basic Properties

The boiling point of R-123 is slightly higher than that of R-11, and the vapor pressure of R-123 is slightly lower than R-11 at similar temperatures. Most of the other refrigeration-specific properties are also similar, indicating that new R-123 chillers will provide operating conditions and performance close to what has been seen with R-11 equipment. New equipment must take into consideration, however, the differences in properties in order to optimize the performance of R-123. When retrofitting R-11 chillers with R-123, the differences in properties will require that changes be made to controls, components, and/or the impeller-drive train in order to minimize performance losses.

Environmental Properties

R-123 has one of the lowest ODP values of all of the HCFC refrigerants. In addition, its low Halocarbon Greenhouse Warming Potential (HGWP) and good overall energy efficiency, combine to give a favorable Total Equivalent Warming Index (TEWI) compared to other options for comfort cooling.

This brochure has been designed to give a broad background of properties and technical considerations to help you use R-123 for your centrifugal chiller installations.

Forane® 123 Basic Property Comparison to R-11

	R-123	R-11
Chemical Formula:	$CHCl_2CF_3$	CCl_3F
Molecular Weight:	152.9	137.4
Boiling Point @ 1 atm:	82.2	74.5
Freezing Point @ 1 atm:	-160.6	-168
Density of Saturated Vapor @ b.p. (lb./cu. ft.):	0.401	0.364
Density of Saturated Liquid @ 80°F (lb./cu. ft.):	91.46	91.9
Critical Temperature (°F):	365.3	388.4
Critical Pressure (psia):	523.6	639.5
Critical Density (lb./cu. ft.):	33.6	34.6
Latent Heat of Vaporization @ b.p. (BTU/lb.):	73.6	78.3
Specific Heat of Liquid @ 80°F (BTU/lb. °F):	0.24	0.212
Specific Heat of Vapor @ 1 atm (BTU/lb. °F):	0.172	0.140
Flammability Limits in Air:	non-flammable	
Ozone Depletion Potential (ODP):	0.015	1.0
Halocarbon Greenhouse Warming Potential (HGWP):	0.02	1.0

Pressure-Temperature Chart

Temp (°F)	123 psig	11 psig
-40	* 28.8	* 28.4
-30	* 28.3	* 27.8
-20	* 27.8	* 27.1
-10	* 26.9	* 26.0
0	* 25.9	* 24.7
10	* 24.5	* 23.1
20	* 22.8	* 21.1
30	* 20.7	* 18.6
40	* 18.1	* 15.6
50	* 14.9	* 12.0
60	* 11.1	* 7.7
70	* 6.5	* 2.6
80	* 1.2	1.6
90	2.5	5.0
100	6.2	8.9
110	10.4	13.4
120	15.2	18.5
130	20.8	24.3
140	27.0	30.8
150	34.2	38.1
160	41.6	46.2
170	51.0	55.3
180	60.9	65.3
190	71.9	76.3
200	84.0	88.4

** Pressures provided in Inches Mercury Vacuum.*

Forane® 123: Engineering Data

Temp (°F)	psia	Density (lb./cu. ft.)		Enthalpy (BTU/lb.)	
		Liquid	Vapor	Liquid	Vapor
-40	0.545	101.1	0.0186	0.00	84.77
-30	0.776	100.3	0.0259	4.35	86.14
-20	1.09	99.49	0.0354	6.51	87.51
-10	1.49	98.70	0.0477	8.69	88.89
0	2.01	97.91	0.0632	10.89	90.28
10	2.68	97.11	0.0826	13.11	91.68
20	3.52	96.30	0.1065	15.35	93.09
30	4.56	95.49	0.1358	17.61	94.50
40	5.85	94.67	0.1711	19.89	95.91
50	7.40	93.84	0.2134	22.20	97.32
60	9.28	93.00	0.2636	24.52	98.74
70	11.51	92.15	0.3228	26.86	100.16
80	14.15	91.29	0.3919	29.22	101.57
90	17.24	90.41	0.4723	31.61	102.98
100	20.84	89.52	0.5651	34.01	104.39
110	25.01	88.62	0.6717	36.44	105.79
120	29.79	87.69	0.7935	38.89	107.18
130	35.25	86.75	0.9323	41.37	108.56
140	41.45	85.79	1.0900	43.87	109.93
150	48.45	84.80	1.2670	46.39	111.29
160	56.32	83.79	1.4680	48.94	112.64
170	65.12	82.75	1.6930	51.52	113.97
180	74.93	81.69	1.9460	54.13	115.28
190	85.81	80.59	2.2290	56.76	116.56
200	97.83	79.45	2.5460	59.43	117.83

To calculate the Latent Heat of Vaporization, subtract the liquid enthalpy from the vapor enthalpy at the desired temperature.

Temperature Conversion: °C = (°F – 32) x 5/9

Pressure Conversion: psig = psia – 14.7 {P > 14.7}
in. Hg Vacuum = (14.7 – psia) x 2.036

Density Conversion: lb./cu. ft. {water = 62.43 lb./cu. ft.}
lb./gal. = lb./cu. ft. ÷ 7.48 {water = 8.35 lb./gal.}
g/ml = lb./cu. ft. x 0.016 {water = 1 g/ml}

Operating Considerations for New Systems

Performance

In new chiller installations, R-123 chillers are sized and specified according to the same industry practices which govern the selection of R-11 equipment. The chillers will have adequate capacity for the job which it is selected.

Lubrication and Material Compatibility

New R-123 chillers are built and delivered with the proper materials of construction and the manufacturer's recommended lubricant. In general, the same lubricants which have been used with R-11 can be used for R-123. If installation procedures or service conditions call for addition of lubricant or replacement of components on a system built for R-123, please consult the equipment manufacturer for specific recommendations.

Considerations for Retrofitting R-11 Installations with R-123

Performance

Testing has shown reduced capacity and efficiency in chillers where the only modification was a change from R-11 to R-123. In order to obtain the maximum performance from R-123, some mechanical modification of the equipment is usually called for. Original equipment manufacturers offer recommendations, and in some cases retrofit kits, that will provide for the best performance when using R-123.

Lubrication

R-123 is chemically compatible, and fully miscible, with the same lubricants which are currently used in R-11 equipment. Manufacturer's recommendations should be followed regarding the choice of lubricant or procedure for oil changes during retrofit.

Materials of Construction

R-123 is chemically stable in contact with common materials of construction. The refrigerant may, however, affect the size, shape, or mechanical properties of plastics or elastomers which are present in R-11 chillers. Each system must be checked carefully for any materials which will not be acceptable when R-123 is introduced into the chiller. Suitable replacement parts should be obtained from the equipment manufacturer.

Personal Exposure and Safe Handling

Elf Atochem provides a Material Safety Data Sheet (MSDS) which contains the latest safety and personal protection information regarding Forane 123. The MSDS is sent to all customers who purchase Forane 123, and the information is updated when necessary.

In general, R-123 has a lower occupational exposure limit than R-11 (based on an 8 hour work day, time-weighted-average). Industry standards, such as ASHRAE Standard 15, "Safety Code for Mechanical Refrigeration", provide detailed guidelines for equipment location, safety precautions, and restrictions involved with using R-123 in water chiller applications. Please comply with all applicable industry standards, building codes, and chemical and equipment manufacturer recommendations which pertain to the use of R-123.

Elf Atochem Cylinder Identification

TYPE	COLOR CODE	SIZES NET LBS.
R-123 ($CHCl_2CF_3$)	Lt. Blue Grey	100 (E), 200 (E)

Other Forane® Alternative Refrigerants

TYPE	COLOR CODE	SIZES NET LBS.
R-22 ($CHClF_2$)	Green	30 (B), 50 (C), 125 (D)
R-134a (CF_3CH_2F)	Light Blue	30 (B), 125 (D)
R-404A	Orange	24 (B), 100 (D)
FX 56	Tan	30 (B)

Container Style

24/30 lb.
(B)

50 lb.
(C)

100/125 lb.
(D)

100/200 lb.
Drum
(E)

elf atochem
ATO

elf atochem
ATO

Published by Elf Atochem North America, Inc., Fluorochemicals, 2000 Market Street, Philadelphia, PA 19103

Forane® 134a

(1, 1, 1, 2 Tetrafluoroethane)

Forane® 134a is an HFC, zero ozone depletion potential (ODP) refrigerant with properties very similar to R-12. It can be used both as a pure refrigerant in a number of traditional R-12 applications, and as a component in refrigerant blends targeted for R-502 and R-22 applications.

Compressor and system manufacturers have begun to sell new equipment which has been specifically designed for R-134a. In addition, laboratory testing and field trials are confirming that R-134a can work in the retrofit of many existing R-12 and 500 installations.

New Equipment

Industries which are successfully making the transition from R-12 to R-134a include automotive air conditioning, other specialized air conditioning or climate control applications, positive pressure centrifugal chillers, medium temperature commercial refrigeration, refrigeration appliances, industrial refrigeration plants, and transport refrigeration.

Retrofit

Applications where R-134a is being proven reliable for retrofitting R-12 systems include R-12 centrifugal chillers, semi-hermetic, reciprocating, and screw refrigeration applications, industrial refrigeration plants, and some hermetic compressor applications. See RETROFIT section for more considerations.

This brochure has been designed to give a broad background of properties and technical considerations to help you determine if Forane 134a will meet your CFC alternatives needs.

Forane® 134a: Basic Property Data

Chemical Formula:	CF_3CH_2F
Molecular Weight:	102.0
Boiling Point @ 1 atm:	- 15.7°F
Freezing Point @ 1 atm:	- 149.8°F
Density of Saturated Vapor @ b.p.:	0.325 lb./cu. ft.
Density of Saturated Liquid @ 80°F:	75.35 lb./cu. ft.
Critical Temperature:	213.8°F
Critical Pressure:	590.3 psia
Critical Density:	31.9 lb./cu. ft.
Latent Heat of Vaporization @ b.p.:	92.5 BTU/lb.
Specific Heat of Liquid @ 80°F:	0.35 BTU/lb. °F
Specific Heat of Vapor @ 1 atm:	0.23 BTU/lb. °F
Flammability Limits in Air:	non-flammable
Workplace Environmental Exposure Level* (WEEL)(8 hour time weighted average):	1000 ppm
Ozone Depletion Potential (ODP)	0
Halocarbon Greenhouse Warming Potential (HGWP):	0.27

**Established by American Industrial Hygiene Association.*

Pressure-Temperature Chart

Temp (°F)	134a psig	12 psig
-50	* 18.7	* 15.4
-40	* 14.8	* 11.0
-30	* 9.9	* 5.5
-20	* 3.7	0.6
-10	1.9	4.5
0	6.5	9.2
10	11.9	14.7
20	18.4	21.1
30	26.1	28.5
40	35.1	37.0
50	45.5	46.7
60	57.5	57.8
70	71.2	70.2
80	86.8	84.2
90	104.0	99.7
100	124.0	117.0
110	147.0	136.0
120	171.0	157.0
130	199.0	181.0
140	229.0	206.0
150	263.0	234.0
160	300.0	264.0
170	341.0	297.0
180	386.0	333.0
190	435.0	372.0
200	489.0	414.0

**Pressures provided in Inches Mercury Vacuum.*

Forane® 134a: Engineering Data

Temp (°F)	psia	Density (lb./cu. ft.)		Enthalpy (BTU/lb.)	
		Liquid	Vapor	Liquid	Vapor
-50	5.49	89.30	0.1304	-2.95	95.68
-40	7.42	88.31	0.1727	0.00	97.18
-30	9.85	87.31	0.2254	2.98	98.68
-20	12.89	86.30	0.2901	5.99	100.18
-10	16.62	85.28	0.3688	9.04	101.67
0	21.16	84.23	0.4634	12.12	103.14
10	26.63	83.17	0.5762	15.23	104.60
20	33.13	82.08	0.7097	18.38	106.04
30	40.80	80.96	0.8667	21.57	107.45
40	49.77	79.82	1.0500	24.79	108.84
50	60.18	78.64	1.2630	28.05	110.20
60	72.17	77.43	1.5100	31.36	111.52
70	85.89	76.18	1.7950	34.72	112.80
80	101.50	74.89	2.1230	38.13	114.03
90	119.10	73.54	2.5010	41.59	115.20
100	139.00	72.13	2.9350	45.12	116.32
110	161.20	70.66	3.4340	48.71	117.36
120	186.00	69.10	4.0090	52.39	118.31
130	213.60	67.46	4.6750	56.14	119.16
140	244.10	65.70	5.4490	60.00	119.88
150	277.70	63.81	6.3580	63.98	120.45
160	314.80	61.74	7.4390	68.10	120.82
170	355.50	59.45	8.7470	72.40	120.93
180	400.30	56.83	10.3700	76.94	120.66
190	449.40	53.73	12.5000	81.83	119.83
200	503.40	49.73	15.5200	87.31	118.00

To calculate the Latent Heat of Vaporization, subtract the liquid enthalpy from the vapor enthalpy at the desired temperature.

Temperature Conversion: °C = (°F – 32) x 5/9

Pressure Conversion: psig = psia – 14.7 {P > 14.7}
in. Hg Vacuum = (14.7 – psia) x 2.036

Density Conversion: lb./cu. ft. {water = 62.43 lb./cu. ft.}
lb./gal. = lb./cu. ft. ÷ 7.48 {water = 8.35 lb./gal.}
g/ml = lb./cu. ft. x 0.016 {water = 1 g/ml}

Performance of Forane® 134a in New Equipment

LUBRICATION

For all R-134a applications, lubrication is a very important consideration.

- Miscibility between refrigerant and oil is critical for many equipment designs. Miscibility is required to ensure oil return to the compressor.
- R-134a is not miscible with mineral oils. Polyolester (POE) lubricants and poly alkylene glycol (PAG) lubricants have been recommended by various equipment manufacturers to be used with R-134a.
- POE and PAG lubricants will absorb moisture quickly. They must be handled carefully to avoid prolonged exposure to air.

Generally, new equipment will be shipped by the manufacturer with a compatible lubricant already charged. All of the manufacturers' recommendations should be followed.

SYSTEM PERFORMANCE

Climate Control

Chillers and specially designed A/C systems have been engineered to use R-134a while providing energy efficiency equivalent to R-12.

- Manufacturers have successfully introduced products for mobile air conditioning and positive pressure chillers using R-134a.

Refrigeration: Low Temperature

- At lower evaporator temperatures the pressure ratio of R-134a rises in relation to R-12, and the capacity may drop off significantly. Check with equipment manufacturers for specific recommendations regarding the use of their equipment with R-134a at lower application temperatures.
- One alternative for low temperature applications is the use of HFC blends, such as Forane® 404A (FX70), which have been designed to replace R-502 in low temperature refrigeration applications.

Refrigeration: Medium and High Temperature Applications

- R-134a can be used in most medium and high temperature R-12 applications.
- An ideal theoretical cycle analysis using the thermodynamic properties of R-134a shows a slight decrease in capacity and efficiency. When improvements, such as liquid subcooling, are introduced into the equation, the performance of R-134a becomes equal to that of R-12. These improvements are being taken advantage of by equipment manufacturers.

Retrofitting with Forane® 134a

Retrofitting of R-12 systems to R-134a is recommended when the projected service and material costs to maintain the system with R-12, over the expected lifetime of the system, exceed the cost of retrofit and maintenance with R-134a. A refrigerant management program may also call for the retrofit of equipment over a specific time frame so that other equipment may be serviced by the recovered R-12.

RETROFIT APPLICATIONS

Centrifugal Chillers

R-12 chillers which are retrofitted to R-134a will generally suffer in capacity and efficiency if no changes are made to the equipment. Manufacturers of chillers will provide engineering recommendations and retrofit kits to ensure the best performance from their equipment.

Automotive A/C

Key issues are lubrication, flushing, and material compatibility. These will determine how expensive the retrofit job will be.

Refrigeration

Larger refrigeration systems can be successfully retrofitted if the following factors are considered:

- Lubricant Flushing - most refrigeration systems require less than 5% residual mineral oil after flushing with POE.
- Compatibility of materials must be checked. Any materials which will cause leaks or failure of the system must be replaced.
- Application Temperature Range - the performance of R-134a should be evaluated at the application temperatures to confirm if it should be used.

Refrigeration: Small Hermetic

Only applicable where the compressor is replaced. Key issues are the effect of residual mineral oil on capillary tubes, time/cost of job, and availability of R-22 based service fluids.

Elf Atochem Cylinder Identification

TYPE	COLOR CODE	SIZES NET LBS.
R-134a (CF_3CH_2F)	Light Blue	30 (B), 125 (D)

Other Forane® Alternative Refrigerants

TYPE	COLOR CODE	SIZES NET LBS.
R-22 ($CHClF_2$)	Green	30 (B), 50 (C), 125 (D)
R-123 ($CHCl_2CF_3$)	Lt. Blue Grey	100 (E), 200 (E)
R-404A	Orange	24 (B), 100 (D)
FX 56	Tan	30 (B)

Container Style

24/30 lb. (B)

50 lb. (C)

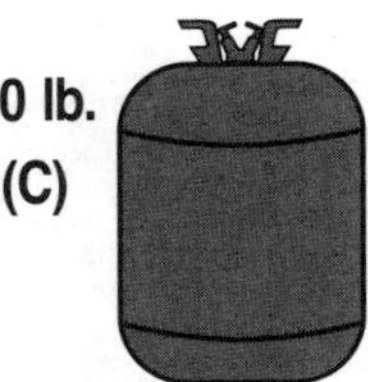

100/125 lb. (D)

100/200 lb. Drum (E)

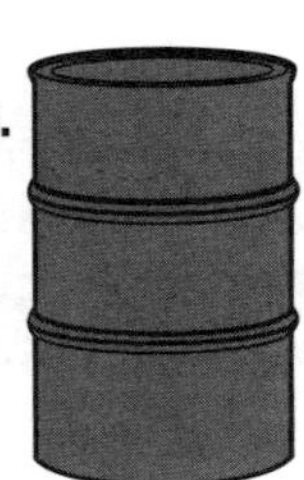

elf atochem

ATO

elf atochem
ATO

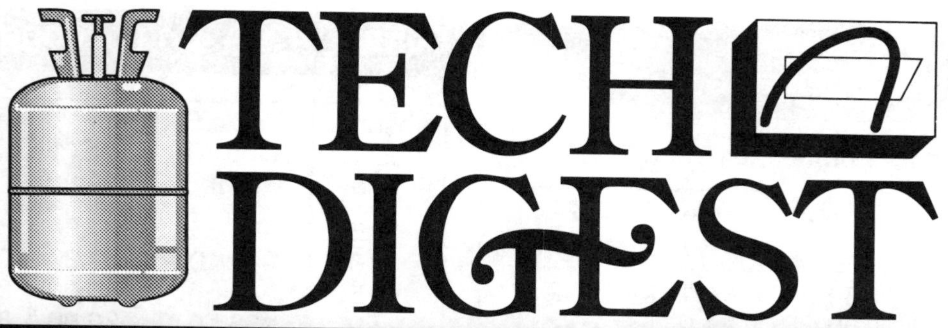

Published by Elf Atochem North America, Inc., Fluorochemicals, 2000 Market Street, Philadelphia, PA 19103

Forane® 404A

Forane® 404A is a zero ozone depletion potential (ODP), near azeotropic blend of HFC refrigerants R-125, R-143a, and R-134a. Forane® 404A is formulated to closely match the properties of R-502, which make it useful for a variety of medium and low temperature refrigeration applications.

New Systems

Forane® 404A has been approved by many refrigeration compressor and system manufacturers for use in new refrigeration equipment. Applications where R-404A equipment is available include food display and storage cases, cold storage rooms, ice machines, transportation, and process refrigeration.

Retrofit

Forane® 404A can be used to retrofit many existing R-502 systems. The physical and refrigeration properties of the blend cause it to behave much like R-502 when used in a retrofit; however it is not intended to be a direct, "drop-in" service fluid for R-502 systems. (See the RETROFIT section).

This brochure provides a broad background of properties and technical information to help apply Forane® 404A to your refrigeration needs.

NOTE: *R-404A is the ASHRAE Standard 34 Number Designation for the blend of R-125/143a/134a (44/52/4 wt %). Prior to the assignment of an ASHRAE number designation, Elf Atochem referred to this blend under the research label Forane® FX 70.*

Forane® 404A: Basic Property Data

Chemical Formula:	R-125	(CF_3CHF_2) - 44 wt %
	R-143a	(CF_3CH_3) - 52 wt %
	R-134a	(CF_3CH_2F) - 4 wt %
Average Molecular Weight:		97.6
Boiling Point @ 1 atm:		- 50.4°F
Density of Saturated Vapor @ b.p.:		0.336 lb./cu. ft.^{3}
Density of Saturated Liquid @ 77°F:		64.86 lb./cu. ft.^{3}
Critical Temperature:		162°F
Critical Pressure:		542 psia
Latent Heat of Vaporization @ b.p.:		88.8 BTU/lb.
Specific Heat of Liquid @ 77°F:		0.359 BTU/lb. °F
Specific Heat of Vapor @ 1 atm, 77°F:		0.208 BTU/lb. °F
Maximum Temperature Glide:		1.5°F
Flammability Limits in Air:		non-flammable*
Ozone Depletion Potential (ODP):		0
Halocarbon Greenhouse Warming Potential (HGWP):		0.94

* *Forane 404A does not propagate flame in ASTM E-681-95 at test temperatures up to 100°C*

Pressure - Temperature Chart

for Forane® 404A and R-502

Temp (°F)	404A (psig)[a]	502 (psig)
-60	* 8.1	* 7.2
-50	* 1.0	* 0.2
-40	3.8	4.1
-30	9.1	9.2
-25	12.2	12.1
-20	15.5	15.3
-15	19.1	18.8
-10	23.1	22.6
-5	27.4	26.7
0	32.1	31.1
5	37.2	35.9
10	42.7	41.0
15	48.6	46.5
20	54.9	52.4
25	61.7	58.8
30	69.1	65.6
35	77.0	72.8
40	85.3	80.5
45	94.4	88.7
50	104.0	97.4
55	114.1	106.6
60	124.9	116.4
65	136.3	126.7
70	148.4	137.6
75	161.4	149.1
80	174.8	161.2
85	189.1	174.0
90	204.1	187.4
95	220.1	201.4
100	236.7	216.2
105	254.3	231.7
110	273.0	247.9
115	334.1	264.9
120	313.4	282.7
125	334.1	301.4
130	356.9	320.8

** Pressures provided in Inches Mercury Vacuum.*

a. The pressure of Saturated Vapor (Dew Point pressure) has been provided for Forane 404A in this chart. This pressure is from 1 to 2 psi lower than the pressure generated by a cylinder of liquid refrigerant at the same temperature. The Dew Point pressure is more meaningful when using a Pressure - Temperature chart for purposes such as checking system operation during charging.

Forane® 404A: Engineering Data

Absolute Pressure psia	Bubble Pt. Temp. (°F) (liq)	Dew Pt. Temp.(°F) (vap)	Density(lb./cu. ft.)		Enthalpy (BTU/lb.)	
			Liquid	Vapor	Liquid	Vapor
5	-86.85	-84.90	85.29	0.123	-13.73	80.10
10	-64.10	-62.30	82.93	0.235	-7.19	83.60
15	-49.65	-48.00	81.37	0.344	-2.91	85.82
20	-38.50	-36.90	80.15	0.449	0.46	87.52
30	-21.60	-20.20	78.26	0.659	5.67	90.05
40	-8.70	-7.30	76.74	0.867	9.77	91.96
50	1.9	3.3	75.46	1.074	13.23	93.50
60	11.1	12.3	74.34	1.282	16.25	94.78
70	19.1	20.3	73.32	1.490	18.96	95.89
80	26.3	27.5	72.39	1.708	21.44	96.96
90	32.9	34.0	71.62	1.911	23.73	97.72
100	38.9	40.0	70.70	2.124	25.97	98.49
110	44.5	45.5	69.92	2.340	27.88	99.18
120	49.7	50.7	69.18	2.588	29.79	99.80
130	54.6	55.6	68.47	2.778	31.61	100.4
140	59.3	60.2	67.79	3.001	33.36	100.9
150	63.7	64.6	67.12	3.227	35.04	101.4
160	67.9	68.3	66.47	3.456	36.55	101.8
170	71.9	72.7	65.84	3.689	38.22	102.2
180	75.7	76.5	65.22	3.925	39.74	102.6
190	79.4	80.2	64.62	4.165	41.22	102.9
200	82.8	83.7	64.02	4.409	42.66	103.2
210	86.3	87.1	63.43	4.657	44.07	103.5
220	89.6	90.4	62.86	4.909	45.45	103.8
230	92.8	93.5	62.28	5.166	46.80	104.0
240	95.9	96.6	61.71	5.428	48.13	104.2
250	98.9	99.6	61.14	5.696	49.43	104.4
260	101.8	102.4	60.58	5.968	50.72	104.5
270	104.6	105.3	60.01	6.247	51.99	104.7
280	107.3	108.0	59.45	6.531	53.24	104.8
290	110.0	110.6	58.89	6.822	54.48	104.9
300	112.6	113.2	59.32	7.120	55.71	105.0
350	124.8	125.3	55.43	8.732	61.74	105.1
400	135.3	136.2	49.79	10.610	67.73	104.7

To calculate the Latent Heat of Vaporization, subtract the liquid enthalpy from the vapor enthalpy at the desired temperature.

Temperature Conversion: °C = (°F – 32) x 5/9

Pressure Conversion: psig = psia – 14.7 {P > 14.7}
in. Hg Vacuum = (14.7 – psia) x 2.036

Density Conversion: lb./cu. ft. {water = 62.43 lb./cu. ft.}
lb./gal. = lb./cu. ft. ÷ 7.48 {water = 8.35 lb./gal.}
g/ml = lb./cu. ft. x 0.016 {water = 1 g/ml}

Considerations for Using Near-Azeotropic Blends

Common refrigerants used in the past were either single component refrigerants, or azeotropic blends which behaved as a single component when used in a refrigeration system. Near-azeotropic blends, such as R-404A, will behave almost the same as azeotropes, such as R-502, for all practical purposes.

- The temperature Glide of R-404A is less than 1.5°F. In most systems this glide is not noticeable compared to normal temperature changes due to pressure drops. Equipment manufacturers indicate potential influences from R-404A's glide on given applications.
- R-404A will not significantly change in composition due to fractionation. There will, however, be a slight difference in composition in the vapor phase which is in equilibrium with liquid, such as in a cylinder. For this reason, Forane 404A should be charged into equipment or systems from the cylinder as a liquid.

Use of Forane® 404A in New Refrigeration Systems

Performance

In new installations, the process for sizing and selecting compressors and other system components for use with R-404A is the same as it has always been for R-502. The compressor capacity, line sizes, etc., will be chosen properly to fit the needs of the job. Operating experience has shown no significant loss of efficiency in R-404A installations, compared to historical R-502 performance.

Lubrication

R-404A requires a polyolester (POE) lubricant to ensure complete miscibility between oil and refrigerant. Miscibility is important for oil return to the compressor, especially in larger systems with long runs of piping. Manufacturers supply equipment with the proper lubricant already charged, or provide specific recommendations on the type or brand of lubricant to be installed in the field.

Material Compatibility

New compressors are constructed with materials which are compatible with R-404A. Follow manufacturers' recommendations regarding materials used in parts which are installed in the field.

Considerations for Retrofitting R-502 Systems for Use with Forane® 404A

Retrofit projects should be included as part of an overall Refrigerant Management Program. Forane 404A can be used in the retrofit of many existing R-502 installations, with the following considerations:

Lubrication

R-404A is not miscible with existing lubricants used in R-502 systems. The mineral oil will need to be replaced with a polyolester (POE) lubricant to a residual mineral oil level less than 5 percent.

Systems Materials

Check Elf Atochem retrofit literature and obtain recommendations from equipment manufacturers regarding compatibility of materials with R-404A. Replace any materials which are not acceptable for use with R-404A.

Obtain procedures, material specifications, and any other recommendations from equipment, component, and lubricant manufacturers, as well as from Elf Atochem.

Pressure Relief

Due to the higher operating pressures associated with the use of Forane 404A as opposed to R-502, consult OEM product specific retrofit requirements for any and all pressure relief modifications and/or requirements.

For Additional Forane® Literature, Training Guides and Case Histories, call

1-800-343-7940

For Retrofit Assistance, call

1-800-RETRO 94

(1-800-738-7694)

Elf Atochem Cylinder Identification

TYPE	COLOR CODE	SIZES NET LBS.
R-404A	Orange	24 (B), 100 (D)

Other Forane® Alternative Refrigerants

TYPE	COLOR CODE	SIZES NET LBS.
R-22 ($CHClF_2$)	Green	30 (B), 50 (C), 125 (D)
R-123 ($CHCl_2CF_3$)	Lt. Blue Grey	100 (E), 200 (E)
R-134a (CF_3CH_2F)	Light Blue	30 (B), 125 (D)
FX 56	Tan	30 (B)

Container Style

24/30 lb. (B)

50 lb. (C)

100/125 lb. (D)

100/200 lb. Drum (E)

elf atochem

ATO

elf atochem
ATO

Published by Elf Atochem North America, Inc., Fluorochemicals, 2000 Market Street, Philadelphia, PA 19103

Forane® 408A

Forane® 408A (FX-10) is a low ozone depletion potential (ODP), near-azeotropic blend of HCFC 22 and HFC refrigerants R-125 and R-143a. Forane 408A has been added to the Forane family of refrigerants to provide a convenient and reliable retrofit solution for medium and low temperature refrigeration systems which are currently using R-502.

Use Forane 408A to Retrofit R-502 Systems

Forane 408A can be used to retrofit many existing R-502 systems. R-408A has been blended to closely match the physical and refrigeration properties of R-502 because the equipment being retrofitted was designed for R-502. R-408A should not be mixed with R-502 or used to top off existing systems. (*See the RETROFIT section for review of additional considerations.*)

Use Forane 404A for New Low and Medium Temperature Systems

Forane 408A is not intended for use in new equipment. Refrigeration applications which were previously designed to use R-502 can now be specified to use a long term alternative HFC blend, Forane 404A. Manufacturers are making compressors and refrigeration systems available for use in food display and storage cases, cold storage rooms, ice machines, transportation, and process refrigeration.

This brochure has been designed to give a broad background of properties and technical considerations to help you apply Forane 408A to your refrigeration needs.

Forane® 408A: Basic Property Data

			R-408A	R-502
Chemical Formula:	R-125	(CF_3CHF_2)	7 wt %	--
	R-143a	(CF_3CH_3)	46 wt %	--
	R-22	($CHClF_2$)	47 wt %	48.8 wt %
	R-115	($CClF_2CF_3$)	--	51.2 wt %
Average Molecular Weight:			87	111.6
Boiling Point @ 1 atm (°F):			- 46.3	- 50.1
Density of Saturated Vapor @ b.p.(lb./cu. ft.):			0.296	0.388
Density of Saturated Liquid @ 77°F(lb./cu. ft.):			66.17	75.91
Critical Temperature(°F):			182.3	180.0
Critical Pressure (psia):			629.5	591.0
Latent Heat of Vaporization @ b.p.(BTU/lb.):			100.7	74.21
Specific Heat of Liquid @ 77°F (BTU/lb. °F):			0.151	0.298
Specific Heat of Vapor @ 1 atm (BTU/lb. °F):			0.180	0.200
Maximum Temperature Glide (°F):			1.0	0
Flammable Limits in Air:			non-flammable*	
Ozone Depletion Potential (ODP, CFC 11 = 1.0):			0.026	0.3
Halocarbon Greenhouse Warming Potential (HGWP, CFC 11 = 1.0):			0.75	4.1

** Forane 408A does not propagate flame in ASTM E-681-85 at test temperatures up to 100°C*

Pressure - Temperature Chart

Temp (°F)	Sat. Vapor R-408A (psig)	R-502 (psig)
-45	0.7	1.9
-40	2.8	4.1
-35	5.1	6.5
-30	7.6	9.2
-25	10.4	12.1
-20	13.5	15.3
-15	16.8	18.8
-10	20.4	22.6
-5	24.4	26.7
0	28.7	31.1
5	33.3	35.9
10	38.3	41.0
15	43.7	46.5
20	49.5	52.4
25	55.8	58.8
30	62.5	65.6
35	69.7	72.8
40	77.4	80.5
45	85.6	88.7
50	94.3	97.4
55	103.6	106.6
60	113.5	116.4
65	124.0	126.7
70	135.1	137.6
75	146.9	149.1
80	159.4	161.2
85	172.5	174.0
90	186.4	187.4
95	201.1	201.4
100	216.6	216.2
105	232.8	231.7
110	250.0	247.9
115	267.9	264.9
120	286.8	282.7
125	306.6	301.4
130	327.4	320.8
135	349.2	341.2
140	371.9	362.6

a. The pressure of Saturated Vapor (Dew Point pressure) has been provided for R-408A for this P-T chart. This pressure is from 1 to 2 psi lower than, for example, the pressure generated by a cylinder of liquid refrigerant at the same temperature. The Dew Point pressure is more meaningful when using a Pressure - Temperature chart for purposes such as checking system operation during charging.

Forane® 408A: Engineering Data

Temp °F	Pressure (psia)		Density(lb./cu. ft.)		Enthalpy (BTU/lb.°F)	
	Sat. Liq.	Sat. Vap.	Sat. Liq.	Sat. Vap.	Sat. Liq.	Sat. Vap.
-45	15.8	15.4	80.46	0.310	-1.400	95.70
-40	18.0	17.5	79.96	0.350	-0.000	96.50
-35	20.3	19.8	79.45	0.393	1.400	97.20
-30	22.9	22.3	78.93	0.440	2.700	97.90
-25	25.7	25.1	78.41	0.491	4.100	98.60
-20	28.8	28.1	77.89	0.547	5.500	99.30
-15	32.2	31.5	77.36	0.608	6.900	99.90
-10	35.9	35.1	76.83	0.674	8.400	100.6
-5	39.9	39.1	76.29	0.745	9.800	101.3
0	44.2	43.4	75.75	0.823	11.30	102.0
5	48.9	48.0	75.19	0.906	12.80	102.6
10	54.0	53.0	74.64	0.997	14.20	103.3
15	59.5	58.4	74.07	1.094	15.70	103.9
20	65.4	64.2	73.50	1.199	17.30	104.5
25	71.7	70.5	72.92	1.312	18.80	105.2
30	78.4	77.2	72.33	1.433	20.40	105.8
35	85.7	84.4	71.74	1.563	21.90	106.4
40	93.4	92.1	71.13	1.703	23.50	107.0
45	101.7	100.3	70.51	1.853	25.20	107.5
50	110.5	109.0	69.89	2.014	26.80	108.1
55	119.8	118.3	69.25	2.187	28.50	108.6
60	129.8	128.2	68.60	2.372	30.20	109.1
65	140.3	138.7	67.93	2.571	31.90	109.6
70	151.5	149.8	67.26	2.783	33.60	110.1
75	163.4	161.6	66.56	3.012	35.40	110.6
80	175.9	174.1	65.85	3.257	37.20	111.0
85	189.1	187.2	65.12	3.519	39.10	111.4
90	203.1	201.1	64.37	3.802	40.90	111.7
95	217.8	215.8	63.60	4.105	42.80	112.1
100	233.3	231.3	62.80	4.432	44.80	112.4
105	249.7	247.5	61.98	4.785	46.80	112.7
110	266.8	264.7	61.12	5.165	48.80	112.9
115	284.9	282.6	60.23	5.577	50.90	113.1
120	303.8	301.5	59.31	6.023	53.10	113.2
125	323.6	321.3	58.34	6.509	55.30	113.2
130	344.4	342.1	57.32	7.040	57.60	113.2
135	366.2	363.8	56.24	7.622	60.00	113.1
140	389.0	386.6	55.09	8.263	62.40	113.0

To calculate the Latent Heat of Vaporization, subtract the liquid enthalpy from the vapor enthalpy at the desired temperature.

Temperature Conversion: °C = (°F – 32) x 5/9

Pressure Conversion: psig = psia – 14.7 {P > 14.7}
in. Hg Vacuum = (14.7 – psia) x 2.036

Density Conversion: lb./cu. ft. {water = 62.43 lb./cu. ft.}
lb./gal. = lb./cu. ft. ÷ 7.48 {water = 8.35 lb./gal.}
g/ml = lb./cu. ft. x 0.016 {water = 1 g/ml}

Considerations for Using Near-Azeotropic Blends

Common refrigerants used in the past were either single component refrigerants, or azeotropic blends which behaved as a single component when used in a refrigeration system. Near-azeotropic blends, such as R-408A will behave almost the same as azeotropes, such as R-502, for all practical purposes.

- The temperature glide of R-408A is less than 1.0°F. This glide is usually not noticeable compared to normal temperature changes due to pressure drops across the tubing, for example. Manufacturers in general have not indicated any special considerations for low-glide blends in normal retrofit applications.

- R-408A will not significantly change in composition due to fractionation. There will, however, be a slight difference in composition in the vapor phase which is in equilibrium with liquid, such as in a cylinder. 408A should therefore be transferred to charging equipment or systems from the cylinder as a liquid.

Considerations for Retrofitting R-502 Systems for Use with Forane® 408A

Retrofit projects should be included as part of an overall Refrigerant Management program. Forane 408A can be used in most existing R-502 installations, with the following considerations:

Performance

In most retrofit applications, R-408A capacity and efficiency are slightly higher than R-502. The compressor, line sizes, and other components will not need replacement, and should operate the same with R-408A as they did with R-502.

Lubrication

R-408A is capable of being used with mineral oil, alkylbenzene oil, or polyolester lubricants. Systems which operate with R-502 and mineral oil, and show adequate lubricant return to the compressor, may continue to use mineral oil with R-408A. Alkylbenzene and/or polyolester may be used alone or in combination with mineral oil in order to improve lubricant miscibility and return to the compressor. Consult any manufacturer's guidelines for additional recommendations.

Material Compatibility

Check Elf Atochem retrofit literature and obtain recommendations from equipment manufacturers regarding compatibility of materials with R-408A. Replace any materials which are not acceptable for use with R-408A. Generally, materials which are compatible with R-22 can be used for R-408A.

Retrofit Procedure

1. Gather baseline data from the sytem while still operating on R-502.
2. Leak check system to identify necessary repairs.
3. Recover existing R-502 charge.
4. If needed, remove mineral oil and replace with alkylbenzene or polyolester.
5. Replace filter driers.
6. Evacuate system using a deep vacuum (at least 250 microns).
7. Charge system with R-408A using liquid phase only. (Approximate charge will be 85-90% of R-502 charge).
8. Properly mark and identify R-408A refrigerant charge for the retrofitted system.
9. Start system and adjust expansion device if needed.

For Additional Forane® Literature, Training Guides and Case Histories, call

1-800-343-7940

For Retrofit Assistance, call

1-800-RETRO 94

(1-800-738-7694)

Elf Atochem Cylinder Identification

TYPE	COLOR CODE	SIZES NET LBS.
R-408A	Medium Purple	24 (B), 100 (D)

Other Forane® Alternative Refrigerants

TYPE	COLOR CODE	SIZES NET LBS.
R-22 ($CHClF_2$)	Green	30 (B), 50 (C), 125 (D)
R-123 ($CHCl_2CF_3$)	Lt. Blue Grey	100 (E), 200 (E)
R-134a (CF_3CH_2F)	Light Blue	30 (B), 125 (D)
R-409A	Tan	30 (B)
R-404A	Orange	24 (B), 100 (D)

Container Style

24/30 lb.
(B)

50 lb.
(C)

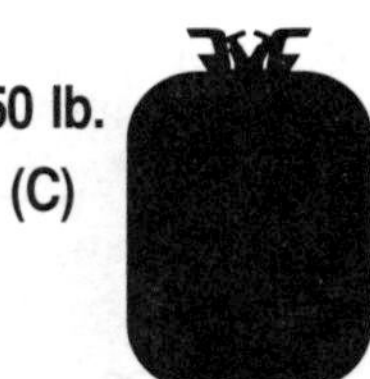

100/125 lb.
(D)

100/200 lb.
Drum
(E)

elf atochem
ATO

elf atochem
ATO

Product Information

orane FX 10 (R-408A) Saturated Properties

essure [psia]	Saturated Liquid T Bubble [F]	Density [lb/ft^3]	Enthalpy [BTU/lb]	Entropy [BTU/lb.R]	Saturated Vapor T Dew [F]	Density [lb/ft^3]	Enthalpy [BTU/lb]	Entropy [BTU/lb.R]	Heat of vaporization [BTU/lb]
10	-62.2	82.18	-5.9	-0.014	-60.9	0.208	93.5	0.235	99.4
12	-55.6	81.52	-4.2	-0.010	-54.3	0.247	94.4	0.234	98.6
14	-49.8	80.94	-2.6	-0.006	-48.6	0.285	95.2	0.232	97.9
16	-44.6	80.42	-1.2	-0.003	-43.4	0.322	96.0	0.231	97.2
18	-39.9	79.95	0.0	0.000	-38.8	0.360	96.6	0.230	96.6
20	-35.6	79.51	1.2	0.003	-34.5	0.397	97.2	0.229	96.0
22	-31.7	79.11	2.3	0.005	-30.6	0.434	97.8	0.228	95.5
24	-28.0	78.73	3.3	0.008	-26.9	0.471	98.3	0.227	95.0
26	-24.5	78.37	4.3	0.010	-23.5	0.508	98.8	0.227	94.5
28	-21.3	78.03	5.2	0.012	-20.2	0.544	99.2	0.226	94.1
30	-18.2	77.70	6.0	0.014	-17.2	0.581	99.6	0.226	93.6
35	-11.2	76.96	8.0	0.018	-10.2	0.671	100.6	0.225	92.6
40	-4.9	76.28	9.9	0.022	-3.9	0.762	101.4	0.224	91.6
45	0.8	75.65	11.5	0.026	1.8	0.852	102.2	0.223	90.7
50	6.1	75.07	13.1	0.029	7.0	0.942	102.9	0.222	89.8
55	10.9	74.53	14.5	0.032	11.9	1.032	103.5	0.221	89.0
60	15.5	74.02	15.9	0.035	16.4	1.122	104.1	0.221	88.2
65	19.7	73.53	17.2	0.038	20.6	1.212	104.6	0.220	87.4
70	23.7	73.07	18.4	0.040	24.6	1.303	105.1	0.220	86.7
80	31.1	72.20	20.7	0.045	32.0	1.484	106.0	0.219	85.3
90	37.8	71.39	22.9	0.049	38.7	1.665	106.8	0.218	84.0
100	44.0	70.64	24.8	0.053	44.8	1.849	107.5	0.217	82.7
110	49.7	69.92	26.7	0.057	50.6	2.033	108.1	0.217	81.4
120	55.1	69.24	28.5	0.060	55.9	2.219	108.7	0.216	80.2
130	60.1	68.58	30.2	0.064	60.9	2.406	109.2	0.216	79.0
140	64.8	67.95	31.8	0.067	65.6	2.596	109.7	0.215	77.8
160	73.6	66.76	34.9	0.072	74.3	2.981	110.5	0.214	75.6
180	81.6	65.62	37.8	0.078	82.3	3.375	111.2	0.213	73.4
200	88.9	64.53	40.5	0.082	89.6	3.778	111.7	0.212	71.2
210	92.4	64.01	41.8	0.085	93.1	3.984	112.0	0.212	70.1
220	95.7	63.48	43.1	0.087	96.4	4.193	112.2	0.211	69.1
230	98.9	62.97	44.4	0.089	99.6	4.405	112.4	0.211	68.0
240	102.1	62.46	45.6	0.091	102.7	4.620	112.5	0.210	66.9
250	105.1	61.96	46.8	0.094	105.7	4.839	112.7	0.210	65.9
260	108.0	61.46	48.0	0.096	108.7	5.061	112.8	0.210	64.8
270	110.9	60.96	49.2	0.098	111.5	5.286	112.9	0.209	63.7
280	113.7	60.47	50.4	0.100	114.3	5.516	113.0	0.209	62.7
290	116.4	59.98	51.5	0.101	117.0	5.749	113.1	0.208	61.6
300	119.0	59.49	52.7	0.103	119.6	5.987	113.2	0.208	60.5
320	124.1	58.51	54.9	0.107	124.7	6.476	113.2	0.207	58.3
340	129.0	57.53	57.1	0.111	129.5	6.985	113.2	0.206	56.1
360	133.6	56.55	59.3	0.114	134.1	7.517	113.2	0.205	53.9
380	138.1	55.55	61.4	0.118	138.6	8.073	113.0	0.204	51.6
400	142.3	54.53	63.6	0.121	142.8	8.658	112.8	0.203	49.2
420	146.5	53.48	65.8	0.125	146.9	9.275	112.6	0.202	46.8
440	150.4	52.41	67.9	0.128	150.9	9.931	112.2	0.201	44.3

FORANE FX 10 (R-408A)

Superheated Vapor - Enthalpy (BTU/lb)

Temp. [F]	Dew Pressure [psia]	SUPERHEATING (R)											
		0	10	20	30	40	50	60	70	80	90	100	110
-80	5.7	90.7	92.3	93.9	95.5	97.1	98.7	100.4	102.1	103.8	105.5	107.3	109.1
-75	6.6	91.5	93.0	94.6	96.2	97.9	99.5	101.2	102.9	104.6	106.4	108.1	109.9
-70	7.7	92.2	93.8	95.4	97.0	98.6	100.3	102.0	103.7	105.4	107.2	109.0	110.8
-65	8.9	92.9	94.5	96.1	97.7	99.4	101.1	102.8	104.5	106.3	108.0	109.8	111.7
-60	10.3	93.6	95.2	96.8	98.5	100.2	101.9	103.6	105.3	107.1	108.9	110.7	112.5
-55	11.8	94.3	95.9	97.6	99.3	100.9	102.7	104.4	106.1	107.9	109.7	111.5	113.4
-50	13.5	95.0	96.7	98.3	100.0	101.7	103.4	105.2	107.0	108.7	110.6	112.4	114.2
-45	15.4	95.7	97.4	99.1	100.8	102.5	104.2	106.0	107.8	109.6	111.4	113.2	115.1
-40	17.5	96.5	98.1	99.8	101.5	103.2	105.0	106.8	108.6	110.4	112.2	114.1	116.0
-35	19.8	97.2	98.8	100.5	102.3	104.0	105.8	107.6	109.4	111.2	113.1	114.9	116.8
-30	22.3	97.9	99.6	101.3	103.0	104.8	106.6	108.4	110.2	112.0	113.9	115.8	117.7
-25	25.1	98.6	100.3	102.0	103.8	105.5	107.3	109.2	111.0	112.9	114.7	116.6	118.6
-20	28.1	99.3	101.0	102.7	104.5	106.3	108.1	109.9	111.8	113.7	115.6	117.5	119.4
-15	31.5	99.9	101.7	103.5	105.2	107.0	108.9	110.7	112.6	114.5	116.4	118.3	120.3
-10	35.1	100.6	102.4	104.2	106.0	107.8	109.6	111.5	113.4	115.3	117.2	119.2	121.1
-5	39.1	101.3	103.1	104.9	106.7	108.5	110.4	112.3	114.2	116.1	118.0	120.0	122.0
0	43.4	102.0	103.8	105.6	107.4	109.3	111.2	113.0	115.0	116.9	118.9	120.8	122.8
5	48.0	102.6	104.4	106.3	108.1	110.0	111.9	113.8	115.7	117.7	119.7	121.7	123.7
10	53.0	103.3	105.1	107.0	108.8	110.7	112.6	114.6	116.5	118.5	120.5	122.5	124.5
20	64.2	104.5	106.4	108.3	110.2	112.2	114.1	116.1	118.1	120.1	122.1	124.1	126.2
25	70.5	105.2	107.1	109.0	110.9	112.9	114.8	116.8	118.8	120.8	122.9	124.9	127.0
30	77.2	105.8	107.7	109.6	111.6	113.6	115.5	117.6	119.6	121.6	123.7	125.7	127.8
35	84.4	106.4	108.3	110.3	112.3	114.2	116.3	118.3	120.3	122.4	124.4	126.5	128.6

FORANE FX 10 (R-408A)

Superheated Vapor - Enthalpy (BTU/lb)

Temp. [F]	Dew Pressure [psia]	SUPERHEATING (R)											
		0	10	20	30	40	50	60	70	80	90	100	110
40	92.1	107.0	108.9	110.9	112.9	114.9	117.0	119.0	121.0	123.1	125.2	127.3	129.4
45	100.3	107.5	109.5	111.5	113.6	115.6	117.6	119.7	121.8	123.9	126.0	128.1	130.2
50	109.0	108.1	110.1	112.1	114.2	116.2	118.3	120.4	122.5	124.6	126.7	128.9	131.0
55	118.3	108.6	110.7	112.7	114.8	116.9	119.0	121.1	123.2	125.3	127.5	129.6	131.8
60	128.2	109.1	111.2	113.3	115.4	117.5	119.6	121.8	123.9	126.1	128.2	130.4	132.6
65	138.7	109.6	111.7	113.9	116.0	118.1	120.3	122.4	124.6	126.8	128.9	131.1	133.4
70	149.8	110.1	112.3	114.4	116.6	118.7	120.9	123.1	125.3	127.5	129.7	131.9	134.1
75	161.6	110.6	112.7	114.9	117.1	119.3	121.5	123.7	125.9	128.1	130.4	132.6	134.9
80	174.1	111.0	113.2	115.4	117.7	119.9	122.1	124.3	126.6	128.8	131.1	133.3	135.6
85	187.2	111.4	113.7	115.9	118.2	120.4	122.7	124.9	127.2	129.5	131.8	134.0	136.3
90	201.1	111.7	114.1	116.4	118.7	121.0	123.2	125.5	127.8	130.1	132.4	134.7	137.1
95	215.8	112.1	114.5	116.8	119.1	121.5	123.8	126.1	128.4	130.8	133.1	135.4	137.8
100	231.3	112.4	114.8	117.2	119.6	122.0	124.3	126.7	129.0	131.4	133.7	136.1	138.5
105	247.5	112.7	115.1	117.6	120.0	122.4	124.8	127.2	129.6	132.0	134.4	136.8	139.2
110	264.7	112.9	115.4	118.0	120.4	122.9	125.3	127.7	130.2	132.6	135.0	137.4	139.8
115	282.6	113.1	115.7	118.3	120.8	123.3	125.8	128.3	130.7	133.2	135.6	138.0	140.5
120	301.5	113.2	115.9	118.6	121.2	123.7	126.2	128.7	131.2	133.7	136.2	138.7	141.1
125	321.3	113.2	116.1	118.8	121.5	124.1	126.7	129.2	131.7	134.3	136.8	139.3	141.8
130	342.1	113.2	116.2	119.0	121.8	124.4	127.1	129.7	132.2	134.8	137.3	139.9	142.4
135	363.8	113.1	116.3	119.2	122.0	124.8	127.4	130.1	132.7	135.3	137.9	140.4	143.0
140	386.6	113.0	116.3	119.3	122.2	125.0	127.8	130.5	133.2	135.8	138.4	141.0	143.6
145	410.5	112.7	116.2	119.4	122.4	125.3	128.1	130.9	133.6	136.3	138.9	141.6	144.2
150	435.4	112.3	116.1	119.4	122.6	125.5	128.4	131.2	134.0	136.7	139.4	142.1	144.8

FORANE FX 10 (R-408A)

Superheated Vapor - Entropy (BTU/lb.R)

Temp. [F]	Dew Pressure [psia]	SUPERHEATING (R)											
		0	10	20	30	40	50	60	70	80	90	100	110
-80	5.7	0.241	0.245	0.249	0.253	0.257	0.261	0.265	0.268	0.272	0.276	0.280	0.283
-75	6.6	0.239	0.243	0.247	0.251	0.255	0.259	0.263	0.267	0.270	0.274	0.278	0.281
-70	7.7	0.238	0.242	0.246	0.250	0.254	0.257	0.261	0.265	0.269	0.272	0.276	0.280
-65	8.9	0.236	0.240	0.244	0.248	0.252	0.256	0.260	0.263	0.267	0.271	0.275	0.278
-60	10.3	0.235	0.239	0.243	0.247	0.251	0.254	0.258	0.262	0.266	0.269	0.273	0.277
-55	11.8	0.234	0.238	0.242	0.245	0.249	0.253	0.257	0.261	0.264	0.268	0.272	0.275
-50	13.5	0.232	0.236	0.240	0.244	0.248	0.252	0.256	0.259	0.263	0.267	0.270	0.274
-45	15.4	0.231	0.235	0.239	0.243	0.247	0.251	0.254	0.258	0.262	0.265	0.269	0.273
-40	17.5	0.230	0.234	0.238	0.242	0.246	0.249	0.253	0.257	0.260	0.264	0.268	0.271
-35	19.8	0.229	0.233	0.237	0.241	0.245	0.248	0.252	0.256	0.259	0.263	0.267	0.270
-30	22.3	0.228	0.232	0.236	0.240	0.243	0.247	0.251	0.255	0.258	0.262	0.266	0.269
-25	25.1	0.227	0.231	0.235	0.239	0.242	0.246	0.250	0.254	0.257	0.261	0.264	0.268
-20	28.1	0.226	0.230	0.234	0.238	0.242	0.245	0.249	0.253	0.256	0.260	0.264	0.267
-15	31.5	0.225	0.229	0.233	0.237	0.241	0.244	0.248	0.252	0.255	0.259	0.263	0.266
-10	35.1	0.225	0.228	0.232	0.236	0.240	0.244	0.247	0.251	0.255	0.258	0.262	0.265
-5	39.1	0.224	0.228	0.231	0.235	0.239	0.243	0.246	0.250	0.254	0.257	0.261	0.264
0	43.4	0.223	0.227	0.231	0.234	0.238	0.242	0.246	0.249	0.253	0.257	0.260	0.264
5	48.0	0.222	0.226	0.230	0.234	0.238	0.241	0.245	0.249	0.252	0.256	0.259	0.263
10	53.0	0.222	0.225	0.229	0.233	0.237	0.241	0.244	0.248	0.251	0.255	0.259	0.262
20	64.2	0.220	0.224	0.228	0.232	0.236	0.239	0.243	0.247	0.250	0.254	0.257	0.261
25	70.5	0.220	0.224	0.227	0.231	0.235	0.239	0.242	0.246	0.250	0.253	0.257	0.260
30	77.2	0.219	0.223	0.227	0.231	0.234	0.238	0.242	0.245	0.249	0.253	0.256	0.260
35	84.4	0.218	0.222	0.226	0.230	0.234	0.237	0.241	0.245	0.248	0.252	0.255	0.259

FORANE FX 10 (R-408A)
Superheated Vapor - Entropy (BTU/lb.R)

Temp. [F]	Dew Pressure [psia]	SUPERHEATING (R)											
		0	10	20	30	40	50	60	70	80	90	100	110
40	92.1	0.218	0.222	0.226	0.229	0.233	0.237	0.241	0.244	0.248	0.251	0.255	0.258
45	100.3	0.217	0.221	0.225	0.229	0.233	0.236	0.240	0.244	0.247	0.251	0.254	0.258
50	109.0	0.217	0.221	0.225	0.228	0.232	0.236	0.240	0.243	0.247	0.250	0.254	0.257
55	118.3	0.216	0.220	0.224	0.228	0.232	0.235	0.239	0.243	0.246	0.250	0.253	0.257
60	128.2	0.216	0.220	0.223	0.227	0.231	0.235	0.239	0.242	0.246	0.249	0.253	0.257
65	138.7	0.215	0.219	0.223	0.227	0.231	0.234	0.238	0.242	0.245	0.249	0.253	0.256
70	149.8	0.214	0.219	0.222	0.226	0.230	0.234	0.238	0.241	0.245	0.249	0.252	0.256
75	161.6	0.214	0.218	0.222	0.226	0.230	0.234	0.237	0.241	0.245	0.248	0.252	0.255
80	174.1	0.213	0.217	0.221	0.225	0.229	0.233	0.237	0.241	0.244	0.248	0.251	0.255
85	187.2	0.213	0.217	0.221	0.225	0.229	0.233	0.236	0.240	0.244	0.247	0.251	0.254
90	201.1	0.212	0.216	0.220	0.224	0.228	0.232	0.236	0.240	0.243	0.247	0.251	0.254
95	215.8	0.212	0.216	0.220	0.224	0.228	0.232	0.236	0.239	0.243	0.247	0.250	0.254
100	231.3	0.211	0.215	0.219	0.223	0.227	0.231	0.235	0.239	0.243	0.246	0.250	0.253
105	247.5	0.210	0.215	0.219	0.223	0.227	0.231	0.235	0.238	0.242	0.246	0.249	0.253
110	264.7	0.209	0.214	0.218	0.222	0.226	0.230	0.234	0.238	0.242	0.246	0.249	0.253
115	282.6	0.209	0.213	0.218	0.222	0.226	0.230	0.234	0.238	0.241	0.245	0.249	0.252
120	301.5	0.208	0.213	0.217	0.221	0.225	0.229	0.233	0.237	0.241	0.245	0.248	0.252
125	321.3	0.207	0.212	0.216	0.221	0.225	0.229	0.233	0.237	0.241	0.244	0.248	0.252
130	342.1	0.206	0.211	0.216	0.220	0.224	0.228	0.233	0.236	0.240	0.244	0.248	0.251
135	363.8	0.205	0.210	0.215	0.219	0.224	0.228	0.232	0.236	0.240	0.244	0.247	0.251
140	386.6	0.204	0.209	0.214	0.219	0.223	0.227	0.232	0.236	0.240	0.243	0.247	0.251
145	410.5	0.202	0.208	0.213	0.218	0.223	0.227	0.231	0.235	0.239	0.243	0.247	0.250
150	435.4	0.201	0.207	0.212	0.217	0.222	0.226	0.231	0.235	0.239	0.243	0.246	0.250

FORANE FX 10 (R-408A)

Superheated Vapor - Specific Volume (ft^3/lb)

Temp. [F]	Dew Pressure [psia]	SUPERHEATING (R)											
		0	10	20	30	40	50	60	70	80	90	100	110
-80	5.7	8.144	8.367	8.590	8.812	9.034	9.256	9.478	9.699	9.921	10.14	10.36	10.58
-75	6.6	7.051	7.243	7.434	7.625	7.816	8.007	8.197	8.387	8.577	8.767	8.956	9.146
-70	7.7	6.131	6.296	6.461	6.626	6.791	6.955	7.119	7.283	7.447	7.611	7.774	7.938
-65	8.9	5.352	5.495	5.638	5.781	5.924	6.066	6.209	6.351	6.493	6.634	6.776	6.917
-60	10.3	4.689	4.814	4.939	5.063	5.188	5.312	5.435	5.559	5.682	5.806	5.929	6.052
-55	11.8	4.123	4.233	4.342	4.451	4.559	4.668	4.776	4.884	4.992	5.100	5.207	5.315
-50	13.5	3.638	3.734	3.830	3.926	4.021	4.116	4.211	4.306	4.401	4.495	4.590	4.684
-45	15.4	3.221	3.306	3.390	3.474	3.558	3.642	3.726	3.810	3.893	3.976	4.059	4.142
-40	17.5	2.860	2.935	3.010	3.085	3.159	3.233	3.307	3.381	3.455	3.528	3.602	3.675
-35	19.8	2.547	2.614	2.680	2.747	2.813	2.879	2.944	3.010	3.075	3.141	3.206	3.271
-30	22.3	2.275	2.334	2.394	2.453	2.512	2.571	2.629	2.688	2.746	2.804	2.862	2.920
-25	25.1	2.037	2.090	2.144	2.197	2.249	2.302	2.354	2.406	2.458	2.510	2.562	2.614
-20	28.1	1.829	1.877	1.925	1.972	2.019	2.067	2.114	2.160	2.207	2.254	2.300	2.346
-15	31.5	1.646	1.689	1.732	1.775	1.818	1.860	1.902	1.945	1.987	2.028	2.070	2.112
-10	35.1	1.485	1.524	1.563	1.601	1.640	1.678	1.717	1.755	1.793	1.830	1.868	1.906
-5	39.1	1.342	1.378	1.413	1.448	1.483	1.518	1.552	1.587	1.621	1.655	1.690	1.723
0	43.4	1.216	1.248	1.280	1.312	1.344	1.376	1.407	1.438	1.470	1.501	1.532	1.562
5	48.0	1.103	1.133	1.163	1.192	1.221	1.250	1.278	1.307	1.335	1.363	1.391	1.419
10	53.0	1.003	1.031	1.058	1.084	1.111	1.137	1.163	1.189	1.215	1.241	1.267	1.292
20	64.2	0.834	0.857	0.880	0.903	0.925	0.947	0.969	0.991	1.013	1.035	1.056	1.078
25	70.5	0.762	0.784	0.805	0.826	0.846	0.867	0.887	0.907	0.927	0.947	0.967	0.987
30	77.2	0.698	0.718	0.737	0.757	0.776	0.795	0.813	0.832	0.851	0.869	0.887	0.905
35	84.4	0.640	0.658	0.676	0.694	0.712	0.730	0.747	0.764	0.781	0.798	0.815	0.832

FORANE FX 10 (R-408A)

Superheated Vapor - Specific Volume (ft^3/lb)

Temp. [F]	Dew Pressure [psia]	SUPERHEATING (R) 0	10	20	30	40	50	60	70	80	90	100	110
40	92.1	0.587	0.604	0.621	0.638	0.654	0.671	0.687	0.703	0.719	0.735	0.750	0.766
45	100.3	0.540	0.556	0.572	0.587	0.603	0.618	0.633	0.648	0.662	0.677	0.692	0.706
50	109.0	0.496	0.512	0.526	0.541	0.555	0.570	0.584	0.598	0.611	0.625	0.638	0.652
55	118.3	0.457	0.471	0.485	0.499	0.513	0.526	0.539	0.552	0.565	0.578	0.590	0.603
60	128.2	0.422	0.435	0.448	0.461	0.474	0.486	0.499	0.511	0.523	0.535	0.546	0.558
65	138.7	0.389	0.402	0.414	0.426	0.438	0.450	0.462	0.473	0.484	0.496	0.507	0.517
70	149.8	0.359	0.371	0.383	0.395	0.406	0.417	0.428	0.439	0.449	0.460	0.470	0.480
75	161.6	0.332	0.344	0.355	0.366	0.376	0.387	0.397	0.407	0.417	0.427	0.437	0.447
80	174.1	0.307	0.318	0.329	0.339	0.349	0.359	0.369	0.379	0.388	0.397	0.407	0.416
85	187.2	0.284	0.295	0.305	0.315	0.324	0.334	0.343	0.352	0.361	0.370	0.379	0.387
90	201.1	0.263	0.273	0.283	0.292	0.302	0.311	0.319	0.328	0.337	0.345	0.353	0.361
95	215.8	0.244	0.253	0.263	0.272	0.281	0.289	0.298	0.306	0.314	0.322	0.330	0.337
100	231.3	0.226	0.235	0.244	0.253	0.261	0.270	0.278	0.285	0.293	0.301	0.308	0.315
105	247.5	0.209	0.218	0.227	0.235	0.244	0.251	0.259	0.267	0.274	0.281	0.288	0.295
110	264.7	0.194	0.203	0.211	0.219	0.227	0.235	0.242	0.249	0.256	0.263	0.270	0.276
115	282.6	0.179	0.188	0.197	0.204	0.212	0.219	0.226	0.233	0.240	0.246	0.253	0.259
120	301.5	0.166	0.175	0.183	0.191	0.198	0.205	0.212	0.218	0.225	0.231	0.237	0.243
125	321.3	0.154	0.162	0.170	0.178	0.185	0.192	0.198	0.205	0.211	0.217	0.223	0.228
130	342.1	0.142	0.151	0.159	0.166	0.173	0.179	0.186	0.192	0.198	0.204	0.209	0.215
135	363.8	0.131	0.140	0.148	0.155	0.162	0.168	0.174	0.180	0.186	0.191	0.197	0.202
140	386.6	0.121	0.130	0.138	0.145	0.151	0.158	0.163	0.169	0.175	0.180	0.185	0.190
145	410.5	0.111	0.120	0.128	0.135	0.142	0.148	0.153	0.159	0.164	0.169	0.174	0.179
150	435.4	0.102	0.112	0.119	0.126	0.133	0.139	0.144	0.150	0.155	0.160	0.164	0.169

FORANE FX 10 (R-408A)

Superheated Vapor - Density (lb/ft^3)

Temp. [F]	Dew Pressure [psia]	SUPERHEATING (R) 0	10	20	30	40	50	60	70	80	90	100	110
-80	5.7	0.123	0.120	0.116	0.113	0.111	0.108	0.106	0.103	0.101	0.099	0.097	0.094
-75	6.6	0.142	0.138	0.135	0.131	0.128	0.125	0.122	0.119	0.117	0.114	0.112	0.109
-70	7.7	0.163	0.159	0.155	0.151	0.147	0.144	0.140	0.137	0.134	0.131	0.129	0.126
-65	8.9	0.187	0.182	0.177	0.173	0.169	0.165	0.161	0.157	0.154	0.151	0.148	0.145
-60	10.3	0.213	0.208	0.202	0.197	0.193	0.188	0.184	0.180	0.176	0.172	0.169	0.165
-55	11.8	0.243	0.236	0.230	0.225	0.219	0.214	0.209	0.205	0.200	0.196	0.192	0.188
-50	13.5	0.275	0.268	0.261	0.255	0.249	0.243	0.237	0.232	0.227	0.222	0.218	0.213
-45	15.4	0.310	0.303	0.295	0.288	0.281	0.275	0.268	0.262	0.257	0.252	0.246	0.241
-40	17.5	0.350	0.341	0.332	0.324	0.317	0.309	0.302	0.296	0.289	0.283	0.278	0.272
-35	19.8	0.393	0.383	0.373	0.364	0.356	0.347	0.340	0.332	0.325	0.318	0.312	0.306
-30	22.3	0.440	0.428	0.418	0.408	0.398	0.389	0.380	0.372	0.364	0.357	0.349	0.342
-25	25.1	0.491	0.478	0.467	0.455	0.445	0.434	0.425	0.416	0.407	0.398	0.390	0.383
-20	28.1	0.547	0.533	0.520	0.507	0.495	0.484	0.473	0.463	0.453	0.444	0.435	0.426
-15	31.5	0.608	0.592	0.577	0.563	0.550	0.538	0.526	0.514	0.503	0.493	0.483	0.474
-10	35.1	0.674	0.656	0.640	0.624	0.610	0.596	0.583	0.570	0.558	0.546	0.535	0.525
-5	39.1	0.745	0.726	0.708	0.691	0.674	0.659	0.644	0.630	0.617	0.604	0.592	0.580
0	43.4	0.823	0.801	0.781	0.762	0.744	0.727	0.711	0.695	0.680	0.666	0.653	0.640
5	48.0	0.906	0.883	0.860	0.839	0.819	0.800	0.782	0.765	0.749	0.734	0.719	0.704
10	53.0	0.997	0.970	0.946	0.922	0.900	0.879	0.860	0.841	0.823	0.806	0.789	0.774
20	64.2	1.199	1.167	1.136	1.108	1.081	1.056	1.032	1.009	0.987	0.966	0.947	0.928
25	70.5	1.312	1.276	1.242	1.211	1.182	1.154	1.127	1.102	1.078	1.056	1.034	1.013
30	77.2	1.433	1.393	1.356	1.322	1.289	1.258	1.229	1.202	1.176	1.151	1.127	1.105
35	84.4	1.563	1.519	1.479	1.440	1.405	1.371	1.339	1.309	1.280	1.253	1.227	1.202

FORANE FX 10 (R-408A)

Superheated Vapor - Density (lb/ft^3)

Temp. [F]	Dew Pressure [psia]	SUPERHEATING (R)											
		0	10	20	30	40	50	60	70	80	90	100	110
40	92.1	1.703	1.655	1.610	1.567	1.528	1.491	1.456	1.422	1.391	1.361	1.333	1.306
45	100.3	1.853	1.800	1.750	1.703	1.660	1.619	1.580	1.544	1.510	1.477	1.446	1.416
50	109.0	2.014	1.955	1.900	1.848	1.801	1.756	1.713	1.674	1.636	1.600	1.566	1.534
55	118.3	2.187	2.121	2.060	2.004	1.951	1.901	1.855	1.811	1.770	1.731	1.694	1.659
60	128.2	2.372	2.299	2.231	2.169	2.111	2.057	2.006	1.958	1.913	1.870	1.830	1.792
65	138.7	2.571	2.489	2.415	2.346	2.282	2.222	2.166	2.114	2.065	2.018	1.974	1.932
70	149.8	2.783	2.693	2.610	2.534	2.463	2.398	2.337	2.279	2.226	2.175	2.127	2.081
75	161.6	3.012	2.911	2.819	2.735	2.657	2.585	2.518	2.455	2.396	2.341	2.289	2.239
80	174.1	3.257	3.144	3.042	2.949	2.863	2.784	2.710	2.641	2.577	2.517	2.460	2.406
85	187.2	3.519	3.393	3.280	3.177	3.082	2.995	2.914	2.839	2.769	2.703	2.641	2.582
90	201.1	3.802	3.660	3.534	3.419	3.315	3.219	3.130	3.048	2.971	2.899	2.832	2.768
95	215.8	4.105	3.946	3.805	3.678	3.562	3.457	3.359	3.269	3.185	3.107	3.034	2.965
100	231.3	4.432	4.253	4.095	3.953	3.825	3.709	3.602	3.503	3.412	3.326	3.247	3.172
105	247.5	4.785	4.582	4.404	4.247	4.105	3.976	3.859	3.751	3.651	3.558	3.471	3.390
110	264.7	5.165	4.934	4.735	4.559	4.402	4.260	4.131	4.012	3.903	3.802	3.707	3.619
115	282.6	5.577	5.313	5.088	4.892	4.717	4.560	4.418	4.289	4.169	4.059	3.956	3.860
120	301.5	6.023	5.721	5.466	5.246	5.052	4.879	4.722	4.580	4.450	4.329	4.218	4.114
125	321.3	6.509	6.160	5.871	5.623	5.407	5.215	5.043	4.887	4.745	4.614	4.493	4.380
130	342.1	7.040	6.634	6.304	6.025	5.784	5.572	5.382	5.211	5.056	4.913	4.781	4.659
135	363.8	7.622	7.147	6.768	6.454	6.185	5.949	5.740	5.553	5.383	5.227	5.084	4.952
140	386.6	8.263	7.701	7.266	6.910	6.609	6.348	6.117	5.912	5.726	5.557	5.402	5.258
145	410.5	8.976	8.304	7.800	7.396	7.059	6.769	6.515	6.289	6.087	5.902	5.734	5.579
150	435.4	9.775	8.959	8.373	7.914	7.535	7.213	6.933	6.686	6.465	6.264	6.082	5.914

Product Information

Forane FX 56 (R-409A) Saturated Properties

Pressure [psia]	Saturated Liquid T Bubble [F]	Density [lb/ft^3]	Enthalpy [BTU/lb]	Entropy [BTU/lb.R]	Saturated Vapor T Dew [F]	Density [lb/ft^3]	Enthalpy [BTU/lb]	Entropy [BTU/lb.R]	Heat vaporizati [BTU/
4	-76.1	92.08	-8.5	-0.021	-60.7	0.092	92.1	0.237	100
6	-62.9	90.88	-5.5	-0.013	-47.5	0.134	93.9	0.233	99
8	-52.9	89.96	-3.1	-0.007	-37.6	0.175	95.2	0.230	98
10	-44.7	89.20	-1.1	-0.003	-29.4	0.215	96.3	0.228	97
12	-37.8	88.55	0.5	0.001	-22.5	0.255	97.2	0.227	96
14	-31.7	87.97	2.0	0.005	-16.5	0.295	98.0	0.226	96
16	-26.3	87.45	3.4	0.008	-11.1	0.334	98.8	0.225	95
18	-21.4	86.97	4.6	0.011	-6.2	0.373	99.4	0.224	94
20	-16.9	86.53	5.7	0.013	-1.7	0.411	100.0	0.223	94
25	-7.0	85.56	8.2	0.019	8.1	0.507	101.3	0.221	93
30	1.5	84.71	10.3	0.023	16.4	0.601	102.4	0.220	92
35	8.9	83.95	12.2	0.027	23.8	0.695	103.3	0.219	91
40	15.5	83.26	14.0	0.031	30.4	0.789	104.2	0.218	90
45	21.6	82.63	15.6	0.034	36.3	0.882	104.9	0.218	89
50	27.1	82.04	17.1	0.037	41.8	0.975	105.6	0.217	88
60	37.0	80.97	19.7	0.043	51.5	1.160	106.8	0.216	87
70	45.8	80.00	22.2	0.048	60.1	1.346	107.8	0.215	85
80	53.6	79.12	24.4	0.052	67.8	1.532	108.7	0.214	84
90	60.7	78.30	26.4	0.056	74.8	1.719	109.5	0.214	83
100	67.3	77.52	28.3	0.059	81.2	1.907	110.2	0.213	82
110	73.4	76.79	30.1	0.063	87.1	2.096	110.9	0.212	80
120	79.1	76.10	31.8	0.066	92.7	2.286	111.4	0.212	79
130	84.5	75.43	33.4	0.069	97.9	2.477	112.0	0.212	78
140	89.5	74.79	34.9	0.071	102.8	2.670	112.4	0.211	77
150	94.3	74.17	36.4	0.074	107.4	2.865	112.9	0.211	76
160	98.9	73.57	37.8	0.077	111.8	3.061	113.3	0.210	75
170	103.3	72.99	39.2	0.079	116.0	3.260	113.7	0.210	74
180	107.4	72.42	40.5	0.081	120.0	3.460	114.0	0.210	73
190	111.5	71.87	41.8	0.084	123.9	3.663	114.3	0.209	72
200	115.3	71.32	43.1	0.086	127.6	3.868	114.6	0.209	71
210	119.1	70.79	44.3	0.088	131.2	4.075	114.9	0.208	70
220	122.7	70.26	45.5	0.090	134.6	4.285	115.1	0.208	69
230	126.2	69.75	46.7	0.092	137.9	4.497	115.3	0.208	68
240	129.5	69.24	47.9	0.094	141.1	4.712	115.5	0.207	67
250	132.8	68.73	49.0	0.096	144.3	4.930	115.7	0.207	66
260	136.0	68.23	50.1	0.097	147.3	5.151	115.9	0.207	65
280	142.1	67.25	52.3	0.101	153.1	5.601	116.1	0.206	63
300	147.9	66.28	54.4	0.104	158.5	6.066	116.4	0.205	6
320	153.4	65.31	56.5	0.108	163.7	6.545	116.5	0.205	60
340	158.7	64.35	58.5	0.111	168.7	7.040	116.6	0.204	58
360	163.8	63.39	60.5	0.114	173.4	7.552	116.7	0.203	56
380	168.7	62.42	62.5	0.117	178.0	8.084	116.6	0.203	54
400	173.4	61.45	64.4	0.120	182.4	8.637	116.6	0.202	53
420	177.9	60.45	66.4	0.123	186.6	9.213	116.5	0.201	50
440	182.3	59.44	68.3	0.126	190.6	9.816	116.3	0.200	4

FORANE FX 56 (R-409A)

Superheated Vapor - Enthalpy (BTU/lb)

Temp. [F]	Dew Pressure [psia]	SUPERHEATING (R) 0	10	20	30	40	50	60	70	80	90	100	110
-80	2.1	89.5	90.9	92.3	93.7	95.2	96.6	98.1	99.6	101.1	102.6	104.2	105.7
-75	2.5	90.2	91.6	93.0	94.4	95.9	97.3	98.8	100.3	101.8	103.4	104.9	106.5
-70	2.9	90.9	92.3	93.7	95.1	96.6	98.0	99.5	101.1	102.6	104.1	105.7	107.3
-65	3.5	91.5	92.9	94.4	95.8	97.3	98.8	100.3	101.8	103.3	104.9	106.5	108.1
-60	4.1	92.2	93.6	95.1	96.5	98.0	99.5	101.0	102.5	104.1	105.7	107.3	108.9
-55	4.8	92.9	94.3	95.7	97.2	98.7	100.2	101.7	103.3	104.8	106.4	108.0	109.7
-50	5.6	93.5	95.0	96.4	97.9	99.4	100.9	102.5	104.0	105.6	107.2	108.8	110.4
-45	6.5	94.2	95.7	97.1	98.6	100.1	101.7	103.2	104.8	106.4	108.0	109.6	111.2
-40	7.5	94.9	96.3	97.8	99.3	100.9	102.4	103.9	105.5	107.1	108.7	110.4	112.0
-35	8.6	95.6	97.0	98.5	100.0	101.6	103.1	104.7	106.3	107.9	109.5	111.1	112.8
-30	9.9	96.2	97.7	99.2	100.7	102.3	103.8	105.4	107.0	108.6	110.3	111.9	113.6
-25	11.3	96.9	98.4	99.9	101.4	103.0	104.6	106.2	107.8	109.4	111.0	112.7	114.4
-20	12.8	97.6	99.1	100.6	102.2	103.7	105.3	106.9	108.5	110.2	111.8	113.5	115.2
-15	14.5	98.2	99.8	101.3	102.9	104.4	106.0	107.6	109.3	110.9	112.6	114.3	116.0
-10	16.4	98.9	100.4	102.0	103.6	105.2	106.8	108.4	110.0	111.7	113.4	115.1	116.8
-5	18.5	99.6	101.1	102.7	104.3	105.9	107.5	109.1	110.8	112.4	114.1	115.8	117.6
0	20.8	100.2	101.8	103.4	105.0	106.6	108.2	109.9	111.5	113.2	114.9	116.6	118.4
5	23.3	100.9	102.5	104.1	105.7	107.3	108.9	110.6	112.3	114.0	115.7	117.4	119.1
10	26.1	101.5	103.1	104.7	106.4	108.0	109.6	111.3	113.0	114.7	116.4	118.2	119.9
20	32.3	102.8	104.5	106.1	107.7	109.4	111.1	112.8	114.5	116.2	118.0	119.7	121.5
25	35.9	103.5	105.1	106.8	108.4	110.1	111.8	113.5	115.2	117.0	118.7	120.5	122.3
30	39.7	104.1	105.8	107.4	109.1	110.8	112.5	114.2	116.0	117.7	119.5	121.3	123.1
35	43.9	104.8	106.4	108.1	109.8	111.5	113.2	114.9	116.7	118.4	120.2	122.0	123.8

FORANE FX 56 (R-409A)

Superheated Vapor - Enthalpy (BTU/lb)

Temp. [F]	Dew Pressure [psia]	SUPERHEATING (R)											
		0	10	20	30	40	50	60	70	80	90	100	110
40	48.3	105.4	107.1	108.7	110.4	112.2	113.9	115.6	117.4	119.2	121.0	122.8	124.6
45	53.2	106.0	107.7	109.4	111.1	112.8	114.6	116.4	118.1	119.9	121.7	123.5	125.4
50	58.3	106.6	108.3	110.0	111.8	113.5	115.3	117.1	118.8	120.6	122.5	124.3	126.1
55	63.9	107.2	108.9	110.7	112.4	114.2	116.0	117.7	119.6	121.4	123.2	125.0	126.9
60	69.9	107.8	109.6	111.3	113.1	114.8	116.6	118.4	120.3	122.1	123.9	125.8	127.7
65	76.2	108.4	110.2	111.9	113.7	115.5	117.3	119.1	121.0	122.8	124.7	126.5	128.4
70	83.1	109.0	110.8	112.5	114.3	116.1	118.0	119.8	121.6	123.5	125.4	127.3	129.2
75	90.3	109.5	111.3	113.1	115.0	116.8	118.6	120.5	122.3	124.2	126.1	128.0	129.9
80	98.1	110.1	111.9	113.7	115.6	117.4	119.3	121.1	123.0	124.9	126.8	128.7	130.6
85	106.3	110.6	112.5	114.3	116.2	118.0	119.9	121.8	123.7	125.6	127.5	129.4	131.4
90	115.1	111.2	113.0	114.9	116.8	118.6	120.5	122.4	124.3	126.3	128.2	130.1	132.1
95	124.4	111.7	113.6	115.4	117.3	119.2	121.1	123.1	125.0	126.9	128.9	130.8	132.8
100	134.3	112.2	114.1	116.0	117.9	119.8	121.7	123.7	125.6	127.6	129.5	131.5	133.5
105	144.8	112.7	114.6	116.5	118.5	120.4	122.3	124.3	126.3	128.2	130.2	132.2	134.2
110	155.8	113.1	115.1	117.0	119.0	121.0	122.9	124.9	126.9	128.9	130.9	132.9	134.9
115	167.5	113.6	115.6	117.5	119.5	121.5	123.5	125.5	127.5	129.5	131.5	133.5	135.6
120	179.9	114.0	116.0	118.0	120.0	122.0	124.0	126.1	128.1	130.1	132.2	134.2	136.3
125	192.9	114.4	116.4	118.5	120.5	122.6	124.6	126.6	128.7	130.7	132.8	134.8	136.9
130	206.7	114.8	116.9	118.9	121.0	123.1	125.1	127.2	129.3	131.3	133.4	135.5	137.6
135	221.2	115.1	117.2	119.4	121.5	123.5	125.6	127.7	129.8	131.9	134.0	136.1	138.2
140	236.4	115.4	117.6	119.8	121.9	124.0	126.1	128.2	130.4	132.5	134.6	136.7	138.8
145	252.4	115.7	118.0	120.1	122.3	124.5	126.6	128.8	130.9	133.0	135.2	137.3	139.5
150	269.3	116.0	118.3	120.5	122.7	124.9	127.1	129.2	131.4	133.6	135.7	137.9	140.1

FORANE FX 56 (R-409A)

Superheated Vapor - Entropy (BTU/lb.R)

Temp. [F]	Dew Pressure [psia]	SUPERHEATING (R) 0	10	20	30	40	50	60	70	80	90	100	110
-80	2.1	0.243	0.247	0.250	0.254	0.257	0.261	0.264	0.267	0.271	0.274	0.277	0.281
-75	2.5	0.241	0.245	0.248	0.252	0.255	0.259	0.262	0.266	0.269	0.272	0.275	0.279
-70	2.9	0.240	0.243	0.247	0.250	0.254	0.257	0.260	0.264	0.267	0.270	0.273	0.277
-65	3.5	0.238	0.241	0.245	0.248	0.252	0.255	0.259	0.262	0.265	0.268	0.272	0.275
-60	4.1	0.236	0.240	0.243	0.247	0.250	0.254	0.257	0.260	0.263	0.267	0.270	0.273
-55	4.8	0.235	0.238	0.242	0.245	0.249	0.252	0.255	0.259	0.262	0.265	0.268	0.271
-50	5.6	0.233	0.237	0.240	0.244	0.247	0.250	0.254	0.257	0.260	0.264	0.267	0.270
-45	6.5	0.232	0.236	0.239	0.242	0.246	0.249	0.252	0.256	0.259	0.262	0.265	0.268
-40	7.5	0.231	0.234	0.238	0.241	0.244	0.248	0.251	0.254	0.257	0.261	0.264	0.267
-35	8.6	0.230	0.233	0.236	0.240	0.243	0.246	0.250	0.253	0.256	0.259	0.263	0.266
-30	9.9	0.228	0.232	0.235	0.239	0.242	0.245	0.248	0.252	0.255	0.258	0.261	0.264
-25	11.3	0.227	0.231	0.234	0.237	0.241	0.244	0.247	0.251	0.254	0.257	0.260	0.263
-20	12.8	0.226	0.230	0.233	0.236	0.240	0.243	0.246	0.249	0.253	0.256	0.259	0.262
-15	14.5	0.225	0.229	0.232	0.235	0.239	0.242	0.245	0.248	0.252	0.255	0.258	0.261
-10	16.4	0.224	0.228	0.231	0.234	0.238	0.241	0.244	0.247	0.251	0.254	0.257	0.260
-5	18.5	0.223	0.227	0.230	0.233	0.237	0.240	0.243	0.246	0.250	0.253	0.256	0.259
0	20.8	0.223	0.226	0.229	0.233	0.236	0.239	0.242	0.245	0.249	0.252	0.255	0.258
5	23.3	0.222	0.225	0.228	0.232	0.235	0.238	0.241	0.245	0.248	0.251	0.254	0.257
10	26.1	0.221	0.224	0.228	0.231	0.234	0.237	0.241	0.244	0.247	0.250	0.253	0.256
20	32.3	0.220	0.223	0.226	0.230	0.233	0.236	0.239	0.242	0.245	0.248	0.252	0.255
25	35.9	0.219	0.222	0.226	0.229	0.232	0.235	0.238	0.242	0.245	0.248	0.251	0.254
30	39.7	0.218	0.222	0.225	0.228	0.231	0.235	0.238	0.241	0.244	0.247	0.250	0.253
35	43.9	0.218	0.221	0.224	0.228	0.231	0.234	0.237	0.240	0.243	0.246	0.249	0.252

FORANE FX 56 (R-409A)

Superheated Vapor - Entropy (BTU/lb.R)

Temp. [F]	Dew Pressure [psia]	SUPERHEATING (R) 0	10	20	30	40	50	60	70	80	90	100	110
40	48.3	0.217	0.220	0.224	0.227	0.230	0.233	0.236	0.240	0.243	0.246	0.249	0.252
45	53.2	0.217	0.220	0.223	0.226	0.230	0.233	0.236	0.239	0.242	0.245	0.248	0.251
50	58.3	0.216	0.219	0.223	0.226	0.229	0.232	0.235	0.238	0.242	0.245	0.248	0.251
55	63.9	0.215	0.219	0.222	0.225	0.229	0.232	0.235	0.238	0.241	0.244	0.247	0.250
60	69.9	0.215	0.218	0.222	0.225	0.228	0.231	0.234	0.237	0.240	0.244	0.247	0.250
65	76.2	0.214	0.218	0.221	0.224	0.228	0.231	0.234	0.237	0.240	0.243	0.246	0.249
70	83.1	0.214	0.217	0.221	0.224	0.227	0.230	0.233	0.236	0.240	0.243	0.246	0.249
75	90.3	0.214	0.217	0.220	0.223	0.227	0.230	0.233	0.236	0.239	0.242	0.245	0.248
80	98.1	0.213	0.216	0.220	0.223	0.226	0.229	0.232	0.236	0.239	0.242	0.245	0.248
85	106.3	0.213	0.216	0.219	0.223	0.226	0.229	0.232	0.235	0.238	0.241	0.244	0.247
90	115.1	0.212	0.216	0.219	0.222	0.225	0.228	0.232	0.235	0.238	0.241	0.244	0.247
95	124.4	0.212	0.215	0.218	0.222	0.225	0.228	0.231	0.234	0.237	0.240	0.243	0.246
100	134.3	0.211	0.215	0.218	0.221	0.224	0.228	0.231	0.234	0.237	0.240	0.243	0.246
105	144.8	0.211	0.214	0.218	0.221	0.224	0.227	0.230	0.234	0.237	0.240	0.243	0.246
110	155.8	0.210	0.214	0.217	0.220	0.224	0.227	0.230	0.233	0.236	0.239	0.242	0.245
115	167.5	0.210	0.213	0.217	0.220	0.223	0.227	0.230	0.233	0.236	0.239	0.242	0.245
120	179.9	0.210	0.213	0.216	0.220	0.223	0.226	0.229	0.232	0.236	0.239	0.242	0.245
125	192.9	0.209	0.213	0.216	0.219	0.223	0.226	0.229	0.232	0.235	0.238	0.241	0.244
130	206.7	0.209	0.212	0.216	0.219	0.222	0.225	0.229	0.232	0.235	0.238	0.241	0.244
135	221.2	0.208	0.212	0.215	0.218	0.222	0.225	0.228	0.231	0.235	0.238	0.241	0.244
140	236.4	0.208	0.211	0.215	0.218	0.221	0.225	0.228	0.231	0.234	0.237	0.240	0.243
145	252.4	0.207	0.211	0.214	0.218	0.221	0.224	0.228	0.231	0.234	0.237	0.240	0.243
150	269.3	0.206	0.210	0.214	0.217	0.221	0.224	0.227	0.230	0.234	0.237	0.240	0.243

FORANE FX 56 (R-409A)

Superheated Vapor - Specific Volume (ft^3/lb)

Temp. [F]	Dew Pressure [psia]	SUPERHEATING (R) 0	10	20	30	40	50	60	70	80	90	100	110
-80	2.1	19.97	20.51	21.04	21.57	22.11	22.64	23.17	23.71	24.24	24.77	25.30	25.84
-75	2.5	16.94	17.39	17.84	18.29	18.73	19.18	19.63	20.08	20.52	20.97	21.42	21.86
-70	2.9	14.44	14.82	15.20	15.58	15.96	16.33	16.71	17.09	17.47	17.84	18.22	18.60
-65	3.5	12.37	12.69	13.02	13.34	13.66	13.98	14.30	14.62	14.94	15.26	15.57	15.89
-60	4.1	10.65	10.92	11.20	11.47	11.74	12.01	12.29	12.56	12.83	13.10	13.38	13.65
-55	4.8	9.203	9.438	9.672	9.906	10.14	10.37	10.61	10.84	11.07	11.31	11.54	11.77
-50	5.6	7.987	8.189	8.391	8.592	8.793	8.995	9.195	9.396	9.597	9.797	9.998	10.198
-45	6.5	6.959	7.134	7.308	7.483	7.657	7.830	8.004	8.177	8.351	8.524	8.697	8.870
-40	7.5	6.087	6.239	6.390	6.541	6.692	6.843	6.994	7.144	7.295	7.445	7.595	7.745
-35	8.6	5.343	5.475	5.607	5.739	5.871	6.002	6.134	6.265	6.396	6.527	6.658	6.788
-30	9.9	4.706	4.822	4.938	5.053	5.168	5.283	5.398	5.513	5.628	5.742	5.856	5.971
-25	11.3	4.159	4.261	4.362	4.464	4.565	4.666	4.767	4.868	4.968	5.069	5.169	5.270
-20	12.8	3.687	3.777	3.866	3.956	4.045	4.134	4.223	4.312	4.401	4.489	4.578	4.666
-15	14.5	3.278	3.358	3.437	3.516	3.595	3.674	3.753	3.832	3.910	3.988	4.067	4.145
-10	16.4	2.923	2.994	3.064	3.135	3.205	3.275	3.345	3.415	3.484	3.554	3.623	3.693
-5	18.5	2.614	2.677	2.740	2.802	2.865	2.927	2.990	3.052	3.114	3.176	3.238	3.299
0	20.8	2.343	2.399	2.456	2.512	2.568	2.624	2.679	2.735	2.790	2.846	2.901	2.956
5	23.3	2.106	2.156	2.207	2.257	2.307	2.358	2.407	2.457	2.507	2.556	2.606	2.655
10	26.1	1.897	1.943	1.988	2.033	2.079	2.124	2.168	2.213	2.258	2.302	2.347	2.391
20	32.3	1.550	1.587	1.624	1.661	1.698	1.735	1.772	1.808	1.845	1.881	1.917	1.953
25	35.9	1.405	1.439	1.473	1.507	1.540	1.574	1.607	1.640	1.673	1.706	1.739	1.771
30	39.7	1.277	1.308	1.338	1.369	1.400	1.430	1.460	1.490	1.520	1.550	1.580	1.610
35	43.9	1.162	1.190	1.218	1.246	1.274	1.302	1.330	1.357	1.384	1.412	1.439	1.466

FORANE FX 56 (R-409A)

Superheated Vapor - Specific Volume (ft^3/lb)

Temp. [F]	Dew Pressure [psia]	SUPERHEATING (R) 0	10	20	30	40	50	60	70	80	90	100	110
40	48.3	1.059	1.085	1.111	1.137	1.162	1.188	1.213	1.238	1.263	1.288	1.313	1.338
45	53.2	0.968	0.992	1.015	1.039	1.062	1.086	1.109	1.132	1.155	1.177	1.200	1.223
50	58.3	0.885	0.907	0.929	0.951	0.972	0.994	1.015	1.036	1.057	1.078	1.099	1.120
55	63.9	0.811	0.832	0.852	0.872	0.892	0.911	0.931	0.950	0.970	0.989	1.008	1.027
60	69.9	0.744	0.763	0.782	0.800	0.819	0.837	0.855	0.873	0.891	0.909	0.927	0.944
65	76.2	0.684	0.701	0.719	0.736	0.753	0.770	0.787	0.803	0.820	0.836	0.853	0.869
70	83.1	0.629	0.646	0.662	0.678	0.694	0.709	0.725	0.740	0.756	0.771	0.786	0.801
75	90.3	0.580	0.595	0.610	0.625	0.640	0.654	0.669	0.683	0.697	0.711	0.726	0.740
80	98.1	0.535	0.549	0.563	0.577	0.591	0.604	0.618	0.631	0.644	0.658	0.671	0.684
85	106.3	0.494	0.507	0.520	0.533	0.546	0.559	0.571	0.584	0.596	0.609	0.621	0.633
90	115.1	0.456	0.469	0.481	0.493	0.505	0.517	0.529	0.541	0.552	0.564	0.575	0.587
95	124.4	0.422	0.434	0.446	0.457	0.468	0.480	0.491	0.502	0.513	0.523	0.534	0.545
100	134.3	0.391	0.402	0.413	0.424	0.434	0.445	0.455	0.466	0.476	0.486	0.496	0.506
105	144.8	0.362	0.373	0.383	0.393	0.403	0.413	0.423	0.433	0.443	0.452	0.461	0.471
110	155.8	0.336	0.346	0.356	0.365	0.375	0.384	0.394	0.403	0.412	0.421	0.430	0.438
115	167.5	0.311	0.321	0.331	0.340	0.349	0.358	0.367	0.375	0.384	0.392	0.401	0.409
120	179.9	0.289	0.298	0.307	0.316	0.325	0.333	0.342	0.350	0.358	0.366	0.374	0.381
125	192.9	0.269	0.277	0.286	0.294	0.303	0.311	0.319	0.326	0.334	0.342	0.349	0.356
130	206.7	0.250	0.258	0.266	0.274	0.282	0.290	0.297	0.305	0.312	0.319	0.326	0.333
135	221.2	0.232	0.240	0.248	0.256	0.263	0.271	0.278	0.285	0.292	0.299	0.305	0.312
140	236.4	0.216	0.224	0.231	0.239	0.246	0.253	0.260	0.266	0.273	0.280	0.286	0.292
145	252.4	0.201	0.208	0.216	0.223	0.230	0.236	0.243	0.249	0.256	0.262	0.268	0.274
150	269.3	0.187	0.194	0.201	0.208	0.215	0.221	0.228	0.234	0.240	0.246	0.251	0.257

FORANE FX 56 (R-409A)

Superheated Vapor - Density (lb/ft^3)

Temp. [F]	Dew Pressure [psia]	SUPERHEATING (R) 0	10	20	30	40	50	60	70	80	90	100	110
-80	2.1	0.050	0.049	0.048	0.046	0.045	0.044	0.043	0.042	0.041	0.040	0.040	0.039
-75	2.5	0.059	0.058	0.056	0.055	0.053	0.052	0.051	0.050	0.049	0.048	0.047	0.046
-70	2.9	0.069	0.067	0.066	0.064	0.063	0.061	0.060	0.059	0.057	0.056	0.055	0.054
-65	3.5	0.081	0.079	0.077	0.075	0.073	0.072	0.070	0.068	0.067	0.066	0.064	0.063
-60	4.1	0.094	0.092	0.089	0.087	0.085	0.083	0.081	0.080	0.078	0.076	0.075	0.073
-55	4.8	0.109	0.106	0.103	0.101	0.099	0.096	0.094	0.092	0.090	0.088	0.087	0.085
-50	5.6	0.125	0.122	0.119	0.116	0.114	0.111	0.109	0.106	0.104	0.102	0.100	0.098
-45	6.5	0.144	0.140	0.137	0.134	0.131	0.128	0.125	0.122	0.120	0.117	0.115	0.113
-40	7.5	0.164	0.160	0.156	0.153	0.149	0.146	0.143	0.140	0.137	0.134	0.132	0.129
-35	8.6	0.187	0.183	0.178	0.174	0.170	0.167	0.163	0.160	0.156	0.153	0.150	0.147
-30	9.9	0.212	0.207	0.203	0.198	0.193	0.189	0.185	0.181	0.178	0.174	0.171	0.167
-25	11.3	0.240	0.235	0.229	0.224	0.219	0.214	0.210	0.205	0.201	0.197	0.193	0.190
-20	12.8	0.271	0.265	0.259	0.253	0.247	0.242	0.237	0.232	0.227	0.223	0.218	0.214
-15	14.5	0.305	0.298	0.291	0.284	0.278	0.272	0.266	0.261	0.256	0.251	0.246	0.241
-10	16.4	0.342	0.334	0.326	0.319	0.312	0.305	0.299	0.293	0.287	0.281	0.276	0.271
-5	18.5	0.383	0.374	0.365	0.357	0.349	0.342	0.334	0.328	0.321	0.315	0.309	0.303
0	20.8	0.427	0.417	0.407	0.398	0.389	0.381	0.373	0.366	0.358	0.351	0.345	0.338
5	23.3	0.475	0.464	0.453	0.443	0.433	0.424	0.415	0.407	0.399	0.391	0.384	0.377
10	26.1	0.527	0.515	0.503	0.492	0.481	0.471	0.461	0.452	0.443	0.434	0.426	0.418
20	32.3	0.645	0.630	0.616	0.602	0.589	0.576	0.564	0.553	0.542	0.532	0.522	0.512
25	35.9	0.712	0.695	0.679	0.664	0.649	0.636	0.622	0.610	0.598	0.586	0.575	0.565
30	39.7	0.783	0.765	0.747	0.730	0.715	0.699	0.685	0.671	0.658	0.645	0.633	0.621
35	43.9	0.861	0.840	0.821	0.802	0.785	0.768	0.752	0.737	0.722	0.708	0.695	0.682

FORANE FX 56 (R-409A)

Superheated Vapor - Density (lb/ft^3)

Temp. [F]	Dew Pressure [psia]	SUPERHEATING (R) 0	10	20	30	40	50	60	70	80	90	100	110
40	48.3	0.944	0.921	0.900	0.880	0.860	0.842	0.824	0.808	0.792	0.776	0.762	0.748
45	53.2	1.033	1.008	0.985	0.963	0.941	0.921	0.902	0.884	0.866	0.849	0.833	0.818
50	58.3	1.130	1.102	1.076	1.052	1.028	1.006	0.985	0.965	0.946	0.927	0.910	0.893
55	63.9	1.233	1.203	1.174	1.147	1.122	1.097	1.074	1.052	1.031	1.011	0.992	0.973
60	69.9	1.344	1.310	1.279	1.249	1.221	1.195	1.169	1.145	1.122	1.100	1.079	1.059
65	76.2	1.462	1.426	1.391	1.359	1.328	1.299	1.271	1.245	1.220	1.196	1.173	1.151
70	83.1	1.589	1.549	1.511	1.476	1.442	1.410	1.380	1.351	1.323	1.297	1.272	1.248
75	90.3	1.725	1.681	1.640	1.600	1.564	1.529	1.495	1.464	1.434	1.406	1.378	1.352
80	98.1	1.871	1.822	1.776	1.734	1.693	1.655	1.619	1.584	1.552	1.521	1.491	1.463
85	106.3	2.026	1.973	1.923	1.876	1.831	1.790	1.750	1.713	1.677	1.643	1.611	1.580
90	115.1	2.192	2.133	2.078	2.027	1.978	1.933	1.890	1.849	1.810	1.773	1.738	1.704
95	124.4	2.370	2.305	2.245	2.188	2.135	2.085	2.038	1.993	1.951	1.911	1.873	1.836
100	134.3	2.560	2.488	2.422	2.360	2.302	2.247	2.196	2.147	2.101	2.057	2.016	1.976
105	144.8	2.763	2.684	2.610	2.542	2.479	2.419	2.363	2.310	2.260	2.212	2.167	2.124
110	155.8	2.979	2.892	2.811	2.736	2.667	2.601	2.540	2.482	2.428	2.376	2.327	2.281
115	167.5	3.211	3.114	3.025	2.943	2.867	2.795	2.728	2.665	2.606	2.550	2.497	2.446
120	179.9	3.458	3.351	3.253	3.163	3.079	3.001	2.928	2.859	2.795	2.734	2.676	2.621
125	192.9	3.723	3.604	3.496	3.396	3.304	3.219	3.139	3.064	2.994	2.928	2.865	2.806
130	206.7	4.006	3.874	3.754	3.645	3.543	3.450	3.362	3.281	3.204	3.133	3.065	3.001
135	221.2	4.310	4.163	4.030	3.908	3.797	3.694	3.599	3.510	3.427	3.349	3.275	3.206
140	236.4	4.635	4.470	4.323	4.189	4.067	3.954	3.850	3.753	3.662	3.577	3.497	3.422
145	252.4	4.984	4.800	4.635	4.487	4.352	4.229	4.115	4.009	3.910	3.818	3.731	3.650
150	269.3	5.358	5.152	4.969	4.804	4.656	4.520	4.395	4.279	4.172	4.072	3.978	3.889

elf atochem

ATO

Refrigeration Case History Forane® 134a

Retrofitting Automotive Air Conditioners from R-12 to Forane® 134a

. . and replacing mineral oil ith Planetelf® PAG lubricant

Automotive air conditioners, also known as mobile air nditioners (MACs), even though small in size do not lack complexity. MACs pose a special problem for retrofit- g due to the presence of elastomer hoses (several mate- s); variable system operation (compressor RPM is a ltiple of engine RPM); multitude of compressor types tary vane, piston, scroll, etc.); expansion device type ed orifice tube or thermal expansion valve (TXV)), etc. of the above, plus a variety of vehicle specific prob- ns, such as age, geographic location, etc. make retrofit- g a MAC a challenging project.

All refrigerant and system handling regulations that ly to stationary air conditioners and refrigeration units, o apply to MACs. In addition, a set of Society of Auto- tive Engineers (SAE) J-standards specific to mobile ap- cations also apply. One of the most important regula- ns deals with the retrofitting of the service ports. Typi- y, MACs have 2 service ports, one on each side of the stem. The high side is a 3/8" flare fitting and the low e a standard 7/16" refrigeration flare fitting, both with external threads. After a system retrofit is completed, these fittings must be changed to Forane 134a approved fittings per SAE J-639 (internal, metric threads) in such a way that the CFC 12 original fittings are permanently disabled.

Regarding the refrigerant choice for a retrofit, overwhelmingly, the mobile air conditioning industry has chosen HFC 134a as the leading candidate and Elf Atochem fully supports this position. However, while HFC 134a is the only pure refrigerant available, there are several other candidates in the market in the form of blends, and servicemen should be aware of them to avoid possible cross contamination of refrigerants in their equipment. The Mobile Air Conditioning Society (M.A.C.S.) has petitioned the U.S. EPA to ban the use of any refrigerant other than HFC 134a for MAC retrofits.

For lubricant oils, there is currently a choice of 2 synthetic materials: Poly Alkaline Glycols (PAGs) or Polyolesters (POEs). Although it varies with the car manufacturer, most have chosen PAGs as their Original Equipment Manufacturers' (OEM) fluid, as well as their retrofit fluid. However, in some instances a manufacturer may recommend the use of a PAG for OEM and a POE for retrofits. Be sure to check with the vehicle manufacturer for any oil specifications if available. If no oils are specified for retrofits, then use the recommended OEM oil.

Elf Atochem North America, Inc.
Fluorochemicals
2000 Market Street
Philadelphia, PA 19103
1-800-245-5858

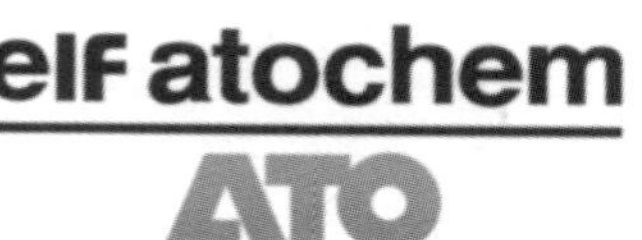

Follow this step-by-step guide to re
CFC 12 to the new

The retrofit procedure that follows is a recommendation developed and tested by Elf Atochem in a fleet of vehicles, and is based on SAE, M.A.C.S. and industry recommendations. In general, if a vehicle manufacturer has developed a specific retrofit procedure, that procedure and not the one listed here should be followed.

1. *Thoroughly leak check and evacuate the system for signs of previous leaks, defective components, etc. Replace or repair as necessary after charge recovery. Empty systems should be charged with a small amount of CFC 12 to leak check.*

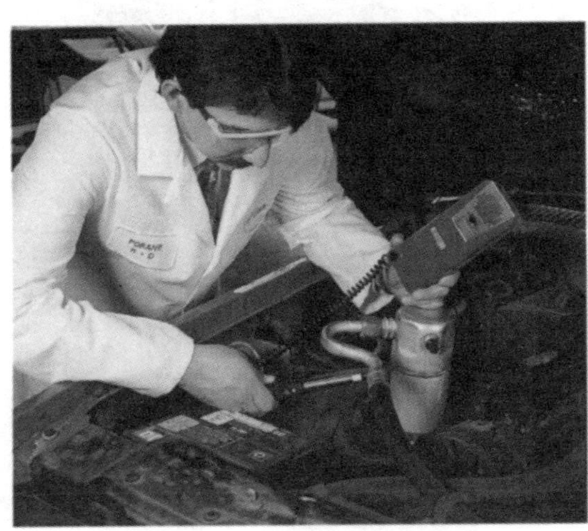

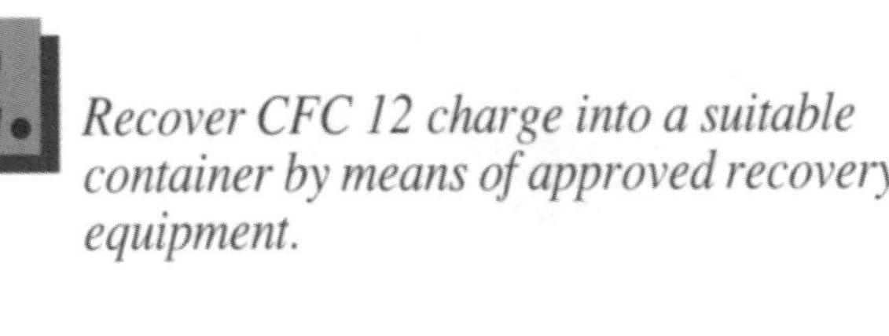

2. *Recover CFC 12 charge into a suitable container by means of approved recovery equipment.*

3. *Pull a system vacuum to 29" of Hg. for 5 minutes. (If not flushing, evacuate at the same level for 45 minutes and go to STEP 7.)*

4. *Connect the power flushing equipment and flush for 30 minutes or longer. Systems with a TXV will need external heat to "open" the valve.*

5. *Recover liquid CFC 12 refrigerant used to flush and evacuate to 29" of Hg. for 30 minutes.*

ıg automotive air conditioners from e® 134a refrigerant

6. *Add the recommended amount of HFC 134a compatible lubricant per system compressor manufacturer's specifications, usually 6 to 8 fl. oz.*

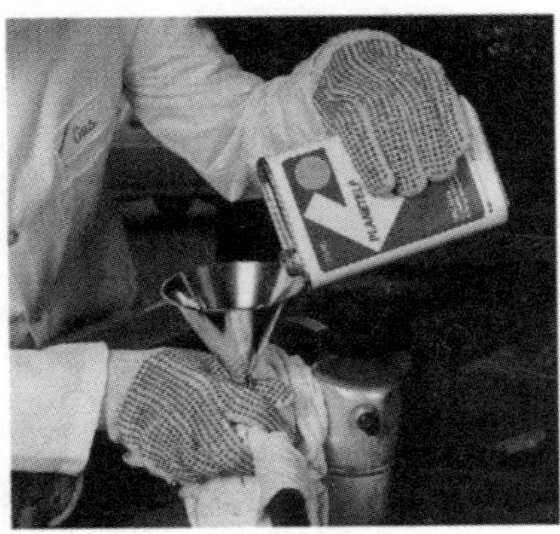

9. *Leak check system again, paying special attention to any connections that may have been worked on.*

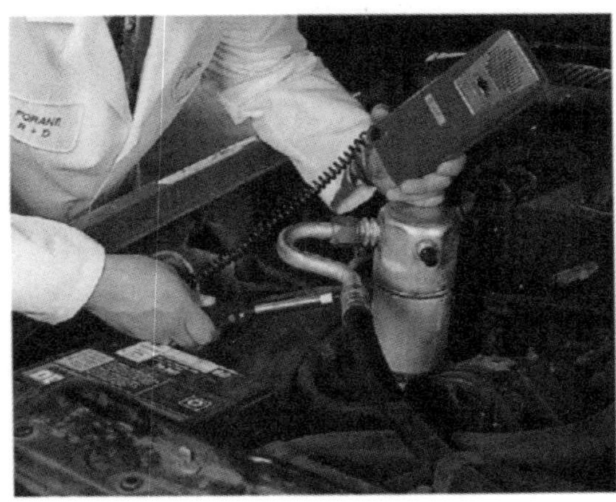

7. *Install SAE approved HFC 134a fittings disabling all other CFC 12 fittings in the system.*

Re-evacuate the system and recharge with Forane 134a using 90% by weight of the original CFC 12 charge.

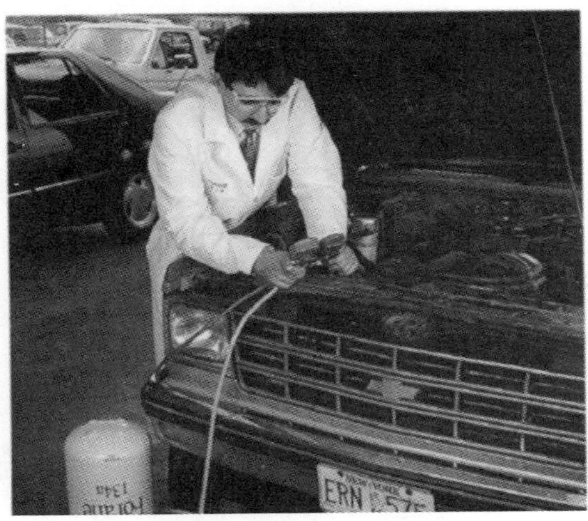

Clearly label the system indicating it has been retrofitted to HFC 134a and a synthetic oil.

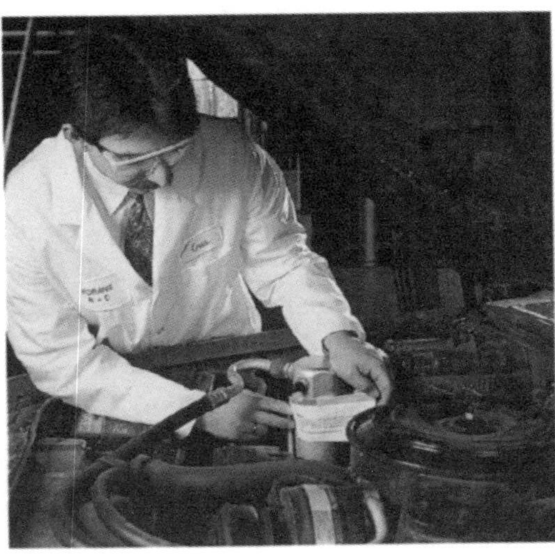

For up-to-the-minute technical advice call 1-800-RETRO94.

If our guidelines differ from Original Equipment Manufacturer's (OEM) guidelines, follow OEM guidelines.

Elf Atochem North America, Inc., Fluorochemicals
2000 Market Street, Philadelphia, PA 19103
1-800-245-5858

Refrigeration Case History Forane® 134a

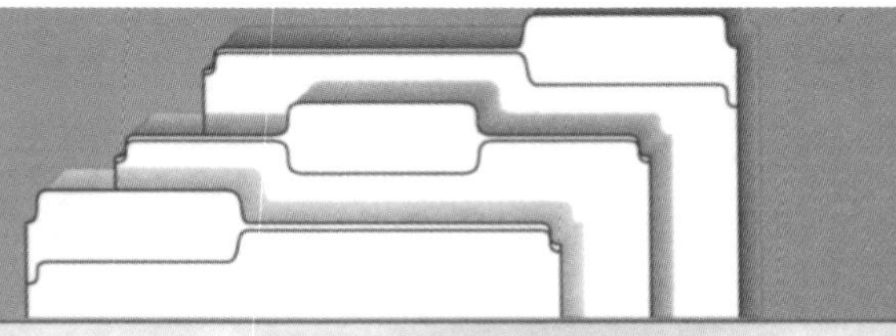

etrofitting Centrifugal Chillers from R-12 o Forane 134a

. and replacing mineral oil with anetelf®ACD polyolester lubricant

stomer	*R. R. Donnelley & Sons Dwight, Illinois plant*
ntractor	*Ruyle Mechanical Peoria, Illinois*
olesaler	*Berkheimer Supply Gary, Indiana*

R. R. Donnelley is one of the world's largest publish- companies. Their Dwight printing plant stretches over 593 sq. ft. The air-cooled centrifugal water chiller ides comfort cooling for the press areas. It is a 1975 em and had been scheduled for routine servicing, ing it an ideal time for the retrofit. The retrofit oc- ed in the heat of Summer, so it was important that it lone quickly and efficiently. The contractor scheduled rything to the minute. The retrofit proceedure took a l of eighteen hours to complete. The remarkable thing at the system was put back into service without a h. The contractor reports it is performing even better n it did with R-12 and as a result, Donnelley is achiev- significant savings in energy costs.

Refrigerant Required	*1,300 lbs. of Forane 134a*
Lubricant	*12 gal. Planetelf ACD 68*
Unit	*Trane CVAA320B high speed high pressure air-cooled centrifugal water chiller*
Compressor	*400 hp centrifugal*

*Elf Atochem North America, Inc.
Fluorochemicals
2000 Market Street
Philadelphia, PA 19103
1-800-245-5858*

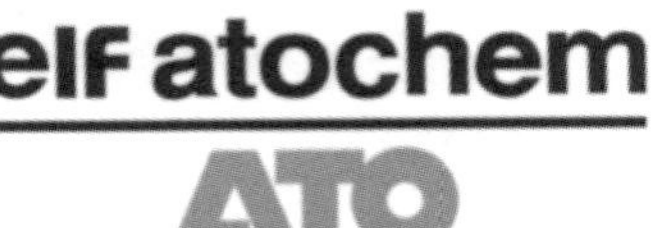

Follow this step-by-step guide
CFC 12 to the nev

Gather baseline data

- Check the system and components for compatibility with Forane 134a and Planetelf® ACD polyolester lubricants
- Check existing performance
- Record overall operating characteristics
- Use data to optimize Forane 134a system in step 8

Leak test system

- Forane 134a will leak in a similar fashion to R-12; repair all leaks prior to recharging system with Forane 134a

3.

Replace Lubricant to start flushing of mineral oil

- Drain mineral oil from all accessible areas and replace with Planetelf ACD lubricant (polyolester)

Run system with new lubricant

- Operate system with new lubricant 24-48 hours with R-12 charge
- Test for mineral oil level; if less than 5% proceed to next step, if not repeat steps 3 and 4

Recover R-12 charge

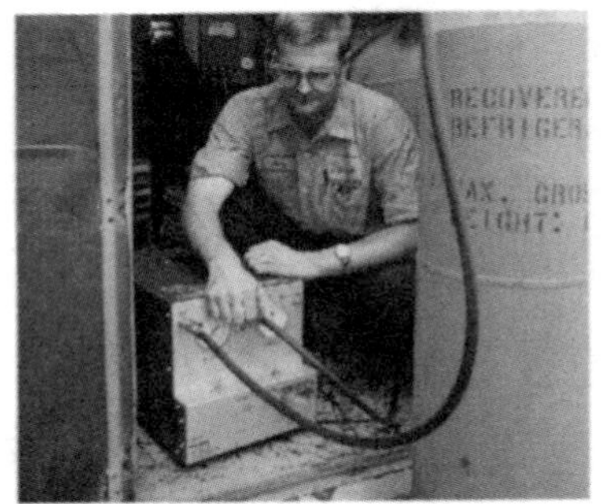

- Use approved recovery device and procedure
- Recover Planetelf lubricant charge and dispose of properly

fitting centrifugal chillers from e® 134a refrigerant

6. *Replace components and evacuate system*

- Replace filters (Use approved desiccant materials (XH-6, XH-9 Type)
- Replace any other components as required
- Evacuate to 1500 microns minimum

7. *Charge with Forane 134a*

- Charge system using pressure-temperature charts (not sightglass) to proper operating conditions (Approx. 90-91% of R-12 charge)
- Leak check system thoroughly

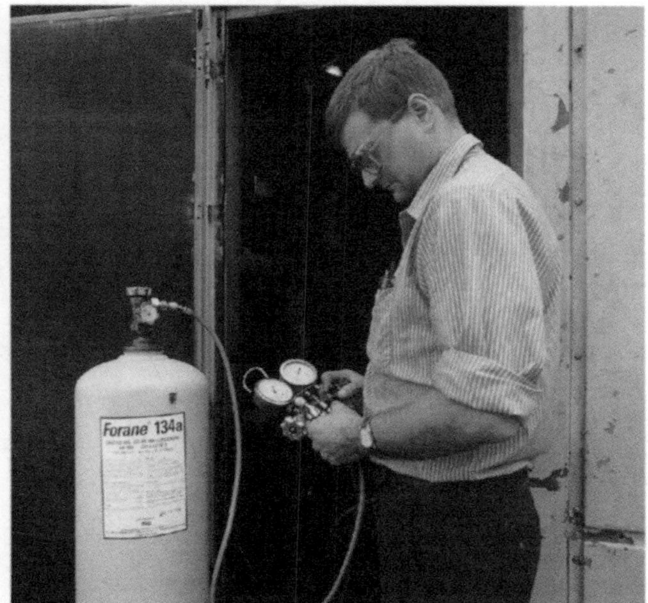

8. *Adjust charge and control settings as needed*

- Reset controls as necessary
- Note: Forane 134a operates approximately 2-5% lower suction pressure and 2-5% higher discharge pressure than R-12

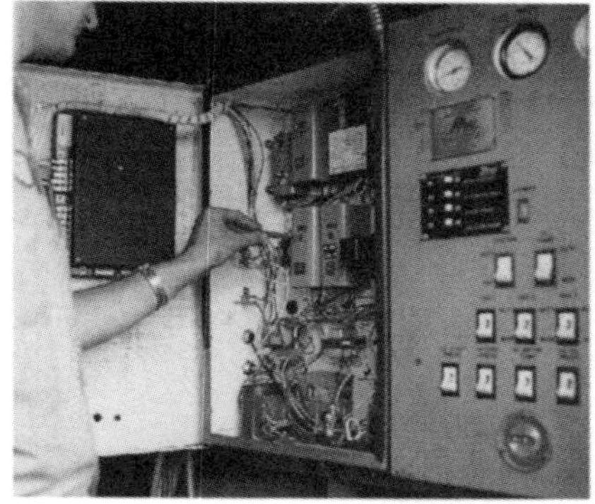

9. *Check operation of the system and re-label unit to reflect refrigerant and lubricant change*

- Indicate new refrigerant and charge for the system to avoid cross contamination of refrigerant

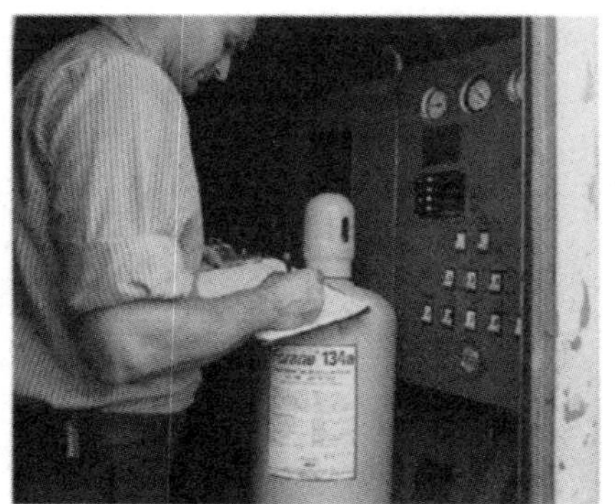

For up-to-the-minute technical advice call 1-800-RETRO94.

If our guidelines differ from Original Equipment Manufacturer's (OEM) guidelines, follow OEM guidelines.

Elf Atochem North America, Inc., Fluorochemicals
2000 Market Street, Philadelphia, PA 19103
1-800-245-5858

elf atochem
ATO

Refrigeration Case History Forane® 134a

lew England Supermarket Retrofits Complete Refrigeration System from R-12 o Forane® 134a

lo System Component Modification r Replacement Was Required, lor Was Business Interrupted.

Customer	*Market Basket Woburn, Massachusetts*
Contractor	*Excel Refrigeration Tewksbury, Massachusetts*
Vholesaler	*Day Supply, 9 Branches in New England (Elf Atochem Distributor for 25 years)*

Produce and Dairy cases that were retrofitted with Forane 134a.

- *76' Meat Cases*
- *48' Poultry Cases*
- *24' Rear Dairy Cases*
- *2 Deli Coolers*
- *Meat Cooler*
- *32' Service Deli*
- *Meat Prep Room*
- *56' 5D Dairy Front*
- *44' 5D Dairy Middle*
- *Poultry Cooler*
- *Island Produce Cases*
- *Fish Cooler*
- *3 Door Reach In*
- *Old Dairy Cooler*
- *Produce Cooler*
- *Wall Produce Cases*

Market Basket, an aggressive chain of 51 supermarkets the New England area, with 4 more planned by the end of 993, has retrofitted the complete refrigeration system in their oburn, Massachusetts store from R-12 to Forane 134a, Elf ochem's single component replacement for CFC 12 that as zero ozone depletion potential.

In a model of efficiency, the retrofit of 2 - 1000 lb. stems and 1 - 300 lb. system was completed over a 5-day eriod during times when the store was closed at the end of e business day. The actual replacement of R-12 by Forane 34a refrigerant was accomplished in 10 hours. The addi- nal retrofit time was consumed in the process of flushing ineral oil from the system. In addition to 2300 lbs. of Forane 134a refrigerant, only new lubricant and a new set of filter driers were required. No system modification or component replacement took place. The expansion valves and crank-case pressure regulator valves were not changed.

A simple flushing procedure using the new polyolester lubricant was used by the contractor, Excel Refrigeration, Tewksbury, Massachusetts. This reduced the mineral oil content to acceptable levels prior to recharging the system with Forane 134a refrigerant.

Today the system is running efficiently and the customer reports no significant cost increases in energy. Market Basket now plans to convert all refrigeration units in all its stores to Forane 134a refrigerant as soon as practicable.

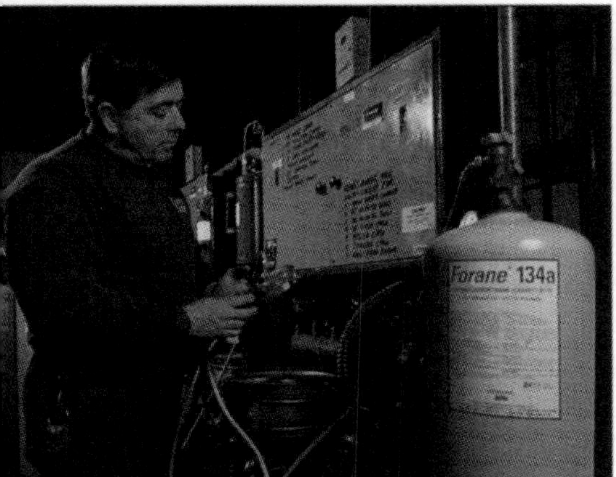

xcel, the contractor, is charging the system with Forane 134a.

Refrigerant Required	*2,300 lbs. of Forane 134a*
Systems	*2 Large Systems 1000 lbs. ea. 1 Small System 300 lb.*
Refrigerated Cases	*8 Product Cases on each 1000 lb. system 25°-30° Suction Temp. Range*
Compressors	*2-20 hp semi-hermetic on each large system 1-10 hp semi-hermetic on small system*

Elf Atochem North America, Inc.
Fluorochemicals
2000 Market Street
Philadelphia, PA 19103
1-800-245-5858

Follow this step-by-step guide to retrofitt
from CFC 12 to the r

1. *Initial system baseline data check with R-12*

- Check existing performance
- Record overall operating characteristics
- This data is used to optimize Forane 134a system in Step 8
- Leak check system thoroughly

2. *Compatibility check of system components, Forane 134a and Planetelf® ACD Polyolester Lubricant*

- Compressor seals and gaskets
- Desiccants: solid core or compacted bead type recommended
- Expansion devices: TEV super heat adjustment may be required

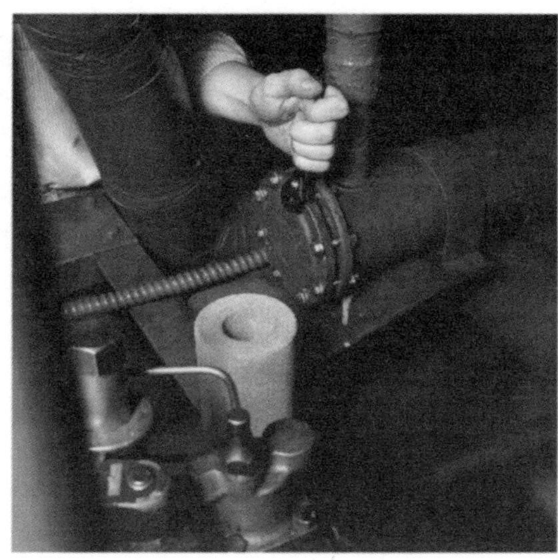

3. *Removal of mineral oil from system*

- Drain mineral oil from compressor and other accessible oil traps
- Replace with equivalent Planetelf ACD polyolester lubricant
- Controls - remove mineral oil, check pressure differentials
- Operate system with R-12 and Planetelf lubricant approximately 24 hours (this procedure insures adequate miscibility of the two lubricants and facilitates the removal of mineral oil from the system)
- Test for mineral oil level; if less than 5% proceed to next step, if not repeat step 3

4. *Recover R-12 from system*

- Use recovery equipment manufacturers' guidelines to recover R-12
- Remove Planetelf from system
- Change filter drier

omplete supermarket refrigeration system
rane® 134a refrigerant

5. *Replace system components if required*

- Use component manufacturers' guidelines
- Repair leaks as required

6. *Evacuate system*

- A minimum evacuation to 1500 microns is required
- Lower levels are desired for most applications
- Evacuate from both high and low sides

7. *Charge system with Forane 134a and Planetelf ACD lubricant*

- Generally the new Forane 134a charge will be approximately 91% of the original R-12 charge (use pressure/temperature chart)
- Identify system with proper R-134a and polyolester lubricant labels
- Leak check system thoroughly

8. *Start system and check for proper operation*

- Reset controls as necessary
- Suction pressures normally operate 5-7% less than R-12 systems
- Discharge pressures normally operate 5-8% higher than R-12 systems

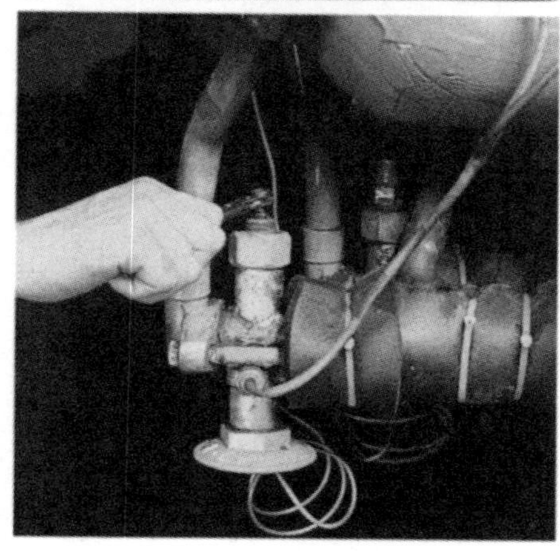

For up-to-the-minute technical advice call 1-800-RETRO94.

If our guidelines differ from Original Equipment Manufacturer's (OEM) guidelines, follow OEM guidelines.

Elf Atochem North America, Inc., Fluorochemicals
2000 Market Street, Philadelphia, PA 19103
1-800-245-5858

ELF LUBRICANT'S PROCEDURE FOR FLUSHING LUBRICANTS FROM REFRIGERATION SYSTEMS

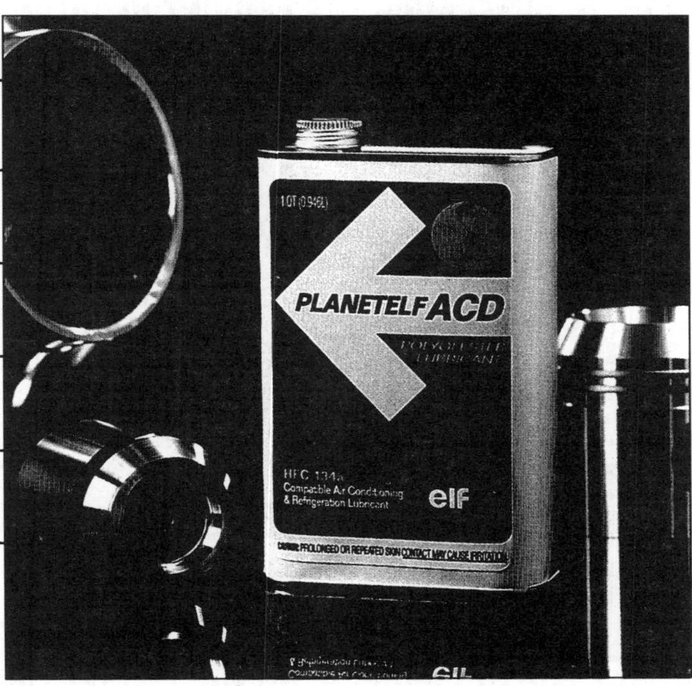

Our Planetelf ACD lubricants – formulated with a polyolester base – are now the lubricants of choice.

When converting refrigeration systems to operate with HFC refrigerants, it's essential that the original lubricant be replaced by an HFC-compatible lubricant.

Any system that now contains R12 refrigerant most likely contains a mineral oil lubricant. Since mineral oil can not be used with R134a refrigerant, it must be flushed out thoroughly and replaced with the correct lubricant. After retrofitting, the system may contain a residue of no more than five-percent mineral oil. Otherwise, the performance of the entire system may be degraded.

The procedure we discuss here offers the best means of performing this flushing process.

WHY ELIMINATE MINERAL OIL?

In CFC systems, mineral oil has been used primarily because it mixes properly with CFC refrigerant.

With the advent of the newer refrigerants such as R134a, mineral oil is no longer suitable because it lacks miscibility, i.e., the ability to mix with them. Miscibility is vital because it aids in the return of oil to the compressor and prevents oil accumulation in the heat exchangers, a condition that would degrade performance.

The new family of lubricants from ELF is ideally suited for all of the new refrigerants.

OVERVIEW OF FLUSHING PROCEDURE

Mineral oil lubricant is removed from the refrigeration system by thorough flushing. Flushing involves charging the refrigeration system with CFC refrigerant and Planetelf polyolester lubricant, operating the system for a period of time, then draining the lubricant. This procedure is repeated until the amount of mineral oil in the drained polyolester lubricant is below 5%.

The amount of residual mineral oil lubricant mixed in with the polyolester lubricant can be determined quickly and accurately by means of a refractometer. The chart on page 2 is then used to convert that refractometer reading to a percentage of residual mineral oil.

That chart can be developed on the site using ordinary graph paper. Also required are a few drops of mineral oil that have been drained from the system prior to flushing, and a quantity of Planetelf lubricant that will be used for flushing.

Dissolved gases within the drained sample must be removed by degassing before using the refractometer.

It is possible to use chemical tests instead of the refractometer, however, these are costly and require handling of potentially hazardous chemicals. We therefore recommend use of a refractometer in all cases.

HOW TO DETERMINE THE AMOUNT OF OIL IN THE SAMPLE

Portable refractometers have a scale that covers a segment of the range between one and one hundred. That portion of the scale from 50 to 100 is required for retrofit purposes. A chart must be created to convert the refractive index to % mineral oil. Such a chart is prepared as follows:

1. Obtain linear (not logarithmic) graph paper.
2. The "Y" axis should be scaled from 50 to 100. (See illustration) This axis will be labeled "Refractive Index Reading."

   The "X" axis should be scaled from 0% to 100%. This axis will be labeled "Percent Mineral Oil."
3. Read the refractive index of the flushing fluid (Planetelf ACD Lubricant). Mark the refractive index for the flushing fluid on the "Y" axis of the chart, above the point representing 0% mineral oil. Then read the refractive index of the lubricant drained from the refrigeration system. It should be undiluted lubricant drained from the compressor, not a mixture of flushing fluid and lubricant. Mark the refractive index for the pure mineral oil on the "Y" axis above the point representing 100% mineral oil.
4. Draw a straight line connecting the refractive index point representing 0% mineral oil with the point representing 100% mineral oil.

To determine percentage of mineral oil in a mixture of mineral oil and flushing fluid, the chart is used to convert the refractive index reading.

CHART FOR CONVERSION OF THE REFRACTIVE INDEX READING TO % MINERAL OIL, SHOWING TYPICAL EXAMPLE

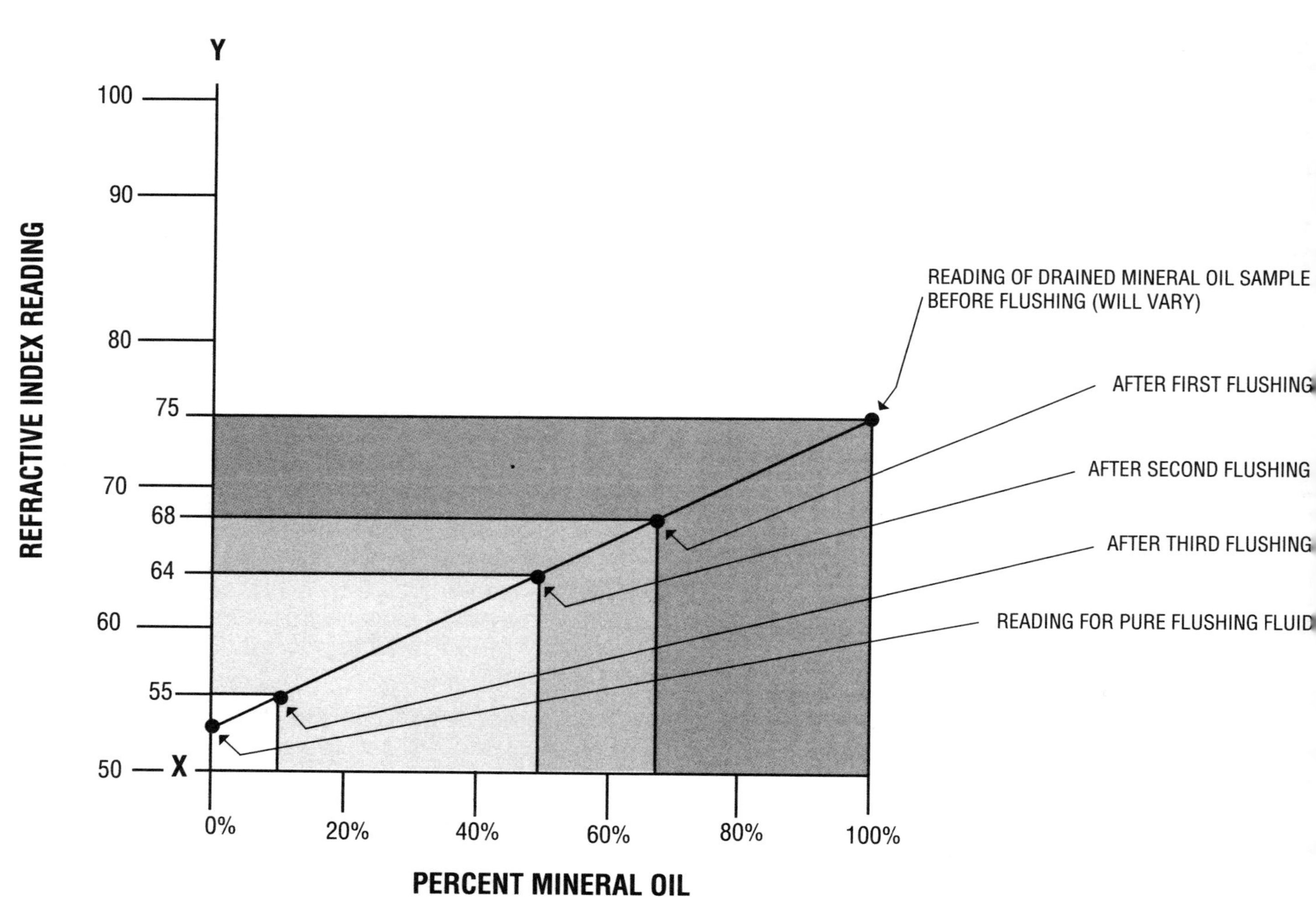

IEASURING THE REFRACTION F THE OIL SAMPLE

efore determining the refraction index of oil om a refrigeration system, the oil sample nust first be degassed because it contains ome dissolved refrigerant that would cause a alse reading.

o prepare the oil sample, take a quantity of bout 10cc and agitate this sample in a vacuum until the foam disappears (about 10 minutes).

The vacuum can be created by connecting an ordinary filter jar to the vacuum pump that is used to drain the lubrication circuit.

The refraction index is also affected by temperature. There- ore, an automatic temperature correction efractometer is recommended. If automatic emperature correction is not available, be ure that the oil temperature is maintained at 8°F/20°C (+ or – 1°).

)igital and optical refractometers are both in vide use, the chief difference being in cost digital types are approx. $800, optical types pprox. $200).

IGITAL REFRACTOMETER, WITH TEMPERATURE CORRECTION

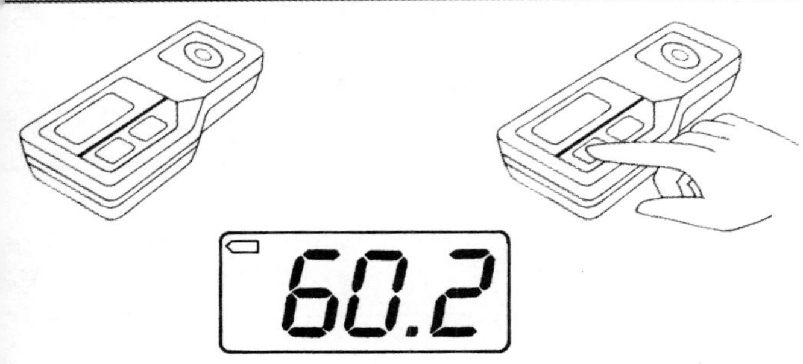

PTICAL REFRACTOMETER, WITH NO TEMPERATURE CORRECTION

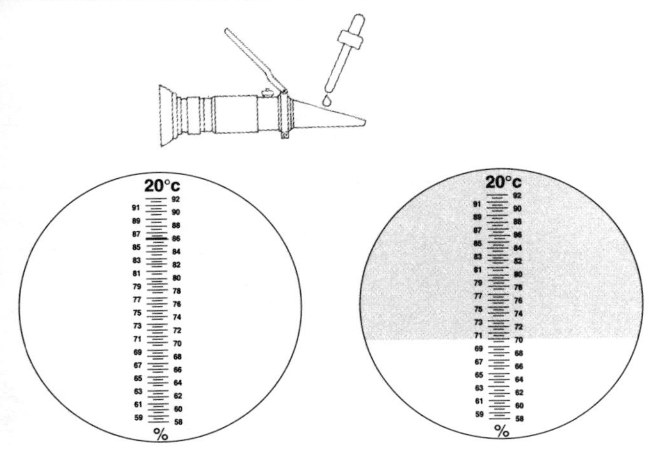

REFRIGERATION FLUID INTERCHANGE CHART

PLANTETELF ACD	32AW	68AW
Mineral Oil & Alkyl Benzene lubricants	▪ Alkyl benzene	▪ Alkyl Benzene
	▪ Calgon C3	▪ Calgon C
	▪ Capella B	▪ Capella D
	▪ Capella WF32	▪ Capella WF68
	▪ Cryol 150	▪ Cryol 300
	▪ Suniso 3GS	▪ Suniso 4G
	▪ Virginia 150	▪ Virginia 300
	▪ Zerice Supreme 32	▪ Zerol 300
	▪ Zerol 150	
Competitive Synthetic Equivalents	▪ BVA Solest 32	▪ BUA Solest 68
	▪ Castrol Icematic SW32	▪ Castrol Icematic SW68
	▪ CPI Solest 35	▪ CPI Solest 60
	▪ CPI Solest LT 32	▪ CPI Solest 68
	▪ ICI Emkarate RL 184	▪ ICI Enkarate 375
	▪ MOBIL EAL 224	▪ MOBIL EAL 226

GLOSSARY OF TERMS

R12 – a refrigerant containing chlorine and other compounds considered harmful to the ozone layer.

R134a – a newly developed refrigerant that is not considered harmful to the ozone layer. R134a is rapidly replacing R12 in most applications.

Mineral oil – The lubricant traditionally used in systems containing R12 refrigerant.

Planetelf ACD – A new, polyolester lubricant that is used in systems containing HFC refrigerant.

Refraction – A method of determining the presence of mineral oil by measuring the bending (refraction) of light by a fluid; commonly reported as a 'refraction index' number and/or chart.

THE FLUSHING PROCEDURE VISUALIZED

First, you should drain the mineral oil lubricant. Retain an oil sample, measure its refraction index and determine its % mineral oil. Then proceed as shown below.

	1. Refill with Planetelf lubricant
	2. Recharge with CFC refrigerant if the refrigerant charge was evacuated.
	3. Operate the system for 24 to 48 hours
	4. Evacuate the refrigerant from system (if required to drain the lubricant)
	5. Drain the lubricant and take a sample
20°C %	6. Measure the refractive index
	7. Convert the refractive index to % mineral oil ***If not within limit, Repeat steps 1 through 7***
1. 2.	8. If within limit: Recover the CFC charge, charge system with Planetelf lubricant and HFC refrigerant.

NOTES

elf lubricants north america 

Planetelf Refrigeration Lubricants
5 North Stiles Street • Linden, NJ 07036 • 1-908-862-9300 • FAX 1-908-862-6885

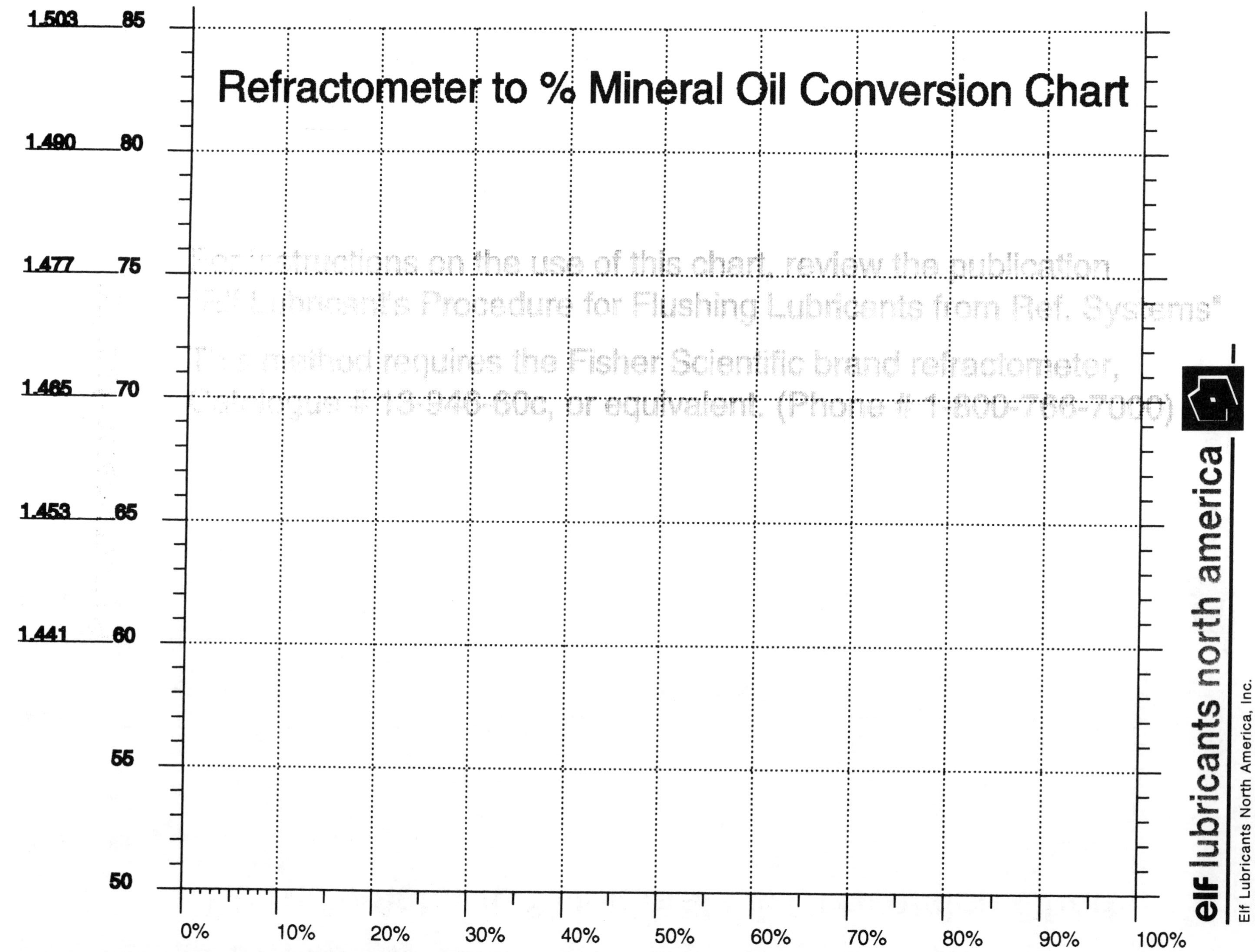

elf lubricants north america

Elf Lubricants North America, Inc.
5 North Stiles Street, PO Box 1063
Linden, NJ 07036-0001
908-862-9300 • FAX 908-862-5087

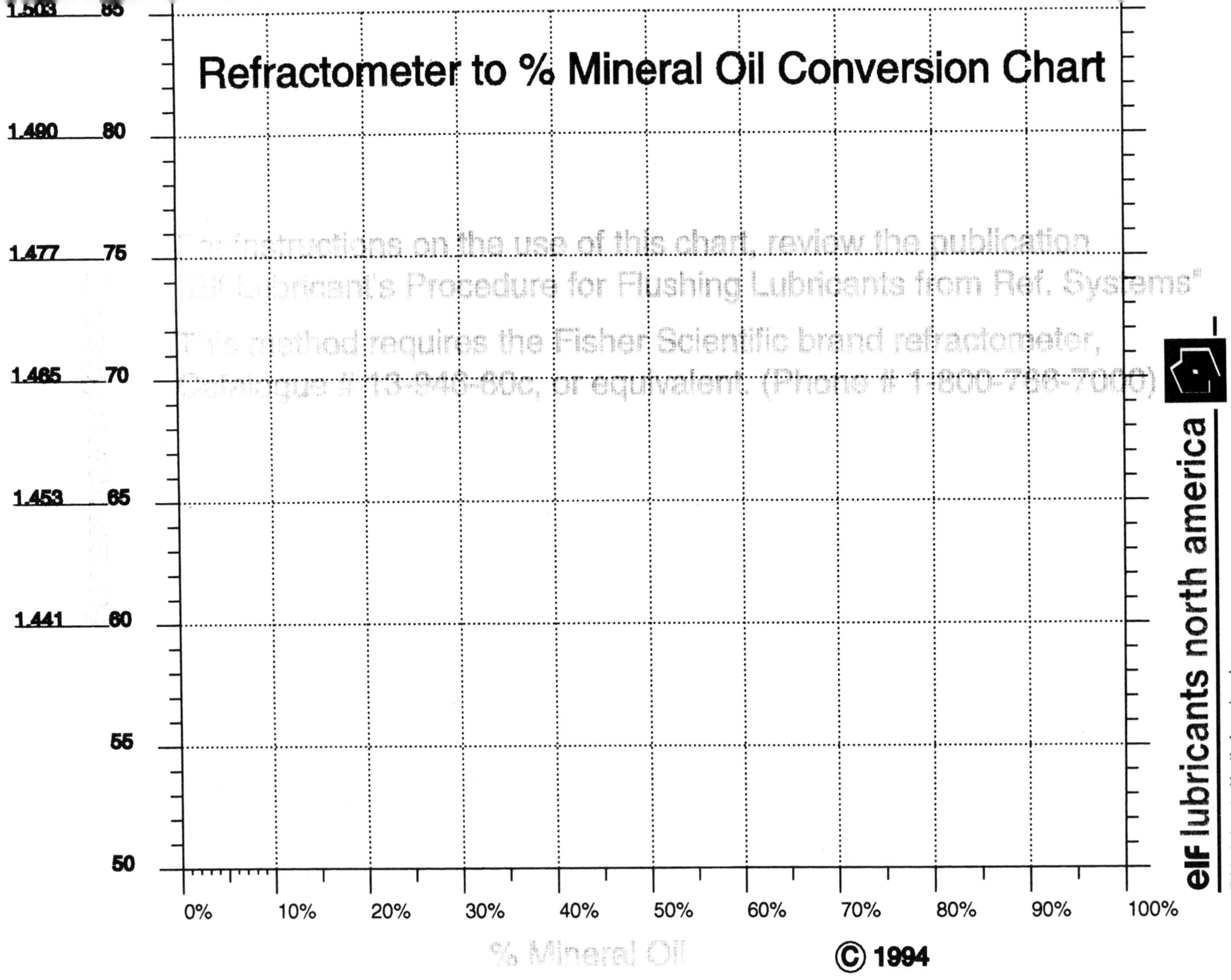

elf lubricants north america

Elf Lubricants North America, Inc.
5 North Stiles Street, PO Box 1063
Linden, NJ 07036-0001
908-862-9300 • FAX 908-862-5087

Refractometer to % Mineral Oil Conversion Chart

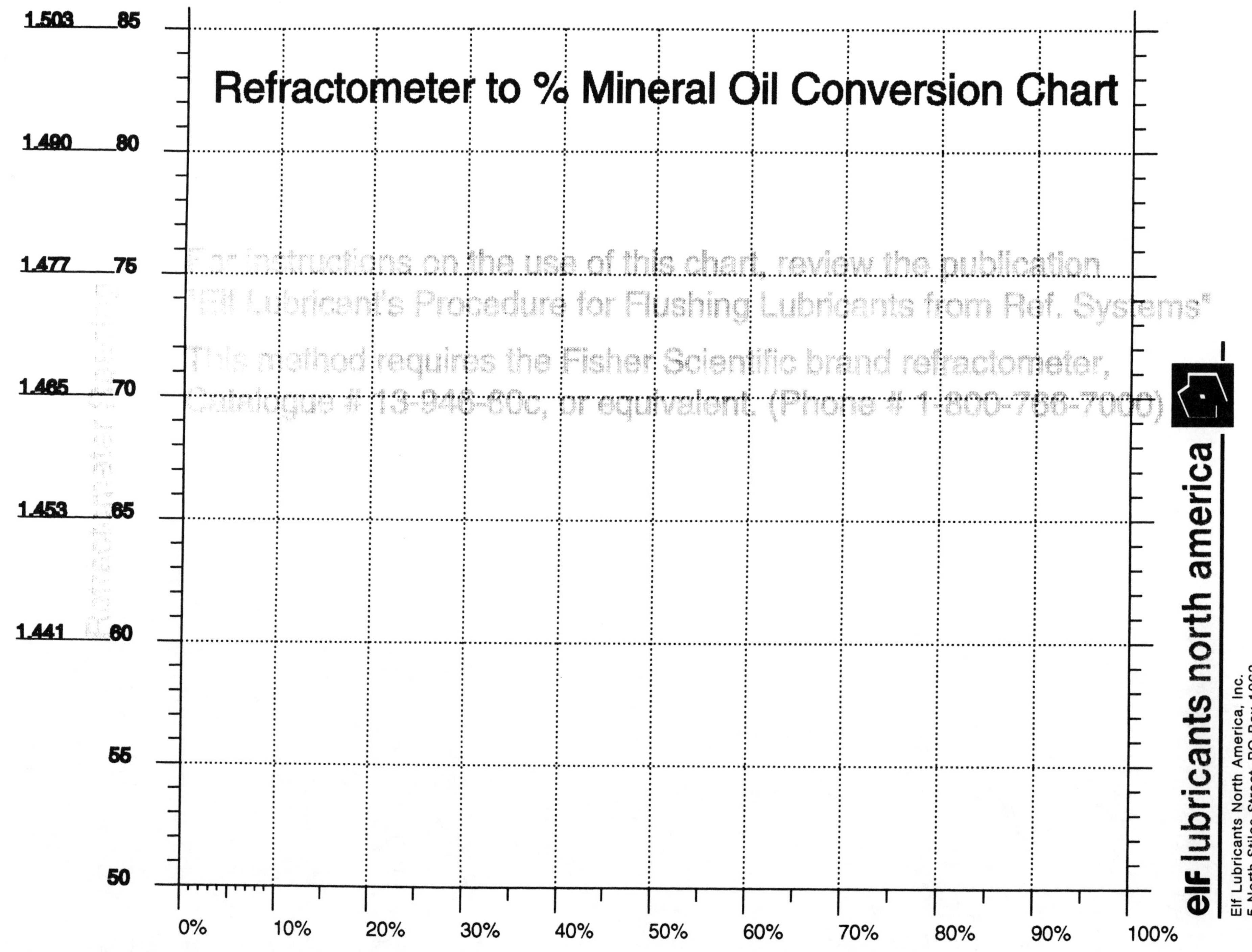

elf lubricants north america

Elf Lubricants North America, Inc.
5 North Stiles Street, PO Box 1063
Linden, NJ 07036-0001
908-862-9300 • FAX 908-862-5087

General Retrofitting Guidelines

It is far easier to retrofit most systems than people ealize. Elf Atochem has developed a nine-step procedure s follows:

- Check original system performance.
- Check system for material compatibility (all parts, materials, valves and controls, etc.).
- Check for appropriate lubricant. Change if necessary.
- Recover refrigerant and drain lubricant.
- Replace/repair system components and repair leaks as necessary.
- Add final charge of appropriate lubricant and evacuate system.
- Charge system with new Forane refrigerant. Adjust charge size as necessary. Re-label system with proper identification.
- Start system and adjust charge to reflect proper pressure/temperature correlation.
- Check system for proper operation and moisture content. Replace filter/dryers if high moisture exists.

elf atochem

Elf Atochem North America, Inc.
2000 Market Street, Philadelphia, PA 19103
800-343-7940

DV-1841- 9/94 - LX

PRODUCT INFORMATION

ALTERNATIVE REFRIGERANT BLENDS

elf atochem

ALTERNATIVE REFRIGERANTS BLENDS – WHO MAKES THEM? WHAT'S IN THEM?

Refrigerant	Manufacturer	ASHRAE#	Components	Application
FX 56	Elf Atochem	R-409A [2]	R-22/124/142b	R-12 Retrofit
FX 10	Elf Atochem	R-408A [2]	R-125/143a/22	R-502 Retrofit
FX 70	Elf Atochem	R-404A	R-125/143a/134a	R-502 New/Retrofit
FX 220	Elf Atochem		R-23/32/134a	R-22 alternative
AZ 50	Allied Signal	R-507 [1]	R-125/143a	R-502 New/Retrofit
AZ 20	Allied Signal	R-410A [2]	R-32/125	R-22 alternative
MP 39, 66	DuPont	R-401A,B	R-22/152a/124	R-12 Retrofit
HP 80, 81	DuPont	R-402A,B	R-125/290/22	R-502 Retrofit
HP 62	DuPont	R-404A	R-125/143a/134a	R-502 New/Retrofit
AC 9000	DuPont	R-407C [2]	R-32/125/134a	R-22 alternative
(Klea) 60, 61	ICI	R-407A,B [1]	R-32/125/134a	R-502 New/Retrofit
(Klea) 66	ICI	R-407C [2]	R-32/125/134a	R-22 alternative
(Isceon) 69L	Rhone Poulenc	R-403B	R-290/22/218	R-502 retrofit
GHG 12	Indianapolis Refrigeration Products	R-406A [1]	R-22/142b/600a	R-12 retrofit
Greeencool 12	GU/Greencool	R-405A [1]	R-22/152a/142b/C318	R-12 retrofit
Greeencool 2018 A,B	GU/Greencool	R-411A,B [2]	R-1270/22/152a	R-22 service
OZ 12	OZ Technologies		R-290/600	R-12 retrofit
HC 12A	OZ Technologies		Hydrocarbons	R-12 service

CFC Refrigerants	HCFC Refrigerants	HFC Refrigerants	Hydrocarbon Refrigerants	Perfluorocarbon Refrigerants
R-11	R-22	R-32 R-143a	R-290 (propane)	R-218
R-12	R-123	R-125 R152a	R-600 (butane)	R-C318
R-115 *(51% in 502 with 49% 22)*	R-124	R-134a	R-600a (isobutane)	
	R-142b		R-1270 (propylene)	

1. *These numbers have been approved for publication in an addendum to ASHRAE Standard 34-1992, Number Designation and Safety Classification of Refrigerants.*
2. *These numbers have been proposed for addition to ASHRAE Standard 34-1992. They will be accepted after completion of a public review process.*

ALTERNATIVE REFRIGERANTS BLENDS, GROUPED BY CFC TYPE

Refrigerant	ASHRAE#	Applications	Lubricant
R-11 ALTERNATIVES			
R-123	R-123	Retrofit or New Centrifugals	Mineral Oil
R-12 ALTERNATIVES			
R-134a	R-134a	R-12 New/Retrofit	Polyester (POE)
FX 56	R-409A	R-12 Retrofit	Mineral Oil/Alkylbenzene
MP 39, 66	R-401A,B	R-12 Retrofit	Alkylbenzene
GHG 12	R-406A	R-12 retrofit	Mineral Oil/Alkylbenzene
Greencool 12	R-405A	R-12 retrofit	Mineral Oil/Alkylbenzene
OZ 12		R-12 retrofit	Mineral Oil
HC 12A		R-12 applications	Mineral Oil
R-502 ALTERNATIVES			
FX 10	R-408A	R-502 Retrofit	Mineral/Alkylbenzene/POE
FX 70	R-404A	R-502 New/Retrofit	Polyester (POE)
AZ 50	R-507	R-502 New/Retrofit	Polyester (POE)
HP 80, 81	R-402A,B	R-502 Retrofit	Mineral Oil + Alkylbenzene
HP 62	R-404A	R-502 New/Retrofit	Polyester (POE)
Klea 60, 61	R-407A,B	R-502 New/Retrofit	Polyester (POE)
Isceon 69L	R-403B	R-502 retrofit	Mineral Oil + Alkylbenzene
R-22 ALTERNATIVES			
FX 220		R-22 alternative	Polyester (POE)
AZ 20	R-410A	R-22 alternative	Polyester (POE)
AC 9000	R-407C	R-22 alternative	Polyester (POE)
(Klea) 66	R-407C	R-22 alternative	Polyester (POE)
Greencool 2018 A,B	R-411A,B	R-22 service	Mineral Oil/Alkylbenzene

ASHRAE NUMBERING SYSTEM

Pure Refrigerants
(based on chemical makeup)

12 CCl_2F_2
134a CH_2F - CF_3

- (a) given based on structure
- (4) number of fluorine atoms
- (3) number of hydrogen atoms, +1
- (1) number of carbon atoms, -1

Blends (Azeotropes - 500 series, Zeotropes - 400 series)

Azeotropes are refrigerant blends which evaporate and condense exactly like a pure component at some temperature and pressure. Azeotropes may not behave this way at all temperatures and pressures, but they will be close.

Zeotropes will show some amount of temperature glide when evaporating or condensing. Some may act like azeotropes (glide is not noticeable in normal operation, less than 3°F). Zeotropes with glides greater than 3°F will have one end of the evaporator warmer than the other. This may impact system performance.

PRESSURE/TEMPERATURE CHART

Temp. °F	12 (psig)	502 (psig)	FX-56 (409A) Liquid	FX-56 (409A) Vapor	FX-10 (408A) (psig)	404A (FX-70) (psig)
-40	11.0*	4.3			2.3	3.8
-30	5.5*	9.4	0.4*	9.9*	7.2	9.1
-25	2.3*	12.3	1.9	6.8*	9.9	12.2
-20	0.6	15.5	4.1	3.7*	12.7	15.5
-15	2.4	19.0	6.5	0.2	15.9	19.1
-10	4.5	22.8	8.8	2.1	19.4	23.1
-5	6.7	26.8	11.7	4.3	23.2	27.4
0	9.2	31.2	14.5	6.5	28.3	32.1
5	11.8	36.0	17.9	9.3	33.0	37.2
10	14.6	41.1	21.3	12.0	38.2	42.7
15	17.7	46.6	25.3	15.3	43.6	48.6
20	21.0	52.5	29.4	18.5	49.6	54.9
25	24.6	58.7	34.1	22.3	55.8	61.7
30	28.5	65.4	38.8	26.1	62.7	69.1
35	32.6	72.6	44.1	30.6	70.0	77.0
40	37.0	80.2	49.5	34.9	77.9	85.3
45	41.7	88.3	55.5	40.2	86.2	94.4
50	46.7	96.9	61.6	45.4	95.1	104.0
55	52.0	106.0	68.6	50.6	104.7	114.1
60	57.7	115.6	75.6	55.7	114.7	124.9
65	63.8	125.8	83.5	63.4	125.5	136.3
70	70.2	136.6	91.4	71.1	136.7	148.4
75	77.0	148.0	100.1	78.9	148.8	161.4
80	84.2	159.9	108.8	86.7	161.6	174.8
85	91.8	172.5	118.9	95.6	175.0	189.1
90	99.8	185.8	128.9	104.4	189.1	204.1
95	108.3	199.7	140.0	114.3	204.1	220.1
100	117.2	214.4	151.0	124.1	219.8	236.7
105	126.6	229.7	163.0	135.2	236.3	254.3
110	136.4	245.8	175.0	146.3	253.6	273.0
115	146.8	262.6	188.4	158.7	272.0	292.7
120	157.7	280.3	201.8	171.1	291.4	313.4
125	169.1	298.7	216.7	185.0	311.7	334.1
130	181.0	318.0	231.6	198.9	332.1	356.9
135	193.5	338.1	247.7	214.0	354.4	
140	206.6	359.1	263.9	229.1	377.1	

*Denotes pressure in inches Hg Vacuum

For Additional Forane Literature, Training Guides, and Case Histories, call **1-800-343-7940**

For Retrofit Assistance, call **1-800-RETRO 94** (1-800-738-7694)

Q. How do you make sense of today's alternative refrigerant blends?

A. These tables will help you translate all the letters and numbers into the basic refrigerant building blocks which make up practically all of the new refrigerant blends.

AlliedSignal Chemicals

The following information is reprinted with permission of AlliedSignal Chemicals:

- *Genetron® AZ-20 Product Brochure*
- *Genetron® AZ-50 Product Brochure*
- *Genetron® 123 Bulletin*
- *Genetron® 134a Bulletin*
- *Genetron® MP Blends: Retrofit Guidelines*
- *Genetron® AZ-50: Retrofit Guidelines*
- *Genetron® 134a: Retrofit Guidelines*

AlliedSignal
CHEMICALS

Genetron® AZ-20 Product Brochure

Fluorocarbons

PRODUCT SPECIFICATIONS

ssay (Min. Wt % of HFC-32/125): 99.8%

oisture (Max. Wt. %): 0.0010

on-Volatile Residue (Max. Vol. %): 0.01

hloride (Max. Wt. %): 0.0001

otal Acidity (Max. mg KOH/gm): 0.0015

on-condensibles in vapor phase (Max. Vol. %): 1.5

SERVICING CONSIDERATIONS

enetron AZ-20 is a 50/50 (wt. %) mixture of HFC-32/125. netron AZ-20 exhibits azeotropic behavior with temperature es that are less than 0.3°F (0.2°C) over the operating range.

/hen compared with a zeotrope, an azeotropic mixture such Genetron AZ-20 will not suffer significant segregation in a tem and will not materially change its composition due to a k. As a result, servicing a system that uses an azeotropic ture is similar to servicing a system that uses a pure fluid.

MATERIALS COMPATIBILITY

he stability of Genetron AZ-20 with metals is excellent. oratory testing has shown that Genetron AZ-20 is compat- with steel, copper, aluminum and brass. The stability of rigerant/oil mixtures is determined using the ASHRAE 97 aled tube method. AZ-20 was studied with several lubri- nts. The tests were conducted in the presence of steel, cop- and aluminum. The time of the exposure was two weeks, h the temperature of the exposure being 200°C (392°F). e stability was judged by both visual observation and mea- ing the fluoride concentration in the tubes.

typical example of the results of such tests with three dif- ent lubricants is shown below. The visual appearance of the tals and the lubricant is unchanged. In addition, the amount fluoride produced in the tube is just barely above the back- ound concentration. This indicates that the lubricant, metals d the refrigerant are compatible under the extreme condi- ns of the tests.

STABILITY OF GENETRON® AZ-20 WITH POLYOL ESTER LUBRICANTS AND METALS

bricant	Lubricant Appearance	Copper	Aluminum	Steel	Fluoride (μg)	AZ-20 Purity
obil L 22	No Change	No Change	No Change	No Change	5	No Change
obil L 32	No Change	No Change	No Change	No Change	6	No Change
strol W 32	No Change	No Change	No Change	No Change	10	No Change

te: Test performed at 200°C (392°F) for 14 days.

PRESSURE VS. TEMPERATURE - GENETRON® AZ-20

Temp. (°F)	Pressure (Psig)	Temp. (°C)	Pressure (kPag)
-40	11.6	-40.0	79.8
-35	14.9	-37.5	100.3
-30	18.5	-35.0	122.5
-25	22.5	-32.5	146.8
-20	26.9	-30.0	173.0
-15	31.7	-27.5	201.4
-10	36.8	-25.0	232.1
-5	42.5	-22.5	265.3
0	48.6	-20.0	301.0
5	55.2	-17.5	339.3
10	62.3	-15.0	380.5
15	70.0	-12.5	424.7
20	78.3	-10.0	472.0
25	87.3	-7.5	522.5
30	96.8	-5.0	576.5
35	107.0	-2.5	634.0
40	118.0	0.0	695.2
45	129.7	2.5	760.3
50	142.2	5.0	829.4
55	155.5	7.5	902.7
60	169.6	10.0	980.4
65	184.6	12.5	1062.6
70	200.6	15.0	1149.5
75	217.4	17.5	1241.3
80	235.3	20.0	1338.1
85	254.1	22.5	1440.1
90	274.1	25.0	1547.5
95	295.1	27.5	1660.5
100	317.2	30.0	1779.1
105	340.5	32.5	1903.7
110	365.0	35.0	2034.4
115	390.7	37.5	2171.4
120	417.7	40.0	2314.8
125	445.9	42.5	2464.8
130	475.6	45.0	2621.7
135	506.5	47.5	2785.5
140	539.0	50.0	2956.5
145	572.8	52.5	3134.9
150	608.1	55.0	3320.8
155	645.0	57.5	3514.4
160	683.4	60.0	3715.9
		62.5	3925.5
		65.0	4143.4
		67.5	4369.7
		70.0	4604.6

Chlorinated Materials and Refrigerants

AlliedSignal does not recommend the use of chlorinated solvents to clean refrigeration systems or components.

Desiccants

Desiccant driers compatible with Genetron AZ-20 are available for O.E.M. field-testing. Individual drier manufacturers should be contacted for specific recommendations.

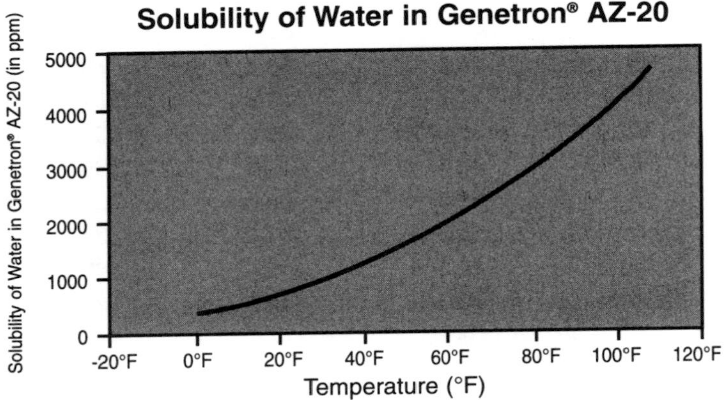

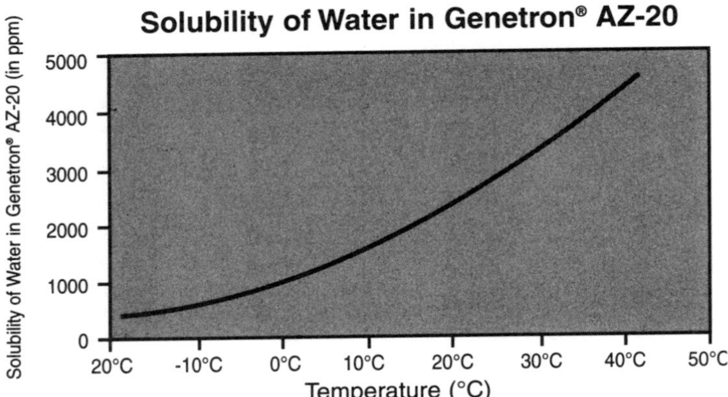

Compatibility with Plastics and Elastomers

The table on the right is a summary of materials compatibility data resulting from tests performed by AlliedSignal and other worldwide industry organizations.

Since there are many different grades and formulations of these materials, we recommend that compatibility testing be performed on the specific grade of materials under consideration when designing new systems.

This data should be used only as a guide to the compatibility of materials with Genetron AZ-20.

The rankings in the table at the right should be used with caution since they are judgements based on limited samplings. Customers should consult with the manufacturer or conduct further independent testing.

SUMMARY OF MATERIALS COMPATIBILITY FOR GENETRON® AZ-20
COMPATIBILITY: PLASTICS/ELASTOMERS

Material	Genetron® AZ-20
Ethylene-Propylene Diene Terpolymer	S
Ethylene-Propylene Copolymer	S
Chlorosulfonated Polyethylene	S
Chlorinated Polyethylene	D
Neoprene (Chloroprene)	S
Epichlorohydrin	D
Fluorinated Rubbers	U
Silicone	D
Polyurethane	D
Nitriles	D
H-NBR	D
Butyl Rubber	D
Polysulfide	S
Nylon	S
Polytetrafluoroethylene	S
PEEK	S
ABS	U
Polypropylene	D
Polyphenyl Sulfide	U
Polyethylene Terephthalate	D
Polysulfone	D
Polyimide	S
Polyetherimide	S
Polyphthalamide	D
Polyamideimide	S
Acetal	D
Phenolic	S

S: Suitable
D: Suitability dependent on formulation
U: Unsuitable

LUBRICANTS

ıs with other HFC's, polyol ester lubricants are recommend- for use with Genetron AZ-20. Many polyol ester lubricants commercially available. Castrol SW 32 and Mobil EAL 32 two polyol ester lubricants that were tested by AlliedSignal. thin a temperature range of -40°F to 140°F (-40°C to 60°C) d a concentration up to 50% lubricant, these two lubricants ıibited complete miscibility with Genetron AZ-20.

ılliedSignal does not recommend specific lubricants. The mpressor and lubricant manufacturers should be consulted a specific recommendation.

SAFETY

ılliedSignal recommends reading the MSDS before using netron AZ-20.

Toxicity

Genetron AZ-20 can be safely used in all of its intended plications when handled in accordance to the Material fety Data Sheet (MSDS). This is based on data developed the Program for Alternative Fluorocarbon Toxicity Testing AFTs, III and V), an international consortium of which liedSignal is a charter member. The conclusion was ached after review of all toxicity results, which confirmed the rinsically low toxicity of the components. AlliedSignal rec- nmends reading the MSDS before using Genetron AZ-20.

Inhalation

AlliedSignal has established a PEL (permissible exposure nit for an eight-hour day and a 40-hour work week) of 1000 m for Genetron AZ-20. Inhalation of the product's vapor ay cause irritation. Vapor inhalation at high concentrations ay result in asphyxiation or the heart may become sensi- zed, causing cardiac arrhythmia. Because of possible distur- ances of cardiac rhythm, catecholamine drugs, such as epi- phrine, should be used with special caution only in situa- ons of emergency life support. Treatment of overexposure to enetron AZ-20 should be directed at the control of symptom.

When concentrations of Genetron AZ-20 reach levels which duce oxygen to 14-16% by displacement, symptoms of sphyxiation will occur. An individual exposed to high con- entrations of Genetron AZ-20 must be given medical atten- on immediately. Adequate ventilation must be provided at all mes.

Skin and Eye Contact

Genetron AZ-20 vapors can irritate the skin and eyes. In liq- id form, it can freeze skin or eyes on contact. If contact with kin should occur, flush the exposed area with lukewarm water ntil all of the chemical is removed. If there is evidence of ostbite, bathe in lukewarm water. Should eye contact occur, mmediately flush with large amounts of lukewarm water for at east 15 minutes, lifting eyelids occasionally to facilitate irriga- on. Seek medical attention as soon as possible.

Leaks

If a large release of Genetron AZ-20 vapor occurs, the area should be evacuated immediately. Vapors may concentrate near the floor, displacing available oxygen. Once the area is evacuated, it must be ventilated using blowers or fans to circulate the air at floor-level.

Flammability

According to ASHRAE Standard 34, Genetron AZ-20 is provisionally classified in safety group A1/A1, i.e., it is non-flammable at 1 Atm. pressure (101.3 kPa) and 64°F (18°C). As defined by the U.S. Department of Transportation (DOT) regulations, flash-point determinations do not apply to Genetron AZ-20. It has no flame limits, and DOT considers it non-flammable (Green Label).

In addition, Underwriters' Laboratory has recognized Genetron AZ-20 as practically non-flammable.

Since Genetron AZ-20 does not have a flash point and is non-flammable, AlliedSignal does not believe classified electrical installations are required and that standard industrial-type electrical installations may be used. It is essential to review and comply with all local building codes and other applicable regulations and laws when using Genetron AZ-20 or any other similar product.

Combustibility

Although Genetron AZ-20 is non-flammable at ambient temperatures and atmospheric pressures, it can become combustible under pressure when mixed with air.

Because of this combustibility potential under pressure, Genetron AZ-20 and air should never be mixed in tanks or supply lines, or allowed to accumulate in storage tanks. Leak-checking should never be done with a mixture of Genetron AZ-20 and air. Leak-checking can be performed safely with a mixture of Genetron AZ-20 and nitrogen.

Thermal Stability

It is important to avoid exposing Genetron AZ-20 to very high temperatures. When exposed to high temperatures, such as those found in flames, Genetron AZ-20 vapors will decompose. This may produce toxic and irritating compounds. Pungent odors released will irritate the nose and throat and generally force evacuation of the area.

Genetron AZ-20 is stable under normal operating conditions. Contact with certain red-hot metals may result in exothermic or explosive reactions and yield toxic and/or corrosive decomposition products. Specific materials to avoid include abraded aluminum surfaces and active metals such as sodium, potassium, calcium, powdered aluminum, magnesium and zinc.

STORAGE and HANDLING

Bulk and Cylinder

Genetron AZ-20 has a higher vapor pressure compared to most of the current refrigerants, particularly Genetron 22 (HCFC-22). For this reason, Genetron AZ-20 must be handled with careful attention to the design pressure rating of the handling equipment. All storage shipping containers -- cylinders, storage tanks, tank trailers or tank cars -- must be specifically designed to handle Genetron AZ-20.

Genetron AZ-20 cylinders must be clearly marked and kept in a cool, dry and properly ventilated storage area away from heat, flames, corrosive chemicals, fumes, explosives and be otherwise protected from damage. Disposable Jugs™ should be discarded in an environmentally safe manner in accordance with all laws and regulations.

Empty cylinders should be returned to AlliedSignal or your Genetron Wholesaler. Under no circumstance should anything be put into the empty cylinder. Once empty, properly close the cylinder valve and replace the valve cap.

Keep cylinders of Genetron AZ-20 out of direct sunlight, especially in warm weather. Genetron AZ-20 expands significantly when heated, reducing the amount of vapor space left in the cylinder. Once the cylinder becomes liquid-full, any further rise in temperature can cause it to burst, potentially resulting in serious personal injury. **Never allow a cylinder to get warmer than 125°F (52°C).**

Always store cylinders above dirt or damp floors to prevent rusting, using a platform or parallel rails. **Secure cylinders in place by means of a rack, chain or rope to prevent them from tipping, falling, rolling or accidentally striking each other or any other object.** If the cylinder valve is broken off, rapid escape of the high pressure contents will propel the cylinder, which could potentially result in serious injury. Keep cylinder caps in place until the cylinder is in use.

The storage area should be away from corrosive chemicals or fumes to avoid damaging effects on the cylinder and threaded areas of the valve. Follow similar precautions for bulk storage and transport systems, ensuring that proper design and operation satisfies the required pressure rating and also avoids external corrosive conditions, overheating or overfilling.

Any evidence of a leak, visual or by a leak detector (see leak detection section), must be corrected immediately by either stopping the leak or transferring all products from the leaking container into a secure container to allow for repairs.

Maintenance should be performed in areas where Genetron AZ-20 has accumulated only after confirming the work area concentrations are below the permissible exposure level (Genetron AZ-20 vapors are heavier than air and can accumulate at floor level). This can be determined using a leak detector capable of sensing Genetron AZ-20. If vapors do accumulate, ventilate the area using fans and other air movers as necessary. Potential sources for further vapor releases should also be eliminated if possible.

A thorough pre-job review must be done to determine t respiratory protection requirements, as well as the other sa ty equipment needed.

Vessels, containers, transfer lines, pumps and other equ ment used with Genetron AZ-20 should not be exposed high-temperature sources (such as welding, brazing and op flames) until they have been thoroughly cleaned and fou free of vapors or liquid. Cylinders must never be exposed welding, brazing or open flames. Exposure to high tempe tures can cause fire, explosion and decomposition of Genetr AZ-20. This may result in the formation of toxic or corros compounds.

When possible, maintenance or cleaning of equipme should be performed without entering the vessel. If a tank any confined-space must be entered, then formal confin space entry procedures <u>must</u> be followed.

Among the requirements of these procedures are that a f qualified work team be used and the confined-space en form be completed and placed at the job site. As a minimu the following guidelines also must be followed:

SAFETY GUIDELINES

1. **Pull all fuses or safety jacks.**
2. **Lock and tag breakers and switches.**
3. **Break and/or blank all lines.**
4. **Test for toxic or flammable atmosphere.**
5. **Test for oxygen deficiency or excessive level – 19.5 percent minimum.**
6. **Assign and instruct observer(s).**
7. **Alert employees in the immediate area to help if needed.**
8. **Provide fresh air supply.**
9. **Wear rescue harness.**
10. **Attach tie line.**
11. **Keep rescue equipment nearby.**
12. **Wear appropriate safety level protective clothing**

LEAK DETECTION

Use leak detectors for pinpointing specific leaks or for m toring an entire room on a continual basis. Leak detectors important for refrigerant conservation, equipment protec and performance, reduction of emissions and protection those coming in contact with the system. Leak testing sho not be performed with mixtures of air and Genetron AZ under pressure. Since Genetron AZ-20 is an HFC mixt use a leak detector capable of detecting an HFC gas.

Types of Leak Detectors

here are two types of leak detectors – leak pinpointers and a monitors. Before purchasing either type, several equipnt factors should be considered, including detection limits, sitivity and selectivity.

/ith selectivity, there are three categories of leak detectors: 1-selective, halogen-selective or compound selective. In neral, the complexity and cost of a leak detector increases its specificity increases.

luorescent dyes approved for use by the equipment manuturer can be added to systems to help pinpoint leaks.

RETROFITTING EXISTING SYSTEMS

ienetron AZ-20 is a leading, long-term non-ozone-depleting ndidate to replace HCFC-22 due to its many favorable permance characteristics. However, the performance propers which make it an attractive candidate to replace HCFC-22 new equipment – higher capacity and higher pressure – ke it difficult to be used in existing systems designed for FC-22. In most cases, mandatory changes would include npressors and thermostatic expansion valves. Condensers d other high-pressure-side components may also require olacing. Depending on the applicable design standard for ssure-containing components and the particular design, en low-pressure-side components may require changing. ovided local building codes permit, and equipment manuturers approve, it may be possible to retain the indoor coil d inter-connecting lines.

ENVIRONMENTAL CONSIDERATIONS

Genetron AZ-20 is a halogenated hydrocarbon. Treatment disposal of wastes generated by use of this product may quire special consideration, depending on the nature of the stes and the means of discharge, treatment or disposal. r more information, refer to the Material Safety Data Sheet SDS).

f discarded unused, Genetron AZ-20 is not considered a azardous waste" by the Resource Conservation and covery Act (RCRA). Because Genetron AZ-20 is consided to have minimum biodegradability, care should be taken avoid releases to the environment.

The disposal of Genetron AZ-20 may be subject to federal, ate and local regulations. Users should conduct disposal erations in compliance with applicable federal, state and cal laws and regulations. Appropriate regulatory agencies so should be consulted before discharging or disposing of aste materials.

RECYCLING and RECLAMATION

The Clean Air Act Amendments of 1990 require mandatory recycling and reclamation of Genetron AZ-20 during maintenance, service or repair of air-conditioning and refrigeration equipment. Recovery equipment is available to recover Genetron AZ-20. AlliedSignal offers a complete refrigerant reclamation program for Genetron AZ-20.

For additional information, call AlliedSignal at

1-800-631-8138

PACKAGING

Genetron AZ-20 is available in a variety of containers. They include 25-lb Disposable Jugs™ and 100-lb returnable cylinders. Larger containers such as one ton (1450-lb) returnable tanks, bulk tank trailers and isotanks will be available in the near future. Consult your Genetron Sales Representative if a larger container is required.

AVAILABLE LITERATURE/TECHNICAL ASSISTANCE

AlliedSignal has a wide range of literature available for all of its environmentally safer Genetron products, covering such topics as reclamation, retrofitting guidelines, product specifications and technical properties. In addition, AlliedSignal technical specialists are available to assist you in all phases of using Genetron AZ-20 – handling and storage and applications assistance. For further information, please write us at:

AlliedSignal Inc.
P.O. Box 1053
Morristown, NJ 07962-1053
Or call us at
1-800-631-8138

GENETRON® AZ-20 THERMODYNAMIC TABLE – ENGLISH UNITS

TEMP (°F)	PRESSURE (Psia)	LIQUID DENSITY (lb/ft³)	VAPOR VOLUME (ft³/lb)	ENTHALPY H_{liq} (Btu/lb)	ENTHALPY ΔH_{vap} (Btu/lb)	ENTHALPY H_{vap} (Btu/lb)	ENTROPY S_{liq} (Btu/lb°F)	ENTROPY S_{vap} (Btu/lb°F)
-60.00	15.87	84.34	3.5603	-4.62	110.17	105.55	-0.0112	0.2645
-58.00	16.72	84.12	3.3891	-4.17	109.99	105.82	-0.0100	0.2638
-56.00	17.62	83.90	3.2276	-3.72	109.80	106.08	-0.0089	0.2631
-54.00	18.55	83.68	3.0752	-3.27	109.61	106.34	-0.0078	0.2624
-52.00	19.53	83.45	2.9312	-2.82	109.42	106.60	-0.0067	0.2617
-50.00	20.54	83.23	2.7952	-2.36	109.22	106.86	-0.0056	0.2610
-48.00	21.60	83.01	2.6666	-1.89	109.01	107.12	-0.0045	0.2603
-46.00	22.70	82.78	2.5449	-1.43	108.81	107.38	-0.0033	0.2597
-44.00	23.84	82.56	2.4298	-0.96	108.59	107.63	-0.0022	0.2590
-42.00	25.03	82.33	2.3208	-0.48	108.36	107.88	-0.0011	0.2584
-40.00	26.27	82.11	2.2176	-0.00	108.13	108.13	-0.0000	0.2577
-38.00	27.56	81.88	2.1198	0.48	107.90	108.38	0.0012	0.2571
-36.00	28.90	81.65	2.0270	0.96	107.67	108.63	0.0023	0.2565
-34.00	30.29	81.42	1.9391	1.45	107.43	108.88	0.0035	0.2558
-32.00	31.73	81.19	1.8556	1.94	107.18	109.12	0.0046	0.2552
-30.00	33.22	80.96	1.7764	2.44	106.93	109.37	0.0058	0.2546
-28.00	34.78	80.73	1.7011	2.94	106.67	109.61	0.0069	0.2540
-26.00	36.39	80.50	1.6296	3.45	106.40	109.85	0.0081	0.2534
-24.00	38.06	80.26	1.5616	3.96	106.13	110.09	0.0092	0.2528
-22.00	39.79	80.03	1.4970	4.47	105.85	110.32	0.0104	0.2523
-20.00	41.58	79.79	1.4354	4.99	105.57	110.56	0.0116	0.2517
-18.00	43.44	79.56	1.3769	5.51	105.28	110.79	0.0128	0.2511
-16.00	45.36	79.32	1.3212	6.04	104.98	111.02	0.0139	0.2506
-14.00	47.34	79.08	1.2681	6.57	104.68	111.25	0.0151	0.2500
-12.00	49.40	78.84	1.2175	7.10	104.37	111.47	0.0163	0.2494
-10.00	51.53	78.60	1.1693	7.64	104.06	111.70	0.0175	0.2489
-8.00	53.73	78.36	1.1233	8.19	103.73	111.92	0.0187	0.2484
-6.00	56.00	78.12	1.0794	8.73	103.41	112.14	0.0199	0.2478
-4.00	58.35	77.87	1.0376	9.29	103.06	112.35	0.0211	0.2473
-2.00	60.77	77.63	0.9976	9.84	102.73	112.57	0.0223	0.2468
0.00	63.27	77.38	0.9594	10.41	102.37	112.78	0.0235	0.2462
2.00	65.86	77.13	0.9230	10.97	102.02	112.99	0.0247	0.2457
4.00	68.52	76.88	0.8881	11.54	101.66	113.20	0.0260	0.2452
6.00	71.27	76.63	0.8548	12.12	101.29	113.41	0.0272	0.2447
8.00	74.11	76.38	0.8230	12.70	100.91	113.61	0.0284	0.2442
10.00	77.03	76.12	0.7925	13.29	100.52	113.81	0.0296	0.2437
12.00	80.05	75.87	0.7633	13.88	100.13	114.01	0.0309	0.2432
14.00	83.15	75.61	0.7354	14.47	99.74	114.21	0.0321	0.2427
16.00	86.35	75.35	0.7087	15.08	99.32	114.40	0.0334	0.2422
18.00	89.64	75.09	0.6830	15.68	98.91	114.59	0.0346	0.2417
20.00	93.03	74.83	0.6585	16.29	98.49	114.78	0.0359	0.2412
22.00	96.52	74.57	0.6350	16.91	98.05	114.96	0.0372	0.2407
24.00	100.11	74.30	0.6124	17.53	97.61	115.14	0.0384	0.2402
26.00	103.81	74.03	0.5908	18.16	97.16	115.32	0.0397	0.2398
28.00	107.60	73.76	0.5700	18.79	96.71	115.50	0.0410	0.2393
30.00	111.51	73.49	0.5501	19.43	96.24	115.67	0.0423	0.2388
32.00	115.52	73.22	0.5310	20.08	95.77	115.85	0.0436	0.2384
34.00	119.65	72.94	0.5126	20.73	95.28	116.01	0.0449	0.2379
36.00	123.89	72.67	0.4949	21.38	94.80	116.18	0.0462	0.2374
38.00	128.24	72.39	0.4780	22.05	94.29	116.34	0.0475	0.2370
40.00	132.71	72.11	0.4617	22.71	93.79	116.50	0.0488	0.2365
42.00	137.30	71.82	0.4460	23.39	93.26	116.65	0.0501	0.2360
44.00	142.01	71.54	0.4310	24.07	92.73	116.80	0.0515	0.2356
46.00	146.85	71.25	0.4165	24.76	92.19	116.95	0.0528	0.2351
48.00	151.81	70.96	0.4025	25.45	91.64	117.09	0.0541	0.2347
50.00	156.89	70.66	0.3891	26.15	91.08	117.23	0.0555	0.2342
52.00	162.11	70.37	0.3762	26.85	90.52	117.37	0.0568	0.2337
54.00	167.46	70.07	0.3637	27.57	89.93	117.50	0.0582	0.2333
56.00	172.94	69.76	0.3517	28.28	89.35	117.63	0.0596	0.2328
58.00	178.56	69.46	0.3402	29.01	88.75	117.76	0.0609	0.2324
60.00	184.32	69.15	0.3290	29.74	88.14	117.88	0.0623	0.2319
62.00	190.21	68.84	0.3183	30.48	87.52	118.00	0.0637	0.2315
64.00	196.25	68.52	0.3080	31.23	86.88	118.11	0.0651	0.2310
66.00	202.44	68.20	0.2980	31.99	86.23	118.22	0.0665	0.2306
68.00	208.77	67.88	0.2883	32.75	85.57	118.32	0.0679	0.2301
70.00	215.25	67.56	0.2790	33.52	84.90	118.42	0.0694	0.2297
72.00	221.88	67.23	0.2701	34.30	84.22	118.52	0.0708	0.2292
74.00	228.67	66.89	0.2614	35.09	83.52	118.61	0.0722	0.2287
76.00	235.61	66.56	0.2530	35.88	82.81	118.69	0.0737	0.2283
78.00	242.71	66.21	0.2449	36.68	82.09	118.77	0.0752	0.2278
80.00	249.97	65.87	0.2371	37.50	81.35	118.85	0.0766	0.2274
82.00	257.39	65.51	0.2296	38.32	80.60	118.92	0.0781	0.2269
84.00	264.98	65.16	0.2222	39.15	79.83	118.98	0.0796	0.2264
86.00	272.74	64.80	0.2152	39.99	79.05	119.04	0.0811	0.2260
88.00	280.66	64.43	0.2083	40.84	78.26	119.10	0.0826	0.2255
90.00	288.76	64.06	0.2017	41.70	77.44	119.14	0.0841	0.2250
92.00	297.03	63.68	0.1953	42.57	76.62	119.19	0.0857	0.2246
94.00	305.47	63.29	0.1891	43.45	75.77	119.22	0.0872	0.2241
96.00	314.10	62.90	0.1831	44.34	74.91	119.25	0.0888	0.2236
98.00	322.90	62.50	0.1773	45.24	74.03	119.27	0.0903	0.2231

GENETRON® AZ-20 THERMODYNAMIC TABLE – ENGLISH UNITS

TEMP (°F)	PRESSURE (Psia)	LIQUID DENSITY (lb/ft³)	VAPOR VOLUME (ft³/lb)	ENTHALPY H_{liq} (Btu/lb)	ENTHALPY ΔH_{vap} (Btu/lb)	ENTHALPY H_{vap} (Btu/lb)	ENTROPY S_{liq} (Btu/lb°F)	ENTROPY S_{vap} (Btu/lb°F)
100.00	331.89	62.10	0.1716	46.15	73.14	119.29	0.0919	0.2226
102.00	341.06	61.69	0.1662	47.08	72.21	119.29	0.0935	0.2221
104.00	350.43	61.27	0.1608	48.02	71.28	119.30	0.0952	0.2216
106.00	359.98	60.84	0.1557	48.98	70.31	119.29	0.0968	0.2211
108.00	369.72	60.40	0.1507	49.94	69.33	119.27	0.0985	0.2206
110.00	379.66	59.95	0.1458	50.93	68.32	119.25	0.1001	0.2201
112.00	389.79	59.49	0.1411	51.92	67.30	119.22	0.1018	0.2195
114.00	400.13	59.02	0.1365	52.94	66.24	119.18	0.1035	0.2190
116.00	410.66	58.54	0.1321	53.97	65.16	119.13	0.1053	0.2185
118.00	421.40	58.05	0.1277	55.02	64.05	119.07	0.1070	0.2179
120.00	432.35	57.54	0.1235	56.09	62.91	119.00	0.1088	0.2174
122.00	443.50	57.02	0.1194	57.18	61.74	118.92	0.1106	0.2168
124.00	454.87	56.49	0.1154	58.30	60.52	118.82	0.1125	0.2162
126.00	466.44	55.93	0.1115	59.44	59.28	118.72	0.1144	0.2156
128.00	478.24	55.36	0.1077	60.60	58.00	118.60	0.1163	0.2150
130.00	490.25	54.77	0.1040	61.80	56.67	118.47	0.1183	0.2144
132.00	502.48	54.16	0.1003	63.02	55.30	118.32	0.1203	0.2137
134.00	514.93	53.52	0.0967	64.29	53.87	118.16	0.1223	0.2131
136.00	527.61	52.85	0.0932	65.59	52.38	117.97	0.1244	0.2124
138.00	540.51	52.16	0.0898	66.93	50.84	117.77	0.1266	0.2117
140.00	553.64	51.43	0.0864	68.33	49.22	117.55	0.1289	0.2110
142.00	567.01	50.66	0.0831	69.78	47.52	117.30	0.1312	0.2102
144.00	580.61	49.84	0.0797	71.31	45.71	117.02	0.1337	0.2094
146.00	594.44	48.97	0.0764	72.91	43.80	116.71	0.1362	0.2085
148.00	608.52	48.03	0.0731	74.61	41.76	116.37	0.1389	0.2077
150.00	622.83	47.02	0.0698	76.43	39.54	115.97	0.1418	0.2067
152.00	637.39	45.91	0.0665	78.40	37.12	115.52	0.1450	0.2056
154.00	652.19	44.66	0.0630	80.58	34.41	114.99	0.1484	0.2045
156.00	667.24	43.23	0.0593	83.06	31.29	114.35	0.1524	0.2032
158.00	682.54	41.51	0.0553	86.01	27.53	113.54	0.1570	0.2016
160.00	698.09	39.28	0.0505	89.87	22.84	112.41	0.1632	0.1995

AZ-20 Thermodynamic Formulas

T_c = 162.500 °F P_c = 717.886 psia ρ_c = 31.2139 lb./cu.ft. T_b = -62.878 °F **MWt.** = 72.558

Vapor pressure correlated as:

$$\ln (P_{vap}/\text{psia}) = A + \frac{B}{T} + CT + DT^2 + \frac{E(F-T)}{T} \ln (F-T)$$

where T is in R

A = 0.1303495663*E*+02 **B** = -0.4165761600*E*+04 **C** = 0.3807471667*E*-03
D = 0.0000000000*E*+00 **E** = 0.0000000000*E*+00 **F** = 0.0000000000*E*+00

Liquid density correlated as:

$$\rho = \rho_c + \sum_{i=1}^{4} D_i (1-T_r)^{i/3}$$

where ρ is in lb./cu.ft.

D_1 = 0.3512693796*E*+02 D_2 = 0.1214476898*E*+03 D_3 = -0.1620426211*E*+03 D_4 = 0.9829573272*E*+02
ρ_c = 0.3121390984*E*+02

Ideal gas heat capacity correlated as:

$$C_p^o = C_1 + C_2 T + C_3 T^2 + C_4 T^3 + C_5/T$$

where C_p^o is in Btu/lb.R and T is in R

C_1 = 0.8363938559*E*-01 C_2 = 0.2339311077*E*-03 C_3 = -0.4207713700*E*-07
C_4 = 0.0000000000*E*+00 C_5 = 0.0000000000*E*+00

Martin-Hou coefficients used:

$$P = \frac{RT}{(v-b)} + \sum_{i=2}^{5} \frac{A_i + B_i T + C_i \exp(-KT_r)}{(v-b)^i}$$

where P (psia), v (cu.ft./lb.), T(R), $T_r = T/T_c$

R = 0.147903 **b** = 0.5201834013*E*-02 **K** = 0.5474999905*E*+01

i	A_i	B_i	C_i
2	-0.6291824867*E*+01	0.3614923532*E*-02	-0.1642519012*E*+03
3	0.2758515284*E*+00	-0.2820548871*E*-03	0.5163036381*E*+01
4	-0.1578745342*E*-02	0.0000000000*E*+00	0.0000000000*E*+00
5	-0.2470426041*E*-04	0.5655830560*E*-07	-0.5439239867*E*-03

TEMP (°C)	PRESSURE (kPa)	LIQUID DENSITY (kg/m³)	VAPOR VOLUME (m³/kg)	ENTHALPY H_{liq} (kJ/kg)	ENTHALPY ΔH_{vap} (kJ/kg)	ENTHALPY H_{vap} (kJ/kg)	ENTROPY S_{liq} (kJ/kg°K)	ENTROPY S_{vap} (kJ/kg°K)
-30.00	274.33	1281.96	0.0935	10.39	246.04	256.43	0.0436	1.0555
-29.00	285.43	1278.57	0.0900	11.48	245.44	256.92	0.0480	1.0533
-28.00	296.89	1275.16	0.0867	12.57	244.84	257.41	0.0524	1.0512
-27.00	308.70	1271.74	0.0835	13.66	244.23	257.89	0.0688	1.0490
-26.00	320.89	1268.31	0.0805	14.77	243.60	258.37	0.0613	1.0469
-25.00	333.46	1264.86	0.0776	15.89	242.95	258.84	0.0657	1.0448
-24.00	346.42	1261.39	0.0748	17.01	242.30	259.31	0.0702	1.0428
-23.00	359.77	1257.91	0.0721	18.14	241.64	259.78	0.0747	1.0407
-22.00	373.53	1254.42	0.0696	19.28	240.96	260.24	0.0792	1.0387
-21.00	387.70	1250.91	0.0671	20.43	240.27	260.70	0.0837	1.0366
-20.00	402.29	1247.38	0.0648	21.58	239.58	261.16	0.0883	1.0346
-19.00	417.31	1243.84	0.0625	22.75	238.86	261.61	0.0928	1.0327
-18.00	432.76	1240.28	0.0604	23.92	238.13	262.05	0.0974	1.0307
-17.00	448.67	1236.71	0.0583	25.11	237.38	262.49	0.1020	1.0287
-16.00	465.03	1233.11	0.0563	26.30	236.63	262.93	0.1065	1.0268
-15.00	481.68	1229.50	0.0544	27.50	235.86	263.36	0.1112	1.0248
-14.00	499.16	1225.87	0.0528	28.71	235.08	263.79	0.1158	1.0229
-13.00	516.95	1222.23	0.0508	29.93	234.29	264.22	0.1204	1.0210
-12.00	535.23	1218.56	0.0491	31.16	233.48	264.64	0.1251	1.0191
-11.00	554.01	1214.87	0.0475	32.40	232.65	265.05	0.1298	1.0172
-10.00	573.31	1211.16	0.0459	33.65	231.81	265.46	0.1344	1.0154
-9.00	593.12	1207.44	0.0444	34.90	230.96	265.86	0.1391	1.0135
-8.00	613.47	1203.69	0.0430	36.17	230.09	266.26	0.1439	1.0117
-7.00	634.36	1199.92	0.0416	37.45	229.21	266.66	0.1486	1.0098
-6.00	655.79	1196.13	0.0402	38.73	228.32	267.05	0.1534	1.0080
-5.00	677.79	1192.31	0.0389	40.03	227.40	267.43	0.1581	1.0062
-4.00	700.36	1188.47	0.0377	41.34	226.47	267.81	0.1629	1.0044
-3.00	723.50	1184.61	0.0365	42.65	225.53	268.18	0.1678	1.0026
-2.00	747.24	1180.72	0.0353	43.98	224.57	268.55	0.1726	1.0008
-1.00	771.57	1176.81	0.0342	45.32	223.59	268.91	0.1774	0.9990
0.00	796.52	1172.87	0.0331	46.67	222.60	269.27	0.1823	0.9973
1.00	822.08	1168.91	0.0321	48.03	221.59	269.62	0.1872	0.9955
2.00	848.28	1164.91	0.0311	49.40	220.57	269.97	0.1921	0.9937
3.00	875.11	1160.89	0.0302	50.78	219.52	270.30	0.1970	0.9920
4.00	902.59	1156.85	0.0292	52.17	218.47	270.64	0.2020	0.9902
5.00	930.74	1152.77	0.0283	53.58	217.38	270.96	0.2070	0.9885
6.00	959.56	1148.66	0.0275	54.99	216.29	271.28	0.2119	0.9868
7.00	989.05	1144.52	0.0266	56.42	215.18	271.60	0.2170	0.9850
8.00	1019.24	1140.34	0.0258	57.86	214.04	271.90	0.2220	0.9833
9.00	1050.14	1136.14	0.0250	59.31	212.89	272.20	0.2271	0.9816
10.00	1081.75	1131.90	0.0243	60.78	211.72	272.50	0.2321	0.9799
11.00	1114.08	1127.62	0.0236	62.25	210.54	272.79	0.2372	0.9782
12.00	1147.14	1123.31	0.0229	63.74	209.32	273.06	0.2424	0.9765
13.00	1180.95	1118.96	0.0222	65.24	208.10	273.34	0.2475	0.9747
14.00	1215.52	1114.58	0.0215	66.76	206.84	273.60	0.2527	0.9730
15.00	1250.86	1110.15	0.0209	68.28	205.58	273.86	0.2579	0.9713
16.00	1286.97	1105.68	0.0203	69.82	204.29	274.11	0.2631	0.9696
17.00	1323.87	1101.17	0.0197	71.38	202.97	274.35	0.2684	0.9679
18.00	1361.58	1096.62	0.0191	72.95	201.64	274.59	0.2736	0.9662
19.00	1400.09	1092.02	0.0185	74.53	200.28	274.81	0.2789	0.9645
20.00	1439.42	1087.37	0.0180	76.12	198.91	275.03	0.2843	0.9628
21.00	1479.58	1082.68	0.0175	77.74	197.50	275.24	0.2896	0.9611
22.00	1520.61	1077.93	0.0170	79.36	196.08	275.44	0.2950	0.9594
23.00	1562.48	1073.14	0.0165	81.00	194.63	275.63	0.3004	0.9576
24.00	1605.21	1068.29	0.0160	82.66	193.15	275.81	0.3059	0.9559
25.00	1648.83	1063.38	0.0155	84.33	191.65	275.98	0.3114	0.9542
26.00	1693.33	1058.42	0.0151	86.02	190.13	276.15	0.3169	0.9525
27.00	1738.73	1053.40	0.0147	87.73	188.57	276.30	0.3224	0.9507
28.00	1785.05	1048.31	0.0142	89.45	187.00	276.45	0.3280	0.9490
29.00	1832.29	1043.16	0.0138	91.19	185.39	276.58	0.3336	0.9472
30.00	1880.46	1037.95	0.0134	92.94	183.76	276.70	0.3393	0.9455
31.00	1929.58	1032.66	0.0130	94.72	182.10	276.82	0.3450	0.9437
32.00	1979.66	1027.30	0.0127	96.52	180.40	276.92	0.3507	0.9419
33.00	2030.70	1021.87	0.0123	98.33	178.68	277.01	0.3565	0.9401
34.00	2082.73	1016.35	0.0120	100.16	176.92	277.08	0.3623	0.9383
35.00	2135.74	1010.76	0.0116	102.02	175.13	277.15	0.3682	0.9365
36.00	2189.77	1005.07	0.0113	103.89	173.32	277.21	0.3741	0.9347
37.00	2244.80	999.30	0.0110	105.79	171.46	277.25	0.3800	0.9328
38.00	2300.86	993.43	0.0106	107.71	169.57	277.28	0.3860	0.9310
39.00	2357.96	987.46	0.0103	109.65	167.64	277.29	0.3921	0.9291
40.00	2416.11	981.38	0.0100	111.62	165.67	277.29	0.3982	0.9272
41.00	2475.32	975.20	0.0098	113.61	163.67	277.28	0.4043	0.9253
42.00	2535.60	968.20	0.0095	115.63	161.62	277.25	0.4105	0.9234
43.00	2596.97	962.48	0.0092	117.68	159.53	277.21	0.4168	0.9214
44.00	2659.43	955.93	0.0089	119.76	157.39	277.15	0.4032	0.9194
45.00	2722.99	949.24	0.0087	121.87	155.20	277.07	0.4296	0.9174
46.00	2787.68	942.40	0.0084	124.00	152.97	276.97	0.4361	0.9154
47.00	2853.50	935.41	0.0082	126.18	150.68	276.86	0.4427	0.9134
48.00	2920.46	928.26	0.0079	128.39	148.34	276.73	0.4493	0.9113

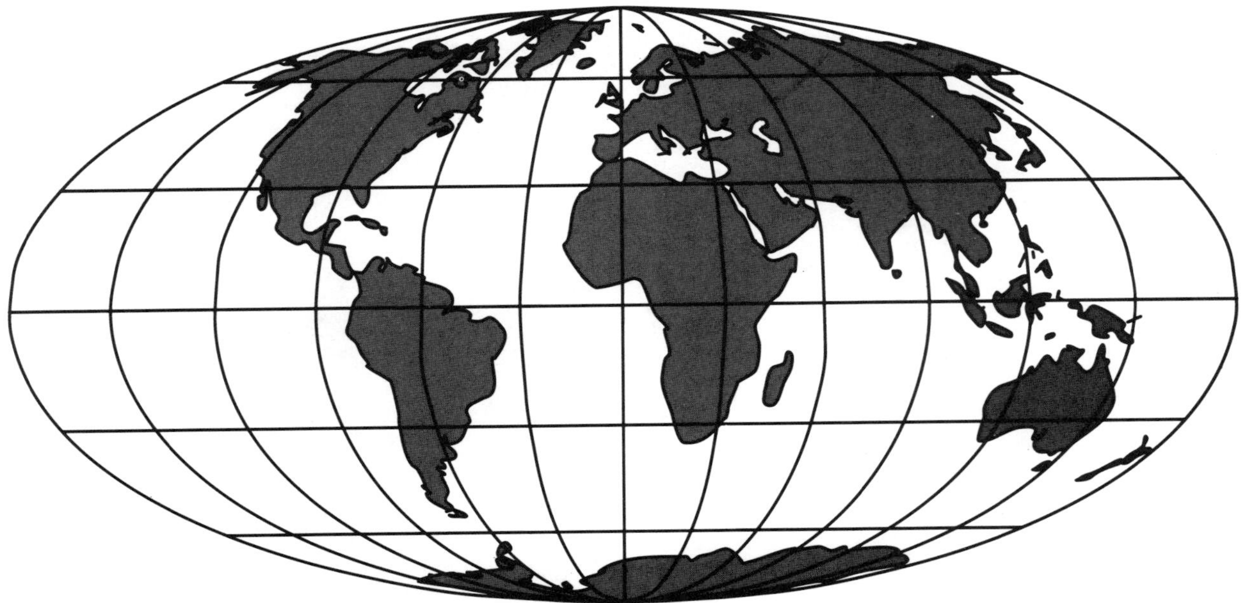

For more information contact your AlliedSignal Fluorocarbons representative.

WORLDWIDE SALES OFFICES

UNITED STATES
AlliedSignal Inc.
Fluorocarbons
P.O. Box 1053
Morristown, NJ 07962-1053
Phone: 800-631-8138
Fax: 201-455-6395

MANUFACTURER'S REPRESENTATIVE
REFRIGERANTS (Southeastern U.S.)
E.V. Dunbar Company
4200 Northside Parkway N.W.
Building 3A
Atlanta, Georgia 30327
Phone: 800-241-2010
Fax: 800-849-0834

LATIN AMERICA-CARIBBEAN
AlliedSignal Inc.
Fluorocarbons
20801 Biscayne Blvd.
Suite #435
Aventura, FL 33180
Phone: 305-931-6465
Fax: 305-931-6762

CANADA
AlliedSignal Inc.
Fluorocarbons
50 Burnhamthorpe Road West
Suite 904
Box 71
Mississauga, Ontario
L5B 3C2
Phone: 905-276-9211
Fax: 905-276-5711

ASIA
AlliedSignal Inc.
Fluorocarbons
Suite 3812-16, Shell Tower
Times Square, 1 Matheson Street
Causeway Bay, Hong Kong
Phone: 852-506-1812
Fax: 852- 506-0192

EUROPE-MIDDLE EAST-AFRICA
AlliedSignal Fluorochemicals
Europe B.V.
Stadsring 163A
3817 BA Amersfoort
The Netherlands
Phone: 033-792300
Fax: 033-792350

AUSTRALIA
AlliedSignal Inc.
Fluorocarbons
71 Queens Road, 2nd Floor
Melbourne, Victoria 3004
Australia
Phone: 61-3-529-1411
Fax: 61-3-510-9837

CUSTOMER SERVICE

HOW TO ORDER

To place an order from anywhere in the continental United States, Hawaii and the Caribbean:

Call: 800-522-8001
Fax: 800-458-9073

In Canada:

Call: 800-553-9749
Fax: 800-553-9750

Outside these areas:

Call: 201- 455-6300
Fax: 201-455-2763

DISCLAIMER

All statements, information and data given herein are believed to be accurate and reliable but are presented without guaranty, warranty or responsibility of any kind, expressed or implied. Statements or suggestions concerning possible use of our products are made without representation or warranty that any such use is free of patent infringement and are not recommendations to infringe any patent. The user should not assume that all safety measures are indicated, or that other measures may not be required.

G525-012
1/95 5K
Printed in USA

AlliedSignal
CHEMICALS

Genetron® AZ-50 (R-507) Product Brochure

Fluorocarbons

Genetron® AZ-50 (R-507)
Properties, Uses, Storage and Handling
Table of Contents

INTRODUCTION

etron® AZ-50 (R-507), (an azeotrope of HFC-125 and 43a, assigned by ASHRAE) has been developed by ignal to serve as a long term substitute for the refrig- R-502. Genetron AZ-50 is a patented*, environmentally non-ozone-depleting substitute that possesses similar efficiency and capacity characteristics to R-502 and intrinsically-low toxicity. Genetron AZ-50 is an excel- frigerant choice for low- and medium-temperature ration applications.

APPLICATIONS

ommercial refrigeration, Genetron AZ-50 serves as a rant in a wide range of applications, such as super- t-display cases, transport refrigeration and ice nes. Genetron AZ-50 also may be used in a number cialty applications to replace R-502.

etron AZ-50 is suitable for both new equipment and ting existing R-502 commercial-refrigeration systems. rally, there will be few if any equipment design es necessary to optimize the performance of on AZ-50 in these applications. For retrofitting com- al refrigeration systems, refer to "Genetron AZ-50 t Guidelines" (G-525-010).

ent No. 5,211,867

PHYSICAL PROPERTIES

English Units

Chemical Name	Pentafluoroethane/1,1,1 Trifluoroethane
Appearance	Clear, colorless gas with a faint ethereal odor
Molecular Formula	CHF_2CF_3/CH_3CF_3
Molecular Weight	98.9
Boiling Point (°F)	-52.1
Critical Temperature (°F)	160
Critical Pressure (psia)	550
Critical Volume (ft³/lb)	0.0320
Critical Density (lb/ft³)	31.2138
Vapor Density @ Boiling Point (lb/ft³)	0.3476
Liquid Density (lb/ft³)	65.36
Liquid Heat Capacity (Btu/(lb)(°F))	0.34
Vapor Heat Capacity (vapor at constant pressure) (Btu/(lb)(°F))	0.211
Heat of Vaporization at Boiling Point (Btu/lb)	86.25
Vapor Pressure (psia)	186.66
Liquid Thermal Conductivity (Btu/hr•ft°F)	0.0366
Vapor Thermal Conductivity (Btu/hr•ft°F)	0.00697[a]
Liquid Viscosity (lbm/ft•h)	0.4456[a]
Vapor Viscosity (lbm/ft•h)	0.0298[a]
% Volatiles by Volume	100
Flammability Limits in Air (vol%)	None
Ozone Depletion Potential (ODP)	0
ASHRAE Safety Group Classification	A1

SI Units

Boiling Point (°C)	-46.7
Critical Temperature (°C)	70.9
Critical Pressure (kPa)	3793.6
Critical Volume (m³/kg)	.002
Critical Density (kg/m³)	500
Vapor Density @ Boiling Point (kg/m³)	5.5679
Liquid Density (kg/m³)	1046.93
Liquid Heat Capacity (kJ/kg·K)	1.44
Vapor Heat Capacity (vapor at constant pressure) (kJ/kg°K)	0.8778
Heat of Vaporization @ Boiling Point (kJ/kg)	200.49
Vapor Pressure (kPa)	1287.01
Liquid Thermal Conductivity (W/m·K)	0.0633[a]
Vapor Thermal Conductivity (W/m·K)	0.0121[a]
Liquid Viscosity (μPa•s)	184.2[a]
Vapor Viscosity (μPa•s)	12.30
% Volatiles by Volume	100
Flammability Limits in air at 1 atm (vol%)	None

[a] Information based on estimated properties

Note: All measurements are at 77°(25° C) and 1 ATM (101.3 kPa) unless otherwise noted.

SPECIFICATIONS

Assay: Minimum Weight percent of all Fluorocarbons.

HFC-125	50%
HFC-143a	50%
Moisture, maximum weight percent	0.0010
Non-Volatile Residue	0.0010
Chloride (wt %)	< 0.0001
Total Acidity (mg KOH/gm)	0.0015
Non-condensibles in vapor phase (vol. %)	1.5%

PERFORMANCE DATA

English Units

The data below indicates performance at Standard Ton Conditions (5°F evaporating and 86°F condensing):

	Genetron® AZ-50	**R-502**
Evaporating Pressure (psig)	40.5	35.9
Condensing Pressure (psig)	197.8	176.6
Compression Ratio	3.85	3.78
Compressor Discharge Temperature (°F)	92.0	99.0
Temperature of Suction Gas (°F)	5	5
Specific Volume of Suction Vapor (cu. ft./lb)	0.82	0.80
Latent Heat of Vaporization (Btu/lb)	75.4	67.3
Net Refrigeration Effect (Btu/lb)	48.6	44.9
Coefficient of Performance (C.O.P.)	4.25	4.35
Horsepower per ton of Refrigeration	1.11	1.08
Refrigerant Circulated per ton (lbs/min.)	4.11	4.45
Compressor Suction Gas Volume per ton (cu. ft./min.)	3.40	3.57
Liquid Circulated per ton (cu. in./min.)	111.5	103.4

SI Units

The data below at cooling load = 1 kw (-15°C evaporating and 30°C condensing):

	Genetron® AZ-50	**R-502**
Evaporating Pressure (kPag)	279.1	247.2
Condensing Pressure (kPag)	1364.0	1217.6
Compression Ratio	3.85	3.78
Compressor Discharge Temperature (°C)	33.5	37.3
Temperature of Suction Gas (°C)	-15	-15
Specific Volume of Suction Vapor (m^3/kg)	0.0510	0.05
Latent Heat of Vaporization (kJ/kg)	175.3	156.5
Net Refrigeration Effect (kJ/kg)	112.9	104.4
Coefficient of Performance (C.O.P.)	4.25	4.35
Refrigerant Circulated per kw(g/s)	8.85	9.58
Compressor Suction Gas Volume per kw(L/s)	0.45	0.48
Liquid Circulated per kw(mL/s)	8.66	8.03

PRESSURE VS. TEMPERATURE

Temperature (°F)	Genetron® AZ-50 (Psig)	Temperature (°C)	Gen[illegible] AZ[illegible] (k[illegible]
-60	5.80*	-45.0	
-55	2.20*	-42.5	[illegible]
-50	0.90	-40.0	[illegible]
-45	3.10	-37.5	[illegible]
-40	5.50	-35.0	[illegible]
-35	8.20	-32.5	[illegible]
-30	11.1	-30.0	[illegible]
-25	14.4	-27.5	[illegible]
-20	17.9	-25.0	[illegible]
-15	21.7	-22.5	[illegible]
-10	25.9	-20.0	[illegible]
-5	30.4	-17.5	[illegible]
0	35.3	-15.0	[illegible]
5	40.5	-12.5	[illegible]
10	46.2	-10.0	[illegible]
15	52.3	-7.5	[illegible]
20	58.8	-5.0	[illegible]
25	65.8	-2.5	[illegible]
30	73.3	0.0	[illegible]
35	81.3	2.5	[illegible]
40	89.8	5.0	[illegible]
45	98.9	7.5	[illegible]
50	108.6	10.0	[illegible]
55	118.9	12.5	[illegible]
60	129.8	15.0	[illegible]
65	141.4	17.5	[illegible]
70	153.6	20.0	[illegible]
75	166.6	22.5	[illegible]
80	180.3	25.0	[illegible]
85	194.9	27.5	[illegible]
90	210.2	30.0	[illegible]
95	226.4	32.5	[illegible]
100	243.6	35.0	[illegible]
105	261.6	37.5	[illegible]
110	280.7	40.0	[illegible]
115	300.8	42.5	[illegible]
120	322.0	45.0	[illegible]
125	344.3	47.5	[illegible]
130	367.8	50.0	[illegible]
135	392.7	52.5	[illegible]
140	418.8	55.0	[illegible]
145	446.3	57.5	[illegible]
150	475.3	60.0	[illegible]
155	505.8	62.5	[illegible]
160	---	65.0	[illegible]
		67.5	[illegible]
		70.0	[illegible]

* (inches Hg - vacuum)

** Gauge Pressure = Absolute - 101.3 kPa

Additional physical properties for Genetron AZ-50 are provided in the appen[illegible]

Genetron® AZ-50 (R-507)

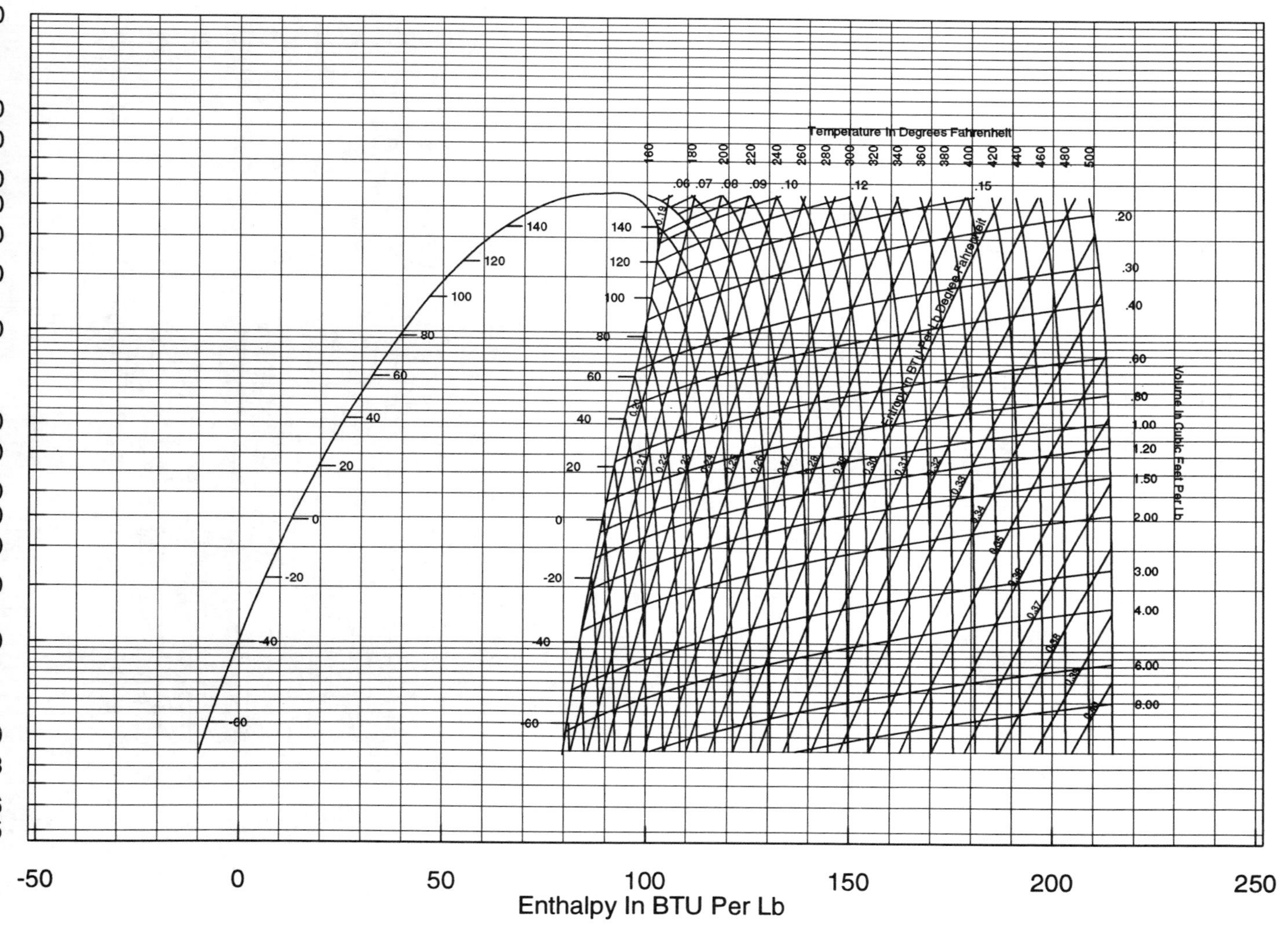

Genetron® AZ-50 (R-507)

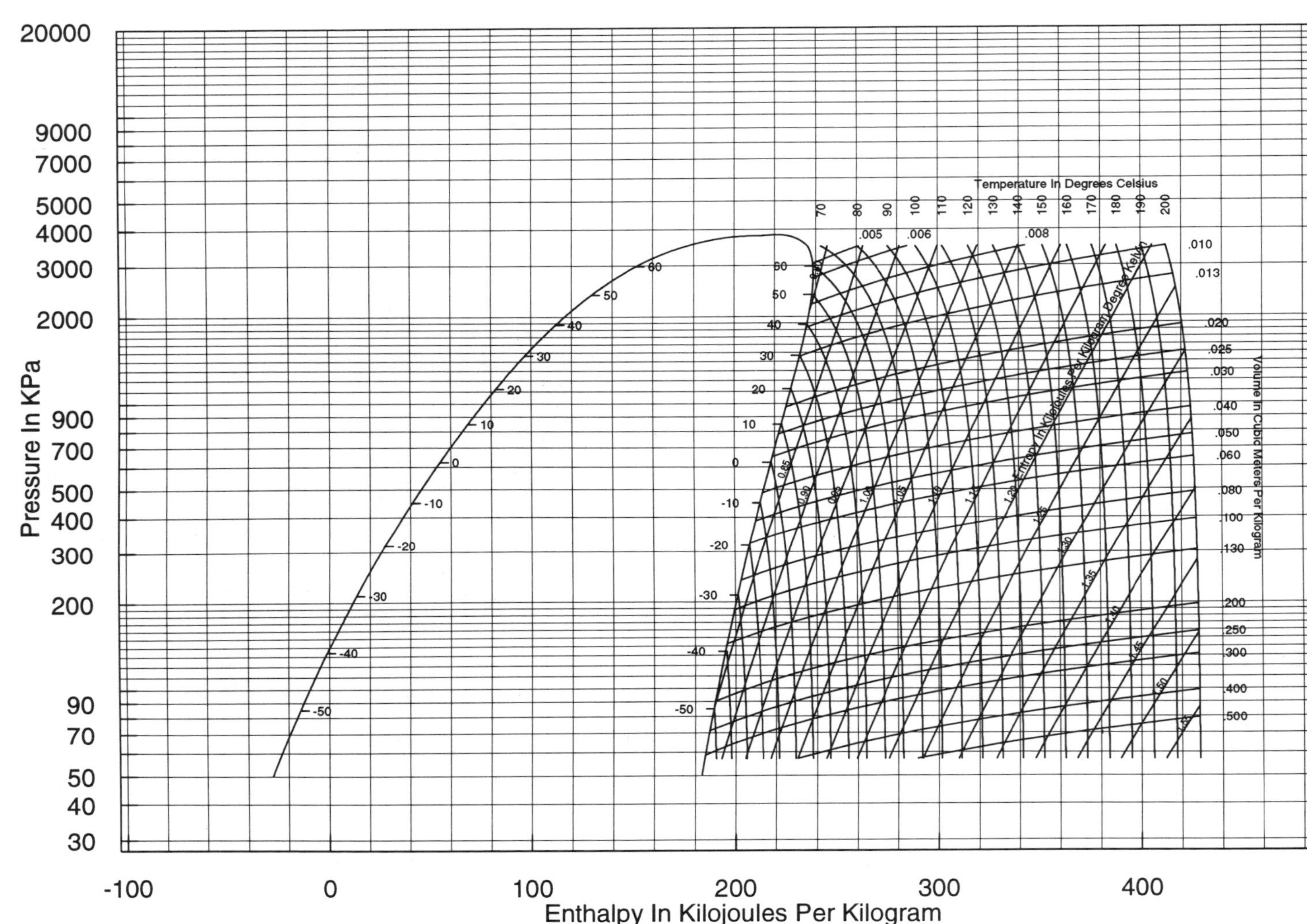

LUBRICANTS

Polyol ester lubricants are to be used with Genetron® AZ- Most compressor manufacturers are recommending spe- polyol ester lubricants. Check with the equipment manu- urer for the recommended lubricants for their system.

Miscibility in Lubricants

Polyol ester lubricants are available in a wide viscosity ge from as low as 15 centistokes (cs) to more than 220 cs 104°F (40°C). Their range of miscibilities with Genetron 50 can vary widely. Miscibility is the ability of the refriger- /lubricant mixture to form a single liquid phase.

Many commercial polyol esters provide miscibility with netron AZ-50 down to low temperatures. As shown in the ure below, the Genetron AZ-50/polyol ester lubricant mis- ility curve is often concave. The refrigerant lubricant mix- e is miscible at low temperatures and becomes immisci- at higher temperatures. These mixtures exhibit lower ical solution temperatures. The lower critical solution nperature is the temperature below which the refrigerant xtures remain miscible over the entire concentration ge.

MISCIBILITY GENETRON® AZ-50 AND POLYOL ESTER LUBRICANTS

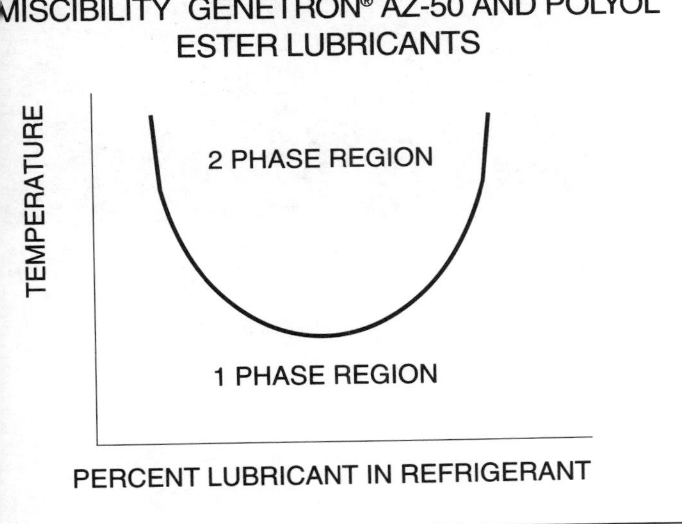

Stability with Metals

The stability of Genetron AZ-50 is very good for virtually applications where R-502 is suitable. Genetron AZ-50 is ompatible with steel, copper, aluminum and brass.

The stability of refrigerant/oil mixtures is determined sing the ASHRAE 97 sealed-tube method. Studies were onducted using sealed tubes of Genetron AZ-50 with poly- ester lubricants in the presence of three metal coupons valve steel, copper and aluminum) for 14 days at 400°F 204°C). The stability was judged through both visual bservation and measuring the fluoride concentration pro- uced in the tube.

On the basis of several such tests, it is clear that Genetron AZ-50 is stable with polyol esters. A typical example of such tests is shown in the table below. Copper, steel and aluminum are stable with Genetron AZ-50 and the polyol esters studied. The stability of the refrigerant, as shown by the fluoride produced and the Genetron AZ-50 chromatographic purity, is excellent.

Stability of Genetron® AZ-50 With Polyol Ester Lubricants and Metals

Lubricant	Lubricant Appearance	Copper	Aluminum	Steel	Fluoride (μG)	AZ-50 Purity
Mobil EAL 22	N.C.	N.C.	N.C.	Very light copper color for the portion immersed in the liquid.	12	N.C.
Mobil EAL 32	N.C.	N.C.	N.C.	N.C.	< 10	N.C.
Castrol SW 32	N.C.	N.C.	N.C.	Slight black spots in the vapor phase region. Portion immersed in liquid is good.	13	N.C.

N.C.= No Change
Note: Test performed at 400°F (204° C) for 14 days.

Chlorinated Materials and Refrigerants

There are three situations in which Genetron AZ-50 and its associated lubricants might come into contact with chlorinated materials and refrigerants. They occur when:

1) A chlorinated solvent is used to clean or flush the system;
2) A system is retrofitted from R-502 to Genetron AZ-50, or
3) R-502 is accidentally charged into a system that contains Genetron AZ-50.

It is recommended that chlorinated materials not be introduced into systems that use Genetron AZ-50 with polyol ester lubricants. While performing retrofits, the service technician should follow appropriate retrofit guidelines to help assure that residual chlorinated compounds are minimized. Genetron AZ-50 alone is chemically compatible with chlorinated materials. However, the polyol ester lubricants used with Genetron AZ-50 can be incompatible with chlorinated materials. Chlorinated materials should not be introduced into Genetron AZ-50 systems that use polyol ester lubricants without prior consultation with the equipment manufacturer.

Genetron® AZ-50/R-502 Mixtures

The mixing of Genetron AZ-50 and R-502 should be minimized. Genetron AZ-50 is an azeotrope of HFC-125 and HFC-143a. R-502 is an azeotrope of HCFC-22 and CFC-115. The mixture of Genetron AZ-50 and R-502 will contain four components: HFC-125, HFC-143a, HCFC-22 and CFC-115. The CFC-115 and HFC-125 may form an azeotrope, and separation of these four components will become difficult. This will make recycling and reclamation very difficult, especially to return to the original composition of the two azeotropes.

EQUIPMENT-RELATED ISSUES

Compatibility: Plastics and Elastomers

With the introduction of Genetron AZ-50, AlliedSignal, in conjunction with leading OEMs, has conducted materials testing to evaluate the compatibility of materials used in refrigerant applications. The following list is a condensed sampling of the testing that has been performed to date. The information on this list is a first-level ranking of the compatibility of the materials. (Note: the compatibility of any specific material will be dependent on its formulation and history.) The ranking, although based on limited sampling, can serve as a useful guide.

Compatibility: Plastics/Elastomers

Material	Genetron® AZ-50	Genetron® AZ-50 Polyol Ester
Ethylene-Propylene Diene terpolymer	S	S
Ethylene-Propylene copolymer	S	S
Chlorosulfonated Polyethylene	S	U
Polyisoprene	D	U
Chlorinated Polyethylene	S	U
Neoprene (Chloroprene)	S	D
Epichlorohydrin	D	U
Polyvinylidene fluoride and copolymer of vinylidene fluoride and hexafluoropropylene	U	U
Silicone	U	D
Polyurethane	D	D
Nitriles	D	D
H-NBR	D	S
Butyl rubber	D	S
Polysulfide	S	U
Nylon	S	D
Polytetrafluoroethylene	S	S
PEEK	S	S
ABS	D	U
Polypropylene	D	D
Polyphenylene sulfide	D	D
Polyethylene terephthalate	S	S
Polysulfone	S	S
Polyimide	S	D
Polyetherimide	S	S
Polyphthalamide	D	U
Polyamideimide	D	S
Acetal	S	U
Phenolic	S	D
Epoxy Laminate	S	S

S: Suitable
D: Suitability dependent on formulation
U: Unsuitable
In either case, rankings should be used with caution since they are judgements based on limited sampling. Customers should consult the manufacturer or do further independent testing.

Desiccants

Three common types of desiccant materials are use making driers. They are molecular sieves, alumina and ca gel. Molecular sieves XH7 and XH9 are recommer by UOP (a major molecular sieve manufacturer) for use Genetron AZ-50. In addition, each drier manufacturer developed driers and filters that are compatible Genetron AZ-50. Such driers can include all three type drier materials.

Solubility of Water in Genetron® AZ-50

The solubility of water in Genetron AZ-50 is shown in graph below. This solubility is comparable to that of wate R-502.

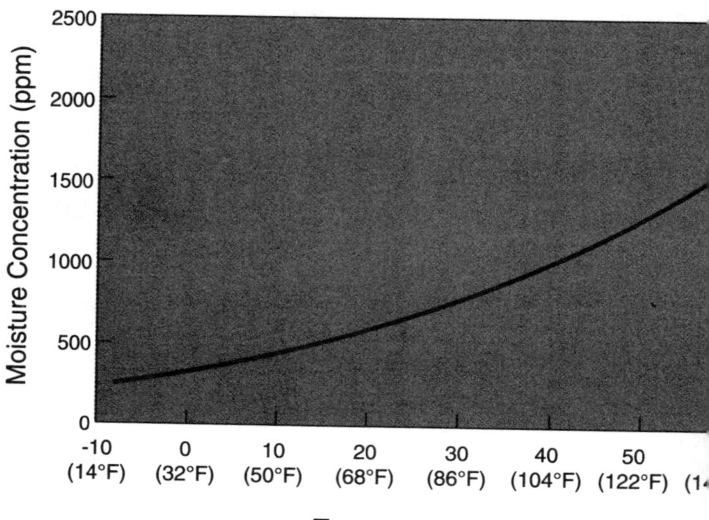

SAFETY

Toxicity

ənetron® AZ-50 can be safely used in all of its intended cations based on data developed by AlliedSignal. This lusion was reached after review of all toxicity results h confirmed the intrinsically low toxicity of the sub- ;e. However, the end-user should read the Material ;y Data Sheet (MSDS) before using Genetron AZ-50.

Inhalation

ənetron AZ-50 is of a low order of acute toxicity in ani- . Vapor inhalation at high concentrations may result in yxiation or cardiac arrhythmia. If vapors are inhaled at concentrations, cardiac irregularities and possibly car- arrest could occur. Under these circumstances the may become sensitized. Do not use adrenaline (epi- rine) if over-exposure to Genetron AZ-50 is suspected. 1 concentrations of Genetron AZ-50 reach levels which ;e oxygen to 14-16% by displacement, symptoms of yxiation will occur. An individual exposed to high con- 'ations of Genetron AZ-50 must be given medical tion immediately. As with most fluorocarbons, ade- ventilation must be provided at all times.

Skin and Eye Contact

ənetron AZ-50 vapors have little or no effect on the and eyes. In liquid form, however, it can freeze skin or on contact. If contact with the skin should occur, flush xposed area with lukewarm water until the chemical is ved. If there is evidence of frostbite, soak in lukewarm . If contact with the eyes should occur, immediately with large amounts of lukewarm water for at least 15 es, occasionally lifting eye lids to facilitate the flushing ss. Seek medical attention immediately.

Leaks

ould a large release of Genetron AZ-50 vapor occur, rea must be evacuated immediately. Vapors may con- ate near the floor, displacing available oxygen. Once rea is evacuated, it must be ventilated using blowers ıs to circulate the air at floor-level.

Flammability

defined by the U.S. Department of Transportation) regulations, flash-point determinations do not apply :-50. It has no flame limits, and DOT considers it non- nable (Green Label). Underwriters' Laboratories ® has recognized Genetron AZ-50 as practically non- nable.

According to ASHRAE Standard 34, Genetron AZ-50 is classified in safety group A1. Since Genetron AZ-50 does not have a flash point and is non-flammable, we do not believe classified electrical installations are required and that standard industrial-type electrical installations may be used. It is essential to review and comply with all local building codes and other applicable regulations and laws when using Genetron AZ-50 or any other similar product.

Combustibility

Genetron AZ-50 is an azeotrope of HFC-125 and HFC-143a and is non-flammable at ambient temperatures and atmospheric pressures. However, when mixed with air, HFCs can be combustible at higher pressures and temperatures.

Because of this combustibility potential under pressure, Genetron AZ-50 and air should never be mixed in tanks or supply lines, or allowed to accumulate in storage tanks. Leak-checking should never be done with a mixture of Genetron AZ-50 and air. Leak-checking can be performed safely with a mixture of Genetron AZ-50 and nitrogen.

Anyone using or handling Genetron AZ-50 should carefully review the Material Safety Data Sheet (MSDS).

Thermal Stability

It is important to avoid exposing Genetron AZ-50 to very high temperatures. When exposed to high temperatures, such as those found in flames, Genetron AZ-50 vapors will decompose. This may produce toxic and irritating compounds. Pungent odors released will irritate the nose and throat and generally force evacuation of the area.

Genetron AZ-50 is stable under normal operating conditions. Contact with certain red-hot metals may result in exothermic or explosive reactions and yield toxic and/or corrosive decomposition products. Specific materials to avoid include abraded aluminum surfaces and active metals such as sodium, potassium, calcium, powdered aluminum, magnesium and zinc.

STORAGE AND HANDLING

Genetron® AZ-50 cylinders must be clearly marked and kept in cool, dry and properly ventilated storage areas away from heat, flames, corrosive chemicals or fumes, explosives and otherwise be protected from damage. Empty cylinders should be returned to your AlliedSignal Wholesaler.

Keep cylinders of Genetron AZ-50 out of direct sunlight, particularly in warm weather. Genetron AZ-50 expands significantly when heated, thereby reducing the amount of vapor space left in the cylinder. Once the cylinder becomes liquid-full, any further rise in temperature can cause the cylinder to burst, resulting in serious personal injury.

NEVER ALLOW A CYLINDER TO GET WARMER THAN 125°F (55°C).

Cylinders always should be raised above dirt or damp floors to prevent rusting. This can be done by using a platform or parallel rails. All containers must be secured in place by means of a rack, chain or rope so they cannot tip, roll or accidentally strike each other or any other object.

The storage area should be away from corrosive chemicals or fumes to avoid damaging effects on the cylinder and threaded areas of the valve.

MAINTENANCE

Maintenance in areas where Genetron AZ-50 can accumulate (Genetron AZ-50 vapors are heavier than air) should be performed only after establishing with a fluorocarbon sniffer that vapor concentrations are below the permissible exposure level. If vapors accumulate, a self-contained breathing apparatus should be used. Vessels, containers, transfer lines, pumps and other equipment should not be exposed to high-temperature sources (such as welding, brazing and open flames) until they have been thoroughly cleaned and found free of vapors. Exposure to these circumstances can cause fire, explosion and decomposition of Genetron AZ-50. This may result in the formation of toxic or corrosive compounds.

When possible, maintenance or cleaning of equipment should be performed without entering the vessel. If a tank must be entered, personnel should be required to use a formal tank-entry procedure based on recognized safety principles. This procedure should include, as a minimum, the following safety guidelines:

SAFETY GUIDELINES

1. **Pull all fuses or safety jacks.**
2. **Lock and tag breaker and switches.**
3. **Break and/or blank all lines.**
4. **Test for toxic or flammable atmosphere.**
5. **Test for oxygen deficiency -- 19.5 percent minimum.**
6. **Assign and instruct observer.**
7. **Alert employees in the immediate area to help if needed.**
8. **Provide fresh air supply.**
9. **Wear rescue harness.**
10. **Attach tie line.**
11. **Keep rescue equipment nearby.**
12. **Wear protective clothing.**

LEAK DETECTION

Leak detectors can be used for pinpointing specific l or for monitoring an entire room on a continuous b Leak detection is important for refrigerant conserva equipment protection and performance, reduction of e sions and protection of those coming in contact with system. No leak testing should be performed with mixt of air and Genetron AZ-50.

Types of Detectors

There are two types of leak detectors -- leak pinpoir and area monitors. Before purchasing either type, se equipment factors should be considered, including dete limits, sensitivity and selectivity.

With regards to selectivity, there are three categori leak detectors: nonselective, halogen-selective or c pound-selective. In general, the complexity and cost leak detector increases as its specificity increa Fluorescent dyes can be added to systems to help pin leaks.

ENVIRONMENTAL CONSIDERATIONS

Genetron AZ-50 is a halogenated hydrocar Treatment or disposal of wastes generated by use of product may require special consideration, dependin the nature of the wastes and the means of discharge, t ment or disposal. For more information refer to Environmental Data sheet supplement to the Mat Safety Data Sheet (MSDS).

discarded unused, Genetron® AZ-50 is not considered azardous waste" by the Resource Conservation and overy Act (RCRA). Because Genetron AZ-50 is considered to have minimum biodegradability, care should be n to avoid releases to the environment.

ne disposal of Genetron AZ-50 may be subject to federtate and local regulations. Users should conduct disl operations in compliance with applicable federal, state local laws and regulations. Appropriate regulatory ncies also should be consulted before discharging or osing of waste materials.

RECLAMATION

he Clean Air Act Amendments of 1990 will require datory recycling and reclamation of Genetron AZ-50 ng maintenance, service or repair of air-conditioning and geration equipment. Your Genetron Wholesaler offers a gerant reclamation program for Genetron AZ-50. A iled description of the AlliedSignal reclamation program ven in brochure R525-638, titled "Genetron® Refrigerant clamation Program." To obtain a copy, call your netron Wholesaler or AlliedSignal at 1-800-631-8138. the name of your nearest Genetron Wholesaler, call 00-522-8001.

RETROFITTING

Applications where Genetron AZ-50 is a suitable retrofit lacement refrigerant include supermarket display cases, k-in coolers, ice machines and other specialty applicas.

Genetron AZ-50 vs. Blends

Where feasible, Genetron AZ-50 is the preferred retrofit lacement for R-502 in most OEM applications. In some ses, however, retrofitting with Genetron AZ-50 may be icult because nearly all of the mineral oil in the system st be removed. For these instances, interim blends such Genetron® HP80 may be a suitable option.

Service technicians should keep in mind that future reguions may further restrict the use of HCFC-containing rigerants and dictate the ultimate use of non-chlorine ntaining refrigerants such as Genetron AZ-50 for servic- R-502 equipment.

Retrofit Lubricants

Genetron AZ-50 is not a "drop in" replacement for R-502. Mineral oils and alkylbenzene lubricants are immiscible with Genetron AZ-50 and must therefore be replaced with polyol ester lubricants. Consult the original equipment manufacturer for the recommended lubricant.

Retrofit Procedures

Retrofit procedures have been developed by AlliedSignal to help technicians perform successful retrofits of R-502 systems utilizing positive-displacement (reciprocating, rotary, scroll or screw) compressors with Genetron AZ-50. However, these should not be used as a substitute for the equipment manufacturer's specific recommendations..

For further information on retrofitting with Genetron AZ-50, refer to the "Genetron AZ-50 Retrofit Guidelines," bulletin G525-010.

PACKAGING

Genetron AZ-50 is available in a variety of containers. They include 25-lb. disposable cylinders, 100-lb. returnable cylinders, and one ton (1750-lb.) returnable tanks. Bulk tank trailers; and isotanks are also available.

TECHNICAL ASSISTANCE

AlliedSignal technical specialists are available to assist customers in all phases of Genetron AZ-50 use. Working with the sales staff, they can offer plans for storage, handling and use. For further information and/or technical assistance on Genetron refrigerants, contact:

AlliedSignal Inc.
Fluorocarbons
P.O. Box 1053
Morristown, NJ 07962-1053
(800) 631-8138

AVAILABLE LITERATURE

AlliedSignal has a wide range of literature available on topics including: reclamation, retrofitting procedures, product specifications and product descriptions. For further information, call AlliedSignal at (800) 631-8138.

Genetron® AZ-50 (R-507) THERMODYNAMIC TABLE

TEMP (°F)	PRESSURE (Psia)	LIQUID DENSITY (lb/ft³)	VAPOR VOLUME (ft³/lb)	ENTHALPY H_{liq} (Btu/lb)	ENTHALPY ΔH_{vap} (Btu/lb)	ENTHALPY H_{vap} (Btu/lb)	ENTROPY S_{liq} (Btu/lb°F)	ENTROPY S_{vap} (Btu/lb°F)
-60	11.80	83.17	3.5367	-6.61	87.72	81.11	-0.0161	0.2034
-58	12.48	82.95	3.3532	-5.95	87.35	81.40	-0.0145	0.2030
-56	13.20	82.73	3.1812	-5.29	86.98	81.69	0.0128	0.2026
-54	13.95	82.51	3.0200	-4.63	86.61	81.98	0.0112	0.2023
-52	14.74	82.28	2.8686	-3.97	86.24	82.27	0.0096	0.2019
-50	15.56	82.06	2.7264	-3.31	85.86	82.55	0.0080	0.2016
-48	16.41	81.83	2.5928	-2.65	85.49	82.84	0.0064	0.2013
-46	17.30	81.61	2.4672	-1.88	85.11	83.13	0.0046	0.2010
-44	18.22	81.38	2.3489	-1.32	84.74	83.42	0.0032	0.2007
-42	19.18	81.16	2.2376	-0.66	84.36	83.70	0.0016	0.2004
-40	20.18	80.93	2.1327	0.00	83.99	83.99	0.0000	0.2001
-38	21.22	80.70	2.0337	0.66	83.61	84.27	0.0015	0.1998
-36	22.30	80.47	1.9404	1.32	83.24	84.56	0.0031	0.1995
-34	23.42	80.25	1.8523	1.96	82.86	84.64	0.0046	0.1993
-32	24.59	80.02	1.7690	2.64	82.48	85.12	0.0062	0.1990
-30	25.80	79.78	1.6903	3.30	82.10	85.40	0.0077	0.1988
-28	27.05	79.66	1.6159	3.96	81.73	85.69	0.0092	0.1986
-26	28.35	79.32	1.5455	4.62	81.35	85.97	0.0107	0.1983
-24	29.70	79.09	1.4700	5.72	80.98	86.25	0.0122	0.1981
-22	31.09	78.85	1.4156	5.93	80.60	86.53	0.0137	0.1979
-20	32.54	78.62	1.3557	6.59	80.22	86.81	0.0152	0.1977
-18	34.03	78.38	1.2989	7.25	79.83	87.08	0.0167	0.1975
-16	35.57	78.14	1.2450	7.91	79.45	87.36	0.0182	0.1973
-14	37.17	77.91	1.1938	8.56	79.08	87.64	0.0197	0.1971
-12	38.82	77.67	1.1452	9.22	78.69	87.91	0.0211	0.1969
-10	40.53	77.43	1.0990	9.88	78.31	88.18	0.0266	0.1967
-8	42.29	77.19	1.0550	10.53	77.93	88.46	0.0240	0.1966
-6	44.11	76.94	1.0132	11.19	77.56	88.74	0.0255	0.1964
-4	45.98	76.70	0.9734	11.84	77.17	89.01	0.0269	0.1962
-2	47.92	76.46	0.9355	12.50	76.78	89.28	0.0283	0.1961
0	49.91	76.21	0.8994	13.15	76.40	89.55	0.0297	0.1959
2	51.97	75.96	0.8649	13.81	76.01	89.82	0.0311	0.1958
4	54.09	75.72	0.8321	14.46	75.63	90.09	0.0325	0.1957
6	56.28	75.47	0.8008	15.11	75.25	90.36	0.0339	0.1956
8	58.53	75.22	0.7708	15.77	74.85	90.62	0.0353	0.1954
10	60.85	74.96	0.7423	16.42	74.47	90.89	0.0367	0.1953
12	63.23	74.71	0.7150	17.07	74.08	91.15	0.0381	0.1951
14	65.69	74.45	0.6889	17.72	73.70	91.42	0.0394	0.1950
16	68.21	74.20	0.6640	18.38	73.30	91.68	0.0408	0.9149
18	70.81	73.94	0.6401	19.03	72.91	91.94	0.0422	0.1948
20	73.48	73.68	0.6173	19.68	72.52	92.20	0.0435	0.1947
22	76.22	73.42	0.5954	20.33	72.13	92.46	0.0449	0.1946
24	79.04	73.16	0.5744	20.98	71.74	92.72	0.0462	0.1945
26	81.94	72.69	0.5544	21.63	71.34	92.97	0.0475	0.1944
28	84.91	72.63	0.5351	22.28	70.95	93.23	0.0488	0.1943
30	87.97	72.36	0.5167	22.93	70.55	93.48	0.0502	0.1942
32	91.11	72.09	0.4990	23.59	70.15	93.74	0.0515	0.1941
34	94.33	71.82	0.4820	24.24	69.75	93.99	0.0528	0.1941
36	97.63	71.54	0.4657	24.89	69.35	94.24	0.0541	0.1940
38	101.02	71.27	0.4500	25.54	68.94	94.48	0.0554	0.1939
40	104.50	70.99	0.4349	26.19	68.54	94.73	0.0567	0.1938
42	108.07	70.71	0.4205	26.85	68.13	94.98	0.0579	0.1937
44	111.73	70.43	0.4066	27.50	67.72	95.22	0.0592	0.1937
46	115.48	70.14	0.3932	28.16	67.30	95.46	0.0605	0.1936
48	119.32	69.85	0.3803	28.81	66.89	95.70	0.0618	0.1935
50	123.26	69.57	0.3679	29.47	66.47	95.94	0.0630	0.1935
52	127.30	69.27	0.3560	30.13	66.04	96.17	0.0643	0.1934
54	131.43	68.98	0.3445	30.78	65.63	96.41	0.0656	0.1933
56	135.67	68.68	0.3334	31.44	65.20	96.64	0.0668	0.1933
58	140.00	68.38	0.3227	32.11	64.76	96.87	0.0681	0.1932
60	144.44	68.08	0.3124	32.77	64.33	97.10	0.0693	0.1931
62	148.99	67.77	0.3025	33.43	63.90	97.33	0.0706	0.1931
64	153.65	67.46	0.2929	34.10	63.45	97.55	0.0719	0.1930
66	158.41	67.15	0.2836	34.77	63.00	97.77	0.0731	0.1930
68	163.29	66.83	0.2747	35.44	62.55	97.99	0.0744	0.1929
70	168.28	66.51	0.2661	36.12	62.08	98.20	0.0756	0.1928
72	173.38	66.19	0.2577	36.79	61.63	98.42	0.0769	0.1928
74	178.60	65.86	0.2497	37.47	61.16	98.63	0.0781	0.1927
76	183.95	65.53	0.2419	38.16	60.68	98.84	0.0794	0.1926
78	189.41	65.19	0.2343	38.84	60.20	99.04	0.0806	0.1926
80	195.00	64.85	0.2270	39.53	59.71	99.24	0.0819	0.1925
82	200.71	64.50	0.2200	40.23	59.21	99.44	0.0831	0.1924
84	206.56	64.15	0.2131	40.93	58.71	99.64	0.0844	0.1924
86	212.53	63.80	0.2065	41.63	58.20	99.83	1.0856	0.1923
88	218.64	63.44	0.2001	42.34	57.67	100.01	0.0869	0.1922
90	224.88	63.07	0.1939	43.06	57.14	100.20	0.0882	0.1921
92	251.26	62.70	0.1878	43.78	56.60	100.38	0.0894	0.1920
94	237.78	62.32	0.1820	44.51	56.04	100.55	0.0907	0.1920
96	244.45	61.93	0.1763	45.25	55.48	100.73	0.0920	0.1919

Genetron® AZ-50 (R-507) THERMODYNAMIC TABLE (continued)

TEMP (°F)	PRESSURE (Psia)	LIQUID DENSITY (lb/ft³)	VAPOR VOLUME (ft³/lb)	ENTHALPY H_{liq} (Btu/lb)	ENTHALPY ΔH_{vap} (Btu/lb)	ENTHALPY H_{vap} (Btu/lb)	ENTROPY S_{liq} (Btu/lb°F)	ENTROPY S_{vap} (Btu/lb°F)
98	251.26	61.54	0.1708	45.99	54.90	100.89	0.0933	0.1918
100	258.22	61.14	0.1655	46.74	54.31	101.05	0.0946	0.1917
102	265.33	60.73	0.1603	47.50	53.71	101.21	0.0959	0.1916
104	272.59	60.32	0.1552	48.27	53.09	101.36	0.0973	0.1915
106	280.02	59.90	0.1503	49.05	52.46	101.51	0.0966	0.1913
108	287.60	59.46	0.1455	49.84	51.81	101.65	0.1000	0.1912
110	295.34	59.02	0.1409	50.65	51.13	101.78	0.1013	0.1911
112	303.25	58.57	0.1363	51.47	50.44	101.91	0.1027	0.1910
114	311.34	58.10	0.1319	52.30	49.73	102.03	0.1041	0.1908
116	319.59	57.62	0.1276	53.15	48.99	102.14	0.1056	0.1907
118	328.02	57.13	0.1234	54.01	48.23	102.24	0.1070	0.1905
120	336.63	56.63	0.1193	54.89	47.45	102.34	0.1085	0.1904
122	345.42	56.11	0.1153	55.80	46.33	102.43	0.1100	0.1902
124	354.40	55.57	0.1114	56.72	45.78	102.50	0.1115	0.1900
126	363.57	55.02	0.1076	57.67	44.90	102.57	0.1131	0.1898
128	372.94	54.44	0.1038	58.65	43.97	102.62	0.1147	0.1896
130	382.50	53.85	0.1001	59.65	43.02	102.67	0.1164	0.1893
132	392.27	53.23	0.0965	60.70	41.99	102.69	0.1181	0.1891
134	402.24	52.58	0.0930	61.77	40.94	102.71	0.1198	0.1888
136	412.42	51.90	0.0895	62.90	39.80	102.70	0.1217	0.1885
138	422.82	51.18	0.0860	64.07	38.61	102.68	0.1236	0.1882
140	433.44	50.42	0.0826	65.29	37.35	102.64	0.1256	0.1878
142	444.28	49.62	0.0792	66.59	35.98	102.57	0.1276	0.1874
144	455.34	48.75	0.0758	67.96	34.51	102.47	0.1299	0.1870
146	466.65	47.82	0.0723	69.43	32.91	102.34	0.1322	0.1866
148	478.19	46.80	0.0689	71.02	31.15	102.17	0.1348	0.1860
150	489.97	45.67	0.0653	72.77	29.18	101.95	0.1376	0.1854
152	502.00	44.39	0.0616	74.74	26.91	101.65	0.1407	0.1847
154	514.29	42.89	0.0577	77.02	24.24	101.26	0.1443	0.1838
156	526.83	41.02	0.0533	79.84	20.86	100.70	0.1488	0.1827
158	539.64	38.36	0.0476	83.86	15.94	99.80	0.1553	0.1811
160	***Above Critical Region***							

Genetron® AZ-50 (R-507) Thermodynamic Formulas

T_c = 159.620 °F $\quad$ P_c = 550.620 psia $\quad$ ρ_c = 31.2138 lb./cu.ft. $\quad$ T_b = -52.114 °F $\quad$ ***MWt.*** = 98.859

Experimental vapor pressure correlated as:

$$\ln (P_{vap}/\text{psia}) = A + \frac{B}{T} + CT + DT^2 + \frac{E(F-T)}{T} \ln (F-T); \; T \text{ Rankine}$$

A = 0.2924862663E+02 $\quad$ B = -0.6980594400E+04 $\quad$ C = -0.3143806111E-01

D = 0.2034543662E-04 $\quad$ E = 0.0000000000E+00 $\quad$ F = 0.0000000000E+00

Experimental liquid density correlated as:

$$\rho \text{ (lb./cu.ft.)} = \rho_c + \sum_{i=1}^{4} D_i (1-T_r)^{i/3}$$

D_1 = 0.4095480193E+02 $\quad$ D_2 = 0.9657367140E+02 $\quad$ D_3 = -0.1373264174E+03 $\quad$ D_4 = 0.9275837300E+02

ρ_c = 0.3121379985E+02

Experimental ideal gas heat capacity correlated as:

$$C_p^o \text{ (Btu/lb.R)} = C_1 + C_2 T + C_3 T^2 + C_4 T^3 + C_5 / T; \; T \text{ Rankine}$$

C_1 = 0.2823005799E-01 $\quad$ C_2 = 0.3937799977E-03 $\quad$ C_3 = -0.1284318010E-06

C_4 = 0.0000000000E+00 $\quad$ C_5 = 0.2273532317E+01

Estimated Martin-Hou coefficients used:

$$P = \frac{RT}{(v-b)} + \sum_{i=2}^{5} \frac{A_i + B_i T + C_i \exp(-KT_r)}{(v-b)^i}$$

P (psia), v (cu.ft./lb.), T (R), $T_r = T/T_c$

R = 0.108554 $\quad$ b = 0.6037684713E-02 $\quad$ K = 0.5474999905E+01

i	A_i	B_i	C_i
2	-0.4399993532E+01	0.2423270433E-02	-0.9431533232E+02
3	0.1832078621E+00	-0.1843217222E-03	0.2850803971E+01
4	-0.1000145627E-02	0.0000000000E+00	0.0000000000E+00
5	-0.1397424811E-04	0.3240541064E-07	-0.2694851636E-03

Genetron® AZ-50 (R-507) THERMODYNAMIC TABLE (continued)

TEMP (°C)	PRESSURE (kPa)	LIQUID DENSITY (kg/m³)	VAPOR VOLUME (m³/kg)	ENTHALPY H_{liq} (kJ/kg)	ENTHALPY ΔH_{vap} (kJ/kg)	ENTHALPY H_{vap} (kJ/kg)	ENTROPY S_{liq} (kJ/kg°K)	ENTROPY S_{vap} (kJ/kg°K)
-30	214.37	1263.10	0.0884	13.79	187.33	201.12	0.0575	0.8280
-29	223.31	1259.71	0.0850	15.17	186.54	201.71	0.0631	0.8272
-28	232.54	1256.30	0.0818	16.54	185.75	202.29	0.0687	0.8264
-27	242.05	1252.89	0.0787	17.92	184.95	202.87	0.0743	0.8257
-26	251.84	1249.46	0.0758	19.28	184.16	203.45	0.0798	0.8250
-25	261.93	1246.02	0.0730	20.67	183.36	204.03	0.0853	0.8243
-24	272.33	1242.57	0.0703	22.04	182.56	204.60	0.0908	0.8236
-23	283.03	1239.10	0.0678	23.42	181.76	205.18	0.0963	0.8229
-22	294.04	1235.62	0.0653	24.79	180.96	205.75	0.1017	0.8223
-21	305.38	1232.13	0.0630	26.16	180.16	206.32	0.1072	0.8217
-20	317.04	1228.62	0.0608	27.53	179.36	206.89	0.1125	0.8211
-19	329.01	1225.10	0.0586	28.90	178.56	207.46	0.1179	0.8205
-18	341.37	1221.56	0.0566	30.27	177.56	208.03	0.1232	0.8199
-17	354.04	1218.00	0.0546	31.64	176.95	208.59	0.1286	0.8194
-16	367.06	1214.43	0.0528	33.00	176.15	209.15	0.1338	0.8189
-15	380.44	1210.85	0.0510	34.37	175.34	209.71	0.1391	0.8183
-14	394.18	1207.24	0.0492	35.74	174.53	210.27	0.1443	0.8178
-13	408.29	1203.62	0.0476	37.10	173.73	210.83	0.1496	0.8174
-12	422.77	1199.98	0.0460	38.47	172.92	211.39	0.1547	0.8169
-11	437.64	1196.32	0.0445	39.83	172.11	211.94	0.1599	0.8164
-10	452.89	1192.65	0.0430	41.20	171.29	212.49	0.1651	0.8160
-9	468.53	1188.95	0.0416	42.56	170.48	213.04	0.1702	0.8156
-8	484.59	1185.24	0.0403	43.92	169.67	213.59	0.1753	0.8152
-7	501.03	1181.50	0.0390	45.29	168.84	214.13	0.1804	0.8148
-6	517.90	1177.75	0.0377	46.65	168.02	214.67	0.1854	0.8144
-5	535.18	1173.97	0.0365	48.01	167.20	215.21	0.1904	0.8140
-4	552.90	1170.17	0.0354	49.37	166.38	215.75	0.1955	0.8136
-3	571.05	1166.35	0.0342	50.74	165.55	216.29	0.2005	0.8133
-2	589.64	1162.51	0.0332	52.10	164.72	216.82	0.2054	0.8129
-1	608.68	1158.64	0.0321	53.46	163.89	217.35	0.2104	0.8126
0	628.17	1154.75	0.0312	54.82	163.06	217.88	0.2153	0.8123
1	648.13	1150.83	0.0302	56.19	162.21	218.40	0.2202	0.8120
2	668.56	1146.89	0.0293	57.55	161.38	218.93	0.2251	0.8117
3	689.47	1142.92	0.0284	58.91	160.54	219.45	0.2300	0.8114
4	710.86	1138.93	0.0275	60.28	159.68	219.96	0.2349	0.8111
5	732.74	1134.90	0.0267	61.65	158.83	220.48	0.2397	0.8108
6	755.13	1130.85	0.0259	63.01	157.98	220.99	0.2446	0.8105
7	778.03	1126.77	0.0251	64.38	157.12	221.50	0.2494	0.8102
8	801.44	1122.65	0.0244	65.75	156.25	222.00	0.2542	0.8100
9	825.38	1118.51	0.0237	67.12	155.38	222.50	0.2590	0.8097
10	849.85	1114.33	0.0230	68.49	154.51	223.00	0.2638	0.8095
11	874.86	1110.12	0.0223	69.87	153.62	223.49	0.2686	0.8092
12	900.43	1105.87	0.0216	71.25	152.73	223.98	0.2733	0.8090
13	926.55	1101.59	0.0210	72.63	151.84	224.47	0.2781	0.8087
14	953.24	1097.27	0.0204	74.01	150.94	224.95	0.2828	0.8085
15	980.51	1092.91	0.0198	75.40	150.03	225.43	0.2875	0.8082
16	1008.37	1088.52	0.0193	76.76	149.13	225.91	0.2923	0.8080
17	1036.81	1084.08	0.0187	78.18	148.20	226.38	0.2970	0.8078
18	1065.87	1079.60	0.0182	79.57	147.28	226.85	0.3017	0.8075
19	1095.54	1075.08	0.0176	80.97	146.34	227.31	0.3064	0.88073
20	1125.83	1070.51	0.0171	82.38	145.38	227.76	0.3111	0.8070
21	1156.76	1065.89	0.0167	83.79	144.43	228.22	0.3158	0.8068
22	1188.33	1061.23	0.0162	85.20	143.46	228.66	0.3205	0.8066
23	1220.55	1056.52	0.0157	86.63	142.48	229.11	0.3252	0.8063
24	1253.44	1051.75	0.0153	88.05	141.49	229.54	0.3299	0.8061
25	1287.01	1046.93	0.0149	89.49	140.48	229.97	0.3346	0.8058
26	1321.26	1042.05	0.0144	90.93	139.47	230.40	0.3393	0.8056
27	1356.21	1037.11	0.0140	92.38	138.44	230.82	0.3441	0.8053
28	1391.87	1032.11	0.0136	93.83	137.40	231.23	0.3488	0.8050
29	1428.25	1027.05	0.0133	95.30	136.34	231.64	0.3535	0.8048
30	1465.36	1021.92	0.0129	96.77	135.27	232.04	0.3583	0.8045
31	1503.21	1016.73	0.0125	98.26	134.17	232.43	0.3630	0.8042
32	1541.82	1011.46	0.0122	99.75	133.07	232.82	0.3678	0.8039
33	1581.20	1006.11	0.0118	101.26	131.94	233.20	0.3726	0.8036
34	1621.36	1000.68	0.0115	102.78	130.79	233.57	0.3775	0.8033
35	1662.32	995.17	0.0112	104.31	129.62	233.93	0.3823	0.8029
36	1704.08	989.58	0.0109	105.86	128.42	234.28	0.3872	0.8026
37	1746.66	983.89	0.0106	107.42	127.21	234.63	0.3921	0.8022
38	1790.08	978.11	0.0103	109.00	125.96	234.96	0.3970	0.8019
39	1834.35	972.22	0.0100	110.59	124.70	235.29	0.4020	0.8015
40	1879.47	966.23	0.0097	112.20	123.41	235.61	0.4070	0.8011
41	1925.48	960.12	0.0094	113.84	122.07	235.91	0.4120	0.8006
42	1972.38	953.90	0.0091	115.49	120.72	236.21	0.4171	0.8002
43	2020.19	947.55	0.0089	117.16	119.33	236.49	0.4223	0.7997
44	2068.92	941.06	0.0086	118.86	117.90	236.76	0.4275	0.7992

Genetron® AZ-50 (R-507) THERMODYNAMIC TABLE (continued)

TEMP (°C)	PRESSURE (kPa)	LIQUID DENSITY (kg/m³)	VAPOR VOLUME (m³/kg)	ENTHALPY H_{liq} (kJ/kg)	ENTHALPY ΔH_{vap} (kJ/kg)	ENTHALPY H_{vap} (kJ/kg)	ENTROPY S_{liq} (kJ/kg°K)	ENTROPY S_{vap} (kJ/kg°K)
45	2118.59	934.43	0.0084	120.59	116.43	237.02	0.4328	0.7987
46	2169.22	927.65	0.0081	122.35	114.91	237.26	0.4381	0.7982
47	2220.82	920.71	0.0079	124.13	113.36	237.49	0.4435	0.7976
48	2273.41	913.60	0.0077	125.95	111.75	237.70	0.4490	0.7970
49	2327.01	906.30	0.0074	127.80	110.10	237.90	0.4546	0.7964
50	2381.63	898.79	0.0072	129.69	108.39	238.08	0.4603	0.7957
51	2437.29	891.07	0.0070	131.62	106.62	238.24	0.4660	0.7950
52	2494.02	883.12	0.0068	133.60	104.78	238.38	0.4719	0.7942
53	2551.83	874.91	0.0066	135.63	102.87	238.50	0.4780	0.7934
54	2610.74	866.42	0.0063	137.72	100.88	238.60	0.4841	0.7925
55	2670.77	857.62	0.0061	139.86	98.81	238.67	0.4905	0.7916
56	2731.94	848.48	0.0059	142.07	96.65	238.72	0.4970	0.7906
57	2794.27	838.97	0.0057	144.36	94.38	238.74	0.5037	0.7896
58	2857.78	829.04	0.0055	146.73	91.99	238.72	0.5106	0.7884
59	2922.50	818.62	0.0053	149.19	89.48	238.67	0.5178	0.7872
60	2988.45	807.67	0.0052	151.77	86.80	238.57	0.5253	0.7859
61	3055.64	796.09	0.0050	154.47	83.97	238.44	0.5332	0.7845
62	3124.11	783.79	0.0048	157.32	80.92	238.24	0.5414	0.7829
63	3193.88	770.62	0.0046	160.34	77.65	237.99	0.5501	0.7812
64	3264.97	756.41	0.0044	163.57	74.09	237.66	0.5595	0.7792
65	3337.40	740.89	0.0042	167.07	70.18	237.25	0.5696	0.7771
66	3411.21	723.71	0.0040	170.91	65.81	236.72	0.5806	0.7746
67	3486.42	704.28	0.0038	175.22	60.82	236.04	0.5930	0.7718
68	3563.05	681.59	0.0036	180.21	54.93	235.14	0.6073	0.7683
69	3641.13	653.59	0.0033	186.33	47.57	233.90	0.6249	0.7639
70	3720.70	614.54	0.0030	194.93	37.04	231.97	0.6496	0.7575

Genetron® AZ-50 (R-507) Thermodynamic Formulas

T_c = 70.900 °C P_c = 3793.559 kPa ρ_c = 499.9982 kg/m³ T_b = -46.73°C ***MWt.*** = 98.859

Experimental vapor pressure correlated as:

$$\ln(P_{vap}/\text{Pa}) = A + \frac{B}{T} + CT + DT^2 + \frac{E(F-T)}{T}\ln(F-T)\ ;\ T\ \text{Kelvin}$$

A = 0.3808714000E+02 B = -0.3878108000E+04 C = -0.5658851000E-01

D = 0.6591921000E+04 E = 0.0000000000E+00 F = 0.0000000000E+00

Experimental liquid density correlated as:

$$\rho\ (\text{kg/m}^3) = \rho_c + \sum_{i=1}^{4} D_i (1-T_r)^{i/3}$$

D_1 = 0.6560344849E+03 D_2 = 0.1546965332E+04 D_3 = -0.2199763184E+04 D_4 = 0.1485849976E+04

ρ_c = 0.4999982453E+03

Experimetnal ideal gas heat capacity correlated as:

$$C_p^o\ (\text{J/mol K}) = C_1 + C_2T + C_3T^2 + C_4T^3 + C_5/T\ ;\ T\ \text{Kelvin}$$

C_1 = 0.1168450165E-02 C_2 = 0.2933759987E-00 C_3 = -0.1722328452E-3

C_4 = 0.0000000000E+00 C_5 = 0.5227897339E+03

Estimated Martin-Hou coefficients used:

$$P = \frac{RT}{(v-b)} + \sum_{i=2}^{5} \frac{A_i + B_iT + C_i\exp(-KT_r)}{(v-b)^i}$$

P (Pa), ***v***(m³/mole), ***T***(K), $T_r = T/T_c$

R = 8.314410 J/mol °K b = 0.3726197247E-04 K = 0.5474999905E+01

i	A_i	B_i	C_i
2	-0.1155474424E+01	0.1145467279E-02	-0.2476798058E+02
3	0.2969257184E-03	-0.5377157208E-06	0.4620309453E-02
4	-0.1000373917E-07	0.0000000000E+00	0.0000000000E+00
5	-0.8626268645E-12	0.3600680308E-14	-0.1663525220E-10

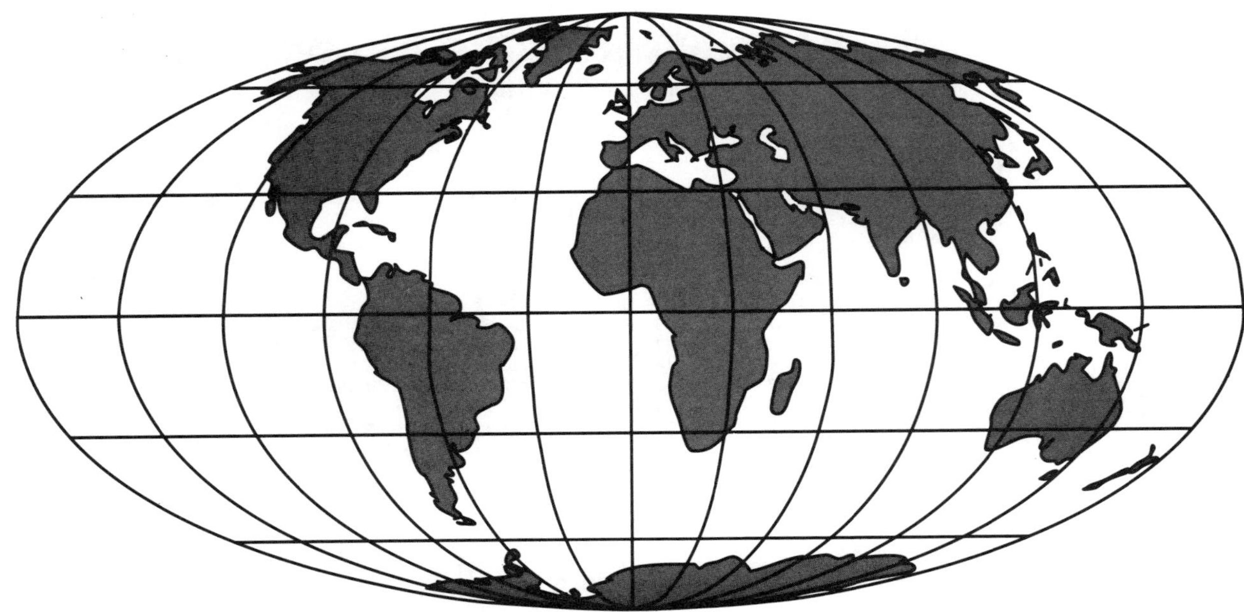

For more information contact your AlliedSignal Fluorocarbons representative.

WORLDWIDE SALES OFFICES

UNITED STATES
AlliedSignal Inc.
Fluorocarbons
P.O. Box 1053
Morristown, NJ 07962-1053
Phone: 800-631-8138
Fax: 201-455-6395

MANUFACTURER'S REPRESENTATIVE
REFRIGERANTS
(Southeastern U.S.)
E.V. Dunbar Company
4200 Northside Parkway N.W.
Building 3A
Atlanta, Georgia 30327
Phone: 800-241-2010
Fax: 800-849-0834

LATIN AMERICA-CARIBBEAN
AlliedSignal Inc.
Fluorocarbons
20801 Biscayne Blvd.
Suite #435
Aventura, FL 33180
Phone: 305-931-6465
Fax: 305-931-6762

CANADA
AlliedSignal Inc.
Fluorocarbons
50 Burnhamthorpe Road West
Suite 904
Box 71
Mississauga, Ontario
L5B 3C2
Phone: 905-276-9211
Fax: 905-276-5711

ASIA
AlliedSignal Inc.
Fluorocarbons
Suite 3812-16, Shell Tower
Times Square, 1 Matheson Street
Causeway Bay, Hong Kong
Phone: 852-506-1812
Fax: 852-506-0192

EUROPE-MIDDLE EAST-AFRICA
AlliedSignal Fluorochemicals
Europe B.V.
Stadsring 163A
3817 BA Amersfoort
The Netherlands
Phone: 033-792300
Fax: 033-792350

AUSTRALIA
AlliedSignal Inc.
Fluorocarbons
71 Queens Road, 2nd Floor
Melbourne, Victoria 3004
Australia
Phone: 61-3-9529-1411
Fax: 61-3-9510-9837

CUSTOMER SERVICE
HOW TO ORDER
To place an order from anywhere in the continental United States, Hawaii and the Caribbean:
Call: 800-522-8001
Fax: 800-458-9073
In Canada:
Call: 800-553-9749
Fax: 800-553-9750
Outside these areas:
Call: 201-455-6300
Fax: 201-455-2763

DISCLAIMER
All Statements, information and data given herein are believed to be accurate and reliable but are presented without guaranty, warranty or responsibility of any kind, expressed or implied. Statements or suggestions concerning possible use of our products are made without representation or warranty that any such use is free of patent infringement and are not recommendations to infringe any patent. The user should not assume that all safety measures are indicated, or that other measures may not be required.

G-525-0
5/95 2
Printed in U

Genetron® 123 Bulletin

Fluorocarbons

Understanding Needs.
Finding Solutions.

Genetron® 123

(Dichlorotrifluoroethane)

Genetron® 123 is a very low-ozone depleting compound that serves as a replacement to CFC-11 in centrifugal chillers.

*Physical Properties:

Chemical formula	$CHCl_2CF_3$
Molecular weight	152.9
Boiling point @ 1 atm, °F	82.2
Critical temperature, °F	363
Critical pressure (psia)	540
Critical density, lb./cu. ft.	34.5
Saturated liquid density @ 86°F lb./cu. ft.	90.4
Heat of vaporization @ boiling point Btu/lb.	72.9
Specific heat of liquid @ 86°F Btu/lb. °F	0.21
Specific heat of vapor at constant pressure (Cp @ 86°F and 1 Atm Btu/lb.°F)	0.17
Flammable range, % volume in air	**Nonflammable
Ozone depletion potential	0.016

Comparative Cycle Performance:

Evaporator temperature = 35°F
Condenser temperature = 105°F
Degrees superheat @ evaporator = 0°F
Degrees subcooling = 0°F
Compressor isentropic efficiency: 75%

	Genetron® 123	Genetron® 11
Evaporator pressure, in Hg	19.5	17.2
Condenser pressure, psig	8.1	10.9
Compression ratio	4.47	4.06
Compressor discharge temperature, °F	122.8	144.0
Coefficient of performance	4.63	4.72
Refrigerant circulation per ton, lb/min	3.29	3.01
Compressor displacement per ton, cfm	21.78	18.2
Liquid flow per ton, cu. in./min	64.1	57.9
Latent heat @ evaporator temp., Btu/lb	76.9	81.0
Net refrigeration effect Btu/lb	60.7	66.4

*Information based on estimated properties

**Based on ASHRAE Standard 34 with match ignition

123 Thermodynamic Table

Temp. (°F)	Pressure (Psia)	Density (lb/ft³)	Vapor Volume (ft³/1b)	H_{liq} (Btu/lb)	Enthalp ΔH_{vap} (Btu/lb)
0	2.00	97.71	15.9382	8.16	79.40
2	2.12	97.54	15.0945	8.58	79.26
4	2.25	97.38	14.3033	9.00	79.12
6	2.38	97.22	13.5607	9.43	78.97
8	2.52	97.05	12.8634	9.85	78.84
10	2.66	96.89	12.2082	10.27	78.70
12	2.82	96.72	11.5923	10.70	78.55
14	2.97	96.56	11.0131	11.13	78.41
16	3.14	96.39	10.4679	11.56	78.26
18	3.31	96.23	9.9545	11.99	78.11
20	3.50	96.06	9.4709	12.42	77.97
22	3.69	95.90	9.0150	12.85	77.82
24	3.88	95.73	8.5851	13.28	77.68
26	4.09	95.56	8.1794	13.72	77.52
28	4.31	95.40	7.7964	14.15	77.38
30	4.53	95.23	7.4347	14.59	77.22
32	4.77	95.06	7.0929	15.03	77.07
34	5.01	94.90	6.7697	15.46	76.92
36	5.26	94.73	6.4639	15.90	76.77
38	5.53	94.56	6.1746	16.35	76.61
40	5.80	94.39	5.9007	16.79	76.45
42	6.09	94.22	5.6412	17.23	76.30
44	6.39	94.05	5.3953	17.68	76.13
46	6.70	93.88	5.1622	18.12	75.98
48	7.02	93.71	4.9411	18.57	75.82
50	7.35	93.54	4.7312	19.02	75.65
52	7.70	93.37	4.5320	19.47	75.49
54	8.06	93.20	4.3429	19.92	75.33
56	8.43	93.03	4.1631	20.37	75.16
58	8.82	92.86	3.9922	20.82	75.00
60	9.22	92.69	3.8297	21.28	74.83
62	9.63	92.51	3.6752	21.73	74.66
64	10.06	92.34	3.5281	22.19	74.49
66	10.51	92.17	3.3880	22.64	74.33
68	10.97	91.99	3.2546	23.10	74.16
70	11.44	91.82	3.1275	23.56	73.98
72	11.94	91.65	3.0064	24.02	73.81
74	12.44	91.47	2.8908	24.49	73.63
76	12.97	91.30	2.7806	24.95	73.45
78	13.52	91.12	2.6755	25.41	73.28
80	14.08	90.94	2.5751	25.88	73.10
82	14.66	90.77	2.4793	26.35	72.91
84	15.26	90.59	2.3877	26.81	72.74
86	15.87	90.41	2.3002	27.28	72.55
88	16.51	90.24	2.2165	27.75	72.37
90	17.17	90.06	2.1366	28.22	72.19
92	17.85	89.88	2.0600	28.70	71.99
94	18.55	89.70	1.9868	29.17	71.81
96	19.27	89.52	1.9167	29.64	71.62
98	20.01	89.34	1.8496	30.12	71.43
100	20.77	89.16	1.7853	30.59	71.24
102	21.56	88.98	1.7237	31.07	71.05
104	22.37	88.79	1.6647	31.55	70.85
106	23.20	88.61	1.6081	32.03	70.66
108	24.06	88.43	1.5538	32.51	70.46
110	24.94	88.25	1.5017	32.99	70.27
112	25.85	88.06	1.4518	33.48	70.06
114	26.78	87.88	1.4038	33.96	69.86
116	27.74	87.69	1.3577	34.45	69.66
118	28.72	87.51	1.3135	34.93	69.46
120	29.74	87.32	1.2710	35.42	69.25

thalpy H_{vap} (Btu/lb)	Entropy S_{liq} (Btu/lb. °F)	Entropy S_{vap} (Btu/lb °F)
87.56	0.0186	0.1913
87.84	0.0195	0.1911
88.12	0.0204	0.1910
88.40	0.0213	0.1909
88.69	0.0222	0.1908
88.97	0.0231	0.1907
89.25	0.0240	0.1905
89.54	0.0249	0.1904
89.82	0.0258	0.1903
90.10	0.0267	0.1903
90.39	0.0276	0.1902
90.67	0.0285	0.1901
90.96	0.0294	0.1900
91.24	0.0303	0.1899
91.53	0.0312	0.1899
91.81	0.0321	0.1898
92.10	0.0330	0.1897
92.38	0.0339	0.1897
92.67	0.0348	0.1896
92.96	0.0356	0.1896
93.24	0.0365	0.1895
93.53	0.0374	0.1895
93.81	0.0383	0.1895
94.10	0.0392	0.1894
94.39	0.0401	0.1894
94.67	0.0409	0.1894
94.96	0.0418	0.1894
95.25	0.0427	0.1894
95.53	0.0436	0.1893
95.82	0.0445	0.1893
96.11	0.0453	0.1893
96.39	0.0462	0.1893
96.68	0.0471	0.1893
96.97	0.0479	0.1893
97.26	0.0488	0.1893
97.54	0.0497	0.1893
97.83	0.0505	0.1894
98.12	0.0514	0.1894
98.40	0.0523	0.1894
98.69	0.0531	0.1894
98.98	0.0540	0.1894
99.26	0.0549	0.1895
99.55	0.0557	0.1895
99.83	0.0566	0.1895
100.12	0.0574	0.1896
100.41	0.0583	0.1896
100.69	0.0591	0.1897
100.98	0.0600	0.1897
101.26	0.0609	0.1897
101.55	0.0617	0.1898
101.83	0.0626	0.1898
102.12	0.0634	0.1899
102.40	0.0643	0.1899
102.69	0.0651	0.1900
102.97	0.0659	0.1901
103.26	0.0668	0.1901
103.54	0.0676	0.1902
103.82	0.0685	0.1903
104.11	0.0693	0.1903
104.39	0.0702	0.1904
104.67	0.0710	0.1905

123 Thermodynamic Table *(continued)*

Temp. (°F)	Pressure (Psia)	Liquid Density (lb/ft³)	Vapor Volume (ft³/1b)	Enthalpy H_{liq} (Btu/lb)	Enthalpy ΔH_{vap} (Btu/lb)	Enthalpy H_{vap} (Btu/lb)	Entropy S_{liq} (Btu/lb °F)	Entropy S_{vap} (Btu/lb °F)
122	30.78	87.13	1.2301	35.91	69.05	104.96	0.0718	0.1905
124	31.84	86.94	1.1909	36.40	68.84	105.24	0.0727	0.1906
126	32.94	86.76	1.1531	36.89	68.63	105.52	0.0735	0.1907
128	34.06	86.57	1.1168	37.38	68.42	105.80	0.0743	0.1908
130	35.21	86.38	1.0818	37.88	68.20	106.08	0.0752	0.1908
132	36.40	86.19	1.0482	38.37	67.99	106.36	0.0760	0.1909
134	37.61	86.00	1.0158	38.87	67.78	106.65	0.0768	0.1910
136	38.85	85.81	0.9847	39.36	67.57	106.93	0.0777	0.1911
138	40.13	85.61	0.9547	39.86	67.35	107.21	0.0785	0.1912
140	41.44	85.42	0.9257	40.36	67.12	107.48	0.0793	0.1913
142	42.78	85.23	0.8979	40.86	66.90	107.76	0.0802	0.1914
144	44.15	85.03	0.8710	41.36	66.68	108.04	0.0810	0.1914
146	45.56	84.84	0.8451	41.86	66.46	108.32	0.0818	0.1915
148	47.00	84.64	0.8201	42.37	66.23	108.60	0.0826	0.1916
150	48.47	84.44	0.7960	42.87	66.01	108.88	0.0835	0.1917
152	49.98	84.25	0.7728	43.38	65.77	109.15	0.0843	0.1918
154	51.53	84.05	0.7504	43.88	65.55	109.43	0.0851	0.1919
156	53.11	83.85	0.7287	44.39	65.32	109.71	0.0859	0.1920
158	54.73	83.65	0.7078	44.90	65.08	109.98	0.0867	0.1921
160	56.38	83.45	0.6876	45.41	64.85	110.26	0.0876	0.1922

123 Thermodynamic Formulas

T_c=363.200 °F P_c=533.097 psia ρ_c=34.5257 lb./cu.ft. T_b=82.166 °F **MWt.**=152.930

Experimental vapor pressure correlated as:

$$\ln(P_{vap}) = A + \frac{B}{T} + CT + DT^2 + \frac{E\,(F-T)}{T}\ln(F-T)$$

where P_{vap} is in psia and T in °R

A=0.2135167313E+02 B=−0.7580945477E+04 C=−0.1151736692E−01
D=0.5341983248E−05 E=0.0000000000E+00 F=0.0000000000E+00

Experimental ideal gas heat capacity correlated as:

$$C_p^o \text{ (Btu/lb. °R)} = C_1 + C_2T + C_3T^2 + C_4T^3 + C_5/T$$

where T is in °R

C_1=0.3627324125E−01 C_2=0.2963321983E−03 C_3=−0.1222965602E−06
C_4=0.0000000000E+00 C_5=0.0000000000E+00

Experimental liquid density correlated as:

$$\rho = \rho_c + \sum_{i=1}^{4} D_i(1-T_r)^{i/3}$$

where ρ is in lb./cu.ft.

D_1=0.5473153636E+02 D_2=0.6881690823E+02 D_3=−0.9265622670E+02 D_4=0.6699838557E+02
ρ_c =0.3452572608E+02

Estimated Martin-Hou coefficients used:

$$P = \frac{RT}{(v-b)} + \sum_{i=2}^{5} \frac{A_i + B_i T + C_i\, exp(-KT_r)}{(v-b)^i}$$

P (psia), v (cu.ft./lb.), T (°R), $T_r = T/T_c$

R = 0.070173 b = 0.5778313758E−02 K = 0.5474999905 + 01

i	A_i	B_i	C_i
2	−0.3461174842E+01	0.1482683303E−02	−0.6375783935E+02
3	0.1271057059E+00	−0.9675560464E−04	0.1712913479E+01
4	−0.5983292209E−03	0.0000000000E+00	0.0000000000E+00
5	−0.7744198272E−05	0.1325431541E−07	−0.1261428005E−03

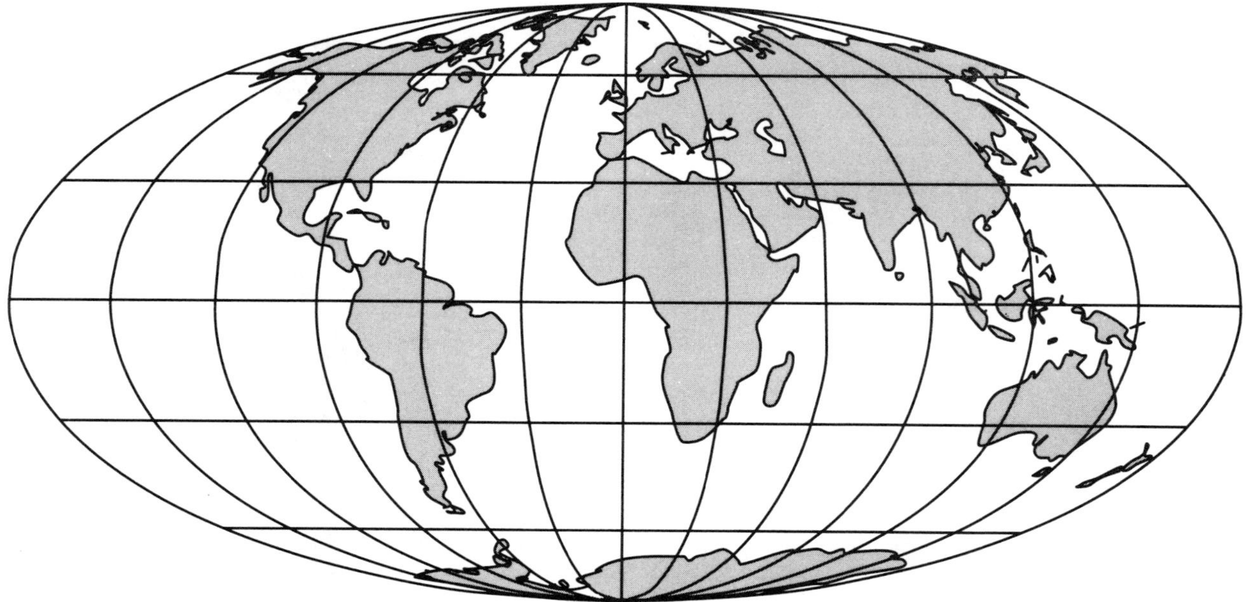

For more information contact your AlliedSignal Fluorocarbons representative.

WORLDWIDE SALES OFFICES

UNITED STATES

AlliedSignal Inc.
Fluorocarbons
P.O. Box 1053
Morristown, NJ 07962-1053
Phone: 800-631-8138
Fax: 201-455-6395

MANUFACTURER'S REPRESENTATIVE

REFRIGERANTS
(Southeastern U.S.)

E.V. Dunbar Company
4200 Northside Parkway N.W.
Building 3A
Atlanta, Georgia 30327
Phone: 800-241-2010
Fax: 800:849-0834

LATIN AMERICA-CARIBBEAN

AlliedSignal Inc.
Fluorocarbons
20801 Biscayne Blvd.
Suite #435
Aventura, FL 33180
Phone: 305-931-6465
Fax: 305-931-6762

CANADA

AlliedSignal Inc.
Fluorocarbons
50 Burnhamthorpe Road West
Suite 904
Box 71
Mississauga, Ontario
L5B 3C2
Phone: 416-276-9211
Fax: 416-276-5711

EUROPE • MIDDLE EAST AFRICA

AlliedSignal Europe N.V.
Fluorocarbons
Haasrode Research Park-Grauwmeer 1
3001 Heverlee (Leuven)
Belgium
Phone: 32-16-391290 or 391291
Fax: 32-16-400159

AUSTRALIA

AlliedSignal Inc.
Fluorocarbons
71 Queens Road, 2nd Floor
Melbourne, Victoria 3004
Australia
Phone: 61-3-529-1411
Fax: 61-3-510-9837

ASIA

AlliedSignal Inc.
Fluorocarbons
E. Wing, 1028 New World Office Building
24 Salisbury Road, Tsimshatsui
Kowloon, Hong Kong
Phone: 852-724-2929
Fax: 852-722-7495

CUSTOMER SERVICE

HOW TO ORDER

To place an order from anywhere in the continental United States, Hawaii and the Caribbean:
Phone: 800-522-8001
Fax: 800-458-9073
In Canada:
Phone: 800-553-9749
Fax: 800-553-9750
Outside these areas:
Phone: 201-455-6300
Fax: 201-455-2763

Genetron® Understanding Needs. Finding Solutions.

B-525-646
11-93 10K
Printed in USA

DISCLAIMER

All statements, information and data given herein are believed to be accurate and reliable but are presented without guaranty, warranty or responsibility of any kind expressed or implied. Statements or suggestions concerning possible use of our products are made without representation or warranty that any such use is free of patent infringement and are not recommendations to infringe any patent. The user should not assume that all safety measures are indicated, or that other measures may not be required

Genetron® 134a Bulletin

Fluorocarbons

Understanding Needs.
Finding Solutions.

Genetron® 134a

(Tetrafluoroethane)

Genetron® 134a is a non-ozone depleting compound and the refrigerant of choice to replace CFC-12 in numerous air conditioning and cooling applications. It replaces CFC-12 in automobile air conditioning, residential, commerical and industrial refrigeration and in certain centrifugal chiller applications.

Physical Properties:

Chemical formula	CF_3CH_2F
Molecular weight	102.03
Boiling point @ 1 atm, °F	-15.1
Critical temperature, °F	214.0
Critical pressure (psia)	589.9
Critical density (lb./cu. ft.)	31.97
Liquid density @ 80°F (lb./cu. ft.)	75.0
Heat of vaporization @ boiling point (Btu/lb.°F)	92.4
Specific heat of liquid @ 80°F (Btu/lb.°F)	0.341
Specific heat of vapor @ constant pressure, 1 atm and 80°F (Btu/lb.°F)	0.204
Flammable range, % volume in air	*None
Ozone depletion potential	0
Greenhouse warmng potential (estimate)	0.285

Comparative Cycle Performance:

Evaporator temperature = 20°F
Condenser temperature = 110°F
Suction superheat = 30°F
Subcooling = 10°F
Compressor isentropic efficiency: 65%

	Genetron®		
	12	22	134a
Evaporator pressure, psig	21.0	43.0	**18.5**
Condenser pressure, psig	136.4	226.3	**146.4**
Compression ratio	4.23	4.17	**4.86**
Compressor discharge temperature, °F	188.1	227.0	**178.3**
Coefficient of performance	2.90	2.79	**2.83**
Refrigerant circulation per ton, lb/min	3.80	2.78	**3.00**
Compressor displacement per ton, cfm	4.51	2.82	**4.55**
Liquid flow per ton, cu. in./min	83.2	67.4	**71.7**
Latent heat @ evaporator temp., Btu/lb	66.5	90.6	**86.9**
Net refrigeration effect Btu/lb	52.7	72.0	**66.7**

*Flame limits measured using ASTM E681 with electrically activated kitchen match ignition source per ASHRAE Standard 34.

134a Thermodynamic Table

Temp. (°F)	Pressure (psia)	Liquid Density (lb/ft³)	Vapor Volume (ft³/1b)	Enthalpy H_{liq} (Btu/lb)	Enthal ΔH_{va} (Btu/
-20	12.95	86.466	3.4174	5.71	93.1
-18	13.63	86.260	3.2551	6.30	92.8
-16	14.35	86.054	3.1019	6.88	92.5
-14	15.09	85.847	2.9574	7.47	92.2
-12	15.87	85.639	2.8209	8.06	91.9
-10	16.67	85.431	2.6919	8.65	91.6
-8	17.51	85.222	2.5699	9.24	91.3
-6	18.38	85.012	2.4546	9.83	91.0
-4	19.29	84.801	2.3454	10.43	90.7
-2	20.23	84.589	2.2420	11.03	90.4
0	21.20	84.377	2.1440	11.63	90.1
2	22.22	84.163	2.0512	12.23	89.8
4	23.27	83.949	1.9632	12.84	89.4
6	24.35	83.734	1.8797	13.44	89.1
8	25.48	83.518	1.8004	14.05	88.8
10	26.65	83.301	1.7251	14.66	88.5
12	27.86	83.084	1.6536	15.27	88.2
14	29.11	82.865	1.5856	15.89	87.8
16	30.41	82.645	1.5210	16.50	87.5
18	31.75	82.425	1.4595	17.12	87.2
20	33.14	82.203	1.4010	17.74	86.8
22	34.57	81.980	1.3452	18.36	86.5
24	36.05	81.757	1.2922	18.99	86.1
26	37.58	81.532	1.2416	19.61	85.8
28	39.16	81.306	1.1934	20.24	85.5
30	40.79	81.079	1.1474	20.87	85.1
32	42.47	80.851	1.1035	21.50	84.7
34	44.21	80.622	1.0617	22.14	84.4
36	45.99	80.392	1.0217	22.77	84.0
38	47.84	80.160	.9835	23.41	83.7
40	49.74	79.928	.9470	24.05	83.3
42	51.70	79.694	.9122	24.69	82.9
44	53.71	79.458	.8788	25.34	82.5
46	55.79	79.222	.8469	25.98	82.2
48	57.93	78.984	.8164	26.63	81.8
50	60.13	78.745	.7871	27.28	81.4
52	62.39	78.504	.7591	27.93	81.0
54	64.71	78.262	.7323	28.58	80.6
56	67.11	78.019	.7066	29.24	80.2
58	69.57	77.774	.6820	29.90	79.8
60	72.09	77.527	.6584	30.56	79.4
62	74.69	77.279	.6357	31.22	79.0
64	77.36	77.030	.6140	31.88	78.6
66	80.09	76.778	.5931	32.55	78.2
68	82.90	76.525	.5731	33.22	77.8
70	85.79	76.271	.5538	33.89	77.4
72	88.75	76.014	.5353	34.56	77.0
74	91.79	75.756	.5175	35.24	76.5
76	94.90	75.496	.5004	35.91	76.1
78	98.09	75.234	.4840	36.59	75.7
80	101.37	74.971	.4682	37.27	75.3
82	104.73	74.705	.4530	37.96	74.8
84	108.16	74.437	.4383	38.65	74.4
86	111.69	74.167	.4242	39.33	73.9
88	115.30	73.895	.4106	40.03	73.4
90	118.99	73.621	.3975	40.72	73.0
92	122.78	73.344	.3849	41.42	72.5
94	126.65	73.065	.3728	42.12	72.1
96	130.62	72.784	.3610	42.82	71.6
98	134.68	72.500	.3497	43.52	71.1

Enthalpy H_{vap} (Btu/lb)	Entropy S_{liq} (Btu/lb °F)	Entropy S_{vap} (Btu/lb °F)
3.81	.0133	.2250
9.11	.0146	.2247
9.40	.0159	.2244
9.70	.0172	.2242
9.99	.0185	.2239
0.29	.0198	.2236
0.58	.0212	.2234
0.87	.0225	.2231
1.17	.0238	.2229
1.46	.0251	.2227
1.75	.0264	.2224
2.04	.0277	.2222
2.33	.0290	.2220
2.62	.0303	.2218
2.91	.0316	.2216
3.19	.0329	.2214
3.48	.0342	.2212
3.76	.0355	.2210
4.05	.0368	.2208
4.33	.0381	.2206
4.62	.0393	.2205
4.90	.0406	.2203
5.18	.0419	.2201
5.46	.0432	.2200
5.74	.0445	.2198
6.02	.0458	.2196
6.29	.0470	.2195
6.57	.0483	.2194
6.85	.0496	.2192
7.12	.0509	.2191
7.39	.0521	.2189
7.66	.0534	.2188
7.93	.0547	.2187
8.20	.0560	.2186
8.47	.0572	.2184
8.74	.0585	.2183
9.00	.0598	.2182
9.27	.0610	.2181
9.53	.0623	.2180
9.79	.0636	.2179
0.05	.0648	.2178
0.31	.0661	.2177
0.57	.0673	.2176
0.82	.0686	.2175
1.08	.0698	.2174
1.33	.0711	.2173
1.58	.0724	.2172
1.83	.0736	.2171
2.08	.0749	.2170
2.32	.0761	.2170
2.57	.0774	.2169
2.81	.0786	.2168
3.05	.0799	.2167
3.29	.0811	.2166
3.52	.0824	.2166
3.76	.0836	.2165
3.99	.0849	.2164
4.22	.0861	.2163
4.44	.0873	.2162
4.67	.0886	.2162

134a Thermodynamic Table *(continued)*

Temp. (°F)	Pressure (psia)	Liquid Density (lb/ft³)	Vapor Volume (ft³/1b)	Enthalpy H_{liq} (Btu/lb)	Enthalpy ΔH_{vap} (Btu/lb)	Enthalpy H_{vap} (Btu/lb)	Entropy S_{liq} (Btu/lb °F)	Entropy S_{vap} (Btu/lb °F)
100	138.83	72.213	.3388	44.23	70.66	114.89	.0898	.2161
102	143.07	71.924	.3283	44.94	70.17	115.11	.0911	.2160
104	147.42	71.632	.3181	45.65	69.68	115.33	.0923	.2159
106	151.86	71.338	.3083	46.37	69.17	115.54	.0936	.2159
108	156.40	71.040	.2988	47.09	68.66	115.75	.0948	.2158
110	161.04	70.740	.2896	47.81	68.15	115.96	.0961	.2157
112	165.79	70.436	.2807	48.54	67.63	116.17	.0973	.2156
114	170.64	70.129	.2722	49.26	67.11	116.37	.0986	.2156
116	175.59	69.819	.2639	50.00	66.57	116.57	.0998	.2155
118	180.65	69.506	.2559	50.73	66.03	116.76	.1011	.2154
120	185.82	69.189	.2481	51.47	65.49	116.96	.1023	.2153
122	191.11	68.868	.2406	52.21	64.94	117.15	.1036	.2152
124	196.50	68.543	.2333	52.96	64.37	117.33	.1048	.2151
126	202.00	68.215	.2263	53.71	63.80	117.51	.1061	.2150
128	207.62	67.882	.2195	54.46	63.23	117.69	.1074	.2150
130	213.36	67.545	.2129	55.22	62.64	117.86	.1086	.2149
132	219.22	67.203	.2065	55.98	62.05	118.03	.1099	.2148
134	225.19	66.857	.2003	56.75	61.44	118.19	.1112	.2147
136	231.29	66.506	.1942	57.52	60.83	118.35	.1124	.2145
138	237.51	66.151	.1884	58.30	60.21	118.51	.1137	.2144
140	243.86	65.789	.1827	59.08	59.58	118.66	.1150	.2143
142	250.33	65.422	.1772	59.86	58.94	118.80	.1162	.2142
144	256.94	65.050	.1719	60.65	58.29	118.94	.1175	.2141
146	263.67	64.671	.1667	61.45	57.62	119.07	.1188	.2139
148	270.54	64.286	.1616	62.25	56.94	119.19	.1201	.2138
150	277.54	63.895	.1567	63.06	56.25	119.31	.1214	.2137
152	284.67	63.496	.1519	63.87	55.55	119.42	.1227	.2135
154	291.95	63.090	.1473	64.70	54.82	119.52	.1240	.2133
156	299.37	62.676	.1428	65.52	54.10	119.62	.1253	.2132
158	306.93	62.254	.1384	66.36	53.35	119.71	.1266	.2130
160	314.64	61.823	.1341	67.20	52.58	119.78	.1279	.2128

134a Thermodynamic Formulas

T_c=213.980 °F P_c=589.871 psia ρ_c=31.9702 lb./cu.ft. T_b=−15.08 °F **MWt.**=102.030

Vapor pressure correlated as:

$$\ln(P_{vap}) = A + \frac{B}{T} + CT + DT^2 + \left(\frac{E\,(F-T)}{T}\right) \ln(F-T)$$

where P_{vap} is in psia and T in °R

A=22.98993635 B=−7243.87672 C=−0.013362956 D=0.692966E−05 E=.1995548 F=674.72514

Liquid density correlated as:

$$\rho = \rho_c + \sum_{i=1}^{4} Di\left(1 - \frac{T}{T_c}\right)^{i/3}$$

where ρ is in lb./cu.ft.

D_1=51.1669818 D_2=63.8999897 D_3=−72.213814 D_4=49.3004419

ρ_c =31.9702477

Ideal gas heat capacity correlated as:

$$C_p^o(\text{Btu/lb. R}) = C_1 + C_2T + C_3T^2 + \frac{C_5}{T}$$

Where C_p^o is in Btu./lb °R and T is in °R

C_1=0.0012557213 C_2=0.00043742894 C_3=−0.1487126E−06 C_5=6.802105688

Martin-Hou PVT Equation:

$$P = \frac{RT}{(v-b)} + \sum_{i=2}^{5} \frac{A_i + B_iT + C_i\exp(-KT_r)}{(v-b)^i}$$

P (psia), v (cu.ft./lb.), T(°R), $T_r = T/T_c$

R = 0.105180
b = 0.005535126747
K = 0.5474999905E+01

i	A_i	B_i	C_i
2	−4.447445323	.002352000740	−131.4300642
3	.08630832505	−.296165168E−04	3.856548532
4	−.001001713054	0	0
5	−.106369059E−05	.107907448E−07	−.000313783768

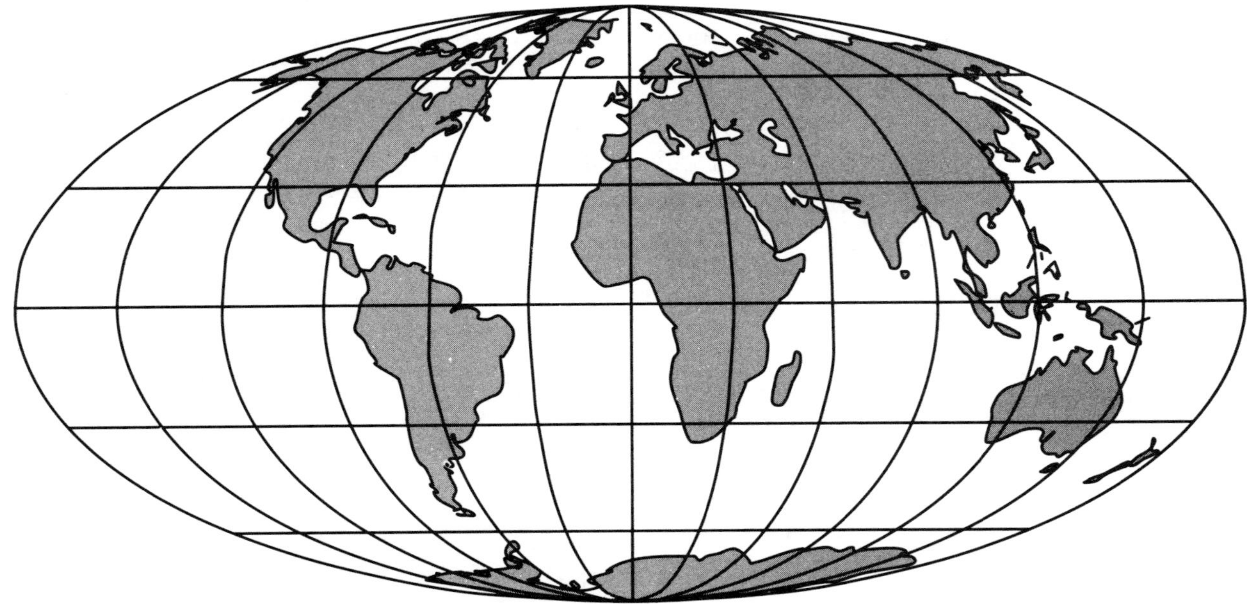

For more information contact your AlliedSignal Fluorocarbons representative.

WORLDWIDE SALES OFFICES

UNITED STATES

AlliedSignal Inc.
Fluorocarbons
P.O. Box 1053
Morristown, NJ 07962-1053
Phone: 800-631-8138
Fax: 201-455-6395

MANUFACTURER'S REPRESENTATIVE

REFRIGERANTS
(Southeastern U.S.)

E.V. Dunbar Company
4200 Northside Parkway N.W.
Building 3A
Atlanta, Georgia 30327
Phone: 800-241-2010
Fax: 800:849-0834

LATIN AMERICA-CARIBBEAN

AlliedSignal Inc.
Fluorocarbons
20801 Biscayne Blvd.
Suite #435
Aventura, FL 33180
Phone: 305-931-6465
Fax: 305-931-6762

CANADA

AlliedSignal Inc.
Fluorocarbons
50 Burnhamthorpe Road West
Suite 904
Box 71
Mississauga, Ontario
L5B 3C2
Phone: 416-276-9211
Fax: 416-276-5711

EUROPE • MIDDLE EAST AFRICA

AlliedSignal Europe N.V.
Fluorocarbons
Haasrode Research Park-Grauwmeer 1
3001 Heverlee (Leuven)
Belgium
Phone: 32-16-391290 or 391291
Fax: 32-16-400159

AUSTRALIA

AlliedSignal Inc.
Fluorocarbons
71 Queens Road, 2nd Floor
Melbourne, Victoria 3004
Australia
Phone: 61-3-529-1411
Fax: 61-3-510-9837

ASIA

AlliedSignal Inc.
Fluorocarbons
E. Wing, 1028 New World Office Building
24 Salisbury Road, Tsimshatsui
Kowloon, Hong Kong
Phone: 852-724-2929
Fax: 852-722-7495

CUSTOMER SERVICE

HOW TO ORDER

To place an order from anywhere in the continental United States, Hawaii and the Caribbean:
Phone: 800-522-8001
Fax: 800-458-9073
In Canada:
Phone: 800-553-9749
Fax: 800-553-9750
Outside these areas:
Phone: 201-455-6300
Fax: 201-455-2763

Genetron® Understanding Needs. Finding Solutions.

B-525-
3-93
Printed in

DISCLAIMER

All statements, information and data given herein are believed to be accurate and reliable but are presented without guaranty, warranty or responsibility of any kind expressed or implied. Statements or suggestions concerning possible use of our products are made without representation or warranty that any such use is free of patent infringement and are not recommendations to infringe any patent. The user should not assume that all safety measures are indicated, or that other measures may not be required

Further Information

For additional information, we invite you to consult your nearest Genetron® Wholesaler at the address and phone number indicated below, or call us at 1-800-631-8138, or fax us at 201-455-6395.

Disclaimer

All statements, information and data given herein are believed to be accurate and reliable, but are presented without guaranty, warranty or responsibility of any kind, expressed or implied. Statements or suggestions concerning possible use of our products are made without representation or warranty that any such use is free of patent infringement, and are not recommendations to infringe any patent. The user should not assume that all safety measures are indicated, or that other measures are indicated, or that other measures may not be required.

P.O. Box 1053
Morristown, NJ 07962-1053

G-525-011
4/95 10K
Printed in USA

Genetron®
MP Blends
Retrofit Guidelines

Fluorocarbons

With the phaseout of CFCs rapidly approaching, existing refrigeration equipment may need to be either replaced with new equipment or retrofitted with alternative refrigerants. By following equipment manufacturers' recommendations and AlliedSignal's guidelines outlined in this publication, service technicians can readily retrofit many existing CFC-12 refrigeration systems to use Genetron® MP Blends.

As the industry moves away from the use of CFCs, refrigerant service personnel will play a key role in the transition to HCFC and HFC alternatives through retrofitting. AlliedSignal has produced this booklet to help service technicians better understand the various technical and operational aspects of carrying out the retrofit procedures using AlliedSignal's new Genetron MP Blends.

Although the information can be helpful as a general guide, **it should not be used as a substitute for the equipment manufacturer's specific recommendations.** For this reason, AlliedSignal strongly recommends contacting the equipment manufacturer for detailed information on retrofitting the specific model under consideration. Also, refer to the Material Safety Data Sheet (MSDS) for safety information on the use of Genetron MP Blends.

Genetron® MP39 and MP66 Blends

Genetron® MP39 and Genetron® MP66 are alternative refrigerants to replace CFC-12 in many medium-temperature refrigeration systems. These blends contain hydrochlorofluorocarbons (HCFCs), chemicals currently regulated by law and scheduled for control beginning in 1996. Both products are mixtures of HCFC-22, HFC-152a and HCFC-124.

Genetron MP39 is a suitable retrofit refrigerant for supermarket display cases, walk-in-coolers, beverage dispensers, vending machines, water coolers and home refrigerators. The use of Genetron MP39 should be limited to applications where the evaporator temperature is above -10°F (-23°C).

Genetron MP66 is designed primarily to replace CFC-12 as a retrofit refrigerant in transport refrigeration. However, where high compression ratios exist, the use of Genetron MP66 can result in significant capacity reductions and excessive discharge temperatures. It is essential that the manufacturer of the equipment be contacted for a recommendation on retrofitting from CFC-12. Genetron MP66 also is suitable for domestic and commercial freezer applications where the evaporator temperature is below -10°F (-23°C).

Should Genetron® MP Blends or Genetron® 134a Be Used?

Where feasible, the preferred retrofit for CFC-12 is Genetron 134a, a non-ozone-depleting refrigerant that will replace CFC-12 in most OEM applications. In some cases, however, retrofitting with Genetron 134a may be difficult because nearly all of the mineral oil in the system must be removed. For these instances, interim-service fluids or blends such as Genetron MP39 or MP66 may be preferred.

Service technicians should keep in mind that future regulations may restrict the use of HCFC-containing refrigerants and dictate the ultimate use of Genetron 134a for servicing CFC-12 equipment.

Genetron MP Blends: Not "Drop-In" Replacements

Genetron MP Blends are not "drop-in" replacements for CFC-12. Since neither Genetron MP39 nor MP66 are azeotropes, each one can segregate. As a result, service technicians must acquaint themselves with modified service procedures to perform each retrofit effectively when using Genetron MP Blends.

The retrofit procedures listed here have been developed by AlliedSignal to address these issues and to help technicians perform successful retrofits of CFC-12 systems utilizing positive-displacement (reciprocating, rotary, scroll or screw) compressors with Genetron MP Blends.

Retrofit Procedures

1. Record Baseline Data

Before making any hardware changes, compare current system operating data with normal operating data. Correct any deficiencies and record final data as a performance baseline. Data should include measurements throughout the system — temperatures and pressures at the evaporator, compressor suction and discharge, and condenser; expansion device, superheat and compressor amps. These measurements will be useful when adjusting the system with Genetron MP Blends during the retrofit.

2. Recover CFC-12 Charge

The CFC-12 charge should be recovered from the system using a recovery machine capable of meeting or exceeding the required levels of evacuation. The charge **must** be collected in a recovery cylinder.

DO NOT VENT THE REFRIGERANT.

Knowing the recommended CFC-12 charge size for the system is helpful. If it is not known, weigh the entire amount of refrigerant removed. This amount can be used as a guide for the initial quantity of Genetron MP39 or MP66 to be charged into the system.

3. Drain the Lubricant

Many small hermetic compressors do not have oil drains, making it necessary to remove the compressor from the system to drain the lubricant. The best point in the system to drain the lubricant is the suction line of the compressor. Using this procedure, it is possible to drain most of the lubricant. Remember that most of the mineral oil must be removed from the system before adding the alkylbenzene lubricant.

For larger systems, the mineral oil should be drained from multiple points in the system. Most of the existing oil can be drained from the compressor crankcase, but particular attention also should be paid to low spots around the evaporator where lubricant often collects. The mineral oil also should be drained from oil separators and/or suction accumulators.

4. Measuring Existing Lubricant

Measure and record the volume of lubricant removed from the system. Compare this amount with the amount recommended by the manufacturer to ensure that the majority of lubricant has been removed. This volume also will be used as a guide to determine the amount of alkylbenzene lubricant to add in the next step.

5. Recharge Compressor with Alkylbenzene Lubricant

Add to the compressor the same volume of alkylbenzene lubricant as the volume of mineral oil drained in step 4. In small systems with short refrigerant lines, the mineral oil may have sufficient miscibility with Genetron MP Blends to achieve adequate oil return to the compressor. However, AlliedSignal recommends using a commercially available alkylbenzene oil of the same viscosity grade as the mineral oil, typically 150 SUS, to ensure optimum performance. Check with the compressor manufacturer for the correct viscosity grade.

6. Reinstall the Compressor

If the compressor was removed to drain the oil, reinstall the compressor following the standard service practices recommended by the manufacturer.

7. Evaluate the Expansion Device

Most CFC-12 systems with expansion valves will operate satisfactorily with Genetron MP39 or MP66. If the system uses a capillary tube, it will need to be replaced with one of greater restriction to achieve satisfactory performance over the complete range of design conditions. AlliedSignal recommends consulting with the equipment manufacturer before replacing the capillary tube.

If the manufacturer's information is not available, the suggested approach is to replace the capillary tube with one of the same diameter, but about 50 percent longer. For example, if the CFC-12 system's capillary tube is 40 inches (1.0 meter) long, its optimum length for MP39 should be approximately 60 inches (1.5 meters). It may be easier and more effective, however, to replace the capillary tube with a properly sized expansion valve.

In most cases, the unit can be operated with the original capillary tube by undercharging the unit with a MP blend. Operation may be satisfactory if the ambient conditions are expected to be relatively constant.

If operation is expected over a wide range of condensing temperatures, unsatisfactory performance may result at both high- and low-condensing temperatures. The potential problems could include liquid floodback and motor overload at high-condensing temperatures, as well as a loss of liquid seal entering the capillary tube at low-condensing temperatures.

8. Replace the Filter Drier

Following system maintenance, a recommended service practice is to replace the filter drier. There are two types of filter driers commonly used in refrigeration equipment — loose-fill and solid-core.

Many, but not all, of the standard loose-fill and solid-core driers used with CFC-12 are compatible with Genetron MP Blends. Check with your Genetron® wholesaler to make sure the replacement filter drier being used is compatible with Genetron MP Blends.

9. Reconnect the System and Evacuate

Use normal service practices to reconnect and evacuate the system. To remove air and other non-condensibles, AlliedSignal recommends evacuating the system to a full vacuum of 1000 microns or less from both sides of the system. Attempting to evacuate a system with the pump connected to only the low side of the system will not adequately remove moisture and non-condensibles such as air. Use a good electronic gauge to measure the vacuum. An accurate reading cannot be made with a refrigeration gauge.

10. Check for System Leaks

Check the system for leaks using normal service practices.

11. Charge System with Appropriate Genetron® MP Blend

When charging the system with either Genetron MP39 or MP66, it is important to remember that these products are blends and not azeotropes. For this reason, special charging procedures are required to ensure optimal system performance.

It is essential when using either MP39 or MP66 that the system be liquid-charged by removing only liquid from the cylinder. Never charge the system with vapor from a MP blend cylinder. Vapor-charging a MP blend will result in the wrong refrigerant composition and may result in a loss of system performance.

The cylinders for both products are equipped with dip tubes to facilitate liquid-removal with the cylinder in the upright position. A throttling valve should be used to control the flow of refrigerant to the suction side to ensure that the liquid is converted to vapor prior to entering the system. NOTE: To prevent compressor damage, do not directly charge liquid into the suction line of the unit.

12. Use Correct Charge Size

Systems being charged with Genetron MP39 or MP66 require a smaller charge size than those using CFC-12. The charge typically will be about 90 percent by weight of the original CFC-12 charge with expansion-valve or optimized capillary-tube systems. If the original capillary tube is used, it will generally be necessary to undercharge the system to prevent liquid floodback to the compressor.

AlliedSignal recommends initially charging the system with 75 percent by weight of the original CFC-12 charge. For medium-temperature refrigeration applications, if the original CFC-12 charge was 100 pounds (50 Kg), initially charge 75 pounds (37.5 Kg) of Genetron MP39. The same procedure is used for Genetron MP66.

13. Check System Operation

Start the system and let conditions stabilize. If the system is undercharged, add additional Genetron MP Blend in increments of 5 percent by weight of the original CFC-12 charge. For example, if the original charge was 100 pounds (50 Kg), charge in increments of 5 pounds (2.5 Kg). Continue until desired operating conditions are achieved.

Compressor suction pressures for Genetron MP39 after stabilization should be within about 1 psi (5 to 10 KPa) of normal system operation with CFC-12 for most medium-temperature systems. Compressor discharge pressures typically will be about 10-20 psi (75-150 kPa) higher than normal system operation with CFC-12. For Genetron MP66, the suction pressure will be close to that of CFC-12 at low evaporator temperatures -20°F (-29°C), but may be as much as 8 or 9 psi (60 kPa) higher at medium temperatures 25°F (-4°C). The discharge pressure may be as much as 70 psi (450 to 500 kPa) higher when exposed to extreme ambient conditions.

It may be necessary to reset the high pressure cutout to compensate for the higher discharge pressures of the MP Blend system. This procedure should be done carefully to avoid exceeding the recommended operating limits of the compressor and other system components. The use of an expansion device not optimized for the system, such as the original capillary tube, will make the system more sensitive to charge and/or operating conditions. As a result, system performance will change more quickly if the system is overcharged (or undercharged) with Genetron MP39 or MP66.

To avoid overcharging, it is best to charge the system by first measuring the operating conditions (including discharge and suction pressures, suction line temperature, compressor amps, superheat) instead of using the liquid-line sight glass as a guide.

14. Label Components and System

After retrofitting the system with an MP Blend, label the system components to identify the type of refrigerant (Genetron MP39 or MP66) and alkylbenzene lubricant (by brand name) in the system. This will help ensure that the proper refrigerant and lubricant will be used to service the equipment in the future.

Retrofit Checklist for Genetron® MP Blends

1. Record baseline data on original system performance. _______
2. Recover CFC-12 refrigerant charge using appropriate recovery equipment. _______
   * Record the amount of CFC-12 removed. _______
3. Drain most of the lubricant from the compressor. _______
4. Measure amount of lubricant removed. _______
5. Recharge compressor with alkylbenzene lubricant. _______
   * Use the same amount that was removed from the existing system. _______
6. Reinstall compressor. _______
7. Evaluate expansion device. _______
   * Replace existing capillary tube with one that is 50 percent longer, or _______
   * adjust the setting of the expansion valve as necessary. _______
8. Replace filter drier with new drier approved for use with Genetron MP39 or MP66. _______
9. Reconnect system and evacuate. _______
10. Recharge system with appropriate Genetron MP Blend. _______
    * Remove Liquid Only from cylinder. _______
11. Check system for leaks. (Re-evaluate system following leak check). _______
12. Use correct charge size. _______
    * Initial charge 75 percent by weight of original CFC-12 charge. _______
    * Record amount of refrigerant charged. _______
13. Check system operation.
    * Adjust charge to achieve desired operating conditions. _______
    * If low, remove liquid only from cylinder in increments of 5 percent of original CFC-12 charge. _______
    * Record the amount of refrigerant added. _______
14. Label components and system for type of refrigerant, i.e. Genetron MP39 or MP66 and lubricant (by brand name). _______

Genetron® MP Blends Temperature/Pressure Tables

Temp °F	MP-39 Bubble Pressure Psig	MP-39 Dew Pressure Psig	MP-66 Bubble Pressure Psig	MP-66 Dew Pressure Psig
-50	13.3*	17.4*	12.1*	16.3*
-45	10.9*	15.5*	9.4*	14.2*
-40	8.1*	13.2*	6.5*	11.8*
-35	5.1*	10.7*	3.3*	9.1*
-30	1.7*	7.9*	.2	6.1*
-25	1.0	4.8*	2.1	2.8*
-20	3.0	1.4*	4.3	.5
-15	5.2	1.2	6.6	2.5
-10	7.7	3.3	9.2	4.7
-5	10.3	5.5	12.0	7.1
0	13.2	8.0	15.1	9.7
5	16.3	10.7	18.4	12.6
10	19.7	13.7	22.0	15.8
15	23.4	16.9	25.9	19.2
20	27.4	20.4	30.1	23.0
25	31.7	24.2	34.6	27.0
30	36.4	28.3	39.5	31.4
35	41.3	32.8	44.8	36.1
40	46.6	37.6	50.4	41.1
45	52.4	42.7	56.4	46.6
50	58.5	48.2	62.8	52.4
55	65.0	54.1	69.6	58.7
60	71.9	60.4	76.9	65.4
65	79.3	67.2	84.7	72.5
70	87.1	74.4	92.9	80.1
75	95.4	82.1	101.6	88.2
80	104.2	90.2	110.9	96.8
85	113.6	98.9	120.7	106.0
90	123.4	108.1	131.0	115.6
95	133.8	117.9	141.9	125.9
100	144.8	128.2	153.4	136.8
105	156.4	139.1	165.5	148.2
110	168.5	150.6	178.3	160.4
115	181.3	162.8	191.6	173.1
120	194.7	175.6	205.7	186.6
125	208.8	189.0	220.4	200.7
130	223.6	203.2	235.9	215.6
135	239.1	218.1	252.0	231.2
140	255.3	233.8	268.9	247.6
145	272.2	250.2	286.6	264.8

Notes:

1. To determine the saturated temperature for a superheat setting, use dew-point pressure. To determine the saturated temperature for a subcooling calculation, use bubble-point pressure.
2. * inches of mercury vacuum
3. The above data is preliminary.

Temp °C	MP-39 Bubble Pressure kPag	MP-39 Dew Pressure kPag	MP-66 Bubble Pressure kPag	MP-66 Dew Pressure kPag
-46	-46.3	-60.1	-42.2	-56.4
-44	-40.5	-55.4	-36.0	-51.3
-42	-34.3	-50.3	-29.3	-45.9
-40	-27.5	-44.8	-22.0	-39.9
-38	-20.2	-38.8	-14.2	-33.4
-36	-12.3	-32.3	-5.8	-26.5
34	-3.8	-25.2	3.2	-18.9
-32	5.3	-17.6	12.9	-10.8
-30	15.1	-9.5	23.2	-2.0
-28	25.5	-.7	34.4	7.4
-26	36.7	8.8	46.2	17.5
-24	48.7	18.9	58.9	28.4
-22	61.4	29.8	72.4	40.0
-20	74.9	41.4	86.7	52.4
-18	89.4	53.8	102.0	65.6
-16	104.7	67.0	118.2	79.8
-14	120.9	81.1	135.4	94.8
-12	138.1	96.1	153.6	110.8
-10	156.4	112.1	172.9	127.7
-8	175.6	129.0	193.3	145.8
-6	196.0	147.0	214.8	164.8
-4	217.5	166.0	237.5	185.0
-2	240.2	186.1	261.4	206.4
0	264.0	207.3	286.6	229.0
2	289.2	229.8	313.1	252.8
4	315.6	253.5	340.9	277.9
6	343.3	278.4	370.1	304.3
8	372.5	304.7	400.8	332.2
10	403.0	332.4	433.0	361.4
12	435.0	361.4	466.6	392.2
14	468.5	391.9	501.9	424.5
16	503.6	424.0	538.8	458.3
18	540.3	457.5	577.3	493.8
20	578.6	492.7	617.5	530.9
22	618.5	529.5	659.5	569.8
24	660.3	568.1	703.3	610.5
26	703.8	608.4	749.0	653.0
28	749.1	650.4	796.5	697.3
30	796.3	694.4	846.0	743.6
32	845.4	740.2	897.5	791.9
34	896.4	788.0	951.0	842.2
36	949.5	837.8	1006.6	894.6
38	1004.6	889.6	1064.3	949.2
40	1061.8	943.6	1124.2	1005.9
42	1121.2	999.8	1186.4	1065.0
44	1182.7	1058.1	1250.8	1126.3
46	1246.5	1118.8	1317.5	1190.0
48	1312.6	1181.7	1386.7	1256.1
50	1381.1	1247.1	1458.2	1324.8
52	1451.9	1314.9	1532.3	1395.9
54	1525.1	1385.2	1608.8	1469.7
56	1600.9	1458.1	1688.0	1546.1
58	1679.1	1533.6	1769.7	1625.2
60	1760.0	1611.7	1854.1	1707.2

Further Information

For additional information, we invite you to consult your nearest Genetron® Wholesaler at the address and phone number indicated below, or call us at 1-800-631-8138.

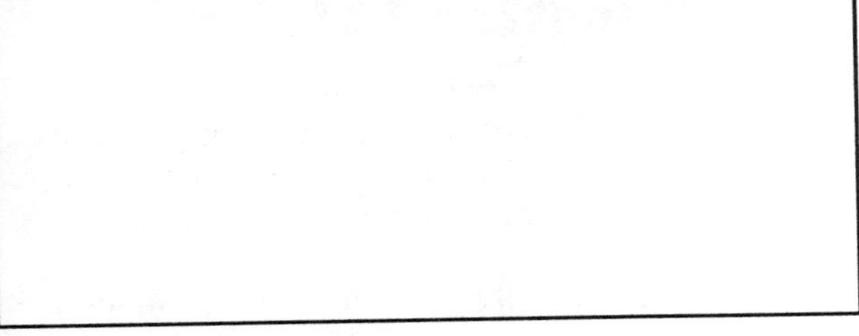

Disclaimer

All statements, information and data given herein are believed to be accurate and reliable, but are presented without guaranty, warranty or responsibility of any kind, expressed or implied. Statements or suggestions concerning possible use of our products are made without representation or warranty that any such use is free of patent infringement, and are not recommendations to infringe any patent. The user should not assume that all safety measures are indicated, or that other measures are indicated, or that other measures may not be required.

P.O. Box 1053
Morristown, NJ 07962-1053

G-525-014
5-94 25K
Printed in USA

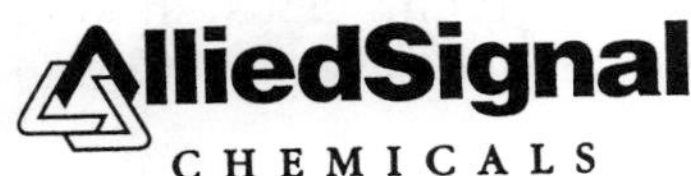

Genetron® 134a

Retrofit Guidelines

Fluorocarbons

Understanding Needs.
Finding Solutions.

With the phaseout of CFCs rapidly approaching, existing refrigeration equipment may need to be either replaced with new equipment or retrofitted with alternative refrigerants. By following equipment manufacturers' recommendations and AlliedSignal's guidelines outlined in this publication, service technicians can readily retrofit many existing CFC-12 refrigeration systems to use Genetron® 134a.

As the industry moves away from the use of CFCs, refrigerant service personnel will play a key role in the transition to HCFC and HFC alternatives through retrofitting. AlliedSignal has produced this booklet to help service technicians better understand the various technical and operational aspects of carrying out retrofits in commercial refrigeration systems using AlliedSignal's Genetron 134a.

Although the information in this publication can be helpful as a general guide, **it should not be used as a substitute for the equipment manufacturer's specific recommendations.** For this reason, AlliedSignal strongly recommends contacting the equipment manufacturer for detailed information on retrofitting the specific model under consideration. And, always refer to the Product Safety Data Sheet (PSDS) for safety information on the use of Genetron 134a.

Genetron 134a

Genetron 134a is the preferred alternative refrigerant to replace CFC-12 in most medium-temperature refrigeration systems. This product is an HFC and therefore is not scheduled for phaseout under current law.

Applications where Genetron 134a is a suitable retrofit refrigerant include supermarket cases, walk-in coolers, beverage dispensers, vending machines, water coolers and home refrigerators. The use of Genetron 134a should be limited to applications where the evaporator temperature is above -10°F (-23°C).

When Should HFC-134a Be Used?

Where feasible, the preferred retrofit for CFC-12 is HFC-134a, a non-ozone-depleting refrigerant that will replace CFC-12 in most OEM applications. In some cases, however, retrofitting with HFC-134a may be difficult because nearly all of the mineral oil in the system must be removed. For these instances, interim-service fluids or blends such as Genetron MP39 or Genetron MP66 may be preferred. If one of these fluids is to be used, refer to bulletin G-525-011 for "Genetron MP Blends Retrofit Guidelines."

Service technicians should keep in mind that future regulations may further restrict the use of

HCFC-containing refrigerants and dictate the ultimate use of HFC-134a for servicing CFC-12 equipment.

Genetron 134a: Not a "Drop-In" Replacement

Genetron 134a is not a "drop-in" replacement for CFC-12. Mineral oils and alkylbenzene lubricants are immiscible with Genetron 134a and must therefore be replaced with new lubricants.

The retrofit procedures listed here have been developed by AlliedSignal to address these issues and to help technicians perform successful retrofits of CFC-12 systems utilizing positive-displacement (reciprocating, rotary, scroll or screw) compressors with Genetron 134a.

RETROFIT PROCEDURES

1. Record Baseline Data

It is desirable to record system performance data prior to retrofit in order to establish the normal operating conditions for the equipment. Data should include temperatures and pressure measurements throughout the system, including the evaporator, compressor suction and discharge, condenser and expansion device. These measurements will be useful when adjusting the system with Genetron 134a during the retrofit.

2. Isolate CFC-12 Charge

The CFC-12 charge should be isolated from the rest of the system by pumping it down into the receiver. If no receiver is present, the refrigerant must be removed from the system using a certified recovery machine capable of meeting or exceeding the required levels of evacuation as specified by the U.S. EPA. The charge **must** be collected in a recovery cylinder.

DO NOT VENT THE REFRIGERANT.

Knowing the recommended CFC-12 charge size for the system is helpful. If it is not known, weigh the entire amount of refrigerant removed. This amount can be used as a guide for the initial quantity of Genetron 134a to be charged into the system.

3. Choose Compressor Lubricant

Mineral oil is typically used as the lubricant for CFC-12 compressors. But, to achieve miscibility of Genetron 134a with the lubricant, a polyol ester must be used.

AlliedSignal recommends using a polyol ester lubricant approved by the compressor manufacturer. Differences among polyol ester-based lubricants make it difficult to assume that they are interchangeable. Check with the compressor manufacturer for the correct viscosity grade and brand for the compressor in the system being retrofitted.

4. Drain the Lubricant

Since many small hermetic compressors do not have oil drains, removal of the compressor from the system may be necessary for draining the lubricant. The best point in the system to drain the lubricant is the suction line of the compressor. Using this procedure, it is possible to drain nearly 95 percent of the lubricant. Remember that most of the mineral oil must be removed from the system before adding the replacement lubricant.

For larger systems, the mineral oil should be drained from multiple points in the system. Particular attention should be paid to low spots around the evaporator where lubricant often collects. The mineral oil also should be drained from oil separators and/or suction accumulators.

5. Measuring Existing Lubricant

Measure and record the volume of lubricant removed from the system. Compare this amount with the amount recommended by the manufacturer to ensure that the majority of lubricant has been removed. This volume also will be used as a guide to determine the amount of polyol ester lubricant to add in the next step.

6. Recharge Compressor with Polyol Ester Lubricant

Add to the compressor the same volume of polyol ester lubricant as the volume of mineral oil drained in step 5.

7. Reinstall the Compressor

Reinstall the compressor following the standard service practices recommended by the manufacturer.

8. Recharge the CFC-12

If the system charge was pumped into the receiver, the balance of the system should be evacuated and then the receiver valves opened. If the original charge was collected in a recovery cylinder, the system should be evacuated and then recharged with the original CFC-12. It may be necessary to "top off" the refrigerant charge to compensate for the small amount lost in draining the mineral oil.

9. Run the Compressor

Run the compressor with the polyol ester lubricant and the CFC-12 for at least 24 hours. Next, drain the polyol ester and recharge with a new charge of the polyol ester. Check the lubricant that was drained to see if the residual mineral oil content is below 5 percent. Test kits are available from several lubricant suppliers that check for residual mineral oil content. Generally, it will require about three charges to get the mineral oil content down to the acceptable level.

10. Continue to Flush the System

Repeat steps 8 and 9 until the residual mineral oil content is below 5 percent. The lubricant that was removed from the compressors in the flushing procedure must be disposed of properly.

11. Evaluate the Expansion Device

Most CFC-12 systems with expansion valves will operate satisfactorily with Genetron 134a. If the system uses a capillary tube, it will need to be replaced with one of greater restriction to achieve satisfactory performance over the complete range of design conditions. AlliedSignal recommends consulting with the equipment manufacturer before replacing the capillary tube.

If the manufacturer's information is not available, the suggested approach is to replace the capillary tube with one of the same diameter, but about 50 percent longer. For example, if the CFC-12 system's capillary tube is 40 inches long, its optimum length for Genetron 134a should be approximately 60 inches. It may be easier and more effective, however, to replace the capillary tube with a properly-sized expansion valve.

In most cases, the unit can be operated with the original capillary tube by undercharging the unit with Genetron 134a. Operation may be satisfactory if the ambient conditions are expected to be relatively constant.

But, if operation is expected over a wide range of

condensing temperatures, unsatisfactory performance may result at both high- and low-condensing temperatures. The potential problems would include liquid floodback and motor overload at high-condensing temperatures, as well as a loss of liquid seal entering the capillary tube at low-condensing temperatures.

12. Replace the Filter Drier

Following system maintenance, a recommended service practice is to replace the filter drier. There are two types of filter driers commonly used in refrigeration equipment — loose-fill and solid-core.

Many, but not all, of the standard loose-fill and solid-core driers used with CFC-12 are compatible with Genetron 134a. Check with your Genetron wholesaler to make sure the replacement filter drier being used is compatible with Genetron 134a.

13. Reconnect the System and Evacuate

Use normal service practices to reconnect and evacuate the system. To remove air and other noncondensibles, AlliedSignal recommends evacuating the system to a full vacuum of 1,000 microns or less from both sides of the system. However, attempting to evacuate a system with the pump connected to only the low side of the system will not adequately remove moisture and non-condensibles such as air. Use a good electronic gauge to measure the vacuum. An accurate reading cannot be made with a refrigeration gauge.

14. Check for System Leaks

Check the system for leaks using normal service practices.

15. Charge System with Genetron 134a

When charging the system with Genetron 134a, use the same charging procedures that you would use for CFC-12 to ensure optimal system performance.

Systems being charged with Genetron 134a require a smaller charge size than those using CFC-12. The charge typically will be about 90 percent by weight of the original CFC-12 charge with expansion-valve or optimized capillary-tube systems. If the original capillary tube is used, it will generally be necessary to undercharge the system to prevent liquid floodback to the compressor.

AlliedSignal recommends initially charging the system with 75 percent by weight of the original CFC-12 charge. For medium-temperature refrigeration applications, if the original CFC-12 charge was 100 pounds, initially charge 75 pounds of Genetron 134a. If the original CFC-12 charge was 300 grams, initially charge 225 grams of Genetron 134a.

16. Check System Operation

Start the system and let conditions stabilize. If the system is undercharged, add additional Genetron 134a in increments of 5 percent by weight of the original CFC-12 charge. For example, if the original charge was 100 pounds, charge in increments of 5 pounds. If the original charge was 300 grams, charge in increments of 15 grams. Continue until desired operating conditions are achieved.

Compressor-suction pressures for Genetron 134a after stabilization should be within about 2 psi of normal system operation with CFC-12 for most medium-temperature systems. Compressor-discharge pressures typically will be about 10-20 psi higher than normal system operation with CFC-12.

It may be necessary to reset the high pressure cutout to compensate for the higher discharge pressures of the Genetron 134a system. This procedure should be done carefully to avoid exceeding the recommended operating limits of the compressor and other system components. The use of an expansion device not optimized for the system, such as the original capillary tube, will make the system more sensitive to charge and/or operating conditions. As a result, system performance will change more quickly if the system is overcharged (or undercharged) with Genetron 134a.

To avoid overcharging, it is best to charge the system by first measuring the operating conditions (including discharge and suction pressures, suction line temperature, compressor amps, super heat) before using the liquid-level sight glass as a guide.

17. Label Components and System

After retrofitting the system with Genetron 134a, label the system components to identify the refrigerant (G-134a) and specify type of polyol ester lubricant (by brand name) in the system. This will help ensure that the proper refrigerant and lubricant will be used to service the equipment in the future.

RETROFIT CHECKLIST FOR GENETRON 134a

1. Record baseline data on original system performance. ______
2. Recover CFC-12 refrigerant charge using appropriate recovery equipment or pump down into receiver. ______
   * Record the amount of CFC-12 removed. ______
3. Choose compressor lubricant. ______
4. Drain at least 90 percent of the lubricant from the compressor. ______
5. Measure amount of lubricant removed. ______
6. Recharge compressor with polyol ester lubricant. ______
   * Use the same amount that was removed from the existing system. ______
7. Reinstall compressor. ______
8. Recharge the original CFC-12. ______
9. Run the System. ______
10. Repeat Flushing Procedure. (steps 4-9) ______
11. Evaluate expansion device. ______
    * Replace existing capillary tube with one that is 50 percent longer or preferably a new expansion valve. ______
12. Replace filter drier with new drier approved for use with Genetron 134a. ______
13. Reconnect system and evacuate. ______
14. Check system for leaks. (Re-evaluate system following leak check) ______
15. Charge system with Genetron 134a. ______
    Use correct charge size. ______
    * Initial charge 75 percent by weight of original CFC-12 charge. ______
    * Record amount of refrigerant charged. ______
16. Check system operation. ______
    * Adjust charge to achieve desired operating conditions. ______
    * If low, remove liquid only from cylinder in increments of 5 percent of original CFC-12 charge. ______
    * Record the amount of refrigerant added. ______
17. Label components and system for type of refrigerant, i.e., Genetron 134a and lubricant. ______

GENETRON® 134a
TEMPERATURE-PRESSURE TABLE

Temperature (°F)	134a (Psig)
-60.00	21.6*
-55.00	20.1*
-50.00	18.5*
-45.00	16.7*
-40.00	14.6*
-35.00	12.3*
-30.00	9.7*
-25.00	6.7*
-20.00	3.5*
-15.00	0.1
-10.00	2.0
-5.00	4.2
0.00	6.5
5.00	9.2
10.00	12.0
15.00	15.1
20.00	18.5
25.00	22.2
30.00	26.1
35.00	30.4
40.00	35.1
45.00	40.1
50.00	45.5
55.00	51.2
60.00	57.4
65.00	64.1
70.00	71.1
75.00	78.7
80.00	86.7
85.00	95.3
90.00	104.3
95.00	114.0
100.00	124.2
105.00	135.0
110.00	146.4
115.00	158.4
120.00	171.2
125.00	184.6
130.00	198.7
135.00	213.6
140.00	229.2
145.00	245.5
150.00	262.9
155.00	281.1
160.00	300.00

* - (in Hg) Vacuum

Genetron®

AZ-50 (R-507)

Retrofit Guidelines

Fluorocarbons

Further Information

For additional information, we invite you to consult your nearest Genetron® Wholesaler at the address and phone number indicated below, or call us at 1-800-631-8138, or fax us at 201-455-6395.

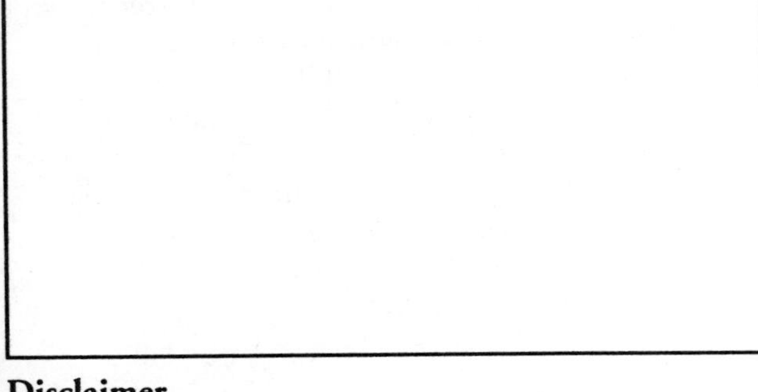

Disclaimer

All statements, information and data given herein are believed to be accurate and reliable, but are presented without guaranty, warranty or responsibility of any kind, expressed or implied. Statements or suggestions concerning possible use of our products are made without representation or warranty that any such use is free of patent infringement, and are not recommendations to infringe any patent. The user should not assume that all safety measures are indicated, or that other measures are indicated, or that other measures may not be required.

P:O. Box 1053
Morristown, NJ 07962-1053

G-525-010
6/95-20K
Printed in USA

With the phaseout of CFCs rapidly approaching, existing refrigeration equipment may need to be either replaced with new equipment or retrofitted with alternative refrigerants. By following equipment manufacturers' recommendations and AlliedSignal's guidelines outlined in this publication, service technicians can readily retrofit many existing R-502 refrigeration systems to use Genetron® AZ-50.

As the industry moves away from the use of CFCs, refrigerant service personnel will play a key role in the transition to HFC alternatives through retrofitting. AlliedSignal has produced this booklet to help service technicians better understand the various technical and operational aspects of carrying out the retrofit procedures using AlliedSignal's new Genetron® AZ-50.

Although the information can be helpful as a general guide, **it should not be used as a substitute for the equipment manufacturer's specific recommendations.** For this reason, AlliedSignal strongly recommends contacting the equipment manufacturer for detailed information on retrofitting the specific model under consideration. Also, refer to the Material Safety Data Sheet (MSDS) for safety information on the use of Genetron AZ-50.

Genetron® AZ-50 (R-507)

Genetron AZ-50 (R-507) is a patented azeotrope (HFC 125/HFC-143a) designed to serve as a long-term alternative to R-502 and HCFC-22 in low- and medium-temperature commercial refrigeration applications. This product contains two HFCs and therefore is not scheduled for phaseout under current law. Applications where AZ-50 is a suitable retrofit refrigerant include supermarket freezer cases, reach in coolers, display cases and ice machines.

Genetron AZ-50: Not a "Drop in" Replacement

Genetron AZ-50 is not a "drop-in" replacement for R-502. Mineral oils and alkylbenzene lubricants, which have been used traditionally with R-502, are immiscible with AZ-50 and must therefore be replaced with new lubricants. The retrofit procedures listed here have been developed by AlliedSignal to address these issues and to help technicians perform successful retrofits of R-502 systems utilizing positive-displacement (reciprocating, rotary, scroll or screw) compressors with AZ-50.

Retrofit Procedures

1. Record Baseline Data

It is desirable to record system performance data prior to retrofit to establish the normal operating conditions for the equipment. Data should include temperatures and pressure measurements throughout the system, including the evaporator, compressor suction and discharge, condenser and expansion device. These measurements will be useful when adjusting the system with AZ-50 during the retrofit.

2. Isolate R-502 Charge

The R-502 charge should be isolated from the rest of the system by pumping it down into the receiver. If no receiver is present, the refrigerant must be removed from the system using a recovery machine capable of meeting or exceeding the required levels of evacuation. The charge must be collected in a recovery cylinder.

DO NOT VENT THE REFRIGERANT.

Knowing the recommended R-502 charge size for the system is helpful. If it is not known, weigh the entire amount of refrigerant removed. This amount can be used as a guide for the initial quantity of AZ-50 to be charged into the system.

3. Choose Compressor Lubricant

Mineral oil or alkylbenzenes are typically used as the lubricants for R-502 compressors. But, to achieve miscibility of the AZ-50 with the lubricant, a polyol ester must be used. AlliedSignal recommends using a polyol ester lubricant approved by the compressor manufacturer. Differences among polyol ester-based lubricants make it difficult to assume that they are interchangeable. Check with the compressor manufacturer for the correct viscosity grade and brand for the compressor in the system being retrofitted.

4. Drain the Lubricant

Since many small hermetic compressors do not have oil drains, removal of the compressor from the system may be necessary for draining the lubricant. The best point in the system to drain the lubricant is the suction line of the compressor. Remember that most of the oil must be removed from the system before adding the replacement lubricant.

For larger systems, the oil should be drained from multiple points in the system. Particular attention should be paid to low spots around the evaporator where lubricant often collects. The oil also should be drained from oil separators and/or suction accumulators.

5. Measuring Existing Lubricant

Measure and record the volume of lubricant removed from the system. Compare this amount with the amount recommended by the manufacturer to ensure that the majority of lubricant has been removed. This volume also will be used as a guide to determine the amount of polyol ester lubricant to add in the next step.

6. Recharge Compressor with Polyol Ester Lubricant

Add to the compressor the same volume of polyol ester lubricant as the volume of oil drained in step 5.

7. Reinstall the Compressor

Reinstall the compressor following the standard service practices recommended by the manufacturer.

8. Recharge the R-502

If the system charge was pumped into the receiver, the balance of the system should be evacuated and then the receiver valves opened. If the original charge was collected in a recovery cylinder, the system should be evacuated and then recharged with the original R-502. It may be necessary to "top off" the refrigerant charge to compensate for the small amount lost in draining the oil.

9. Run the Compressor

Run the compressor with the polyol ester lubricant and the R-502 for at least 24 hours. Next, drain the polyol ester and recharge with fresh polyol ester. Check the lubricant that was drained. Be sure the residual oil content is below 5%. Test kits are available from several lubricant suppliers for this purpose. It usually requires about three charges to get the oil content under 5%.

It usually requires about three charges to get the oil content under 5%.

10. Continue to Flush the System

Repeat steps 4 through 9 until the residual oil content is below 5%. The lubricant that was removed from the compressors in the flushing procedure must be disposed of properly.

11. Evaluate the Expansion Devices

Most R-502 systems with any of the common expansion devices will operate satisfactorily with AZ-50; however, it may be necessary to adjust the superheat. AlliedSignal recommends consulting with the equipment manufacturer whenever possible.

12. Replace the Filter Drier

Following system maintenance, a recommended service practice is to replace the filter drier. There are two types of filter driers commonly used in refrigeration equipment—loose-fill and solid-core.

Many, but not all, of the standard loose-fill and solid-core driers used with R-502 are compatible with AZ-50. Check with your wholesaler to make sure the replacement filter drier being used is compatible with AZ-50.

13. Reconnect the System and Evacuate

Use normal service practices to reconnect and evacuate the system. To remove air and other non-condensibles, AlliedSignal recommends evacuating the system to a full vacuum of 1,000 microns or less from both sides of the system. However, attempting to evacuate a system with the pump connected to only the low side of the system will not adequately remove moisture and non-condensibles such as air. Use a good electronic gauge to measure the vacuum. An accurate reading cannot be made with a refrigeration gauge.

14. Check for System Leaks

Check the system for leaks using normal service practices.

15. Charge System with Genetron® AZ-50

When charging the system with AZ-50, use the same charging procedures that you would use for R-502 to ensure optimal system performance.

Systems being charged with AZ-50 require a smaller charge size than those using R-502. The charge typically will be about 85 percent by weight of the original R-502 charge with expansion-valve or optimized capillary systems.

AlliedSignal recommends initially charging the system with 75 percent by weight of the original R-502 charge. For medium-temperature refrigeration applications, if the original R-502 charge was 100 pounds (50 Kg), initially charge 75 pounds (37.5 Kg) of AZ-50. If the original R-502 charge was 300 grams, initially charge 225 grams of AZ-50.

16. Check System Operation

Start the system and let conditions stabilize. If the system is undercharged, add additional AZ-50 in increments of 5 percent by weight of the original R-502 charge. For example, if the original charge was 100 pounds (50 Kg), charge in increments of 5 pounds (2.5 Kg). If the original charge was 300 grams, charge in increments of 15 grams. Continue until desired operating conditions are achieved.

Compressor-suction pressures for AZ-50 after stabilization should be within about 2 psi (15 kPa) of normal system operation with R-502 for most medium- and low-temperature systems. Compressor-discharge pressures typically will be about 18-25 psi (125-170 kPa) higher than normal system operation with R-502.

It may be necessary to reset the high pressure cutout to compensate for the higher discharge pressures of the AZ-50 system. This procedure should be done carefully to avoid exceeding the recommended operating limits of the compressor and other system components.

To avoid overcharging, it is best to charge the system by first measuring the operating conditions (including discharge and suction pressures, suction line temperature, compressor amps, super heat) before using the liquid-level sight glass as a guide.

17. Label Components and System

After retrofitting the system with AZ-50, label the system components to identify the type of refrigerant (Genetron® AZ-50) and specify type of polyol ester lubricant (by brand name) in the system. This will help ensure that the proper refrigerant and lubricant will be used to service the equipment in the future.

Retrofit Checklist for Genetron® AZ-50

1. Record baseline data on original system performance. _______
2. Recover R-502 refrigerant charge using appropriate recovery equipment or pump down into receiver. _______
   * Record the amount of R-502 removed. _______
3. Choose compressor lubricant. _______
4. Drain as much of the lubricant from the compressor as possible. _______
5. Measure amount of lubricant removed. _______
6. Recharge compressor with polyol ester lubricant. _______
   * Use the same amount that was removed from the existing system. _______
7. Reinstall compressor. _______
8. Recharge the System using the original R-502. _______
9. Run the System. _______
10. Repeat Flushing Procedure until 95% pure POE oil. (steps 4-9) _______
11. Evaluate expansion device. _______
12. Replace filter drier with new drier approved for use with Genetron AZ-50. _______
13. Reconnect system and evacuate. _______
14. Charge system with Genetron AZ-50. _______
    Use correct charge size. _______
    * Initial charge 75 percent by weight of original R-502 charge. _______
    * Record amount of refrigerant charged. _______
15. Check system for leaks. (Re-evaluate system following leak check) _______
16. Check system operation. _______
    * Adjust charge to achieve desired operating conditions. _______
    * If low, charge in increments of 5 percent of original R-502 charge. _______
    * Record the amount of refrigerant added. _______
17. Label components and system for type of refrigerant, i.e. Genetron AZ-50 and lubricant (by brand name). _______

Genetron® AZ-50 (R-507) Temperature/Pressure Tables

Temp °F	Pressure Psig
-60	5.8*
-55	2.2*
-50	0.9
-45	3.1
-40	5.5
-35	8.2
-30	11.1
-25	14.4
-20	17.9
-15	21.7
-10	25.9
-5	30.4
0	35.3
5	40.5
10	46.2
15	52.3
20	58.8
25	65.8
30	73.3
35	81.3
40	89.8
45	98.9
50	108.6
55	118.9
60	129.8
65	141.4
70	153.6
75	166.6
80	180.3
85	194.9
90	210.2
95	226.4
100	243.6
105	261.6
110	280.7
115	300.8
120	322.0
125	344.3
130	367.8
135	392.6
140	418.8
145	446.3
150	475.3
155	505.9

Notes:

1. * inches of mercury vacuum

Temp °C	Pressure kPag
-50	-15
-48	-6
-46	4
-44	14
-42	26
-40	38
-38	51
-36	65
-34	80
-32	96
-30	113
-28	131
-26	151
-24	171
-22	193
-20	216
-18	240
-16	266
-14	293
-12	321
-10	352
-8	383
-6	417
-4	452
-2	488
0	527
2	567
4	610
6	654
8	700
10	749
12	799
14	852
16	907
18	965
20	1025
22	1087
24	1152
26	1220
28	1291
30	1364
32	1440
34	1520
36	1603
38	1689
40	1778
42	1871
44	1968
46	2068
48	2172
50	2280
52	2393
54	2509
56	2631
58	2756
60	2887
62	3023
64	3164
66	3310
68	3462
70	3619

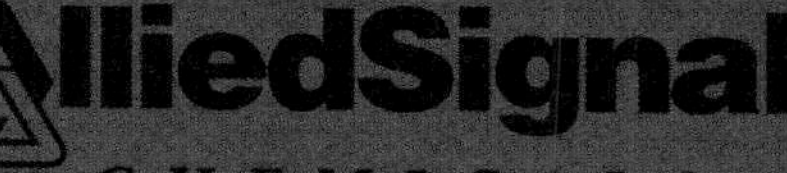

Genetron® Products Brochure

Fluorocarbons

Genetron® Products

CFC 113 — Trichlorotrifluoroethane ($C_2Cl_3F_3$) Used in low capacity centrifugal chiller packaged units. Operates with very low system pressures, high gas volumes. Also used as an intermediate in the manufacture of specialty lubricants.

HCFC 141b* — Dichlorofluoroethane (CCl_2FCH_3) The leading substitute for CFC-11 in rigid foam blowing insulation applications, such as: construction (commercial, residential and public) appliances and transport vehicles.

HCFC 123* — Dichlorotrifluoroethane ($CHCl_2CF_3$) A very low ozone depleting compound that serves as a replacement for CFC 11 in centrifugal chillers.

CFC 11 — Trichlorofluoromethane (CCl_3F) A blowing agent for rigid foam blowing insulation applications, such as: construction (commercial, residential and public) appliances and transport vehicles. Also a refrigerant used in centrifugal chillers.

CFC 114 — Dichlorotetrafluoroethane ($C_2Cl_2F_4$) Intermediate in pressure and displacement. Principally used with chillers for higher capacities or for lower evaporator temperature process type applications.

SELECTED PHYSICAL DATA

	CFC 113	HCFC 141b*	HCFC 123*	CFC 11	CFC 114
Substitutes (See Legend Below)		■	■		
ASHRAE Number	R-113	R-141b	R-123	R-11	R-114
Molecular Weight	187.4	116.95	152.91	137.4	170.9
Boiling Point @ 1 Atmos (°F)	117.6	89.7	82.2	74.9	38.8
Freezing Point @ 1 Atmos (°F)	-31	-154.3	-160.6	-168	-137
Critical Temperature (°F)	417	410.4	363.2	388	294
Critical Pressure (psia)	499	673.0	533.1	640	473
Saturated Liquid Density @ 86°F (lb./cu.ft.)	96.8	76.31	90.41	91.4	89.8
Specific Heat of Liquid @ 86°F (Btu/lb.°F)	0.22	0.35	0.21	0.21	0.24
Specific Heat of Vapor @ Constant Pressure. (Cp), @ 86°F and 1 Atmos. (Btu/lb.°F)	0.15[1]	0.17[1]	0.17	0.14	0.17
Specific Heat Ratio of Vapor (k=Cp/Cv) @ 86°F and 1 Atmos.	1.08[1]	—	1.10	1.13	1.08
Flammability and Explosivity. (Based on ASHRAE Standard 34 with Match Ignition)††	None	7.6-17.7†	None	None	None
ANSI/ASHRAE Standard 34-1992 Safety Group Classification	A1	N.C.†††	B1	A1	A1

[1]@ 0.2 Atmos Press. (CFC 113)

[1]@ 0.2 Atmos Press. (HCFC 141b)

LEGEND:

- ■ **CFC 11** Substitutes
- □ **CFC 12** Substitutes
- ■ **R-502** Substitutes
- ■ **CFC 13 / R-503** Substitutes
- ■ **HCFC 22** Substitutes

HCFC 22 — Chlorodifluoromethane ($CHClF_2$) As a refrigerant, operates with higher system pressures but low compressor displacement. Popular in residential, commercial and industrial applications. Also used as an intermediate to produce fluoropolymers and as a blowing agent in rigid foam applications.

Blend 407C* — Difluoromethane Pentafluoroethane Tetrafluoroethane ($CH_2F_2/CHF_2CF_3/CF_3CH_2F$) A long-term, non-ozone-depleting replacement for HCFC-22 in various air-conditioning applications, as well as in positive displacement refrigeration systems. It is a ternary blend of HFC-32/HFC-125/HFC-134a.

Azeotrope 502 — Azeotrope ($CHClF_2/CClF_2CF_3$) An azeotropic mixture used in low- and medium-temperature refrigeration applications.

SELECTED PHYSICAL DATA

	HCFC 22	Blend 407C*	Azeotrope 502
Substitutes (See Legend Above)	□ ■	■	
ASHRAE Number	R-22	R-407**	R-502
Molecular Weight	86.5	86.2	111.6
Boiling Point @ 1 Atmos (°F)	-41.4	-46.6▲	-49.8
Freezing Point @ 1 Atmos (°F)	-256	—	—
Critical Temperature (°F)	205	189.1	180
Critical Pressure (psia)	722	699.1	591
Saturated Liquid Density @ 86°F (lb./cu.ft.)	73.3	70.6	74.4
Specific Heat of Liquid @ 86°F (Btu/lb. °F)	0.31	0.36	0.30
Specific Heat of Vapor @ Constant Pressure. (Cp), @ 86°F and 1 Atmos. (Btu/lb.°F)	0.20	0.20	0.17
Specific Heat Ratio of Vapor (k=Cp/Cv) @ 86°F and 1 Atmos.	1.18	1.14	1.14
Flammability and Explosivity. (Based on ASHRAE Standard 34 with Match Ignition)††	None	None	None
ANSI/ASHRAE Standard 34-1992 Safety Group Classification	A1	A1/A1	A1

NOTE: 502 is an azeotropic mixture consisting of HCFC-22 ($CHClF_2$) 48.8% by weight and CFC 115 ($CClF_2CF_3$), 51.2% by weight.

* Preliminary information based on estimated properties.
** Provisional number assigned by ASHRAE.
▲: Bubble point temperature.
†: Upper and lower vapor flammability (Vol.%).
††: ASTM E681-85 Match ignition ambient conditions.
†††: N.C. Not Classified.
Ω: @ -30°F.

afluoroethane ($CHClFCF_3$) ential medium refrigerant for lications. It is eplace CFC-12 t in sterilizing as. A potential ent for CFC-11 in rigid foam applications.

Difluoroethane (CHF_2CH_3) Used as an aerosol propellent and a blowing agent for thermo plastic foams. Also used as a component in refrigerant blends.

Tetrafluoroethane (CF_3CH_2F) A refrigerant to replace CFC-12 in auto air conditioning, as well as refrigeration systems in residential, commercial and industrial applications. Also used as a blowing agent in rigid foam insulation.

Dichlorodifluoromethane (CCl_2F_2) A very versatile refrigerant in reciprocating and rotary type equipment and in some centrifugal designs. Also used as diluent in a sterilant gas, and as a blowing agent in rigid foam applications.

Chlorodifluoromethane Difluoroethane Chlorotetrafluoroethane ($CHClF_2/CH_3CHF_2/CHClFCF_3$) An interim replacement for CFC-12 in medium-temperature commercial refrigeration systems. Contains HCFC-22/ HFC-152a/HCFC-124.

Azeotrope (CCl_2F_2/CH_3CHF_2) An azeotropic mixture which has slightly higher vapor pressures and provides higher capacities from the same compressor displacement.

Chlorodifluoromethane Difluoroethane Chlorotetrafluoroethane ($CHClF_2/CH_3CHF_2/CHClFCF_3$) An interim replacement for CFC-12 in low-temperature commercial refrigeration systems. Contains HCFC-22/ HFC-152a/HCFC-124.

Chlorodifluoromethane Chlorotetrafluoroethane Chlorodifluoroethane ($CHClF_2/CF_3CHClSF/CH_3CClF_2$) An interim replacement for CFC-12 in refrigeration systems. Contains HCFC-22/ HCFC-124/HCFC-142b.

HCFC 124	HFC 152a*	HFC 134a	CFC 12	Blend MP39*	Azeotrope 500	Blend MP66*	Blend 409A*
□	□	□		□		□	□
R-124	R-152a	R-134a	R-12	R-401A	R-500	R-401B	R409A**
136.5	66.05	102.03	120.9	94.4	99.3	92.9	97.45
10.3	-11.29	-15.1	-21.6	-26.5▲	-28.3	-29.5▲	-32.4▲
-326	-178.6	-141.9	-252	—	-254	—	—
252	236.4	214	234	228.7	222	226.4	228.9
525	651.5	589.8	597	600.0	642	596.1	673.1
83.6	55.34	74.17	80.7	74.0	71.1	74.0	74.8
0.27	0.342	0.36	0.24	0.30	0.30	0.30	0.2962
0.17	0.2516	0.21	0.15	0.18	0.18	0.17	0.169
1.09	1.15	1.12	1.14	1.15	1.14	1.15	1.15
None	3.9-16.9†	None	None	None	None	None	None
N.C.†††	A2	A1	A1	A1/A1	A1	A1/A1	A1/A1

NOTE: 500 is an azeotropic mixture consisting of CFC 12 (CCl_2F_2), 73.8% by weight and HFC 152a (CH_3CHF_2), 26.2% by weight.

Azeotrope (CHF_2CF_3/CH_3CF_3) -50 is a non-ozone epleting azeotropic HFC-125 and HFC- has been primarily place R-502 in low temperature com- eration applications upermarket display and ice machines.

Pentafluoroethane (CHF_2CF_3) A candidate substitute for use in low temperature refrigerant applications. Low critical temperature may limit use as a stand alone fluid.

Pentafluoroethane Propane Chlorodifluoromethane ($CHClF_2/CHF_2CF_3/C_3H_8$) An interim replacement for retrofitting low- and medium-temperature commercial refrigeration systems.

Azeotropic Mixture (CH_2F_2/CHF_2CF_3) AZ-20 is an azeotropic mixture of HFC-32 and HFC-125. It has been designed to replace HCFC-22 in air conditioning and refrigeration applications.

Chlorotrifluoromethane ($CClF_3$) A specialty low temperature refrigerant used in the low stage of cascade systems to provide evaporator temperatures in the range of -75°C.

Trifluoromethane (CHF_3) A specialty low temperature refrigerant that may be used to replace CFC-13 and R-503 in the low stage of cascade systems.

Azeotrope ($CHF_2/CClF_3$) An azeotropic mixture which is used in the low stage of cascade type systems where it provides gains in compressor capacity and in low temperature capability.

Azeotrope AZ-50*	HFC 125	Blend HP80*	Azeotropic Mixture AZ-20*	CFC 13	HFC 23	Azeotrope 503
■ ■ ■	■	■	■ ■		■	
R-507	R-125	R-402A	R-410A**	R-13	R-23	R-503
98.9	120.0	101.6	72.6	104.5	70.0	87.5
-52.1	-55.8	-56.6▲	-62.9	-114.6	-115.7	-126.1
—	-153	—	—	-294	-247	—
160	151	168.3	163	84	78	67
550	525	615.0	720	561	701	632
63.8	72.3	68.5	64.8	82.4 Ω	74.7	78.5 Ω
0.35	0.35	0.34	0.41	0.24 Ω	0.33 Ω	0.28 Ω
0.22	0.19	0.18	0.21	0.13 Ω	0.16 Ω	0.14 Ω
1.11	1.09	1.13	1.17	1.18 Ω	1.24 Ω	1.21 Ω
None	None	None	None	None	None	None
A1	N.C.†††	A1/A1	A1/A1	A1	N.C.†††	N.C.†††

NOTE: AZ-50 is an azeotropic mixture consisting of HFC-125) 50% by weight and HFC-143a (CH_3CF_3), 50% by weight.

.S. Patent 5,211,867 AlliedSignal Inc.

NOTE: AZ-20 is an azeotropic mixture consisting of HFC-32 (CH_2F_2) 50% by weight and HFC-125 (CHF_2CF_3), 50% by weight. U.S. Patent 4,978,467 AlliedSignal Inc.

European Patent-533,673

NOTE: 503 is an azeotropic mixture consisting of HFC-23 (CHF_2) 40.1% by weight and CFC-13 ($CClF_3$), 59.9% by weight.

U.S. Patent 3,640,869 Allied Chemical Corp.

Genetron® Products
VAPOR PRESSURES

TEMP °F	113	141b	123	11	114	14
35.0	25.1*	20.7*	19.5*	17.1*	2.2*	7
40.0	24.4*	19.5*	18.1*	15.5*	0.4	10.
45.0	23.7*	18.1*	16.6*	13.8*	2.1	12
50.0	22.9*	16.7*	15.0*	12.0*	3.9	15.
55.0	21.9*	15.1*	13.1*	9.9*	5.9	18.
60.0	20.9*	13.4*	11.2*	7.7*	8.0	21.
65.0	19.8*	11.5*	9.0*	5.3*	10.3	25.
70.0	18.6*	9.4*	6.6*	2.7*	12.7	28.
75.0	17.2*	7.2*	4.1*	0.1	15.3	32.
80.0	15.8*	4.8*	1.3*	1.6	18.2	37.
85.0	14.2*	2.3*	0.9	3.2	21.2	41
90.0	12.4*	0.2	2.5	4.9	24.4	46.
95.0	10.5*	1.7	4.2	6.8	27.8	51.
100.0	8.5*	3.2	6.1	8.8	31.4	56.
110.0	3.8*	6.6	10.2	13.2	39.4	68.
120.0	0.7	10.4	15.0	18.3	48.4	82.
130.0	3.8	14.6	20.5	24.0	58.4	97.

TEMP °F	124	152a	134a	12	BUBBLE (liq) MP39	DEW (vap) MP39	500	BUBBLE (liq) MP66	DEW (vap) MP66	BUBBLE (liq) 409A	DEW (vap) 409A	22	BUBBLE (liq) 407C	DEW (vap) 407C	502	BUBBLE (liq) 404A	DEW (vap) 404A	AZ-50**	125	BUBBLE (liq) HP80	DEW (vap) HP80	AZ-2
-40.0	22.0*	16.0*	14.7*	11.0*	3.8*	12.5*	7.6*	7.2*	11.3*	5.2*	13.2*	0.6	3.3	3.2*	4.1	5.1	4.7	5.5	7.3	8.5	7.1	11.
-35.0	20.7*	13.9*	12.3*	8.4*	2.3*	10.1*	4.6*	4.0*	8.7*	1.9*	10.7*	2.6	5.7	0.3	6.5	7.6	7.2	8.2	10.1	11.3	9.9	14.
-30.0	19.3*	11.5*	9.7*	5.5*	0.7*	7.3*	1.2*	0.4*	5.9*	0.9	7.9*	4.9	8.3	2.3	9.2	10.3	9.9	11.1	13.2	14.5	13.0	18.
-25.0	17.7*	8.8*	6.8*	2.3*	1.1	4.3*	1.2	1.8	2.7*	2.9	4.8*	7.5	11.1	4.6	12.1	13.3	12.9	14.3	16.5	17.9	16.2	22.
-20.0	15.9*	5.9*	3.6*	0.6	3.1	0.9*	3.2	3.9	0.4	5.1	1.4*	10.2	14.3	7.1	15.3	16.6	16.2	17.8	20.2	21.6	19.9	26.
-15.0	13.9*	2.6*	0.0	2.5	5.3	1.4	5.4	6.3	2.3	7.4	1.2	13.2	17.7	9.8	18.8	20.2	19.8	21.7	24.3	25.7	23.8	31.
-10.0	11.6*	0.5	2.0	4.5	8.9	3.4	7.8	8.9	4.4	10.0	3.2	16.5	21.4	12.9	22.6	24.1	23.7	25.8	28.6	30.1	28.1	36.
-5.0	9.1*	2.4	4.1	6.7	10.3	5.6	10.4	11.7	6.7	12.9	5.5	20.1	25.5	16.2	26.7	26.3	27.9	30.3	33.4	34.8	32.8	42.
0.0	6.4*	4.6	6.5	9.2	13.2	8.0	13.3	14.8	9.3	16.0	8.0	24.0	29.9	19.8	31.1	33.0	32.5	35.2	38.6	40.0	37.8	48.
5.0	3.4*	6.9	9.1	11.8	16.3	10.6	16.4	18.2	12.0	19.3	10.6	28.3	34.7	23.8	35.9	37.9	37.5	40.5	44.1	45.6	43.3	55.
10.0	0.1*	9.5	12.0	14.7	19.7	13.5	19.7	21.9	15.0	22.9	13.6	32.8	39.9	28.2	41.0	43.3	42.9	46.2	50.2	51.6	49.2	62.
15.0	1.7	12.3	15.1	17.7	23.3	16.7	23.3	25.9	18.3	26.8	16.8	37.8	45.5	32.9	46.5	49.1	48.6	52.2	56.6	58.0	55.5	70.
20.0	3.7	15.3	18.4	21.1	27.3	20.1	27.2	30.2	21.8	31.0	20.0	43.1	51.6	38.0	52.5	55.3	54.9	58.8	63.6	65.0	62.3	78.
25.0	5.8	18.6	22.1	24.6	31.6	23.8	31.4	34.9	25.7	35.5	24.0	48.8	58.1	43.6	58.8	62.0	61.6	65.8	71.1	72.4	69.6	87.
30.0	8.1	22.2	26.1	28.5	36.2	27.8	36.0	39.9	29.8	40.4	28.0	54.9	65.1	49.6	65.6	69.2	68.8	73.3	79.1	80.4	77.4	96.
35.0	10.6	26.1	30.4	32.6	41.1	32.2	40.8	45.3	34.3	45.6	32.4	61.5	72.5	56.0	72.8	76.1	76.5	81.3	87.7	88.9	85.8	107.
40.0	13.3	30.3	35.0	37.0	46.4	36.8	46.0	51.0	39.1	51.1	37.1	68.5	80.6	63.0	80.5	85.1	84.7	89.8	96.9	97.9	94.8	118.0
45.0	16.2	34.8	40.0	41.7	52.1	41.9	51.6	57.2	44.3	57.1	42.1	76.1	89.1	70.6	88.7	93.9	93.6	98.9	106.7	107.6	104.3	129.
50.0	19.4	39.6	45.4	46.7	58.2	47.3	57.5	63.8	49.9	63.4	47.6	84.1	98.3	78.6	97.4	103.2	103.0	108.6	117.1	117.8	114.5	142.
55.0	22.8	44.8	51.2	52.1	64.7	53.1	63.8	70.8	55.9	70.1	53.4	92.6	108.0	87.3	106.6	113.2	113.0	118.8	128.2	128.8	125.3	155.5
60.0	26.5	50.4	57.4	57.8	71.6	59.4	70.6	78.3	62.3	77.3	59.6	101.6	118.4	96.6	116.4	123.7	123.6	129.7	140.0	140.3	136.7	169.6
65.0	30.4	56.3	64.0	63.8	79.0	66.0	77.7	86.3	69.1	84.9	66.2	111.3	129.4	106.5	126.7	134.9	134.9	141.3	152.5	152.6	148.9	184.6
70.0	34.6	62.7	71.1	70.2	86.9	73.2	85.3	94.8	76.4	92.9	73.2	121.4	141.0	117.1	137.6	146.8	146.9	153.6	165.7	165.6	161.8	200.6
75.0	39.1	69.4	78.6	77.0	95.2	80.8	93.4	103.7	84.2	101.5	80.7	132.2	153.4	128.4	149.1	159.4	159.6	166.6	179.7	179.3	175.4	217.4
80.0	43.9	76.6	86.7	84.2	104.0	88.9	101.9	113.2	92.5	110.5	88.7	143.7	166.4	140.4	161.2	172.7	173.0	180.3	194.5	193.8	189.9	235.3
85.0	49.0	84.3	95.2	91.7	113.4	97.5	110.9	123.2	101.3	120.0	97.2	155.7	180.2	153.2	174.0	186.7	187.2	194.8	210.2	209.0	204.4	254.1
90.0	54.4	92.4	104.3	99.7	123.3	106.7	120.5	133.7	110.6	130.0	106.2	168.4	194.8	166.8	187.4	201.5	202.1	210.2	226.7	225.1	221.0	274.1
95.0	60.2	101.1	113.9	108.2	133.7	116.4	130.5	144.8	120.6	140.6	115.7	181.8	210.2	181.2	201.4	217.1	217.9	226.4	244.1	242.0	237.8	295.1
100.0	66.3	110.2	124.1	117.0	144.7	126.8	141.1	156.4	131.1	151.7	125.8	196.0	226.3	196.5	216.2	233.5	234.5	243.5	262.4	259.8	255.6	317.2
110.0	79.7	130.1	146.3	136.2	168.5	149.2	163.9	181.5	153.9	175.7	147.6	226.4	261.1	229.7	247.9	268.8	270.3	280.6	301.8	298.0	293.7	365.0
120.0	94.7	152.3	171.1	157.3	194.8	174.3	189.2	209.0	179.4	202.1	171.9	260.0	299.5	266.7	282.7	307.1	309.8	321.9	345.3	339.9	335.6	417.7
130.0	111.4	177.0	198.7	180.5	223.7	202.2	216.9	238.9	207.6	231.1	198.9	297.0	341.5	307.7	320.6	350.3	353.1	367.8	393.1	385.8	331.5	475.6
140.0	129.9	204.2	229.2	205.9	255.3	233.1	247.4	271.5	238.8	262.7	228.6	337.4	387.4	353.1	362.6	396.9	400.4	418.7	445.4	435.8	431.5	538.9
150.0	150.4	234.2	262.8	233.7	289.8	267.1	280.7	306.6	273.2	297.1	261.3	381.7	437.3	403.1	408.4	447.5	452.0	475.3	502.4	490.1	485.8	608.1

TEMP °F	13	23	503
-120.0	4.5*	3.9*	3.1
-110.0	2.1	2.9	9.3
-100.0	7.6	9.0	16.9
-95.0	10.8	12.7	21.4
-90.0	14.3	16.8	26.3
-85.0	18.2	21.3	31.8
-80.0	22.5	26.3	37.7
-75.0	27.2	31.8	44.2
-70.0	32.3	38.0	51.3
-65.0	37.8	44.6	59.0
-60.0	43.9	52.0	67.3
-55.0	50.4	60.0	76.4
-50.0	57.6	68.7	86.1
-45.0	65.1	78.1	96.6
-40.0	57.6	68.7	107.8
-35.0	82.2	99.4	119.9
-30.0	91.6	111.3	132.8
-25.0	101.7	124.1	146.7
-20.0	112.5	137.8	161.4

Pressure: Psig

*** inches mercury vacuum**
**** AZ-50 as an azeotrope of 125/143a.**
***** AZ-20 is an azeotropic mixture of 32/125.**

edSignal Fluorocarbons

orld Leader in the Full-Service Supply of Environmentally Safer Fluorocarbons

dSignal Fluorocarbons

ese changing times, it's important to have a knowledgeable arbon supplier that can help your business make the transi- environmentally safer fluorocarbon products. At AlliedSignal carbons, we continuously strive to be that full-service supplier and our other worldwide customers.

broad product line we offer features Genetron®, Genesolv® and e® brand alternatives for virtually every application – air condi- and refrigeration, blowing-agent, precision-cleaning, sterilant- rosol and other specialty uses.

global customer-service commitment encompasses meeting rent and future needs of our customers as well as ensuring y can make a smooth transition away from CFCs. We provide stomers with comprehensive technical and applications sup- nd we serve as a valuable information resource offering a full ment of informational material and literature–ranging from al bulletins and product brochures to government-regulation s and instructional videos.

onditioning

riety of environmentally safer alternatives is available from ignal Fluorocarbons for the air conditioning industry.

the unitary-air-conditioning market, we have commercialized one-depleting replacements for HCFC-22, including Genetron and Genetron 407C.

etron AZ-20 is a patented, UL-recognized azeotropic mixture -32/125 that has shown better energy efficiency than HCFC- esting performed with unitary air conditioning equipment.

alternative refrigerants for centrifugal chillers include Genetron d 134a. Genetron AZ-50 (R-507) and AZ-20 are available for e displacement chiller applications.

major supplier to the world's leading automotive manufactur- e developed a non-ozone-depleting refrigerant, Genetron 134a, omotive air conditioning systems.

igeration

elp the commercial refrigeration industry meet the require- of the CFC phaseout, AlliedSignal offers a broad line of R-502 CFC-22 replacements for low- and medium-temperature refrig- systems.

leading alternative is Genetron AZ-50 (R-507), an azeotropic e of HFC-125/143a that can be used in both low- and medium- rature refrigeration systems in new-equipment and retrofit ations. AZ-50 has been approved by the world's leading refrig- compressor, component and system manufacturers. It is cur- used in hundreds of refrigeration systems worldwide–in indus- ood-service, supermarket and other applications.

er R-502 and HCFC-22 alternative products include Genetron which can be used in both low- and medium-temperature sys- HP80 is also available as an excellent interim product for low- edium-temperature applications.

medium-temperature systems, we manufacture interim products P39 and MP66 for retrofitting applications. And we also manu- e Genetron 134a as a long-term non-ozone-depleting refrigerant dium-temperature refrigeration systems, in both new equipment ations and retrofit projects.

rofitting

rofitting existing refrigeration systems to environmentally safer erants plays a major role in the refrigeration industry's move away from CFCs. AlliedSignal encourages its customers to retrofit these systems now to help insure their smooth operation over the long term.

Comprehensive information is available to help retrofit refrigeration systems to all of our alternative refrigerants. In addition to technical and applications support services, we have step-by-step retrofit guidelines, an instructional video and computer software programs that help answer questions on the performance of our products when retrofitted in various applications.

We also provide a comprehensive reclamation program, enabling contractors and end-users to return used refrigerant to our network of Genetron Wholesalers for reclamation and eventual re-use.

Technical Expertise

An integral part of AlliedSignal's $250 million investment to commercialize alternative fluorocarbon products is the company's Fluorine Products Technology Center. This world-class research facility in Buffalo, N.Y., plays a leading part in the company's customer-application support programs. Some of the work performed at the Center includes materials compatibility, lubricant miscibility and system performance testing.

To help maintain AlliedSignal's leadership position in the alternative fluorocarbon industry, the facility's scientists are continuing their research and development of next-generation products.

Blowing Agents

AlliedSignal is leading the worldwide blowing agent industry's conversion away from CFC-11 and 12 to environmentally safer, interim alternatives. The alternative products currently available to our construction, transportation, industrial and appliance customers include Genetron 141b, 142b, 22, 134a and blends of HCFC-142b/HCFC-22. The superior thermal-insulating properties and materials compatibility of these products make them ideal blowing agents for producing a variety of high-value urethane and styrene-based insulating foams. Additionally, Genetron 134a and 152a are acceptable non-VOC alternatives for non-insulating thermo plastic foams.

Although HCFC blowing agents are excellent interim replacements for CFCs, AlliedSignal has accelerated its efforts to develop a chlorine-free third-generation blowing agent to meet the long-term needs of its worldwide customers.

Specialty Products

A variety of environmentally safer fluorocarbons and technical support services are also available from AlliedSignal for the worldwide specialty products markets.

We currently supply fluorocarbon-based propellants to the essential-use sectors of the specialty-aerosol industry, which includes metered-dose inhalers and some industrial applications. We have also developed Genetron 152a as a non-ozone-depleting, non-VOC propellant for consumer aerosol products.

For the sterilant gas industry, we offer the environmentally safer Oxyfume 2000 (mixture of ethylene oxide and HCFC-124) to replace the CFC-based 12/88 mixture used to sterilize hospital equipment and medical devices. A next-generation sterilant gas–Oxyfume 3000–is under development.

Genesolv 2000 and 2004 are available to the electronic-precision-cleaning markets. And we are in the development stages of a Genesolv 3000 third-generation precision-cleaning product.

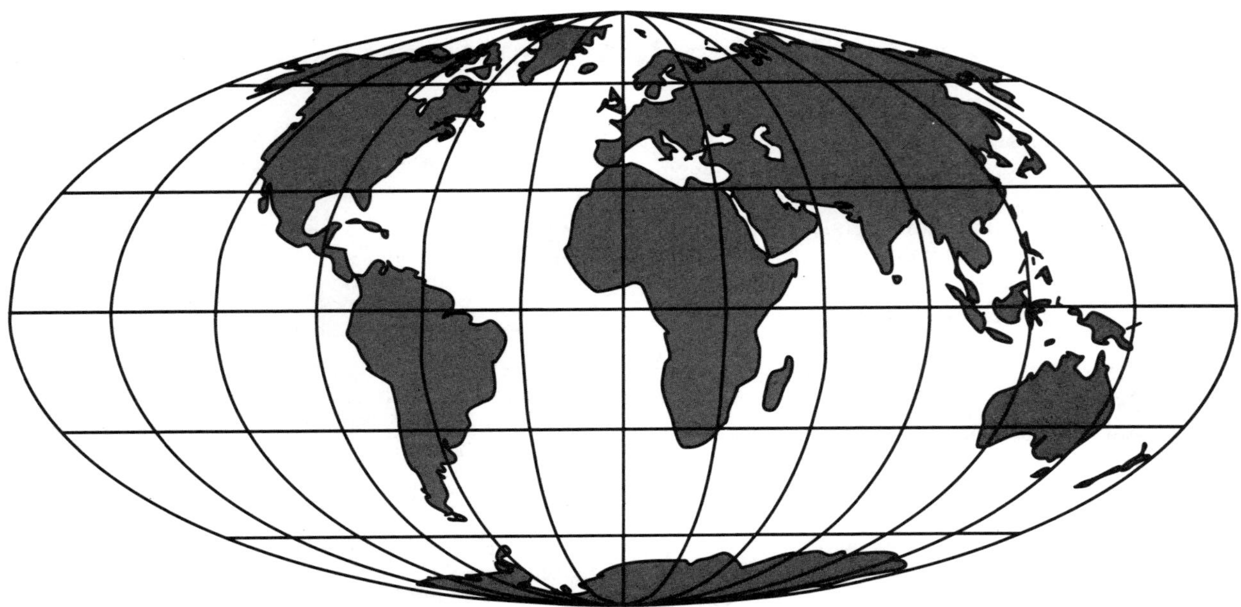

For more information contact your AlliedSignal Fluorocarbons representative.

WORLDWIDE SALES OFFICES

UNITED STATES
AlliedSignal Inc.
Fluorocarbons
P.O. Box 1053
Morristown, NJ 07962-1053
Phone: 800-631-8138
Fax: 201-455-6395

MANUFACTURER'S REPRESENTATIVE
REFRIGERANTS (Southeastern U.S.)
E.V. Dunbar Company
4200 Northside Parkway N.W.
Building 3A
Atlanta, Georgia 30327
Phone: 800-241-2010
Fax: 800-849-0834

LATIN AMERICA-CARIBBEAN
AlliedSignal Inc.
Fluorocarbons
20801 Biscayne Blvd.
Suite #435
Aventura, FL 33180
Phone: 305-931-6465
Fax: 305-931-6762

CANADA
AlliedSignal Inc.
Fluorocarbons
50 Burnhamthorpe Road West
Suite 904
Box 71
Mississauga, Ontario
L5B 3C2
Phone: 905-276-9211
Fax: 905-276-5711

ASIA
AlliedSignal Inc.
Fluorocarbons
Suite 3812-16, Shell Tower
Times Square, 1 Matheson Street
Causeway Bay, Hong Kong
Phone: 852-506-1812
Fax: 852- 506-0192

EUROPE-MIDDLE EAST-AFRICA
AlliedSignal Fluorochemicals
Europe B.V.
Stadsring 163A
3817 BA Amersfoort
The Netherlands
Phone: 033-792300
Fax: 033-792350

AUSTRALIA
AlliedSignal Inc.
Fluorocarbons
71 Queens Road, 2nd Floor
Melbourne, Victoria 3004
Australia
Phone: 61-3-529-1411
Fax: 61-3-510-9837

CUSTOMER SERVICE
HOW TO ORDER
To place an order from anywhere in the continental United States, Hawaii and the Caribbean:
Call: 800-522-8001
Fax: 800-458-9073
In Canada:
Call: 800-553-9749
Fax: 800-553-9750
Outside these areas:
Call: 201- 455-6300
Fax: 201-455-2763

G525-00
1/95 50
Printed in US

Genetron® Refrigerants

G-113 TRICHLOROTRIFLUOROETHANE CCl_2FCClF_2 B.P. 117.6°F

G-123 DICHLOROTRIFLUOROETHANE $CHCl_2CF_3$ B.P. 82.2°F

G-11 TRICHLOROFLUOROMETHANE CCl_3F B.P. 74.5°F

G-114 DICHLOROTETRAFLUOROETHANE $CClF_2CClF_2$ B.P. 38.6°F

G-124 CHLOROTETRAFLUOROETHANE $CHClFCF_3$ B.P. 10.5°F

G-134a TETRAFLUOROETHANE CF_3CH_2F B.P. -15.1°F

G-12 DICHLORODIFLUOROMETHANE CCl_2F_2 B.P. -21.6°F

G-500 AZEOTROPE G-12/152a B.P. -28.3°F

G-22 CHLORODIFLUOROMETHANE $CHClF_2$ B.P. -41.5°F

G-502 AZEOTROPE G-22/115 B.P. -49.8°F

AZ-50 AZEOTROPE G-125/143a B.P. -52.1°F

G-125 PENTAFLUOROETHANE CHF_2CF_3 B.P. -55.4°F

G-32 DIFLUOROMETHANE CH_2F_2 B.P. -61.0°F

AZ-20 AZEOTROPIC MIXTURE G-32/125 B.P. -62.9°F

G-13 CHLOROTRIFLUOROMETHANE $CClF_3$ B.P. -114.6°F

G-23 TRIFLUOROMETHANE CHF_3 B.P. -115.6°F

G-503 AZEOTROPE G- 23/13 B.P. -126.1°F

Genetron® Refrigerants Pressure Temperature Chart

Fluorocarbons

Understanding Needs.
Finding Solutions.

LIQUID DENSITY OF GENETRON® REFRIGERANTS

		Temperature °F			Temperature °F		
		-80	-40	0	40	80	120
G-113	#/ft.³	—	106.3	103.6	100.6	97.4	94.1
	#/gal.	—	14.2	13.8	13.4	13.0	12.6
G-123	#/ft.³	104.1	100.9	97.7	94.4	90.9	87.3
	#/gal.	13.9	13.5	13.1	12.6	12.2	11.7
G-11	#/ft.³	104.2	101.3	98.3	95.1	91.9	88.5
	#/gal.	13.9	13.5	13.1	12.7	12.3	11.8
G-114	#/ft.³	105.1	101.6	97.9	94.0	89.9	85.4
	#/gal.	14.0	13.6	13.1	12.6	12.0	11.4
G-124	#/ft.³	100.7	97.0	93.1	88.9	84.3	79.2
	#/gal.	13.5	13.0	12.4	11.9	11.3	10.6
G-134a	#/ft.³	92.4	88.5	84.4	79.9	75.0	69.2
	#/gal.	12.3	11.8	11.3	10.7	10.0	9.2
G-12	#/ft.³	98.4	94.7	90.7	86.3	81.5	75.9
	#/gal.	13.2	12.7	12.1	11.5	10.9	10.1
G-500	#/ft.³	87.9	84.3	80.5	76.3	71.8	66.6
	#/gal.	11.7	11.3	10.8	10.2	9.6	8.9
G-22	#/ft.³	91.9	88.0	83.8	79.3	74.1	68.1
	#/gal.	12.3	11.8	11.2	10.6	9.9	9.1
G-502	#/ft.³	95.8	91.4	86.7	81.5	75.5	68.0
	#/gal.	12.8	12.2	11.6	10.9	10.1	9.1
AZ-50*	#/ft.³	85.4	80.9	76.2	71.0	64.9	56.6
	#/gal.	11.4	10.8	10.2	9.5	8.7	7.6
G-125	#/ft.³	97.5	92.6	87.2	81.1	73.6	63.2
	#/gal.	13.0	12.4	11.7	10.8	9.8	8.4
G-32	#/ft.³	77.8	73.7	69.4	64.7	59.4	52.8
	#/gal.	10.4	9.8	9.3	8.6	7.9	7.1
AZ-20**	#/ft.³	86.5	82.1	77.4	72.1	65.9	57.5
	#/gal.	11.6	11.0	10.3	9.6	8.8	7.7
G-13	#/ft.³	90.2	84.1	77.0	67.7	48.9	—
	#/gal.	12.1	11.2	10.2	9.0	6.5	—
G-23	#/ft.³	85.4	79.5	72.0	61.9	—	—
	#/gal.	11.4	10.6	9.6	8.3	—	—
G-503	#/ft.³	86.4	80.2	72.3	61.1	—	—
	#/gal.	11.6	10.7	9.7	8.2	—	—

*AZ-50 is an azeotrope of HFC 125 and HFC 143a
**AZ-20 is an azeotropic mixture of HFC 32 and HFC 125

G525-002
1-95-25K
Printed in U.S.A.

Genetron®
Understanding Needs. Finding Solutions.

P.O. Box 1053, Morristown, New Jersey 07962-1053
1-800-631-8138

System Evacuation

Prior to charging with refrigerant, good practice calls for evacuation to deep vacuum levels to remove non-condensible gases and also to evaporate and remove any trapped moisture from within the system. The chart below shows the equivalence of low pressure readings in microns with other familiar pressure/vacuum units. It also lists the temperature at which water will vaporize at each pressure.

PRESSURE VACUUM EQUIVALENTS

Absolute pressure above zero base		Vacuum below one atmosphere	Approximate fraction at one atmosphere	Vaporization temperature of H_2O in °F @ each pressure
microns	PSIA	Inches of mercury		
0	0	29.92	–	–
50	.001	29.92	1/15000	-50
100	.002	29.92	1/7600	-40
150	.003	29.92	1/5100	-33
200	.004	29.91	1/3800	-28
300	.006	29.91	1/2500	-21
500	.010	29.90	1/1500	-12
1,000	.019	29.88	1/760	1
2,000	.039	29.84	1/380	15
4,000	.077	29.76	1/190	29
6,000	.116	29.69	1/127	39
10,000	.193	29.53	1/76	52
15,000	.290	29.33	1/50	63
20,000	.387	29.13	1/38	72
30,000	.580	28.74	1/25	84
50,000	.967	27.95	1/15	101
100,000	1.93	25.98	2/15	125
200,000	3.87	22.05	1/4	152
500,000	9.67	10.24	2/3	192
760,000	14.696	0	1 Atmos.	212

Genetron® Pressure Temperature Chart

°F	G-113	G-123	G-11	G-114	G-124	°F
-20	29.0	27.6	26.9	22.8	15.9	-20
-15	28.8	27.3	26.5	21.7	13.9	-15
-10	28.6	26.8	25.9	20.5	11.6	-10
-5	28.4	26.3	25.3	19.2	9.2	-5
0	28.1	25.8	24.6	17.7	6.4	0
5	27.9	25.1	23.9	16.1	3.4	5
10	27.5	24.4	23.0	14.3	0.1	10
15	27.1	23.6	22.1	12.3	1.7	15
20	26.7	22.7	21.0	10.1	3.7	20
25	26.3	21.7	19.8	7.7	5.8	25
30	25.7	20.6	18.5	5.1	8.1	30
35	25.1	19.4	17.1	2.3	10.6	35
40	24.4	18.0	15.6	0.4	13.3	40
45	23.7	16.5	13.8	2.1	16.3	45
50	22.9	14.9	12.0	3.9	19.4	50
55	21.9	13.0	9.9	5.8	22.8	55
60	20.9	11.0	7.7	7.9	26.5	60
65	19.8	8.9	5.3	10.2	30.4	65
70	18.6	6.6	2.7	12.6	34.6	70
75	17.2	4.0	0.1	15.2	39.1	75
80	15.8	1.2	1.6	18.0	43.9	80
85	14.2	0.9	3.2	21.0	49.0	85
90	12.4	2.5	4.9	24.2	54.4	90
95	10.5	4.2	6.8	27.6	60.2	95
100	8.5	6.1	8.8	31.2	66.3	100
105	6.3	8.1	10.9	35.0	72.8	105
110	3.8	10.3	13.2	39.1	79.7	110
115	1.2	12.6	15.7	43.4	87.0	115
120	0.8	15.1	18.3	48.0	94.7	120
125	2.2	17.7	21.1	52.9	102.8	125
130	3.8	20.6	24.0	58.0	111.4	130
135	5.5	23.4	27.1	63.4	120.4	135
140	7.3	26.8	30.5	69.1	129.9	140
145	9.2	30.2	34.0	75.1	139.9	145
150	11.2	33.8	37.7	81.4	150.4	150

°F	G-134a	G-12	G-500	G-22	G-502	AZ-50 (G-507)	G-125	AZ-20 (G-410A)*	°F
-60	21.6	19.0	16.9	11.9	7.1	5.9	3.1	1.2	-60
-55	20.2	17.3	14.9	9.2	3.8	2.3	0.4	3.4	-55
-50	18.6	15.4	12.7	6.1	0.1	0.9	2.4	5.8	-50
-45	16.8	13.3	10.3	2.7	1.9	3.1	4.7	8.6	-45
-40	14.7	11.0	7.5	0.6	4.1	5.5	7.3	11.6	-40
-35	12.3	8.3	4.5	2.6	6.6	8.2	10.1	14.9	-35
-30	9.7	5.4	1.1	4.9	9.2	11.1	13.2	18.5	-30
-25	6.8	2.3	1.3	7.4	12.1	14.3	16.5	22.5	-25
-20	3.6	0.6	3.3	10.2	15.4	17.8	20.2	26.9	-20
-15	0.0	2.5	5.5	13.2	18.8	21.7	24.3	31.7	-15
-10	2.0	4.5	7.9	16.5	22.6	25.8	28.7	36.8	-10
-5	4.1	6.8	10.5	20.1	26.7	30.3	33.4	42.5	-5
0	6.5	9.2	13.3	24.0	31.1	35.2	38.6	48.6	0
5	9.1	11.8	16.4	28.2	35.9	40.5	44.1	55.2	5
10	12.0	14.7	19.8	32.8	41.0	46.2	50.2	62.3	10
15	15.1	17.7	23.4	37.7	46.6	52.2	56.7	70.0	15
20	18.4	21.1	27.3	43.1	52.5	58.8	63.6	78.3	20
25	22.1	24.6	31.5	48.8	58.8	65.8	71.1	87.3	25
30	26.1	28.5	36.0	54.9	65.6	73.3	79.1	96.8	30
35	30.4	32.6	40.9	61.5	72.9	81.3	87.7	107.1	35
40	35.0	37.0	46.1	68.5	80.6	89.8	96.9	118.0	40
45	40.1	41.7	51.6	76.0	88.8	98.9	106.7	129.7	45
50	45.4	46.7	57.6	84.0	97.5	108.6	117.1	142.2	50
55	51.2	52.1	63.9	92.6	106.7	118.8	128.2	155.5	55
60	57.4	57.7	70.6	101.6	116.5	129.8	140.0	169.6	60
65	64.0	63.8	77.8	111.2	126.8	141.3	152.5	184.6	65
70	71.1	70.2	85.4	121.4	137.7	153.6	165.7	200.6	70
75	78.6	77.0	93.4	132.2	149.2	166.6	179.7	217.4	75
80	86.7	84.2	102.0	143.6	161.3	180.3	194.5	235.3	80
85	95.2	91.8	111.0	155.7	174.0	194.8	210.2	254.1	85
90	104.3	99.8	120.5	168.4	187.4	210.2	226.7	274.1	90
95	113.9	108.2	130.6	181.8	201.5	226.4	244.1	295.1	95
100	124.1	117.2	141.1	195.9	216.2	243.5	262.4	317.2	100
105	134.9	126.5	152.3	210.7	231.7	261.6	281.6	340.5	105
110	146.4	136.4	164.0	226.3	248.0	280.7	301.8	365.0	110
115	158.4	146.8	176.3	242.7	265.0	300.8	323.1	390.7	115
120	171.1	157.6	189.2	259.9	282.8	321.9	345.3	417.7	120
125	184.5	169.0	202.8	277.9	301.4	344.3	368.7	445.9	125
130	198.7	181.0	217.0	296.8	320.9	367.8	393.1	475.6	130
135	213.5	193.5	231.9	316.5	341.3	392.6	418.7	506.5	135
140	229.2	206.6	247.4	337.2	362.6	418.7	445.4	539.0	140
145	245.6	220.3	263.7	358.8	358.8	446.3	473.3	572.8	145
150	262.8	234.6	280.8	381.4	408.4	475.3	502.4	608.1	150
155	281.0	249.5	298.5	405.1	433.0	505.8	—	645.0	155
160	299.9	265.1	317.1	429.8	458.7	—	—	683.4	160

°F	G-23	G-13	G-503	°F	G-23	G-13	G-503
-160	24.2	23.7	21.1	-35	99.4	82.2	120.0
-155	22.8	22.4	19.1	-30	111.3	91.6	132.9
-150	21.2	20.8	16.8	-25	124.1	101.7	146.7
-145	19.3	18.9	14.2	-20	137.8	112.5	161.5
-140	17.1	16.8	11.1	-15	152.5	124.0	177.2
-135	14.4	14.3	7.5	-10	168.2	136.2	193.9
-130	11.4	11.4	3.4	-5	185.0	149.1	211.7
-125	7.9	8.1	0.6	0	203.0	162.9	230.5
-120	3.9	4.5	3.2	5	222.1	177.5	250.5
-115	0.3	0.3	6.1	10	242.4	192.9	271.7
-110	2.9	2.2	9.3	15	264.0	209.2	294.1
-105	5.8	4.7	12.9	20	286.9	226.3	317.8
-100	9.1	7.6	17.0	25	311.2	244.5	342.9
-95	12.7	10.8	21.4	30	337.1	263.6	369.3
-90	16.8	14.3	26.4	35	364.5	283.7	397.2
-85	21.3	18.2	31.8	40	393.5	304.8	426.6
-80	26.3	22.5	37.7	45	424.3	327.1	457.6
-75	31.9	27.1	44.2	50	457.0	350.5	490.2
-70	38.0	32.3	51.3	55	491.6	375.1	524.6
-65	44.7	37.9	59.0	60	528.3	401.0	560.7
-60	52.0	43.9	67.4	65	567.3	428.2	598.7
-55	60.0	50.5	76.4	70	608.7	456.9	—
-50	68.7	57.5	86.1	75	652.7	487.2	—
-45	78.2	65.2	96.6	80	—	519.5	—
-40	88.4	73.4	107.9	85	—	—	—

Vapor Pressure-psig
Blue Figures (In. Hg) Vacuum

* Provisional Number Assigned by ASHRAE

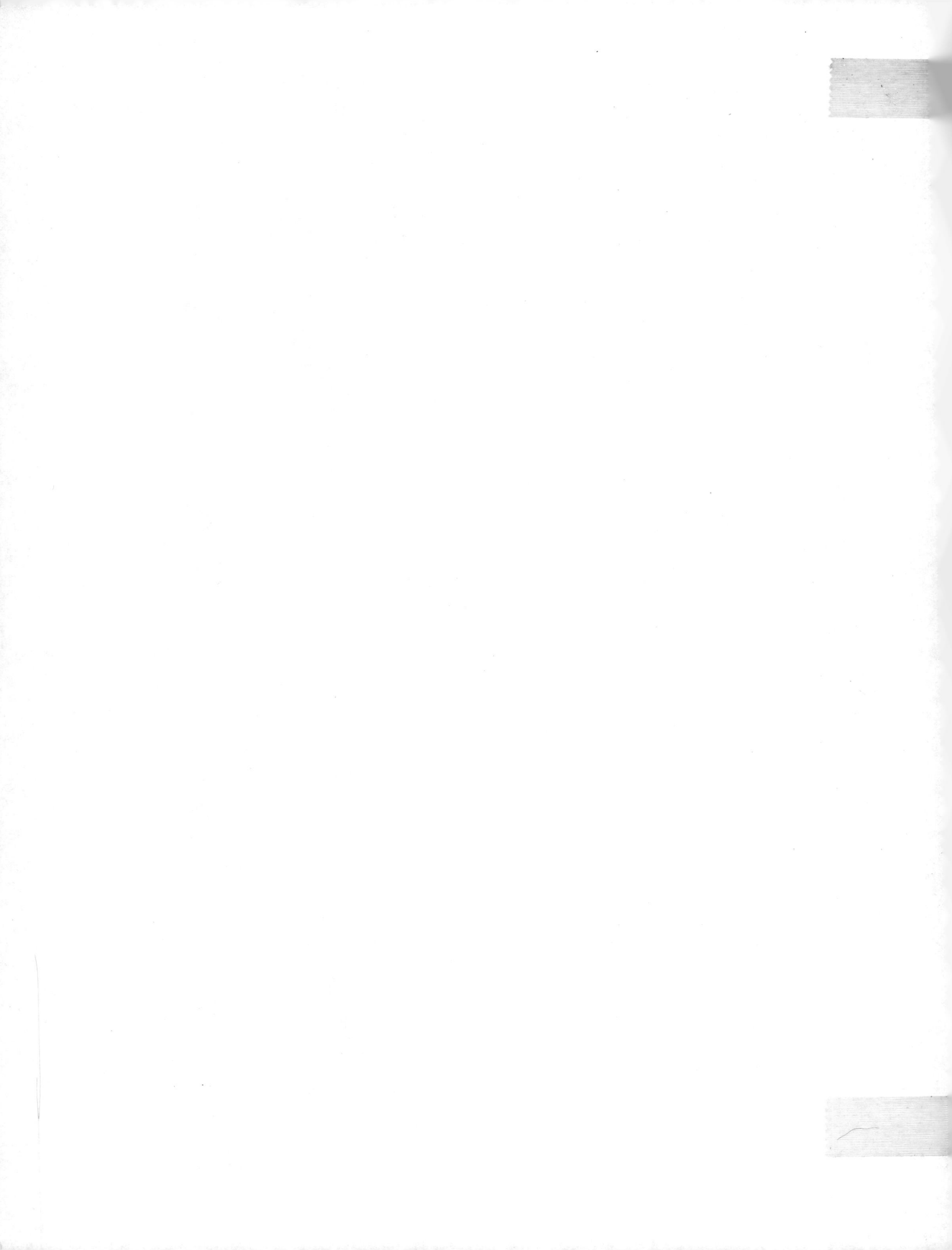